ICPP'98

Proceedings

1998 International Conference on Parallel Processing

Editor

Ten H. Lai
The Ohio State University

Minneapolis, Minnesota
August 10-14, 1998

Sponsored by

The International Association for Computers and Communications
The Ohio State University

IEEE
COMPUTER
SOCIETY

Los Alamitos, California

Washington • Brussels • Tokyo

IEEE Computer Society Order Number PR08650
ISBN 0-8186-8650-2
ISBN 0-8186-8651-0 (case)
ISBN 0-8186-8652-9 (microfiche)
IEEE Order Plan Catalog Number 98EX205
ISSN 0190-3918

Additional copies may be ordered from:

IEEE Computer Society	IEEE Service Center	IEEE Computer Society	IEEE Computer Society
Customer Service Center	445 Hoes Lane	13, Avenue de l'Aquilon	Asia/Pacific Office
10662 Los Vaqueros Circle	P.O. Box 1331	B-1200 Brussels	Watanabe Bldg., 1-4-2
P.O. Box 3014	Piscataway, NJ 08855-1331	BELGIUM	Minami-Aoyama
Los Alamitos, CA 90720-1314	Tel: + 1-908-981-1393	Tel: + 32-2-770-2198	Minato-kuTokyo 107-0062
Tel: + 1-714-821-8380	Fax: + 1-908-981-9667	Fax: + 32-2-770-8505	JAPAN
Fax: + 1-714-821-4641	mis.custserv@computer.org	euro.ofc@computer.org	Tel: + 81-3-3408-3118
E-mail: cs.books@computer.org			Fax: + 81-3-3408-3553
			tokyo.ofc@computer.org

Editorial production by Bob Werner

Cover art design and production by Alex Torres

Printed in the United States of America by Technical Communication Services

Table of Contents

1998 International Conference on Parallel Processing

Keynote Address: The Future of Vectors in a Scalable World
Speaker: Steve Oberlin, Vice President, Cray Research

Session 1A: Theory/Algorithms
Chair: George Karypis, University of Minnesota

Session 1B: Parallel Simulation
Chair: Richard Enbody, Michigan State University

Session 1C: Mobile Computing
Chair: Zhi-Li Zhang, University of Minnesota

Session 2A: Applications and Algorithms I
Chair: Hal Sudborough, University of Texas at Dallas

Session 3C: Distributed Shared Memory
Chair: Dhabaleswar Panda, Ohio State University

Keynote Address: Implementing Parallelism on Silicon
Speaker: C.L. Wu, National Chiao Tung University, Taiwan

Session 4A: Applications and Algorithms II
Chair: Sandeep Gupta, Colorado State University

Session 4B: Memory/Storage Management
Chair: Xiaodong Zhang, College of William and Mary

Panel Session: Convergence Points on Commercial Parallel Systems: Do We Have the Node Architecture? Do We Have the Network? Do We Have the Programming Paradigm?
Organizer and Moderator: H.J. Siegel, Purdue University

Panelists:
Hank Dietz, Purdue University
Jose Duato, Universidad Politecnica de Valencia, Spain
Steve Scott, Cray Research/Silicon Graphics
Thomas Sterling, JPL/Caltech
Craig Stunkel, IBM Research
Stephen Wheat, Intel

Keynote Address: Where is the Internet Heading to? From Workplace to Livingspace
Speaker: Iwao Toda, Fujitsu Labs, Japan

Session 6A: Scientific Computing
Chair: Yousef Saad, University of Minnesota

Session 6B: Scheduling
Chair: Sajal K. Das, University of North Texas

Session 6C: Collective Communication
Chair: Jose Duato, Universidad Politecnica de Valencia, Spain

Session 7A: Software Techniques
Chair: Matthew O'Keefe, University of Minnesota

Session 7B: Load Balancing/Performance
Chair: Chita R. Das, Pennsylvania State University

Session 7C: Wormhole Networks
Chair: Craig Stunkel, IBM T.J. Watson Research

Preface

In its great tradition, the International Conference on Parallel Processing has once again compiled a distinctive program. In response to its call for papers, a total of 214 papers from around the world were submitted to ICPP-98. Each paper was assigned to at least three referees and/or program committee members for review. About 80 committee members and over 300 referees have participated in the review process. Based on the reviews provided by the referees and committee members, the program chair and vice chairs collectively selected 72 papers for inclusion in the technical program. The following table summarizes the submissions and acceptances in the different areas:

Areas	Submitted	Accepted
Architecture/Networking	63	22
Compilers	30	10
Resource Management	36	12
Algorithms/Applications	35	11
Multimedia/Mobile	14	5
Network Based Computing	23	8
Fault Tolerance	13	4
Totals	214	72

The 72 papers accepted have been organized as 24 sessions, on a wide variety of topics. In addition to the paper sessions, there will be three keynote speeches and a panel session. We are grateful to our keynote speakers Dr. Steve Oberlin of Cray Research, Professor C.L. Wu of National Chiao Tung University, Taiwan, and Dr. Iwao Toda of Fujitsu Labs, Japan; and to Dr. H.J. Siegel of Purdue University for organizing the exciting panel session.

Many other individuals have contributed to the success of the conference. We would like to thank all of the authors who have submitted papers to the conference. We also wish to thank the entire program committee and all the referees for providing valuable reviews in a timely fashion. Special thanks are due to the Program Vice Chairs for their excellent job in organizing the program committee, overseeing the review process, and selecting papers for the program. Our thanks also go to the Tutorials Chair, Pen-Chung Yew; the Workshops Chair, Chita Das; the Award Chair, Makoto Takizawa; the Publicity Chair, Sandeep Gupta; the Publication Chair, Tom Page; the International Liaisons, Michel Raynal, Makoto Takizawa, and Hyunsoo Yoon; and the Local Arrangements Chair, Subburajan Ponnuswamy. The assistance of Wuchi Feng, Jianping Jiang, Elizabeth O'Neill, and Min-te Sun is greatly appreciated. Finally, our profound gratitude to Professor Tse-yun Feng and Professor Ming T. Liu for their guidance, support, and encouragement in running the conference.

David Du
University of Minnesota
General Chair

Ten H. Lai
The Ohio State University
Program Chair

Organizing and Program Committees

General Chair
David Du, University of Minnesota

Program Chair
Ten H. Lai, Ohio State University

Program Vice Chairs

Architectures
Dhabaleswar Panda, Ohio State University

Compilers and Languages
David Lilja, University of Minnesota

OS and Resource Management
C.T. Howard Ho, IBM Almaden Research Center

Algorithms and Applications
Joseph F. JáJá, University of Maryland

Networking and Protocols
Norio Shiratori, Tohoku University, Japan

Multimedia and Mobile Computing
Wuchi Feng, Ohio State University

Network-Based Computing
Kai Li, Princeton University

Fault Tolerance and Reliability
Füsun Özgüner, Ohio State University

Organizing Committees

Tutorials Chair
Pen-Chung Yew, University of Minnesota

Workshops Chair
Chita R. Das, Pennsylvania State University

Award Chair
Makoto Takizawa, Tokyo Denki University, Japan

Publicity Chair
Sandeep Gupta, Colorado State University

Referees

Toshihiko Ando

Bulent Abali

Kota Abe

Dharma P. Agrawal

Manish Ahluwalia

Selim G. Akl

Elif Albuz

Shahzad Ali

Cristiana Amza

Jennifer Anderson

Anish Arora

Todd M. Austin

Bhed Bahadur Bista

David A. Bader

Prith Banerjee

Mohammad Banikazemi

Rami Baroody

Sujoy Basu

Riccardo Bettati

Randeep Bhatia

Ricardo Bianchini

Angelos Bilas

Robert Bjornson

Anthony Bolmarcich

Rajendra V. Boppana

Bella Bose

Mark Brehob

Shuki Bruck

Nicholas J. Carriero

Henri Casanova

Chi-Chao Chang

Huey-Ling Chen

Ming-Syan Chen

Wen-Shyen Eric Chen

Yuh-Shyan Chen

Yuqun Chen

Paul Y.S. Cheung

Yanghee Choi

B-K Chung

Sung Woo Chung

Grzegorz Czajkowski

Donglai Dai

Stefanos N. Damianakis

Chita R. Das

Sajal K. Das

Samir R. Das

Tony DeWitt

Ewa Deelman

Xiaotie Deng

Peter A. Dinda

Jose Duato

Pradeep K. Dubey

Cezary Dubnicki

Michel Dubois

S. Dutt

Shantanu Dutt

Sandhya Dwarkadas

Guy Edjlali

Thorsten von Eicken

Victor Eijkhout

Kattamuri Ekanadham

Richard J. Enbody

Mary M. Eshaghian

Ike Evans

Alessandro Fabbri

Graham E. Fagg

Wu-chi Feng

Renato J. Figueiredo

Kevin Foltz

L. Fong

Hubertus Franke

Vincent W. Freeh

O. Frieder

Ophir Frieder

Michael Furman

Dr. Guang Gao

Guang Gao

Yuan Gao

Ye Ge

Robert A. van de Geijn

Robert van de Geijn

Arjan van Gemund

Sanjeev Ghai

Somnath Ghosh

Ashvin Goel

Rohit Goyal

Ronald Greenberg

Dave Grove

Vinod Grover

Junjie Gu

Lee Guan

Sudipto Guha

Anshul Gupta

Manish Gupta

John Gustafson

Soonhoi Ha

Torben Hagerup

Jonathan Hal

Mary Hall

Vivek Halwan

Daniel J. Harvey

Manzoor Hashmani

Gerd Heber

Tamir Heyman

Hiroaki Higaki

Teruo Higashino

Wai-Hong Ho

Howard Ho

Jennifer Hou
Ching-chi Hsu
Windsor Hsu
Yarsun Hsu
Deyu Hu
Oscar Ibarra
Tetsuo Ideguchi
Akira Idoue
Sotiris Ioannidis
Yutaka Ishibashi
Fumio Ishizaki
Nayeem Islam
Michael Iverson
Ravishankar Iyer
Tom Jacob
E.E. Jan
Dongming Jiang
Changli Jiao
G. Jin
David B. Johnson
Don Johnson
Doug Joseph
Tetsuro Kakeshita
Manabu Kato
Kenji Kawahara
Ram Kesavan
Ashfaq Khokhar
Samir Khuller
JunSeong Kim
Sung Chun Kim
Yoonhee Kim
Shigetomo Kimura
Chung-Ta King
Erturk Kocalar
Cory Kosak
Charles "Buck" Krasic
Ulrich Kremer
Sanjeev Kumar
Yu-Kwong Kwok
Feipei Lai

Mario Lauria
Paul LeMahieu
Mark Leair
Jenq Kuen Lee
Joohan Lee
Yongjoon Lee
Jie Li
Z. Li
Zhiyuan Li
Cheng Liao
Yao-Nan Lien
David Lilja
Beng-Hong Lim
Hock-Beng Lim
Wei Lin
Mikko Lipasti
Pangfeng Liu
Yew-Huey Liu
F. Lombardi
Honghui Lu
Yuan Lu
Qian-Rong Ma
Nihar R. Mahapatra
Kia Makki
S. Makki
Sam Makki
Evangelos P. Markatos
Ami Marowka
Martonosi
Rami Melhem
Padmanabhan Menon
Gerard G.L. Meyer
Maged M. Michael
Sam Midkiff
Dejan Mircevski
Tadanori Mizuno
Prasant Mohapatra
Vijay Moorthy
Jose E. Moreira
David Mount

Yuko Murayama
Ravi Nair
Yoshihiro Nakahira
A.K. Nanda
David Nassimi
Richard Neves
Chris J. Newburn
Satoshi Nishiyama
Nicholas A. Nystrom
Hiroyuki Ohsaki
Hitoshi Oi
Yuji Oie
S. Olariu
Yen-Jen Oyang
F Ozguner
Loic Prylli
Michael A. Palis
Yi Pan
Alessandro Panconesi
D.K. Panda
Santosh Pande
Vsevolod Panteleenko
Marios Papaefthymiou
Behrooz Parhami
E.K. Park
Myong-Soon Park
Sung-Yong Park
Yoonho Park
Sanjay J. Patel
David Petrou
Timothy M. Pinkston
M. Cristina Pinotti
Niki Pissinou
James S. Plank
Greg Plaxton
L Potter
Jean-Pierre Prost
Xiaohan Qin
Ilkyeun Ra
Radharamanan Radhakrishnan

Balaji Raghavachari

Mukund Raghavachari

C.S. Raghavendra

Karthick Rajamany

Ram Rajamony

Sanguthevar Rajasekaran

Ryan Rakvic

Ramachandran

R Raman

J. Ramanujam

John Ramirez

Balkrishna Ramkumar

Parthasarathy Ranganathan

A.L. Narasimha Reddy

Kees van Reeuwijk

Dan Revel

Jennifer Rexford

Marc D. Riedel

Johan Ringstrom

Jerry Roth

Sumit Roy

Rudrajit Samanta

Vasilis Samoladas

Steven Samorodin

Erich Schikuta

David E. Schimmel

Assaf Schuster

Eric J. Schwabe

Loren Schwiebert

Cristiana Bentes Seidel

Chandra Sekharan

Dimitrios Serpanos

Severance

Hazim Shafi

Gautam Shah

Shamik Sharma

Kai Shen

Jang-Ping Sheu

Shibata

Hiroshi Shigeno

Wei-Kuan Shih

M. Singhal

Henk J. Sips

Rajeev Sivaram

Ben Smith

Andrew Sohn

Jon A. Solworth

Arun K. Somani

Ruud Sommerhalder

Claudio Roland Sonnenburg

Neelam Soundarajan

Evan Speight

Pradip Srimani

Harini Srinivasan

Per Stenstrom

Robert Stets

Erich Strohmaier

Craig Stunkel

Y.J. Suh

Yoram J. Sussmann

Kenji Suzuki

Kaoru Takahashi

Masaru Takesue

Makoto Takizawa

Hong Tang

Parimala Thulasiraman

Ramki Thurimella

Josep Torrellas

Farnaz Mounes-Toussi

Jenn-Yuan Tsai

Chau-Wen Tseng

Yu-Chee Tseng

Masahiko Tsukamoto

Hung-Ying Tyan

Richard Uhlig

Sriram Vajapeyam

D. Vengroff

Jeffrey Vetter

Koichi Wada

Jonathan Walpole

Bin Wang

Biing-Feng Wang

David S.L. Wei

Shu-Shang Sam Wei

Wang Wei

Jennifer Welch

Avishai Wool

C. Eric Wu

Jean-Lien C. Wu

Jie Wu

Haiyan Xu

Lihao Xu

Jingling Xue

Sudhakar Yalamanchili

Ushio Yamamoto

Ming-Hour Yang

Tao Yang

Wuu Yang

Yuanyuan Yang

Baoqing Ye

Yi Ye

Chi-Hsiang Yeh

Honesty Young

Robert Yves

Brad Vander Zanden

Jinsuo Zhang

Li Zhang

Wu Zhao

Yuan Zhou

Yuanyuan Zhou

Huican Zhu

Keynote Address
The Future of Vectors in a Scalable World

Speaker: Steve Oberlin, Vice President
Cray Research

Session 1A
Theory/Algorithms

Chair: George Karypis
University of Minnesota

Simulating PRAM with a MSIMD model (ASC)

Darrell Ulm
University of Akron
Department of Math and Computer Science
Akron, Ohio
dulm@math.uakron.edu

Johnnie W. Baker
Kent State University
Department of Math and Computer Science
Kent, Ohio 44242
jbaker@mcs.kent.edu

Abstract: The ASC (MSIMD) model for parallel computation supports a generalized version of an associative style of computing that has been used since the introduction of associative SIMD computers in the early 1970's. In particular, this model supports data parallelism, constant time maximum and minimum operations, one or more instruction streams (ISs) which are sent to a unique set in a dynamic partition of the processors, and assignment of tasks to the ISs using control parallelism. ASC also allows a network to interconnect the processing elements (PEs). This paper shows how ASC can simulate synchronous PRAM, and the converse. These results provide an important step in defining the power of associative model in terms of PRAM which is the most studied parallel model. Also, these simulations will provide numerous algorithms for ASC by giving an automatic method of converting algorithms from PRAM to ASC.

Keywords : *computational models, parallel models, PRAM, associative computing, ASC, data parallel, massively parallel, SIMD, parallel algorithms*

1. Introduction

The ASC (Associative Computing) model was developed by Johnnie W. Baker, Jerry L. Potter, and others at Kent State University[16]. This model is a generalization of the SIMD paradigm where each of up to k instruction streams (IS) sends commands to a unique set in a dynamic partition of the SIMD processors. A wide range of different types of algorithms and several very large programs have been implemented using the ASC language including a parallel optimizing compiler for ASC, two rule-based inference engines, and an associative PROLOG interpreter[15][16][7][2][6][20][21]. The goal of this paper is to simulate PRAM, a popular model of computing, with ASC; this provides an automatic transfer of PRAM algorithms to ASC with runtime bounds. PRAM is the best known model of parallel computation, and more algorithms have been written for it than any other parallel model. By simulating PRAM, ASC can utilize all PRAM algorithms.

Much previous work has been done concerning simulating PRAM with parallel computers. The work here expands what was known previously by combining existing network methods with the added power gained by having one or more instruction streams that can coordinate and communicate globally.

2. ASC: A Generalized Data Parallel Model

Hillis and Steele[10] defined a the data parallel programming paradigm in the early 1980s, but this work did not provide a complete computational model. The ASC model extends this concept to be a complete programming computational model. It is appropriate to have a model that emphasizes data parallel programming, even though other computational models may be capable of supporting it. Other recently developed models such as BSP and LogP tend to focus on MIMD and distributed computing concepts and thus capture this style of computing best[5]. Furthermore, a 1991 survey reported that 90 percent of parallel applications are data parallel in nature[4].

This section describes the associative model of computation presented in the IEEE Computer article "ASC: An Associative Computing Paradigm," which is based on work done at Kent State University[16]. Also, see [1][2][11][15]. The model can be supported efficiently on a wide variety of existing platforms. Moreover, ASC is a model for a currently buildable, multi-purpose parallel computer which supports a wide array of applications from grand challenge applications requiring massive parallelism to on-chip parallelism for PC interactive graphics. The model reduces the arduous chore of task allocation and embodies the intuitive and well accepted method of data parallel programming. There are many data parallel languages available that ASC encompasses and also an actual language called ASC[16]. The ASC language has been implemented on various platforms such as Thinking Machine's CM-2,

Goodyear/Loral/Lockheed-Martin's Aspro, the Wavetracer, personal computers, and UNIX workstations.

The data parallel style of programming is actually very sequential in nature, and therefore is much easier to master by traditional sequential programmers than MIMD programming which employs task allocation, load balancing, synchronization points, etc. A standard associative language (such as ASC) is implementable across many distinct platforms providing true portability for parallel algorithms[16]. No specific machine architecture is required to effectively use the ASC model. It can be efficiently implemented on PCs, single workstations, SIMDs, MIMDs, and distributed systems. This model is intended to standardize the concept of associative computing and to provide a basis for complexity analysis for data parallel and associative algorithms[8].

2.1. Description of ASC

The ASC model is a hybrid SIMD/MIMD model and is capable of both styles of programming. A frequent criticism of SIMD programming is that several PEs may be idle during if-else or case statements. The instruction streams provide a way to concurrently process conditional statements by partitioning the PEs among the ISs.

In the most basic terms, the *associative model (ASC)* has an large array of processing elements (PEs) and one or more instruction streams (ISs), each of which broadcast their instructions to a unique set in a dynamic partition of all PEs. The number of ISs is normally expected to be small in comparison to the number of PEs. The multiple ISs supported by the ASC model allows greater efficiency, flexibility, and reconfigurability than is possible with only one IS. An ASC machine with j ISs and n PEs will be written as $ASC(n, j)$. Each PE (or *cell*) has a local memory and ASC supports the associative processing concept, which is to locate objects by content instead of by location in the combined local memory of the PEs. This is accomplished by searching a specified field of each PE for a given data item. Each PE is capable of performing local arithmetic and logical operations and the other usual functions of a sequential processor other than issuing instructions.

Cells can be either active, inactive, or idle. Active cells execute the program broadcast from an IS. An inactive cell is in an ISs group of cells, but does not execute instructions until the IS instructs inactive cells to become active again. Idle cells are currently inactive and contain no essential program data but may be re-assigned as an active cell at a later time. ISs can be active or idle. An active IS is currently issuing instructions to a group of cells or waiting to perform a join. An idle IS is not assigned to any PEs and is waiting until another IS forks, partitioning its PEs between itself and a new previously inactive IS. All PEs may be assigned to one IS in a single operation. Also, a PE can change the IS to

which it listens dynamically using local data and comparisons. This, in fact, is the only form of IS switching needed for the ASC simulation of PRAM presented in this paper. For instance, if an IS broadcasts some value to a set of PEs, the PEs could set this value to their active IS in the next instruction cycle, or choose not to switch.

ASC specifically supports data parallelism; the data reduction operations of *and, or, min* and *max*; one or more instruction streams (ISs), each of which is sent to a distinct set in a dynamic partition of the processors; broadcasting by the ISs; and task assignment to ISs using control parallelism or data locality which allows PEs to switch ISs based on local data. The ASC model is shown in Figure 1, and there are three networks, real or virtual, shown in Figure 1: the PE interconnection network, the IS interconnection network, and the network between the PEs and ISs.

There are no restrictions on the type of cell network used with the ASC model. It could be the mesh, hypercube, shuffle-exchange, or many others. The programmer does not need to worry about the actual network present or the routing scheme, but only that ASC is capable of generalized routing with some latency. Some of the most obvious choices for an actual ASC machine are the linear array or the mesh because of the ease to implement them in VLSI and their expandability.

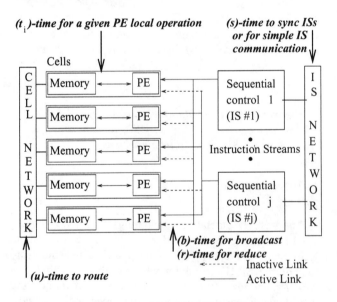

Figure 1. The ASC Model

To ensure running time predictability of the data parallel model on actual machines, the basic operations of the model are abstracted into a few parameters: u is the time to perform a routing of a word among all PEs (a word from each PE to any other PE location), t_i is the time to perform a sequential PE local operation indexed $1 \leq i \leq v$ where v is the number of different operations, s is the maximum time for an IS communication or to synchronize ISs, b is the

4

time to broadcast, and r is the time to do a data reductions *and, or, min, max* involving active PEs. The b parameter also gives the worst case time for an IS to write a single word, while r is the upper bound time for and IS reading from one PE. If the value of v is one then t will represent t_1. The speed of I/O can be measured as the amount of time it takes to read or write a word of information with a secondary storage unit and is represented by d. Other important parameters are the number n of PEs and the number of j ISs.

3. Simulation of PRAM

This section presents algorithms for ASC to simulate PRAM Most notably, the ASC to PRAM simulation achieves a constant lower bound when the PRAM algorithm uses the same order of shared memories as ASC ISs. A specific case is when an ASC(n,1) machine simulates a priority CRCW algorithm employing only $O(1)$ shared memories, then a cycle is simulated in $\theta(1)$ time.

Results in [13][14][4] show that network models, with PEs having a constant bound on the number of links per node *(bounded degree networks)*, can simulate a priority CRCW cycle in $O(\log n)$ with high probability. Thus by combining the one IS ASC simulation presented here with existing methods that use networks, the resulting simulation has a has a runtime of $\theta(1)$ when emulating a constant number of shared memories, and a probabilistic upper bound of $O(\log n)$ for certain logarithmic diameter bounded degree networks (like the hypercube). Moreover, for any network these simulations have a upper-bound of $route(n)$, where $route(n)$ is the amount of time in terms of n to perform a priority CRCW operation using the network. For example, a mesh network could perform this operation in $O(\sqrt{n})$[19].

When *simulation* of a model is performed there are various operations to consider. For parallel models, the operations that need to be simulated are parallel execution of processors and data movement between processors[3]. These are determined with a mapping of processor resources from one model to another and with the algorithmic emulation of operations. When the time complexity of each operation performed in a cycle is divided by the complexity to perform the same operations on the machine being simulated, the maximum time to emulate any operation gives the slowdown of the simulation and also an indication of the relative powers of the two machines or how different they are [13][14][4]. Similar models should simulate each other in nearly the same amount of time. A stronger model simulates a weaker model in significantly less time than conversely.

3.1. A Synchronous Definition of PRAM

A PRAM(n,m) machine is defined as a collection of n sequential (RAM) machines and a set of m global memories. Each RAM of the PRAM has an instruction set, a local memory, and a specific address in the range $(0...n-1)$[9]. During one cycle of execution, each processor executes the same instruction with different data synchronously. The instruction can be a local computation, a read from a global memory $(0...m-1)$, or a write into global memory $(0...m-1)$. Almost all known PRAM algorithms are for synchronous PRAM[17]. It is assumed that one machine cycle takes a constant amount of time regardless of hardware requirements to build such a machine. This paper deals mainly with priority CRCW and combining CRCW although the EREW and CREW simulations are also derived. Priority CRCW allows the PE with the largest address to write its value when several PEs are writing to the same global memory. With combining CRCW, all PEs which write to the same location are combined by some arithmetic or logical operation such as addition. A diagram of PRAM is shown in Figure 2.

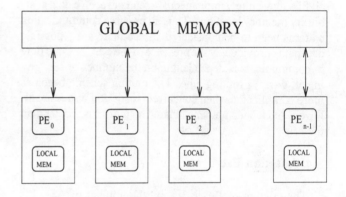

Figure 2. PRAM

3.2. Why Simulate PRAM with ASC?

ASC is a practical data parallel model for real machines, and there is a wealth of PRAM algorithms, so it is of interest to obtain ASC algorithms by simulating PRAM. Many PRAM algorithms map very well to ASC while some may need adjustment in terms of reducing communications at perhaps the cost of performing more computations, especially when considering *parallel slackness* which is defined as the ratio of data to the number of processors. In other words, there should be sufficiently more data than processors so that a parallel algorithm runs optimally.

One algorithm that maps very well to ASC is the $O(\log n)$ expected time PRAM convex hull algorithm that assumes a random distribution of points[12]. It is shown in this section that an ASC machine with only one IS and no network can simulate priority CRCW with a constant number of shared memories in constant time. There are no doubt many other useful priority CRCW algorithms that also use a constant number of shared memories, and these have a corresponding ASC algorithm that executes in the same time. Even without a PE network, ASC has intrinsic capabilities to perform some operations faster than PEs connected only by a bounded degree network since such a network can not perform a 1-to-n broadcast operation in less time than an order of the diameter of the network. For example a mesh needs $\theta(\sqrt{n})$ time to broadcast data, and a hypercube needs $\theta(\log n)$ time to broadcast[19][14].

3.3. Operations Needed for Simulation

To simulate PRAM with any machine, three operations need to be handled: parallel execution of the PEs, reading from the shared memories, and writing to the shared memories[3]. It is assumed that the ASC machine has the same number of PEs and that an ASC PE has the same computational power as a PRAM PE. However, the PRAM reads and writes are highly parallel and complex in nature since all PEs may either simultaneously send or receive data at arbitrary memory locations. Thus all possible communication patterns need to be considered. Since there are j possible data paths provided by the presence of the ASC ISs, the time to communicate is dependent upon the number of ISs, giving an $O(n/j)$ routing time. The routing scheme becomes more complicated when concurrent reads and writes are allowed, and when number of shared memories is greater than the PEs.

3.4. Notation Used

The number of PEs is n, and the number of ASC ISs is j. There are m shared PRAM memories, and it is assumed that PRAM is synchronous. The term *priCRCW* will denote all PRAMs up to and including the power of *priority CRCW*, and the term *comCRCW* will imply all CRCW PRAMs at least as powerful as *combining CRCW PRAM*. The combining CRCW resolves write conflicts by combining data written to a shared memory with some operator (e.g. $+, -, /, *, MIN, MAX, AND, OR, ...$).

3.5. ASC Simulation of Concurrent Read

Without a PE network, the concurrent read operation of CRCW(n,m) is simulated with ASC(n,j) in $O(n/j)$ time with high probability. Figure 3 shows the ASC algorithm. The m PRAM shared memories are hashed into ASC's n PEs, divided more or less equally between each PE. Each IS also *manages* about an equal number of PEs and thus the memories stored in those PEs. This PE to IS assignment is also based on an optimal hashing function. When PRAM

PEs are concurrently reading, this is simulated by each IS collecting, on average, $O(n/j)$ read requests from the PEs. This step is accomplished in $O(n/j)$ with a high probability if an optimal hashing function (uniform parallel hashing) is assumed. Then each IS processes $O(n/j)$ read requests in $O(n/j)$ time, reading the required data from the n PEs. This is possible because each IS may connect to j strictly disjoint subsets of PEs.

* *Gather O(n) read requests to the j ISs ($O(n/j)$ avg. time)*
1 for all PEs and ISs do in parallel
2   set all PEs to *active*
3   if (a PE is not reading) then set the PE to *inactive*
4   *assign* each PE to IS that manages the read request
5   while (any (PEs are $active$))
6   all ISs *select* an arbitrary active PE
7   *select* other PEs reading from same memory
8   *insert* read request into IS read-request list
9   set these selected PEs to *inactive*
* *Read O(n) data requests into j ISs ($O(n/j)$ avg. time)*
10   set all PEs to *active*
11   *assign* each PE to IS which manages memory to be read
12   while (any (PEs are $active$))
13   process next entry in ISs read-request list
14   ISs read a hashed(memory) into read-request list
* *Broadcast read data into requesting PEs ($O(n/j)$ avg. time)*
15   if (a PE is not reading) then set the PE to *inactive*
16   *assign* each PE to IS which manages the memory to be read
17   while (any entries in IS lists are unprocessed)
18   process next entry in ISs read-request list
19   select PEs reading from memory location of this entry
20   broadcast read data into requesting PEs from IS list

Figure 3. $O(n/j)$ **Algorithm to Simulate CR Synchronous priCRCW(n,m) on ASC(n,j)**

3.6. Examining CR Algorithm

Figures 4, 5, 6, and 7 show an example of the major simulation steps of a concurrent read. The following steps referring to Figure 3 show the operations taken to simulate one concurrent read. First, in line 1 all PEs and ISs perform operations in parallel. At line 2 all PEs are made active. Line 3 forces any PEs that are not reading to be temporarily inactive and no longer perform any operations. Line 4 forces each PE listen to the IS processor which manages the PE holding the memory location it wishes to read. In the $5th$ line, iterations are performed until all PEs are inactive and thus have had their read requests saved in the ISs. At line 6 each IS selects an arbitrary PE out of all of its active PEs to save its read-request in a list located at an IS. Each read-request will be saved in only one list in an ISs, one list

6

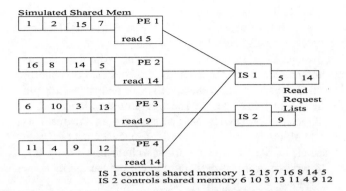

Figure 4. ASC Simulation of PRAM Concurrent Read: building of read request lists

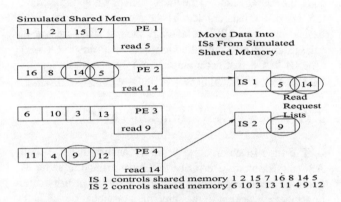

Figure 5. ASC Simulation of PRAM Concurrent Read: moving data to ISs

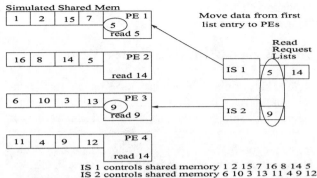

Figure 6. ASC Simulation of PRAM Concurrent Read: handle first entries, and send data that was read to PEs

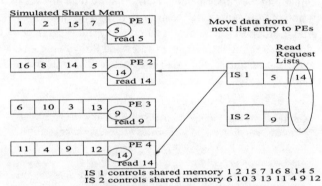

Figure 7. ASC Simulation of PRAM Concurrent Read: handle second entries, and send data that was read to PEs

per IS. For each IS the selected PE's read-address is compared with all other active listening PEs during line 7, and all PEs with the same read request are made active. Line 8 saves the read request (memory location, initial requesting PE) in a list for each IS. The selected PEs which are all reading from the same location concurrently are made inactive at step 9. This process continues until all PEs have their requests stored in a list in each IS. Since there are n PEs and j ISs, an optimal hashing scheme will yield $O(n/j)$ list entries per IS. If there there are only k distinct read locations, where $k \leq n$, the time to complete lines 1-9 is $\theta(1)$.

Lines 10-14 bring data to be read from the PEs into the ISs, which in lines 15-20 is broadcast to the original requesting PEs. Continuing the line by line description, line 10 sets the PEs to be active again, and line 11 assigns PEs to the ISs which manage their shared memories (each IS manages $O(n/j)$ PEs and therefore $O(m/j)$ memories). Line 12 loops while any PEs are still active. Line 13 considers the next read request stored in the IS request list starting from the first entry in the list. At line 14, each IS reads data from the requested memory address in one of the PEs and saves this data at the same location of the list. See Figure 5

for an example of where the data is read.

The lines from 15-20 send this data back out to the PEs that are reading. Line 15 sets PEs inactive if they are not reading. Line 16 assigns each active PE to the IS that manages the memory of that PEs original read request. A loop is made in line 17 until all list entries are processed in the ISs. These lists can be empty if there were no read requests for memories that PE managed, or the lists can contain anywhere from a constant number of requests up to an average of $O(n/j)$ entries. Line 18 fetches the next entry in each IS list starting with the first. PEs that are reading at the memory location of this entry are selected in line 19, and then line 20 broadcasts the data to these PEs.

All operations except the loops are assumed to take a constant amount of time in ASC. Thus the limiting factor is the size of any read request list. Because there are n PEs, on average the lists should be $O(n/j)$ in size, and the entire read process takes $O(n/j)$ with high probability. If all PEs are reading from only k shared memories where $k \leq n$ then the size of the lists will be $O(k/j)$ and the time to complete a concurrent read is $O(k/j)$. Figures 6 and 7 show the data being moved out to the PEs.

3.7. ASC Simulation of Concurrent Write

In $O(n/j)$ time, ASC(n,j) can also simulate concurrent write of priority CRCW(n,m) with high probability using a method very similar to the concurrent read simulation. An overview only is given due to the correspondence between the two algorithms. The ASC algorithm is shown in Figure 8. Again, the shared memory of PRAM is stored in the PEs, hashed among each PE. The memory addressing scheme is the same as the concurrent read algorithm in that each IS manages a roughly equal number of PEs (and shared memory) based on a hashing function. While concurrent writing, data needs to be moved from potentially all n PEs to the PEs containing the target memory cells. If more than one PE is writing to the same cell, the priority rule states that the PE with the highest self address is allowed to write. This is handled by selecting the maximum addressed PE with the ASC reduction operation across a set of active PEs in constant time.

* Gather $O(n)$ write requests into IS lists ($O(n/j)$ time)
* Use reduce max when > 1 PE writes to same location
1 for all PEs and ISs do in parallel
2   set all PEs to active
3   if (a PE is not writing) then set the PE to inactive
4   assign PEs to IS that manages memory request to write
5   while (any (PEs are active))
6   all ISs select maximum active PE
7   select other PEs writing to same memory
8   For each IS, reduce with MAX selected write requests
9   insert reduced write data in IS write-request list
10   set these selected PEs to inactive
* write $O(n)$ data out to memories hashed in PEs ($O(n/j)$ time)
11   set all PEs to active
12   assign each PE to IS that manages memory to write
13   while (any entries in write-request list remain)
14   process next entry in IS's write-request list
15   each IS, WRITEs one data into hashed location

Figure 8. $O(n/j)$ **Algorithm to Simulate CW Synchronous priCRCW(n,m) on ASC(n,j)**

3.8. Examining CW Algorithm

The steps of the for simulating a concurrent write with ASC is shown in Figure 8. Without great detail, similar but shorter than the reading algorithm, lines 1-10 form $O(n/j)$ sized lists of PE write requests with a high probability. When several PEs are trying to write to the same

location, the ASC maximum reduction operation is used to store the PE write request of the largest addressed PE. Thus write conflicts are resolved in constant time.

Lines $11 - 15$ write the data in the write request lists currently located in the ISs to the correct PEs. First, line 11 sets PEs back to active status. Line 12 assigns each PE to the IS which manages it. The algorithm then loops in line 13, each IS processing one list entry from their own lists until all are considered. Line 14 fetches the next entry in each ISs write request list starting with the first. Lastly, line 15 writes a word of data into the correct hashed memory location.

Much like the concurrent read algorithm, all statements except loops are assumed to take a constant time in the ASC model. The simulation of PRAM priority concurrent write takes the average time of the loops each of which is based on the size of the lists created. If the memories are optimally hashed into the n PE, on average the list sizes created in each IS are $O(n/j)$ and the algorithm also runs in $O(n/j)$ time. If $k \leq n$ distinct memories are written into, then the list size s $O(k/j)$, and the algorithm runs in $O(k/j)$.

4. Overview of ASC simulation of PRAM

The time to complete a priority concurrent write with ASC(n,j) simulating priority CRCW(n,m) is the same as that for completing a concurrent read. By the priority rule, multiple PEs writing to the same memory location are handled in one constant time step, using the ASC maximum reduction operation, so the write operation finishes in $O(n/j)$ time. If there are reads or writes involving only k memories, where $0 \leq k \leq n$, then the time can be written as $O(k/j)$. In short, any n processor PRAM algorithm that requires only a constant number of shared memories is simulated with an ASC(n,1) machine in $O(1)$. An example of this is shown in a paper by M. Atwah where the PRAM algorithm to solve the convex hull problem for n randomly distributed points is solved in $O(\log n)$ time with only a constant number of shared memories[2]. There are no doubt many efficient priority CRCW algorithms that require only a constant number of shared memories. These algorithms can execute on a simple one IS ASC machine in the same time as on a PRAM.

Furthermore, by obvious transitivity ASC(n,j) simulates the weaker CREW(n,m) and EREW(n,m) PRAM in the same time as it simulates priority CRCW(n,m)[18][12]. If the number of PRAM shared memories is of the same order as the number of instruction steams, $m = O(j)$, then ASC(n,j) simulates priority CRCW(n,j) in $O(1)$. It may be interesting to note that no matter how much memory or ISs are present, as long as all PEs write to a subset of memory cells that is constant in size, then a step of simulation on ASC(n,1) takes constant time. So it is possible for the simulation to run in $\theta(1)$ extra time per machine cycle in the best situation.

5. Considerations when ASC has a PE Network

If the ASC machine simulating PRAM has an interconnection network between the PEs, traditional methods can be used to simulate PRAM with the network alone, not using the ISs to route data. The simulation of PRAM with parallel machines that have PEs with local memories and a network has is well studied. The concurrent read and write problem is essentially a routing problem on the network. For instance simulation methods that use a mesh network exist where the time to simulate each cycle is $O(\sqrt{n})$. This is fact is the same time it takes to sort n data items on a mesh with n processors. Simulation methods for other networks exist with a bounded number of connection per node (bounded degree networks). The fastest simulates PRAM in probabilistic $O(\log n)$ time, while a wide variety of constant and non-constant degree networks simulate PRAM in average time $O(D)$ where D is the diameter. These networks include the cube-connected cycles, butterfly, shuffle-exchange, mesh, hypercube, star, etc[14][3]. The shared memories are generally hashed amongst the local memory of the n PEs similarly to the ASC simulation method.

However, even if the PRAM being simulated has a constant number of shared memories (e.g., one shared memory), the network simulation of PRAM time is still lower bounded by the diameter of the network, or the time it takes one PE to send a message to another PE. The priority ASC simulation of priCRCW with a constant number of shared memories requires $\theta(1)$ time which is better than the network methods cited above perform.

When ASC has a network, the ASC simulation of PRAM is a hybrid algorithm consisting of a simulation algorithm using only the network, and the ASC method as presented previously. This hybrid algorithm proceeds by performing one network routing step, and then alternately one ASC routing step with a constant extra cost in time and space. Whenever one of the methods finishes a single cycle of simulation, the other algorithm is terminated, and the next cycle is then started. At worst, if both methods finish at the same time, the simulation requires only a constant factor more time, and is no worse than the time for the fastest method to complete. At best, when considering $k \leq n$ shared memories, this hybrid algorithm simulates a step of PRAM in $O(min(k/n, route(n))$ where $route(n)$ is a function of the number of n PEs it takes to simulate one cycle of PRAM using the PE network, and $O(k/n)$ is the time to simulate PRAM with ASC. The ASC method has the capability of improving the fastest simulation of PRAM time, even with the one IS ASC machine. The best running time of this hybrid algorithm is $\theta(1)$ for a constant number of shared memories and is no worse than $O(route(n))$ using a network simulation method.

Reexamining the PRAM algorithm for convex hull on random data points, the fastest known network method to simulate this algorithm on a logarithmic diameter network (e.g., a hypercube, cube-connected cycles, or butterfly) takes $O(\log n)$ simulation steps each of $O(\log n)$ time for a total execution time of $O(\log^2 n)$. However the ASC method alone, or the ASC-Network hybrid method, executes this algorithm in optimal $O(\log n)$ time, an improvement over existing bounded degree network algorithms.

6. An Obvious PRAM Simulation of ASC

This section presents a way to simulate ASC(n,j) with combining CRCW(n,m). It is included for completeness, even though the algorithm is simple, in order to provide some way to compare the two models. Combining CRCW (comCRCW) is used since it simplifies implementing the ASC reduction operators of AND, OR, MAX, and MIN by having the power to make such combinations.

The n PRAM PEs perform the same operations that the ASC PEs can perform, and the IS information for IS_k is stored in $PE_{k\ MOD\ n}$ where $0 \leq k \leq j$. The $PE_{k\ MODn}$ simulate the operations of instruction stream k, and it is assumed that each PRAM PE also has the power of an IS.

However, since ASC ISs are asynchronous, the execution of all ISs is done iteratively in j steps. Since j steps are taken regardless, all control communication between ISs finishes in $O(j)$ time by having each PE simulating an IS write and read synchronization information to a j sized array stored within a single shared memory (assuming that a shared memory has j words). Since EREW and CREW PRAM simulate the CRCW using the same number of PEs and shared memories with a known extra cost of $O(n/m + \log n)$, the extra time for these two models to simulate ASC are easily obtained from the $O(j)$ combining CRCW simulation[12][18].

7. Conclusions of ASC-PRAM simulations

It has been shown how the ASC model can simulate PRAM, and a means for PRAM to simulate ASC has been given. The results in this section allow the number of ISs and shared memories to be unbounded to allow wide comparisons of the models. Table 1 summarizes the current simulation results for the indicated models. Table 2 shows the comparison of PRAM and ASC when the amount of shared memory is proportional to the number of ISs or $m = O(j)$. When this is true, ASC(n,m) simulates priCRCW(n,m) in constant time with a constant amount of space, while comCRCW(n,m) simulates ASC(n,m) in $O(m)$ time with $O(m/n)$ extra space required per PE. The actual number of ASC ISs implementable is no doubt a slow growing function of n, yet even ASC with one IS has a great deal of computational power in practice[15].

simulate	with	time
ASC(n,j)	RAM	$O(n + j)$
priCRCW(n,m)	ASC(n,j)	$O(n/j)$
ASC(n,1)	comCRCW(n,m)	$O(1)$
ASC(n,1)	CREW(n,m)	$O(n/m + \log n)$
ASC(n,j)	comCRCW(n,m)	$O(j)$
ASC(n,j)	CREW(n,m)	$O(\frac{jn}{m} + j * \log n)$

Table 1. Overview of Simulation Times

simulate	with	time
priCRCW(n,m)	ASC(n,m)	$O(1)$
ASC(n,m)	comCRCW(n,m)	$O(m)$
ASC(n,m)	CREW(n,m)	$O(n + m * \log n)$
priCRCW(n,1)	ASC(n,1)	$O(1)$
ASC(n,1)	comCRCW(n,1)	$O(1)$

Table 2. Comparative Simulation Times for PRAM and ASC when $m = cj$ (c is a constant), and for $j = m = 1$

The main goal and future direction of this work is to provide a theoretical foundation for a parallel programming system (ASC) that can be implemented on virtually any type of machine, sequential or parallel, tightly bound or loosely coupled, and to show that ASC has the power to execute well known PRAM algorithms, some of which optimally. Allowing parallel slackness, even difficult PRAM algorithms such as sorting or FFT could be simulated with ASC optimally. It is hoped that this model will enable portable parallel programs to be written for existing and future machines in such a way that the masses of programmers accept the data parallel model as easily as they accept classic sequential programming, finally creating a bridge to practical parallel programming.

References

[1] S. G. Akl. *Parallel Computing: Models and Methods*. Prentice Hall, New York, 1997.

[2] M. Atwah. Computing the convex hull on the associative model. Master's project, Kent State University, Math and Computer Science (MSB), August 1994.

[3] Y. Aumann and A. Schuster. Deterministic pram simulation with constant memory blow-up and no time-stamps. In *Proceedings of the Third Symposium on the Frontiers of Massively Parallel Computation*, pages 22–29, College Park, MD, October 8-10, 1990. IEEE Computer Society Press.

[4] T. Blank and J. R. Nickolls. A grimm collection of mimd fairy tales. In *Proceedings of the Fourth Symposium on the Frontiers of Massively Parallel Computation*, pages 448–457, McLean, VA, October 19-21, 1992. IEEE Computer Society Press.

[5] Culler-Karp-Patterson-Sahay-Schauser-Santos-Subramonian-Eicken. Logp: Towards a realistic model of parallel computation. *Proceedings of the ASC SIGPLAN Symposium on Principles and Practice of Parall el Programming*, pages 235–261, 1993.

[6] P. W. "Darrell Ulm. Solving a two-dimensional knapsack problem on simd computers. In *International Conference on Parallel Processing*, volume 3, pages 181–184, 1992.

[7] M. C. Esenwein. Parallel string matching algorithms using associativve computing and mesh with multiple broadcast. Master's project, Kent State University, Math and Computer Science (MSB), 1995.

[8] A. Falkoff. Algorithms for parallel search memories. *J. Associative Computing*, pages 488–511, March 1962.

[9] S. Fortune and J. Wyllie. Parallelism in random access machines. *Proceeding of the ASC Symposium on the Theory of Computing*, pages 114–118, 1978.

[10] S. Hillis. Data parallel algorithms. *Communications of the ACM*, 29(12):1170–1183, December 1986.

[11] K. F. Hioe. Asprol (associative programming language). Master's project, Kent State University, Math and Computer Science (MSB), August 1986.

[12] J. JaJa. *An Introduction to Parallel Algorithms*. Addison-Wesley, Reading, Massachusetts, 1992.

[13] Z. Lin, Olariu. Simulating enhanced meshes with applications. *Parallel Processing Letters*, 3(1):59–70, 1993.

[14] R. Palis. Packet routing and pram emulation on star graphs and leveled networks. *Journal of Parallel and Distributed Computing*, (20):145–157, 1994.

[15] J. Potter. *Associative Computing — A Programming Paradigm for Massively Parallel Computers*. Plenum Publishing, N.Y., 1992.

[16] Potter-Baker-Scott-Bansal-Leangsuksun-Asthagiri. Asc: An associative computing paradigm. *IEEE Computer*, pages 19–25, November 1994.

[17] M. Quinn. *Parallel Computing:: Theory and Practice*. McGraw Hill, 1994.

[18] J. Rife, editor. *Synthesis of Parallel Algorithms*. Morgan Kofmann Publishers, San Mateo, CA, 1993.

[19] K. Thompson. Sorting on a mesh connected computer. *Communications of the ACM*, 20(4):263–271, April 1977.

[20] D. Ulm and J. Baker. Solving a two-dimensional knapsack problem on a mesh with multiple buses. In *International Conference on Parallel Processing*, volume 3, pages 168–171, 1995.

[21] D. Ulm and J. Baker. Virtual parallelism by self-simulation of the multiple instruction stresm associative model. *Proceedings of the International Conference on Parallel and Distributed Proce ssing Techniques and Applications*, III:1421–1430, August 1996.

Pancake Problems with Restricted Prefix Reversals and some Corresponding Cayley Networks

Douglas W. Bass and I. Hal Sudborough
Computer Science Program
The University of Texas at Dallas
Richardson, Texas USA

Abstract

The pancake problem [7, 10, 14] concerns the number of prefix reversals ("flips") needed to sort the elements of an arbitrary permutation, which is the diameter of the n-dimensional Pancake network [2, 3, 14, 15]. We restrict the problem by allowing only a few of the possible n-1 flips. Let f_i denote a flip of size i We consider sets with either O(1) flips or $\log_2 n$ flips, and explore their corresponding Cayley networks, such as:

*The **Subcube**$_n$ network, for $n = 2^k$, defined by the $\log_2 n$ flips $\{f_2, f_4, f_8 \ldots f_n\}$. Subcube$_n$ is isomorphic to a network obtained from an (n - 1) dimensional hypercube, Q_{n-1}, by deleting all but $\log_2 n$ of the edges incident to each of its nodes, has diameter (3n / 2)-2 (we give an optimum routing algorithm), and hosts Q_{n-1} with nearly optimum dilation.*

*The **Triad**$_n$ network where n is odd and $\lfloor n / 2 \rfloor$ mod $4 \neq 0$, defined by the set of flips $\{f_{\lfloor n/2 \rfloor}, f_{\lceil n/2 \rceil}, f_n\}$. Triad$_n$ has n! nodes and diameter $\Theta(n \log_2 n)$. Both the n-dimensional shuffle-exchange [18] [22] and shuffle-exchange permutation [17] networks can be emulated by Triad$_n$ with constant slowdown.*

Keywords: Pancake problem, sorting permutations, fixed-degree Cayley networks, hypercubes, edge deletion, cube-connected cycles, diameter, routing, embeddings, shuffle-exchange network, shuffle-exchange permutation network.

I. Introduction

The pancake problem [7] concerns the number of prefix reversals or *flips* needed to sort the elements of a permutation. Let f(n) be the maximum number needed to sort any permutation on n symbols. The best bounds known for f(n) are $15n / 14 \le f(n) \le (5n + 5) / 3$ [14], [10].

While O(n) flips are sufficient to sort using the set of all n - 1 possible flips, the degree of the associated pancake network is a linear function of the size of the permutations being sorted. Let f_i represent a flip of size i. For example, a flip of size 4, *i. e.*, f_4, on eight symbols has the effect of

changing, say, 3 5 1 2 4 6 8 7 into 2 1 5 3 4 6 8 7. f_4 is the permutation 4 3 2 1 5 6 7 8. Suppose we have a group G (for example, the symmetric group S_n), and a subset S of G (for example, a set of 3 flips). If every element of G can be generated as a finite product of the elements of S, then the elements of S are called *generators*, and S is called a *generating set* of G. We also say that S *generates* G. If G is a group and S generates G, then the *Cayley network Cay(G, S)* is a network where the nodes are the elements of G, and the edges are all ordered pairs (s, t) where t = sg, for some g $\in$ G and s $\in$ S [15]. Investigating the number of sorting steps needed with sets of only 3 flips is equivalent to investigating the diameter of Cayley networks of degree 3 on S_n and its subgroups. Cayley graphs have been extensively studied [1], [4], [15] as bases for interconnection networks, due to their many desirable properties, including regularity, vertex-symmetry and recursive or near-recursive substructure. Recently, a number of Cayley networks of degree O(1) have been proposed. [20], [17], [16]. Some examples of fixed-degree Cayley networks are shown in Table 1, with diameter results in [21], [5] and [16].

Network	# Nodes	Degree	Diameter
TC_n	$n2^n$	3	$2n-1$
SEP_n	n!	3	$\Theta(n^2)$
Incomplete k-ary n-cube	k^n	4	$\Theta(kn)$

Table 1. Comparing recently introduced fixed-degree Cayley networks

If we find a set S of three flips that allows us to sort in O(f(n)) sorting steps, then we have found a Cayley network of degree 3 on S_n with O(f(n)) diameter. If we find a set of three flips that does not allow us to sort all permutations, then we have found a Cayley network of degree 3 on a subgroup of S_n.

11

II. Subcube$_n$, a network isomorphic to a spanning subnetwork of a hypercube.

Menger's Theorem states if a network has vertex-connectivity k, then any two distinct nodes are connected by k vertex-disjoint paths [11]. As the binary hypercube Q_n has vertex-connectivity n, perhaps some, or even most of the links can be removed from Q_n without affecting its diameter. This has been a subject of recent research [8], [6] [13]. It has been shown that $(n-2)2^{n-1} + 1 - \left\lceil \dfrac{2^n - 1}{2n - 1} \right\rceil$ links can be removed from Q_n without increasing its diameter [6]. However, the resulting network is not regular. It is also known that the cube-connected cycles network of dimension n (CCC$_n$) is a spanning subnetwork of $Q_{n + \log n}$, when n = 2^k for some k > 1 [18]. We now introduce a Cayley network of degree $\log_2$ n isomorphic to a spanning subnetwork of Q_{n-1}.

Consider the set $F_n = \{f_2, f_4, f_8, ..., f_n\}$ of flips to be performed on permutations of length n, where n = 2^k for some k ≥ 1. Consider the group $G(F_n)$ that F_n generates. Let Subcube$_n$ be defined as Cay($G(F_n)$, F_n). The set of flips never moves individual elements out of their original blocks of lengths 2, 4, ..., n. Consider the identity permutation I_n = 1 2 ... n of n distinct unsigned symbols. The ith block of size $r = 2^p$, for some p (1 ≤ p ≤ k), in any permutation $\pi = \pi_1 \pi_2 ... \pi_n$ of I_n consists of the symbols $\pi_{(i-1)r+1}$, $\pi_{(i-1)r+2}$, ..., $\pi_{(i-1)r+r}$. A permutation π is in G(F) if and only if for all i and all p, there exists a j such that the symbols in the ith block of size r of I_n are exactly the symbols in the jth block of size r of π. This can be shown be downward induction on r. Somewhat equivalently we show the following.

Lemma 1: Subcube$_n$ is a network with 2^{n-1} nodes.

Proof: Proof by induction on n. Subcube$_2$ has 2 nodes ((1 2), (2 1)). Suppose for the inductive step Subcube$_n$ has 2^{n-1} nodes. Subcube$_{2n}$ generates 2^{n-1} permutations of elements 1 through n, by the flips of F_n. Subcube$_{2n}$ can bring elements n + 1 through 2n into positions 1 through n by f_{2n}. Subcube$_{2n}$ can now generate 2^{n-1} permutations of elements n + 1 through 2n, by the flips of F_n. The first n positions could be occupied by either elements 1 through n, or elements n + 1 through 2n. There are 2^{n-1} permutations of element 1 through n, and 2^{n-1} permutations of elements n + 1 through 2n. Subcube$_{2n}$ is therefore the product of the three objects Subcube$_n$, Subcube$_n$ and Subcube$_2$, and has $2^{n-1} * 2^{n-1} * 2 = 2^{2n-1}$ nodes. ν

The blocks of elements that must be reversed to route from the identity to a node in Subcube$_n$ can be represented by a bit string of n - 1 values b_1, b_2 ..., b_{n-1}, which is constructed from left to right by the following:

- $b_1 = 1$ ⇔ The string of all elements need to be reversed by f_n.
- $b_2 = 1$ ⇔ The string formed by the symbols in the 1st block of length n / 2 of I_n, wherever it is, needs to be reversed.
- $b_3 = 1$ ⇔ The string formed by the symbols in the 2nd block of length n / 2 of I_n, wherever it is, needs to be reversed...

In general...

- $b_k = 1$, where k = $\left(\displaystyle\sum_{j=0}^{i} 2^j \right) + t$, for some t (1 ≤ t ≤ 2^{i+1}) ⇔ The string formed by the symbols in the tth block of length n / (2^{i+1}) of I_n, wherever it is, needs to be reversed.

Example: Consider the permutation 6 5 8 7 3 4 2 1. F_8 = $\{f_2, f_4, f_8\}$, and this permutation will be mapped to a bit string of length 7. To obtain this permutation from the identity using the flips of F_8, elements 1 through 8 of the identity must be reversed by f_8, resulting in 8 7 6 5 4 3 2 1, so $b_1 = 1$. The elements 1 through 4 (the 1st block of length n / 2 of I_n), do not have to be reversed, so $b_2 = 0$. The elements 5 through 8 must be reversed, giving 5 6 7 8 4 3 2 1, so $b_3 = 1$. b_4, b_5, b_6 and b_7 represent the reversals of the pairs of elements (1, 2), (3, 4), (5, 6) and (7, 8), respectively. Elements 1 and 2 do not have to be reversed, so $b_4 = 0$. The remaining pairs of elements must be reversed, giving 6 5 8 7 3 4 2 1, and a corresponding bit string of 1 0 1 0 1 1 1.

Theorem 1: Subcube$_n$ is isomorphic to a spanning subnetwork of Q_{n-1} of degree $\log_2$ n.

Proof: Let M_1: Subcube$_n$ → Q_{n-1} be the mapping described above. It follows from the definition of obtaining the bit string $b_1 b_2 ... b_{n-1}$ that for any permutation in $G(F_n)$ there is a unique binary string in $\{0, 1\}^{n-1}$. So, M_1 is one-to-one. We need to show that M_1 is an isomorphism. Let π and π' be permutations in $G(F_n)$ such that $\pi f_i = \pi'$, for some f_i in F_n. If $f_i = f_n$, i. e., π' is the reversal of the entire permutation π, then $M_1(\pi)$ and $M_1(\pi')$ differ in position 1. If $f_i = f_{n/2}$, then π' is obtained by reversing the first half of π, so $M_1(\pi)$ and $M_1(\pi')$ differ in either position 2 or 3. That is, if the entire string is reversed, then this half size reversal toggles bit 3; otherwise, it toggles bit 2. If $f_i = f_{n/k}$, then $M_1(\pi)$ and $M_1(\pi')$ differ in one and only one of the positions k through 2k - 1. If π has the jth block of length n / k of I_n in positions 1 through n / k, then $M_1(\pi)$ and $M_1(\pi')$ differ in position k + j -1. Thus, M_1 is an isomorphism between $N(F_n)$ and a spanning subnetwork of Q_{n-1}. ν

12

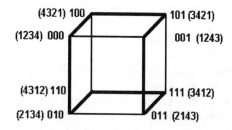

Figure 1. Subcube₄ (dark edges) is a spanning subnetwork of Q₃

Subcube$_n$ contains 2^{n-1} permutations, and is isomorphic to Q_{n-1} with a particular set of $n - 1 - (\log_2 n)$ of the edges incident to each node were removed. Figure 1 shows the relationship between Subcube₄ and Q₃.

Suppose we are trying to route in Subcube$_n$ to a permutation π'. Algorithm ROUTE (shown in Figure 2) returns the sequence of flips required to route from π to π', which through the isomorphism M_1 can also be viewed as a sequence of bit toggles to route between nodes in Q_{n-1}.

Example: Suppose we wished to route from 3 4 1 2 7 8 6 5 to 8 7 6 5 1 2 4 3. Algorithm ROUTE returns the sequence $\{f_4, f_2, f_4, f_8, f_4, f_2\}$ to route from $\{3\ 4\ 1\ 2\ 7\ 8\ 6\ 5\}$ to $\{8\ 7\ 6\ 5\ 1\ 2\ 4\ 3\}$, *i. e.*, from $\{0\ 1\ 1\ 1\ 1\ 0\ 1\}$ to $\{1\ 1\ 0\ 0\ 1\ 0\ 0\}$ in Q_7.

The maximum length of the sequence returned by Algorithm ROUTE is an upper bound on the diameter of Subcube$_n$.

Theorem 2: The diameter of Subcube$_n \le (3n / 2) - 2$.

Proof: Figure 1 shows that Subcube₄ is a simple cycle of length 8. Therefore its diameter is 4. Because of the definition of Subcube$_n$, Subcube$_n$ contains Subcube$_{n/2}$ as a subnetwork. Consider the algorithm ROUTE in Figure 2. In the worst case, (a) the elements in positions 1 through n / 2 need to be arranged, taking no more flips than the diameter of Subcube$_{n/2}$, (b) the elements in positions (n / 2)+1 through n are moved to positions 1 through n / 2 by the flip f_n, taking 1 flip, (c) the elements that were in positions (n / 2) + 1 through n, but are now in positions 1 through n / 2 need to be arranged, again taking no more flips than the diameter of Subcube$_{n/2}$, and (d) the elements in positions 1 through n / 2 are moved back to positions (n / 2) + 1 through n by the flip f_n, taking 1 flip. Thus, the diameter of Subcube$_n$ is described by the recurrence relation D(n) = 2D(n / 2) + 2, D(4) = 4, whose solution is (3n / 2) - 2. ν

Table 2 shows how Subcube$_n$ compares with Q_{n-1}. Since Subcube$_n$ has 2^{n-1} nodes, its diameter is $\Theta(\log N)$, where N is the number of nodes.

```
Algorithm ROUTE(π, π', n)
begin
  if n = 2 then
    begin
      if π₁ ≠ π'₁ then
        f₂
    end
  else
    if the first n / 2 elements of π are same as the
    first n / 2 elements of π' then
      begin
        ROUTE({π₁...π_size / 2}, {π'₁...π'_size / 2}, n / 2)
        Apply fₙ to π
        ROUTE({π₁...π_size / 2},
            {π'_size π'_size - 1... π'_(size / 2) + 1}, n / 2)
        Apply fₙ to π
      end
    else
      begin
        ROUTE({π₁...π_size / 2},
            {π'_size π'_size - 1... π'_(size / 2) + 1}, n / 2)
        Apply fₙ to π
        ROUTE({π₁...π_size / 2}, {π'₁...π'_size / 2}, n / 2)
      end
end
```

Figure 2. A routing algorithm for Subcube$_n$

Measure	Subcube$_n$	Q_{n-1}
Degree = f(n)	log n	n
Diameter = f(n)	(3n / 2) - 2	n
Degree = f(N)	log((log N) + 1)	log N
Diameter = f(N)	(3/2)((log N)+1)	log N

Table 2. Comparing Subcube$_n$ with Q_{n-1}

A generating set G is called *minimal* if and only if removing any generator causes the set to generate a smaller set [15].

Lemma 2: F_n is a minimal generating set.

Proof: If f_2 is removed from the generating set, then one can never separate individual elements of blocks of four contiguous elements, so the result is a smaller set. If f_k is removed, where $2 < k < n$, then individual elements in the range k / 2 through 3k / 2 cannot be separated from each other, resulting in a smaller set. If f_n is removed, then the elements in the range n / 2 through n cannot be moved, resulting in a smaller set. ν

The *fault tolerance* of a network is the minimum number of nodes that must be removed to disconnect the network. A network is *complete* when there is a link between each pair of nodes. The fault tolerance of a non-complete network is one less than its vertex-connectivity. A regular network of degree d and fault-tolerance d-1 is *maximally fault tolerant*.

Theorem 3: $N(F_n)$ is maximally fault tolerant.

Proof: This follows from Lemma 3 and the fact that all Cayley networks with minimal generating sets are maximally fault tolerant [12]. ∨

III. Properties of generating sets

If the inverse of every generator is again in the generating set, then the Cayley network will be undirected. Cayley networks generated by sets of flips are always undirected, since every flip is its own inverse.

Theorem 4: Let f(n) be the diameter of any undirected Cayley network on S_n generated by a set of O(1) generators. Then, $f(n) = \Omega(n \log_2 n)$.

Proof: Start with the identity permutation and apply all k generators. k + 1 nodes have now been reached. Apply all k generators again to all the nodes that have been reached. No more than $k + 1 + (k * (k - 1)) = k^2 + 1$ nodes could be reached, because one of the generators is the inverse of a previously applied generator. Repeat this process d times. No more than $k + 1 + (k *(k - 1)^{d-1})$ nodes could be reached. When $k + 1 + (k * (k - 1)^{d-1}) = n!$, then all nodes are reached. $k + 1 + (k * (k - 1)^{d-1}) = \Theta(k^d)$. If $n! = \Theta(k^d)$, then $\log_2 n! = \log_2(\Theta(k^d)) = \log_2 k^d + \Theta(1)$, which is $d \log_2 k + \Theta(1)$. Since $\log_2 n! = \Omega(n \log_2 n)$, $d = \Omega(n \log_2 n)$. ∨

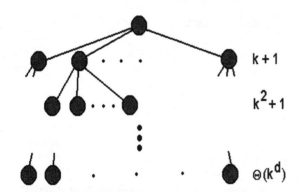

Figure 3. The maximum number of nodes that can be reached by d sorting steps

Consider the elements of a permutation π arranged in order around a circle so that π_n is adjacent to π_1. Let d(i, j) be the minimum circular distance between elements i and j. Let π and σ be two permutations

on n symbols. Then let the **displacement**
$$D(\pi, \sigma) = \sum_{i=1}^{n-1} d(\sigma_i, \sigma_{i+1}) - \sum_{i=1}^{n-1} d(\pi_i, \pi_{i+1}).$$ If σ is the permutation that results from applying the flip of size i to π, then $D(i) = D(\pi, \sigma)$. Notice that $D(n) = 0$, since there is no change in the relative circular positions of the elements. In general, $D(i) = O(i^2)$ for $i \le n / 2$, and $D(i) = O((n - i)^2)$ for $i > n / 2$. Consider the permutation $\pi = 1\ 3\ 5\ ...\ n - 1\ 2\ 4\ 6\ ...\ n$. Then $D(\pi, I_n) = (n / 2)(n / 2) + ((n / 2) - 1)((n / 2) - 1) - (n - 1) = n^2 / 2 - 2n + 2$. In order to sort in k steps, a set of flips must contain a flip with a displacement of at least $(n^2 / 2 - 2n + 2) / k$. Substituting $k = O(n \log_2 n)$, it follows that a set of flips must contain a flip with a displacement of $\Omega(n / \log_2 n)$.

Theorem 5: A generating set of flips must contain a flip of size i where $O(\sqrt{n / \log n}) \le i \le n - O(\sqrt{n / \log n})$, if it allows sorting in $\Theta(n \log_2 n)$ flips.

While the following sets of flips are able to sort an arbitrary permutation, they take $\Omega(n^2)$ steps, because the maximum displacement of any flip in any of these sets is O(1): $\{f_2, f_{n-1}, f_n\}$, $\{f_{n-2}, f_{n-1}, f_n\}$, $\{f_{n-3}, f_{n-2}, f_n\}$, $\{f_3, f_{n-1}, f_n\}$ where n is odd, $\{f_2, f_{n-2}, f_n\}$ where n is odd, $\{f_{n-3}, f_{n-1}, f_n\}$, where n is odd, and $\{f_3, f_{n-2}, f_n\}$, where n is even.

IV. The Triad network $Triad_n$.

$Triad_n$, where n is odd, is the network on S_n where the generating set is $\{f_{\lfloor n/2\rfloor}, f_{\lceil n/2\rceil}, f_n\}$. $Triad_n$ has n! nodes and 3n! / 2 edges. This network is an attempt to keep the benefits of fixed-degree Cayley networks on S_n, (vertex-symmetry, n! nodes, fixed-degree, routing equivalent to sorting) while attaining a network of optimal asymptotic diameter. $Triad_n$ has much better diameter, *i. e.*, $\Theta(n \log_2 n)$, than the recently studied shuffle-exchange permutation network, SEP_n, which has $\Theta(n^2)$ diameter [5].

Figure 4. A portion of Triad₇

Let LEFT(i, j, k) be defined as a left shuffle (cyclic shift) of elements π_i through π_j by k positions. Let RIGHT(i, j, k) be defined similarly, but for a right shuffle, and let EXCHANGE(i, i + 1) denote LEFT(i, i + 1, 1). If $(G_1, G_2, ..., G_n)$ is a sequence of generators, then let $(G_1, G_2, ..., G_n)^i$ represent i successive applications of that sequence.

Theorem 6: $Triad_n$ is a Cayley network on S_n for $n \geq 5$ where n is odd and $\lfloor n/2 \rfloor \bmod 4 \neq 0$.

Proof: Since SEP_n is known to be a Cayley network on all of S_n, we show $Triad_n$ to be a Cayley network on all of S_n by showing that a sequence of $Triad_n$ generators produce the generators of SEP_n, namely {LEFT(1, n, 1), RIGHT(1, n, 1), EXCHANGE(1, 2)}. When n is odd, LEFT(1, n, 1) can be accomplished by the sequence {$f_{\lceil n/2 \rceil}$, f_n, $f_{\lceil n/2 \rceil}$, $f_{\lceil n/2 \rceil}$, f_n, $f_{\lceil n/2 \rceil}$}. A right shuffle can be simulated by applying the left shuffle sequence in reverse order. LEFT(1, n, k) = LEFT(1, n, 1)^k. When $\lfloor n/2 \rfloor \bmod 4 \neq 0$, EXCHANGE($\lfloor n/2 \rfloor$, $\lceil n/2 \rceil$) is effected by the sequence ($f_{\lceil n/2 \rceil}$, LEFT(1, n, 2), ($f_{\lceil n/2 \rceil}$, LEFT (1, n, 1))$^{\lfloor n/2 \rfloor}$). Elements π_1 and π_2 can be transposed by the sequence {RIGHT(1, n, $\lfloor n/2 \rfloor$ - 1), EXCHANGE($\lfloor n/2 \rfloor$, $\lceil n/2 \rceil$), LEFT(1, n, $\lfloor n/2 \rfloor$ - 1)}. As the three generators of SEP_n can be simulated by sequences of $Triad_n$ generators, $Triad_n$ is a Cayley network on S_n where n is odd and $\lfloor n/2 \rfloor \bmod 4 \neq 0$. ν

If n is even, then the generators of SEP_n cannot be simulated by the above method. If $\lfloor n/2 \rfloor \bmod 4 = 0$, then $f_{\lfloor n/2 \rfloor}$, $f_{\lceil n/2 \rceil}$, f_n all correspond to even numbers of transpositions. When this is the case, EXCHANGE($\lfloor n/2 \rfloor$, $\lceil n/2 \rceil$) cannot be done, and the largest set that can be generated is the alternating group.

In order to prove the $O(n \log_2 n)$ bound for the diameter of $Triad_n$, we describe operations that can be simulated by an $O(1)$ length sequence of $Triad_n$ generators. We can use these operations as a macro to prove our bound. If LEFT(i, j, k) can be simulated by a given sequence, then RIGHT(i, j, k) can be simulated by applying that sequence in reverse order.

1) *RIGHT(1, $\lceil n/2 \rceil$, 1)* : $f_{\lceil n/2 \rceil}$, $f_{\lceil n/2 \rceil}$.
2) *LEFT($\lceil n/2 \rceil$, n, 1)* : f_n, RIGHT(1, $\lceil n/2 \rceil$, n), f_n. *LEFT(1, n, 1)* : $f_{\lceil n/2 \rceil}$, f_n, $f_{\lceil n/2 \rceil}$, $f_{\lceil n/2 \rceil}$, f_n, $f_{\lceil n/2 \rceil}$.
3) *LEFT($\lfloor n/2 \rfloor$, $\lceil n/2 \rceil$ + 1, 1)* : LEFT($\lceil n/2 \rceil$, n, 1), RIGHT(1, $\lceil n/2 \rceil$, 1), RIGHT($\lceil n/2 \rceil$, n, 1), LEFT(1, $\lceil n/2 \rceil$, 1).
4) *LEFT($\lceil n/2 \rceil$ + 1, n, 2)* : RIGHT($\lceil n/2 \rceil$, n, 1), RIGHT($\lfloor n/2 \rfloor$, $\lceil n/2 \rceil$ + 1, 1), RIGHT($\lceil n/2 \rceil$, n, 1), RIGHT($\lfloor n/2 \rfloor$, $\lceil n/2 \rceil$ + 1, 1).
5) *LEFT(1, $\lfloor n/2 \rfloor$, 2)* : f_n, LEFT($\lceil n/2 \rceil$ + 1, n, 2), f_n.
6) $\pi_1 \pi_2 \ldots \pi_n \longrightarrow \pi_1 \pi_2 \ldots \pi_{\lfloor n/2 \rfloor} \pi_{\lceil n/2 \rceil - 1)} \pi_{\lceil n/2 \rceil + 1)} \pi_{\lceil n/2 \rceil} \ldots \pi_n$: RIGHT(1, $\lceil n/2 \rceil$, 1), LEFT($\lceil n/2 \rceil$, n, 1), RIGHT(1, $\lceil n/2 \rceil$, 1), LEFT($\lceil n/2 \rceil$, n, 1), LEFT(1, n, 2), RIGHT($\lceil n/2 \rceil$, n, 2).

We will partition elements p through r by shuffling π_q into position $\lceil n/2 \rceil$. Since we have RIGHT(1, $\lceil n/2 \rceil$, 1), and LEFT($\lceil n/2 \rceil$, n, 1), we can use the right and left ends of the permutation as the tops of two "stacks" for elements p through q and elements q + 1 through r, respectively. The

element in position $\lceil n/2 \rceil$ will be pushed onto one of these two stacks. When k < n elements are being partitioned, sometimes the last element between p and q is moved to its stack while there are still elements between q + 1 and r in positions $\lceil n/2 \rceil$ + 1, $\lceil n/2 \rceil$ + 2, ..., $\lceil n/2 \rceil$ + k. In the same way, sometimes the last element between q + 1 and r is moved to its stack while there are still elements between p and q in positions $\lfloor n/2 \rfloor$, $\lfloor n/2 \rfloor$ - 1, ... $\lfloor n/2 \rfloor$ - k. To resolve this, we apply RIGHT(1, $\lfloor n/2 \rfloor$, 2), or LEFT($\lceil n/2 \rceil$ + 1, n, 2), as needed.

At this point, the elements p through q are in positions 1 through q - p + 1, and the elements q + 1 through r are in positions n - r + q + 1 through n. We must put the partitioned halves back into their original positions without disturbing the relative positions of the other elements. We shuffle the elements p through q into positions $\lceil n/2 \rceil$ - p + q through $\lceil n/2 \rceil$. We move the elements q + 1 through r into positions $\lceil n/2 \rceil$ + 1 through $\lceil n/2 \rceil$ + r by the sequence (RIGHT($\lceil n/2 \rceil$, n, 1), RIGHT($\lfloor n/2 \rfloor$, $\lceil n/2 \rceil$ + 1, 1))$^{r-q}$. It doesn't matter that the relative position of some of the elements between p and q are being changed by this sequence, because the partition around q is not being disrupted.

SORT(π, p, r, n)
   begin
      if (r - p) $\geq$ 1 **then**
      begin
         q $\Downarrow$ (p + r) / 2
         Partition π so that elements p through q
            are in positions p $\pm$ k through
            q $\pm$ k in arbitrary order, and
            elements q + 1 through r are in
            positions q + 1 $\pm$ k through r $\pm$ k, for
            some k $\leq$ n / 2
         SORT(π, p, q, n)
         SORT(π, q + 1, r, n)
      end
      if (r - p + 1 = n) **then**
         Shuffle 1 into position 1 in as few flips as
         possible
   end

Figure 5. A routing algorithm for $Triad_n$

The algorithm will eventually get to the point of partitioning two elements. We move the two elements into positions $\lfloor n/2 \rfloor$ - 1 and $\lfloor n/2 \rfloor$. We then apply the sequence that changes $\pi_1 \pi_2 \ldots \pi_n$ into $\pi_1 \pi_2 \ldots \pi_{\lfloor n/2 \rfloor} \pi_{(\lfloor n/2 \rfloor - 1)} \pi_{(\lceil n/2 \rceil + 1)} \pi_{\lceil n/2 \rceil} \ldots \pi_n$. It doesn't matter that the elements in positions $\lceil n/2 \rceil$ and $\lceil n/2 \rceil$ + 1 are being transposed, because the algorithm will resolve them later. This strategy will not work for putting n - 1 and n in order, because it

15

would disrupt the position of 1 and 2. In the proof of Theorem 3, we mentioned that the sequence $\{f_{\lceil n/2\rceil}$, LEFT$(1, n, 2), (f_{\lfloor n/2\rfloor}$, LEFT$(1, n, 1))^{\lfloor n/2\rfloor}\}$ will transpose the elements in positions $\lfloor n/2\rfloor$ and $\lceil n/2\rceil$ in O(n) flips. We will use this sequence if and only if n and n - 1 need to be transposed. This completes the description of the partitioning algorithm, which is given in full detail below. Selected statements are numbered to describe the number of moves required by the algorithm.

Theorem 7: The diameter of Triad$_n$ is $\Theta(n \log_2 n)$.

Proof: When PARTITION(π, p, q, r) is called, and less than n elements are being partitioned, then either 1), the right end of the elements to be partitioned are in position $\lceil n/2\rceil$, or 2) the left end of the elements to be partitioned are in position $\lceil n/2\rceil + 1$. Statement 5) therefore requires O(n) flips, where n is the number of elements being partitioned. Statements 6) through 12) require O(1) flips and are executed O(n) times, therefore requiring O(n) flips. Statements 1) and 2) require O(1) flips. Statements 3) and 4) require O(n) flips, but are only executed once throughout all the calls to PARTITION. Therefore, if there are n elements to be partitioned, then PARTITION requires O(n) flips. The number of flips required by SORT is described by the recurrence T(n) = 2T(n / 2) + O(n), because PARTITION requires O(n) flips, and it takes O(n) flips to put n - 1 and n in the proper order, and shuffle 1 into position 1 at the end. The solution of the recurrence is O(n $\log_2$ n). Since the diameter of Triad$_n$ is Ω(n $\log_2$ n) by Theorem 4, the diameter of Triad$_n$ is Θ(n $\log_2$ n). ∨

Corollary 1: Triad$_n$ is a Cayley network of degree 3 on S_n with asymptotically optimal diameter (up to constant factors).

Example: Consider the permutation 7162543. We will first partition the entire permutation: $7162543 \xrightarrow{(2)} 2716543 \xrightarrow{(4)} 2715436 \xrightarrow{(4)} 2714365 \xrightarrow{(2)} 4271365 \xrightarrow{(2)} 1427365 \xrightarrow{(4)} 1423657$. Now we will partition 1 through 4. $1423657 \xrightarrow{(12)} 5714236 \xrightarrow{(4)} 5712364 \xrightarrow{(2)} 2571364 \xrightarrow{(2)} 1257364 \xrightarrow{(32)} 1257436 \xrightarrow{(4)} 5712436$. 1 and 2 are in order, therefore put 3 and 4 in order. $5712436 \xrightarrow{(18)} 2436571 \xrightarrow{(30)} 2345671 \xrightarrow{(6)} 1234567$. While this permutation was selected at random, putting 3 and 4 in order had the happy consequence of putting 5 and 6 in order as well.

PARTITION(π, p, q, r)
begin
  if $(r = p)$ **then**
    do nothing
  else if $(r - p)=1$ **then**
  begin
    if r is before p **then**
      if $p \neq n-1$ or $n-2$ **then**
      begin
1)   Move r and p to positions $\lfloor n/2\rfloor - 1$ and $\lfloor n/2\rfloor$
2)   Change $\pi_1\,\pi_2\ldots\pi_n$ into $\pi_1\,\pi_2\ldots\pi_{\lfloor n/2\rfloor}\,\pi_{(\lfloor n/2\rfloor-1)}\,\pi_{(\lceil n/2\rceil+1)}\,\pi_{\lceil n/2\rceil}\ldots\pi_n$
      end
      else
      begin
3)   Move p and r to positions $\lfloor n/2\rfloor$ and $\lceil n/2\rceil$
4)   Apply $\{f_{\lceil n/2\rceil}$, LEFT$(1, n, 2),$ $(f_{\lfloor n/2\rfloor}$, LEFT$(1, n, 1))^{\lfloor n/2\rfloor}\}$
      end
  end
  else
  begin
5) Move the element corresponding to q to position $\lceil n/2\rceil$
    while there are elements between p and q in positions $q + 1$ to r **do**
    begin
      if the element in position $\lceil n/2\rceil$ is between p and q **then**
6)   RIGHT$(1, \lceil n/2\rceil, 1)$ // 2 flips
      else
7)   LEFT$(\lceil n/2\rceil, n, 1)$ // 4 flips
    end
    while there are elements between p and q not on the right end **do**
8)   RIGHT$(1, \lfloor n/2\rfloor, 2)$ // 34 flips
    while there are elements between $q + 1$ and r not on the left end **do**
9)   LEFT$(\lceil n/2\rceil + 1, n, 2)$ // 32 flips
    while there are elements between p and q on the right end **do**
10)   LEFT$(1, \lceil n/2\rceil, 1)$ // 2 flips
    while there are elements between $q + 1$ and r on the left end **do**
    begin
11)   RIGHT$(\lceil n/2\rceil, n, 1)$ // 4 flips
12)   RIGHT$(\lfloor n/2\rfloor, \lceil n/2\rceil + 1, 1)$ // 12 flips
    end
  end
end

Figure 6. A partitioning algorithm for Triad$_n$

16

In the algorithm PARTITION, statement 5 takes $6(q - p)$ flips, or roughly $3n$ flips, where n is the number of elements being partitioned. Statements 6 and 7 take at most $4n$ flips. Statements 8 and 9 will be executed no more than $n / 2$ times, adding at most $17n$ flips. Statement 10 will be executed $n / 2$ times, adding n flips. Statements 11 and 12 will be executed $n / 2$ times, adding $8n$ flips, for a total of $3n + 4n + 17n + n + 8n = 33n$. The constant is less when only 2 elements are being partitioned. Therefore the recurrence equation is $T(n) = 2T(n / 2) + 33n$, $T(1) = 0$, whose solution is $33(n \log_2 n)$.

V. Embeddings Into Triad$_n$.

Since the efficiency of many parallel algorithms in dependent on the topology of the interconnection network, it is useful to determine a rough upper bound on the number of Triad$_n$ flips required to simulate moves in other networks.

The star network is bipartite, with the bipartition based on permutations with even and odd numbers of transpositions. Let the mapping M_2 be as follows:

- If π is an even permutation, then $M_2(\pi) = \pi$
- If π is odd, then $M_2(\pi) = (\pi_2 \ \pi_3 \ \dots \ \pi_{(\lfloor n / 2 \rfloor - 1)} \ \pi_1 \ \pi_{\lceil n / 2 \rceil} \dots \pi_n)$

Theorem 8: M_2 embeds S_n into Triad$_n$ with dilation $n + O(1)$

Theorem 9: M_2 embeds SEP$_n$ into Triad$_n$ with dilation $O(1)$

We will construct an embedding of the shuffle-exchange network of dimension n, SE$_n$ into Triad$_n$ by constructing an embedding of SE$_n$ into SEP$_n$. Let $G = (V, E)$ and $H = (V', E')$ be two networks, and let f be a function mapping nodes in V to subsets of V' other than the empty set. f is called a *dilation d one-to-many embedding* if for every pair of adjacent nodes u and v in V, 1) f(u) and f(v) share no nodes in common, and 2) there is a node x in f(u) and a node y in f(v) such that the distance in H between x and y is $\leq d$ [9], [19]. It should be noted that in one-to-many embeddings there is no need for communication between distinct host nodes that serve as images of the same guest processor. This is so, because hosts for a given guest compute exactly the same information. They represent redundant copies of the same guest computation.

Let M_3 be a one-to-one mapping between a bit string B of SE$_n$ and the permutations $M_3(B)$ of SEP$_n$ as follows:

- $B_1 = 0 \Leftrightarrow 1$ is to the left of 2 in $M_3(B)$
- $B_2 = 0 \Leftrightarrow$ the rightmost element of $\{1, 2\}$ is to the left of the leftmost element of $\{3, 4\}$ in $M_3(B)$
- $B_3 = 0 \Leftrightarrow 3$ is to the left of 4 in $M_3(B)$

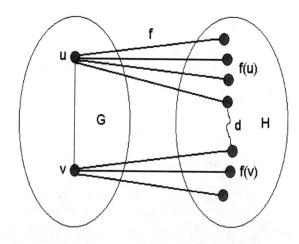

Figure 7. A dilation d one-to-many embedding of G into H

- $B_4 = 0 \Leftrightarrow$ the rightmost element of $\{3, 4\}$ is to the left of the leftmost element of $\{5, 6\}$ in $M_3(B)$
    - *
    - *
    - *
- $B_{n-1} = 0 \Leftrightarrow n - 1$ is to the left of n in $M_3(B)$.
- $B_n = 1 \Leftrightarrow$ the element in position n is swapped with the element in position 1 in $M_3(B)$

Consider the bit string $B = 0\ 1\ 1\ 1\ 1\ 0\ 1$. $B_1 = 0$, so 1 is to the left of 2 in $M_3(B)$ $(1\ 2\ *\ *\ *\ *\ *)$. B_2 and B_3 are 1, so 4 is to the left of 3 in $M_3(B)$, and 2 (the rightmost element of $\{1, 2\}$) is to the right of 4 (the leftmost element of $\{3, 4\}$) in $M_3(B)$ $(1\ 4\ 2\ *\ *\ *\ *)$. B_4, B_5 and B_6 yield $1\ 4\ 2\ 6\ 3\ 5\ 7$. Since $B_7 = 1$, the elements in positions 1 and 7 are swapped, and $M_3(B) = 7\ 4\ 2\ 6\ 3\ 5\ 1$.

Let M_4 be a one-to-many mapping between the bit strings of SE$_n$ and the permutations of SEP$_n$ as follows. $M_4(B)$ contains $M_3(B)$ for all bit strings B in SE$_n$. If B and B' are two bit strings, and B' is obtained by applying k right shuffles to B, then take $M_3(B)$, apply k right shuffles, and add the resulting permutation to $M_4(B')$. $M_4(B)$ contains n elements for all bit strings B. For example, since the bit string $0\ 1\ 1\ 1\ 1\ 0\ 1$ is obtained by applying a right shuffle to $1\ 1\ 1\ 1\ 0\ 1\ 0$, then $M_4(0\ 1\ 1\ 1\ 1\ 0\ 1)$ includes $M_3(1\ 1\ 1\ 1\ 0\ 1\ 0) = (2\ 4\ 1\ 5\ 3\ 7\ 6)$, shuffled right by 1 position $(6\ 2\ 4\ 1\ 5\ 3\ 7)$.

Theorem 10: M_4 is a dilation $O(1)$ one-to-many embedding of SE$_n$ into SEP$_n$.

Theorem 11: M_4 composed with M_2 is a dilation $O(1)$ one-to-many embedding of SE$_n$ into Triad$_n$.

Acknowledgments

The authors would like to thank Linda Morales of Nortel for her helpful comments on the draft of this paper.

References

[1] S. B. Akers and B. Krishnamurthy. A group-theoretic model for symmetric interconnection networks. *IEEE Tr*ansactions on Computers*, 38(4):555-566, April 1989.

[2] S. G. Akl and K. Qiu. A Novel Routing Scheme on the Star and Pancake Networks and Its Applications. *Parallel Computing* 19(1):95-101, 1993

[3] S. G. Akl, K. Qiu and I. Stojmenovic. Fundamental Algorithms for the Star and Pancake Interconnection Networks with Applications to Computational Geometry. *Networks*, special issue on Interconnection Networks and Algorithms

[4] F. Annexstein, M. Baumslag and A. L. Rosenberg. Group action graphs and parallel architectures. *SIAM Journal on Computing*, 19(3):544-569, June 1990

[5] D. Bass and I. H. Sudborough. On the Shuffle-Exchange Permutation Network. In *Proceedings of the 3rd International Symposium on Parallel Architectures, Algorithms and Networks (ISPAN '97)*, Los Alamitos, California, December 1997

[6] A. Bouabdallah, C. Delorme and S. Djelloul. Edge deletion preserving the diameter of the hypercube. *Discrete Applied Mathematics*, 63, 1995, 91-95.

[7] H. Dweighter, Amer. Math. Monthly 82 (1975), 1010.

[8] P. Erdos, P. Hamburger, R. Pippert, W. Weakley. Hypercube Subgraphs with Minimal Detours. *Journal of Graph Theory*, 23, 1996, 119-128

[9] L. Gardner, Z. Miller, D. Pritikin and I. H. Sudborough. Embedding Hypercubes into Pancake, Cycle Prefix and Substring Reversal Networks. In *Proceedings of the 28th Annual Hawaii International Conference on System Sciences*, Los Alamitos, California, January 1995

[10] W. H. Gates and C. H. Papadimitriou. Bounds for sorting by prefix reversal. *Discrete Math.*, vol. 27, pages 47-57, 1979.

[11] A. Gibbons. *Algorithmic Graph Theory*, Cambridge University Press, Cambridge, England, 1985.

[12] C. Godsil, Connectivity of minimal Cayley graphs, *Arch. Math.* 37, 1981, 473-476.

[13] N. Graham and F. Harary. Changing and unchanging the diameter of a hypercube. *Discrete Applied Mathematics*, 37/38, 1992, 265-274.

[14] M. Heydari and I. H. Sudborough. On the diameter of the pancake network. *Journal of Algorithms*, vol. 25, pages 67-94, 1997

[15] M.-C. Heydemann, Cayley graphs and interconnection networks. In G. Hahn and G. Sabidussi (eds.), Graph Symmetry. Kluwer Academic Publishers, The Netherlands, 1997.

[16] D. M. Kwai and B. Parhami. A Class of Fixed-Degree Cayley-Graph Interconnection Networks Derived by Pruning k-ary n-cubes. In *Proceedings of the 26th International Conference on Parallel Processing*, Los Alamitos, California, August 1997

[17] S. Latifi and P. K. Srimani. A new fixed degree regular network for parallel processing. In *Proceedings of the Eighth IEEE Symposium on Parallel and Distributed Processing*, pages 152-159, Los Alamitos, California, October 1996.

[18] F. T. Leighton. *Introduction to Parallel Algorithms and Architectures: Arrays, Trees, Hypercubes*. Morgan Kaufmann Publishers, San Mateo, California, 1992.

[19] Z. Miller, D. Pritikin and I. H. Sudborough. Near embeddings of hypercubes into Cayley graphs on the symmetric group. *IEEE Transactions on Computers*, vol. 43(1) 1994, 13-22.

[20] P. K. Srimani and P. Vadapalli. Trivalent Cayley graphs for interconnection networks. *Information Processing Letters*, vol. 54, pages 329-335, 1995.

[21] P. K. Srimani and P. Vadapalli. Shortest routing in trivalent Cayley graph network. *Information Processing Letters*, vol. 57, pages 183-188, 1996

[22] H. Stone. Parallel processing with the perfect shuffle. *IEEE Transactions on Computers*, C-20(2):153-161, February 1971

Session 1B
Parallel Simulation

Chair: Richard Enbody
Michigan State University

Parallel Optimistic Logic Simulation
with Event Lookahead

Hong K. Kim   Jack Jean
Department of Computer Science and Engineering
Wright State University
Dayton, OH 45435
Email: {hkim,jjean}@cs.wright.edu

Abstract

Parallel discrete event simulation (PDES) on general-purpose machines can reduce the logic simulation time for large circuits considerably. However, it generates more events than necessary for certain high activity circuits and produces inconsistent execution times over different circuits. This is because glitches contribute to a sizable portion of events during a simulation. The proposed Event-lookahead Time Warp (ETW) algorithm can look ahead, combine and execute multiple events at each gate optimistically, and recover from an error by using a rollback mechanism as used in the original Time Warp algorithm. As a result, it reduces unnecessary events and produces more consistent execution times and reasonable speedups.

1 Introduction

Parallel discrete-event simulation (PDES) has been used to reduce the simulation time for some large circuits. PDES can be classified into two groups: synchronous and asynchronous simulations. Asynchronous simulations in turn can be classified into two categories: *conservative* [5] and *optimistic* [6, 7]. The asynchronous optimistic approach, so called Time Warp, has been used to achieve a greater degree of parallelism. It processes events at first based on an optimistic but not necessarily true assumption and, if a false evaluation of some gates is detected, recovers from the error using a rollback mechanism.

Most parallel logic simulations using discrete event-driven techniques do not consistently perform well over different circuits simulated [1, 4]. For some circuits with high activity, the PDES can perform poorly compared to other simulations because of multiple evaluations at each gate for the same input vector. In this paper, an optimistic PDES algorithm, called Event-lookahead Time Warp (ETW), is proposed for parallel logic simulation. The algorithm combines multiple events into one by looking ahead so to ease the multiple evaluation problem of the optimistic event-driven simulations. It is especially effective for high activity circuits which provide more opportunities for event combining. As a result, it enables the application of PDES to high-activity circuits and it produces more consistent performance over different circuits.

Among several parallel simulation algorithms, the Time Warp has a greater degree of parallelism and does not have synchronization overhead and blocking problem [5] (or eventually deadlock problem). However, the Time Warp may cause a lot of rollback and the performance is inconsistent for different circuits. To improve the Time Warp algorithm, many techniques have been proposed including adaptive process scheduling [10], bounding window [14, 17], and partitioning and load balancing [8, 9]. This paper addresses the multiple evaluation problem of the Time Warp algorithm that causes higher amount of rollback and degrades performance. The problem can be improved by using the ETW, in which events with *different* timestamps at each gate can be combined and executed at the same time. This special feature of the ETW algorithm makes it different from other simulation models, such as synchronous PDES and asynchronous conservative PDES. In a synchronous PDES, only events with the same timestamp are executed at the same time. In asynchronous conservative PDES, combining multiple events with different timestamps may cause heavy blocking overhead (or deadlock problem). The ETW can look ahead and combine multiple events at a gate optimistically, and recover from a look-ahead error by using a modified rollback mechanism as used in the original Time Warp algorithm.

The rest of the paper is organized as follows. Section 2 describes the Event-lookahead Time Warp and its rationale. Section 3 presents an efficient priority queue to support the ETW. In Section 4, the simulation environments and experimental results are described. Section 5 concludes this paper.

2 Event-lookahead Time Warp

In the logic simulation of digital circuits, each gate receives signals from their input ports. Because of circuit delays, the output of a logic gate may contain a short pulse, called a *glitch*, at a time when steady state analysis predicts that the output should not change. A glitch in the logic simulation causes one or more than one event at the gate where the glitch occurs and it may trigger some extra events or glitches at other gates. Glitches therefore contribute to a sizeable portion of events during a simulation. Since glitches can be ignored most of the times, this paper proposes an Event-lookahead Time Warp (ETW) algorithm to ignore events caused by glitches and examines the resulting improvement on simulation speed.

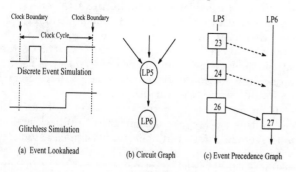

Figure 1: Ignoring circuit glitches in ETW

Figure 1 (a) shows two output waveforms of a gate where a clock cycle is within two neighboring clock boundaries, each indicated by a vertical dashed line. For simulation, input vectors are applied only at consecutive clock boundaries and a clock cycle is assigned to be a fixed number of simulation time slots, e.g., 100. The top waveform in the figure has one glitch whose existence does not influence the operation of the circuit. The bottom waveform is a "cleaner" version of the top one where the glitch is removed. Note that the timing about when the output state changes is still available in the bottom waveform. Figure 1 (b) shows part of a circuit graph where a circle represents a logic gate or a flip-flop. The computations associated with each gate (or flip-flop) are grouped as a *logical process* (LP) during the following description. Unlike the standard definition of logical process that contains several physical processes [7], an LP is used for each gate or flip-flop in this paper. The gate LP5 has three input ports and one output port. Figure 1 (c) shows that the gate LP5 receives three events from other predecessor gates where the numbers 23, 24, 26 are timestamps and, with the conventional TW, each event in the LP5 may generate a new event to the LP6. Because the first two events are for a glitch in Figure 1 (a), it would speed up the simulation to send only one event to LP6. This is the basic idea of the event-lookahead TW algorithm.

In PDES, a gate may be evaluated multiple times for a single input vector due to events with different timestamps. Since the effect of an event may override the effect of earlier events, some intermediate events may not be necessary. The conventional Time Warp

executes unprocessed events one by one from an event list. Each time the event that has the smallest timestamp is executed. The ETW looks ahead to consider future events and combines multiple events occurred within the same clock cycle at each gate. Those events that get combined and executed together may have different timestamps which record the exact timing of events. This is different from the Yaddes system [11] which combines and executes events with the *same* timestamp to an LP.

The parallel ETW algorithm has the following advantages:

1. *It reduces unnecessary intermediate events.*

2. *It can be applied efficiently to circuits of different activity levels:* The ETW is expected to be efficient for both low activity circuits and high activity circuits, while the TW is good only for low activity circuits and the compiled-code simulation is good only for high activity circuits.

3. *It leads to more balanced workload:* When the number of processors is large, a conservative algorithm generates a lot of null messages, while an optimistic algorithm produces a lot of anti-messages and erroneous events. Since the ETW simulation produces smaller number of events for each input vector and the number of events arrived at each node is less dynamic, it is easier to balance workload with the ETW.

Unlike the compiled-code simulation, the ETW does not require that all possible events for the current clock period have arrived when a gate is evaluated. The available events from the same input vector are evaluated and, if it turns out that the evaluation is premature, the latest valid states are recovered using a rollback mechanism. The ETW algorithm is designed and implemented by modifying the conventional TW algorithm. In the following paragraphs, the conventional TW algorithm is briefly described and then the ETW algorithm is introduced.

The Conventional TW The conventional TW algorithm that uses the *smallest timestamp first scheduling* works as follows. The events are ordered in each processor according to their timestamps. Multiple processors handle different parts of a circuit and execute events at different paces, sending events to other processors if needed. As shown in the procedure *Conventional_TW_main()* in Figure 2, each processor executes a nested while loop until there is no more unprocessed event. The inner loop repeatedly identifies and evaluates the event with the smallest timestamp, updates states, and produces and sends new events. Note that rollbacks are triggered by events from either the local processor or remote processors. The rollbacks from the local processor are handled within the procedure *evaluate_event*().

```
Conventional_TW_main() {
  while(there is unprocessed event over any processor){
    For each external event e from remote processors,
      call rollback_or_enqueue(e);
    while(there is unprocessed event in this processor){
      select an event, e_i, with the smallest timestamp
      evaluate_event(e_i);
      /* may generate events or cause rollbacks */
      token_passing_and_fossil_collection_if_needed();
      /* GVT (Global Virtual Time)-Computation */
      For each external event e from remote processors,
        call rollback_or_enqueue(e);
    }
  }
}
evaluate_event(e) {
  evaluate the logic gate output;
  if(there is an output transition) {
    generate a new event e_n;
    if(the destination processor is remote)
      send_event_to_other_processor(e_n);
    else rollback_or_enqueue(e_n);
  }
}
  /* with a new event, update an event list */
rollback_or_enqueue(e) {
  if((event e is anti-message) or
      (e's timestamp < Local Virtual Time))
    rollback(e);
  else enqueue(e);
}

rollback(e) {
  Undo all processed events whose timestamps are
    greater than or equal to the timestamp of e
}
```

Figure 2: Conventional Time Warp algorithm

An ETW Example Figure 3 (a) shows an example to illustrate the ETW algorithm. The waveform shown in the example may appear at the output of a logic gate resulting from event evaluation. In this figure, suppose events e_1, e_2, ..., and e_7 are in the event queue and they are all for the same clock cycle. (Note that the clock boundary is pre-specified by assigning a large enough timestamp range per input vector. As a result, the ETW can be applied to circuits even when there is no global clock.) The ETW first updates the gate input signal values by considering all those seven events and evaluates the gate output value

at e_7. Depending on the output value, there is either none or one new event to generate corresponding to those seven events. If a new event is generated, as is the case in this example, it is because there is a "valid" waveform transition that is not considered as a glitch. The new event generated in this example corresponds to the waveform transition at e_6. To get the correct timing of the waveform transition, there is a need to evaluate e_6 and then e_5. However there is no need to evaluate e_1, e_2, e_3, and e_4. If there is no more event received for the gate during this clock cycle, then the waveform is considered to contain exactly one signal transition at e_6 and two glitches, one at e_1 and e_3 and the other at e_4 and e_5, are removed as a result. In this example, to check if there is a "valid" waveform transition, the logic gate output before event e_1 is used as a reference for comparison. Because of that, there is no "valid" waveform transition at e_3 or e_5.

If an anti-message arrives to cancel e_5 before the end of this clock cycle, a sequence of rollback actions is triggered. First of all, the input signals associated with each event are updated. The events are then re-evaluated backwards, starting from e_7, going through e_6 and e_4, and ending with e_3. The reason to stop at e_3 instead of e_6 is that, as shown in Figure 3 (b), the waveform transition triggered by e_4 is no longer due to a glitch once e_5 is canceled. In that case, the new event previously triggered by e_6 needs to be canceled with an anti-message. In addition, a new event is generated at e_4 because it represents the last signal transition in the clock cycle. Note that only one glitch is removed from the waveform.

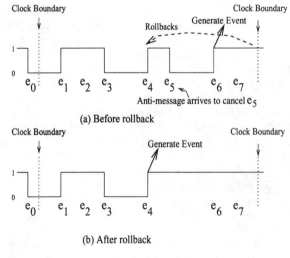

(a) Before rollback

(b) After rollback

Figure 3: ETW rollback mechanism

The above technique can also be applied to flip-flops. Input signals of flip-flops can be classified into two types, sensitive and insensitive ones. Sensitive input signals such as asynchronous preset and reset are similar to input signals of logic gates in that they affect the output signal without waiting for a clock transition. Insensitive signals such as the J and K inputs of a JK-flip-flop affect the output signal only at a clock boundary. The ETW technique explained in the previous paragraph can be applied to sensitive inputs without modification. As to the insensitive inputs, their effects are only evaluated at clock boundaries and events are generated only at those times, if necessary.

The ETW Algorithm The ETW is implemented by modifying two procedures of the conventional TW. They are the procedures $evaluate\_event()$ and $rollback()$. The events are ordered in each LP according to their timestamps. A pseudo code of the detail modification is shown in Figure 4.

```
/* Two modified procedures for the ETW*/
evaluate_event(e) {
  from the event queue for the LP that contains e, let
      E be the set of all the events that are in the
      current clock cycle, denote e_L as the event with
      the largest timestamp in E, and compute
      the input signals at each event in E.
  evaluate the logic gate output at e_L.
  if(there is an output transition at e_L) {
      from events in E that are earlier than e_L, find
          the last event that does not produce an output
          transition, denoted as e_s.
      generate an event e at e_{s+1}
      /* e_{s+1} is the event right after e_s */
      if (the destination processor of event e is remote)
          send_event_to_other_processor(e);
      else rollback_or_enqueue(e);
  }
}
rollback(e) {
  from events that are earlier than e, find the last
      event that dose not produce an output transition,
      denoted as e_s.
  undo all processed events whose timestamps are
      greater than or equal to the timestamp of e_{s+1},
      the event right after e_s.
}
```

Figure 4: More details in the ETW

The procedure $evaluate\_event()$ needs to be replaced because, when encountered with multiple events that are within the same clock cycle but with different timestamps, the ETW approach may generate events only for the last one that triggers an output signal transition while the TW approach generates an event for every output transition. As a result, the

checking of whether there is an output transition is done in a different way. As explained in the previous example, events e_3 and e_5 in Figure 3 (a) do not produce output transition with ETW even though they do with TW.

From the event queue for the LP that contains e, let E be the set of all the events that are in the current clock cycle. Not shown in Figure 4 is that, in the procedure $evaluate\_event()$, state saving is performed during the forming of the event set E so to facilitate future rollbacks. The state of each gate is defined to be the logic levels of its input signals and contains n bits, where n is the number of input ports. The state of a flip-flop includes the logic levels of both its inputs and outputs. The state saving and updating is performed after the inclusion of each event.

As to the difference of TW and ETW in the procedure $rollback()$, when there is a need to rollback an event e, only e and events later than e are considered in the TW while events earlier than e are also considered in the ETW. This is because, in the ETW, an event may be combined with later events so to reduce the number of new events. As a result, when one of the later events is rolled back, the earlier event may need to be reconsidered for the possibility of generating new events. In the previous example, when the event e_5 in Figure 3 (a) is canceled, the events e_3 and e_4 need to be evaluated again, the event e_4 should be rolled back, and a new event is generated at e_4 accordingly.

Low rollback cost is required to get a good performance for optimistic simulations. In order to reduce the rollback ratio by increasing the probability that all possible events arrive when a gate is selected for evaluation, the scheduling of logical processes is significant. This may be achieved by developing several techniques for the ETW: (1) An efficient queue structure is needed to support the run-time scheduling of active logical processes for different circuits including circuits with feedback loops. Such an efficient queue structure will be described in the next section. (2) A good partitioning algorithm is required to minimize interprocessor communication and to achieve better concurrency. Such partitioning algorithm was developed for parallel logic simulation and used in this paper [8].

3 Governor Heap

Among current scheduling algorithms, the smallest-timestamp-first method can reduce rollbacks to a reasonable level. The most commonly used data structure to support the method is either a priority queue based on a splay tree data structure [16] or the Calendar queue [3]. (More detail in performance comparison can be found in [13].) In either case, the events for different logical processes (gates/flip-flops) are mixed together as long as those processes are assigned to the same processor. Note that for a typical simulation, a processor handles thousands of logical processes while each logical process has few events per input vector. Since the ETW looks ahead and combines events *for the same logical process*, events should be stored according to their LPs and events for the same LP should be stored close to each other. Because of this reason, a *governor heap* as illustrated in Figure 5 is proposed.

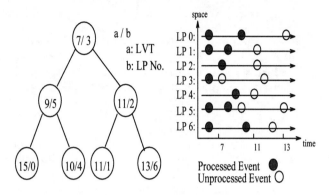

Figure 5: A Governor heap

A governor heap contains a fixed-size heap and multiple linked lists, one for each LP (gate/flip-flop). Events for each LP are sorted in a linked list according to their timestamps. Each linked list has a "governor" that has the smallest timestamp for the LP. All the governors in a processor form the fixed-size heap structure. Each heap node has two values: its Local Virtual Time (LVT) and the LP number (or gate number). The governors are ordered in the heap according to their timestamps so that the root of the heap is for the unprocessed event that has the smallest timestamp in the processor. The right-hand side of Figure 5 shows multiple linked lists, one for each LP. The horizontal axis represents the simulation time in LVT and the vertical axis indicates the seven LPs in a processor.

The governor heap is scalable with the circuit size because the height of the heap structure grows logarithmically with the number of gates in each processor while the length of each individual event list usually does not increase with the circuit size. It is very efficient in supporting the ETW for large-scale simulations because of the following characteristics:

1. Finding events to be combined is much faster with the governor heap than with other data structures because those events reside in a single *short* linked list.

2. The management of an anti-message can be considered as a delete operation. The rollback operation first finds and deletes the target event in the event list of the given LP. If the LVT is changed in the linked list, the heap structure needs to be updated.

3. Fossil collection operation can be performed in each linked list locally. There is no need to update the heap structure since fossil collection does not change any LVT.

The governor heap is similar to several queue implementations in previous works and two differences are noted here. (1) In [3, 12, 15], an event list or heap contains events associated with many different simulation objects. In the governor heap, each simulation object (a gate/flip-flop) has its individual event list. This feature is important in supporting the ETW. (2) The heap size in the governor heap is fixed, while that in other works [12, 15, 16] is not fixed. The heap memory space for the governor heap can be allocated statically and inactive objects are not deleted and still exist in the bottom of the heap. This can reduce the overhead of memory allocation.

4   Simulation Results

This section describes our simulation environment for gate-level logic simulation and presents performance results on parallel machines. The performance of the ETW is compared with the original TW algorithm in terms of several factors that influence performance.

4.1   Simulation Model and Environment

Table 1 summarizes the characteristics of the circuits used as test cases, including several of the largest ISCAS benchmark circuits [2] and a 16-bit array multiplier. A *unit-delay model* was used for the simulations. That means, the gate propagation delay is the same for all inputs and for all gates/flip-flops. The unit-delay assumption is not necessary for the ETW algorithm and the multiple-delay model and the zero-delay model can also be used.

Governor Heap Scalability Table 2 summarize the efficiency of the proposed governor heap on sequential simulations. Here, *efficiency* is defined as the number of events committed per second during simulation. For each circuit, the total number of events, the total execution time, and the efficiency shown in Table 2 are produced on a DEC alpha workstation when using both 100 and 1000 input vectors. With the different number of input vectors and several different circuits, the efficiency ranges from 11,689 to 18,136 events/sec and that illustrates the scalability of the governor heap. Furthermore, the tables show that the execution time increases slightly more than linearly with both the number of randomly generated input vectors and the circuit size. For example, even though the size of the 32-bit multiplier is about four times than that of the 16-bit multiplier, the execution time of the 32-bit multiplier is about four times that of the 16-bit multiplier with 1000 input vectors and is no more than six times with 100 input vectors.

Table 1: Benchmark Circuits

Circuit	No of gates	No of edges	No of primary inputs	No of primary outputs	No of flip-flops
ISCAS c6288	3376	5728	32	32	0
16-bit multiplier	2080	3552	32	32	0
ISCAS s9234	5808	8182	36	39	211
ISCAS s13207.1	8651	11803	62	152	638
ISCAS s38417	23843	33664	28	106	1636
ISCAS s38584.1	20717	34182	38	304	1426

Table 2: Scalability evaluation of the governor heap (the ETW).

Circuit	100 input vectors			1000 input vectors		
	No of Events	Execution Time (in sec.)	Efficiency (events/sec.)	No of Events	Execution Time (in sec.)	Efficiency (events/sec.)
ISCAS s9234	192248	10.6	18136	1806542	134.6	13422
ISCAS s13207.1	257211	14.3	17987	2453584	209.9	11689
ISCAS s38417	811598	53.1	15284	8068325	573.5	14068
ISCAS s38584.1	1093303	73.4	14895	11341134	815.5	13907

4.2 ETW Simulation Performance

The experiments have been performed on an IBM SP2 which is a parallel processor with 64 computing nodes interconnected by a high-speed multistage network. Each node of the SP2 has a 67 MHz processor and 64 Mbytes of memory. For communication library, the Message Passing Interface (MPI) is adopted. One thousand random input vectors have been used for the simulation of each circuit. For efficient partitioning, a concurrency preserving partitioning algorithm is used [8].

Efficient and Consistent Performance Table 3 compares the results of the ETW and the original TW simulation in the parallel environment with 10 processors on the IBM SP2. For both TW and ETW, global synchronization is used once every 100 input vectors. Several factors that influence simulation time are summarized in Table 3. They include

- the total number of events executed. It can be considered as the amount of workload.

- the ratio of external events which is defined as the number of inter-processor events divided by the total number of events. A larger ratio means more inter-processor communication.

- the ratio of erroneous events which is the number of erroneous events divided by the total number of events. A larger ratio means more rollbacks.

- the load imbalance factor which is defined as $m * p/n - 1$ where m is the maximum number of events among p processors and n is the total number of events. The factor is zero for a perfectly balanced workload. Note that erroneous events are not included in calculating the load imbalance factor.

- the total execution time which excludes the time for partitioning, reading input vectors, and printing output vectors.

- the efficiency which is defined as the average number of events committed per second.

From Table 3, it appears that the 16-bit multiplier with the TW algorithm produces a lot more events compared to the other circuit (*s38417*). With the ETW algorithm, the event-lookahead operation drastically reduces the number of events for the 16-bit multiplier. In either circuit, the ETW gets better performance than the TW algorithm in terms of the total number of events, the ratio of external events, the ratio of erroneous events, load imbalance factor, the efficiency, and the execution time. Even though the ETW dose not balance workload explicitly, it usually leads to more balanced workload because of less dynamic behavior of the ETW. In particular, the ETW simulation is five times faster for the multiplier and 20% faster for *s38417*.

Table 3: The Comparison of TW and ETW with 10 processors

Experiment		Total No. of Events	Ratio of External Events	Ratio of Erroneous Events	Load Imbalance Factor	Execution Time (sec.)	Efficiency (no./sec.)
Circuit	Protocol						
16 − bit	TW	22910747	.30	.49	.26	506.46	23070
Multiplier	ETW	4186271	.24	.26	.14	101.82	30424
	TW	9784096	.06	.21	.22	152.82	50578
s38417	ETW	8452743	.06	.19	.16	126.55	54102

Table 4: ETW execution time (in seconds) and speedups

Experiment		No. of Processors						
Circuit	Metric	1	2	4	8	10	16	32
16 − bit	Exe. Time	461.2	332.2	232.1	151.2	101.8	87.2	132.7
multiplier	Speedup	1.00	1.38	1.98	3.05	4.53	5.29	3.47
	Exe. Time	701.8	417.1	240.9	135.7	126.6	109.6	51.9
s38417	Speedup	1.00	1.68	2.91	5.17	5.54	6.40	13.52

Table 4 shows the ETW execution time in seconds and speedups of those two circuits with different numbers of SP2 processors. The speedup results for the multiplier are pretty good considering that there are only 2080 gates. It also shows that more processors can be used effectively for the larger circuit (s38417) with ten times more gates.

Execution times for four different circuits are shown in Table 5. For those three large sequential circuits, the speedups are reasonably good. Particularly, the s13207.1 circuit has better speedup when 24 or smaller number of processors are used. A speedup of 12.8 is achieved with 24 processors. However, when 32 processors are used, that reduces to 11.1 and the s38417 circuit with larger number of gates has a better speedup of 13.5. For small number of processors, the obtained execution times are more consistent and the speedups are reasonably good for different circuits.

The previous results were obtained with 1000 input vectors for each simulation run. In order to reduce the workload imbalance, the amount of rollback, and the event list length, several bounded window techniques [14, 17] can be used by introducing global synchronization periodically. Note that global synchronization, if used too frequently, causes a lot of overhead or blocking among processors and degrades the performance of parallel simulation. Simulation results on the ETW show that, even though global synchronization once every input vector reduces erroneous events to less than 1%, global synchronization once for every 100 input vectors outperforms those with more frequent global synchronization. This is because the ETW with its lower rollback cost allows less frequent global synchronization.

5 Conclusions

Most previous simulators have limitations on some specific types of circuits. For example, the parallel discrete event simulation (PDES) does not perform well for high-activity circuits and the parallel oblivious simulation does not perform well for low-activity circuits. The proposed Event-lookahead Time Warp (ETW) technique improves PDES by combining multiple events and reducing the number of events. The resulting algorithm is very efficient for different circuits and the improvement is particularly clear for high-activity circuits. Unlike the compiled-code simulation, it does not require the static evaluation order of gates and is therefore applicable to synchronous circuits with or without feedback loops. In addition, it can be applied to multi-delay model and provides timing information even though glitches are removed.

Acknowledgments

This research is supported by an Ohio State Board of Regent Research Investment grant. The authors would like to thank the Argonne National Laboratory and the Ohio Supercomputer Center for allowing the use of their IBM SP2 machines.

References

[1] M. L. Bailey, J. V. Briner Jr., and R. D. Chamberlain, "Parallel Logic Simulation of VLSI Systems," ACM Computing Surveys, Vol. 26, No. 3, pp. 255-294, September 1994.

[2] F. Brglez, D. Bryan, and K. Kozminski, "Combinational Profiles of Sequential Benchmark Circuits," Proc. of the IEEE International Symp. on Circuits and Systems, pp. 1929-1934, 1989.

[3] Randy Brown, "Calendar Queues: A Fast O(1) Priority Queue Implementation for the Simulation Event Set Problem," Communication of the

Table 5: The ETW Execution Time (in seconds)

Circuits	No. of Processors							
	1	2	4	8	10	16	24	32
16 − bit multiplier	461.2	332.5	232.1	151.1	138.9	87.1	82.2	154.7
s13207.1	219.8	167.9	76.4	41.9	33.0	23.6	17.2	19.8
s38417	701.0	417.1	240.9	135.6	132.9	109.6	86.6	51.9
s38584.1	1094.2	728.6	502.7	364.9	336.1	245.1	165.6	128.6

ACM, Vol. 31, No. 10, pp.1220-1227, October 1988.

[4] Roger D. Chamberlain, "Parallel Logic Simulation of VLSI Systems," Proc. of the 32nd Design Automation Conf., pp. 139-143, 1995

[5] K. M. Chandy and J. Misra, "Asynchronous Distributed Simulation via a Sequence of Parallel Computations," Communications of the ACM, Vol. 24, No. 11, pp. 198-206, April 1981.

[6] R. M. Fujimoto, "Parallel Discrete Event Simulation," Communications of the ACM, Vol. 33, No. 10, pp. 30-53, October 1990.

[7] D. R. Jefferson, "Virtual Time," ACM Trans. on Programming Languages and Systems, Vol. 7, No. 3, pp. 404-425, July 1985.

[8] Hong K. Kim and Jack Jean, "Concurrency Preserving Partitioning (CPP) for Parallel Logic Simulation," Proc. of 10th Workshop on Parallel and Distributed Simulation, pp. 98-105, 1996.

[9] V. Krishnaswamy, G. Hasteer, and P. Banerjee, "Load Balancing and Work Load Minimization of Overlapping Parallel Tasks," Proc. of the 1997 International Conf. on Parallel Processing, August 1997.

[10] A. C. Palaniswamy and P. A. Wilsey, "Scheduling Time Warp Processes using Adaptive Control Techniques," Proceeding of the 1994 Winter Simulation Conference, pp. 731-738, December 1994.

[11] B. R. Preiss, "The Yaddes Distributed Discrete Event Simulation Specification Language and Execution Environment," Proc. of the SCS Multiconference on Distributed Simulation, pp. 139-144, January 1989.

[12] R. Rönngren and R. Ayani, "Efficient Implementation of Event Sets in Time Warp," Proc. of 7th Workshop on Parallel and Distributed Simulation, pp. 101-108, 1993.

[13] R. Rönngren and R. Ayani, "A Comparative Study of Parallel and Sequential Priority Queue Algorithms," ACM Trans. on Modeling and Computer Simulation, Vol. 7, No. 2, pp. 157-209, April 1997.

[14] L. M. Sokol, B. K. Stucky, and V. S. Hwang, "MTW: A Control Mechanism for Parallel Discrete Simulation," Proceedings of the 1989 International Conference on Parallel Processing, Vol. 3, pp.250-254, 1989.

[15] J. Steinman, "Discrete-Event Simulation and the Event Horizon Part 2: Event List Management," Proc. of 10th Workshop on Parallel and Distributed Simulation, pp. 170-178, 1996.

[16] R. E. Tarjan and D. D. Sleator, "Self-Adjusting Binary Search Trees," Journal of the ACM, Vol. 32, No. 3, pp. 652-686, July 1985.

[17] S. Turner and M. Xu, "Performance evaluation of the bounded Time Warp algorithm," Proc. of 6th Workshop on Parallel and Distributed Simulation, pp. 117-128, 1992.

On-line Configuration of a Time Warp Parallel Discrete Event Simulator*

Radharamanan Radhakrishnan, Nael Abu-Ghazaleh,
Malolan Chetlur and *Philip A. Wilsey*
Computer Architecture Design Laboratory
Dept. of ECECS, PO Box 210030, Cincinnati, OH 45221–0030
(513) 556-4779, phil.wilsey@uc.edu

Abstract

In Time Warp simulations, the overheads associated with rollbacks, state-saving and the communication induced by rollbacks are the chief contributors to the cost of the simulation; thus, these aspects of the simulation have been primary targets for optimizations. Unfortunately, the behavior of the Time Warp simulation is highly dynamic and greatly influenced by the application being simulated. Thus, the suggested optimizations are only effective for certain intervals of the simulation. This paper argues that the performance of Time Warp simulators benefits from a dynamic on-line decision process that selects and configures the sub-algorithms implementing the different aspects of the simulator to best match the current behavior of the simulation. In particular, we study control strategies to dynamically: (i) adjust the checkpointing (or state-saving) interval (ii) select the cancellation strategy (lazy or aggressive), and (iii) determine the policy for aggregating the application messages (an optimization that significantly improves the performance in message passing environments). The strategies have been implemented in the WARPED *Time Warp simulation kernel and the performance obtained via the dynamically controlled optimizations is shown to surpass that of their best performing static counterparts.*

1   Introduction

Time Warp is an optimistic synchronization model that has been used extensively for parallel discrete event simulation [10]. It offers several advantages over conservative synchronization approaches [19] and has the potential to outperform them [9]. Unfortunately, Time Warp simulators have yet to realize this potential consistently. The performance of the simulator is affected by the choice of sub-algorithms implementing the different aspects of the simulation kernel, and the internal parameter settings for these sub-algorithms (we call these algorithms and their set of internal parameters, the *configuration* of the simulator). If an unsuitable configuration is

chosen, the simulator suffers from problems such as instability (due to excessive rollbacks), excessive (erroneous) optimistic computation, high memory usage [23] and high communication overheads caused by excessive rollbacks [6]. Thus, careful choice of the configuration of the simulator is imperative for efficient execution.

The choice of an efficient configuration is complicated by the highly dynamic and unpredictable nature of the Time Warp model. In addition, the simulation may pass through different phases where the optimal configuration changes. Several researches have recognized this dynamic nature, and suggested adaptive techniques for optimizing specific aspects of the simulator [7, 14, 20, 29]. The use of adaptive techniques in a distributed application is difficult because changes that are affected locally have secondary system-wide effects. This is especially true for the Time Warp model because the progress of the simulation is nondeterministic. This paper investigates the use of on-line configuration in Time Warp simulators. It develops a general feedback control framework [1] for implementing on-line configuration, and illustrates its success in Time Warp simulators by using it to control three different facets of the simulator operation.

The remainder of the paper is organized as follows. Section 2 describes Parallel Discrete Event Simulation (PDES), and the Time Warp model. Section 3 presents the control model used for on-line configuration. Section 4 introduces periodic check-pointing, and develops the control system used to configure the checkpoint period. Section 5 presents message cancellation algorithms and develops the control system used to dynamically switch among them. Section 6 describe the dynamic message aggregation optimization of the communication module of Time Warp, and develops the control model for optimizing the size of the aggregation window. The control models are analyzed, and the performance results are shown in Section 8. Finally, Section 9 contains some concluding remarks.

2   Time Warp

In a Time Warp synchronized discrete event simulation, *Virtual Time* [10] is used to model the passage of the time in the simulation. Changes in the state of the simulation occur as

---

*Support for this work was provided in part by the Advanced Research Projects Agency under contracts J–FBI–93–116 and DABT63–96–C–0055.

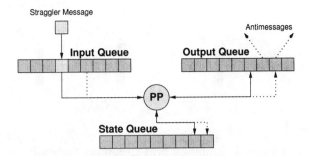

Figure 1. A Simulation Object in a Time Warp Simulation

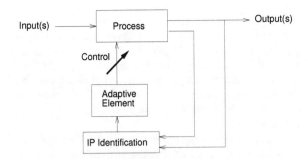

Figure 2. Feedback Control

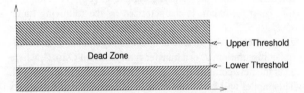

Figure 3. Thresholding for Cancellation

events are processed at specific virtual times. In turn, events may schedule other events at future virtual times. The virtual time defines a total order on the events of the system. The simulation state (and time) advances in discrete steps as each event is processed. The simulation is executed via several simulator processes, called simulation objects. Each simulation object is constructed from a physical process (PP) and three history queues. Figure 1 illustrates the structure of a simulation object. The input and the output queues store incoming and outgoing events respectively. The state queue stores the state history of the simulation object. Each simulation object maintains a clock that records its Local Virtual Time (LVT). Simulation objects interact with each other by exchanging time-stamped event messages. One departure from Jefferson's original definition [10] of Time Warp is that simulation objects are placed into groups called "logical processes" (LPs).

The simulation objects must be synchronized in order to maintain the causality of the simulation; although each simulation object processes local events in their (locally) correct time-order, events are not globally ordered. Fortunately, each event need only be ordered with respect to events that affect it (and, conversely, events it affects); only a partial order of the events is necessary for correct execution [11]. Synchronization protocols can be classified into *conservative* [19], and *optimistic* protocols [8, 10]. In a conservatively synchronized simulation, an event is executed only when the simulation object receives guarantees that all other simulation objects will not produce an event that will invalidate it; each simulation object must have reached an LVT time equal to the time of the event to be processed[1]. Accordingly, total order in processing the events is enforced.

Under optimistically synchronized protocols (*e.g.,* the Time Warp model [10]), simulation objects execute their local simulation autonomously, without explicit synchronization. A causality error arises if a simulation object receives a message with a time-stamp earlier than its LVT value (a *straggler* message). In order to allow recovery, the state of the simulation object and the output events generated are saved in history queues as each event is processed. When a straggler message is

---

[1] There is a model dependent tolerance for this condition; the more general condition is that the LVT of other simulation objects is within a *lookahead* value of the event time.

detected, the erroneous computation must be undone — a *rollback* occurs. The rollback process consists of: (i) the state of the simulation object is restored to a state prior to the straggler message time-stamp, and (ii) erroneously sent output messages are canceled (by sending *anti-messages* to nullify the original message).

The global progress time of the simulation, called Global Virtual Time (GVT), is defined as the lowest of the LVT values of the simulation objects [8, 13, 18]. Periodic GVT calculation is necessary to reclaim memory space used by history queues; history items with a time-stamp lower than GVT are no longer needed, and are deleted to make room for new history items.

3 Linear Feedback Control Systems

In feedback control systems, the system behavior is changed in response to observed output values, in order to force the system to a desired state [1]. More precisely, a feedback control system samples output values and adjusts input values in order to meet some performance criteria (Figure 2). For example, in a Time Warp simulator, the output may be the number of events committed between GVT cycles, the number of events rolled back upon receipt of a straggler message, LVT, or any other information that can be observed about the system. Such values that have been used in several investigations for dynamically adjusting simulation parameters [2, 14, 17, 20, 21, 22, 28].

Virtually all dynamic control investigations have also used data filtering techniques to smooth and to prevent spurious data points from causing wide variations in parameter adjustment. In this research, we have found that non-linear thresholding functions are best suited for damping the selection of which cancellation strategy to use. A thresholding function defines boundaries on input values that determine the output value produced. For example, Figure 3, demonstrates the filtration process used for the dynamic control of the cancellation strategies (discussed in more detail in Section 5). Two thresholds are used with a dead zone lying between the thresholds. In this example, the function changes its value only after it moves into the shaded region above or below each threshold. When the input falls in the dead zone, the function continues to produce the same output.

Unlike analog control systems, the feedback control logic competes for the same CPU cycles that are used for useful computation. Thus, control should not be adapted at a high frequency, or the overhead for tuning the simulator will outweigh the benefits from the better configuration [26]. A configuration control system, is characterized by the following tuple: $< O, I, S, T, P >$, where O is the sampled output, I is the current state of the parameter under configuration, S is the initial configuration, T is a transfer function from O to I', where I' is the new configuration, and P is the configuration period. This model will be further elaborated in the remainder of this paper, where the performance tuning of three independent aspects of Time Warp simulators using on-line configuration is discussed.

4   Check-pointing Strategies

Check-pointing is necessary to protect against erroneous optimistic computation. Each Logical Process (LP) must periodically save its local state such that, in the event of a causality error, a rollback to a correct state is possible. Time Warp objects with large states require considerable memory space as well as CPU cycles for state saving. In general, states are saved after every event execution. However, the check-pointing cost can be reduced by saving the state infrequently. In the simple case, a Time Warp simulator checkpoints every χ events; this scheme is called *Periodic Check-pointing*. Figure 4 illustrates a process rolling back upon the receipt of a straggler message (white circle). The shaded circles denote events and the filled boxes denote state saving points. Since check-pointing does not occur after every processed event, a rollback will have to re-execute any intermediate events (*coast forward*). Thus, an optimal checkpoint interval must balance the cost of check-pointing vs. the coast of the coast-forward phase. Excessively large check-pointing periods will have long coast-forward phases but low check-pointing cost. The opposite is true for excessively small check-pointing periods.

Using periodic state saving, the arrival of a straggler message may require the system to rollback to an earlier state than necessary and coast forward [8]. While coasting forward, no messages are sent out to the other processes in the system (the previously sent messages are correct). The difficulty of periodic state saving is determining an appropriate fixed frequency for check-pointing. Some applications operate best with a fairly small value; while others require much larger values [3, 25]. Currently, no practical techniques for statically analyzing simulation applications to decide the checkpoint frequency are known — motivating investigations into dynamically adjusting the checkpoint interval.

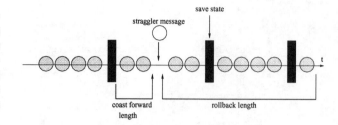

Figure 4. Rollback and Coasting Forward (χ = 4)

There have been a variety of proposals to dynamically controlling the checkpoint interval [7, 14, 21, 29]. These techniques employ adaptive control to dynamically establish values for the checkpoint interval. Some of the performance parameters monitored in these studies include the average time to execute one event, the average time to save the process state, and the number of rollbacks. All of the studies sample the output values for each individual process, and recalculate the optimal checkpoint interval infrequently.

Both Lin [14] and Palaniswamy [21] derive an analytical model of a Time Warp simulator and use the model to derive a formula for dynamically establishing values for the checkpoint interval. Unfortunately, each approach results in a fairly complex formula that requires significant processing overhead for evaluation and data capture. Consequently, we developed a feedback control system for dynamically adapting the check-pointing interval [7]. This control system may be described using the tuple $< E_c, \chi, 1, A, P >$. More precisely, the control system monitors a cost index, E_c, for check-pointing that is the sum of the state saving costs and the coasting forward costs in the interval starting at the previous invocation. χ is the checkpoint interval, the parameter under configuration. The control system operates under the assumption that the optimal period results in the minimum value for E_c. Simulation starts with an initial period of 1. The transfer function, A, is the following: at every control invocation, if E_c is not observed to have increased significantly, the check-pointing period is incremented; otherwise, it is decremented. P is the period for the invocation of the control process. The control system converges to the optimal period, assuming the single minima assumption holds.

5   Cancellation Strategies

The performance of the simulator is highly dependent on the efficiency of the cancellation strategy employed to undo the effects of erroneous computation (the sending of anti-messages). Two known cancellation strategies exist [8]: *aggressive-cancellation*, and *lazy-cancellation*. Under aggressive-cancellation, the arrival of a straggler message forces the immediate generation of an anti-message to cancel erroneous outputs. In contrast, lazy cancellation delays sending anti-messages until forward processing demonstrates, by comparison of old and new output, that the original output messages were incorrect. Thus, there is a potential for reduction in communication, as well as wasted optimistic computation. The performance under lazy-cancellation is better than aggressive cancellation if the regenerated output messages do not differ widely from the prematurely sent messages.

Studies have shown that lazy-cancellation can perform better than aggressive-cancellation, but that, even within the same application domain, some models perform better under aggressive cancellation [2, 28]. In our experiments using digital systems models [27] written in the hardware description language VHDL [24], we observed that:

- Neither aggressive nor lazy-cancellation is clearly superior to the other.
- The optimal strategy is sensitive to the partitioning scheme.
- Different LPs within the same application operate best under different cancellation strategies.
- Within a single LP, the optimal cancellation strategy varies over the lifetime of the simulation.
- The optimal cancellation strategy depends on the the the application and the platform.

Accordingly, a static selection of the cancellation strategy does not yield the optimal configuration.

Most Time Warp simulators support the two cancellation strategies in the form of a compile-time (or simulation-time) switch — the selection of the cancellation strategy is the responsibility of the user. Lin's analysis [12] demonstrates that even with a number of unrealistic assumptions, a static analysis to determine the optimal cancellation strategy is complex and requires perfect knowledge of the simulation. Thus, we propose that the selection can be performed dynamically by the simulator using on-line configuration. The control model for dynamically selecting the cancellation strategy can be described as $< HR, I, Aggressive, A, P >$. HR is the *Hit Ratio*, an index defined on the observed cancellation of the simulator. I is the selected cancellation strategy; $I \in \{Aggressive, Lazy\}$. The initial state of the system is *Aggressive* cancellation. A is the heuristic used in determining which strategy to use next, and P is the period between the invocation of the control process. The remainder of this section will describe HR and A in detail.

As a result of our experiments, we have found that the optimal cancellation strategy in the simulation correlates well with a performance index we call the Hit Ratio (HR). HR is a measure of how productive an LP's premature computations were in its recent past. Under aggressive-cancellation, an LP is said to have a *Lazy Aggressive Hit* if it generates the same message before and after a rollback, otherwise it is said to have a *Lazy Aggressive Miss*. Each LP maintains a dynamic record of the past n output message comparisons. The number of comparisons, n, is statically controlled (by the user) and is called the *Filter Depth*. In order to update HR under aggressive-cancellation, the simulation must continue to monitor whether the sent messages have different values after the rollback. The overhead of this comparison is small. The time required to switch between the two strategies is negligible with respect to the rollback time. The *Hit Ratio* is then defined as follows:

$$Hit\ Ratio = \frac{\#Lazy\ Aggressive\ Hits\ +\ \#Lazy\ hits}{Filter\ Depth\ Comparisons}$$

The cancellation strategy is determined using a thresholding function whose input is the *Hit Ratio*. The threshold to switch from aggressive to lazy-cancellation is called A2L_Threshold and the threshold to switch from lazy to aggressive-cancellation is called L2A_Threshold. These two thresholds can have the same value in which case the dead zone is eliminated. If the Hit Ratio is high (*e.g.,* 0.4) then it the LP favors lazy-cancellation. Conversely, if it is low (*e.g.,* 0.2) then the LP favors aggressive-cancellation. These thresholds are fixed at compile time (optimal values for them are currently determined empirically).

One possible heuristic for switching between the algorithms is to monitor the HR. The simulation starts with aggressive-cancellation. Whenever HR rises over A2L_Threshold, the simulation is switched to lazy-cancellation. If HR falls below L2A_Threshold, the simulation is switched back to aggressive-cancellation. Thrashing between strategies (continuous switching among them) is minimized using: (i) a large filter depth; (ii) the infrequent invocation of the control mechanism; and (iii) the hysteresis introduced by the "dead-zone" between the two thresholds.

6 Dynamic Message Aggregation

Dynamic Message Aggregation (DyMA) is an optimization to the Time Warp communication system that matches the communication behavior to the underlying communication system. Using DyMA, the communication module of each LP collects application messages destined to the same LP, that occur in close temporal proximity, and sends them as a single physical message. Since there is a large overhead associated with each message (regardless of the message size), significant improvement in performance is possible. The decision on when to send the messages is made by the *aggregation policy*.

Clearly, the higher the number of messages aggregated, the greater the reduction in the communication overhead. The longer the messages are delayed, the greater the number of messages aggregated. However, delaying messages excessively harms the performance of the receiving LP. Thus, aggregation policies must balance the potential gain from additional message aggregation, to the potential loss at the receiving LP. It is difficult to determine a static balance between the two factors; the communication behavior of Time Warp simulators is highly dynamic and unpredictable. While static window sizes (in time, or number of messages) for aggregation yield some performance improvement, better overall performance results from dynamic control of the aggregate size.

In specifying the window size, we seek to balance the benefits resulting from aggregating more messages, versus the harm from delaying messages excessively. These two factors are modeled as: (i) Aggregation Optimistic Factor (AOF): AOF is the gain from delaying the messages; it is proportional to the rate of reception of messages to be sent. If AOF is high, a large number of messages are aggregated without excessive delay;

and (ii) Aggregation Pessimistic Factor (APF): APF models the harm from delaying the messages. It is proportional to the age of the aggregate. Note that both of these factors vary with the nature of the application, and may change dynamically within the lifetime of the simulation.

Initially, a static policy that aggregates messages for a fixed time, called *Fixed Aggregation Window* (FAW), was developed. The age of the first message received by the aggregation layer is tracked. Once this age reaches a constant value (the size of the window), the aggregate message is sent. The advantage of this policy is its low overhead; only a single check of the current aggregate age (time that the aggregate has been alive) against the constant window size is required. This policy provides a static balance between AOF and APF, making it insensitive to changes in the communication behavior of the application. No matter how high (or low) the message arrival rate is, the fixed window size is used. Since the chosen window size significantly affects the performance of this policy, dynamic control of the balance between AOF and APF is desirable.

A dynamic policy, called *Simple Adaptive Aggregation Window* (SAAW), is suggested. SAAW extends FAW to adapt the window size with the message arrival rate. The initial aggregation window is specified statically as in the case of FAW. During simulation, the message rate achieved by an aggregate is calculated *when the aggregate is sent* and used to decide what the aggregation window for the next aggregate should be. Changing the aggregation window size allows policy to adapt its behavior to vary with the behavior of the application. For example, if the application is exhibiting bursty communication behavior, the aggregation window size is increased to take advantage of the higher AOF. The overhead for implementing SAAW is slightly higher than FAW; there is an additional computation to determine the window size when the aggregate is sent.

$< R(age), W, W_{initial}, SAAW, everyAggregate >$ describes the control system used by the SAAW strategy. $R(age)$ is the rate of reception of messages, modified to reflect the age of the aggregate. Thus, an aggregate a_1 that achieves a message reception rate r is considered to have a higher modified rate than an aggregate a_2 with the same rate r if the age of a_1 is smaller than that of a_2. W is the window size, which is the parameter being configured. $W_{initial}$ is the initial window size. SAAW is the control heuristic; in our implementation, W is increased if $R(age)$ has increased relative to the last aggregate, and vice versa. Finally, the window size is adapted as each aggregate is sent.

7 The Experimental Environment

The WARPED simulation kernel provides the functionality to develop applications modeled as discrete event simulations [15, 16]. Considerable effort has been made to define a standard programming interface to hide the details of Time Warp from the Application Programming Interface (API). All Time Warp specific activities such as state saving and rollback are performed by the kernel without intervention from the application. Consequently, an implementation of the WARPED inter-

face can be constructed using either conservative [19] or optimistic [4, 8] parallel synchronization techniques. Furthermore, the simulation kernel can operate as a sequential kernel.

The WARPED system is composed of a set of C++ class and template libraries which the user accesses in several ways. Where the kernel needs information about data structures within the application, they are passed into kernel template classes. When kernel data or functions need to be made available to the user, they can be accessed by one of two mechanisms: inheritance and method invocation. A more detailed description of the internal structure and organization of the WARPED kernel is available on the www at http://www.ececs.uc.edu/~paw/warped.

The results reported in this paper were obtained by executing two different simulation models on a network of SUN (SPARC 4 and 5) workstations interconnected by 10Mb Ethernet. To fully test the system, the network of workstations chosen for the experiments were not dedicated to the experiments. Five sets of measurements were taken at two different times and the average of these values were then reported. The two models (available in the WARPED distribution) are:

SMMP: The SMMP application models a shared memory multiprocessor. Each processor is assumed to have a local cache with access to a common global memory (The model is somewhat contrived in that requests to the memory are not serialized—*i.e.,* main memory can have multiple requests pending at any given moment). The model is generated by a C++ program which lets the user adjust the following parameters: (i) the number of processors/caches to simulate, (ii) the number of LPs to generate, (iii) the speed of cache, (iv) the speed of main memory, and (v) the cache hit ratio. The generation program partitions the model to take advantage of the fast intra-LP communication. The model configuration used in the experiments reported herein is 16 processors simulated using 4 LPs. The cache speed is set to 10 nanoseconds and the main memory for 100 nanoseconds. The cache hit ratio is set as 90%. This application has 100 simulation objects. Each processor generates a user specified number of memory requests. Each request (also referred to as a test vector) is in fact a token that contains information about its creation time, the creator (simulation) processor, and the time at which this request should be satisfied.

RAID: The RAID application models the RAID Disk Arrays which is a method of providing a vast array of storage [5] with a higher I/O performance than several large expensive disks. This application incorporates a flexible model of a RAID Disk Array and can be configured in various sizes of disk arrays and request generators. Each request is in fact a token that carries information about the number of disks, the number of cylinders, number of tracks, number of sectors, size of each sector and specific information about which stripe to read and parity information. The following configuration is used for the data reported in this paper: 20 source processes generate 1000 requests each to 8 disks via 4 forks. The application is partitioned into 4 LPs.

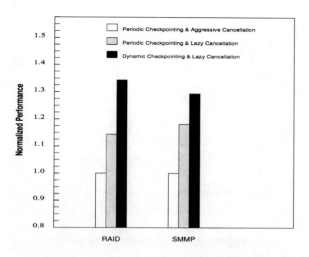

Figure 5. Dynamic Check-pointing (normalized results)

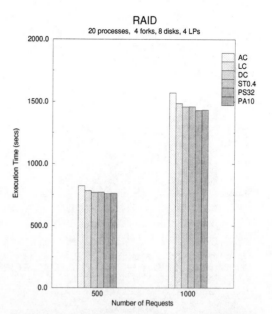

Figure 6. Execution Time vs. Number of requests

8 Analysis

The performance of the check-pointing algorithms is shown in Figure 5. The SMMP model processed 11,300 committed events per second when no dynamic optimizations were used; RAID processed 10,917 committed events per second. The all-static optimizations case was used as the base value against which the results are normalized (*i.e.*, 1.0 in the graph represents 11,300 committed events per second for SMMP when periodic check-pointing and aggressive cancellation is used). Dynamic check-pointing improved the performance of the simulation by 30% in the best case.

The performance of dynamic-cancellation relative to aggressive and lazy-cancellation for both applications was studied. Figure 6 is a plot of execution time as a function of the number of requests for RAID for the following cancellation strategies:

- AC : Aggressive-cancellation
- LC : Lazy-cancellation
- DC : Dynamic-cancellation with Filter Depth = 16, A2L_Threshold = 0.45 and L2A_Threshold = 0.2
- ST0.4 : Dynamic-cancellation with a single threshold, A2L_Threshold = L2A_Threshold = 0.4
- PS32 : Dynamic-cancellation with the cancellation strategy permanently set after 32(Filter Depth) comparisons
- PA10 : Dynamic-cancellation with the cancellation strategy permanently set to aggressive if 10 successive comparisons result in misses

In this application, all disk objects favor lazy-cancellation while all the fork objects favor aggressive-cancellation. In the model configuration chosen for this investigation, there are more disk objects than fork objects. Consequently,

lazy-cancellation provides better performance than aggressive-cancellation. Dynamic-cancellation performs better than lazy-cancellation due to the fact that all objects strictly favor either aggressive or lazy-cancellation. DC and ST0.4 perform 1.5% faster than lazy-cancellation while PS32 and PA10 provide a 2.5% speedup (because the cost of doing passive comparison is completely avoided by the objects which favor aggressive-cancellation).

Figure 7 shows the execution time as a function of the number of requests for SMMP for the following cancellation strategies:

- AC, LC, and DC remain the same as before
- PS : Dynamic-cancellation with the cancellation strategy permanently set after 64 (Filter Depth) comparisons
- PA : Dynamic-cancellation with the cancellation strategy permanently set to aggressive if 10 successive comparisons result in misses

In this application, all the objects strictly favor lazy-cancellation. This results in a 15% speedup over aggressive cancellation. Consequently all the variations of dynamic-cancellation perform on par with lazy-cancellation. PS64 performs slightly better than DC and PA because it permanently switches into lazy cancellation after 64 comparisons and does not have to monitor the hit (misses) throughout the simulation.

Figures 8 and 9 show the performance of the FAW and SAAW policies for different aggregate ages on a network of SUN SPARC workstations. Clearly, aggregation yields considerable speedup (30% in the best case) on a network of workstations. There appears to an "optimal" window size for which the aggregation performance is best for each application. Window sizes less than that are too conservative; additional aggregation is possible without hurting performance. Conversely, window sizes greater than the optimal value delay the messages excessively, nullifying the benefit obtained from the additional aggregation. The SAAW strategy is superior to FAW

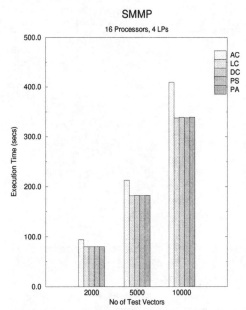

SMMP
16 Processors, 4 LPs

Figure 7. Execution Time vs. Number of requests

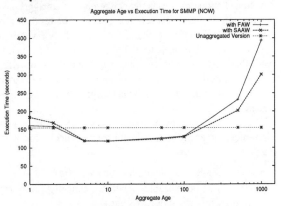

Figure 8. DyMA results for SMMP

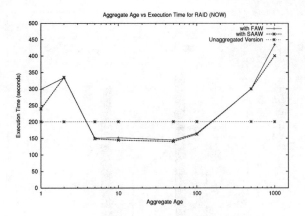

Figure 9. DyMA results for RAID

because it is able to converge on the optimal window size dynamically. Note here that a window size is statically fixed for the FAW strategy whereas the statically fixed window size for the SAAW strategy is only the initial window size. We expect that with more sophisticated adaption of the window size, additional performance improvement can be obtained.

9 Concluding Remarks

The performance of Time Warp depends on the nature of the application being simulated. The choice of the sub-algorithms to implement several of the simulator functions, as well as the parameter settings for these sub-algorithms significantly affect performance; the settings of these sub-algorithms and parameters are collectively called the configuration of the simulator. Most simulators operate with a static configuration that is either set by default or determined by the user at compile or simulation time. However, a static configuration is limited

because: (i) it is difficult to determine an optimal configuration statically; (ii) the optimal configuration may vary during the simulation time; and (iii) the optimal configuration may be different across LPs in the same simulation.

This paper demonstrates that the performance of Time Warp simulators will benefit from dynamic control of its configuration to match the current behavior of the simulator. It presents a linear-control model for on-line configuration of the simulation. The model is different from traditional control theory because data-sampling and parameter adjustment are intrusive; these operations contend for processor-cycles that can be used for useful computation. In addition, this control process is, by necessity, imprecise. Consider, that: (i) changes of the local LP configurations will have secondary effects (on other LPs and the system), and tertiary effects that are reflected back to the LP; these effects are difficult to quantify; and (ii) because data-sampling and parameter adjustment are intrusive, it is usually not feasible to implement the most accurate control system if it is too complex. This was illustrated in the periodic saving control system, where our simple heuristic outperformed the more rigorous (but more costly) techniques.

The on-line configuration model was used to adapt the behavior of different facets of the simulation. In particular, control strategies for dynamic adjustment of (i) checkpoint interval (ii) cancellation strategy (lazy or aggressive), and (iii) dynamic aggregation of application messages were presented. The public domain WARPED Time Warp simulation kernel was modified to implement these optimizations. Performance results for the control strategies demonstrate that adaptive schemes can improve performance. Because of the imprecise nature of the control systems, it is nearly impossible to find the optimal settings for them. We relied on empirical data to guide the design of the control systems. We believe that further analysis of the parameters of the control model will allow better control systems to be constructed and yield further improvement in performance.

References

[1] ASTROM, K. J., AND WITTENMARK, B. *Adaptive Con-*

trol. Addison Wesley, Reading, MA, 1989.

[2] BALL, D., AND HOYT, S. The adaptive time-warp concurrency control algorithm. In *Distributed Simulation* (Jan. 1990), Society for Computer Simulation, pp. 174–177.

[3] BELLENOT, S. State skipping performance with the time warp operating system. In *6th Workshop on Parallel and Distributed Simulation* (Jan. 1992), Society for Computer Simulation, pp. 53–61.

[4] CHANDY, K. M., AND SHERMAN, R. Space-time and simulation. In *Distributed Simulation* (1989), Society for Computer Simulation, pp. 53–57.

[5] CHEN, P. M. Raid: High-performance, reliable secondary storage. *ACM Computing Surveys 26*, 2 (June 1994), 145.

[6] FERSCHA, A. Probabilistic adaptive direct optimism control in time warp. In *Proc. of the 9th Workshop on Parallel and Distributed Simulation (PADS 95)* (June 1995), pp. 120–129.

[7] FLEISCHMANN, J., AND WILSEY, P. A. Comparative analysis of periodic state saving techniques in time warp simulators. In *Proc. of the 9th Workshop on Parallel and Distributed Simulation (PADS 95)* (June 1995), pp. 50–58.

[8] FUJIMOTO, R. Parallel discrete event simulation. *Communications of the ACM 33*, 10 (Oct. 1990), 30–53.

[9] FUJIMOTO, R. M. Time warp on a shared memory multiprocessor. *Transactions of Society for Computer Simulation* (July 1989), 211–239.

[10] JEFFERSON, D. Virtual time. *ACM Transactions on Programming Languages and Systems 7*, 3 (July 1985), 405–425.

[11] LAMPORT, L. Time, clocks, and the ordering of events in a distributed system. *Communications of ACM* (July 1978), 558–565.

[12] LIN, Y. Estimating the likelihood of success of lazy cancellation in time warp simulations. *International Journal in Computer Simulation* (1996).

[13] LIN, Y.-B. Memory management algorithms for optimistic parallel simulation. In *6th Workshop on Parallel and Distributed Simulation* (Jan. 1992), Society for Computer Simulation, pp. 43–52.

[14] LIN, Y.-B., PREISS, B. R., LOUCKS, W. M., AND LAZOWSKA, E. D. Selecting the checkpoint interval in time warp simulation. In *Proc of the 7th Workshop on Parallel and Distributed Simulation (PADS)* (July 1993), Society for Computer Simulation, pp. 3–10.

[15] MARTIN, D. E., MCBRAYER, T., AND WILSEY, P. A. WARPED: A time warp simulation kernel for analysis and application development, 1995. (available on the www at http://www.ece.uc.edu/~paw/warped/).

[16] MARTIN, D. E., MCBRAYER, T. J., AND WILSEY, P. A. WARPED: A time warp simulation kernel for analysis and application development. In *29th Hawaii International Conference on System Sciences (HICSS-29)* (Jan.

1996), H. El-Rewini and B. D. Shriver, Eds., vol. Volume I, pp. 383–386.

[17] MATSUMOTO, Y., AND TAKI, K. Adaptive time-ceiling for efficient parallel discrete event simulation. In *Object-Oriented Simulation Conference (OOS '93)* (Jan. 1993), T. Beaumariage and C. Roberts, Eds., Society for Computer Simulation, pp. 101–106.

[18] MATTERN, F. Efficient algorithms for distributed snapshots and global virtual time approximation. *Journal of Parallel and Distributed Computing 18*, 4 (Aug. 1993), 423–434.

[19] MISRA, J. Distributed discrete-event simulation. *Computing Surveys 18*, 1 (Mar. 1986), 39–65.

[20] PALANISWAMY, A., AND WILSEY, P. A. Adaptive bounded time windows in an optimistically synchronized simulator. In *Third Great Lakes Symposium on VLSI* (1993), pp. 114–118.

[21] PALANISWAMY, A., AND WILSEY, P. A. Adaptive checkpoint intervals in an optimistically synchronized parallel digital system simulator. In *VLSI 93* (Sept. 1993), pp. 353–362.

[22] PALANISWAMY, A., AND WILSEY, P. A. Scheduling time warp processes using adaptive control techniques. In *Proceedings of the 1994 Winter Simulation Conference* (Dec. 1994), J. D. Tew, S. Manivannan, D. A. Sadowski, and A. F. Seila, Eds., pp. 731–738.

[23] PALANISWAMY, A., AND WILSEY, P. A. Parameterized time warp: An integrated adaptive solution to optimistic pdes. *Journal of Parallel and Distributed Computing 37*, 2 (Sept. 1996), 134–145.

[24] PERRY, D. L. *VHDL*, 2nd ed. McGraw–Hill, New York, NY, 1994.

[25] PREISS, B. R., MACINTRYE, I. D., AND LOUCKS, W. M. On the trade-off between time and space in optimistic parallel discrete-event simulation. In *6th Workshop on Parallel and Distributed Simulation* (Jan. 1992), Society for Computer Simulation, pp. 33–42.

[26] RADHAKRISHNAN, R., MOORE, L., AND WILSEY, P. A. External adjustment of runtime parameters in time warp synchronized parallel simulators. In *11th International Parallel Processing Symposium, (IPPS '97)* (Apr. 1997), IEEE Computer Society Press, pp. 260–266.

[27] RAJAN, R., RADHAKRISHNAN, R., AND WILSEY, P. A. Dynamic cancellation: Selecting time warp cancellation strategies at runtime. *International Journal in Computer Simulation* (1997). (forthcoming).

[28] REIHER, P. L., WIELAND, F., AND JEFFERSON, D. R. Limitation of optimism in the time warp operating system. In *Winter Simulation Conference* (Dec. 1989), Society for Computer Simulation, pp. 765–770.

[29] RÖNNGREN, R., AND AYANI, R. Adaptive checkpointing in time warp. In *Proc. of the 8th Workshop on Parallel and Distributed Simulation (PADS 94)* (July 1994), Society for Computer Simulation, pp. 110–117.

Session 1C
Mobile Computing

Chair: Zhi-Li Zhang
University of Minnesota

On the Impossibility of Min-Process Non-Blocking Checkpointing and An Efficient Checkpointing Algorithm for Mobile Computing Systems

Guohong Cao and Mukesh Singhal
Department of Computer and Information Science
The Ohio State University
Columbus, OH 43210
E-mail: {gcao, singhal}@cis.ohio-state.edu

Abstract

Mobile computing raises many new issues, such as lack of stable storage, low bandwidth of wireless channel, high mobility, and limited battery life. These new issues make traditional checkpointing algorithms unsuitable. Prakash and Singhal [14] proposed the first coordinated checkpointing algorithm for mobile computing systems. However, we showed that their algorithm may result in an inconsistency [3]. In this paper, we prove a more general result about coordinated checkpointing: there does not exist a non-blocking algorithm that forces only a minimum number of processes to take their checkpoints. Based on the proof, we propose an efficient algorithm for mobile computing systems, which forces only a minimum number of processes to take checkpoints and dramatically reduces the blocking time during the checkpointing process. Correctness proofs and performance analysis of the algorithm are provided.

1 Introduction

A distributed system is a collection of processes that communicate with each other by exchanging messages. A mobile computing system is a distributed system where some of processes are running on *mobile hosts* (MHs), whose location in the network changes with time. To communicate with MHs, a conventional distributed system is augmented with *mobile support stations* (MSSs) that act as access points for the MHs by wireless networks.

The mobility of MHs raises some new issues [11] pertinent to the design of checkpointing algorithms: locating processes that have to take their checkpoints, energy consumption constraints, lack of stable storage in MHs, and low bandwidth for communication with MHs. These features make traditional checkpointing algorithms for distributed systems unsuitable for mobile computing systems.

Coordinated checkpointing is an attractive approach for transparently adding fault tolerance to distributed applications, since it avoids domino effect [10] and minimizes the stable storage requirement. In this approach, the state of each process in the system is periodically saved on the sta-

ble storage, which is called a checkpoint of the process. To recover from a failure, the system restarts its execution from a previous consistent global checkpoint saved on the stable storage. A system state is said to be consistent if it contains no *orphan message*; i.e., a message whose receive event is recorded in the state of the destination process, but its send event is lost [10, 16]. In order to record a consistent global checkpoint, processes must synchronize their checkpointing activities. In other words, when a process takes a checkpoint, it asks (by sending checkpoint requests to) all relevant processes to take checkpoints. Therefore, coordinated checkpointing suffers from high overhead associated with the checkpointing process.

Much of the previous work [5, 9, 10] in coordinated checkpointing has focused on minimizing the number of synchronization messages and the number of checkpoints during the checkpointing process. However, these algorithms (called *blocking algorithm*) force all relevant processes in the system to block their computations during the checkpointing process. Checkpointing includes the time to trace the dependency tree and to save the states of processes on the stable storage, which may be long. Moreover, in mobile computing systems, due to the mobility of MHs, a message may be routed several times before reaching its destination. Therefore, blocking algorithms may dramatically reduce the performance of these systems [6].

Recently, nonblocking algorithms [6, 15] have received considerable attention. In these algorithms, processes need not block during the checkpointing by using a checkpointing sequence number to identify orphan messages. However, these algorithms [6, 15] assume that a distinguished initiator decides when to take a checkpoint. Therefore, they suffer from the disadvantages of centralized algorithms, such as poor reliability, bottle neck, etc. Moreover, these algorithms [6, 15] require all processes in the system to take checkpoints during checkpointing, even though many of them may not be necessary. If they are modified to permit more processes to initiate checkpointing, which makes them truly distributed, the new algorithms will suffer from another problem: in order to keep the checkpoint sequence number updated, any time a process takes a checkpoint, it has to notify all processes in the system. If each process can initiate a checkpointing, the network would be flooded with control messages and processes might waste their time taking unnecessary checkpoints.

Prakash-Singhal algorithm [14] was the first algorithm to combine these two approaches. More specifically, it forces only a minimum number of processes to take checkpoints and does not block the underlying computation during checkpointing. However, we showed that their algorithm may result in an inconsistency [3]. In this paper, we prove a more general result about coordinated checkpointing: there does not exist a non-blocking algorithm that forces only a minimum number of processes to take their checkpoints. Based on this proof, we propose an efficient checkpointing algorithm for mobile computing systems that forces only a minimum number of processes to take checkpoints and dramatically reduces the blocking time during checkpointing.

The rest of the paper is organized as follows. Section 2 presents preliminaries. In Section 3, we prove that there does not exist a non-blocking algorithm that forces only a minimum number of processes to take their checkpoints. Section 4 presents an efficient checkpointing algorithm for mobile computing systems. Performance analysis of the algorithm is provided in Section 5. Section 6 concludes the paper.

2 Preliminaries

2.1 Computation Model

A mobile computing system consists of a large number of *mobile hosts* (MHs) [1] and relatively fewer static hosts called *mobile support stations* (MSSs). The number of MSSs is denoted by N_{mss} and that of MHs by N_{mh} with $N_{mh} \gg N_{mss}$. The MSSs are connected by a static wired network, which provides reliable $FIFO$ delivery of messages. A *cell* is a logical or geographical coverage area under an MSS. An MH can directly communicate with an MSS by a reliable $FIFO$ wireless channel only if it is present in the cell supported by the MSS.

The distributed computation we consider consists of N sequential processes denoted by $P_1, P_2, \cdots, P_N$ running concurrently on fail-stop MHs or MSSs. The processes do not share a common memory or a common clock. Message passing is the only way for processes to communicate with each other. The computation is asynchronous: each process runs at its own speed and messages are exchanged through reliable communication channels, whose transmission delays are finite but arbitrary.

Each checkpoint taken by a process is assigned a unique sequence number. The $i^{th}(i \geq 0)$ checkpoint of process P_p is assigned a sequence number i and is denoted by $C_{p,i}$. The ith *checkpoint interval* [12] of process P_p denotes all

the computation performed between its ith and $(i+1)^{th}$ checkpoint, including the ith checkpoint but not the $(i+1)^{th}$ checkpoint.

2.2 New Issues in Mobile Computing

There are some new issues in mobile computing systems that complicate the design of such systems.

Locating MHs: When a mobile host MH_1 wants to send a message m to another mobile host, say MH_2, MH_1 sends m to its local MSS, say MSS_p, via a wireless link. MSS_p forwards m to MH_2's local MSS, say MSS_q, over the static network. Finally, MSS_q forwards m to MH_2 via the wireless link. Since MHs move from one cell to another, the location of an MH is not fixed. As a result, MSS_p needs to first locate MH_2 before it can forward m to MSS_q. The cost to locate an MH is referred to as the *search cost* [11]. Even though many routing protocols [2, 8] have been proposed to reduce the search cost, it can still be significant. Therefore, a checkpointing algorithm should try to avoid or reduce the search cost.

Energy and bandwidth requirements: The battery of an MH has a limited life. To save energy, an MH powers down individual components during periods of low activity [7]. This strategy is referred to as the *doze mode* operation. An MH in the doze mode is woken up on receiving a message. Therefore, energy conservation and low bandwidth constraints require a checkpointing algorithm to minimize the number of synchronization messages.

Due to the vulnerability of mobile computers to catastrophic failures, e.g., loss, theft, or physical damage, the disk storage on an MH cannot be considered to be stable [1]. Therefore, we utilize the stable storage at MSSs to store checkpoints of MHs. Then, to take a checkpoint, an MH has to transfer a large amount of data to its local MSS over the wireless link. Since the wireless network has low bandwidth, and MHs have relatively low computation power, a checkpointing algorithm should only force a minimum number of processes to take checkpoints.

2.3 Non-blocking Algorithms

Most of the existing coordinated checkpointing algorithms [5, 10] rely on the two-phase protocol and save two kinds of checkpoints on the stable storage: *tentative* and *permanent*. In the first phase, the initiator takes a tentative checkpoint and forces all relevant processes to take tentative checkpoints. Each process informs the initiator whether it succeeded in taking a tentative checkpoint. A process may refuse to take a checkpoint depending on its underlying computation. After the initiator has received positive acknowledgments from all relevant processes, the algorithm enters the second phase. If the initiator learns that all processes have successfully taken tentative checkpoints, it asks them to make their tentative checkpoints permanent; otherwise, it asks them to discard their tentative checkpoints. A process, on receiving the message from the initiator, acts accordingly. Note that after a process takes a tentative checkpoint in the first phase, it remains blocked until it receives the decision from the initiator in the second phase.

A non-blocking checkpointing algorithm does not require any process to suspend its underlying computation. When processes do not suspend their computations, it is possible for a process to receive a computation message from another process, which is already running in a new checkpoint interval. If this situation is not properly dealt with, it may result in an inconsistency. For example, in Figure 1, P_2 initiates a checkpointing. After sending checkpoint requests to P_1 and P_3, P_2 continues its computation. P_1 receives the checkpoint request and takes a new checkpoint, then it sends $m1$ to P_3. Suppose P_3 processes $m1$ before it receives the checkpoint request from P_2. When P_3 receives the checkpoint request from P_2, it takes a checkpoint (see Figure 1). In this case, $m1$ becomes an orphan.

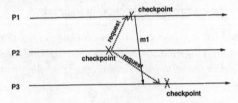

Figure 1: Inconsistent checkpoints

Most of non-blocking algorithms [6, 15] use a Checkpoint Sequence Number (csn) to avoid inconsistencies. In these algorithms, a process is forced to take a checkpoint if it receives a computation message whose csn is greater than its local csn. For example, in Figure 1, P_1 increases its csn after it takes a checkpoint and appends the new csn to $m1$. When P_3 receives $m1$, it takes a checkpoint before processing $m1$ since the csn appended to $m1$ is larger than its local csn.

This scheme works only when every process in the computation can receive each checkpoint request and then increases its own csn. Since Prakash-Singhal algorithm [14] forces only part of processes to take checkpoints, the csn of some processes may be out-of-date, and may not be able to avoid inconsistencies. Prakash-Singhal algorithm attempts to solve this problem by having each process maintain an array to save the csn, where $csn_i[i]$ has been the expected csn of P_i. Note that P_i's $csn_i[i]$ may be different from P_j's $csn_j[i]$ if there is no communication between P_i and P_j for several checkpoint intervals. By using csn and the initiator identification number, they claim that their non-blocking algorithm can avoid inconsistencies and minimize the number of checkpoints during checkpointing. However, we showed that their algorithm may result in an inconsistency [3]. Next, based on a new concept, called "z-dependency", we prove

a more general result: "there does not exist a non-blocking algorithm that forces only a minimum number of processes to take their checkpoints."

3 Proof of Impossibility

Definition 1 If P_p sends a message to P_q during its ith checkpoint interval and P_q receives the message during its jth checkpoint interval, then P_q *z-depends* on P_p during P_p's i^{th} checkpoint interval and P_q's j^{th} checkpoint interval, denoted as $P_p \prec_j^i P_q$.

Definition 2 If $P_p \prec_j^i P_q$, and $P_q \prec_k^j P_r$, then P_r *transitively z-depends* on P_p during P_r's k^{th} checkpoint interval and P_p's i^{th} checkpoint interval, denoted as $P_p \overset{*}{\prec}_k^i P_r$ (we simply call it "P_r transitively z-depends on P_p" if there is no confusion).

Proposition 1

$$P_p \prec_j^i P_q \Longrightarrow P_p \overset{*}{\prec}_j^i P_q$$
$$P_p \overset{*}{\prec}_j^i P_q \wedge P_q \overset{*}{\prec}_k^j P_r \Longrightarrow P_p \overset{*}{\prec}_k^i P_r$$

The definition of "z-depend" here is different from the concept of "causal dependency" used in the literature. We illustrate the difference between causal dependency and z-depend using Figure 2. Since P_2 sends $m1$ before it receives $m2$, there is no causal dependency between P_1 and P_3 due to these messages. However, these messages do establish a z-dependency between P_3 and P_1: $P_3 \prec_{j-1}^{k-1} P_2 \wedge P_2 \prec_{i-1}^{j-1} P_1 \Longrightarrow P_3 \overset{*}{\prec}_{i-1}^{k-1} P_1$.

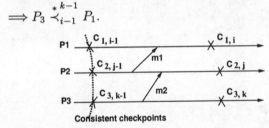

Figure 2: The difference between causal dependency and z-depend

Definition 3 A *min-process* checkpointing algorithm is an algorithm satisfying the following condition: when a process P_p initiates a new checkpointing and takes a checkpoint $C_{p,i}$, a process P_q takes a checkpoint $C_{q,j}$ associated with $C_{p,i}$ if and only if $P_q \overset{*}{\prec}_{i-1}^{j-1} P_p$.

In coordinated checkpointing, to keep consistency, the initiator forces all dependent processes to take checkpoints. Each process, which takes a checkpoint, recursively forces its dependent processes to take checkpoints. Koo-Toueg algorithm [10] uses this scheme, and it has been proved [10] that this algorithm forces only a minimum number of processes to take checkpoints. In the following, we prove that

Koo-Toueg algorithm is a min-process algorithm and a min-process algorithm forces only a minimum number of processes to take checkpoints. To simplify the proof, we use "$P_p \vdash_i^j P_q$" to represent the following: P_q causally depends on P_p when P_q is in the ith checkpoint interval and P_p is in the jth checkpoint interval.

Proposition 2
$$P_p \vdash_i^j P_q \implies P_p \overset{*}{\prec}_i^j P_q$$
$$P_p \overset{}{\prec}_i^j P_q \implies P_p \vdash_i^j P_q$$

Lemma 1 *An algorithm forces only a minimum number of processes to take checkpoints if and only if it is a min-process algorithm.*

Proof. It has been proved [10] that Koo-Toueg algorithm forces only a minimum number of processes to take checkpoints; so we only need to prove the following: in [10], when a process P_p initiates a new checkpointing and takes a checkpoint $C_{p,i}$, a process P_q takes a checkpoint $C_{q,j}$ associated with $C_{p,i}$ if and only if $P_q \overset{*}{\prec}_{i-1}^{j-1} P_p$.

Necessity: In [10], when a process P_p initiates a new checkpoint $C_{p,i}$, it recursively asks all dependent processes to take checkpoints. For example, P_p asks P_{k_m} to take a checkpoint, P_{k_m} asks $P_{k_{m-1}}$ to take a checkpoint, and so on. If a process P_q takes a checkpoint $C_{q,j}$ associated with $C_{p,i}$, then, there must be a sequence:
$$P_q \vdash_{s_{k_1}}^{j-1} P_{k_1} \wedge P_{k_1} \vdash_{s_{k_2}}^{s_{k_1}} P_{k_2} \wedge \cdots \wedge$$
$$P_{k_{m-1}} \vdash_{s_{k_m}}^{s_{k_{m-1}}} P_{k_m} \wedge P_{k_m} \vdash_{i-1}^{s_{k_m}} P_p \quad (1 \le m \le N)$$
$$\implies P_q \overset{*}{\prec}_{s_{k_1}}^{j-1} P_{k_1} \wedge P_{k_1} \overset{*}{\prec}_{s_{k_2}}^{s_{k_1}} P_{k_2} \wedge \cdots \wedge$$
$$P_{k_{m-1}} \overset{*}{\prec}_{s_{k_m}}^{s_{k_{m-1}}} P_{k_m} \wedge P_{k_m} \overset{*}{\prec}_{i-1}^{s_{k_m}} P_p$$
$$\implies P_q \overset{*}{\prec}_{i-1}^{j-1} P_p$$

OR
$$P_q \vdash_{i-1}^{j-1} P_p$$
$$\implies P_q \prec_{i-1}^{j-1} P_p$$
$$\implies P_q \overset{*}{\prec}_{i-1}^{j-1} P_p$$

Sufficiency: If $P_q \prec_{i-1}^{j-1} P_p$, when P_p initiates a new checkpoint $C_{p,i}$, P_q takes a checkpoint $C_{q,j}$ associated with $C_{p,i}$; otherwise, if $P_q \overset{*}{\prec}_{i-1}^{j-1} P_p$, then there must be a sequence:
$$P_q \prec_{s_{k_1}}^{j-1} P_{k_1} \wedge P_{k_1} \prec_{s_{k_2}}^{s_{k_1}} P_{k_2} \wedge \cdots \wedge$$
$$P_{k_{m-1}} \prec_{s_{k_m}}^{s_{k_{m-1}}} P_{k_m} \wedge P_{k_m} \prec_{i-1}^{s_{k_m}} P_p \quad (1 \le m \le N)$$
$$\implies P_q \vdash_{s_{k_1}}^{j-1} P_{k_1} \wedge P_{k_1} \vdash_{s_{k_2}}^{s_{k_1}} P_{k_2} \wedge \cdots \wedge$$
$$P_{k_{m-1}} \vdash_{s_{k_m}}^{s_{k_{m-1}}} P_{k_m} \wedge P_{k_m} \vdash_{i-1}^{s_{k_m}} P_p$$
Then, when P_p initiates a new checkpoint $C_{p,i}$, P_p asks P_{k_m} to take a checkpoint, P_{k_m} asks $P_{k_{m-1}}$ to take a checkpoint, and so on. In the end, P_{k_1} asks P_q to take a checkpoint. Then, P_q takes a checkpoint $C_{q,j}$ associated with $C_{p,i}$. $\square$

Definition 4 A *min-process non-blocking* algorithm is a min-process checkpointing algorithm which does not block the underlying computation during checkpointing.

Lemma 2 *In a min-process non-blocking algorithm, assume P_p initiates a new checkpointing and takes a checkpoint $C_{p,i}$. If a process P_r sends a message m to P_q after it takes a new checkpoint associated with $C_{p,i}$, then P_q takes a checkpoint $C_{q,j}$ before processing m if and only if $P_q \overset{*}{\prec}_{i-1}^{j-1} P_p$.*

Proof. According to the definition of min-process, P_q takes a checkpoint $C_{q,j}$ if and only if $P_q \overset{*}{\prec}_{i-1}^{j-1} P_p$. Thus, we only need to show that P_q should take $C_{q,j}$ before processing m. It is easy to see, if P_q takes $C_{q,j}$ after processing m, m becomes an orphan (as in Figure 1). $\square$

From Lemma 2, in a min-process non-blocking algorithm, when a process receives a message m, it must know if the initiator of a new checkpointing transitively z-depends on it during the previous checkpoint interval.

Lemma 3 *In a min-process non-blocking algorithm, there is not enough information at the receiver of a message to decide whether the initiator of a new checkpointing transitively z-depends on the receiver.*

Proof. The proof is by construction (using a counter-example). In Figure 3, assume messages $m6$ and $m7$ do not exist. P_1 initiates a checkpointing. When P_4 receives $m4$, there is a z-dependency as follows:
$$P_2 \overset{*}{\prec}_0^0 P_4 \wedge P_4 \overset{*}{\prec}_0^0 P_1 \implies P_2 \overset{*}{\prec}_0^0 P_1.$$
However, P_2 does not know this when it receives $m5$. There are two possible approaches for P_2 to get the z-dependency information:

Approach 1: Tracing the in-coming messages. In this approach, P_2 gets the new z-dependency information from P_1. Then, P_1 has to know the z-dependency information before it sends $m5$ and appends the z-dependency information to $m5$. In Figure 3, P_1 cannot get the new z-dependency information ($P_2 \overset{*}{\prec}_0^0 P_1$) unless P_4 notifies P_1 of the new z-dependency information when P_4 receives $m4$. There are two ways for P_4 to notify P_1 of the new z-dependency information: first is to broadcast the z-dependency information (not illustrated in the figure); the other is to send the z-dependency information by an extra message $m6$ to P_3, which in turn sends to P_1 by $m7$. Both of them dramatically increase message overhead. Since the algorithm does not block the underlying computation, it is possible that P_1 receives $m7$ after it sends out $m5$ (as shown in the figure). Then, P_2 still cannot get the z-dependency information when it receives $m5$.

Approach 2: Tracing the out-going messages. In this approach, since P_2 sends message $m3$ to P_5, P_2 hopes to get the new z-dependency information from P_5. Then, P_5 has to know the new z-dependency information and it would like to send an extra message (not shown in the figure) to notify P_2. Similarly, P_5 needs to get the new z-dependency information from P_4, which comes from P_3, and finally from P_1. Certainly, this requires much more extra messages than Approach 1. Similar to Approach 1, P_2 still cannot get the z-dependency information in time since the computation is in progress. □

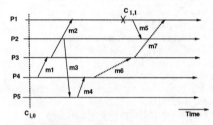

Figure 3: Tracing the dependency

Theorem 1 *No min-process non-blocking algorithm exists.*

Proof. From Lemma 2, in a min-process non-blocking algorithm, a receiver has to know if the initiator of a new checkpointing transitively z-depends on the receiver, which is impossible from Lemma 3. Therefore, no min-process non-blocking algorithm exists. □

Corollary 1 *No non-blocking algorithm forces only a minimum number of processes to take checkpoints.*

Proof. The proof directly follows from Lemma 1 and Theorem 1. □

Remarks

Netzer and Xu [12] introduced the concept of "zigzag" paths to define the necessary and sufficient condition for a set of local checkpoints to lie on a consistent checkpoint. Our definition of "z-depend" captures the essence of "zigzag" paths. If an initiator forces all its "transitively z-dependent" processes to take checkpoints, the resulting checkpoints are consistent, and no "zigzag" path exists among them. If the resulting checkpoints are consistent, then there is no "zigzag" path among them, and all processes on which the initiator "transitively z-depends" have taken checkpoints. However, there is a distinctive difference between a "zigzag" path and "z-depend". A "zigzag" path is used to evaluate whether the existing checkpoints are consistent; thus, it is mainly used to find a consistent recovery line in an uncoordinated checkpointing algorithm. It has almost no use in a coordinated checkpointing algorithm since a consistent recovery line is guaranteed by the synchronization messages. The "z-depend" is proposed for coordinated checkpointing and it reflects the whole synchronization process of coordinated checkpointing, e.g., in the proof of Lemma 1, "z-depend" is used to model the checkpointing process. Based on "z-depend", we found and proved the impossibility result. It is impossible to prove the result only based on "zigzag" paths.

4 A Min-Process Checkpointing Algorithm

From Theorem 1, no min-process non-blocking algorithm exists. There are two directions in designing efficient coordinated checkpointing algorithms. First is to relax the non-blocking condition while keeping the min-process property. The other is to relax the min-process condition while keeping the non-blocking property. The new constraints in mobile computing system, such as low bandwidth of wireless channel, high search cost, and limited battery life, suggest that the proposed checkpointing algorithm should be a min-process algorithm. Therefore, we develop an algorithm that relaxes the non-blocking condition; that is, it is a min-process algorithm; however, it minimizes the blocking time.

4.1 Handling Node Mobility

Changes in the location of an MH complicate the routing of messages. Messages sent by an MH to another MH may have to be rerouted because the destination MH disconnected from the old MSS and is now connected to a new MSS. Many routing protocols for the network layer, to handle MH mobility, have been proposed [8].

An MH may be disconnected from the network for an arbitrary period of time. At the application level, the checkpointing algorithm may generate a request for the disconnected MH to take a checkpoint. Delaying a response to such a request, until the MH reconnects with some MSS, may significantly increase the completion time of the checkpointing algorithm. Thus, we propose the following solution to deal with disconnections.

We observe that only local events can take place at an MH during the disconnect interval. No message send or receive event occurs during this interval. Hence, no new dependencies with respect to other processes are created during this interval. The dependency relation of an MH with the rest of the system, as reflected by its local checkpoint, is the same no matter when the local checkpointing is taken during the disconnect interval.

Suppose a mobile host MH_i wants to disconnect from its local MSS_p. MH_i takes a local checkpoint and transfers its local checkpoint to MSS_p as $disconnect\_checkpoint_i$. If MH_i is asked to take a checkpoint during the disconnect interval, MSS_p converts $disconnect\_checkpoint_i$ into MH_i's new checkpoint and uses the message dependency information of MH_i to propagate the checkpoint request. MH_i also sends $disconnect(sn)$ message to MSS_p on the MH-to-MSS channel supplying the sequence number sn of the last message received on the MSS-to-MH channel. On the receipt of MH_i's $disconnect(sn)$, MSS_p knows the last message that MH_i has received and buffers all computation messages received until the end of the disconnect interval.

Later, MH_i may reconnect at an MSS, say MSS_q. If MH_i knows the identity of its last MSS, say MSS_p, it sends a $reconnect(MH_i, MSS_q)$ message to MSS_p through MSS_q. If MH_i lost the identity of its last MSS for some reason, then MH_i's $reconnect$ request is broadcasted over the network. On receiving the $reconnect$ request, MSS_p transfers all the support information (the checkpoint, dependency vector, buffered messages, etc.) of MH_i to MSS_q, and clears all information related to the disconnection. Then, MSS_q forwards the buffered messages to MH_i. With this, the reconnect routine terminates and the relocated mobile host MH_i resumes normal communication with other MHs (or MSSs) in the system.

4.2 The Checkpointing Algorithm

Data structures at MSSs: In mobile computing systems, all communications to and from an MH pass through its local MSS. Therefore, when an MSS receives an application message to be forwarded to a local MH, it first updates the dependency information that it maintains for the MH, and then forwards it to the MH. The dependency information is recorded by boolean vector R_i for process P_i. The vector has n bits, representing n processes. When $R_i[j]$ is set to 1, it represents that P_i depends on P_j. For every P_i, R_i is initialized to 0 except $R_i[i]$, which is initialized to 1. When a process P_i running on an MH, say MH_p, receives a message from a process P_j, MH_p's local MSS sets $R_i[j]$ to 1.

First phase of the algorithm: When a process running on an MH initiates a checkpointing, it sends a checkpoint $request$ to its local MSS, which will be the *proxy MSS* (If the initiator runs on an MSS, then the MSS is the proxy MSS). The proxy MSS sends $R\_request$ messages to all MSSs in the system (denoted by S_{mss}) to ask for dependency vectors. In response to the $R\_request$, each MSS returns the dependency vectors that it maintains for processes running on the MHs in its cell. Having received all the dependency vectors, the proxy MSS constructs an $N \times N$ dependency matrix with one row per process, represented by the dependency vector of the process. Based on the dependency matrix, the proxy MSS can locally calculate all the processes on which the initiator transitively depends. This is essentially the same as finding the transitive closure of the initiator in the dependency tree which is constructed using the dependency vectors. Then, it can be transformed to a matrix multiplication [4]. After the proxy MSS finds all the processes that need to take checkpoints, it adds them to the set S_{forced} and broadcasts S_{forced} to all MSSs, which are waiting for the result. When an MSS receives S_{forced}, it checks if any processes in S_{forced} are also in its cell. If so, the MSS sends checkpoint $request$ messages to them. Any process receiving a checkpoint $request$ takes a checkpoint and sends a $response$ to its local MSS. After an MSS has

received all $response$ messages from the processes to which it sent checkpoint $request$ messages, it sends a $response$ to the proxy MSS. The following is the formal description of the first phase.

Algorithm executed at the proxy MSS:
for $\forall i(MSS_i \in S_{mss})$, send a $R\_request$ message to MSS_i;
Upon receiving all R vectors from each MSS_i do
    construct matrix D; calculate(D);

Algorithm executed at an MSS, say MSS$_k$:
Upon receiving $R\_request$ from the proxy MSS:
    for $\forall i(Location(P_i) \in Cell_k)$, send R_i to the proxy MSS;
    Upon receiving S_{forced} from the proxy MSS:
    for $\forall i(Location(P_i) \in Cell_k \land P_i \in S_{forced})$, send a
    checkpoint $request$ to P_i;
    continue its computation;
Upon receiving $response$ messages from all processes to which it
sends $request$ messages:
    send a $response$ to the proxy MSS;

Algorithm executed at any process P$_i$:
Upon receiving a $request$ from MSS_j:
    take a checkpoint, send a $response$ to MSS_j;

Calculate (D : N $\times$ N)
/* D_i denotes the dependency vector of process P_i. Assume
   P_j is the initiator. */
$A = D_j$; $D_j = D_j \times D$
While $A \neq D_j$ do $\{A = D_j; D_j = D_j \times D; \}$
$S_{forced} = \phi$;
for $\forall i(D_j[i] = 1)$, $S_{forced} = S_{forced} \cup P_i$;

Second phase of the algorithm: After the proxy MSS has received a $response$ from every MSS, the algorithm enters the second phase. If the proxy MSS learns that all processes have successfully taken tentative checkpoints, it .asks them to make their tentative checkpoints permanent. Otherwise, it asks them to discard their tentative checkpoints. A process, on receiving the message from the proxy MSS, acts accordingly (Techniques to reduce discarded checkpoints can be found in [13]).

An example: In Figure 4, D_i denotes the dependency vector of process P_i. When P_1 initiates a checkpointing, the proxy MSS constructs the dependency matrix D, and calculates $D_1 \times D = (1\ 1\ 1\ 0\ 0)$. Since $(1\ 1\ 1\ 0\ 0) \times D = (1\ 1\ 1\ 0\ 0)$, based on the procedure *Calculate*, $S_{forced} = \{P_1, P_2, P_3\}$. Thus, P_1 asks P_2 and P_3 to take checkpoints.

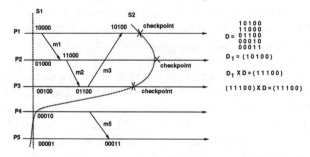

Figure 4: Checkpointing and dependency information

4.3 Proof of Correctness

Lemma 4 *A process takes a checkpoint if and only if the initiator transitively depends on it.*

Proof. In the proposed algorithm, the proxy MSS uses the procedure *calculate* to find out the transitive closure of the initiator. During the execution of *calculate*, no new dependency relation is formed since MSSs are blocked. Therefore, a process P_i belongs to S_{forced} if and only if the initiator transitively depends on P_i. Since an MSS only sends a checkpoint *request* to a process in S_{forced}, a process P_i takes a checkpoint only if the initiator transitively depends on P_i. Thus, we only need to show that a process receives a checkpoint and takes a checkpoint if the initiator transitively depends on it.

If P_i is running on a MSS_p, a checkpoint *request* is sent to P_i when S_{forced} reaches MSS_p. If P_i is running on an MH, say MH_j, which is in MSS_p's cell, then there are three possibilities when S_{forced} reaches MSS_p:

Case 1: MH_j is still connected to MSS_p: the *request* is forwarded to MH_j, then to P_i.

Case 2: MH_j is disconnected from the network: MSS_p takes a checkpoint on the behalf of P_i by converting *disconnect_checkpoint_i* into P_i's new checkpoint.

Case 3: MH_j has moved to MSS_q (handoff): MSS_p forwards the *request* to MSS_q, which forwards it to MH_j, then to P_i by the underlying network as explained in Section 4.1.

Thus, if the initiator transitively depends on P_i, P_i receives a checkpoint *request* and takes a checkpoint. □

Theorem 2 *The algorithm creates a consistent global checkpoint.*

Proof. The proof is by contradiction. Assume there is a pair of processes P_p and P_q such that at least one message m has been sent from P_q after P_q's last checkpoint $C_{q,j}$ and has been received by P_p before P_p's last checkpoint $C_{p,i}$. We also assume $C_{p,i}$ is associated with the initiator P_r's checkpoint $C_{r,k}$. Then, based on Lemma 3:

P_p takes a checkpoint $\Longrightarrow P_p \overset{*i-1}{\prec}_{k-1} P_r$.

P_p receives m from $P_q \Longrightarrow P_q \overset{j}{\prec}_{i-1} P_p$.

$P_q \overset{j}{\prec}_{i-1} P_p \wedge P_p \overset{*i-1}{\prec}_{k-1} P_r \Longrightarrow P_q \overset{*j}{\prec}_{k-1} P_r$

$P_q \overset{*j}{\prec}_{k-1} P_r \Longrightarrow P_q$ takes a checkpoint.

Thus, the sending of m is recorded at P_q. A contradiction. □

5 Performance Analysis

The performance of a checkpointing algorithm is determined by three parameters: the blocking time (in the worst case), the synchronization message overhead (in the worst case), and the number of checkpoints required during checkpointing. Since $N_{mh} \gg N_{mss}$, to simplify the analysis, we assume that all processes are running on MHs and there is only one process running on each MH.

Notations

C_{static}: cost of sending a message between any two MSSs.

$C_{wireless}$: cost of sending a message from an MH to its local MSS (or vice versa).

$C_{broadcast}$: cost of broadcasting a message in the static network.

C_{search}: cost incurred to locate an MH and forward a message to its current local MSS, from a source MSS.

T_{static}: average message delay in the static network.

$T_{wireless}$: average message delay in the wireless network.

$T_{checkpoint}$: average delay to save a checkpoint on the stable storage, including the time to transfer the checkpoint from an MH to its local MSS.

T_{search}: average delay incurred to locate an MH and forward a message to its current local MSS.

Performance of our algorithm

The blocking time: After an MSS has sent all its local dependent vectors to the proxy MSS, it blocks (cannot forward messages) until it receives S_{forced} from the proxy MSS. Therefore, the blocking time is $2T_{static}$.

The synchronization message overhead: The message overhead includes the following. The request and reply messages from the initiator to its proxy MSS: $2C_{wireless}$. The proxy MSS broadcasts $R\_request$, S_{forced}, and *make_permanent* messages to all MSSs: $3C_{broadcast}$. MSSs send dependency vectors and *response* messages to the proxy MSS: $2N_{mss} * C_{static}$. MSSs send checkpoint *request* and *make_permanent* messages to necessary MHs and receive *response* messages from them. In the worst case, it is $3N_{mh} * C_{wireless}$. Therefore, the total message overhead (worst case) is $2C_{wireless} + 3C_{broadcast} + 2N_{mss} * C_{static} + 3N_{mh} * C_{wireless}$.

The number of checkpoints: Similar to Koo-Toueg algorithm [10], our algorithm forces only a minimum number of processes to take checkpoints.

Comparison with other algorithms

Table 1 compares our algorithm with two representative approaches for coordinated checkpointing. Koo-Toueg algorithm [10] has the lowest overhead (based on our three parameters) among the blocking algorithms [5, 9, 10] which try to minimize the number of synchronization messages and the number of checkpoints during checkpointing. The algorithm in [6] has the lowest overhead (based on our three parameters) among the non-blocking algorithms [6, 15]. We do not compare our algorithm with Prakash-Singhal algorithm since it may result in inconsistencies, and there is no easy solution to fix it without increasing overhead.

As shown in Table 1, compared to Koo-Toueg algorithm, our algorithm avoids the search cost (which is significant) and dramatically reduces the blocking time from

Algorithm	Blocking time	Messages	Checkpoints
Koo-Toueg [10]	$N_{mh} * (4 * T_{wireless}$ $+T_{checkpoint} + T_{search})$	$N_{mh} * (6 * C_{wireless} + C_{search})$	MIN
[6]	0	$N_{mh} * (3 * C_{wireless} + C_{search})$	MAX
Our algorithm	$2 * T_{static}$	$2C_{wireless} + 3C_{broadcast} + 2N_{mss} * C_{static}$ $+3N_{mh} * C_{wireless} \approx 3N_{mh} * C_{wireless}$	MIN

Table 1: **A comparison of performance.** $N_{mh} \gg N_{mss}$, $T_{wireless} \gg T_{static}$, $C_{wireless} \gg C_{static}$, and $MAX \gg MIN$ most of times. In general [8], the local MSS of the source MH is unaware of the current location of the target MH, and will have to "search" the network, i.e., query all MSSs, to discover the MSS that is local to the target MH. Then, $C_{search} = C_{broadcast} + 2 * C_{static}$ and $T_{search} = 3 * T_{static}$.

$N_{mh} * (4 * T_{wireless} + T_{checkpoint} + T_{search})$ to $2 * T_{static}$. Besides avoiding the search cost, our algorithm cuts the message overhead by half compared to Koo-Toueg algorithm. Compared to [6], our algorithm avoids the search cost and minimizes the number of checkpoints during checkpointing. Note that there maybe many applications running in a system: some of them have higher reliability requirement, and others do not. Also, different processes run at their own speed. Then, some processes may need to take checkpoints more frequently than others. However, the algorithm in [6] forces all processes in the system to take checkpoints. Thus, our algorithm significantly reduces the message overhead and checkpointing overhead compared to [6].

6 Conclusions

The major contribution of this paper is not just to present an efficient checkpointing algorithm, but to prove a more general result about coordinated checkpointing; that is, there does not exist a non-blocking algorithm that forces only a minimum number of processes to take their checkpoints. The result suggest that there are two directions in designing efficient coordinated checkpointing algorithms: first is to relax the non-blocking condition while keeping the min-process property and the other is to relax the min-process condition while keeping the non-blocking property. The new constraints in mobile computing system, such as low bandwidth of wireless channel, high search cost, and limited battery life, favor that the checkpointing algorithm should be a min-process algorithm. Following this direction, we proposed a min-process algorithm which dramatically reduces the blocking time from $N_{mh} * (4 * T_{wireless} + T_{checkpoint} + T_{search})$ in Koo-Toueg algorithm to $2 * T_{static}$. In our algorithm, only MSSs are blocked for a duration of $2 * T_{static}$. More specifically, the MSSs cannot send messages during these $2 * T_{static}$. However, they can do other computations and even receive messages.

References

[1] Arup Acharya and B.R. Badrinath. "Checkpointing Distributed Applications on Mobil Computers". *the Third Intl.*

Conf. on Parallel and Distributed Information Systems, Sep. 1994.

[2] P. Bhagwat and C.E. Perkins. "A Mobile Networking System Based on Internet Protocol (IP)". *USENIX Symp. on Mobile and Location Independent Computing*, August 1993.

[3] G. Cao and M. Singhal. "On Consistent Checkpointing in Distributed Systems". *OSU Technical Report #OSU-CISRC-9/97-TR44*, 1997.

[4] T. Cormen, C. Leiserson, and R. Rivest. "Introduction to Algorithms". *MIT Press*, 1990.

[5] Y. Deng and E.K. Park. "Checkpointing and Rollback-Recovery Algorithms in Distributed Systems". *Journal of Systems and Software*, pages 59–71, April 1994.

[6] E.N. Elnozahy, D.B. Johnson, and W. Zwaenepoel. "The Performance of Consistent Checkpointing". *Proc. of the 11th Symp. on Reliable Distributed Systems*, pages 86–95, Oct. 1992.

[7] G.H. Forman and J. Zahorjan. "The Challenges of Mobile Computing". *IEEE Computer*, pages 38–47, April 1994.

[8] J. Ioannidis, D. Duchamp, and G.Q. Maguire. "Ip-based Protocols for Mobile Internetworking". *Pro. of ACM SIGCOMM Symp. on Communication, Architectures and Protocols*, pages 235–245, Sep. 1991.

[9] J. Kim and T. Park. "An Efficient Protocol For Checkpointing Recovery in Distributed Systems". *IEEE Trans. on Parallel and Distributed Systems*, Aug. 1993.

[10] R. Koo and S. Toueg. "Checkpointing and Rollback-Recovery for Distributed Systems". *IEEE Trans. on Software Engineering*, pages 23–31, Jan. 1987.

[11] P. Krishna, N.H. Vaidya, and D.K. Pradhan. "Recovery in Distributed Mobile Environments". *IEEE Workshop on Advances in Parallel and Distributed System*, Oct. 1993.

[12] R. Netzer and J. Xu. "Necessary and Sufficient Conditions for Consistent Global Snapshots". *IEEE Trans. on Parallel and Distributed System*, Feb. 1995.

[13] R. Prakash and M. Singhal. "Maximal Global Snapshot with Concurrent Initiators". *Proc. of the Sixth IEEE Symp. on Parallel and Distributed Processing*, pages 344–351, Oct. 1994.

[14] R. Prakash and M. Singhal. "Low-Cost Checkpointing and Failure Recovery in Mobile Computing Systems". *IEEE Trans. on Parallel and Distributed System*, pages 1035–1048, Oct. 1996.

[15] L.M. Silva and J.G. Silva. "Global Checkpointing for Distributed Programs". *Proc. of the 11th Symp. on Reliable Distributed Systems*, pages 155–162, Oct. 1992.

[16] R.E. Strom and S.A. Yemini. "Optimistic Recovery In Distributed Systems". *ACM Trans. on Computer Systems*, pages 204–226, August 1985.

Rerouting Connections in Mobile ATM Networks

Gopal Dommety
Computer and Information Science
Ohio State University
dommety@cis.ohio-state.edu

Malathi Veeraraghavan
Bell Laboratories
Lucent Technologies
mv@bell-labs.com

Mukesh Singhal
Computer and Information Science
Ohio State University
singhal@cis.ohio-state.edu

Abstract

This paper presents an algorithm for optimizing the route of a connection that becomes suboptimal due to operations such as handoffs and location-based reroutes, and applies this algorithm to the handoff management problem in networks with hierarchical link state routing protocols such as PNNI (Private Network-to-Network Interface)-based ATM (Asynchronous Transfer Mode) networks. The route optimization algorithm uses hierarchical route information of the connection and summarized topology and loading information of the network to determine a "crossover node" such that adjusting the connection from that crossover node results in an optimally routed connection.

Handoff management schemes that perform local rerouting of connections have been proposed in order to support fast handoffs. These methods result in suboptimally routed connections. In this paper, we demonstrate how this route optimization algorithm can be used to optimize the route of a connection after such a handoff is executed, as the second phase of a two-phase handoff scheme. This route optimization procedure can also be executed as part of the handoff procedure resulting in a one-phase handoff scheme. Applying this route optimization algorithm, we propose two one-phase schemes, the one-phase optimal scheme and the one-phase minimal scheme. A comparative performance analysis of one- and two- phase handoff schemes is presented. Measures of comparison are handoff latency and the amount of network resources used by a connection. Handoff latency in the one-phase optimal scheme is greater than that in the two-phase schemes, and handoff latency in the one-phase minimal scheme is smaller than that in the two-phase schemes. The one-phase methods show a significant increase in efficiency of the connection compared to the two-phase methods.

Key words: Connection rerouting, route optimization, handoff management, PNNI routing protocol.

1. Introduction

In connection-oriented networks, location and handoff management procedures are needed to support user mobility. *Location management* procedures are needed to track mobiles and locate them in order to establish a connection to a mobile. *Handoff* procedures are needed to reroute connections on which the mobile user is communicating while moving. In both these sets of procedures, paths taken by connections could become "suboptimal" (a path is classified as being "suboptimal" if it is not the shortest path between the endpoints of the connection). For example, most handoff schemes propose performing a local connection reroute rather than an end-to-end connection reroute to keep handoff latencies low. Such reroute operations could result in making the connection path suboptimal. Similarly, location management schemes that propose setting up the connection to the home location of a mobile and then rerouting the connection to the mobile's current location based on location data provided by the home node could result in suboptimal connection paths. It is important to optimize routes of connections since suboptimal paths imply an inefficient usage of network resources.

In [1], we proposed an algorithm for optimizing the route of a connection and applied it to the location management problem. This paper presents a modified version of that algorithm and applies it to the handoff management problem. Based on this algorithm, we propose two solutions for the handoff management problem. In the first solution, the rerouting procedure is integrated into the handoff procedure (*one-phase method*). In this method, as a user moves from one base station to another, an optimal path to the new base station is determined and the connection is rerouted. In the second solution, the route optimization procedure is executed after a fast handoff procedure is completed (*two-phase method*). In this method, the handoff procedure consists of first performing a fast reroute of the connection to the new base station (which may result in a suboptimally routed connection), followed by an optimization of the route of the connection subsequently.

Since the route optimization algorithm is being applied to the problem of handoff management in PNNI-based ATM networks, we begin by providing background information on the PNNI standard and summarize prior work on handoff management in Section 2. In Section 3, we state the "base" rerouting problem, and provide a solution to this problem in Section 4. Section 5 describes how this solution can be integrated with the handoff management procedures. Finally, Section 6 presents results of a comparative performance analysis of the handoff schemes, and Section 7 provides a summary of the paper.

2. Background

In this section, we first present a brief overview of the PNNI-based ATM networks, and then summarize prior work on handoff management.

2.1 Overview of PNNI standards

PNNI-based ATM networks [2] are arranged in hierarchical peer groups as shown in Fig. 1. The lowest level

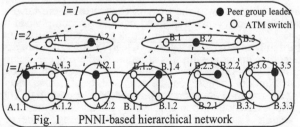

Fig. 1   PNNI-based hierarchical network

($l = L$) consists of ATM switches connected in arbitrary topologies. Each peer group has an elected *Peer Group*

Leader (PGL). Nodes within a peer group exchange topology, loading and reachability information using the *PNNI routing protocol*. The PGL of each peer group represents all the nodes within its peer group in the higher-level peer group and sends summarized topology/loading/reachability information about its lower-level peer group to its peers in the higher-level peer group. Each higher-level peer node broadcasts this summarized information to all its nodes in the lower-level peer group. Using this technique, each node has topology/loading/reachability data about its own peer group and all its ancestor peer groups. For example, in Fig. I, node A.1.1 has the topology information of the entire peer group A.1, as well as the topologies of peer group A and the top-level ($l = 1$) peer group.

The *PNNI signaling protocol standard* defines connection setup and release procedures. In order to set up a connection, the first switch receiving the connection setup request determines the hierarchical source route for that connection. The computed hierarchical source routes are carried as *DTL* (Designated Transit Lists) parameters in the signaling SETUP message [2]. A DTL is list of node identifiers, where a node at the lowest level is a switch, while at higher levels, a node is a logical group node that represents a peer group. A stack of DTLs is used to specify the complete path of a connection from the current node to the destination with one DTL for each level. The exact path (DTLs) within each peer group is computed at the *ingress border node* of the peer group, which then pushes a DTL specifying the path for that peer group on to the stack of DTLs. While computing the path through a peer group, the ingress border node of a peer group uses the next entry in the next DTL (the one corresponding to the next higher level peer group) as the target for exiting this peer group. In case there is only one DTL remaining (i.e., next DTL does not exist), the destination address is used to determine the route. The *egress border node* of a peer group pops DTLs that are exhausted from the stack. "Optimality" of connection paths in PNNI-based networks should be regarded within the context of this hierarchical organization of switches. In other words, because of the hierarchical organization, the "shortest-path" computed by PNNI may not be the true shortest-path. This penalty is paid in return for network scalability.

2.2 Prior work on handoff management

Handoff management consists of procedures to reroute connections on which a mobile user is communicating while moving. Various handoff schemes have been proposed in [3-9]. A *generalized handoff scheme*, which allows for the realization of different handoff schemes proposed in [3-9], can be implemented by changing the node serving as the *CrossOver Switch* (COS), from which point connections are rerouted to the mobile at its new location. In other words, as mobile moves from one base station to another a crossover switch is selected and a new segment is set up from the COS to the new base station. Fig. 2 shows that if the COS is chosen to be the far end switch on the connection, handoff can be accomplished in *one-phase*, i.e., an optimal route is achieved requiring no further route optimization. Clearly, handoff latency becomes an issue with this scheme. At the other extreme, if the COS is statically assigned to be the old base station, low handoff latencies can be achieved, but the path taken by the rerouted connection could become suboptimal. The path extension scheme, anchor switch scheme, and dynamic COS search schemes shown in Fig. 2 lie in-between these extremes. In the path extension scheme, the COS is assigned to be the switch attached to the old base station. In the anchor switch scheme, the COS is statically

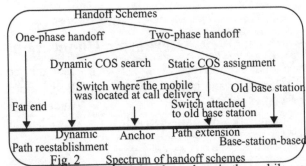

Fig. 2   Spectrum of handoff schemes

assigned to be the switch in whose domain the mobile was located at the time of call delivery. In the dynamic COS search scheme, the COS is selected dynamically with the search typically being limited to a local area for fast handoffs. Fig. 2 classifies the dynamic COS search and the static COS assignment schemes as *two-phase* schemes since they require route optimization after the completion of the handoff. We believe that two-phase handoff schemes will be needed due to considerations of handoff latency. Hence, in this paper we propose a scheme to optimize the route of a connection that becomes suboptimal due to handoffs. From the spectrum of schemes shown in Fig. 2, we observe that if the dynamic COS search scheme is applied to find the optimal COS, such a scheme can be classified as a *one-phase dynamic COS search scheme*. Our proposed one-phase dynamic COS search scheme will be presented in Section 5.2.

3. Problem statement

In this section, we state the base rerouting problem and demonstrate how the route optimization problems created in the handoff management schemes can be mapped to the base rerouting problem.

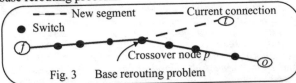

Fig. 3   Base rerouting problem

Consider a connection between two end points f and o in Fig. 3 (where f is used to denote the "far end" and o is used to denote the "old point"). The problem is to reroute the connection $f-o$ to create a connection from node f to node t (target node). Next, we demonstrate how the route optimization problems created in the handoff management schemes can be mapped to this base problem.

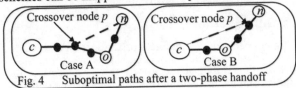

Fig. 4   Suboptimal paths after a two-phase handoff

The suboptimality resulting from the two-phase handoff schemes shown in Fig. 2 is illustrated in Fig. 4, where node c is the constant end (these schemes are general and can be applied to the case where both terminals are mobiles), node o is the COS, and node n is the switch attached to the new base station (or the new base station). In the case of path extension scheme, the handoff procedure is performed by extending the path from the old switch to the new switch. Therefore, node o corresponds to the switch attached to the old base station, also referred to as the old switch. In this case, the suboptimal path from

c to o (old switch) to n (new switch) needs to be rerouted to form an optimal path from c to n by either rerouting the c-o segment toward the target node n (case A in Fig. 4), or by rerouting the o-n segment toward the target node c (case B in Fig. 4). In either case, the problem reduces to that illustrated in Fig. 3.

In the anchor switch scheme shown in Fig. 2, the COS, i.e., node o in Fig. 3, is the anchor switch (the switch in whose domain the mobile was located at the time of call delivery). In the base-station-based handoff scheme, node o is the old base station, and in the two-phase dynamic COS scheme, node o is a local switch through which the connection was rerouted during the fast handoff. In all the above schemes, the route optimization problem reduces to the problem of Fig. 3 after identifying whether the segment c-o or o-n needs to be rerouted to the corresponding target node (n or c, respectively).

Finally, as observed in Section 2.2, the dynamic COS search handoff scheme can be converted from a two-phase scheme to a one-phase scheme if the old connection is rerouted from an optimal crossover node to the new location. Such a scheme can be viewed as one in which optimal rerouting is performed during the handoff. In this case, the same problem illustrated in Fig. 3 needs to be solved wherein node f corresponds to the constant end c, node o corresponds to the old switch, and node t corresponds to the new switch.

Table 1 summarizes the mapping to the base rerouting problem. In the two-phase schemes, after the completion of the first phase (handoff procedure) rerouting is needed on one of the two segments. Definition of the "closeness" of two nodes needed to select between case A and case B is provided in Section 5.1.

Table 1: Mapping to the base rerouting problem

Scheme	Case	f	o	t
Two-phase	o is "closer" to c than n	n	o	c
	o is "closer" to n than c	c	o	n
One-phase dynamic COS	for all cases	c	o	n

Next, we address the issue of selecting the node that initiates the route optimization procedure. To determine the crossover node, the network needs to compute the shortest path between nodes f and t, and then determine the overlap between the new path f-t and the old path f-o. In the one-phase dynamic COS scheme, since it is desirable to keep the handoff latency low, it becomes necessary for node o or t to initiate the route optimization procedure. The choice of the nodes between o and t depends on several factors such as type of handoff (backward or forward), and availability of existing path information (discussed in Sections 4.1 and 4.2). In the rerouting required for the suboptimal paths caused by the two-phase schemes, any of nodes f, o, or t could initiate the route optimization procedures. As shown in Table 1, the assignment of nodes (c, o, and n) in the two-phase schemes to nodes f, o and t is such that o and t are close while f is the distant node. This implies that selecting either nodes o or t as the initiating node will lead to smaller processing delays.

4 Route optimization algorithm

There are four steps involved in solving the base rerouting problem, (i) determining a crossover node p, (ii) establishing a new segment between p and t, (iii) switching user data from the old segment to the new segment, and (iv) releasing the old segment from p to o. Procedure for switching of user data from the old segment to the new segment depends on the scenario in which the route optimization is applied, and is therefore discussed in Section 5. The fourth step of releasing the old segment can be performed using the standard signaling procedures. Next, we present a solution to the problem of determining a crossover node p for the base rerouting problem, and discuss how the new segment can be set up. Ideally, the crossover node p should be such that the path f-p-t is the shortest path between f and t, while at the same time, there should be a maximal overlap in the paths of the old connection f-o and the new connection f-t. We refer to such a crossover node as the *minimal crossover node* for the two paths f-o and f-t.

While finding the minimal crossover node has both the advantages of minimizing the resources required by the new connection and minimizing the new segment setup/old segment release overhead, there are certain constraints in the PNNI standard (in its current form) that do not allow for the determination of this node. In the PNNI standard, there is currently

(i) no requirement mandating that all nodes retain the hierarchical path of a connection after it is established, and
(ii) a restriction that only nodes that created a DTL (Designated Transit List) can change that DTL.

The minimal crossover node determined under these constraints is defined as the *optimal crossover node* since it is a node p such that f-p-t is an optimal path, and as much overlap as is possible between the old and new paths is achieved within the constraints of the PNNI standard.

Thus, we have defined two types of crossover nodes, the optimal crossover node and the minimal crossover node. We present procedures to determine the optimal crossover node in Section 4.1 and minimal crossover node in Section 4.2. The details of the two procedures and the relationship between them is illustrated in Fig. 5. Fig. 5 shows the crossover node determination procedure when old node (o) initiates the procedure. Variation of the procedure when the target node (t) initiates, is omitted due to space considerations [10]. The notation used in the description of these procedures is listed in Table 2.

4.1 Optimal crossover node determination

Two aspects of the PNNI based networks that are fundamental to the optimal crossover node determination procedure are: i) every node only has summarized information regarding the topology of the network (nodes outside of a peer group do not have information regarding the internal structure of that peer group) and ii) connections are routed using hierarchical source routing. The basis of this procedure is that if a connection is routed using source routing and the nodes outside a peer group do not know the internal details of the peer group, then the connection to any node within the peer group will follow the same route until the first node (ingress border node) of that peer group.

The location of the optimal crossover node depends on the exact relation between the ancestors-are-siblings levels of the nodes f, o, and t.

If $a_{of} < a_{ot}$ (Case I of Fig. 6), the scenario is one in

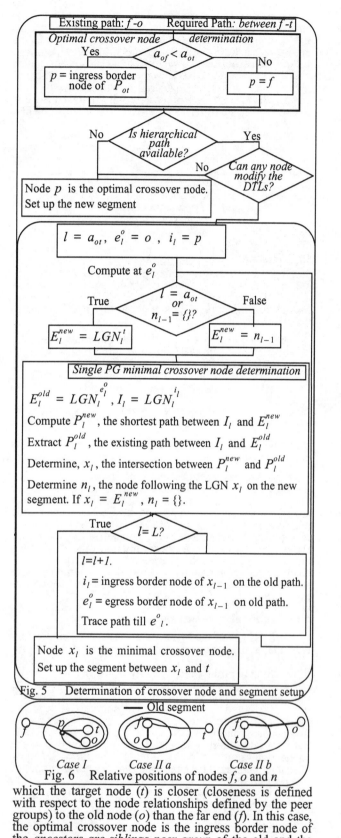

Fig. 5 Determination of crossover node and segment setup

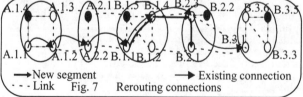

Fig. 6 Relative positions of nodes f, o and n

procedure for the $f-o$ connection entered peer group P_{to}. Since nodes contain only the summarized topology

Table 2: Notation

Symbol	Meaning
P_{ij}	*Ancestors-are-siblings peer group* of two nodes i and j is the lowest peer group in the hierarchy at which ancestors of both nodes belong to the same peer group.
a_{ij}	The *ancestors-are-siblings level* of two nodes i and j, is the level at which the ancestors of the two nodes i and j belong to the same peer group, i.e., the level of their ancestors-are-siblings peer group.
LGN_l^{phy}	Logical group node ancestor of the physical switch phy at level l. For example, in Fig. 1, the $LGN_1^{A1.1}$ is A.
x_l	Minimal crossover peergroup of level l. x_L (value of l is L) is the minimal crossover node.
i_l	Ingress border node of x_{l-1} on the old path. If l is equal to a_{ot}, i_l is the optimal crossover node p.
E_l^{new}	Logical group node of ingress border node e_l^n or a node adjacent to x_{l-1} on the new path P_{l-1}^{new}.
P_l^{old}	Hierarchical path of the existing connection segment between the logical group nodes I_l and E_l^{old}. This path is specified in terms of the logical groups nodes of level l.

and reachability information, nodes outside a peer group cannot distinguish between exact locations of the different nodes reachable through that peer group. Therefore, a connection from the far end to either the target or the old node will follow the same route until it reaches the ingress node (p) of the *ancestors-are-siblings peer group* of the old and the target nodes (P_{to}). Once the connection setup arrives at the ingress node p, it computes the source route to the exact location. Therefore, at p, the connection to the target node (t) would have a different source route than a connection to the old node (o). Hence, an optimal path can be obtained by adjusting the existing connection from the crossover switch p.

Example: Consider the scenario in which there is an existing connection between A.1.1 (far end) and B.3.1 (old node), and a new connection between A.1.1 and B.2.1 (target node) is desired (see Fig. 7). In this case a_{of}, a_{ot} and

A.1.4 A.1.3 A.2.1 B.1.5 B.1.4 B.2.3 B.2.2 B.3.6 B.3.5
B.3.1
A.1.1 A.1.2 A.2.2 B.1.1 B.1.2 B.2.1 B.3.3

→ New segment → Existing connection
- - - Link Fig. 7 Rerouting connections

P_{to} are 1, 2, and B, respectively. Since $a_{of} < a_{ot}$, the crossover node is the ingress border node of peer group B,

which the target node (t) is closer (closeness is defined with respect to the node relationships defined by the peer groups) to the old node (o) than the far end (f). In this case, the optimal crossover node is the ingress border node of the *ancestors-are-siblings peer group* of the old and the target nodes (P_{to}) through which the connection setup

which is B.1.1. Therefore, the optimal path between A.1.1 and B.2.1 is achieved by setting up a new segment from B.1.1 to B.2.1, as shown in Fig. 7.

If $a_{of} > a_{ot}$ (Case II a of Fig. 6), the scenario is one in which the old node (o) is closer to the far end (f) than to the target node (t). In this situation, there may not be any segment common between the existing connection and the new desired connection. Therefore, the optimal crossover node is the far end (f). The new path is optimal since the entire path between the far end and the target node is being set up.

If $a_{of} = a_{ot}$ (Case II b of Fig. 6), the scenario is one in which the target node is closer ($a_{ft} > a_{fo}$) to the far end than to the old node or equidistant ($a_{ft} = a_{fo}$) to the far end and the old node. In this situation too, there may not be any segment common between the existing connection and the new desired connection. The optimal crossover node is the far end (f). Fig. 5 shows the optimal crossover node determination procedure described above.

It should be noted that during the route optimization phase of the two-phase schemes, only *Case I* of Fig. 6 is possible (see Table 1) since by choice, f is the "far end" node. In the one-phase scheme, all three cases are possible. *Case I of Fig. 6* is expected to occur frequently as majority of the movements occur from one base station to another that are typically "near" each other.

4.2 Minimal crossover node determination

As explained earlier, it is possible that a part of the existing segment from the optimal crossover node to the old node is in common with the new segment. For example, in Fig. 7, while B.1.1 is the optimal crossover node, B.2.3 is the minimal crossover node. Next, we describe a procedure to determine the minimal crossover point.

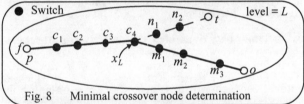

Fig. 8   Minimal crossover node determination

Consider the scenario in which the far end switch, old switch and the target switch are in the same level-L peer group as shown in Fig. 8. In this case, the optimal crossover node is the far end switch since $a_{of} = a_{ot}$ (Case IIb of Fig. 6). To determine the minimal crossover node, the node initiating the procedure (node o or t) needs to first compute the shortest path from node f to node t and then compare it with the old path $f - o$. Since the PNNI routing protocol is a link-state routing scheme, this operation can be easily done. Nodes f, o and t maintain the same topological information about the peer group allowing a node to determine the shortest path between two other nodes.

For the scenario shown in Fig. 8, node o (or node t) computes the shortest path between f and t to be $\{f, c_1, c_2, c_3, c_4, n_1, n_2, t\}$. It knows the path of the old connection as being $\{f, c_1, c_2, c_3, c_4, m_1, m_2, m_3, o\}$. By comparing the old and the new paths, it determines the *minimal crossover node to be the point of intersection of the two paths closest to o* (c_4). Henceforth, we refer to the above-described procedure as the *single PG minimal crossover node determination routine*, and is applied on paths through a single peer group.

Next, extensions of this procedure to the scenario in which nodes f, o and t belong to different level-L peer groups is described. The extensions are based on the following observations:

(i) the end-to-end hierarchical route stored at a node on the path consists of a stack of DTLs, with each DTL representing a path through a peer group at a level of the hierarchy as viewed by that node (see Section 2.1), and

(ii) there is always a peer group at which the ancestors of nodes f, o and t belong to the same peer group.

Given these observations, we begin the minimal crossover node determination by having node o exercise the *single PG minimal crossover node determination routine* for the paths through the peer group at which ancestors of nodes f, o and t are siblings. This leads to the determination of a *minimal crossover peer group* rather than the identification of the actual minimal crossover node. The minimal crossover peer group contains the minimal crossover node, but given the hierarchical structure of the network, node o has no detailed information about the inside structure of this minimal crossover peer group. This makes it necessary to execute the next step of the procedure at a node that lies inside this minimal crossover peer group.

For this purpose, the old connection is traced from node o until the egress border node of the identified minimal crossover peer group on the old connection is reached. This node can then perform the single PG minimal crossover node determination routine for the paths through the minimal crossover peer group to determine the next lower-level minimal crossover peer group. This procedure is applied recursively until a physical switch is identified as the minimal crossover node.

Node t can initiate the minimal crossover node determination only if information regarding the detailed path of the existing connection is available. If node t initiates the minimal crossover node determination procedure, minimal crossover node determination procedure can be executed while setting up the new segment [10]. In other words, the new segment setup is initiated by specifying the hierarchical source route to the minimal crossover peergroup. The ingress border node of this minimal crossover peergroup computes the next lower-level minimal crossover peer group and specifies the route internal to the minimal crossover peer group. This procedure is applied recursively until the minimal crossover node is determined. The details of the minimal crossover node determination algorithm are presented in Fig. 5. Detailed explanation of the algorithm is given in [10].

5   Application to handoff management

In this section, we integrate the route optimization algorithm described in Section 4 into the handoff management schemes described in Section 2.2.

5.1   Second phase of two-phase handoff schemes

In this section, we present a route optimization procedure that can be used to reroute a connection after a fast handoff procedure is completed, as the *second phase* of *two-phase handoff* schemes. In the first phase, a fast local rerouting of the connection to the new location is performed. This could result in a connection that is routed suboptimally. In order to optimize the connection route that resulted from the fast rerouting, a route optimization procedure is executed. Instead of optimizing the route after every handoff, this route optimization procedure could be carried out after multiple handoffs. The need for route optimization is dictated by several factors, such as optimality of the current path, duration of the call, QoS

(Quality of Service) requirements of the connection, etc.

The route optimization procedure after handoff consists of *four* steps. *First*, the connection segment to reroute and the corresponding target node are selected. *Second*, a crossover node between the old and the new paths is determined, and a new segment is set up between that crossover node and the target node. *Third*, using "Tail" signals and buffering, user data is switched over from the old path to the new path. *Fourth*, the old segment is released using standard signaling procedures.

Step1: Connection segment and target node determination: As illustrated in the two cases of Fig. 4, the first task in optimizing the route of a connection locally rerouted through node o is to identify which of the two segments, $c-o$ or $o-n$ needs to be rerouted. The corresponding target nodes for the rerouting operation become n and c, respectively.

Table 1 presents a method of choosing the connection segment and the target node based on the relative "closeness" of the nodes to each other. Ideally, the choice of the connection segment and the target node should be such that the length of the new segment is minimized, thereby, reducing the signaling load, route optimization delay, and the number of cells that need to be buffered. A definition of *closeness* (based on the assumption that the distance between two nodes is inversely proportional to their ancestors-are-siblings level) with the objective of minimizing the length of the new segment is as follows: For three nodes x, y and z, node x is closer to node y than to node z if the ancestors-are-sibling level of nodes x and z is less than or equal to the ancestors-are-sibling level of nodes x and y, i.e., $a_{xz} \le a_{xy}$. For example, if $a_{oc} < a_{on}$ *(Case I of Fig. 6)*, the old switch is closer to the new switch of the mobile. It should be noted that the optimality of the resulting connection path is *independent* of the choice of the target node.

Step 2: Determination of the crossover node and setting up of the new segment: The crossover node is determined using the procedures described in Section 4. If either hierarchical path information is not available or only the nodes that created the DTL can change the DTL, the procedure (see Fig. 5) determines the optimal crossover node. Otherwise, minimal crossover node is determined. In order to set up a new segment between the target node and the crossover node, the identity of the crossover switch is required. Therefore, the existing connection is traced (i.e., a COS_SELECT message is sent along the existing path) till the crossover node. Furthermore, if the detailed path of the existing connection is available, the target node can combine the procedures of COS determination and new segment setup [10].

Step 3: Switching of user data from the old to the new path: Procedures to switch user cells from the old to the new path depend on the acceptable amount of cell loss and out-of-sequence cells, and the support for switching and buffering available in various network elements. For applications that do not require lossless handoffs, once the new segment is formed, user data is switched to the new path as soon as the new segment is set up. In other words, the switching fabric in the target node (or COS) is configured to transmit/receive on the new path without coordinating with the COS (or target node).

For applications requiring lossless and in-sequence cells, "Tail" signals and buffering are used to switch user data from the old path to the new path. Tail signals are special cells sent on the same virtual circuit as the user

cells (in-band signals). Tail signals should be easily distinguishable from user cells. For instance, they could be special RM (Resource Management) cells [12]. These Tail signals are sent to signal the switching of user data to the new segment. For bidirectional connections, user data is to be switched in both the directions, downstream (from COS to the Target node) and upstream (from the target node to the COS). For each direction, we can buffer either at the COS or at the target node. Therefore, there are four possible alternatives for switching bidirectional connections. We will illustrate procedures for buffering both upstream and downstream cells at the target node. Procedures for the other two alternatives can be obtained similarly [10].

Fig. 9 illustrates the procedure for switching of user cells

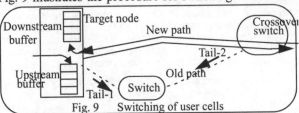

Fig. 9   Switching of user cells

by buffering only at the target node. After the new segment is set up, the upstream cells and the downstream cells received on the new path are buffered and a Tail signal (shown as Tail-1 in Fig. 9) is sent in the upstream direction (towards the COS) by the target node. After receiving this Tail signal, the switch fabric (to receive/transmit cells on the new path) is configured at the COS, and a Tail signal (shown as Tail-2 in Fig. 9) is sent in the downstream direction. On receipt of the Tail signal from the COS, cells in the upstream and downstream buffers are sent first, and then the switch fabric at the target node is configured. All the transit nodes on the old path can release the connection in the appropriate direction as and when they see the corresponding *Tail* signals.

5.2   One-phase dynamic COS search handoff scheme

In this section, we present a *one-phase dynamic COS (CrossOver Switch) search handoff scheme* in which an optimal connection path is achieved while rerouting the connection from the old base station to the new base station. Handoff procedures, typically involve functions such as identification of the new base station, rerouting of the wireline connection between the far end and the old base station to the new base station, radio link establishment between the mobile and the new base station, etc. In this paper, we are only concerned with the connection rerouting aspect of the handoff. This rerouting of the connection during a handoff involves four steps, 1) determination of the crossover node, 2) setting up of the new segment, 3) switching of user data onto the new segment, and 4) releasing the old segment.

Handoff signaling depends on factors such as the type of handoff initiation (mobile initiated, mobile assisted, and base station initiated), type of handoff detection (forward handoff and backward handoff), and type of data transmission during handoff (soft handoff and hard handoff). In this paper, we will illustrate the procedures for a subset of the scenarios, and procedures for other scenarios can be developed similarly [10].

Steps 1 and 2: Determination of the crossover node and setting up of the new segment: The crossover node is determined using the procedure described in Section 4. If the *detailed path* of the existing connection is not available, i.e., node o initiates the route optimization procedure, the crossover node is first determined by tracing the existing connection and then the new segment is set up. If the *detailed path of the existing connection is available,* the new segment can be set up directly by the target node [10], i.e., the procedures of determining the crossover node and setting up the new segment are combined. In Section 6, we compare the performance of these schemes with and without the detailed path information.

Steps 3 and 4: Switching of user data and releasing of the old connection: Procedures to switch user cells from the old to the new path depend on type of data transmission during handoff, type of handoff detection, acceptable amount of cell loss and out-of-sequence cells, and the support for switching and buffering available. For applications requiring lossless and in-sequence cell delivery, "Tail" signals described in section 5.1 and buffering are used to switch user data from the old path to the new path.

During a hard handoff, data transfer is switched over from the old base station to the new base station, i.e., data cannot be sent to and received from both the old and new base stations. Typically, the radio link is disconnected from the old base station and a new radio link is established to the new base station. In order to switch user data in the upstream direction (from the mobile), upstream cells are buffered by the mobile when radio link to the old base station is disconnected until the radio link with the new base station is established [10].

For switching user data in the downstream direction, two buffering alternatives are possible: buffering at the new base station (or the switch attached to the new base station) and buffering at the COS. Fig. 10 illustrates the

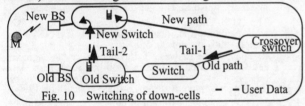

Fig. 10   Switching of down-cells   − − User Data

procedure for switching of user downstream cells by buffering at the new switch. After the new segment is set up, the switch fabric is configured at the COS and a Tail (Tail-1) signal is sent by the COS to the old switch indicating that no more cells will be sent on the old path. On receipt of the Tail-1 signal, the old switch sends the buffered cells followed by a Tail (Tail-2) signal to the new switch. The new switch first sends the cells received from the old switch and on receipt of the Tail signal, sends the cells received on the new path to the mobile. This procedure requires a temporary connection between the new switch (or base station) and the old switch (or base station). Procedure for switching of user downstream cells by buffering at the COS and procedures for soft handoff are presented in [10]. Using these buffering and forwarding techniques, lossless handoff is achieved.

6   Numerical results

In this section, we present the results of a comparative performance analysis of one-phase and two-phase handoff schemes. In particular we compare the proposed one-phase dynamic COS search handoff scheme (optimal and minimal), and the two-phase handoff scheme in which the first phase consists of a quick path extension from the old switch to the new switch (see Fig. 2). While evaluating the performance of the two-phase scheme, two scenarios are considered: *i)* there is a direct link between the old and the new switch, and *ii)* there is no direct link between the old

and the new switch. We also compare the performance of the one-phase schemes with and without detailed information regarding the path of the existing connection.

As discussed earlier, there is a trade-off between handoff latency and resource utilization in one- and two- phase methods. Using an analytic model, we analyze this trade-off. Expressions to estimate the handoff latencies and the resource utilization are derived in [10].

Table 3: Notation and input parameters

Symbol	Meaning	Value
L	Number of peer group levels in the network (see Fig. 1).	5
m_i	Number of peer nodes in a peer group of level i.	10
p_i	Average length of the "shortest-path" between nodes of a peer group at level i, $p_{L+1} = 1$	3
S_d	Delay incurred at a switch during connection setup.	2.33 ms
C_m	Delay incurred at a transit switch to transport a COS_SELECT message.	1 ms

In order to compare the one- and two- phase schemes, a 10-level large hierarchical network consisting of 100,000 switches is considered. Values of input parameters assumed for this numerical computation are shown in Table 3. The probability distributions used for calling patterns and user mobility are derived in [10]. Input parameters S_d and C_m are estimated from measured data [11].

The variation of handoff delays and the resource utilization (number of hops) for different values of $a_{\rho n}$ (ancestors-are-siblings level of the old and the new switches) for the one- and the two-phase methods is shown in Fig. 11.

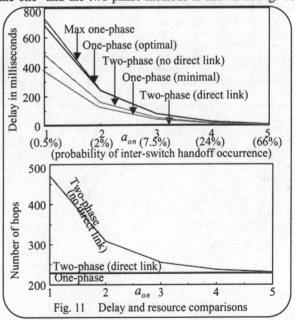

Fig. 11   Delay and resource comparisons

From the plot showing the variation in *inter-switch handoff delay,* three observation are made. *i)* One-phase optimal scheme incurs a higher average delay than that of the two-phase path extension scheme. *ii)* One-phase minimal scheme incurs a lower delay than that of the two-phase path extension scheme (with no direct link). *iii)* Maximum delay in the one-phase scheme is significantly higher than in the two-phase scheme.

Next, we discuss the variation in handoff delay with a variation in the value of a_{on}. The handoff delay in all the schemes increases with a decrease in the value of a_{on} (the lower the value of a_{on}, the greater the distance between the old and new locations). The handoff latency for the one-phase optimal scheme is similar to that of the two-phase scheme for high values of a_{on}, but significantly higher than in the two-phase scheme for low values of a_{on}. It is interesting to note that majority of the inter-switch handoffs (estimated to be 90% of the inter-switch handoffs) occur at high a_{on} values (see Fig. 11). Therefore for most of the handoffs, the handoff latency will be low in the one-phase handoff scheme [10].

If the detailed path of the existing connection is available, as described in Section 5.2, the new segment can be set up directly by the new switch, instead of first determining the COS by tracing the old connection and then setting up the new segment. Fig. 12 show the variation in inter-

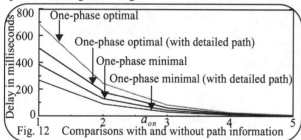

Fig. 12   Comparisons with and without path information

switch handoff delay in the one-phase handoff scheme with and without detailed path information. From the plots we observe that the handoff delay can be significantly reduced (about 27% in the one-phase optimal scheme) if detailed path information is available.

The variation in the number of hops in the resulting connection after rerouting is given in Fig. 11. The one-phase method shows a slight increase in efficiency of connection routes compared to the two-phase method when there is a direct link between the old and the new switches, and a significant increase in efficiency of connection routes when there is no direct link between the old and the new switches. In the two-phase handoff scheme, the connection path after route optimization is performed will be the same as the resulting connection after the one-phase handoff. Therefore, the route optimization phase of the two-phase handoff method will result in a significant improvement in the utilization of communication resources. However, there is an overhead associated the route optimization procedure. This overhead can be reduced by performing route optimization after multiple handoffs instead of performing the route optimization procedure after every handoff.

7. Summary

In this paper, we presented an algorithm for optimizing the route of a connection that becomes suboptimal due to operations such as handoffs. This algorithm can be easily implemented in networks with hierarchical link state routing protocols such as PNNI-based ATM networks. A base rerouting problem was defined as one in which a connection from a far end node f to an old node o needs to be rerouted to a target node t such that the resulting connec-

tion extends from f to t. The rerouting algorithm consists of finding a "crossover node," setting up a new segment from the crossover node to the target node, and releasing the old segment from the crossover node to the old node. Variations of the algorithm include methods to determine two types of crossover nodes, *optimal and minimal*, and methods to initiate the route optimization at the *target node or the old node*.

The second part of the paper describes the application of this rerouting algorithm to the handoff problem. This algorithm can be applied as a *second-phase of two-phase handoff schemes*, where the first phase consists of a local route modification as the user moves, or in an integrated *one-phase handoff scheme*. A comparative performance analysis of the one-phase and two-phase handoff schemes was presented. The one-phase optimal scheme incurs an average handoff latency that is twice as much as the one-phase minimal scheme, while the two-phase scheme incurs an average handoff latency that is about 30% more than the one-phase minimal scheme. The variation in which the route optimization is initiated at the target node is better than the one in which the route optimization is initiated at the old node (by about 27% using the optimal variation). Finally, the amount of network resources saved by selecting the optimal crossover node in the one-phase handoff scheme or by performing the route optimization in the second phase in two-phase schemes is shown to be significant.

References

[1]   G. Dommety, M. Veeraraghavan, and M. Singhal, "Route optimization in mobile ATM networks", *ACM/IEEE International Conference on Mobile Computing and Networking*, Budapest, Hungary, Sept. 1997, pp. 43-54.

[2]   The ATM Forum Technical Committee, "Private Network-Network Specification Interface v1.0 (PNNI 1.0)," March 1996, af-pnni-0055.000.

[3]   R. Yuan, S. K. Biswas, D. Raychaudhuri, "A Signaling and Control Architecture for Mobility Support in Wireless ATM Networks," *Proc. of IEEE International Conference on Communications*, Dallas, Texas, June 1996.

[4]   M. Veeraraghavan, M. Karol and K. Y. Eng, "Mobility and Connection Management in a Wireless ATM LAN", *IEEE Journal on Selected Areas in Communications*, Vol. 15, No. 1, January 1997, pp. 50-68.

[5]   H. Mitts, H. Hansen, J. Immonen, S. Veikkolainen, "Lossless handover for wireless ATM," *Proc. of ACM Mobicom '96*, New York, pp. 85-96.

[6]   W. Chen, "Impact of Anchor rerouting based inter-switch handoffs in Wireless ATM Access Networks," *Proc. of IEEE International Conference on Communications*, Dallas, Texas, June 1996.

[7]   P. P. Mishra, M. B. Srivastava, "Evaluation of Virtual Circuit Rerouting Strategies for Mobility Support in ATM Networks," *IEEE Intl. Conference on Distributed Computing Systems*, Baltimore, Maryland, August 1997.

[8]   B. A. Akyol and D. C. Cox, "Rerouting for handoff in a Wireless ATM Network," *IEEE Personal Communications Magazine*, October 1996, pp. 26-33.

[9]   C-K. Toh, "Performance Evaluation of Crossover Switch Discovery Algorithms for Wireless ATM LANs," *Proc. of IEEE INFOCOM '96*, San Francisco, California.

[10] G. Dommety, M. Veeraraghavan, and M. Singhal, "Rerouting connections in mobile ATM networks", Techinical Report, Department of Computer and Information Science, Ohio State University, OSU-CISRC-8/97-TR37.

[11] M. Veeraraghavan, G. L. Choudhury, and M. Kshirsagar, "Implementation and Analysis of Parallel Connection Control", *IEEE INFOCOM*, Kobe, Japan, April 1997.

[12] The ATM Forum Technical Committee, "ATM User-Network Interface (UNI) Signaling Specification Version 4.0," January 1996, ATM Forum/95-1434R9.

Session 2A
Applications and Algorithms I

Chair: Hal Sudborough
University of Texas at Dallas

A Parallel Algorithm for Timing-driven Global Routing for Standard Cells

Zhaoyun Xing
Sun Microsystems Laboratories
901 San Antonio Road
Palo Alto, CA 94303
xing@eng.sun.com

Prithviraj Banerjee *
Center for Parallel and Distributed Computing
Northwestern University
2145 Sheridan Road, Evanston, IL 60208
banerjee@ece.nwu.edu

Abstract

The timing-driven global routing problem is an extremely important and time consuming phase of any automated layout system. In this paper, by integrating high performance interconnection tree construction, wire-sizing, and switch-able segment channel optimization together, we propose an adaptive timing-driven global routing algorithm which minimizes the timing delay as well as circuit area. Our experiments on MCNC benchmarks show that our timing-driven global routing algorithm reduces the maximum path delays significantly from the global router TimberWolfSC. Based on this adaptive timing-driven global routing algorithm, a parallel algorithm on timing-driven global routing for standard cells is given. This algorithm has been implemented on an 8 processor IBM J-40 shared memory multi-processor by using the Message Passing Interface (MPI). Our experimental results show good speedup and circuit delay results for this parallel algorithm using MCNC benchmark circuits.

1 Introduction

In deep sub-micron fabrication technology, the interconnection delay contributes up to 70% of the clock cycles of high performance circuits. As a result, global routing becomes a very important phase of any automated layout system. In a standard cell design environment, timing-driven global routing determines the interconnection topology of signal nets and the allocation and assignment of feedthroughs such that the circuit delay is minimized. Several timing-driven global routing algorithms have been proposed for standard

*This research was supported in part by the Semiconductor Research Corporation under contract SRC 96-DP-109 and the Advanced Research Projects Agency under contract DAA-H04-94-G0273 administered by the Army Research Office.

cell design [5, 6], while none of those fully takes advantage of the row-based standard cell design technologies. The minimization of the interconnection delays along the dominant paths determines the performance of the timing-driven global routing. Numerous researchers have worked on the interconnection topology construction. A good survey is given in [7].

The timing-driven global routing problem is also a very time consuming phase of the layout synthesis. For contemporary designs containing 100,000 cells and nets, global routers can easily take several hours to perform their operation. Based on TimberWolfSC, in [17], three different parallel algorithms were proposed based on TWGR. Two of them provided good speedups and quality. While various parallel algorithms have been developed in the part for minimizing the wire length and area [1, 2, 13, 14, 16, 17], there is no work on parallel timing-driven global routing.

In this paper, first, by integrating high performance interconnection tree construction, wire-sizing, and switch-able segment channel optimization together, we propose an adaptive timing-driven global routing algorithm which minimizes the timing delay as well as circuit area. Subsequently, based on this algorithm, we propose a parallel algorithm on timing-driven global routing for standard cells. This algorithm has been implemented on an 8 processor IBM J-40 by using the Message Passing Interface (MPI). Our experimental results show good speedup and circuit delay results for this parallel algorithm.

2 Related Work

2.1 Signal Net Delay Minimization

Among various interconnection topology construction algorithms, two models have been used to approximate the signal source-sink delays. The first model assumes that the delay is proportional to the path wire-length, and it is therefore called the linear delay model. The second is called the Elmore delay model which gives much more accurate approximation than the linear model [3]. Throughout this paper, we use the Elmore delay model.

Most of the existing tree topology construction algorithms for the general signal net minimize either one source-sink delay (the sink is called critical sink,) the maximum source-sink delay, or the weighted sum of all source-sink delays. Also, they are greedy [7]. Starting from only the source pin, the tree grows one pin at a time. In each step, a new sink pin is added into the tree such that the objective function increase is minimized. The new sink pin can be connected to the source pin or a sink pin which is in the tree already. This algorithm is called the Elmore Routing Tree algorithm (ERT.) If in addition, the new sink is also allowed to connected to any point on an existing tree edge, this algorithm is called the Steiner Elmore Routing Tree (SERT.) The new point on the edge which minimizes the objective is called the Steiner point. So far, SERT is the best polynomial time delay minimization algorithm with a complexity of $O(n^4)$, where n is the number of sinks on the net.

2.2 Wire Sizing

In a modern design, the wire sizing can reduce the circuit delay by up to 40% [4]. Cong et al. proposed an efficient algorithm to optimize the weighted source sink delay assuming that there are only a finite number of wire-sizes available. This wire-sizing method is called discrete wire-sizing [4]. Chen et al. generalized the wire-size optimization by assuming a wire can take a real range of sizes. This method is called continuous wire-sizing [3].

2.3 Global Router TimberWolfSC

The TimberWolfSC global router (called TWGR in the paper) fully exploits modern row-based technologies [9], and has the following advantages: (1) the solution quality is independent of the routing order of the nets, (2) it takes advantage of electrically equivalent pins, and (3) it handles multi-pin nets. The goal of TWGR is to minimize the total area of the chip by minimizing the total channel density and minimizing the number of feedthroughs in various rows (which increase the row widths).

TWGR roughly consists of five steps. Figure 1 illustrates the execution of TWGR on a simple circuit. There are 3 rows and one net with 3 pins. (a) Step 1

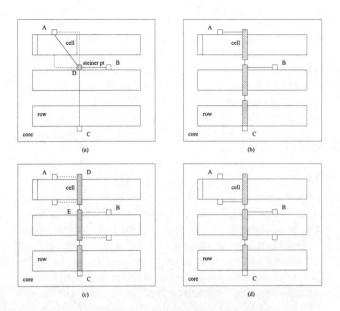

Figure 1: TimberWolf Global Router.

builds the approximate Steiner tree for each net. The Steiner point D is added. Step 2 determines the shape of each L-shape switch-able segment. Segment AD is a L-shape switch-able segment. (b) Step 3 assigns the feedthroughs for each net. Step 4 connects each net. (c) Step 5 flips switch-able net segments to optimize their channels. Assume pins A and B have equivalences on the opposite sides of their cells, then AD and EB are the switch-able net segments. (d) Final routing connections of the net.

3 Adaptive Global Routing

In this section, by integrating high performance interconnection tree construction, wire-sizing, and switch-able segment channel optimization together, we propose an adaptive timing-driven global routing algorithm which minimizes the timing delay as well as circuit area. We will describe each step of our algorithm separately.

3.1 Adaptive Coarse Global Routing

At the beginning of global routing, the coarse global routing is used to make interconnections for each net and estimate the feedthrough distribution.

We first label the primary input or register cells as level 0. The net is labeled the level of the cell where its source pin belongs to. Label any cell the level of the maximum level of the nets it is connected to plus one. The critical paths can be identified as follows. First, using the SERT algorithm [7] and assuming all the sinks have the same weight, we build the interconnection trees for all the nets in this level. Then, the delay of a given cell is computed. The arriving time for the source pins of all the nets in this level is known, and thus the arriving time of all the sink pins of all the nets in this level can be calculated. We perform this procedure on the next level. After the last level, we know the maximum delay and how critical a source-sink pair is on any given net.

The net tree topologies will be improved iteratively. During each iteration we reduce the maximum delay by a step size $\delta > 0$, and use this delay as our target max delay. First set the latest finish time of pins on the primary output cell and register cells to this target delay, then backward propagate the latest finish time all the way to the sink pins of the level 1, and initialize the arriving time for the pins on the primary input cells or register cells 0. Starting from level 1, set the weight of the sink pin of any net in the current level as the reverse of the difference of its latest finish time and the arriving time of the net source pin. SERT can be used to reconstruct net tree topologies and the maximum path delay can be reevaluated. If the maximum delay is smaller than that of a later iteration, double the step-size δ. Otherwise, cut δ by half. If the step size is too small, the adaptive improvement is terminated; otherwise, this process continues.

3.2 Interconnection Improvement

After feedthrough estimation in coarse global routing, feedthroughs can be added in. Since the location information for each pin is accurate, the maximum path delay can be reduced by reconstructing the net interconnections. To reduce the net order dependence, in each iteration, we first generate a random permutation of the net order. According to this random order and SERT, we rebuild the Steiner tree for each net. After each sweep, we reestimate the feedthrough needs and add them in. We perform this procedure on the next iteration.

3.3 Feedthrough Assignment

After the feedthroughs are added into the cell rows, many net segments may demand a feedthrough at specific location on a specific row. Since the feedthroughs cannot overlap, only one net segment can get the feedthrough exactly at a place where it wants. The other net segments must make a detour. To minimize the maximum path delay, the net segments on the critical path cannot be detoured.

In the coarse global routing we have already made the estimation of the delays of each net segment. We can use the slack of a net segment as the weight to determine its feedthrough assignment priority. Assume AB is a net segment and node A is the parent of node B in the net interconnection tree. Its slack is defined as the difference between the latest finish time of B and the earliest arrival time of A and the propagation delay from A to B. The smaller the slack, the more critical the segment is.

When doing feedthrough assignment, for a given row, all the net segments which demand feedthrough in this row will be sorted according the slack weight. In the increasing slack order, each net segment picks the feedthrough which is the closest to the location it requests.

3.4 Timing-driven Net Reconnection

After feedthrough assignment, all nets have the feedthroughs they need. They have to be reconnected, and each pin can be connected only with pins or feedthroughs which are in the same or adjacent rows. we use the ERT algorithm to build the connection tree[7]. But in the ERT algorithm, it assumes that each sink pin can be connected to any pin which is in the partially built tree. When executing the ERT algorithm, we set the distance between pins or feedthroughs in different rows to infinity.

3.5 Wire-sizing

After we reconnect all the feedthroughs and pin of each net, in this step, wire-sizing is used to further reduce the maximum path delay. Though wire-sizing can reduce the maximum path delay, it will increase the area. The reason is that wire-sizing increases the number of tracks or the height of the design.

3.6 Switch-able Net Segment Channel Optimization

As in [9], to take advantage of the standard cell design style, the switch-able segment channel optimization is used to minimize the design area. We use an iterative improvement approach. In each iteration, we randomly pick a switch-able net segment and flip it to its opposite channel. If the channel density decreases, we save it otherwise proceed to the the next iteration.

3.7 Experimental Results

We have implemented the adaptive timing-driven global routing algorithm on a Sun SparcServer 1000E. We report our results over 4 circuits. All experimental results are run on the SUN SparcCenter 1000E.

The test circuits are from the MCNC layout synthesis benchmarks.

In Table 1, we reports the maximum path delay and area results on those benchmark circuits. The wire-sizes are chosen from the set $\{.3\ \mu m, .6\ \mu m, 0.9\ \mu m, 1.2\ \mu m\}$. Due to the excessive running time, when running the benchmark circuits avq.small and avq.large, we discard the nets with more than 100 pins. On the average, the adaptive timing-driven global routing algorithm without wire-sizing reduces the timing delay from TimberWolfSC by 16% with an area increase of only 2%, and the running time decreases by 18 %. The adaptive timing-driven global routing algorithm with wire-sizing reduces the timing delay from TimberWolfSC by 39% with an area increase of 51%, and the running time is increased by 35%.

		ST	BI	AS	AL	change
	Delay(ns)	2.14	25.01	113.35	130.89	0.0
TW	Area (mm^2)	15.44	102.21	686.38	863.20	0.0
	Runtime(s)	22.20	567.90	3,455	4,623	0.0
	Delay(ns)	1.83	20.94	98.92	98.57	-16.9
NW	Area (mm^2)	15.43	106.72	700.60	878.64	+2.06
	Runtime(s)	23.50	144.50	3,391	4,657	-18.9
	Delay(ns)	1.46	14.30	78.36	60.46	-39
WS	Area (mm^2)	18.19	138.99	1,203	1,514	51
	Runtime(s)	30.30	942.20	4,165	5,494	35

Table 1: Results on the maximum path delay, area, and running time of TWGR(TW), the adaptive timing-driven global routing without wire-sizing (NW), and the adaptive timing-driven global routing with wire-sizing(WS). The test circuits are Struct(ST), Biomed(BI), Avq.small(AS), and Avq.large(AL). The change refers to the percentage change from Timber-Wolf global routing.

4 Parallel Timing-driven Global Routing Algorithm

In this section, based on the adaptive timing-driven global routing algorithm proposed in Section 3 and the parallel routing algorithm for area minimization techniques of [17], we propose a parallel timing-driven global routing algorithm. Since there are strong interactions between the cells in the same row and their adjacent rows, the cells and rows are partitioned into contiguous blocks. Figure 2 illustrates a two processor partition for a design with 4 rows of cells. the focus of our parallel timing-driven global routing algorithm is to propose a good net partition and minimize the data synchronization in each global routing step.

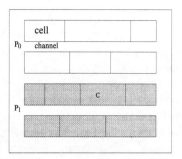

Figure 2: Cell and row partition.

4.1 Net Partition

Several net partitioning schemes were proposed in [17]. One scheme involves partitioning the nets by the center of their pins, called *center partition*. Nets can also be partitioned by the number of pins which fall in the row block of a processor. The net will be assigned to the processor which owns most of the pins for the net. This scheme is called *density partition*. If the processor location of a net is determined by the lower-left corner of the net, the scheme is called *Locus partition*, which is used in the LocusRoute global router [15]. To balance the computation load, each net is assigned a weight. Since each time a net is traversed the computation complexity may be some power of its pin count, the weight given to it is the αth power of pin count for some positive number α. If $\alpha = 1$, the net partition is linear weight partition.

As pointed out in [18], depending on the running complexity of each net-wise traversing, a well chosen α can make the net partition well balanced. Since the complexity of interconnection tree construction can go up to $O(n_0^5)$, α should be chosen in the range of 2 - 3 to balance the computation load. Also, the interconnection tree building is done level by level. Therefore, the net partition should be level balanced, i.e., the net partition should be done on a level basis.

4.2 Parallel Coarse Global Routing

There are two major components in the adaptive coarse global routing. The first is the interconnect topology construction using SERT. Since nets are partitioned, it can be done independently across all the processors. The second is the delay and slack evaluation of the primary outputs and registers. The calculation is done level by level. The inputs of a cell may be on some nets which belong to different processors. For example, in Figure 3, cell C has two inputs which are signal net 1 and 2, and net 1 and net 2 belong to p_0 and p_1 respectively. To calculate the arrival time of pin C_3, the pin of cell C which is on the signal net 3, processor p_1, the owner of cell C, has to wait for p_0 to send the arrival time of C_2. In each iteration of the parallel adaptive coarse global routing, the nets are processed level by level. In each level, after the topology of each net is given, the arrival times of the sink pins of each net can be calculated. Those arrival times are synchronized. Then all the input delays of all the cells in the next level are known. This process proceeds to the next level.

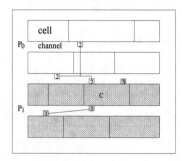

Figure 3: Parallel coarse global routing.

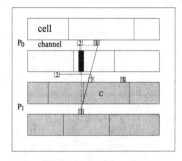

Figure 4: Synchronize the feedthrough needs.

4.3 Parallel L-shape Segment Optimization

When optimizing the L-shape segments, since some nets may go across the rows which belong to different processors, those nets will request feedthroughs at rows not owned by their processors. In Figure 4, net 1 belongs to p_1 and net 2 belongs to p_0. If the segment of net 1 tilts up, then both of them request a feedthrough at the dark shaded coarse global routing grid. This grid is owned by p_0. p_1 must inform p_0 of the feedthrough request of net 1. This is done by synchronization in the parallel timing-driven global routing algorithm.

4.4 Parallel Interconnection Improvement

In the interconnection improvement step, the feedthroughs are added to make a more accurate high performance interconnect for each net. Feedthroughs are owned by the processor which owns the row. In Figure 5, net 2 requests a feedthrough on row 2. After that feedthrough is added in, all the cells to the right of cell A will be shifted right. Thus, the pin of the cell C on net 1 will be shifted right. But net 1 belong to processor 1. p_0 needs to inform p_1 of the new location of pin C_1. In the parallel interconnect improvement, all the processors first add in all the requested feedthroughs, then the pin location of the net will be updated by the processor which owns the cell. Finally, all processors can rebuild the more accurate high performance interconnect.

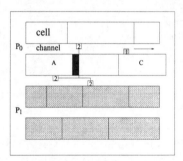

Figure 5: Parallel interconnection improvement.

4.5 Parallel Feedthrough Assignment

After the interconnect tree of each net is fixed, it is clear how many feedthroughs are needed at each coarse global routing grid. They will be added in and be assigned to those nets which request them. When doing parallel timing-driven feedthrough assignment, the slacks on each wire segment must be collected. For a given row, the crossing segments may come from different processors. As in Figure 4, net 1 and net 2 each request a feedthrough at the same spot, and they are owned by two different processors. Recall before interconnect is built for each net, the slack of each wire segment is calculated. In the parallel timing-driven feedthrough assignment, all processors collect the slacks of all the segments which cross rows they own. Then independently all processors sort the segments in each row by their slacks and then do the feedthrough assignment.

4.6 Parallel Net Reconnection and Wire-sizing

After the feedthroughs are assigned to some net by the processor which owns them, they have to be sent to the processor which owns the net. In Figure 6, upon request, feedthroughs A and B are added and assigned by p_0. Assume B is assigned to net 1. Since net 1 belongs to p_1, B has to be sent to p_1. In the parallel net reconnection, feedthroughs, which are assigned to some nets which are owned by other processors, are sent to the other processors. Then, independently, all processors can rebuild the connection by using ERT and then do the wire-sizing.

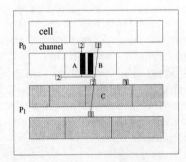

Figure 6: Collect feedthroughs.

4.7 Parallel Switchable Net Segment Channel Optimization

The switch-able net segment channel optimization step reduces the total number of tracks by flipping the switch-able net segments from above/below channel of each row to the below/above channel. A shared channel will result in an overhead of synchronization and an inaccurate track number. This problem is solved by distributing each net segment to the processor which owns the area where the net segment locates. In Figure 7, net 2 has one switch-able net segment AB. It can be switched from the top channel to the bottom channel to CD. This segment belongs to p_0, though net 2 belongs to p_1. Net segment FG will be assigned to p_1.

4.8 Complexity Analysis

Throughout this section, we assume p is the number of processors, n is the number of nets, and n_0 is the maximum number of pins on any net. Since after we have a net partition, all the steps in the timing-driven coarse global routing algorithm can be executed independently except the communication overheads; we only

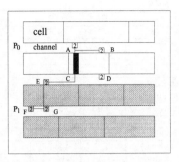

Figure 7: Parallel switch-able segment optimization.

need to measure the overheads. In each level of the interconnection, the broadcasting occurs for all the pins; it takes $O(\sum_1^n n_i) = O(nn_0)$ time. The overhead in the adaptive coarse global routing step is $O(nn_0)$. Since the number of segments distributed by each processor before the timing-driven feedthrough assignment, the number of feedthroughs distributed by each processor after the timing-driven feedthrough assignment, and the number of segments before the switch-able net segment channel optimization are all $O(nn_0)$, the overhead of those steps are $O(nn_0)$. When doing the switch-able net segment channel optimization, there are $O(nn_0/r)$ segments in each shared channel, thus the overhead is $O(nn_0)$. Therefore, the total running complexity of the parallel timing-driven algorithm is $(nn_0^4)/p + O(nn_0)$. If in each level the net partition is well balanced, in theory we can expect good speedup.

4.9 Experimental Results

We implemented our parallel timing-driven global routing algorithm by using the Message Passing Interface (MPI)[12], which has become a standard for portable parallel programming and is available on a range of parallel architectures. We tested our parallel implementation using 3 circuits from the MCNC layout synthesis benchmarks on an 8 processor IBM J-40 shared memory multiprocessor. Table 2 lists the delay, area, and runtime results of 2, 4, and 8 processors. From this table, we can see that our parallel timing-driven global routing algorithm provides fairly good speedups (on the average, 3 of 8 processors) and controls the area degradation (on the average, 2.3% of 8 processors.) Also, it reduces the circuit delay from the one processor run (6% of 8 processor.)

4.10 Impact of Net Partition

This section evaluates the impact of the level based net partition algorithm using three different geometrical net partitioning algorithms in each net level on the

N		BI	AS	AL	AVG
1	Delay(ns)	4.04	34.88	13.50	
	Area (mm^2)	48.73	210.40	246.88	
	Runtime(s)	685.10	2370.00	3353.90	
2	Delay(ns)	3.75	28.48	11.96	
	change	-7.16	-18.33	-11.44	-12.2
	Area (mm^2)	48.28	203.77	239.17	
	change	-0.93	-3.15	-3.12	-2.4
	Runtime(s)	380.00	1525.70	1729.10	
	Speedup	1.80	1.55	1.94	1.8
4	Delay(ns)	3.97	28.44	11.81	
	change	-1.59	-18.45	-12.51	-10.7
	Area (mm^2)	48.44	208.63	246.22	
	change	-0.59	-0.84	-0.27	-0.6
	Runtime(s)	310.10	1160.40	1430.50	
	Speedup	2.21	2.04	2.34	2.2
8	Delay(ns)	3.88	29.52	13.51	
	change	-3.94	-15.36	0.07	-6.3
	Area (mm^2)	49.23	216.80	254.33	
	change	1.03	3.04	3.02	2.3
	Runtime(s)	223.70	868.50	1082.00	
	Speedup	3.06	2.73	3.10	3.0

Table 2: Results on the maximum path delay, area, and running time. N: processor number, change refers the percentage change from single processor run, and AVG: average. The test circuits are Struct(ST), Biomed(BI), Avq.small(AS), and Avq.large(AL).

area, delay and runtime of our parallel timing-driven global routing algorithm. The level based net partitioning algorithm partitions each level of nets by one of the geometrical partition algorithms. Those geometrical net partition algorithms include center partition, density partition, and Locus partition.

Figure 8 compares the 4 processor results on the scaled area, scaled delay, and scaled running time for the MCNC benchmark BIOMED on an IBM J-40. From these results, we conclude that the level based net partition algorithm using density geometrical partitioning algorithm in each net level is the best.

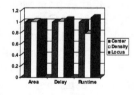

Figure 8: Impact of Net Partitions.

4.11 Impact of Synchronization

Synchronization is very expensive in any parallel application, yet it is important to control the quality of the results. There are two update synchronizations in the parallel global routing algorithm.

The first is in the stage of timing-driven coarse global routing, which is used to synchronize the feedthrough information. After the topology of each interconnection is determined, each segment is assumed to be routed by some one bend L-shaped wire. To reduce the order dependence of the segments processed, a segment is randomly picked from the whole segment pool. By evaluating the needed feedthrough number and channel density change when the side of an L-shaped segment is switched, the L-shape for this segment can be determined. This process will be executed N_c times, where N_c is proportional to the number of nets. Each time the side of a segment is switched, the feedthrough information will change. The number f_c stands for the number of synchronizations throughout this switching improvement process.

The second is in the stage of the switch-able net segment optimization, which is used to synchronize the track information of the shared channels. After each net is reconnected with their feedthroughs, to optimize the channel placement of each switch-able net segment and reduce the order dependence of the segment processed, we randomly pick one switch-able net segment and determine its channel by evaluating the channel track change when the segment is flipped to the opposite channel. This process will also be executed N_t times, where N_t is proportional to the number of nets. For a p processor parallel implementation, there are $p - 1$ shared channels. When the switch-able net segment is flipped from or into the shared channel, the channel track information will change. The number f_t stands for the number of synchronizations throughout this flipping improvement process.

Ideally, f_c and f_t should be equal to the number of switching N_c or the number of flipping N_t made to follow the sequential algorithm quality but then this will limit the parallelism. If f_c or f_t are too small there will be a lot of parallelism, but the quality of the resulting solution will be extremely poor. Hence it is important to determine an optimal value of f_c and f_t to tradeoff the run times with the quality. Figure 9 and Figure 10 compare the 4 processor results of scaled area, scaled delay, and scaled running time for MCNC benchmark BIOMED on an IBM J-40.

Since there is no significant decrease in the circuit area and delay when f_c or f_t increases. f_c and f_t should be in the range of 5 - 10. Obviously, f_c and f_t will be circuit size dependent. For BIOMED, we have 5000 nets, and the optimal number is about 5-10. Hence the frequency of updates should be $0.01N$, where N is the number of nets in the circuit. The results in Table 2 use this criterion and the level based net partition algorithm using density geometrical partition in each net level.

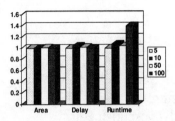

Figure 9: Impact of synchronization with $f_t = 1$. f_c takes the different values.

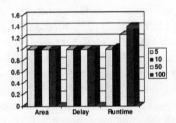

Figure 10: Impact of synchronization with $f_c = 1$. f_t takes the different values.

4.12 Conclusion

In this paper, first by integrating high performance interconnection tree construction, wire-sizing, and switch-able segment channel optimization together, we propose an adaptive timing-driven global routing algorithm which minimizes the timing delay as well as circuit area. Our experiments on MCNC benchmarks show that our timing-driven global routing algorithm reduces the maximum path delays significantly from the global router TimberWolfSC.

Subsequently, we proposed a parallel algorithm to reduce the excessive running time of our timing-driven global router. Our experiments on an 8 processor IBM J-40 shared memory multiprocessor show good speedup and circuit delay and area results. While various parallel routing algorithms have been developed in the past for minimizing the wire-length and area, this is the first work on parallel timing-driven global routing for standard cells.

References

[1] P. Banerjee, *Parallel Algorithms for VLSI Computer-Aided Design*, PTR Prentice Hall, Englewood Cliffs, New Jersey 07632, 1994.

[2] R. J. Brouwer and P. Banerjee. "PHIGURE: A Parallel Hierarchical Global Router," *Proc. 27th Design Automation Conf.*, pp. 360–364, June 1990.

[3] C. Chen and D. F. Wong, "A Fast Algorithm for Optimal Wire-Sizing under Elmore Delay Model," *Proc. IEEE ISCAS*, May 1996. pp 412 - 415.

[4] J. Cong and K. Leung, "Optimal Wire-sizing under the Distributed Elmore Delay Model," *Proc. IEEE ICCAD*, July 1993. pp. 634-639.

[5] J. Cong and P. Madden, "Performance Driven Global Routing for Standard Cell Design," *Proc. Intl Symp on Physical Design*, CA, April, 1997, pp 73 - 80.

[6] J. Huang, et al, "An Efficient timing-driven global routing algorithm," *Proc. ACM/IEEE DAC*, 1993, pp. 596 - 600.

[7] A. B. Kahng and G. Robins, *On Optimal Interconnections for VLSI*, Kluwer Academic Publishers, 1995.

[8] C. Lee. "An Algorithm for Path Connections and its Applications", *IRE Trans. Electronic Computers*, vol. VEC-10, pp. 346–365, Sept. 1961.

[9] K. Lee and C. Sechen, "A New Global Router for Row-Based Layout", *Proc. of ICCAD-88*, pp. 180–183, Nov. 1988.

[10] M. Martonosi and A. Gupta. "Tradeoffs in Message Passing and Shared Memory Implementations of a Standard Cell Router," *Proc. Int. Conf. Parallel Processing (ICPP89)*, pp. III:88–96, Aug. 1989.

[11] E. E. Moore. "The Shortest Path through a Maze. *Annals of the Computation Laboratory of Harvard University*, vol. 30, pp. 285–292, 1959.

[12] Message-Passing Interface Forum, "Document for a Standard Message-passing Interface," University of Tennessee, Knoxville, TN, Tech. Rep. CS-93-214, 1993.

[13] R. Nair, S. J. Hong, S. Liles, and R. Villani. "Global Wiring on a Wire Routing machine," *Proc. 19th Design Automation Conf.*, pp. 224–231, June 1982.

[14] O. A. Olukotun and T. N. Mudge. "A Preliminary Investigation into Parallel Routing on a Hypercube," *Proc. Design Automation Conf.*, pp. 814–820, June 1987.

[15] J. Rose, "LocusRoute: A Parallel Global Router for Standard Cells" *Proc. of 25th DAC*, pp. 189–195, June 1988

[16] J. Rose, "Parallel Global Routing for Standard Cells," *IEEE Trans. Computer-aided Design Integrated Circuits Systems*, pp. 1085–1095, Oct. 1990.

[17] Z. Xing and P. Banerjee, "Parallel Global Routing Algorithms for Standard Cells," *Proc. Intl. Parallel Processing Symposium*, 1996.

[18] Z. Xing and P. Banerjee, "Parallel Global Routing Algorithms for Standard Cells," submitted to *IEEE Trans. on CAD*, 1996.

Performance Analysis and Optimization of a
Parallel Carbon Molecular Dynamic Code on a Cray T3E *

Mihai Horoi
Department of Physics
Central Michigan University
Mt. Pleasant, MI 48859 USA
horoi@phy.cmich.edu

Richard J. Enbody
Dept. of Computer Science and Engineering
Michigan State University
East Lansing, MI 48824 USA
enbody@cse.msu.edu

Abstract

An analysis of the primary factors influencing the performance of a parallel implementation on a Cray T3E of a Carbon Molecular Dynamics code developed at Department of Physics and Astronomy at Michigan State University is presented. We show that classical load-sharing techniques combined with careful analysis of Amdahl's law can be successfully used to significantly increase the performance of the code. This report describes the quantitative analysis of these factors and the solutions used to diminish or eliminate their effects. By slightly modifying the code we reduced its sequential portion to less than 0.1%. We also demonstrate that the MPI collective communications implementation on the Cray T3E dramatically reduces the communication overhead for our code. In the end, a speedup of 170 was obtained using 256 Cray T3E processing elements. These results create the prospect of simulating the dynamics of 1,000-atom nanotubes in the microsecond regime ($\approx$ 1,000,000 time steps).

1. Introduction

The newly emerging nanostructure science, in dealing with nanoscale entities like carbon nanotubes, needs computationally intensive efforts to simulate the interplay between classical and quantum degrees of freedom specific to the nanometer scale. A code which simulates the self-assembly of carbon nanostructures from individual atoms has been developed at the Center for Fundamental Materials Research at Michigan State University. The goal of this approach is to simulate the growth of carbon nanotubes, a new synthetic material of amazing strength that is related to the C_{60} "buckyball". These processes occur on an extremely short length scale of $\gtrsim 10^{-10}$ meters and equally short time scale of $\gtrsim 10^{-13}$ seconds[1, 2, 3], beyond the scope of direct experimental observation and existing computational tools. Simulating these processes will be important for optimizing the synthesis of these materials. Precise interatomic forces are calculated using a Linear Combination of Atomic Orbitals (LCAO) technique that is based on the *ab initio* Local Density Functional formalism[4]. The many-body LCAO Hamiltonian, combined with the recursion technique [5], allows a semi-analytical evaluation of forces acting on individual atoms that is (i) computationally efficient, (ii) suitable for massively parallel computers, and (iii) shows a linear scaling of required computational resources with the number of atoms.

This paper presents the analysis done during the process of creating an efficient parallel implementation, and the resulting improvements in performance. We illustrate how one can use Amdahl's law to analyze the characteristics of a program to achieve significant speedup. The core of this report describes the quantitative analysis of these factors and the solutions used to diminish or eliminate their effects.

There were three stages of development of the parallel version of the Carbon Molecular Dynamics (CMD) code. Our experience in the initial stages influenced our choices in the final version. We will briefly outline those experiences, and then concentrate on the final stage.

The initial phases used the simple Lennard-Jones gasseous interaction to allow the computer scientists to concentrate on the structure and communication of the implementation. Based on research at Sandia National Labs [15] we began with a spatial decomposition of the problem. That is, we assigned regions of space to each processor and moved particle states among processors as particles moved through space. The Sandia work indicated that spatial decomposition significantly reduced communication for the Lennard-Jones force model. Our first implementations were on BBN NUMA (non-uniform memory access) shared-memory machines and on early SGI Challenge shared-memory machines. The code used dynamic load balancing and had sufficiently low overhead to achieve results comparable to others' work on a CM-5 [10, 11]. However, the implementation was limited to a shared-memory machine, and it appeared that a distributed-memory model was necessary to achieve our performance goals. We then ported a modified Lennard-Jones version to an Intel Paragon [9]. The modified Lennard-Jones attempted to incorporate some of the unique features of CMD which would complicate parallelization. The most important of those was the need for "neighbors-of-neighbors" in force computation which both increased the communication and eliminated many short cuts which the simple Lennard-Jones allows. Our version of dynamic load-balancing for distributed memory included "neighbors-of-neighbors" so it required much more overhead than the shared-memory version without "neighbors-of-neighbors". Additional overhead occurred because the state of particles had to be communicated and the distributed-memory load-balancing required additional synchronization.

Successful, load-balanced, Lennard-Jones implementations exist on shared-memory machines [15], but we could not sufficiently reduce overhead using the more complex CMD code. On the basis of our experience we calculated the data movement necessary for dynamic load balancing on a distributed-memory machine using spatial decomposition, and compared it to the communication needed for a particle decomposition. Particle decomposition, the assignment of a fixed number of particles to processors, can be satisfactorily statically load-balanced for the relatively homogeneous calculations of interest to us. That analysis indicated that the communication load is roughly the same in both cases. Therefore, we chose the particle decomposition for our next phase. The simplicity of particle decomposition, particularly with respect to load balancing, let us concentrate on a correct implementation and then on an efficient implementation.

Before beginning further implementation we also explored the dynamically load balanced packages which others have developed. Examples include LPARX [14], CHAOS [13], and MAPS [12]. The generality and ease-of-use of those approaches create implementations with overhead to large for us to meet our performance target. Even though our problem is not particularly fine grained, those packages work best for coarser grained problems than ours. Our need for a million timesteps of simulation demands low overhead for each time step in order to run a sufficient number of timesteps in a reasonable amount of time.

Our final phase began with a particle decomposition of the CMD code for a parallel environment and ended with code tuned for the Cray T3E architecture.

The first port of the code was done for a cluster of DEC Alpha stations using the PVM message passing library, and later adjusted for a massively parallel computational environment on the Cray T3E 600/900 at the Pittsburgh Supercomputer Center. The initial Cray T3E implementation, based on the PVM message passing library, was not very efficient; the speedup limit was 39.

By a careful analysis of Amdahl's law we identified the most important factors limiting the performance:

- the magnitude of the sequential fraction of the code,

- the communication overhead, and

- the work imbalance on different processors.

Simulating these effects on sequential and parallel computers enabled us to measure the their magnitude allowing us to eliminate or diminish their role. Crucial to these efforts was the identification of the most important contribution to the sequential portion of the code which we were able to rewrite to integrate it into the parallel portion of the code. The second most important effect, the communication overhead, was dramatically diminished by using the efficient implementation of the MPI collective communication routines on the Cray T3E architecture.

Using these improvements we were able to obtain an *effective speedup* (comparison with the best sequential time) of 170 when using 256 of the Cray T3E 900 processing elements (PEs) (Figure 9). With a time step of 1×10^{-14} seconds, one can simulate the dynamics of 512-atom nanotubes for 0.01 μsec (1000000 timesteps) in 36 hours of wall-clock time using 256 PEs of the Cray T3E 900.

This paper is organized as follows: Section 2 gives a brief description of the CMD code relevant for the parallel implementation and of some techniques used in the early parameterization approach. Section 3 analyzes the main factors leading to the inefficiency of the implementation described in Section 2. Section 4 presents new improvements added to the parallel code based on the analysis of Section 3 and their effects on the performance. Section 5 is devoted to conclusions and outlook.

2. PVM Implementation

The sequential CMD code was designed and optimized so it will scale linearly with the number particles, N. To achieve this goal, the already simplified tight-binding approach [6] to the electron Hamiltonian was further approximated using recursion techniques to calculate the local electron densities [5]. The tight-biding approximation by itself scales as $O(N^3)$, while the recursion techniques method scales as $O(N)$ without decrease in accuracy (see Table 2 of Ref. [5] for a comparison of *ab initio*, tight-binding, and recursion techniques results for carbon atoms). Of particular importance to users of the code, the recursion-technique was validated by numerous experimental results [2].

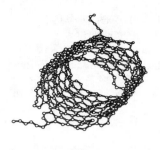

(a) 480-atom nanotube at 350°K

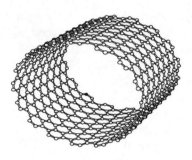

(b) 512-atom nanotube at 0°K

Figure 1. Carbon nanotube examples.

To have an appreciation of the computer resources used by different approaches to carbon molecular dynamics consider that for a few hundred particles, *ab initio* calculations require a few **days** of CPU on an average workstation for each time step, the tight-binding approach needs tens of minutes to solve the same problem, while the recursion technique needs only a few seconds. Even though this method was applied to the aggregation of carbon atoms, the method is quite general and could be used with any other atomic species forming covalent bonds. A successful parallel implementation of this code could provide a very useful tool for performing a large class of molecular dynamics simulations.

A special assumption of this code, which makes it scale as $O(N)$ rather then $O(N^3)$ (or worse), is to consider the contribution to the electron energy associated with an atomic site due only to some neighboring atomic sites. In order to calculate the force acting on one atom, the approach used here considers the contribution from the electrons belonging to the neighboring sites situated in a sphere of radius $R \approx 2.5$ Å, and as a second-order effect the contribution

of all neighbors of the first layer of neighbors. The second-order effect of "neighbors-of-neighbors" turned out to also be an important constraint for the parallel implementation (see Section 3).

In porting this code to a parallel environment we decided to follow the following criteria:

- make the smallest possible number of modifications,

- ensure that the results are identical to those given by the sequential code, and

- use the simplest but most effective parallel techniques to avoid unnecessary overhead.

The sequential code has 5400 lines and 64 subroutines written in FORTRAN 77. We decided to use load sharing techniques, which are generally useful for scientific codes that repeat similar calculations a large number of identical entities (particles). It is important to note that the CMD code is not "embarrassing parallel." The code must synchronize each time the forces are calculated, and results from each processor must be known to all other processors. At each time step it calculates the forces acting on each atom, integrates the equation of motions using the 4th-order Runge-Kutta method, and uses the new coordinates to calculate the new forces acting on each atom. In order to implement the load sharing techniques we had to identify the part of the code that is the most computationally intensive, cut it in equal loads and share these loads among the processors. We determined that the loop calculating the force acting on each atom is the most time consuming one, and we cut it in almost equal pieces, depending on the number of atoms and the number of PEs available (see also Section 3).

The first version of the port was done for a cluster of 6 DEC Alpha workstations connected via a DEC Giga Switch using PVM. Load sharing techniques in a master-slave approach were implemented to parallelize the loop calculating the force acting on each atom. The master shares the burden of calculating the force acting on the atoms, and does all other work, including the integration of equation of motion. The portion of code subjected to the parallelization process is organized as follows: the master first sends all coordinates to all slaves, calculates the first layer of neighbors for all atoms, calculates the second layer of each for some of the atoms (see also Section 3) for which it also calculates the forces, and gathers back the forces calculated by slaves (which have done the same calculations). The results on the 6 DEC Alpha cluster were good, but not significant for testing the scalability of the code: a speedup between 5 and 6 was obtained.

To test the scalability of the parallel implementation, we adjusted the PVM version for the Cray T3E at Pittsburgh Supercomputer Center (PSC). This PVM implementation was tuned up for a homogeneous architecture using raw data communication and the PVM implementation of broadcasting. These improvements account for a 5% increase in the performance over a straight port of the Alpha-PVM code.

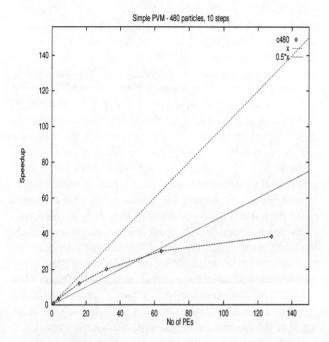

Figure 2. Intial speedup vs. number of PEs using PVM.

In our study we use three nanotube configurations which are of interest for the ongoing research in this area: (C480) a 480-carbon atom nanotube heated at 350°K, Figure 1(a); (C512) a 512-carbon atom nanotube at 0°K, Figure 1(b); and (C1024) a 1024-carbon atom nanotube at 0°K (not shown here). Due to limitations in the available supercomputer resources we integrated the configurations (C480) and (C512) for 10 time steps, and the configuration (C1024) for 5 time steps. Calculating over a few time steps is not useful for studying physical properties of nanotubes, but is sufficient for determining the correctness of the port and the speedup. In fact, using few time steps is a worst case comparison since startup costs are not amortized across many time steps. The speedups for configuration (C480), using up to 128 PEs are presented in Figure 2. To calculate the speedup we always compare the wall-clock time given by the parallel version of the code with the best 1PE time given by the original sequential code. The lines denoted by "x" and "0.5*x" describe the region of High Efficiency defined by Kuck in [7]. One can see that when using more than 50 processors the speedup falls below the "0.5*x" line reaching a "point of no return" [7], beyond which the performance never increases. The maximum speedup reached was 39. The next section analyzes the factors leading to this limited performance and reveals methods to improve it.

```
subroutine force
  call broadcast_coordinates
  call cluster1 ( n_atoms )
  do iatom = atom_start, atom_end
    call cluster2 ( iatom )
    call calculate_force
  enddo
  call gather_results
```

Figure 3. Pseudocode of the parallelized portion of the code before optimization.

	Before Optimization					After
N	T_{tot}	T_{loop}	ΔT	$1 - \gamma$	$T_{cluster1}$	$1 - \gamma'$
480	1850	1833	17	0.009	16	0.0005
512	1304	1276	28	0.022	28	0.001
1K	2672	2560	112	0.042	112	0.001

Table 1. Sequential component code before $(1 - \gamma)$ and after $(1 - \gamma')$ the optimization.

3. Amdahal's Law Analysis

In order to understand the factors responsible for the limited performance previously described, we use Amdahl's law to analyze our parallel implementation. According to Amdahl [8], the speedup S is given by

$$S = \frac{T_1}{\frac{\gamma T_1}{\bar{\eta} P} + (1 - \gamma)T_1 + T_{comm}} , \qquad (1)$$

where T_1 represents the sequential (1PE) time, P is the number of PEs, γ represents the fraction of code which can be fully parallelized (1-γ is the sequential fraction), $\bar{\eta}$ describes the average imbalance of the load on each PE, and T_{comm} represents the total communication overhead. Note that as P increases the sequential portion $(1$-$\gamma)T_1$ can dominate even for relatively large values of γ. For example, code which is 90% parallel ($\gamma = .9$), is perfectly balanced ($\bar{\eta} = 1$), and has no communication ($T_{comm} = 0$) can achieve a maximum speedup of 10 for any number of processors.

We identified the main three factors limiting the performance of our code as: γ, T_{comm}, and $\bar{\eta}$. The remainder of this report describes the quantitative analysis of these factors and the solutions used to diminish or eliminate their effects.

To measure the sequential fraction of the code, 1-γ, we measured the total time used for calculation, T_{tot}, and the time spent in the loop containing the load shared among the PEs. Pseudocode describing that portion of the code is presented in Figure 3.

The results of these simulations are in Table 1. One can observe that the sequential fraction of the code is in the range 1-5%. (The $T_{cluster1}$ and $(1 - \gamma')$ columns will be discussed later.) Even though the sequential fraction of the code does not account for more than 1% for the configuration (C480), Amdahl's law predicts a maximum ideal speedup ($\bar{\eta} = 1$, $T_{comm} = 0$) of 59 when 128 PEs are used. This result alone explains the largest part of the limitation in performance described in Section 2. This factor is expected to further limit the performance of the parallel code for configurations with more atoms, such as (C512) and (C1024), due to the O(N^2) number of operations involved in the **cluster1** routine.

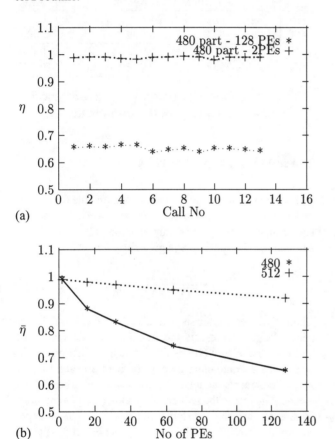

(a)

(b)

Figure 4. Imbalance factor η for different calls of the force routine.

To understand the difference between the above estimate and the results in Figure 2, we simulated the contribution of the average imbalance $\bar{\eta}$. At the root of this imbalance is the difficulty of equally distributing a relatively small number of atoms (480) on a relatively large number of PEs that can be used on the Cray T3E at PSC: up to 512 PEs. Figure 4 presents the results of these simulations. Panel (a) shows the imbalance factor η for different calls of the force routine. For 2 PEs (480 is evenly divisible by 2), one observes

a small imbalance due to slightly different workload for different atoms, while for 128 PEs the decrease in imbalance factor is significant. Panel (b) shows the variation of the average imbalance with the number of PEs. One can observe that the most important factor influencing the imbalance is the degree of incomensurability of the number of PEs with the number of atoms, i.e. the result of the modulus division of the number of atoms to the number of PEs. Taking into account this factor, the maximum ideal speedup ($T_{comm}=0$) for configuration (C480) will be 50 (see Eq. [1]), when 128 PEs are used. The final factor of difference between this ideal result and the result obtained with the real code ($S_{128}=39$) can be accounted by the communication overhead, T_{comm}. It turns out to be more difficult to simulate a quantitative estimation of T_{comm}. Instead, we wrote a synthetic code simulating the broadcasting of the coordinates from master to slave and the gathering of the forces from slaves to master. The goal of this code was to investigate different T_{comm} factors. PVM currently lacks an efficient implementation of the corresponding routine (very recent documentation shows progress in this direction), but the MPI message passing library has a very elegant, and very efficient collective communication approach. Assuming that the busiest communication link is the master, we estimated the *effective* throughput (total amount of data received and sent back by all slaves in unit of time) at that link. Figure 5 shows the results of these simulations for the Cray T3E at PSC and for the SP2 at Cornell Theory Center (MPI only). One can see that the MPI collective communication on the Cray T3E is significantly better than the PVM communication. These results clearly indicate the MPI collective communications as a much better message passing approach for the parallel version of the CMD code.

It is also interesting to understand the *effective* communication throughput of 16 Gbit/s obtained with MPI for 128 PEs. The Cray T3E interconnect router has 6 bidirectional links for each node. The maximum payload for each link is 480 MB/s = 3.84 Gbit/s, which cannot directly account for the 16 Gbit/s throughput obtained in our simulation. The only explanation for this unusually high communication throughput could be a very efficient, hardware supported, implementation of the MPI broadcast routine. In that case the amount of data moved from the master to the interconnect router is a constant as a number of PEs, and the effective throughput increases almost linearly with the number of PEs (it is slightly lower due to O[log(P)] number of routing operations). Without broadcast capabilities (see results of PVM or SP2) the amount of data handled by the master grows as O(P), the communication overhead increases linearly with the number of PEs, and the effective throughput, after an initial increase is falling dawn.

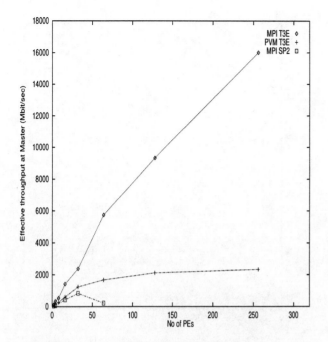

Figure 5. Effective throughput of data at master using different message-passing libraries.

```
subroutine force
  call broadcast_coordinates
  do iatom = atom_start, atom_end
    call cluster1&2 ( iatom )
    call calculate_force
  enddo
  call gather_results
```

Figure 6. Pseudocode after reduction of sequential fraction.

4. Optimization Strategies and Performance Improvements

To improve the performance of the code we tried to diminish the effects of all three factors analyzed in Section 3. To reduce the effect of the sequential fraction of code we further analyzed possible contributors to that part. We found that the call to the **cluster1** routine (see Figure 3) is responsible for the largest contribution to the sequential fraction of the code (Table 1). This routine calculates the first layer of neighbors of all atoms, as explained in Section 2. The **cluster2** routine, calculating the second layer of neighbors for each atom, appeared in the loop in the original sequential code. It uses the results saved by the **cluster1** routine and is able to save approximately 10% of the total time in the original sequential code. It was a valuable optimization for the sequential code, but it hurts the parallel implementation.

Our strategy was to include the calculation done by the

cluster1 routine in the loop allowing calculation of both layers of neighbors in a scalable way. The new version of the code (in pseudocode) is shown in Figure 6. The new code is slower by approximately 11% for 1 PE ($T_1' \approx 1.11 T_1$), but it scales very well when the number of PEs is increased. A simulation to quantify the remaining sequential fraction of code shows a decrease of $1 - \gamma'$ to less than 0.1% (see last column in Table 1).

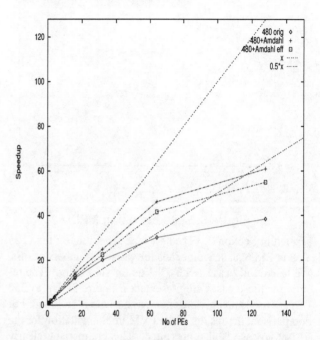

Figure 7. Improvement after reduction of sequential portion of code.

We tested the effect of these modifications for the case discussed at the end of Section 2. The new results, in comparison with the old ones are presented in Figure 7. The effective speedup included in the figure is defined with respect to the best 1 PE time given by the original sequential code, $S_{eff}(P) = \frac{T_1}{T_P'}$. One can see that, even for the relatively imbalanced case of 480 atoms, a significant improvement in performance is obtained. However, the speedup eventually falls from the region of High Efficiency [7].

To diminish the effect of the communication overhead we incorporated the MPI collective communication routines due to their exceptional performance described in Section 3. That is, the code now incorporates both a reduction of the sequential portion and improved communication. The results for the 480-atom configuration are presented in Figure 8 in comparison with the results of the initial PVM calculation described in Section 2. One can see a major improvement in the performance, all new speedups laying in the region of High Efficiency [7]. These results are still distorted by the imbalance effect. To eliminate the effect of this factor we study configurations (C512) and (C1024) de-

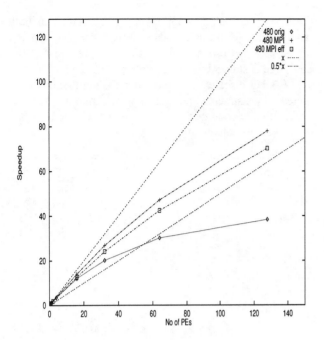

Figure 8. Speedup using MPI.

scribed in Section 2. (The new load scheduler on the Cray T3E at PSC can schedule jobs for variable numbers of PEs. We tested only cases with 2^m PEs for simplicity.) The results for these cases are presented in Figure 9. Up to 256 PEs are used and only the effective speedup is included. For comparison, the results of the PVM implementation for the 512-atom case is also presented. This comparison clearly shows the effect of the very efficient MPI implementation when the imbalance is not present ($\bar{\eta} \approx 1$).

Both MPI results for the 512-atom and 1024-atom configurations scale very well: the effective speedups laying in the region of High Efficiency [7]. A maximum effective speedup of 170 was obtained for the 1024-atom configuration using 256 PEs.

Another interesting facet of our achievements can be viewed when comparing our best time simulating 1024 particles with 256 PEs and the corresponding times obtained using different available workstations. Table 2 presents these times (first row indicates the results obtained for the workstations currently available to the MSU group that uses the sequential version of this code), and the corresponding absolute speedup

$$S_{abs} = \frac{T_{computer}}{T_{CrayT3Eminim}} . \tag{2}$$

Here $T_{computer}$ assumes that no other user consumes CPU resources, while $T_{CrayT3Eminim}$ is the wall-clock time on the Cray T3E 900. One can observe a factor of more than 1,000 in absolute speedup between the Cray T3E 900 and the average workstation available to the researchers.

It would be interesting to study a 1024-atom nanotube

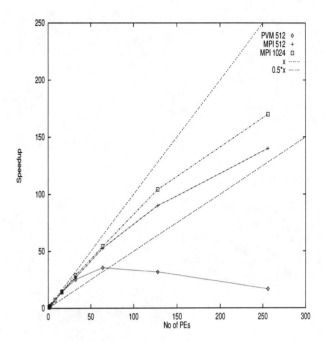

Figure 9. Final speedup incorporating all modification vs. load-balanced PVM.

Computer	480	512	1024
1PE RS/6000	544	1082	1142
4PE SuperSparc	235	561	606
1PE T3E-600	112	210	239
1PE T3E-900	75	140	172

Table 2. The absolute speedup (Eq. 2) for 480, 512 and 1024-particle nanotubes.

at the 0.01 microsecond time scale, i.e. approximately 1,000,000 time steps. By extrapolating the results obtained for 5 time steps to 1,000,000 time steps, one can estimate that it will take 4.67 years to finish this calculations on the RS/6000 workstation, while it will take only 36 hours on the Cray T3E 900 using 256 PEs.

All these results clearly prove that it is worth using high performance, massively parallel computers, such as the Cray T3E 900, for solving the most challenging technological and scientific problems.

5. Summary and Outlook

A Carbon Molecular Dynamics code was efficiently parallelized for the Cray T3E architecture. Using 256 PEs of the Cray T3E 900, a maximum speedup of 170 was obtained integrating the equations of motions for 1,024 particles.

A load sharing approach combined with a careful analysis of Amdahl's Law proved to be a very useful technique in optimizing the performance of the parallel code. We found a high performance implementation of the MPI collective communication on the Cray T3E. By reducing the sequential fraction of the code, using the MPI collective communication, and balancing the workload among the PEs we obtained a boost in performance of more than 400% when more than 128 PEs are used.

A factor of 1,000 increase in speed was reached, comparing our best T3E 900 results with the results obtained on average, available workstations. This result demonstrates the utility of using modern massively parallel computers to obtain computational solutions for the most challenging technological and scientific problems.

The combined approach presented here is quite general from both physics and computational point of view. The recursion technique approach is not limited to carbon atoms, and can be used for other atoms such as silicon or germanium. From a computational point of view, the techniques we developed for this project have potential application for any type of code which involves the broadcasting and gathering of data with synchronization.

Increasing the number of particles up to several thousands is possible using this techniques. The complexity of the code as well as the complexity of the communication is $O(N)$. One can actually see a small increase in performance between the (C512) and the (C1024) due to a slightly better balance in the latter case. The limitation on the number of particles is related to the limitation in physical memory available on each PE board. If the code's virtual length becomes larger than the available single PE physical memory, other techniques (e.g., shared memory techniques) should be used. We are confident that we can efficiently simulate a few hundred thousands particles using the present approach.

Increasing the number of processors deserves more investigation. In particular it will be interesting to study the effect of the $O[\log(P)]$ number of routing operations on the performance of the broadcasting operation.

Our target goal for the next 3-5 years is to integrate the equations of motion of 1,000 particles for more than 10,000,000 time steps (the 0.1 microsecond regime). Presently, we can integrate the equations of motion of 1,000 particles for 350,000 time steps in 12 hours using 256 PEs of the Cray T3E 900.

Acknowledgment We thank Prof. D. Tománek for the continuous support and very useful discussions about the physics involved in his carbon molecular dynamic code.

References

[1] M. S. Dresselhaus, G. Dresselhaus, and P. C. Eklund, *Science of Fullerenes and Carbon Nanotubes*, (Academic Press Inc., 1996 San Diego)

[2] A. Thess, R. Lee, P. Nikolaev, H. Dai, P. Petit, J. Robert, C. Xu, Y. H. Lee, S. G. Kim, D. T. Colbert, G. Scuseria, D. Tománek, J. E. Fisher, and R. E. Smalley, Science **273**, 483 (1996).

[3] Robert F. Service, *Science* **270**, 1119 (1995); Walt A. de Heer, A. Châtelain, and D. Ugarte, *Science* **270**, 1179 (1995).

[4] Y. H. Lee, S. G. Kim, and D. Tománek, Phys. Rev. Lett. **78**, 2393 (1997)

[5] W. Zhong, D. Tománek, and G. F. Bertsch, Solid State Comm. **86**, 607 (1993).

[6] D. Tománek, and M. Schluter, Phys. Rev. Lett. **67**, 2331 (1991).

[7] D. J. Kuck, High Performance Computing, Oxford University Press, 1996.

[8] G. M. Amdahl, *Validity of Single Processor Approach to Achieving Large-Scale Computing Capability*, Proc. AFIPS Conf., pp 483-485, Reston, VA, 1967.

[9] Enbody R, Purdy R, Severance C, "Dynamic Load Balancing," Proceedings of the 7th SIAM Conference, February 1995, pages 645-646.

[10] Severance C, Enbody R, "Evolving Dynamic Load Balancing to Shared Memory Parallel Processors at Supercomputing 1994 Conference". November 1994

[11] Nesbeitt, P., Enbody, R. J., Bulgac, A., Tomanek, D., Overney, G., Severance, C., "A Topology- and Problem-Independent Scalable Parallel Approach to Molecular Dynamics Simulation", Sixth SIAM Conference on Parallel Processing for Scientific Computing, March, 1993, pp. 170 - 173.

[12] R. Williams, S. Karmesin, "MAPS: An Efficient Parallel Language for Scientific Computing", Center for Advanced Computing Research Tech Report, Caltech.

[13] Hwang Y-S., Das R., Saltz J., Hodoscek M., and Brooks B., "Parallelizing Molecular Dynamic Programs for Distributed Memory Machines: An Application of the CHAOS Runtime Support Library," U. of Maryland Tech Report CS-TR-3374, 1994.

[14] Kohn, S, Baden, S., "Irregular Coarse-Grain Data Parallelism Under LPARX," J. of Scientific Programming, to appear.

[15] Plimpton. S.J. , "Fast Parallel Algorithms for Short-Range Molecular Dynamics," J. Comp. Phys., 117:1-19, March 1995.

Parallel Algorithms for Airline Crew Planning on Networks of Workstations[*]

Christos Goumopoulos, Panayiotis Alefragis, Efthymios Housos
Department of Electrical & Computer Engineering, Computer Laboratory
University of Patras, GR-265 00 Rio Patras, Greece
{goumop, alefrag, housos}@ee.upatras.gr

Abstract

The crew planning problem has been successfully solved on a loosely connected network of workstations (NOW) using advanced computational techniques and efficient communication patterns. The parallelization of the successful sequential system of Carmen Systems AB guarantees that the results are immediately useful and applicable to a large number of airlines scheduling problems. The parallel pairing generator component of the crew scheduling process achieves a linear speedup on the number of processors and can be efficiently scaled to a large number of processors. The novel parallel optimizer approach of the paper also achieves almost linear speedups for large problems solved on a small number of workstations. The Lufthansa problems that were used in our experiments validate our theoretical results and prove the value and usefulness of our work.

1. Introduction

The use of resource planning optimization techniques in industrial applications is imperative for the present competitive environment of the global economies and can significantly reduce operational costs. A typical example is the transportation industry where scheduling applications like crew scheduling [9] and crew rostering [4] lead to very large and difficult optimization problems with long computation times. Solving such problems in acceptable time with exact algorithms is impossible due to the combinatorial explosion that characterizes most of these problems. Heuristics are often used in order to reduce the search space and improve the computational tractability of these problems. In any case the run times of these procedures are very high, which makes the use of

parallel processing imperative [3]. In addition the use of parallel processing is driven by the fact that close to day of operations solutions are also desired due to the continuously changing business environment.

The application example and the algorithms described in this paper were in part supported by the European ESPRIT/HPCN project PAROS (Parallel Large Scale Automatic Crew Scheduling) [1,24]. The project started in 1996 with Lufthansa Deutsche Airlines (LH) as the industrial user, Carmen Systems AB, the University of Patras and the Chalmers University of Technology as the other partners. LH supplied important large problems and optimization requirements in the area of crew planning. PAROS is an effort to improve the automatic crew scheduling system produced and marketed by Carmen Systems with the use of high performance computing and modeling techniques. Performance improvements will allow considering more realistic scheduling periods while giving the marketing department additional time to satisfy the market needs.

The network of workstations that has been selected as the parallel processing platform is a cost effective and widely available computation model. Computers connected through high performance networks can be used as parallel machines. The availability of faster workstations in the past ten years has allowed the airlines to reduce the use of mainframes and thus reduce their computational costs. This, however, did create a thrashing computational effect when it comes to large combinatorial problems. The use of networks of workstations for the solution of a single problem minimizes this effect. The emphasis was to develop new software for efficient coordination and cooperation of networked workstations to achieve higher productivity and faster solutions for the crew planning problem. While there exist attempts to solve the crew planning problem on high end parallel hardware [17], this paper focuses on issues that arise in parallelizing this problem on a cluster of workstations.

---

[*] This work has been supported by the ESPRIT HPCN program.

The rest of the paper is organized as follows. In section 2 we describe the crew planning problem and the prevailing solution methodology. The parallel algorithms developed for the two most time critical components of the solution process, the pairing generator and the pairing optimizer, are discussed in sections 3 and 4. Theoretical performance analysis of the proposed parallel algorithms is also presented. In section 5 experimental results from typical Lufthansa crew scheduling problems are shown. Finally, conclusions and future directions of this work are discussed in section 6.

2. Airline Crew Planning Process

The crew planning department receives the schedule from the aircraft scheduling department at regular time intervals and has to create legal round trips in such a way as to satisfy the crew requirements of all flights. The optimal set of trips must comply with the general safety regulations, the company operating policies and the union requirements, while minimizing the total cost. The basic activity to be planned is called *leg* and involves a single departure and a single arrival. Legs are connected into round-trips also called *pairings* that depart and return to specific crew bases. Given the flight table and the distribution of the crews among the crew bases, the planning process may be separated as follows:

- selection of the flight legs to be covered
- pairing generation and optimization
- assignment of the pairings to individual crew members

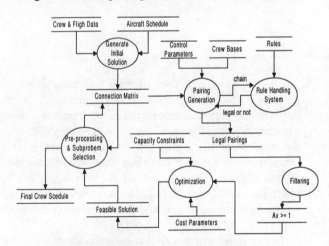

Figure 1. Carmen System DFD

Since the number of possible pairings extends into millions and possibly billions obtaining a meaningful set of pairings, to be given to the optimization procedure, is quite complex and time consuming. The generation of a meaningful set of pairings is aided either by special pre-processing filtering techniques [14] or optimizer feedback

based processes [16]. The optimization phase involves the selection of a set of pairings in order to cover all flight legs while minimizing the total solution cost.

The solution methodology of the Carmen system [2] is shown in (Figure 1) and is presently in production at Air France, Alitalia, British Airways, KLM, Lufthansa, SAS, and Swissair. A typical run of the Carmen system consists of 50-100 iterations. The main system components are the pairing generation and the optimization modules.

The total number of possible pairings depends on the structure of the flight network. A typical short haul fleet for Lufthansa has about 800 daily legs and about 5000 weekly legs. A typical pairing in this fleet contains on the average twelve legs, and since a leg can be connected to at least ten new legs at each major airport, this produces close to 10^{12} pairings. To reduce the number of pairings requires an intelligent generation procedure. The optimizer that will be examined and parallelized in this paper is quite fast and achieves high quality results for problems up to one million pairings. Within the Carmen system and for all of the Lufthansa fleets that were tested, the generator always requires five to eight times more execution time than the optimizer or about 70-85% of the total runtime.

3. Parallel Pairing Generator

3.1. Pairing Generation Algorithm Description

The pairing generator creates legal pairings by connecting legs to each other. The pairing generator is aided by a pre-processed *connection matrix* that shows the acceptable connections between pairs of legs. In addition, there exists a legality module that calculates the properties of each chain and validates all the applicable rules. The connection matrix represents in mathematical terms a directed connection graph among the legs. A node of the graph corresponds to a leg and an edge represents a legal pair-wise connection. The possible non-zero elements of the matrix for a typical fleet of 1000 legs can be from 10,000 to 100,000.

The most efficient algorithm, with respect to memory needs, for the pairing generation process is the depth first search (Figure 2). The search always begins from a subset of legs known as *start legs*. The search is limited by a maximum number of branches to be considered in each node of the search graph. This maximum number of connecting branches is known as the *search width* and its typical value range from 10-20 connections. Every leg chain is checked for legality. Illegal paths are not further investigated which implies that the incremental rules must have a monotonic behavior.

Input: A set of start legs $S = \{s_1, s_2, \ldots, s_k\}$, Connection Matrix CM, set of rules R, search width $SW(P)$ as a function of the working days covered by P, where P denotes a chain of legs

```
procedure GENERATE
    Work queue WQ ← S
    while (WQ not empty) do
        node ← GET_NEXT(WQ)
        SEARCH(node)
    endwhile
endprocedure
procedure SEARCH(node)
    P ← ADD(node)
    if TEST_LEGALITY(P, R) then
        if P is a COMPLETE pairing then
            OUTPUT(P)
        endif
        while SW(P) is not violated do
            r ← GET_NEXT_CONNECTION(node, CM)
            SEARCH(r)
        endwhile
    endif
    P ← REMOVE(node)
endprocedure
```

Figure 2. Serial Pairing Generation Algorithm

3.2. Parallelization Approach

An examination of the serial algorithm in Figure 2 reveals the ability for exploiting parallelism during the pairing generation phase. The majority of the computation time occurs in the *SEARCH* procedure. By distributing the contents of the work queue *WQ*, thereby dividing the computational work among several processors we can reduce the computation time. The amount of computational work done in the *SEARCH* procedure for each element of the *WQ* is highly variable and unpredictable. This implies that the parallelization must incorporate dynamic load balancing mechanisms.

The parallel programming approach used for the parallel generator is the manager/worker model. The manager executes the *GENERATE* procedure and the workers execute the *SEARCH* procedure. The manager broadcasts the connection matrix to every worker at the beginning of the run. This implies that the parallel process involves the distribution of a forest of search trees to the available workers. The manager distributes dynamically the start legs and the search width information to the workers on a worker demand driven manner. The workers generate all the legal pairings and return them to the manager. The communication between the manager and the workers is asynchronous and there is no need for communication between the workers. The manager is composed of two threads, one responsible for the

distribution of the input data to the workers and the other for collecting the output from the workers. This scheme improves the efficiency and the scalability of the parallel generator, despite of the centralized nature of the manager. The typical mapping involves the assignment of each worker to a different processor.

The design goal of all parallel processing applications is to minimize the idle time of each worker and the communication among the processors. To minimize idle time application specific load balancing is done and an overlapping between computation and communication is attempted. To minimize communication we use large messages, that is, the workers do buffering and compression of the pairings in order to reduce the network latency penalty and the volume of the communicated data.

3.3. Application Specific Features

Dynamic Load Balancing. Load balancing is achieved by implementing a dynamic workload distribution scheme in the manager that implicitly takes into account the speed and the current load of each machine. The number of start legs that are sent to each worker are also changing dynamically using a fading algorithm. In the beginning a sufficient number of start legs is given and near the end only a single start leg is assigned to each worker. This scheme attempts to balance the network traffic and the load balancing sensitivities. In (1) the number of start legs (n) assigned to each worker as a function of the number of the remaining start legs (r) is shown.

$$n = \begin{cases} \max(1, \min(UB, floor(N_{TOTAL}/(P \cdot \log 2(N_{TOTAL}/P))))) & \text{if } r = N_{TOTAL} \\ \max(1, f(r) \cdot n) & \text{if } 3nP \le r < N_{TOTAL} \\ 1 & \text{if } r < 3nP \end{cases} \quad (1)$$

N_{TOTAL} is the total number of start legs for the current iteration of the problem, UB is an upper bound for the initial work distribution and $f(r)$ is a monotonic decay function in [0,1]. The initial work assignment depends on the number of processors (P) and N_{TOTAL} and is done simultaneously for all the workers. In addition, efficiency is also improved by pre-fetching the start legs from the manager. A worker requests the next set of start legs before they are needed. It can then perform computation while its request is being serviced by the manager.

Because the search tree that corresponds to each start leg may be very irregular a further refinement of the load balancing scheme is also implemented as the end of the pairing generation is approached. The manager decreases the granularity of the search tree at a lower level and assigns sub-trees to the workers (Figure 3).

Fault Tolerance. For production level reliability the parallel generator is able to recover from task and host failures. The notification mechanism of PVM [11] is used to provide application level fault tolerance to the generator. A worker failure leads to the loss of some pairings that either have not been generated, or have been generated but not sent. Consequently, this part of the generation tree must be recalculated by some worker task. The manager keeps the current computing state of each worker and in case failure it is used for reassigning the unfinished part of the work.

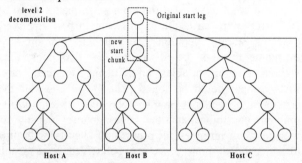

Figure 3. Decomposition of the search tree

The program that called the parallel generator detects the failure of the manager and can start a new manager, as the manager uses a checkpointing mechanism to store state information. The responsibility of the new manager is to reset the workers and to request only the generation of the pairings that have not been generated.

Dynamic Task Creation and Local User Priority. Another powerful feature of the parallel pairing generator is its ability to utilize the availability of new processor nodes and to return to their owners machines that must not be used in the parallel virtual machine any longer. It is possible to add a new host at any time to the virtual parallel machine, and this will cause a new worker to be started automatically. The system also respects the workstation owner's priorities. This is implemented with the suspend/resume set of services. In simple terms, the worker suspends its operation if the machine load (CPU, memory, swap space) is over some specified limits and resumes its operation if the machine load is below a specified limit. When a worker is in suspend mode it is considered blocked and the manager keeps this worker in a list of suspended tasks. Periodically, the manager requests from the worker information concerning its machine load and if the load is below the specified limit the manager moves the worker to the active list of workers. If the worker remains in suspend mode for a long period of time, it is considered as failing, and is removed completely from the system. The rate of the load checking operation defines the performance overhead; interaction of about once every minute creates a very small performance overhead (<0.1%).

4. Parallel Pairing Optimizer

4.1. Pairing Optimization Problem Definition

The pairing optimization problem is modeled as a *set covering* or *set partitioning* 0-1 constraint satisfaction problem [20]. A small number of general capacity constraints also exist but are not considered in this paper.

Let $A = (a_{ij})$ be a 0-1 m x n matrix and $C = (c_j)$ be a vector of size n. Let the sets $M = \{1, \dots ,m\}$ and $N = \{1, \dots ,n\}$ correspond to the rows and columns of A. The value c_j ($j \in N$) represents the cost of column j (pairing j). We assume, without loss of generality, that $c_j \geq 0$, $\forall j \in N$. We say that a column $j \in N$ covers row $i \in M$, if $a_{ij} = 1$. We say that a subset of columns $S \subseteq N$ is a solution to the set covering problem, if for each row $i \in M$, there is at least one column $j \in S$ with $a_{ij} \neq 0$. The target of the optimization algorithm is to select the subset S that minimizes the sum of the corresponding c_j's. In mathematical terms the problem can be written as

$$\min \sum_{j \in N} c_j x_j \qquad (2)$$

$$s.t. \sum_{j \in N} a_{ij} x_j \geq 1, \ x_j \in \{0,1\}, \ i \in M, \ j \in N \qquad (3)$$

where $x_j = 1$ if $j \in S$ and $x_j = 0$ otherwise. The large problems we were concerned have up to one million variables and typically between a few hundred to a few thousand constraints. They are very sparse, usually having only 5 to 10 nonzero entries per column.

The set covering problem is *NP*-hard, and many algorithms have been proposed for exact [10] as well as approximate problem solutions [7,27]. The exact approaches are often based on the branch and bound search technique, which although can be successfully parallelized on the NOW architecture [5,19], has a prohibitive computation time for very large problems. Since our goal was to solve large crew scheduling problems the approximate solution algorithm proposed in [27] was selected for parallelization. This is also the algorithm used in the current serial Carmen system and is particularly efficient for this class of problems.

4.2. High Level Optimization Description

The optimization algorithm can be categorized as an iterative Lagrangian relaxation heuristic algorithm [25]. The algorithm manipulates the Lagrangian *cost vector* $\overline{c}$, which is initialized to the cost vector C. The goal of the manipulation is to create a sign pattern for the elements of $\overline{c}$, which corresponds to a feasible solution S (usually well within 1% of the optimum), given that $\forall x_j \in S$, $\overline{c}_j < 0$. In the sequential algorithm all the problem constraints are iterated, one at a time, updating the corresponding $\overline{c}$ entries. The algorithm is summarized in Figure 4.

Input: 0-1 mxn constraint matrix A, cost vector C

$\overline{c} \leftarrow C, \kappa \leftarrow 0, \forall\, i \in M\, s^i \leftarrow 0$

repeat

    for each constraint i **do**

        $r^j \leftarrow CANCEL(\overline{c}, s^i)$ // cancel out the last contribution

        $r^-, r^+ \leftarrow SELECTION(r^j)$ // select the critical values r^-, r^+

        $s^i \leftarrow CONTRIBUTION(r^-, r^+, \kappa)$ // compute new contribution

        $\overline{c} \leftarrow UPDATE(r^j, s^i)$ // update $\overline{c}$ to its new value

    endfor

    $\kappa \leftarrow INCREASE(\kappa)$ // κ parameter sets the convergence speed

until no sign changes in $\overline{c}$

for each variable $j \in N$ **do**

    if $\overline{c}_j < 0$ **then** $x_j \leftarrow 1$ **else** $x_j \leftarrow 0$

Figure 4. Serial Optimization Algorithm

---

r^j represents a local temporary copy of the $\overline{c}$ entries that correspond to constraint i, r^- and r^+ are the smallest and the second smallest entries of r^j, also called *critical variables* for a particular constraint, s^i is the contribution of constraint i to $\overline{c}$ and $\kappa \in [0,1)$. For each constraint i there exists a unique sparse vector s^i, due to the fact that the algorithm requires the cancellation of the previous contribution to $\overline{c}$ before a constraint is iterated again.

4.3. Parallelization Approach

The parallelization of the optimization process must be done within a single iteration in order to retain the convergence characteristics of the method. The first parallelization attempt used a row-wise decomposition approach. Theory and results on this scheme can be found in [12]. A second approach based on the column-wise decomposition of the problem called *variable based decomposition* (VBD)[1] was pursued.

The VBD approach is realized by distributing subsets of variables (columns) to each processor. Each processor is then responsible for a part of $\overline{c}$ and the corresponding part of the A-matrix. Some of the operations needed for the constraint update can be conveniently done locally (e.g., CANCEL, UPDATE), but the CONTRIBUTION operation requires communication. Each worker process, first executes in parallel the SELECTION operation to find the local minimum values, and then communicates them to the manager process. The manager calculates and broadcasts to the workers the contribution s^i of the current constraint i to the reduced cost vector. Lastly, the workers perform the UPDATE operation and proceed with the next constraint. The communication involves the transmission of a large number of small messages, which makes the use of an efficient low latency communication network an imperative requirement. The VBD advantage is the small communicated data volume, which is proportional to the number of worker processes and the constraints of the problem. Load balancing is very important for the VBD approach and a simple and effective strategy is to send randomly selected variables to each worker process [26,23].

It can be observed that the main performance issue of the VBD approach is the requirement to perform $O(m)$ synchronization operations per global iteration. To overcome this and based on the fact that constraints without common variables can be iterated independently, such groups should be found [21]. If we consider the constraint dependence graph where the nodes are the problem constraints and the edges connect constraints with common variables, the problem of identifying groups of independent constraints can be solved as a graph coloring problem. All the constraints colored with the same color are independent. The fact that the graph coloring problem is *NP*-hard is not so crucial, since there is no need for an optimal solution but for a reasonable approximation [22,26]. A non-optimal fast graph coloring algorithm based on [18] is used for the creation of the constraint groups. If a constraint set g contains only independent constraints, then the CONTRIBUTION operation can be performed group-wise for all $|g|$ constraints at once. The UPDATE operation can now be delayed till the end of each constraint group. The benefit of this approach is that without changing the convergence characteristics of the algorithm we have managed to reduce the number of the communicated messages and synchronization steps from the total number of constraints to the number of independent constraint groups. This strategy was first done on an SGI Origin 2000 at the Chalmers University of Technology, with a speedup of 7 when 8 processors were used [22,26]. However, it can not be used directly on a conventional network of workstations, due to the high latency of the interconnection network. To make this strategy more viable for NOWs a low latency communication network is needed [6,15] with hardware routers, which allows simultaneous communications of all processors. In addition, an optimized message passing implementation [8] is necessary, which eliminates memory copies and uses an efficient protocol stack.

To overcome the limitations of traditional and inexpensive networks an algorithmic improvement of the previous parallel algorithm was attempted. The variation is based on a "lazy" updating procedure of $\overline{c}$. Only the common variables with the constraint group that will be iterated next (PARTIAL_UPDATE operation, see Figure 5) is updated. The reduced cost vector is then fully updated (*FULL_UPDATE* operation), based on the contributions of the previous constraint group, during the time the manager process calculates the contribution to $\overline{c}$ of the current constraint group. This approach overlaps computation with both communication and previous idle time due to synchronization, given that the full cost vector update takes a significant amount of time. The computation time is slightly increased, and the relaxation may have no benefit at all in the extreme case of a problem with a structure that does not permit the creation of constraint groups with a small number of common variables among them. Figure 5 shows a high level description of the lazy VBD worker algorithm.

Input: A subset of variables $V_k \subseteq N$, cost vector $C(V_k)$, set of constraint groups $G = \{g_1, g_2, ..., g_r\}$, where $g_i = \{i \mid i \in M, \forall j \in g_i \ i \text{ and } j \text{ are independent}\}$

Worker Algorithm:
$\overline{c} \leftarrow C(V_k)$, $\kappa \leftarrow 0$, $\forall i \in M \ s^i \leftarrow 0$
repeat
    for each constraint group $g_i \in G$ **do**
        for each constraint $i \in g_i$ **do**
            $r^i \leftarrow CANCEL(\overline{c}, s^i)$
            $r^-_{local}, r^+_{local} \leftarrow SELECTION(r^i)$ // local values are selected
            $B \leftarrow BUFFER(r^-_{local}, r^+_{local})$
        endfor
        $SEND(B, manager)$ // manager computes *CONTRIBUTION* of g_i
        $\overline{c} \leftarrow FULL\_UPDATE(s^{gi-1})$ // update with the contributions of the previous constraint group
        $s^{gi} \leftarrow RECEIVE(B, manager)$ // receive from manager the contribution of group g_i
        $\overline{c} \leftarrow PARTIAL\_UPDATE(s^{gi})$ // do only the necessary updates for next group, leave work for later
    endfor
    $\kappa \leftarrow INCREASE(\kappa)$
until no sign changes in $\overline{c}$
for each variable $j \in V_k$ **do**
    if $\overline{c}_j < 0$ **then** $x_j \leftarrow 1$ **else** $x_j \leftarrow 0$
endfor

Figure 5. High-level "lazy" VBD Algorithm

The size of the reduced cost vector $\overline{c}$ for each processor k is $|V_k|$ and the contribution of a constraint group s^{gi}, is the combination of the contributions s^i of all the constraints of group g_i.

4.4. Theoretical Performance Analysis

The modeling of the execution time for a global iteration of the optimization algorithm as a function of the problem size, the number of processors and other algorithm and hardware characteristics is attempted. The analysis assumes that we have balanced distribution of work and an unloaded network with no special structure,

on which global operations require P messages. T_P^{iter} is the iteration time on P processors, NZ and m are the number of non-zero entries and the rows in the constraint matrix respectively, t_s and t_w are the communication latency and cost per word and t_c is the time to complete a basic floating-point operation.

Sequential Algorithm
The serial implementation has iteration time

$$T_1^{iter} = \lambda_1 \cdot t_c \cdot NZ + \mu \cdot m \cdot t_c + \lambda_2 \cdot t_c \cdot NZ \cong \lambda \cdot t_c \cdot NZ \quad (4)$$

where λ, λ_1, λ_2, μ are constants. The first term corresponds to the execution time of the operations *CANCEL* and *SELECTION*, the second corresponds to the *CONTRIBUTION* operation, and the third to the *UPDATE* operation. Based on profiling results the first and third phases take over 95% of the total execution time, which is equally divided among them.

Analysis of the "lazy" VBD approach
In the basic VBD approach the first and the third phase of the algorithm is parallelized, having as a trade-off $m+m$ global reduction/broadcast operations. The expected speedup is thus

$$S \cong \frac{P \cdot T_1^{iter}}{2 \cdot P^2 \cdot m \cdot t_s + T_1^{iter}} \quad (5)$$

In the next paragraphs we make a more detailed analysis of the VBD approach with the constraint groups and the lazy update as in theory, and in practice, proved to be a very successful parallelization technique.

For each constraint group the required communication will be the communication time for each worker process to send the local r^- and r^+ values to the manager process and the communication time required by the manager process to send back to the worker processes the computed values.

$$t_{group}^{comm} = 2 \cdot \sum_{k=1}^{P} \left(t_s + \sum_{i=1}^{q} p_r \cdot t_w \right) \quad (6)$$

where p_r and p_s is the volume of the communicated data per constraint in words, and q is the number of constraints in the group. In our implementation $p_r = p_s$. If the problem constraints are partitioned in NG independent constraint groups, using a coloring algorithm, the required communication time will be

$$T_{COMM} = \sum_{i=1}^{NG} t_{group}^{comm} = 2 \cdot P \cdot NG \cdot t_s + 2 \cdot P \cdot m \cdot p_r \cdot t_w \quad (7)$$

With the lazy variable update the idle time of the worker processes is minimized because the communication time (T_{COMM}) and the manager computation time tend to overlap with the computation time used by the worker during the update of the cost vector (*FULL_UPDATE* operation). The idle time of the worker processes with the "lazy" variable update can be approximated as

$$T_{IDLE} \cong \max(0, \frac{2 \cdot P \cdot T_{COMM} - T_1^{iter}}{2 \cdot P})$$ (8)

However, a computation overhead T_{OVER} is introduced

$$T_{OVER} = \lambda_2 \cdot t_c \cdot \sum_{i=1}^{NG} \gamma_i$$ (9)

where γ_i is the number of common variables between each consequent pair of constraint groups. This is due to the fact that additional calculations have to be done to determine and partially update the reduced cost vector. The expected parallel iteration time would thus be

$$T_P^{iter} = T_{OVER} + T_{PHASE-1} + T_{IDLE} + T_{PHASE-3}$$

$$= \lambda_2 \cdot t_c \cdot \sum_{NG} \gamma_i + \frac{T_1^{iter}}{P} + \max(0, \frac{2 \cdot P \cdot T_{COMM} - T_1^{iter}}{2 \cdot P})$$ (10)

For a reasonable number of processors and for large problem instances, T_1^{iter} is much larger than the required communication time, and the third term of (10) tends to zero, and thus

$$T_P^{iter} = \lambda_2 \cdot t_c \cdot \sum_{NG} \gamma_i + \frac{T_1^{iter}}{P}$$ (11)

which makes the expected speedup equal to

$$S \cong \frac{P \cdot T_1^{iter}}{P \cdot \lambda_2 \cdot t_c \cdot \sum_{NG} \gamma_i + T_1^{iter}}$$ (12)

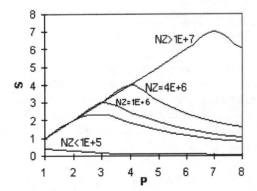

Figure 6. "Lazy" VBD speedup curves for various problem sizes

Based on (12) the expected speedups for various problem sizes of the "lazy" VBD approach are presented in Figure 6. We have assumed an Ethernet based NOW (t_c=0.0293μs, t_s=1500μs, t_w=5μs), 80 constraint groups from the graph coloring and 5% of the non-zeros of a processor common between subsequent constraint groups.

5. Experimental Results

We have measured the performance of the parallel generator and the parallel "lazy" VBD optimizer implementation, using typical crew scheduling problems from Lufthansa. In addition, we report results of the first prototype that integrated the parallel modules in the Carmen system for the same problems. The experiments have been performed on a network of HP715/100 workstations interconnected by standard 10Mbps Ethernet. All workstations used were of almost equal speed (2.89 SPECint95). The implementation of the parallel generator used the PVM message passing library [11] version 4.3, while the implementation of the optimizer used the HP-MPI optimized library [13] version 1.2. PVM provides support for dynamic resource and process control and robustness, used by the parallel generator application. MPI supports asynchronous and non-blocking communication operations, which help the overlap between computation and communication, which is vital for the parallel optimizer. All the programs were written in ANSI C++. The values presented were obtained with exclusive use of the processors and the network.

Name	dl_kopt	dl_splimp	dl_gg	wk_gg
legs	1087	946	946	6196
pairings	159073	318938	396908	594560
CPUs	Time in seconds			
1	10860	20760	26460	31380
2	5563	10797	13771	16834
4	2804	5448	7061	8436
6	1892	3686	4536	5338
8	1385	2797	3466	4312
10	1112	2181	2818	3288

Table 1. Results of parallel generator

The parallel generator and optimizer were tested with four different problems of various sizes. In Table 1 we can see the characteristics of these problems and the runtimes of the parallel generator for different number of workstations. The parallel generation time decreases in all cases almost linearly with respect to the number of workstations used.

The output of the generator module then became the input to the optimization filtering module as it is shown in Figure 1. The filtering module attempts to reduce the size of the constraint matrix by finding equivalent columns and rows and eliminating duplicate or redundant elements. In Table 2 we give the characteristics of the filtered problems and the performance results of the parallel "lazy" VBD optimizer, with NZ representing the number of non-zero elements and s the sparsity ratio of the matrix.

Name	dl_kopt	Dl_splimp	dl_gg	wk_gg
Legs	705	641	643	5287
Pairings	156197	316958	393908	590063
NZ	1826456	4074017	4555324	9890583
s (%)	1.65697	1.98101	1.79009	0.51
CPUs	Time in seconds			
1	951.53	1498.13	2763.12	4071
2	634.54	932.14	1493.57	2035.48
3	365.90	739.76	1001.13	1380,53
4	259.32	434.19	752.89	1041.76

Table 2. Results of "lazy" VBD optimizer

The quality of the solution remains as in the sequential execution while the speedup that is achieved is quite significant. Particularly, for the larger problem *lh_wk_gg*, the speedups are excellent because a small number of large constraint groups exist for this problem. Consequently, the granularity of the computation work is coarse-grained, the communication with the manager is sparse and the idle time is close to zero. In addition, the structure of the problem, which is characterized by long and sparse constraints, makes the overlap between consequent constraint groups minimum. This implies that the overhead term is also minimized. From the experimental results it can be concluded that the theoretical analysis does hold and the ability to use networks of existing workstations for this work is validated. For the problems of this experiment the use of more workstations does not improve the execution time. As it can be seen from Figure 6 about eight workstations can be maximally used efficiently for practical crew scheduling problems.

The parallel components have been integrated in a prototype system, coexisting with the sequential Carmen components. These sequential components take 5-15% of the total runtime on the average, depending on the size of the problem. We run the test problems with the prototype system and we report the results in Table 3. The total runtime of the parallel system is the sum of the parallel generation time, the parallel optimization time and the time spent in the sequential components of the system. The execution of the serial Carmen system on an equivalent machine is also reported. We reduced the execution time about five times for the three problems, and four times for the last problem. The last problem is a large weekly scheduling example where the problem initialization time as well as the connection matrix pre-

processing is significant which increases even further the proportion of the sequential components.

name	Parallel prototype				Serial	
	Generator (10 CPUs)	Optimizer (4 CPUs)	Sequential Part	Total	Total	Speedup
dl_kopt	1112	259.32	909.44	2280.7	12992.6	5.69
dl_slimp	2181	434.19	2225.81	4841.0	24483.9	5.05
dl_gg	2818	752.89	2922.31	6493.2	32145.4	4.95
wk_gg	3288	1041.76	6381.18	10710.	41832.1	3.90

Table 3. Results of the Carmen system with the integrated parallel modules

6. Conclusions and Future Work

In this paper we presented the prevailing methodology for the solution of the crew planning problem and parallel algorithms for the solution of the main steps of this process. The architecture assumed in the paper and in the ESPRIT/HPCN research project PAROS, involves the use of existing interconnected workstations. The idea has been to better utilize the existing infrastructure for the solution of hard and time consuming combinatorial problems that appear in the context of airline crew scheduling.

The parallelization of the generator and the optimizer will give rise to new business advantages for the Carmen System product. Detailed analysis of the various parallelization approaches for both the generator and the optimizer are presented and the experimental results of the best parallel algorithms on a set of real Lufthansa problems is presented. The improved performance of the system can be used to solve larger problems and/or to increase the problem solution quality. The speed and quality of these parallel methods are therefore critical for the overall efficiency of an airline. The demand for such processes increases even further with the ongoing deregulation of the airline operations in Europe.

On a more technical level, an attempt will be made to avoid the generator manager collection of all the pairings produced by the generator workers. This collection is currently performed due to the fact that a global filtering operation must be done. If this global filtering could be done in parallel, there would be no need to collect all the pairings thus reducing the communication expense of the system. Another implication of this could be that the generator workers could in practice be the same with the optimization workers. In addition, the parallelization of the connection matrix creation and preprocessing step before the generation will be also examined because it has become now the system bottleneck. Lastly, the synthesis of the "lazy" VBD approach with the sub-problem selection approach of [26] will be investigated.

Acknowledgments

We would like to thank D.Ioannidis, D.Koulopoulos, G.Thomopoulos and C.Valouxis for the fruitful talks and the support in the development and testing of the parallel algorithms. D.Wedelin for his effort in helping us understand the innovative ideas behind the optimization algorithm and his support in difficult situations in the development stage. T.Takkula and P.Sanders for their effort in improving the serial implementations of the optimization algorithm and their cooperation in examining alternative parallelization approaches. We would also like to thank C.Hjorring and O.Liljenzin for the close cooperation in integrating the various parallel modules in the Carmen system. Lastly, we would like to thank all the partners of the PAROS ESPRIT project for their input and support.

References

[1] Alefragis, P., C. Goumopoulos, E. Housos, P. Sanders, T. Takkula and D. Wedelin, " Parallel crew scheduling in PAROS ", EuroPar '98, September 1-4, 1998 Southampton, UK, accepted for publication.

[2] Anderson, E., et. al., *OR in the airline industry*, chapter Crew Pairing Optimization, pp. 228-258, Kluwer Academic Publishers, Boston, London, Dordrecht, 1997.

[3] Barutt, J., T. Hall, "Airline crew scheduling - supercomputers and algorithms", *30th Annual Symposium AGIFORS* 1990, 351-358; and *SIAM News* 23 (6), 19-22, November 1990.

[4] Bianco, L., et. al., "A heuristic procedure for the crew rostering problem", *European Journal of Operational Research*, 58 (1992), pp. 272-283.

[5] Bixby, R. E., W. Cook, A. Cox, E. K. Lee, "Parallel Mixed Integer Programming", Center for Research on Parallel Computation Research Monograph CRPC-TR95554, 1995.

[6] Boden, N. J., D. Cohen, R. E. Felderman, A. E. Kulawik, C. L. Seitz, J. N. Seizovic, W.-K. Su, "Myrinet: A gigabit per second Local Area Network", *IEEE-Micro*, 15(1):29-36, Feb. 1995.

[7] Caprara, A., M. Fischetti, P. Toth, "A Heuristic Method for the Set Covering Problem", in *Lecture Notes in Computer Science*, pages 72-84, 1996.

[8] Chien, A. et. al., "High Performance Virtual Machines (HPVM): Clusters with Supercomputing APIs and Performance", *Eighth SIAM Conference on Parallel Processing for Scientific Computing* (PP97); March, 1997.

[9] Chu, H. D., E. Gelman, E. L. Johnson, "Solving large scale crew scheduling problems", *European Journal of Operational Research*, 97 (1997), pp. 260-268.

[10] Fisher, M. L., P. Kedia, "Optimal Solutions of Set Covering/Partitioning Problems using Dual Heuristics", *Management Science* 36 pp. 674-688, 1990.

[11] Geist, G., A. Beguelin, J. Dongarra, W. Jiang, R. Mancheck, V. Sunderam, *PVM: Parallel Virtual Machine*, MIT Press, 1994.

[12] Goumopoulos, C., P. Alefragis, E. Housos, " High Performance Airline Crew-Pairing Optimization ", European Parallel and Distributed Systems Conference (Euro-PDS98), July 1-3, 1998 Vienna, AUSTRIA, accepted for publication.

[13] HP MPI User's Guide, 3rd Edition, DSW-493.

[14] Housos, E., T. Elmroth, "Automatic Subproblem Optimization for Airline Crew Scheduling", *Interfaces* 27:5, September-October 1997, pp. 68-77.

[15] IEEE, Standard for the scalable coherent interface (SCI), 1993. IEEE Std 1596-1992.

[16] Lavoie S., M. Minoux, E. Odier, "A new approach of crew pairing problems by column generation and application to air transport", European Journal of Operational Research, 35 (1988), pp. 45-58.

[17] Marsten, R., R. Subramanian, S. Martin, "RALPH: Crew Planning at Delta Air Lines", Technical Report, Cutting Edge Optimization, 1997.

[18] Mehrotra, A., M. A. Trick, "A clique generation approach to graph coloring", INFORMS Journal of Computing, 8 pp. 344-354, 1996.

[19] Mitra, G., I. Hai, M. T. Hajian, , "A Distributed Processing Algorithm for Solving Integer Programs Using a Cluster of Workstations", *Parallel Computing*, 23(6): 733-753, 1997.

[20] Nemhauser, G. L., L.A. Wolsey, *Integer and Combinatorial Optimization*, Wiley - Interscience, 1988.

[21] PAROS consortium (Chalmers), *D5.3b Parallel optimizer experiment*, Technical Report, May 1997.

[22] PAROS consortium (Chalmers), *D5.4b Optimizer prototype*, Technical Report, May 1997.

[23] PAROS consortium (Univ of Patras), *D7.2 Dependence analysis and task graph generation of the process for parallel execution*, Technical Report, Dec. 1997.

[24] PAROS consortium, Technical annex for the Esprit project 20.115: Parallel large scale automatic scheduling, PAROS, January 1996.

[25] Reeves, C. R., *Modern Heuristic Techniques for Combinatorial Problems*, chapter Lagrangian Relaxation, pp. 243-299, McGraw-Hill, 1997.

[26] Sanders, P., T. Takkula, D. Wedelin, "High Performance Integer Optimization for Crew Scheduling", in preparation.

[27] Wedelin, D., "An Algorithm for Large Scale 0-1 Integer Programming with Application to Airline Crew Scheduling", Annals of Operations Research, 57 pp. 283-301, 1995.

Session 2B
Networks of Workstations

Chair: David Lilja
University of Minnesota

Improving Performance of Networks of Workstations by using Disha Concurrent*

F. Silla, A. Robles and J. Duato
Grupo de Arquitecturas Paralelas
Dpto. Inf. de Sistemas y Computadores
Universidad Politécnica de Valencia
Camino de Vera s/n. 46071 - Valencia, SPAIN
{fsilla,arobles,jduato}@gap.upv.es

Abstract

Networks of workstations are currently emerging as a cost-effective alternative to parallel computers. Recently, deadlock recovery techniques have been shown to be an alternative to deadlock avoidance. Disha Concurrent is a progressive deadlock recovery scheme able to simultaneously redirect several deadlocked messages through a deadlock-free lane. Unlike deadlock avoidance techniques, Disha provides true fully adaptive routing without using virtual channels to guarantee deadlock freedom. In this paper, we analyze the application of Disha to networks of workstations. We propose an implementation of Disha on irregular networks that allows concurrent deadlock recovery, proving that this implementation is always able to recover from deadlock. A new switch organization and a new flow control protocol are proposed to support Disha. Performance evaluation results show that applying Disha to irregular networks increases network throughput by a factor of up to 3.5, and also reduces latency with regard to other routing algorithms based on deadlock avoidance techniques.

1. Introduction

Currently, networks of workstations (NOWs) are being considered as a cost-effective alternative to parallel computers, since they are scalable and provide the incremental expansion capability required in parallel computing environments. Proposals like Autonet [12], Myrinet [4], and ServerNet [5] use point-to-point links between switching elements instead of the traditional bus used in computer networks, and also support networks with irregular topology.

Routing algorithms in irregular networks are much different from those used in regular ones, due to the irregular connections between switches. The irregularity makes deadlock avoidance quite complicated. Several deadlock-free routing algorithms have been proposed [12, 10]. These schemes avoid deadlock by prohibiting cyclic dependencies between channels, thus restricting routing considerably. To overcome this constraint, a general methodology for the design of adaptive routing algorithms for irregular networks has been proposed in [13]. Algorithms designed according to this methodology improve network throughput considerably, and reduce message latency.

Recently, deadlock recovery techniques [11, 1, 2] have been shown to be a valid alternative to deadlock avoidance. Deadlock recovery techniques assume that deadlocks are not frequent, and thus do not impose any restriction on routing functions, thereby allowing deadlocks to form. The goal is to make the common case fast and deal with the infrequent cases when deadlock does occur. Deadlock recovery has the advantage of allowing true fully adaptive minimal routing without using virtual channels devoted to deadlock avoidance. Nowadays, virtual channels have been widely accepted and its use is generalized. However, in NOWs with wormhole switching, the use of long links implies the use of deep buffers, therefore requiring a large silicon area. Thus, applying deadlock recovery techniques could provide a higher adaptivity while using less dedicated resources to handle deadlocks.

Disha [1, 2] is a deadlock recovery scheme based on progressive re-direction of deadlocked packets through a deadlock-free lane. Progressive deadlock recovery techniques achieve more performance than deadlock avoidance ones because they require less resources to handle deadlocks. So far, Disha has been analyzed on regular networks like k-ary n-cubes, where it has been shown to be very effective, but it has not been applied to irregular networks yet.

*This work was supported by the Spanish CICYT Grant TIC97–0897–C04–01

80

Applying Disha to irregular networks will allow routing all the messages over minimal paths without requiring virtual channels to guarantee deadlock freedom. However, virtual channels could be used to increase performance.

In this paper, we study whether Disha contributes to increase network performance with respect to current deadlock avoidance techniques in networks with irregular topology. The main contributions of this paper are a routing scheme for deadlocked messages that allows concurrent deadlock recovery while guaranteeing that all the deadlocked messages are delivered, and a detailed performance evaluation of Disha on networks with irregular topology. In particular, we prove that the proposed implementation of Disha is always able to recover from deadlock. Likewise, a switch organization and a flow control protocol to support the proposed implementation of Disha have been proposed. First, an overview of current deadlock recovery techniques is presented in Section 2, also describing two deadlock detection mechanisms. The way to apply Disha to irregular networks is presented in Section 3, while the performance of this implementation is evaluated in Section 4. Finally, in Section 5, some conclusions are drawn.

2. Deadlock Recovery

Deadlock recovery techniques, unlike deadlock avoidance mechanisms, do not impose any restriction on routing functions, allowing deadlocks to form in the interconnection network. However, these techniques require mechanisms to detect and manage deadlocks when they occur. When a deadlock is detected, one or more packets are forced to release the resources they are holding, allowing other packets to use them, and breaking the deadlock.

There are several actions that can be taken to release the resources occupied by deadlocked packets. Deadlock recovery techniques can be classified as progressive and regressive. Progressive deadlock recovery techniques deallocate resources from non-deadlocked packets (normal packets) and reassign them to deadlocked packets for quick delivery. On the other hand, regressive techniques deallocate resources from deadlocked packets, usually killing them (abort-and-retry).

2.1. Progressive Deadlock Recovery

Progressive techniques detect deadlocks at intermediate nodes containing the message header. Instead of killing the deadlocked packet, progressive recovery allows resources to be temporarily deallocated from normal packets and assigned to the deadlocked packet so that it can reach its destination. Once the deadlocked packet is delivered, resources are reallocated again to the preempted packets. Disha [1, 2] is based in this policy.

We are interested in implementing Disha in networks of workstations. To support Disha, each switch must be equipped with an additional central buffer, or Deadlock Buffer. In general, these buffers form what is collectively a deadlock-free recovery lane shared by all the physical channels of the switch. The mechanism that makes the recovery lane deadlock-free is specific to how recovery resources are allocated to deadlocked packets. Implementation can be based on restricted access (Disha Sequential [1]) or structured access (Disha Concurrent [2]) to the deadlock buffers.

Both deadlock handling techniques, Disha Sequential and Disha Concurrent, are very similar, allowing fully adaptive routing on some set of resources while providing dedicated resources to escape from deadlocks. However, Disha Concurrent makes possible that several deadlocks can be recovered from concurrently. It ensures deadlock freedom by the existence of a routing subfunction that is connected and has no cyclic dependencies between deadlock recovery resources [2]. Disha routing subfunction is usually defined by the deadlock buffers. For concurrent recovery, more than one deadlock buffer may be required at each switch for some network topologies. However, the number of deadlock buffers per switch should be kept minimal. Otherwise, crossbar size would increase, increasing propagation delay. Likewise, because several deadlocks can be recovered from simultaneously, an arbiter is required at each switch so that simultaneous requests for the use of deadlock buffers coming from different input channels can be handled.

Deadlock recovery techniques are useful only if deadlocks are rare. Otherwise, the overhead produced by deadlock detection and buffer releasing would degrade performance considerably. It was shown in [9] that deadlocks rarely occur when sufficient routing freedom is provided. In fact, the frequency of deadlock decreases considerably when virtual channels are used.

2.2. Deadlock Detection Mechanisms

Most deadlock detection mechanisms use only crude timeouts on blocked messages. This makes the mechanism susceptible to mistaking congestion for deadlocks. False deadlock detections may saturate the limited bandwidth offered by recovery resources. Thus, the selection of the timeout value for deadlock detection is a critical issue.

Recently, an improved deadlock detection mechanism has been proposed [7]. Instead of measuring the time a message is blocked, this mechanism measures the time the channels requested by a given message are inactive (i.e., the messages occupying them remain blocked). This mechanism can be implemented by using a counter and a one-bit flag (inactivity flag) associated with each output physical channel. The counter is incremented every clock cycle and is reset when a flit is transmitted across the physical out-

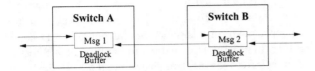

Figure 1. Deadlock in the recovery lane.

put channel. The counter output is continuously compared with a given threshold. If it is greater than this threshold, the inactivity flag is set indicating that the physical output channel is inactive. This flag is reset when a flit is transmitted across the physical channel. Every time a message is routed, if all the feasible output virtual channels are busy, then the inactivity flags associated with the corresponding physical output channels are checked. If all of these flags are set, then the message is presumed to be involved in a deadlock. It should be noted that this mechanism will detect all possible deadlocks, but also some false deadlocks (although much fewer than the timeout mechanism) depending on the threshold used. Thus, the mechanism must be properly tuned, choosing the appropriate threshold.

3. Applying Disha to Irregular Networks

We have chosen Disha Concurrent to implement concurrent deadlock recovery on irregular networks. In [2], it has been shown that a single deadlock buffer is enough to guarantee concurrent deadlock recovery on a 2-dimensional mesh. However, building a deadlock-free recovery lane on an irregular topology with a single deadlock buffer is not an easy task. Indeed, it may be impossible. Consider the following. Let us assume that it is possible to define a Hamiltonian path in the network. The recovery lane could use that path to deliver deadlocked messages. In order to do so, it is necessary to label the switches according to their position in the path. Messages detected as deadlocked at a given switch and destined for a workstation attached to a higher-labeled switch would be sent in the "up" direction along the path. Likewise, deadlocked messages destined for a workstation attached to a lower-labeled switch would be sent in the "down" direction. Now, consider two deadlocked messages traveling in opposite direction along the Hamiltonian path. If a single deadlock buffer per switch is used, those messages will deadlock when they reach two neighboring switches in the path.

Figure 1 depicts the situation. Message 1 has reached the deadlock buffer at switch A and requests the one at switch B. Similarly, message 2 reserved the deadlock buffer at switch B and is requesting the one at switch A. Obviously, there is a deadlock. However, this situation can be solved by using two deadlock buffers (central buffers) at each switch:

one for messages traveling in the "up" direction and another one for messages traveling in the "down" direction.

If we analyze other patterns that can be embedded in a topology, like an Eulerian path or a tree, the situation is the same: Messages traveling along the recovery lane may deadlock if a single deadlock buffer is used. Among those patterns, trees have interesting properties. First, it is possible to define a tree containing all the switches in any topology. Second, the diameter of a tree is much shorter than that of a Hamiltonian path or an Eulerian path. Third, there exist efficient routing algorithms for networks with embedded trees that are able to use all the links in the network. Therefore, we propose implementing the recovery lane required for Disha Concurrent by using two deadlock buffers per switch and the up/down routing scheme [12] as the routing subfunction. In this case, the recovery lane is replaced with a recovery network.

Up/down routing is deadlock-free. In Autonet networks [12], it is implemented with edge buffers. However, when central buffers are used, it is not guaranteed the absence of deadlock. We propose the following implementation of up/down routing when using two central buffers: Buffers will be labeled as the "up" and "down" buffers, respectively. Messages detected as deadlocked at a given switch will be routed through the "up" buffer at that switch. When the up/down routing algorithm selects an "up" link, the message will use the "up" buffer at the next switch. Otherwise, it will use the "down" buffer. This implementation is deadlock-free, as proved in the next lemma.

Lemma 1 *Up/down routing with two central buffers is deadlock-free.*

Proof: We proceed by contradiction. Let us assume that there is a deadlocked configuration. This configuration cannot involve "up" and "down" buffers because transitions from "down" buffers to "up" buffers are not allowed. Therefore, the deadlocked configuration only involves "up" or "down" buffers but not both of them. This implies that only "up" or "down" channels are used by the deadlocked messages. However, as indicated in [12], each cycle in the network has at least one link in the "up" direction and one link in the "down" direction. Thus, deadlock is not possible, contrary to the initial assumption. □

In order to use the central buffers and the up/down routing algorithm as the Disha recovery network, a breadth-first spanning tree must be computed, assigning a direction to each physical link. The routing rule is the same as when routing on edge buffers: a legal route must traverse zero or more "up" buffers followed by zero or more "down" buffers. As a consequence, the routing table for the Disha recovery network is just like the Autonet one. For normal packets, a true fully adaptive minimal routing algorithm is used. Again, before routing can be performed at each switch, the

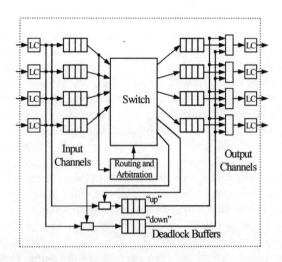

Figure 2. Architecture of the Disha switch.

routing table must be filled. Recovering from deadlock is always possible as proved in the next theorem.

Theorem 1 *The resulting routing algorithm is always able to recover from deadlock.*

Proof sketch: Recovering from deadlock is always possible because: 1) all deadlocks are detected; 2) when a message is detected as deadlocked, it is forwarded through the "up" buffer at the current switch; 3) deadlocked messages can be delivered by using the up/down routing algorithm implemented on the deadlock buffers; 4) messages being routed on the deadlock buffers cannot deadlock again.

3.1. Switch organization

The only changes required in the switch hardware with respect to a conventional switch are the use of a second routing table in the Routing and Arbitration Unit, the addition of two central buffers (Deadlock Buffers), and some hardware to detect deadlocks. This additional hardware requires less silicon area than an additional virtual channel per physical link to avoid deadlock. The deadlock detection hardware consists of a counter, a one-bit flag and some logic associated with each output physical link.

When a message is detected as deadlocked, it is routed until delivered by using the deadlock buffers and the second routing table. Deadlock buffers are organized as shown in Figure 2. As deadlock buffers can be reached from all the input links, an arbiter is required to handle concurrent requests from deadlocked messages arriving through different input links. Flits stored in the deadlock buffers are given a higher priority and can be transmitted over busy links by preempting normal message transmission. High

priority flits are distinguished from normal flits by using the protocol described in the next section. A second arbiter is needed to arbitrate between concurrent requests to the same output link from both deadlock buffers.

Finally, it should be noted that it is necessary to request buffer space at the next switch before starting the transmission of flits from one of the deadlock buffers because the corresponding deadlock buffer at the next switch may be occupied by flits from another deadlocked message. This is handled by the protocol described in the next section.

3.2. Flow Control

NOWs have specific flow control requirements. These requirements arise because, in general, links are narrow and long. Moreover, different links usually have different lengths. Therefore, the flow control protocol proposed in previous implementations of the Disha deadlock recovery scheme [8] is not appropriate in this environment. Flow control requirements in NOWs were already analyzed in [14], proposing a flow control protocol that supports virtual channels and channel pipelining by using control flits and block multiplexing. This protocol transmits several data flits every time a virtual channel gets the physical channel, in order to minimize the use of control flits. A virtual channel will transmit its identifier, and then it will send data flits until the message blocks or has been completely transmitted. At this time, the next ready virtual channel will transmit its identifier followed by data flits, and so on.

In this section, we extend the flow control protocol proposed in [14] in order to support Disha. Disha needs to reserve a deadlock buffer in the next switch before starting to send data flits. Buffer reservation is implemented by using three control flits: "Disha REQ", "Disha ACK", and "Disha NACK". To reserve a deadlock buffer at the next switch, a "Disha REQ" control flit is inserted into the normal data flow and transmitted to the next switch. On receiving this flit, if the requested deadlock buffer is free then a "Disha ACK" control flit is sent back through the reverse physical channel. If the requested buffer is busy or the arbiter assigns the buffer to another request, a "Disha NACK" control flit is returned. If a "Disha ACK" is received, the full bandwidth is allocated to the requesting deadlocked message; if a "Disha NACK" is received, the switch will try another valid outgoing channel.

Once a deadlock buffer has been reserved at the next switch, three additional control flits are required to handle data flit transmission. These control flits work exactly in the same way as the ones required to implement virtual channels [14], except that a higher priority is assigned to deadlock buffers. These control flits work as follows: First, a "Select Disha" control flit is sent before data flits belonging to a deadlocked message are forwarded to the next switch.

If the receiving deadlock buffer is filled up to the upper watermark [4], a "Disha STOP" control flit is returned to stop flit transmission. On reception of this control flit, physical bandwidth may be allocated to another virtual channel. When a deadlock buffer empties below the lower watermark [4], a "Disha GO" control flit is returned. When this control flit is received, the bandwidth of the physical channel is immediately allocated to the deadlocked message.

It should be noted that the reservation of deadlock buffers is much slower than the reservation of edge buffers. This is due to the fact that deadlock buffers may receive requests from different links, therefore requiring arbitration.

4. Performance Evaluation

In this section, we evaluate the behavior of Disha in NOWs, and compare its performance with the performance achieved by a deadlock avoidance-based routing algorithm. Several deadlock detection mechanisms can be used to support a deadlock recovery scheme. We have studied the behavior of the Disha deadlock recovery scheme using two different deadlock detection mechanisms: timeouts and the mechanism proposed in [7], referred to as NDM. We have compared these results with the performance achieved by the adaptive routing algorithm presented in [13] as MA-2vc and the up/down routing algorithm [12].

4.1. Network Model

Instead of using an analytical model, we used a simulator to evaluate the deadlock recovery and avoidance schemes. We have measured message latency and throughput.

Message latency should also include software overhead at source and destination workstations. Traditionally, it has been assumed that this overhead has a main influence on NOW performance. Recently, the performance evaluation of the message passing library implementation for Myrinet networks, known as BIP [3], has showed that overhead software is below 5 microseconds (4.3 microseconds for 0 bytes messages). Taking into account the current bandwidth of Myrinet networks, equal to 160MB/s, 800 bytes messages would be enough for making the hardware latency of messages, between adjacent switches, equal to the overhead software. Moreover, given that only a fraction of the maximum bandwidth is used, the message length could be lower to 800 bytes. In [6], the communication characteristics of three different application under the MPI programming model on an IBM SP2 have been analyzed. The communication patterns of these applications is formed by very long messages (average length greater than 30 KB). Thus, we can assume that the overhead software influence on final message latency will not be important, and we will only consider network hardware latency in this study.

In the switch model used, we have assumed that it takes one clock cycle to compute the routing algorithm, one clock cycle to transmit one flit across the internal crossbar and also that the switch needs one clock cycle to decode the control flits. Propagation time along the physical channel has been fixed to four cycles, while data are injected into the physical channel, which is pipelined, at a rate of one flit per cycle. According to [14], the input buffer size has been set to 27 flits, since fly time is four cycles (27 flits because 27 cycles is three times the maximum round trip delay plus the time needed to decode the control flits). The size of the deadlock buffer has also been set to 27 flits. With respect to the output buffer size, we have set it to four flits.

Each switch has a routing control unit that selects the output channel for a message as a function of its destination workstation, the input channel and the output channel status. Table look-up routing is used. The routing control unit can only process one message header at a time. It is assigned to waiting messages in a demand-slotted round-robin fashion. When a message gets the routing control unit but it cannot be routed because all the alternative output channels are busy, it must wait in the input buffer until its next turn. A crossbar inside the switch allows multiple messages traversing it simultaneously without interference. It is configured by the routing control unit each time a successful routing is made. We have studied the performance of the deadlock recovery scheme in networks with one and two virtual channels per physical channel.

With respect to the network model, network topology has been generated randomly and is completely irregular. For the sake of simplicity, all the switches in the network have the same size. We have assumed 8-port switches. Four of the ports will be used to connect to different processors and the other four ports are used to connect to other switches.

We have evaluated the full range of traffic, from low load to saturation. On the other hand, we have considered that message destination is randomly chosen among all the workstations in the network. For message length, 16-flit, 64-flit, 128-flit, and 256-flit messages were considered. Also, we have run simulations for mixed traffic composed of 16-flit and 128-flit messages, with 10%, 30%, 50%, and 70% short messages. For network size, 16-switch, 32-switch, and 64-switch networks were evaluated. The simulations were run for a number of cycles high enough to deliver 100,000 messages after the network reached the steady state.

4.2. Simulation Results

Figure 3(a) shows the average message latency for a network with 32 switches and one virtual channel per physical channel. Disha is implemented using the timeout deadlock detection mechanism. We analyzed timeouts ranging from

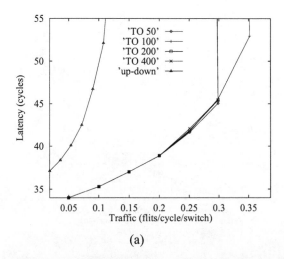

(a)

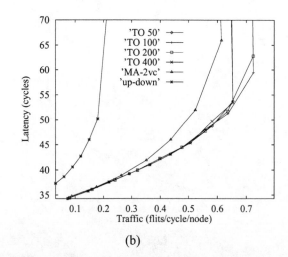

(b)

Figure 3. Message latency versus traffic for Disha when using the timeout detection mechanism in a network with 32 switches. Message length is 16 flits. (a) 1 virtual channel. (b) 2 virtual channels.

50 to 10,000 cycles, although only results for 50, 100, 200, and 400 cycles are plotted. Results for the up/down routing algorithm are also presented. Message length is 16 flits. As can be seen, the Disha mechanism reduces latency and increases throughput significantly, due to the use of fully adaptive minimal routing. The best results are achieved when the timeout is tuned to 100 cycles. For the remaining timeouts, the behavior of the network is similar.

Figure 3(b) shows the results for a 32-switch network and two virtual channels per physical channel when message length is 16 flits. As above, only results for timeouts equal to 50, 100, 200, and 400 cycles are displayed. For comparison purposes, results for a network that implements the up/down routing scheme with two virtual channels per physical channel and results for the MA-2vc routing algorithm are displayed. As can be seen, improvement in performance with respect to the up/down routing algorithm is slightly greater than when only one virtual channel is used. This is due to the fact that the frequency of deadlock decreases when more resources (virtual channels) are used, thus improving the behavior of Disha. However, when compared with the MA-2vc routing algorithm, Disha benefits are small. The reason is that the MA-2vc scheme provides minimal routing in most cases when network load is low. As shown in the figure, Disha achieves a lower message latency only from medium to high network load. This is due to the fact that in this range the MA-2vc adaptive virtual channel (new channel) begins to saturate and messages are routed along the up/down virtual channel (original channel), which does not provide minimal routing. On the other hand, simulation results indicate that the number of messages detected as deadlocked remains small until saturation. How-

ever, messages often must wait for a long period of time due to congestion. This contributes to make differences in performance small. Comparing the results in Figure 3(b) with the results presented in [15], we can conclude that the benefits of Disha when applied to a network with two virtual channels are smaller than the benefits obtained when the number of virtual channels per physical channel is increased from two to three in the MA routing algorithm. This means that with three virtual channels, the MA routing algorithm is able to provide minimal routing in most cases. However, the internal crossbar size is much smaller when using Disha than when using MA with three virtual channels.

Figures 4(a) and 4(b) display the average message latency for a network with 32 switches and one and two virtual channels per physical channel, respectively, when message length is 128 flits. Displayed timeouts range from 200 to 800 cycles, although simulated timeouts range from 200 to 10,000. Results are similar to those obtained when message length is 16 flits. The only difference is that in this case the achieved throughput is slightly higher, especially when one virtual channel is used, due to a better use of the input buffer. When message length is 64 or 256 flits (not shown), the maximum achieved throughput is similar to the 128-flit message case. In the case of mixed traffic (16 and 128 flit messages), results are also similar. Moreover, we have observed that the optimal timeout value is roughly four times the message length. This timeout is the optimal from the point of view of maximum throughput achieved, although it slightly increases latency near saturation. In the case of mixed traffic, the optimal value is approximately four times the maximum message length.

Figure 5 shows the behavior of Disha for 16, 32, and 64-

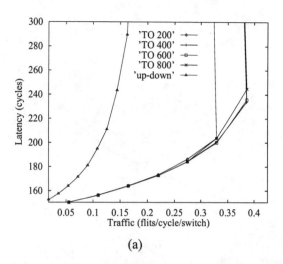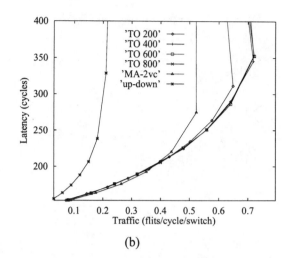

(a)   (b)

Figure 4. Message latency versus traffic for Disha when using the timeout detection mechanism in a network with 32 switches. Message length is 128 flits. (a) 1 virtual channel. (b) 2 virtual channels.

switch networks when message length is 128 flits, and compares it with the behavior of a deadlock avoidance-based routing algorithm. The timeout used is 400 cycles, since this is the one that achieves the best performance for 128-flit messages. Figure 5(a) shows the case of a network with one virtual channel per physical channel. As network size increases, the benefits of using Disha also increase. In the case of a small network (16 switches), using Disha (labeled in Figure 5 as "16 Disha") achieves a 50% improvement in throughput with respect to the up/down routing algorithm. In the case of medium-sized networks, throughput increases by a factor of 2.6, while in large networks (64 switches), improvement factor is about 3.5. For each network size, the Disha mechanism achieves lower latency than up/down routing. On the other hand, Figure 5(b) shows the case for a network with two virtual channels per physical channel. In this case, Disha is compared with the MA-2vc routing algorithm. For small networks, using Disha does not improve performance. In medium and large networks Disha improves performance but improvement is much smaller than for networks with one virtual channel. The reason is that in small networks, messages routed with the MA2-vc algorithm follow minimal paths in most cases. Disha behaves like an additional fully adaptive virtual channel. As shown in [15], adding a third virtual channel to the MA-2vc algorithm does not improve performance in small networks, and increases throughput only in medium and large networks. When applying Disha to irregular networks, the increase in performance is comparable to the increase obtained when adding a fully adaptive virtual channel.

We have also evaluated Disha with the NDM deadlock detection mechanism [7]. We have simulated the NDM

mechanism with thresholds of 16, 32, 64, 128, and 256 cycles for different message lengths and network sizes. In general, there is no significant difference with respect to the results obtained with the timeout mechanism. The reason is that for low load no deadlock occurs. As network load increases, the NDM mechanism achieves a slightly lower latency than the timeout mechanism since some false deadlocks are detected when using timeouts. When the network is close to saturation, the NDM mechanism detects approximately one tenth of the false deadlocks detected by the timeout mechanism. However, since the number of detected deadlocks is high, the recovery paths provided by Disha become congested, and none of the mechanisms are able to achieve higher throughput.

5. Conclusions

In this paper, we have analyzed the application of a progressive deadlock recovery technique, known as Disha Concurrent [2], to NOWs.

In order to support Disha in networks with irregular topology, we have proposed a new switch organization that includes two deadlock buffers (central buffers) per switch. These buffers form a Disha recovery network that uses the up/down routing scheme. We have proved that this Disha recovery network is deadlock-free and is always able to recover from deadlock. Also, a flow control protocol that matches the requirements of NOWs and supports the new switch organization has been proposed.

Performance evaluation shows that Disha reduces latency and increases throughput significantly with regard to current deadlock avoidance techniques [12, 13], especially

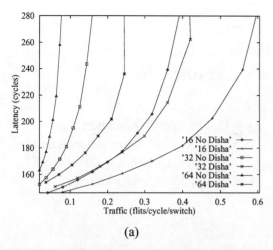

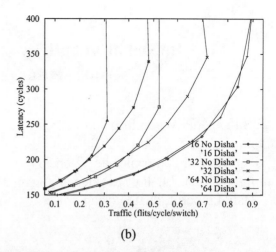

(a)   (b)

Figure 5. Evolution of the performance of Disha with network size. Message length is 128 flits and timeout is 400 cycles. (a) Network with 1 virtual channel. (b) Network with 2 virtual channels.

in medium and large networks, due to the fact that all of the messages follow minimal paths. Network throughput is increased by a factor of up to 3.5. As it has been shown, Disha behaves as an additional fully adaptive minimal virtual channel. In fact, the benefits of applying Disha are similar to the benefits obtained when an additional virtual channel per physical channel is introduced in the network. However, the internal crossbar size is much smaller when using Disha. Thus, Disha provides a feasible mechanism to improve performance without the need for adding more virtual channels, while adding a simple hardware support.

References

[1] Anjan K. V. et al., "DISHA: A deadlock recovery scheme for fully adaptive routing," in *Proc. of the 9th Int. Parallel Processing Symp.*, Apr. 1995.

[2] Anjan K. V., T. M. Pinkston and J. Duato, "Generalized theory for deadlock-free adaptive routing and its application to Disha concurrent," in *Proc. of the 10nd Int. Parallel Processing Symp.*, Apr. 1996.

[3] Available at http://lhpca.univ-lyon1.fr/bip.html

[4] N. J. Boden et al., "Myrinet - A gigabit per second local area network," *IEEE Micro*, pp. 29–36, Feb. 1995.

[5] R. Horst, "ServerNet deadlock avoidance and fractahedral topologies," in *Proc. of the Int. Parallel Processing Symp.*, pp. 274–280, Apr. 1996.

[6] S. Karlsson and M. Brorsson, "A comparative Characterization of Communication Patterns in Applications Using MPI and Shared Memory on an IBM SP2, 2nd Int. Workshop, CANPC, Jan. 1998

[7] J. M. Martínez et al., "Sofware-based deadlock recovery technique for true fully adaptive routing in wormhole networks," in *ICPP*, Aug. 1997.

[8] T. M. Pinkston et al., "WARRP core: optoelectronic implementation of network-router deadlock-handling mechanisms," in *Applied Optics*, Jan. 1998.

[9] T. M. Pinkston and S. Warnakulasuriya, "On deadlocks in interconnection networks," in *Proc. of the 24th Int. Symp. on Computer Architecture*, June 1997.

[10] W. Qiao and L. M. Ni, "Adaptive routing in irregular networks using cut-through switches," in *Proc. of the 1996 Int. Conf. on Parallel Processing*, Aug. 1996.

[11] D. S. Reeves, E. F. Gehringer and A. Chandiramani, "Adaptive routing and deadlock recovery: A simulation study," in *Proc. of the 4th Conf. on Hypercube Concurrent Computers and Applications*, Mar. 1989.

[12] M. D. Schroeder et al., "Autonet: A high-speed, self-configuring local area network using point-to-point links," SRC research report 59, DEC, Apr. 1990.

[13] F. Silla et al., "Improving the Efficiency of Adaptive Routing in Networks with Irregular Topology," in *1997 Int. Conf. on High Perf. Computing*, Dec. 1997.

[14] F. Silla and J. Duato, "On the Use of Virtual Channels in Networks of Workstations with Irregular Topology," in *1997 Parallel Computing, Routing, and Communication Workshop*, June 1997.

[15] F. Silla and J. Duato, "Tuning the Number of Virtual Channels in Networks of Workstations with Irregular Topology," in *10th Int. Conf. on Parallel and Dist. Computing Syst.*, Oct. 1997.

Impact of Adaptivity on the Behavior of Networks of Workstations under Bursty Traffic *

F. Silla, M. P. Malumbres and J. Duato
Dpto. Inf. de Sistemas y Computadores
Universidad Politécnica de Valencia
Camino de Vera, 14, 46071–Valencia, Spain
{fsilla,mperez,jduato}@gap.upv.es

D. Dai and D. K. Panda
Dept. of Computer and Information Science
Ohio State University, Columbus, OH 43210-1277
{dai,panda}@cis.ohio-state.edu

Abstract

Networks of workstations (NOWs) are becoming increasingly popular as an alternative to parallel computers. Typically, these networks present irregular topologies, providing the wiring flexibility, scalability, and incremental expansion capability required in this environment. Similar to the evolution of parallel computers, NOWs are also evolving from distributed memory to shared memory. However, distances between processors are longer in NOWs, leading to higher message latency and lower network bandwidth. Therefore, we can expect the network to be a bottleneck when executing some parallel applications on a NOW supporting a shared-memory programming paradigm.

In this paper we analyze whether the interconnection network in a NOW is able to efficiently handle the traffic generated in a DSM with the same number of processors. We evaluate the behavior of a NOW using application traces captured during the execution of several SPLASH2 applications on a DSM simulator. We show through simulation that the adaptive routing algorithm previously proposed by us almost eliminates network saturation due to its ability to support a higher sustained throughput. Therefore, adaptive routing becomes a key design issue to achieve similar performance in NOWs and tightly-coupled DSMs.

1. Introduction

Research in parallel computers has focused on multicomputers and multiprocessors during the last decades. Large-scale parallel computers evolved from multicomputers to distributed shared-memory multiprocessors, either with cache coherence or without cache coherence. The higher architectural complexity required to provide a sin-gle memory address space is worth its cost. It provides a simpler programming model in which communication is achieved by accessing shared memory locations, and synchronization is performed by using barriers. Additionally, sequential applications that require a large amount of memory to be executed efficiently can be directly ported to DSMs. In general, this is not possible in a multicomputer because each processor has a relatively small local memory.

Due to the increasing computation power of microprocessors and the high cost of parallel computers, networks of workstations (NOWs) are being considered as a cost-effective alternative for small-scale parallel computing. NOWs do not provide the computing capacity available in multicomputers and multiprocessors, but they meet the needs of a great variety of parallel computing problems at a lower cost. Moreover, the nature of NOWs makes them scalable and allows an incremental expansion of the system.

Recent network products, like Autonet [17], Myrinet [1], and ServerNet [11], use point-to-point links between switching elements instead of the traditional shared mediums (like Ethernet) used in computer networks. These NOWs usually present an irregular topology as a consequence of the needs in a local area network. Moreover, instead of being a direct network, NOWs are often arranged as switch-based interconnects, thus reducing the number of switches required for a given number of processors.

Research in NOWs is advancing relatively fast because the research effort made on parallel computers is now being transferred to this raising environment.

As a natural evolution from local area networks, most interconnects for NOWs only provide support for message-passing. These networks consist of a network interface card that is plugged into the I/O bus of each workstation, and one or more switches interconnecting the interface cards through point-to-point links [1]. In general, the bandwidth provided by currently available interface cards and switches is high enough for the requirements of message-passing ap-

*This work was supported by the Spanish CICYT under Grant TIC97–0897–C04–01

plications. However, the performance of some parallel applications is limited by message latency. Most of this latency is due to the software messaging layer. Several attempts have been made to reduce this bottleneck [8].

As parallel computers, NOWs are also evolving from distributed memory to shared memory. Some commercial interface cards support the shared-memory programming model. This is the case for the SCI-PCI adapter from Dolphin [5]. However, this card does not support cache coherence in hardware because memory traffic cannot be seen from the I/O bus. Also, interface cards are reaching the limits of I/O buses[1]. In order to provide a higher bandwidth and lower latency, some researchers have started to develop interface cards that are plugged into the memory bus. Some experimental NOWs provide support for shared-memory [16], also implementing a cache-coherence protocol that allows out-of-order delivery of messages.

2. Motivation

A decade ago, the invention of wormhole switching led to very fast interconnection networks. As a consequence, the interconnection network was no longer the bottleneck in a multicomputer. However, DSMs[2] require faster interconnection networks than multicomputers because messages are shorter (a typical message consists of a cache line and some control information) and much more frequent. While the interconnection network is not the bottleneck yet, some researchers began to report that a lower latency [21] and a higher network bandwidth [2] may significantly reduce the execution time of several parallel applications. As processor clock frequency is increasing at a faster rate than network bandwidth, the interconnection network may become a bottleneck within the next few years [7].

The situation is more critical for NOWs supporting a single memory address space. Physical distance between processors is higher in NOWs than in DSMs, leading to higher latency (due to the propagation delay) and lower bandwidth (due to the use of narrower links)[3]. Additionally, the use of irregular topologies makes routing and deadlock handling much more complex. Existing routing algorithms are either deterministic [1] or provide some degree of adaptivity [17]. They provide non-minimal paths and an unbalanced use of physical links. As a consequence channel utilization is low, reducing the effective network bandwidth even more. Therefore, we can expect the network to be a bottle-

neck when executing some parallel applications on a NOW supporting a shared-memory programming paradigm. Taking into account that NOWs are evolving from distributed memory to shared memory, it is important to analyze the behavior of parallel applications on these machines, also providing solutions to alleviate the bottleneck.

In this paper, we take on such a challenge. We analyze whether the interconnection network in a NOW is able to handle the traffic supported by the network in a DSM when executing some parallel applications. In particular, we evaluate different routing algorithms on NOWs with irregular topology, using traces from parallel applications. These traces were captured from the execution of SPLASH2 applications (Barnes-Hut, Water, Radix, and LU) on a DSM simulator with a hardware cache-coherence protocol. The main goal of this study is to determine whether the interconnection network in a NOW becomes a bottleneck when executing the same applications. Therefore, we fed the network in a simulated NOW with the same traces captured from the execution of those applications in a DSM simulator. We show that the slower interconnection network available in a NOW becomes a bottleneck, saturating during some periods of time. The use of adaptive routing algorithms, derived by using a methodology previously developed by us [20] helps to alleviate such bottlenecks.

The main contribution of this paper is a study of the network behavior in a NOW under the traffic generated by several shared-memory parallel benchmarks executed on a DSM simulator with the same processors. This study provided the following insights:

- Network traffic is bursty, as other studies showed. Shared-memory parallel applications are usually programmed by splitting computation into several steps. At the end of each step, processes update global variables and synchronize, leading to bursty traffic.

- Peak traffic saturates the network for all the applications we analyzed when using routing algorithms from commercial systems. The lower effective network bandwidth available in a NOW compared to a DSM leads to saturation. Therefore, execution time will be longer in a NOW, even if it uses the same processors, than in a DSM with the same number of nodes.

- Architectural improvements that increase channel utilization and throughput, like adaptive routing and virtual channels, considerably reduce the time duration when the network is saturated. Therefore, this architectural improvements allow NOWs to achieve performance similar to a DSM with the same number of processors.

Section 3 presents the trace mechanism used to evaluate interconnection networks. In Section 4, the performance of

---

[1] For example, link bandwidth in Myrinet is 160 Mbytes/s. ServerNet II [9] provides links with 1 Gigabit/s peak bandwidth. However, a 32-bit PCI bus running at 33 MHz only achieves a peak bandwidth of 133 Mbytes/s.

[2] Throughout this paper, the terminology 'DSM' is used to refer to tightly-coupled distributed shared memory systems like DASH, FLASH, SGI Origin, etc.

[3] For example, Cray T3E routers [19] use 14 data wires per link. ServerNet II [9] and Myrinet [1] use serial and 8-bit links, respectively.

different routing algorithms is evaluated using application traces. Finally, in Section 5 some conclusions are drawn.

3. A Simulation Model Based on Application Message Traces

In general, the interconnection network is not the bottleneck in current DSM systems. Therefore, techniques that improve network throughput are of little interest in this environment [21]. Nowadays, DSMs and NOWs are designed by using the same processors. The main architectural differences between these machines are the interconnection network and communication assisting circuitry such as the node controller. In this paper, we focus on the network. In a NOW, links are usually longer and narrower than in a DSM, therefore increasing latency and reducing bandwidth. However, the lower message latency achieved by the network in a DSM may have a very small impact on the execution time of parallel applications. In general, performance could be reasonably comparable in a DSM and a NOW when using the same processors, unless the interconnection network saturates. If it saturates, messages are queued in the injection queue at the source nodes, drastically increasing message latency and seriously degrading performance. The following question arises: Is the interconnection network the bottleneck in a NOW? Will the network in a NOW be able to handle the traffic supported by the network in a DSM without saturating? Note that only a fraction of the network bandwidth is used in a DSM during the execution of parallel applications [21]. Therefore, despite the lower effective bandwidth provided by a NOW, this bandwidth may be enough for the requirements of parallel applications.

To answer the above question, we gathered message traces at the node controller during the execution of several parallel applications on an execution-driven DSM simulator. Then, we fed the interconnection networks of a NOW with those traces in order to analyze if it can handle the same amount of traffic without saturating. In particular, we evaluated the performance of several routing algorithms for irregular networks by using message traces generated by an execution-driven simulation of several SPLASH2 benchmark applications.

The simulated hardware DSM system used an architecture similar to the FLASH machine [12]. The system had 64 nodes connected by an 8×8 mesh with a bandwidth of 400 MB/s/link and 15 ns per-hop delay. The processor in each node was assumed to be a 200 MHz single-issue microprocessor with a perfect instruction cache and a 128 KB 2-way set associative data cache with a line size of 64 bytes. The cache was assumed to operate in dual-port mode using write-back and write-allocate policies. The instruction latencies, issue rules, and memory interface were modeled based on the DLX design [10]. The memory bus was

assumed to be 8 bytes wide. On a memory block access, the first word of the block was assumed to be returned in 30 processor cycles; the successive words follow in a pipelined fashion. The machine used a full-mapped, invalidation-based directory coherence protocol [13]. The node controller took 14 cycles to process an incoming (or outgoing) request or reply. The network interface took 15 cycles to construct and 8 cycles to dispatch a message. The synchronization protocol assumed was queuing based similar to the one used in DASH [14]. Our simulated architecture used the sequential memory consistency model. A cache miss stalls the processor until the critical word of data is returned.

Four applications Barnes, LU, Radix, and Water, all ported from the SPLASH2 suite [22] were used in this study. The problem sizes (listed in Table 1) for the applications were selected with two considerations. First, they are reasonably large to generate realistic network behavior. Second, the sizes of resulting trace files are manageable.

Application	Problem Size
Barnes-Hut	$8K$ particles, $\theta = 1.0$, 4 time steps
LU	512×512 doubles, 8×8 blocks,
Radix	$1M$ keys, $1K$ radix, max $1M$
Water	512 molecules, 4 time steps

Table 1. Applications and their input sizes.

Figure 1 shows the total number of messages injected into the network per time unit. Note that the plot shows the total number of messages generated by all the processors during each 500,000-cycle time interval. As can be seen in Figure 1(a), there are several bursts of traffic during the execution of the Barnes-Hut application. This bursty traffic may instantly saturate the network. If saturation occurs, messages are stored in an injection queue at the source node. Thus, depending on the ability of the network to process this kind of traffic, the overall execution time may be considerably affected. Note that the shared tree is completed at the end of each burst and the processors are not able to proceed until this phase finishes. Figure 1 also shows the traffic pattern of the Water, LU, and Radix applications. Bursty traffic can also be observed in these applications as well.

4. Performance Evaluation

In this section, we compare the performance of the up/down routing scheme (UD) [17] and our minimal adaptive (MA-2VC) routing algorithm [20]. The latter requires two virtual channels per physical channel. In order to make a fair comparison, we have also evaluated the up/down routing algorithm with two virtual channels (UD-2VC).

Our simulator models the network at the flit level. We used traces to drive the simulator. The performance mea-

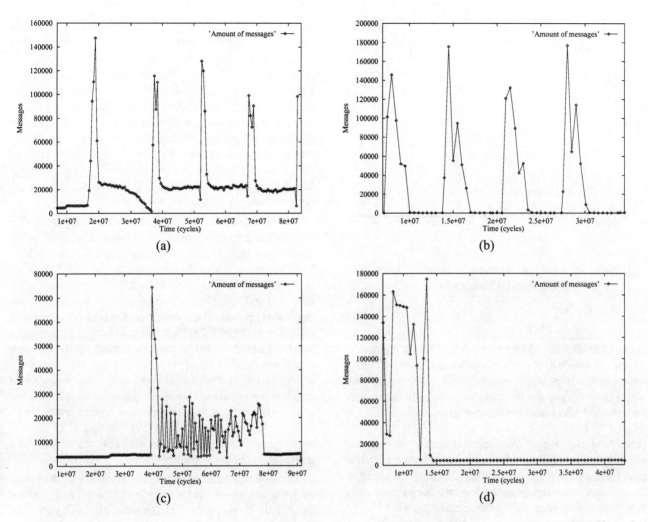

Figure 1. Number of messages injected during the execution time of (a) Barnes, (b) Water, (c) LU, and (d) Radix applications.

sure is message latency because total execution time is determined by the trace file. Message latency lasts since the message is queued at the network interface until its last flit is received at the destination node. It is measured in clock cycles. We obtained the average message latency for each set of 50,000 received messages during program execution. When traffic is intense, a more detailed analysis is required. Thus, when presenting simulation results we will make a zoom of the plot in the critical points by gathering measurements every 5,000 received messages.

As can be seen in Figure 1, there are time intervals in which the message injection rate increases considerably. At these points some messages would be lost if the queues were not deep enough. The time spent waiting on the source queue is also considered in the message latency. We consider the network becomes saturated when the average num-

ber of messages stored in these queues is higher than one.

With respect to the network model, the network is composed of a set of switches. Network topology is completely irregular was generated randomly. For the sake of simplicity, we assumed that there are exactly 4 processors connected to each switch. Also, two neighboring switches are connected by a single link. Finally, all the switches in the network have the same size. We assumed that each switch has 4 ports available to connect to other switches.

4.1. Simulation Results

Figure 2 shows the average message latency in each time interval versus time during the Barnes-Hut execution for the three routing algorithms (UD, UD-2VC, and MA-2VC) on a network with 64 processing elements and 16 switches. Each processor has one injection channel. As seen, message

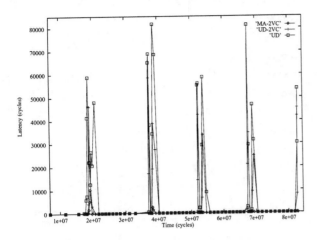

Figure 2. Average message latency versus time during Barnes-Hut execution.

latency remains very low for the three routing algorithms during the whole execution except for five short periods of time, where it increases considerably. Comparing this figure with Figure 1(a), it can be seen that these saturation points correspond to the bursty points mentioned in Section 3. Let us analyze saturation in more detail. The UD routing algorithm produces a very high latency at these points, as well as the UD-2VC routing scheme, which achieves a slightly lower latency. However, the MA-2VC routing algorithm reduces latency drastically in the first two bursty points and even avoids saturation during the remaining ones.

The scale in Figure 2 does not allow us to study the differences in latency when the interconnection network is not heavily loaded. Also, the behavior during the saturation points cannot be clearly seen. We could have used logarithmic scale in the Y axis in order to show these issues. However, after trying with logarithmic scale, we realized that they were difficult to study and, in any case, they did not clearly show the behavior of the routing algorithms during saturation. Therefore, the plots in Figure 3 are zooms that display all these issues properly. Note that in these plots, measures are taken every 5,000 received messages instead of every 50,000 messages as in Figure 2. The consequence is that sudden spikes in latency are not hidden because latency data represented in the plots are the average from a fewer amount of messages. Thus, these plots show the response of the interconnection network more accurately than the plot in Figure 2. This remark is also valid for the zooms of the other SPLASH2 applications shown in this paper.

Figure 3(a) — a detail of the bottom part of Figure 2 — shows the differences in latency when the network is not heavily loaded. As can be seen in this figure, the three routing schemes behave similarly for low loads, as it was ex-

pected after the study in [20]. The UD routing algorithm achieves the highest latency, as expected, while the lowest latency is achieved by the MA-2VC routing algorithm. However, this difference is not significant because the highest difference is about five clock cycles. It is interesting to compare these latencies with the theoretical base latency for wormhole in the absence of contention, which is about 50 cycles for the average distance between nodes and the average message length in the traces. The similarity between the theoretical base latency and the latency obtained in the simulations indicates that during these periods of time the network load is really low.

Figure 3(b) is a zoom of the first saturation point in Figure 2. It can be seen that the UD routing scheme needs seven times more time to process this traffic peak than the MA-2VC algorithm. Also, with respect to the UD-2VC algorithm, MA-2VC behaves more than four times faster. Figures 3(c) and 3(d) show similar results for the second and third bursty points. These results confirm the conclusions in [20], where the MA-2VC algorithm achieved a throughput several times greater than the UD routing algorithm using a uniform distribution of message destinations. However, differences in throughput are more noticeable when application traces are used. This result indicates that there are hot spots in the network due to repetitive communication patterns. In this situation, the MA-2VC routing algorithm behaves comparatively better than with uniform traffic, since it is a fully adaptive algorithm.

An issue that needs some specific study is why the bursty traffic spikes are so hard to handle by the different routing algorithms, specially the UD algorithm. From Figure 1(a), we can see that the injection rate never exceeds 200,000 messages per interval of 500,000 cycles, with 64 processors and 16 switches. This is only a rate of 1 msg/proc/160 cycles. Moreover, messages in a DSM machine are small (they are control messages and cache lines), so why the spikes are so difficult to handle?. We have analyzed the message length distribution in the trace file. Short messages (5 bytes) represent 61.42% of the messages, while long messages (69 bytes) account for 38.57% of the total number of messages. Therefore, the average message length is 29.68 bytes. Taking measures at 5,000 cycle intervals, the maximum amount of information injected into the network per interval is 96,861 bytes. This means an injection rate of 1.21 bytes/switch/cycle. However, simulations carried out with synthetic load and the message length distribution mentioned above show that a network consisting of 16 switches using the UD routing algorithm saturates at an injection rate of 0.37 bytes/switch/cycle. As a consequence, the network becomes completely saturated.

In the case of the other SPLASH2 applications, similar results were obtained when their traces were used to drive the simulator. Figures 4 and 5 show the simulation results

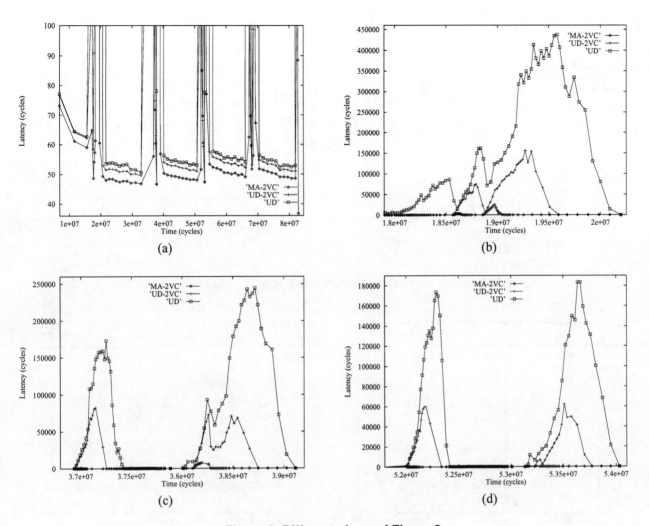

Figure 3. Different views of Figure 2.

for the Water and LU applications, respectively (results for Radix are not shown to save space). Two plots are shown for each application. The first one displays the overall application behavior, and the second one presents a detail of one of the bursty points. In general, it can be seen that the UD routing algorithm is not able to manage the total traffic generated by the processors in the saturation periods, reaching excessive latency values. On the other hand, the UD-2VC behaves better than UD, but the network also saturates. Thus, the use of virtual channels, by itself, does not solve the problem. However, the MA-2VC routing algorithm avoids the network saturation at these points for all the applications under study. Although the figures do not accurately show the behavior of MA-2VC at the bursty points, this routing algorithm never saturates the network for these three applications. In particular, at Figure 4(b), we can see the second bursty point, and the maximum latency values achieved by MA-2VC, UD-2VC, and UD are 60, 31,700,

and 300,000 respectively. This shows the importance of using a minimal adaptive routing scheme.

These results are very important from an architectural point of view. As mentioned, NOWs are migrating from distributed memory to shared memory. This evolution needs faster interconnection networks. As shown above, current NOWs are not ready to support the traffic generated by shared-memory applications. The introduction of virtual channels and a minimal routing algorithm like the MA-2VC algorithm contribute to meet the requirements of NOWs.

5. Conclusions

Networks of workstations are becoming increasingly popular as a cost-effective alternative to parallel computers. Typically, these networks connect processors using irregular topologies [1, 11]. Irregularity provides the wiring flexibility, scalability and incremental expansion capabil-

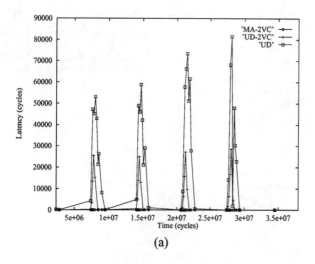

(a)

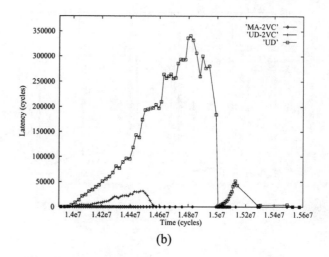

(b)

Figure 4. Average message latency versus time during Water execution.

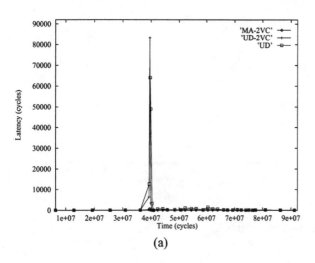

(a)

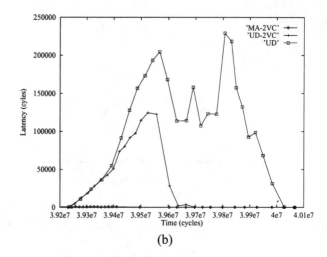

(b)

Figure 5. Average message latency versus time during LU execution.

ity required in this environment. Similar to the evolution of parallel computers, NOWs are also evolving from distributed memory to shared memory. Some commercial interface cards support the shared-memory programming model [5]. Some experimental NOWs provide support for shared-memory [16], also implementing a cache-coherence protocol that allows out-of-order delivery of messages.

In this paper we analyzed whether a NOW with irregular topology is able to handle the traffic supported by the interconnection network in a DSM with the same number of processors. This analysis has been performed by simulating the behavior of networks with irregular topology, using traces from parallel applications. These traces were captured from the execution of SPLASH2 applications (Barnes-Hut, Water, Radix, and LU) on a distributed shared-memory multi-

processor (DSM) simulator with 64 processors and a hardware cache-coherence protocol. We studied the network behavior using different routing algorithms, highlighting the application requirements with respect to the services provided by the network. This study provided the following insights:

- Network traffic is bursty, as already known.
- In the parallel applications we analyzed, peak traffic saturates the network for all the applications when using routing algorithms from commercial systems. Therefore, the lower effective bandwidth provided by the network in a NOW is not enough to achieve the same performance as in a DSM.
- Architectural improvements that increase channel utilization and throughput, like adaptive routing and

virtual channels, considerably reduce network contention and message latency. Therefore, these architectural improvements allow a NOW to achieve performance similar to that of a DSM with the same number of processors.

In summary, this paper shows that several parallel applications for shared-memory machines produce bursty traffic, and that our fully adaptive routing algorithm handles bursty traffic much more efficiently than the up/down routing algorithm with the same network parameters. Therefore, the use of fully adaptive routing algorithms and virtual channels may considerably improve performance when the applications tend to saturate the network at some point during the execution. As a consequence, the use of fully adaptive routing and virtual channels may considerably reduce the total application execution time in a NOW.

As for future work, we plan to develop a complete DSM testbed that includes our irregular network simulator, so that we could estimate the reduction of total application execution time when fully adaptive routing algorithms are used.

References

[1] N. J. Boden et al., "Myrinet - A gigabit per second local area network," *IEEE Micro*, Feb. 1995.

[2] G. T. Byrd et al., "Evaluation of communication mechanisms in invalidate-based shared memory multiprocessors," in *Proc. of the 1997 PCRCW*, June 1997.

[3] D. Dai and D. K. Panda. "Reducing Cache Invalidation Overheads in Wormhole DSMs Using Multidestination Message Passing, in *Int. Conf. on Parallel Processing*, Aug 1996.

[4] D. Dai and D. K. Panda, "How we can design better networks for DSM Systems?," in *Proceedings of the 1997 Parallel Computer Routing and Communication Workshop*, June 1997.

[5] Dolphin, *The Dolphin SCI Interconnect*, available at http://www.dolphinics.no.

[6] J. Duato, "On the design of deadlock-free adaptive routing algorithms for multicomputers: Design methodologies," in *Proc. of Parallel Architectures and Languages Europe 91*, June 1991.

[7] J. Duato, S. Yalamanchili and L. M. Ni, *Interconnection Networks: An Engineering Approach*. IEEE Computer Society Press, 1997.

[8] T. von Eicken et al., "Active messages: A mechanism for integrated communication and computation," in *Proc. of the 19th Int. Symp. on Computer Architecture*, June 1992.

[9] D. Garcia, "Servernet II," in *1997 Parallel Computer Routing and Communication Workshop*, June 1997.

[10] J. L. Hennessy and D. Patterson. *Computer Architecture: A Quantitative Approach*, Morgan Kaufmann, 1990.

[11] R. Horst, "ServerNet deadlock avoidance and fractahedral topologies," in *Proc. of the Int. Parallel Processing Symp.*, Apr. 1996.

[12] J. Kuskin et al, "The Stanford FLASH Multiprocessor, in *Proc. of the Int. Symp. on Computer Architecture*, 1994.

[13] D. Lenoski et al, "The Directory-Based Cache Coherence Protocol for the DASH Multiprocessor, in *Proc. of the 17th Annual Symp. on Computer Architecture*, May 1990.

[14] D. Lenoski, et al., "The Stanford DASH multiprocessor," *IEEE Computer*, vol. 25, no. 3, March 1992.

[15] J. Miguel, et al., "Assessing the performance of the new IBM SP2 communication subsystem," Technical Report 96–06–01, Department of Electrical and Computer Engineering, University of California, Irvine, June 1996.

[16] A. G. Nowatzyk, et al., "S-Connect: From networks of workstations to supercomputer performance," *Proc. of the 22nd Int. Symp. on Comp. Architecture*, June 1995.

[17] M. D. Schroeder et al., "Autonet: A high-speed, self-configuring local area network using point-to-point links," Technical Report SRC research report 59, DEC, April 1990.

[18] S. L. Scott and G. Thorson, "Optimized routing in the Cray T3D," *Proc. of the Workshop on Parallel Computer Routing and Communication*, May 1994.

[19] S. L. Scott and G. Thorson, "The Cray T3E networks: adaptive routing in a high performance 3D torus," in *Proc. of Hot Interconnects IV*, Aug. 1996.

[20] F. Silla and J. Duato, "Improving the Efficiency of Adaptive Routing in Networks with Irregular Topology," in *1997 Int. Conf. on High Perf. Computing*, Dec. 1997.

[21] A. S. Vaidya et al., "Performance benefits of Virtual Channels and Adaptive Routing: An Application Driven Study," in *Int. Conf. on Supercomputing*, 1997

[22] S. C. Woo et al., "The SPLASH-2 Programs: Chracterization and Methodological Considerations, in *Int. Symp. on Computer Architecture*, 1995.

Implementation and Performance Evaluation of Locust

Manish Verma
Silicon Graphics Inc.
verma@engr.sgi.com

Tzi-cker Chiueh
Computer Science Department
State University of New York at Stony Brook
chiueh@cs.sunysb.edu

Abstract

Locust is a distributed shared virtual memory system that exploits compile-time data dependency information to address the issues of false sharing, cache coherence overhead, and affinity process scheduling. This paper reports the results and their analysis of a comprehensive performance evaluation study of the first Locust prototype, which is implemented on a 12-node Pentium cluster running FreeBSD and is fully operational for a year. The results show that for the set of regular programs tested, the performance of Locust is within 1-8% of that of message passing system implemented on the same hardware/software platform. The main performance gain of Locust as compared to existing weak cache consistency models mainly comes from the elimination of unnecessary synchronizations using the generational cache coherence protocol, and the function-shipping approach of implementing synchronization operations.

1. Introduction

Existing performance improvement techniques to distributed shared virtual memory (DSVM) systems are fundamentally based on the following principle: Exploit the application-specific semantics of the parallel programs so that temporary inconsistency does not lead to incorrect program execution. *Locust* [9], pushes this principle to the limit by exploiting the compile-time data dependency information directly. The thesis of the *Locust* project is that by exploiting the data dependency information of parallel applications, the performance of a DSVM system can closely approximate that of a message-passing system. In *Locust*, parallel programs are statically partitioned into indivisible tasks. Data dependencies among a parallel program's tasks are exploited in *Locust* to address the issues of false sharing, coherence maintenance, prefetching, and affinity scheduling. The novel architectural features of *Locust* include a *generation-based cache coherence* (GCC) protocol that eliminates unnecessary coherence traffic, a *producer-initiated data transfer* mechanism that minimizes the access delay of data con-

sumers, and a *function-shipping* synchronization mechanism that reduces synchronization-induced network traffic to its minimum. Because compilers may not be able to generate accurate data dependency information for all programs, *Locust* provides a generic write update/invalidate protocol called the UDD (Unknown Data Dependency) protocol to maintain cache coherence for those program segments whose data dependency information cannot be statically determined. In the general case, *Locust* allows switching between GCC and UDD protocols during the execution of a single parallel program.

We have successfully implemented the first *Locust* prototype, running under FreeBSD UNIX and on top of a set of Pentium-90 machines connected by a 100-Mbps/sec Fast Ethernet. To make efficient use of the network hardware, we also built a low-latency communications subsystem called *Pupa* [9] that bypasses the TCP/IP protocol stack. Although compiler-controlled cache coherence mechanisms [2] have been investigated by several researchers previously, to our knowledge *Locust* is one of the first, if not the first, successful complete implementations. In this paper, we focus on the results and analysis of a detailed performance evaluation study of the first prototype of *Locust*. Section 2 reviews previous works in this area to distinguish the unique aspects of *Locust*. Section 3 briefly describes the software architecture of *Locust* and its prototype implementation. Section 4 presents the detailed performance evaluation of *Locust*, and its comparison with other programming models implemented on the same hardware and operating system. Section 5 concludes this paper with a summary of the main results.

2. Related Work

Munin [1] classifies shared variables into different categories and uses different consistency maintenance mechanisms optimized for each category. It implements *release consistency* by enforcing consistency only at where synchronization operations are performed. Munin also supports a *multiple writer* protocol to allow multiple writes to the same page simultaneously without changing the program semantics. Treadmarks [6] is an off-shoot of Munin. Treadmarks is a user level implementation and uses a variant of release consistency called the *lazy release consistency*, which further reduces the coherence traffic by postponing sending data updates to nodes until they perform an acquire operation. A follow-on work [4] combines the parallelization compiler technology from Parascope and Treadmarks to improve the performance of DSVM by exploiting compile-time knowledge. The focus of this work is on message aggregation and reduction of synchronization overhead. *Locust*, in contrast, uses the generational cache coherence framework to unify all these optimizations. Utilizing the information available in an application program to design better coherence mechanism has been explored further in the Tempest [7] system. Although application-specific protocols enhance performance, they also burden the programmers with the responsibility of writing their own protocols. Midway [10] provided object-level granularity for coherence management. It supports the *entry consistency* model where every shared object is associated with a lock, and a thread is guaranteed a consistent view of the object when it acquires the lock associated with it. Midway employs a time-stamp based mechanism to keep track of what data associated with a particular lock have changed since a node last acquired that lock. This is in some sense similar to *Locust*'s generation number checking. The key difference is that Midway performs the check remotely while *Locust*'s check can be done completely locally. The SAM [8] system's *values* and *accumulators* are similar to our *producer-consumer* and *commutative-mutex* objects. There, the emphasis is on task parallelism and not data parallelism. Unlike SAM, *Locust* keeps versions of an object in the same storage. Applications do not need to explicitly specify which versions need to be used when nor at what time a particular version of an object is no longer needed. Although *Locust* doesn't specify any particular memory consistency model, the generation-based cache coherence scheme actually implements a weak consistency model constrained only by data dependency relations. *Locust*'s function-shipping synchronization mechanism is unique among all the systems we have examined so far. In addition, unlike *Locust*, where load balancing and cache coherence are integrated in a single framework, the issue of load balancing is rarely addressed in existing DSVM systems.

3. The Locust System

3.1. Programming Model

Locust targets at array-based scientific and engineering parallel applications written in high level parallel programming languages using the Single-Program-Multiple-Data (SPMD) model. A parallel program is statically partitioned into indivisible tasks. Tasks that are independent of one another and thus could be executed in parallel are grouped into *generations* or *phases*, which are also units of scheduling and execution. Tasks are assumed to be known at compile time. As a result, *Locust* cannot efficiently support programs that dynamically fork new tasks, or so-called *irregular* applications.

Data in parallel programs are annotated by programmers and grouped into three types - *constant*, *mutual-exclusion* and *producer-consumer*. Data items that are written once and never modified again are declared as *constants*, which are replicated at all nodes in the beginning of the execution. At most one task in a generation can write to a *producer-consumer* data item; other tasks in that generation can read it, but they can use the value of the data item from the previous generation. *Mutual-exclusion* objects are those that are explicitly protected by synchronization variables.

3.2. Cache Coherence

3.2.1. The GCC Protocol

Producer-consumer data are kept coherent using a generational cache coherence (GCC) protocol [2]. The basic idea of this scheme is based on the single assignment principle – whenever a shared data structure, say, A, gets updated, the system assigns a new name to it. Subsequent accesses to A are required to use the newest name. Consequently, the access to A from a node that had cached an earlier version of A will cause a cache miss because of name mismatch. Unlike other cache coherence mechanisms this scheme does not require explicit invalidation messages, thus reducing network traffic.

Every task is associated with a *task generation number* (TGN), which is the same as the phase number in which the task executes. Every data object is augmented with a *valid generation number* (VGN) attribute, which represents *the phase number until which the current value stored in the object remains valid*. When a shared object is updated, its VGN is changed to *the TGN of the generation in which the next update to this object would occur*. If a shared object is modified several times within a task, only the *last* write entails a modification of the object's VGN. Initially all shared objects have a VGN equal to 0, and the phase numbers start from 1, i.e, no task can have a TGN equal to 0.

During the execution of a task, the *first* read access to each shared object is preceded by a software check that compares the task's TGN with the object's VGN. If the task's TGN is larger than the object's VGN, the target objects are either not cached at this node or cached but stale. Otherwise, the most up-to-date version is available locally. In case the required version of the object is not available locally, the task blocks itself, passively waiting for the producer task to send it the most up-to-date value of that object. Computation continues when the required version becomes available. On a write, the new value of the object is sent to the tasks that would need it next, and the VGN of this object is set to the TGN of the task that would modify this object next. Note that only the *last* write to each object in a phase needs to modify the VGN and start a data transfer. Note that destinations of data updates are tasks and not nodes. This provides extra flexibility for scheduling and load balancing.

The benefits of the generational cache coherence mechanism are threefold. First, producer-initiated data transfer in *Locust* helps overlap communication and computation by sending the data to the consumers at the earliest moments, like message passing systems. Secondly, network traffic is reduced because of the elimination of unnecessary coherence traffic due to false sharing and sequential consistency. In addition, explicit request messages from the consumers are also avoided. Third, there is no need for barrier synchronization at the end of each phase because the generation numbers implicitly order the read/write operations from the tasks. As a result, tasks from different generations can execute simultaneously.

3.2.2. The UDD Protocol

Locust also provides a fall-back mechanism called the UDD protocol to maintain cache coherence during the execution of those code segments for which exact data dependencies can not be determined at compile time. The UDD protocol uses a weak consistency model similar to the *release consistency* [5] model. Each data item is associated with a "locking" data structure. Shared data items must be acquired/released before/after being manipulated. There are three acquire modes: *exclusive*, *non-exclusive* and *unprivileged*.

Acquiring a data item in either the exclusive or non-exclusive mode ensures that the value of the data item delivered to the acquirer is up to date. Howver, only when a node acquires a data item in the exclusive mode, it becomes its new *owner*. All exclusive and non-exclusive acquire and release operations must go through its current owner. Ownership change information is sent to all nodes caching the particular data item to facilitate subsequent acquire operations. Only *owners* can modify a data item. After the data item is modified, the owner node sends an update or invalidate message to only those nodes that are currently caching it, by exploiting data dependency information.

Acquiring a data item in the unprivileged mode does not guarantee data consistency. If a data item is cached locally and its update/invalidate message does not reach this node before a subsequent access, the stale value will

be returned. All previous update/invalidate messages are guaranteed to have taken effect on return from a *barrier* operation, which ensures data consistency even when the program uses unprivileged acquires to access data. Due to relaxed consistency requirements, unprivileged release operations are not necessary.

3.3. The Run-Time System

The *Locust* run-time system consists of four modules which are linked to the user program at compile time - (i) *coordinator*, (ii) *computation*, (iii) *owner*, and (iv) *synchronization* modules. The coordinator module maintains the task graph and schedules tasks on the computation modules. Computation modules execute the tasks. Synchronization and mutual-exclusion modules are responsible for synchronization operations and operations on mutual-exclusion data. Owner modules manage the data items governed by the UDD protocol.

A parallel application is started by instantiating the coordinator module at one node. It in turn starts a process on each of the other nodes and then assumes the role of the scheduler from then on. The process started on each node act as a combination of the computation module, the owner module and the synchronization module. The coordinator maintains the task graph and schedules tasks on the computation nodes based on data affinity information among the tasks, and the current load on the associated nodes. Affinity-based scheduling attempts to schedule tasks that work on the same portion of the data to the same node. Each computation node periodically sends its current load estimate to the coordinator At present the current CPU load is estimated as the average number of runnable processes in the past 10 secs sampled at every 5 seconds. The coordinator uses this load estimate to predict the future load on that machine until more up-to-date load information becomes available. Fewer tasks are scheduled on heavily loaded nodes than on lightly loaded nodes.

Locust exploits the fact that the DSVM is implemented completely in software and adopts a function-shipping approach to implement synchronization primitives. The idea is to manage the synchronization data structures on a single node, and to expose a set of synchronization primitives semantically richer than simple read/write to other nodes. All *mutual-exclusion* objects of a parallel program are managed by the *synchronization servers*. These objects are not cached at the computation nodes so every operation on these objects must go through the appropriate servers. When an application attempts to access a *mutual-exclusion* object, it does not go through the process of acquiring the lock associated with that object, retrieving the object, modifying the object locally, and releasing the lock. Instead it simply sends a request to the synchronization server

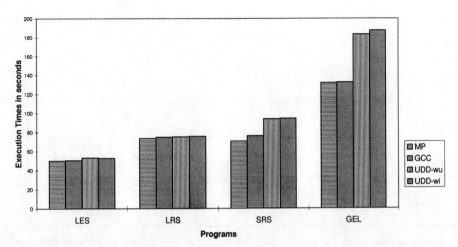

Figure 1: *Relative execution time of the four programs under different programming modes.*

with the name of the object and the operation that it needs to perform on that object. The server performs the requested operation and sends the result back to the computation node. There are two types of synchronization servers implemented in *Locust*. *Centralized Synchronization and Mutual-Exclusion Server (CSMS)* manages global synchronization operations and mutual-exclusion data objects that are uniformly accessed from all tasks. *Distributed Synchronization and Mutual-Exclusion Servers (DSMS)* manage mutual-exclusion data items that are accessed predominantly by a limited set of tasks, and usually co-locate with where the tasks are scheduled. The advantage of this approach is a significant reduction of network traffic. Essentially synchronization is implemented by shipping functions to the data rather than the other way around. Note that this approach is different from the centralized reduction facilities supported by other systems in that we can support arbitrarily complex user defined mutual exclusion operations through the synchronization servers.

Due to space constraints, please refer to [9] [3] for related work as well as *Locust*'s design and implementation details.

4. Performance Evaluation

4.1. Methodology

For performance evaluation and comparison, we use four applications with different data sharing and communication patterns. These applications are Laplace equation solver (LES), Gaussian Elimination (GEL), Long range particle dynamics simulation (LRS), and Short range particle dynamics simulation (SRS). Since we do not have a *Locust* compiler, the annotations to these applications as required by *Locust* are hand-generated.

The experimental setup consists of a network of PCs connected by a Fast Ethernet. Each PC has a P90 CPU, 16 MBytes of main memory and a 256-KByte second-level cache. The PCs are connected to the network by SMC EtherPower 10/100 adapters which are based on DEC 21140 chipsets. The hub used to connect the network is a SMC TigerHub 100. The PCs run FreeBSD 2.1.0, with *Pupa* as the message passing system. All experiments, unless otherwise specified, are run with 10 computation nodes.

We compare the performance of *Locust* with message passing systems, and generic distributed shared memory systems running the UDD protocol under using write update and write invalidate schemes. Message passing programs are expected to yield the best performance. A major goal of this study is to determine how closely *Locust* can approximate the performance of message passing programs, as well as the performance advantages of the GCC protocol over the UDD protocol.

4.2. Execution Time and Speedup

Figure 1 presents the overall execution time of the four applications under the four programming modes. The message passing programs and the GCC programs are labeled MP and GCC respectively. The UDD programs running under the write update and the write invalidate schemes are labeled UDD-wu and UDD-wi respectively. Breakdown of the execution times is presented in Table 1. The average speedups achieved for each program is shown is the last column. The values presented in the table for each component of the execution time are the averages of those component across all nodes for multiple runs of the programs. All timing measurements are in seconds.

The *wait for data* column accounts for the time spent waiting for data to arrive and the time spent at synchronization points. The column *send time* accounts for the

Program	Test Environment	Execution Time (sec)	Computation Time (sec)	Wait for data (sec)	Send time (sec)	Overhead (sec)	Speedup
LES	Uniprocessor	487.41	487.41	-	-	-	-
	Message Passing	50.00	48.63	0.70	0.38	0.29	9.75
	GCC	50.53	48.79	0.81	0.48	0.44	9.65
	UDD WU	53.23	49.68	2.63	0.62	0.30	9.16
	UDD WI	52.81	50.38	1.68	0.60	0.14	9.23
LRS	Uniprocessor	704.75	704.75	-	-	-	-
	Message Passing	73.41	69.87	3.26	0.27	0.00	9.60
	GCC	74.85	70.58	2.75	0.31	1.20	9.42
	UDD WU	75.15	70.71	3.81	0.34	0.29	9.38
	UDD WI	75.71	71.69	3.74	0.04	0.24	9.31
GEL	Uniprocessor	898.75	898.75	-	-	-	-
	Message Passing	131.97	95.22	34.37	2.32	0.06	6.81
	GCC	132.41	96.32	28.35	3.00	4.74	6.79
	UDD WU	183.27	95.10	79.14	7.16	1.87	4.89
	UDD WI	187.38	96.37	82.52	5.39	3.10	4.80
SRS	Uniprocessor	645.14	645.14	-	-	-	-
	Message Passing	70.58	61.11	8.23	1.12	0.02	9.14
	GCC	76.19	61.81	8.52	1.35	4.51	8.47
	UDD WU	93.06	64.28	14.62	2.52	11.64	6.93
	UDD WI	93.65	64.82	15.80	2.61	10.42	6.89

Table 1: *Breakdown of the execution times for the four applications under different modes. All times are in seconds. The uniprocessor times are execution times of sequential programs written to solve the respective problems.*

time spent by the programs in explicit calls to send and update routines. It does not include time for those data send operations initiated by the run time system in response to requests from other nodes. Remote nodes can interrupt the computation at a node for write update and write invalidate programs. As a result, the *computation times* for these programs are slight overestimates of the actual computation times. Everything else not covered by the other columns is shown under the *overhead* column. The uniprocessor times are the execution times of sequential programs written to solve the corresponding problems. The sequential programs were run on a machine with 32 MBytes of main memory to avoid paging.

4.2.1 GCC vs. Message Passing

GCC programs perform within 1% of the performance of the corresponding message passing programs for three of the four applications. Performance of SRS is not as good. However, it is still within 8% of the performance of the corresponding message passing program. Much of the extra overhead incurred by the GCC program for SRS comes from the operations of the distributed synchronization and mutual exclusion servers. However, this overhead is still substantially smaller than those associated with the UDD programs.

4.2.2 GCC vs. UDD

The UDD write update and write invalidate programs perform well for the computation intensive applications such as LES and LRS. These applications have regular data sharing patterns and each data item is writ-

ten to by only one node throughout the execution of the program. So there are no write shared data. The programs have been written to issue the read requests as soon as possible to maximally overlap computation and communication[1]. As a result, time spent waiting for data is minimized. Thus there is no significant difference between the performance of write update and write invalidate programs. Moreover, these programs also use data dependency information to some extent in the sense that the data partitioning used is the same as GCC programs.

The only major factor that amounts to the performance difference between GCC and UDD programs for LES and LRS is the need for explicit synchronization operations such as obtaining locks and the barrier synchronization at the end of each iteration in the UDD programs. By design the GCC protocol does not require explicit synchronization. The UDD programs are expected to perform worse if data dependency information is not used for data partitioning and a more coarser coherence unit, such as a virtual memory page, is used.

The performance differences between GCC and UDD write update/invalidate are more evident in the case of GEL and SRS. These programs have also been optimized as the former two. However, the performance difference is more telling because of more write sharing in these programs. As before, part of the performance difference comes from the explicit synchronization operations. Another major difference between the performance of the the GCC and UDD programs comes

---

[1]The system allows a split-phase locking scheme in which programs make one call to send out a lock request and a separate call to wait for the lock and the data to arrive. Between the two calls they can work on other computation.

Program	Environment	Total message count (x1000)	Coordinator message count (x1000)	Total traffic (Mbytes)	Coordinator traffic (Mbytes)
LES	Message Passing	20.00	0.00	23.60	0.00
	GCC	24.64	4.64	23.93	0.27
	UDD WU	27.05	4.64	24.31	0.27
	UDD WI	37.32	4.64	24.87	0.27
LRS	Message Passing	18.00	0.00	24.70	0.00
	GCC	19.19	1.19	24.76	0.07
	UDD WU	20.30	1.19	25.41	0.07
	UDD WI	24.85	1.19	25.24	0.07
GEL	Message Passing	132.41	0.00	153.05	0.00
	GCC	230.46	98.07	159.19	5.74
	UDD WU	375.72	99.33	171.22	5.80
	UDD WI	415.43	99.33	168.84	5.80
SRS	Message Passing	90.91	0.00	22.71	0.00
	GCC	94.85	4.63	26.46	0.27
	UDD WU	426.45	4.63	88.18	0.27
	UDD WI	476.62	4.63	53.34	0.27

Table 2: *Network traffic in terms of number of messages and number of bytes during the execution of the four applications under different modes.*

from the fact that the GCC programs use the centralized and the distributed synchronization and mutual-exclusion servers for computation on data items that are write shared by more than one node.

For GEL, GCC uses the CSMS server to compute the index of the row with the maximum element in each iteration. Whereas, each node in the UDD program has to actively participate in this computation by locking the global maximum element and the index information and comparing them against the local values. This leads to more communication and serialization overhead. The performance difference between GCC and write-update UDD programs is due to this serialization and the explicit synchronization overhead. The write-invalidate UDD version performs even worse than the write-update UDD program. This is because in the write update program, the pivot row is sent to all other nodes as soon as it it computed, so that the computation can proceed immediately. However, in the write invalidate program as the pivot row is computed, an invalidate message is sent to all other nodes, and they must subsequently send a request for this new row. Consequently the computation is delayed until a reply is received. This extra wait time accounts for the performance difference between the write update and write invalidate program. Note that a similar wait for data in LES and LRS did not lead to any significant performance difference. This is because LES and LRS are computation intensive programs and in each iteration there were other computations that could be carried out while waiting for new updates to arrive. In contrast, for GEL no other computation in each iteration can proceed until the pivot row update has arrived. Although GEL starts as a program with a fair amount of computation in each iteration, as the execution proceeds, each node performs less and less computation in each iteration since one variable is eliminated in each iteration. However, the amount of

communications stays constant in each iteration. Thus towards the end of the execution nodes spend most of their time communicating and waiting for data.

In SRS the contents of each boundary cell can potentially be modified by multiple tasks. As a result, during the execution of UDD programs, multiple nodes require write access to any given cell. Since write access is permissible only after the cells have been acquired in the exclusive mode, the execution of the program is serialized to some extent. In contrast, in the GCC version, the cells are managed by the DSMS servers. Each task sends the operations it needs to perform on each cell to the DSMS server that manages that cell. The DSMS server performs the updates and sends the new value to the tasks that need to read the state of the cell in the next phase. The function-shipping approach to managing mutual exclusion data items is responsible for the performance difference between the GCC and UDD programs. As before, the other reason for the reduced performance of UDD programs is the need for explicit synchronization operations for acquiring shared data and the per-iteration barrier synchronization The performance difference between the write update and write invalidate programs is not significant because the programs overlap computation and communication using split-phase data acquisition as in LES and LRS.

4.3. Communication Overhead

Table 2 compares the communication overheads of the four versions of the parallel applications. We measure the total number of messages as well as the total number of bytes communicated. The traffic to and from the coordinator node is isolated to indicate the scheduling overhead. The total number of bytes exchanged by the UDD write update/invalidate programs is significantly larger than that exchanged by message passing

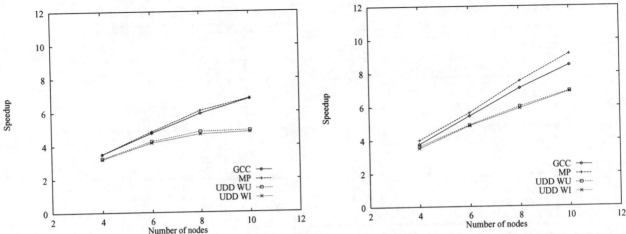

Figure 2: *Scalability of different programming models for varying numbers of processors for GEL and SRS.*

and GCC programs only for the SRS application. However, in terms of the number of messages, the difference is more apparent. Compared to the GCC programs, the UDD write update/invalidate programs generate twice as many messages for GEL and four times as many messages for the SRS application. Since the performance of parallel program depends on both the number of bytes and the number of messages exchanged, the UDD write update/invalidate programs are more likely to suffer in a network with lower bandwidth or in a configuration with larger number of nodes. Some of the additional messages associated with UDD programs are due to explicit synchronization operations. The write update programs are likely to generate spurious update messages when data is sent to nodes where it is not needed. Write invalidate programs do not have spurious updates but they have to send invalidate messages. Write invalidate programs also generate read requests and replies. As a result, write invalidate programs generate more messages but fewer bytes than write update programs.

Because SRS involves more intensive write sharing, the number of bytes transferred is relatively high for the UDD version. The amount of write sharing in GEL is less. Therefore the total number of bytes exchanged by the UDD version is not significantly higher than those in the GCC version. GCC programs are quite comparable to message passing programs in terms of both the total number of bytes and the total number of messages exchanged. Only in the case of GEL does the GCC version incur a significantly higher overhead in terms of the total number of messages. This overhead is not due to the messages exchanged during the real computation but mostly due to a large number of messages to and from the coordinator node, since the shared memory versions of GEL uses a large number of generations.

The coordinator overhead is negligible in terms of the number of bytes in all cases. But the number of mes-

sages to and from the coordinator are admittedly quite large in some cases. These messages are required for exchanging information regarding scheduling of generations, task execution completion, generation completion etc. Each piece of information is sent in one separate message for ease of implementation. There is room for further optimization by packing more than one piece of information into one message. This optimization should benefit both the GCC and the UDD programs.

4.4 Scalability

To test the scalability of different programming modes, we ran the four applications under configurations of 4, 6, 8 and 10 nodes. The program data sets and the number of iterations were kept the same for all configurations. In GCC and UDD, each generation contains the same number of tasks as the number of nodes in the system. LES and LRS scale well under each programming mode. So Figure 2 only shows the speedups of GEL and SRS under different programming models. The speedups of the UDD programs for GEL saturate with 8 nodes. On the other hand, the message passing and GCC programs seem capable of scaling to larger configurations. The reason why UDD versions do not scale as well is the excessive network traffic during the program execution. In general, GCC programs scale almost as well as the message passing programs for all applications. Moreover, the trend shows that the programs can scale to configurations with more than 10 nodes.

4.5. Impact of Task Granularity

By task granularity, we mean the size of the data partition operated on by a single task. Finer task granularity provides more flexibility for load balancing. We ran each application varying the task granularity so that

Program	Tasks Per Phase	Execution Time (sec)	Computation Time (sec)	Wait for work (sec)	Wait for data (sec)	Send time (sec)	Overhead (sec)	Speedup
LES	10	50.53	48.79	0.00	0.81	0.48	0.44	9.65
	20	51.34	49.12	0.00	0.93	0.74	0.56	9.49
	40	52.65	50.25	0.00	1.04	0.78	0.58	9.26
	60	52.82	50.26	0.00	1.16	0.80	0.60	9.23
	80	52.96	50.33	0.00	1.26	0.79	0.58	9.20
LRS	10	74.85	70.58	0.00	2.75	0.32	1.20	9.42
	20	74.73	70.39	0.00	2.93	0.41	1.00	9.43
	40	75.77	70.59	0.00	3.15	0.63	1.40	9.30
	60	76.50	69.91	0.00	3.30	1.03	2.25	9.21
	80	80.16	71.58	0.00	3.80	1.46	3.32	8.79
GEL	10	132.41	96.32	2.52	28.35	3.00	2.22	6.79
	20	133.04	96.42	2.35	28.47	3.23	2.57	6.76
	40	135.06	96.52	1.74	29.92	3.64	3.24	6.65
	60	137.67	96.90	1.70	31.27	4.12	3.68	6.53
	80	143.75	97.44	0.76	36.33	4.67	4.55	6.25
SRS	10	76.19	61.81	0.00	8.52	1.35	4.51	8.47
	20	76.98	61.56	0.00	9.34	1.46	4.63	8.39
	40	80.45	62.59	0.00	9.27	2.56	6.03	8.02
	60	81.95	62.72	0.00	10.34	2.61	6.28	7.87
	80	82.46	62.57	0.00	10.90	2.71	6.28	7.82

Table 3: *Breakdown of the execution times for GCC programs when the task granularity is varied. The numbers in the "tasks per phase" column, indicate the number of tasks in each generation. The larger this number, the smaller the task granularity.*

there were 10, 20, 40, 60 and 80 tasks in each generation. The number of computation nodes used in this experiment were 10. The execution time breakdown is shown in Table 3, and the communication overhead is presented in Table 4. The programs do not show any significant performance deterioration with decreasing granularity. The execution times for all programs increase by less than 10% when the task granularities are reduced by a factor of 8. The network traffic increases as expected since the data items are smaller and must be exchanged independently. The column *wait for work* shows the average time the nodes spent waiting for the coordinator node to schedule tasks. The nodes never go idle for LES, LRS and SRS. In the case of GEL, however, the computation nodes do need to wait because the coordinator is not capable of keeping up with the computation nodes. This is due to the relatively small amount of work in each iteration towards the end of the computation. As the task granularity decreases, the visible coordinator overhead actually decreases, because with decreasing granularity, other communication overheads increase and the time the coordinator takes to schedule tasks is masked by these overheads. The moderate performance loss with reduced task granularity encourages the use of fine-grained scheduling for load balancing. Moreover, it demonstrates that the coordinator and the CSMS server can handle a large number of tasks before becoming a bottleneck.

5. Conclusion

In this paper we present a detailed evaluation of *Locust*, a fully operational compiler-directed distributed shared

virtual memory system. We have compared the performance of four regular parallel applications running under the GCC protocol, under the message passing mode, and under an aggressive directory-based cache coherence protocol — the UDD protocol, all based on the same hardware and software platforms. We show that GCC programs perform within 1-8% of the performance of the message passing programs. All programming modes perform well for computation intensive programs that do not use write sharing heavily, as long as judicious data partitioning is used to avoid false sharing. The major performance difference between GCC and UDD comes from the overhead incurred by UDD programs associated with explicit calls to synchronization operations such as lock, unlock and barrier synchronization. These synchronization operations are completely eliminated by the GCC protocol. The other performance advantage of GCC is that GCC programs exchange a significantly fewer number of messages than UDD programs. *Locust*'s function shipping approach to global reduction operations and update operations on write shared data also contributes to significant performance improvement. In terms of scalability, GCC programs scale almost as well as message passing programs up to 10 nodes and appear to be capable of scaling well to larger configurations. However, for applications with write sharing, UDD programs stop to scale for configurations beyond a smaller number of nodes.

Acknowledgement

This research is supported by an NSF Career Award MIP-9502067, NSF MIP-9710622, NSF IRI-9711635,

Program	Tasks per phase	Total message count (x1000)	Coordinator message count (x1000)	Total traffic (Mbytes)	Coordinator traffic (Mbytes)
LES	10	24.64	4.64	23.93	0.27
	20	40.64	4.64	42.81	0.33
	40	40.64	4.64	42.94	0.46
	60	40.84	4.84	43.08	0.60
	80	40.84	4.84	43.21	0.73
LRS	10	19.19	1.19	24.76	0.07
	20	19.55	1.19	25.27	0.08
	40	20.27	1.19	26.28	0.11
	60	30.94	1.24	27.58	0.14
	80	42.28	1.24	28.90	0.17
GEL	10	230.46	98.07	159.19	5.74
	20	245.00	98.23	161.50	7.13
	40	273.93	98.37	166.11	9.90
	60	307.06	102.72	170.89	12.84
	80	336.02	102.90	175.50	15.61
SRS	10	94.85	4.63	26.46	0.27
	20	94.88	4.63	26.50	0.33
	40	172.81	4.63	47.70	0.46
	60	173.07	4.83	48.06	0.60
	80	173.16	4.83	48.65	0.73

Table 4: *Network traffic in terms of number of messages and number of bytes for GCC programs executed with varying task granularities.*

a contract 95F138600000 from Community Management Staff's Massive Digital Data System Program, as well as fundings from Sandia National Laboratory, Reuters Information Technology Inc., and Computer Associates/Cheyenne Inc.

References

[1] J. K. Bennett, J. B. Carter, and W. Zwaenepoel. Munin: Distributed shared memory using multi-protocol release consistency. In *Proceedings of Operating Systems of the 90s and Beyond. International Workshop Proc., Dagstuhl Castle, Germany, 8-12 July 1991*, pages 56–60, Berlin, Germany, 1991. Springer-Verlag.

[2] T. Chiueh. A generational approach to compiler-controlled multiprocessor cache coherence. In *Proceedings of 22nd International Conference on Parallel Processing*, August 1993.

[3] T. Chiueh and M. Verma. A compiler-directed distributed shared memory system. In *Proceedings of the 9th International Conference on SuperComputing*, July 1995. Also available at http://www.cs.sunysb.edu/~manish/locust.

[4] S. Dwarkadas, A. Cox, and W. Zwaenepoel. An integrated compile-time/run-time software distributed shared memory system. In *Proc. of the 7th International Conference on Architectural Support for Programming Languages and Operating Systems*, pages 186–197, October 1996.

[5] K. Gharachorloo, D. Lenoski, J. Laudon, P. Gibbons, A. Gupta, and J. Hennesy. Memory consistency and event ordering in scalable shared-memory multiprocessors. In *Prodeecings of the 17th Annual International Symposium on Computer Architecture*, pages 15–26, May 1990.

[6] P. Keleher, A. L. Cox, S. Dwarkadas, and W. Zwaenepoel. Treadmarks: Distributed shared memory on standard workstations and operating systems. In *Proceedings of the 1994 Winter USENIX Conference*, pages 115–132, Jan 1994.

[7] Steven K. Reinhardt, James R. Laurus, and David A. Wood. Tempest and typhoon: User-level shared memory. In *Proceedings of the 21st Annual International Symposium on Computer Architecture*, April 1994.

[8] Daniel Scales and Monica Lam. Design and evaluation of a shared object system for distributed memory machine. In *1st USENIX Symposium on Operating Systems Design and Implementation*, pages 101–114, Nov 1994.

[9] M. Verma. *A Compiler-Directed Shared Memory System*. PhD thesis, ECSL-TR-33, Computer Science Department, State University of New York at Stony Brook,, http://ecsl.cs.sunysb.edu/ chiueh/tr/TR33.ps.Z, December 1996.

[10] B. N. Bershad M. J. Zekauskas and W. A. Sawdon. The Midway distributed shared memory system. In *Proceedings of the 1993 IEEE CompCon Conference*, pages 528–537, Feb. 1993.

Session 2C
Routing

Chair: Yu-Chee Tseng
National Central University, Taiwan

An Analytical Model of Duato's Fully-Adaptive Routing Algorithm in *k*-Ary *n*-Cubes

Ould-Khaoua

Department of Computer Science
University of Strathclyde
Glasgow G1 1XH, UK

Abstract

Analytical models of deterministic routing in wormhole-routed k-ary n-cubes have widely been reported in the literature. Although many fully-adaptive routing algorithms have been proposed to overcome the performance limitations of deterministic routing, there has been hardly any study that describes analytical models for these algorithms. This paper proposes a queueing model for obtaining latency measures in wormhole-routed k-ary n-cubes with fully-adaptive routing, based on Duato's algorithm [9]. The validity of the model is demonstrated by comparing analytical results with those obtained through simulation experiments.

1. Introduction

K-ary *n*-cubes have been popular multicomputer networks due to their desirable properties, such as ease of implementation, recursive structures, and ability to exploit communication locality to reduce message latency. The binary hypercube and 2-dimensional torus are the most common instances of *k*-ary *n*-cubes. The former has been used in early multicomputers like the Cosmic Cube [23] and iPSC/2 [21] while the latter has become popular in recent systems, such as the J-machine [20], CRAY T3E [5] and CRAY T3D [15].

Wormhole switching [24] (also widely known as "wormhole routing") has been very popular in practical multicomputers as it makes latency independent of the message distance in the absence of blocking. In wormhole routing, a message is broken into *flits* (a few bytes each) for transmission and flow control. The *header* flit (containing routing information) governs the route and the remaining data flits follow in a pipelined fashion. If the header is blocked, the data flits are blocked in situ.

A routing algorithm, which specifies how messages select their network path, greatly influences network performance. A critical requirement for any routing algorithm is to ensure *deadlock freedom*; deadlock situation occurs when no message can advance towards its destination because of filled queues. Most existing multicomputers use *deterministic* routing for deadlock avoidance, and is based on the concept of *virtual channels* [6]. A virtual channel has its own flit queue, but shares the bandwidth of the physical channel with other virtual channels in a time-multiplexed fashion. Deadlock is avoided by forcing messages to visit virtual channels in a strict order. A typical example of deterministic routing is the dimension-ordered routing in the hypercube, where messages visit dimensions in a pre-defined order. In the high-radix *k*-ary *n*-cube, besides the dimension-ordered routing between dimensions, two virtual channel per physical channels are required to prevent deadlock within a dimension due to the wrap-around connections.

Deterministic routing has been widely adopted in practice due to its simplicity and minimal requirement for virtual channels [15, 20, 21, 23]. However, messages with the same source and destination addresses always take the same route. Therefore, they cannot take advantage of alternative paths, that a topology may provide, to avoid blocking, and thus reduce their latency. Many *fully-adaptive* routing algorithms have been proposed, where a message can use any of the available paths between a given pair of nodes to advance towards its destination [10, 11, 18, 19, 25].

Linder & Harden [18] have extended the concept of virtual channels to virtual networks, developing fully-adaptive routing algorithms for *k*-ary *n*-cube. They have shown that $(n+1)2^{n-1}$ virtual channels are required per physical channel to ensure deadlock-freedom. This high virtual channels requirement translates into high hardware complexity, which can significantly reduce router speed, decreasing the overall network performance [3]. The high cost of adaptivity has motivated researchers to develop fully-adaptive algorithms that require a moderate number of virtual channels [10, 11, 19, 25].

Duato [10] has recently described a fully-adaptive algorithm that allows efficient router implementation because it can use as a few as 2 or 3 virtual channels per physical channel to ensure deadlock-freedom for the hypercube and high-radix k-ary n-cube respectively. The algorithm divides the virtual channels into two classes: a and b. At each routing step, a message can adaptively visit any available virtual channel from class a. If all the virtual channels belonging to class a are busy, it crosses a virtual channel from class b using dimension-ordered routing. The virtual channels of class b define a complete virtual deadlock-free sub-network, which acts like a "drain" for the sub-network built from the class a virtual channels. Fully-adaptive routing algorithms that require a few virtual channels per physical channel have also been discussed in [19, 25].

The first multicomputers and routers that use fully-adaptive routing have recently been reported. The Cray T3E [5] and the Reliable router [9] are two examples that use Duato's routing algorithm. Before adaptive routing can be widely adopted in commercial parallel systems, it is necessary to have clear understanding of the factors that affect their potential performance. Analytical models are cost-effective and efficient tools that can help designers to analyse the performance of adaptive routing algorithms to ensure their successful introduction in future multicomputers.

Analytical models of deterministic routing in wormhole-routed k-ary n-cubes have been widely reported in the literature [1, 4, 7, 12, 13, 14, 17]. More recently, Boura $et\ al$ [2] have presented a model for fully-adaptive routing in the hypercube. Developing such a model is more complicated in high-radix k-ary n-cubes. This stems from the fact that when a message reaches a given router, it is not clear how many hops are left to be made along a given dimension; as the hops already made can belong either to the same or a different dimension. The problem is further exacerbated as the number of dimensions increases. The problem does not exist for the hypercube since a message can cross at most one channel along a dimension, and therefore it is easier to work out how many dimensions are left for a message to visit to reach its destination.

This paper presents an analytical model to compute message latency in wormhole-routed high-radix k-ary n-cubes ($k>2$) with fully-adaptive routing, based on Duato's algorithm. The discussion concentrates on k-ary n-cubes with uni-directional channels, but can easily be adapted for the bi-directional case. Although the model is developed for the uniform traffic pattern, we will discuss in later sections how it can be extended to deal with non-uniform traffic containing communication locality.

The rest of the paper is organised as follows. Section 2 describes the node structure in k-ary n-cubes. Section 3 outlines the analytical model while Section 4 validates the model through simulation. Finally, Section 5 concludes this study.

2. Node Structure

The k-ary n-cube contains $N = k^n$ nodes, arranged in n dimensions, with k nodes per dimension [7]. Each node is connected to its nearest neighbours in each dimension. Let dimensions be numbered from 1 to n. A node, x, can then be labelled by an $n \times 1$ address vector with x_i being the node's position in its dimension i. A node at address $x = (x_1, .., x_{i-1}, x_i, x_{i+1}, .. x_n)$ $(0 \leq x_i \leq k-1)$ $(1 \leq i \leq n)$ is connected to node $x = (x_1, .., x_{i-1}, x_i + 1 \text{ modulo } k, x_{i+1}, .., x_n)$ along dimension i

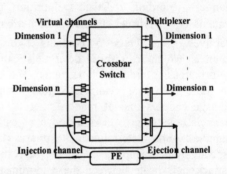

Fig. 1: Node structure in k-ary n-cubes.

Each node consists of a processing element (PE) and router, as shown in Figure 1. The PE contains a processor and some local memory. The router has $(n+1)$ input and $(n+1)$ output channels. A node is connected to its neighbouring nodes through n inputs and n output channels. The remaining channels are used by the PE to inject/eject messages to/from the network respectively. Messages generated by the PE are transferred to the router through the injection channel. Messages at the destination are transferred to the local PE through the ejection channel. The router contains one-flit buffers for incoming virtual channels. The input and output channels are connected by a $(n+1)V$ - way crossbar switch, V being the number of virtual channels which can simultaneously connect multiple input to multiple output channels in the absence of channel contention.

3. The model

The model is based on the following assumptions, which are commonly accepted in the literature [1, 2, 4, 7, 12, 13, 14, 17].

a) Message destinations are uniformly distributed across the network nodes.

b) Nodes generate traffic independently of each other, and which follows a Poisson process with a mean rate of m_g messages/cycle.

c) Message length is exponentially distributed with a mean of M flits, each of which requires one-cycle transmission time across a physical channel

d) The local queue at the injection channel in the source node has infinite capacity.

e) Messages at the destination node are transferred to the local PE one at time through the ejection channel.

f) V ($V>2$) virtual channels are used per physical channel. According to Duato's algorithm, class a contains $(v-2)$ virtual channels, which are crossed adaptively, and class b contains two virtual channels, which are crossed deterministically (e.g. in an increasing order of dimensions). When there are more than one available virtual channel, a message chooses one at random. Let the virtual channels belonging to class a and b be called the adaptive and deterministic virtual channels respectively. To simplify the model derivation, no distinction is made between the deterministic and adaptive virtual channels when computing the different virtual channels occupancy probabilities.

g) The router's pipelining time is one cycle (i.e. it takes one cycle to move a flit from an input to output channel inside the router).

The mean message latency is composed of the mean network latency, S, that is the time to cross the network, and the mean waiting time seen by message in the source node, W_s. However, to model the effects of virtual channels multiplexing, the mean message latency has to be scaled by a factor, $\overline{V}$, representing the average degree of virtual channels multiplexing, that takes place at a given physical channel. Therefore, we can write

$$Latency = (S + W_s)\overline{V} \qquad (1)$$

Calculation of the mean network latency (S):

Under the uniform traffic pattern, the average number of hops that a message makes along each of the n dimensions and across the network, $\overline{k}$ and $\overline{d}$ respectively, are given by

$$\overline{k} = (k-1)/2 \qquad (2)$$
$$\overline{d} = n\overline{k} \qquad (3)$$

The mean network latency, S, consists of two parts: one is the delay due to the actual message transmission time, and the other is due to blocking in the network. Given that a message makes, on average, $\overline{d}$ hops to reach its destination, S can be written as

$$S = M + \overline{d} + \sum_{i=1}^{\overline{d}} B_i + W_{ej} \qquad (4)$$

where M is the message length, B_i is the mean blocking time seen by a message at the ith hop channel $(1 \le i \le \overline{d})$, and W_{ej} is the mean waiting time at the ejection channel in the destination node.

A message is blocked at the ith hop channel when all the adaptive virtual channels of the remaining dimensions to be visited, and also the deterministic virtual channels of the lowest dimension still to be visited are busy. Fully-adaptive routing allows a message to choose any channel to advance towards its destination, resulting in an equal and balanced traffic load on all channels. Therefore, a message sees the same mean waiting time across all the channels. However, it sees different probability of blocking at each hop as the number of alternative paths changes from one hop to another. If W_b and P_{b_i} denote the mean waiting time and probability of blocking at the ith hop channel, the mean blocking time can therefore be written as

$$B_i = P_{b_i} W_b \qquad (5)$$

To compute P_{b_i} we need to compute firstly the probability that all adaptive virtual channels at a dimension are busy, P_a, and secondly the probability that all adaptive and deterministic virtual channels at a dimension are busy, P_d. To compute P_a, three cases are considered.

a) V virtual channels are busy. This implies that all adaptive virtual channels are busy.

b) $(V-1)$ virtual channels are busy. The number of

combinations where $(V-1)$ out of V virtual channels are busy is $\binom{V}{V-1}$. Only two combinations out of $\binom{V}{V-1}$ result in all adaptive virtual channels being busy.

c) $(V-2)$ virtual channels are busy. The number of combinations where $(V-2)$ out of V virtual channels are busy is $\binom{V}{V-2}$. Only one combination out of these results in all adaptive virtual channels being busy.

Similarly, to obtain the second probability, P_d, two cases are considered.

a) V virtual channels are busy. This means that all adaptive and the required deterministic virtual channels are busy.

b) $(V-2)$ virtual channels are busy. In this case, only two combinations out of $\binom{V}{V-1}$ result in all adaptive and the deterministic virtual channels being busy.

Let P_v be the probability that v virtual channels at a given physical channel are busy (P_v is determined below). Taking into account the different cases mentioned above, P_a and P_d are found to be

$$P_a = P_V + \frac{2P_{V-1}}{\binom{V}{V-1}} + \frac{P_{V-2}}{\binom{V}{V-2}} \qquad (6)$$

$$P_d = P_V + \frac{2P_{V-1}}{\binom{V}{V-1}} \qquad (7)$$

The total number of adaptive virtual channels that a message can select during its next hop depends on the number of dimensions still to be visited. When a message arrives at the ith hop channel, it has already made $(i-1)$ hops, which are, in turn, a combination of h_j $(1 \le j \le n)$ $(0 \le h_j \le \bar{k})$ hops made along each of the n dimensions. To compute the probability that a message still has to visit a given dimension, we need to enumerate the number of ways to distribute the $(i-1)$ hops among the n dimensions. To do so, let us refer to the following result from the combinatorial theory [22, 26].

Proposition: *The number of ways to distribute r like objects into m different cells, such that no cells contains less than p objects and not more than $p+q-1$ objects is the coefficient of x^{r-pm} in the*

expansion of the polynomial $P(x) = (1-x^q)^m (1-x)^{-m} = (1+x+x^2+...+x^{q-1})^m$.

In what follows, we will refer to the coefficient of x^{r-pm} as $N_p^{p+q-1}(r,m)$, and which can be shown to be [22]

$$N_p^{p+q-1}(r,m) = \sum_{l=0}^{m} (-1)^l \binom{m}{l} \binom{r-mp-lq+m-1}{m-1} \qquad (8)$$

If the hops made by a message are treated as indistinguishable objects, and the visited dimensions as different cells, the above proposition can be used to compute the number of ways to distribute hops among the dimensions. Under the uniform traffic pattern, a message makes, on average, $\bar{k}$ hops along each of the n dimensions. So, when message arrives at the ith hop channel, the number of ways to distribute the $(i-1)$ hops among the n dimensions such that the message has made at least one hop along each dimension is simply $N_1^{\bar{k}}(i-1,n)$.

To determine the probability that a message still has to visit a given dimension, let us follow a typical message, that makes $\bar{d}$ hops under the uniform traffic pattern. When message arrives at the ith hop channel, the following cases need to be considered.

a) When $1 \le i \le \bar{k}$, a message still has to visit the channels in the n dimensions and, therefore, can choose among adaptive virtual channels belonging to these dimensions.

b) When $\bar{k} \le i \le 2\bar{k}$, a message may have crossed one dimension. The number of ways to distribute the $(i-1)$ hops along the n dimensions such that the message has made at least one hop per dimension is $N_1^{\bar{k}}(i-1,n)$. Similarly, the number of ways to distribute the $(i-1)$ hops such that the message has entirely crossed one dimension is $\binom{n}{1} N_1^{\bar{k}}(i-1-\bar{k},n-1)$. Therefore, the probability that a message has crossed one dimension is given by

$$P_i^1 = \frac{\binom{n}{1} N_1^{\bar{k}}(i-1-\bar{k},n-1)}{\binom{n}{1} N_1^{\bar{k}}(i-1-\bar{k},n-1) + N_1^{\bar{k}}(i-1,n)} \qquad (9)$$

Hence, the probability that it still has to visit all the n dimensions can be written as

109

$$P_i^0 = 1 - P_i^1 = \frac{N_1^{\bar{k}}(i-1,n)}{\binom{n}{1} N(i-1-\bar{k}, n-1) + N_1^{\bar{k}}(i-1,n)} \quad (10)$$

Generally, when $j\bar{k}+1 \le i \le (j+1)\bar{k}$ $(1 \le j \le n-2)$ or $(n-1)\bar{k}+1 \le i \le n\bar{k}-n$, a message may have crossed up to j dimensions. The probability of such a case occurring is given by

$$P_i^j = \frac{\binom{n}{j} N_1^{\bar{k}}(i-1-j\bar{k}, n-j)}{\sum\limits_{l=0}^{j} \binom{n}{l} N_1^{\bar{k}}(i-1-l\bar{k}, n-l)} \quad (11)$$

The probability that it still has to visit the channels of all the n dimensions is

$$P_i^0 = 1 - \sum_{l=1}^{j} P_i^l = \frac{\binom{n}{j} N_1^{\bar{k}}(i-1-j\bar{k}, n-j)}{\sum\limits_{l=0}^{j} \binom{n}{l} N_1^{\bar{k}}(i-1-l\bar{k}, n-l)} \quad (12)$$

c) When $n\bar{k}-n+1 \le i \le n\bar{k}$, a message has definitely crossed $n_c = i - (n\bar{k}-n+1)$ dimensions. Let $i_r = i-1-n_c\bar{k}$ and $n_r = n-n_c$ be the remaining hops and dimensions respectively after crossing the n_c dimensions. The message may also have crossed up to j dimensions, j is such that $j\bar{k} < i_r$ $(0 \le j < n_r)$. For $(i-1)$, the probability that the message has crossed $n_c + j$ dimensions is given by

$$P_i^{n_c+j} = \frac{\binom{n_r}{j} N_1^{\bar{k}}(i_r - j\bar{k}, n_r - j)}{\sum\limits_{l=0}^{j} \binom{n_r}{l} N_1^{\bar{k}}(i_r - l\bar{k}, n_r - l)} \quad (13)$$

The probability that it still has to visit the channels of all the n_r dimensions can be written as

$$P_i^{n_c} = 1 - \sum_{l=1}^{j} P_c^{n_c+l} = \frac{N_1^{\bar{k}}(i_r, n_r)}{\sum\limits_{l=0}^{j} \binom{n_r}{l} N_1^{\bar{k}}(i_r - l\bar{k}, n_r - l)} \quad (14)$$

It is worth noting that in k-ary n-cubes where $n \ll \bar{k}$ and thus, $n \ll \bar{d}$, case (c) can be ignored without introducing serious inaccuracies in the model's predictions of message latency. This is because the weighted contribution of case (c) to the mean network latency is negligible compared to that of (a) and (b).

Suppose that after making a given number of hops, a message has crossed, say, j dimensions. At its next hop, the message can use $(n-j)(v-2)$ adaptive virtual channels at the remaining $(n-j)$ dimensions to be visited and also it can use one of the two deterministic channels at the lowest dimension to be visited according to deterministic routing. Combining the above three cases, and using equations (5) to (7) yield the probability of blocking, P_{b_i}, at the ith channel as

$$P_{b_i} = \begin{cases} P_a^{n-1} P_d & 1 \le i \le \bar{k} \\ \sum\limits_{l=0}^{j} P_i^l P_a^{n-l-1} P_d & \begin{array}{l} j\bar{k}+1 \le i \le (j+1)\bar{k} \\ (1 \le j \le n\text{-}2) \end{array} \\ \sum\limits_{l=0}^{j} P_i^{n_c+l} P_a^{n-(n_c+l)-1} P_d & n\bar{k}-n+1 \le i \le n\bar{k} \end{cases} \quad (15)$$

Given that blocking has occurred, a message waits for a deterministic virtual channel at the lowest dimension still to be visited. To determine the mean waiting time, W_b, to acquire a virtual channel, a physical channel is treated as an M/G/1 queue with a mean waiting of [16]

$$W_b = \frac{\rho \bar{x}(1+C_x^2)}{2(1-\rho)} \quad (16)$$

$$\rho = m_c \bar{x} \quad (17)$$

$$C_x^2 = \frac{\sigma^2}{\bar{x}^2} \quad (18)$$

where m_c is the traffic rate on network channels, $\bar{x}$ is the mean service time, and σ_x^2 is the variance of the service distribution. The traffic rate, m_c, is determined as follows. Since a router has n output channels and the PE generates, on average, m_g messages in a cycle, the rate of messages received by each channel is

$$m_c = \frac{m_g \bar{d}}{n} \quad (19)$$

As adaptive routing distributes traffic evenly across the network, the mean service time at each channel is the same, and is equal to the mean network latency, therefore $\bar{x} = S$. Since the minimum service time at a channel is equal to the message length, M, following a suggestion of [12], the variance of the service time distribution can be approximated as

$$\sigma_x^2 = (S-M)^2 \quad (20)$$

110

As a result, the mean waiting time becomes

$$W_b = \frac{m_c S^2 (1 + \frac{(S-M)^2}{S^2})}{2(1 - m_c S)} \qquad (21)$$

In the steady state, the rate of messages, that exit the network through the ejection channel, is equal to the injection rate of messages, which is equal to the generation rate, m_g. Given that the utilisation of the ejection channel is $m_g M$, the mean waiting time at the ejection channel is given by

$$W_{ej} = m_g M^2 \qquad (22)$$

Equation (4) reveals that S is a function of B_i while equation (5) and (21) show that B_i is a function of S. Given that a closed-form solution to this inter-dependency is very difficult to determine, S and B_i are computed using iterative techniques for solving equations.

Calculation of the waiting time at the source (W_s):

The mean waiting time in the source node is calculated in a similar way to that for a network channel (equation 16). A message in the source node can enter the network through any of the V virtual channels. Modelling the injection channel in the source node as an M/G/1 queue, with the mean arrival rate m_g / V and mean service time S with an approximated variance $(S - M)^2$, yields the mean waiting time as

$$W_s = \frac{\frac{m_g}{V} S^2 (1 + \frac{(S-M)^2}{S^2})}{2(1 - \frac{m_g}{V} S)} \qquad (23)$$

Calculation of the average degree of virtual channels multiplexing ($\overline{V}$):

The probability, P_v, that v virtual channels at a given physical channel are busy, can be determined using a Markovian model [8]. State V_v corresponds to v virtual channels being busy. The transition rate out of state V_v to V_{v+1} is m_c, where m_c is the traffic rate on a given channel (equation 19), while the rate out of V_v to V_{v-1} is $1/S$. The transition rate out of the last state, V_V, is reduced by m_c to account for the arrival of messages while a channel is in this state. In the steady state, the model yields the following probabilities.

$$q_v = \begin{cases} 1 & v = 0 \\ q_{v-1} m_c S & 0 < v < V \\ q_{v-1} \dfrac{m_c}{1/S - m_c} & v = V \end{cases} \qquad (24)$$

$$P_v = \begin{cases} \dfrac{1}{\displaystyle\sum_{l=0}^{V} q_l} & v = 0 \\ P_{v-1} m_c S & 0 < v < V \\ P_{v-1} \dfrac{m_c}{1/S - m_c} & v = V \end{cases} \qquad (25)$$

In virtual channel flow control, multiple virtual channels share the bandwidth of a physical channel in a time-multiplexed manner. The average degree of multiplexing of virtual channels, that takes place at a given physical channel, is given by [8]

$$\overline{V} = \frac{\displaystyle\sum_{v=0}^{V} v^2 P_v}{\displaystyle\sum_{v=0}^{V} v P_v} \qquad (26)$$

4. Validation

The above model has been validated by means of a discrete-event simulator, operating at the flit level. Each simulation experiment was run until the network reaches its steady state, that is until a further increase in simulated network cycles does not change the collected statistics appreciably. Extensive validation experiments have been performed for several combinations of network sizes, message lengths, and virtual channels. However, for the sake of specific illustration, latency results are presented for the following cases only.

- Network size is $N = 8^2$ and 8^3 nodes.
- Number of virtual channels $V = 3$ and 5.
- Mean message length $M = 32$ and 64 flits.

Figures 2 and 3 depict mean message latency results predicted by the above model plotted against those provided by the simulator as a function of traffic injected in the 8-ary 2-cube and 8-ary 3-cube. The results have revealed that in the steady state traffic regions, the analytical model yields latency predictions which are in close agreement with those provided by the simulator in most considered cases (within 5% error in the steady state region).

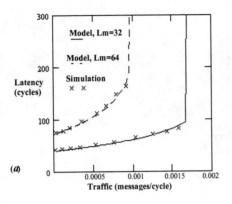

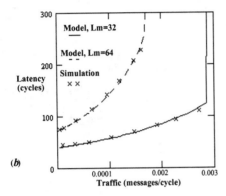

Fig. 2: Validation of the model against simulation in the 8-ary 2-cube. a) *V*=3, **b)** *V*=5.

The above model yields good latency predictions when the mean message length is greater or equal to the average message distance. As an example, for the 8-ary 2-cube, a mean message length, that is greater or equal to *M*=8 flits, allows the model to make accurate estimations. The model overestimates latency at shorter messages because network latency (equation 4) is computed assuming that a message can occupy a number of channels that is equal to the network average distance. Nonetheless, the model can be adapted to improve its accuracy for short messages. If a message can span a set of *s* channels at a time, the latency seen by a message to cross those *s* channels is computed, and then used, instead of the mean network latency, in the calculation of the blocking times and probability of virtual channels occupancy to reduce the overestimation.

The above modelling approach can be easily extended to account for communication locality using a simple locality model, proposed by Agrawal [1], as it allows the probabilities of blocking to be determined in a similar way to that of the uniform traffic case. Let *f* define the *locality fraction*, which is the fraction of

nodes that are potential candidates to receive a message from a source node. Moreover, for a given source node, message destinations are chosen randomly from the *n*-dimensional sub-cube with *fN* nodes centred at the source node. Destinations chosen uniformly over the entire network nodes corresponds to *f*=1. For a given fraction of locality *f*, destination nodes for messages originating at a source node at an address $x = (x_1,.., x_{i-1}, x_i, x_{i+1},.. x_n)$ $(0 \le x_i \le k-1)$ $(1 \le i \le n)$ are uniformly chosen from the set of nodes at $x = (x'_1,.., x'_{i-1}, x'_i, x'_{i+1},.. x'_n)$ $(x_i \le x'_i \le x_i + \sqrt[n]{fN} - 1$ modulo *k*).

With the above locality model, the average number of channels that a message visits along a dimension and across the network are given by

$$\bar{k}_f = \frac{(fN)^{1/n} - 1}{2} \tag{27}$$

$$\bar{d}_f = n\bar{k}_f \tag{28}$$

The mean message latency can be obtained by simply replacing the average message distances $\bar{k}$ and $\bar{d}$ with the new $\bar{k}_f$ and $\bar{d}_f$ in the above model.

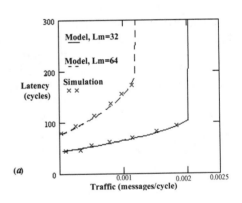

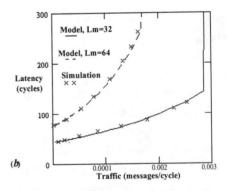

Fig. 3: Validation of the model against simulation in the 8-ary 3-cube. a) V=3, b) V=5.

5. Conclusion

There have been many fully-adaptive routing algorithms proposed in the literature for wormhole-routed k-ary n-cubes to overcome the performance limitations of deterministic routing. There has been hardly any study, however, that proposes analytical models for these algorithms. This paper has presented an analytical model to compute message latency in wormhole-routed high-radix k-ary n-cubes with fully-adaptive routing, based on Duato's algorithm. The model is based on realistic assumptions, widely used in similar studies. Simulation experiments have revealed that results from the analytical model are in close agreement with those obtained through simulation.

References

[1]   A. Agarwal, Limits on interconnection network performance, *IEEE Trans. Parallel & Distributed Systems* 2, 1991, 398-412.

[2]   Y. Boura, C.R. Das, T.M. Jacob, A performance model for adaptive routing in hypercubes, *Proc. Int. Workshop Parallel Processing*, Dec. 1994, 11-16.

[3]   A.A. Chien, A cost and performance model for k-ary n-cubes wormhole routers, *IEEE Trans. Parallel & Distributed Systems*, 9(2), 1998, 150-162.

[4]   B. Ciciani, M. Colajanni, C. Paolucci, An accurate model for the performance analysis of deterministic wormhole routing, *11th Int. Parallel Processing Symposium*, 1997, 353-359.

[5]   Cray Research Inc., The Cray T3E scalable parallel processing system, on Cray's web page at http://www.cray.com/PUBLIC/product- info/T3E.

[6]   W.J. Dally, C.L. Seitz, Deadlock-free message routing in multiprocessor interconnection networks, *IEEE Trans. Computers* C36(5), 1987, 547-553.

[7]   W.J. Dally, Performance analysis of k-ary n-cubes interconnection networks, *IEEE Trans. Computers* C-39(6), 1990, 775-785.

[8]   W.J. Dally, Virtual channel flow control, *IEEE Trans. Parallel & Distributed Systems* 3(2), 1992, 194-205.

[9]   W.J. Dally *et al*, The reliable router: A reliable and high-performance communication substrate for parallel computers, *Proc. 1st Workshop on Parallel Computer Routing & Communication*, K. Bolding & L. Snyder (Eds.), *LCNS*, Springer-Verlag, May 1994, 241-255.

[10]   J. Duato, A New theory of deadlock-free adaptive routing in wormhole routing networks, *IEEE Trans. Parallel & Distributed Systems* 4(12), 1993, 320-1331.

[11]   J. Duato, P. Lopez, Performance evaluation of adaptive routing algorithms for k-ary n-cubes, *Proc. 1st Workshop on Parallel Computer Routing &* *Communication*, K. Bolding & L. Snyder (Eds.), *LCNS*, Springer-Verlag, May 1994, 45-59.

[12]   J.T. Draper, J. Ghosh, A Comprehensive analytical model for wormhole routing in multicomputer systems, *JPDC* 32, 1994, 202-214.

[13]   R. Greenberg, L. Guan, Modelling and comparison of wormhole routed mesh and torus networks, *Proc. 9th IASTED Int. Conf. Parallel and Distributed Computing and Systems*, 1997.

[14]   W.J. Guan, W.K. Tsai, D. Blough, An analytical model for wormhole routing in multicomputer interconnection networks, *Proc. ICPP*, 1993, 650-654.

[15]   R.E. Kessler, J.L. Schwarzmeier, CRAY T3D: A new dimension for Cray Research, *in CompCon*, Spring 1993, 176-182.

[16]   L. Kleinrock, Queueing Systems Vol. 1, John Wiley, New York, 1975.

[17]   J. Kim, C.R. Das, Hypercube communication delay with wormhole routing, *IEEE Trans. Computers* C-43(7), July 1994, 806-814.

[18]   D.H. Linder, J.C. Harden, An adaptive and fault tolerant wormhole routing strategy for k-ary n-cubes, *IEEE Trans. Computers* C-40(1), 1991, 2-12.

[19]   X. Lin, P.K. Mckinley, L.M. Lin, The message flow model for routing in wormhole-routed networks, *Proc. ICPP*, 1993, 294-297.

[20]   M. Noakes, W.J. Dally, System design of the J-machine, *Proc. Advanced Research in VLSI* MIT Press, 1990, 179-192.

[21]   S.F. Nugent, The iPSC/2 direct-connect communication technology, *Proc. Conf. on Hypercube Concurrent Computers & Applications* Vol. 1, 1988, 51-60.

[22]   J. Riorda, An introduction to combinatorial analysis, [Chp. 5, 104-105], John Wiley & Sons, 1958

[23]   C.L. Seitz, The Cosmic Cube, *CACM* 28, Jan. 1985, 22-33.

[24]   C.L. Seitz, The hypercube communication chip, Dep. Comp. Sci., CalTech, Display File 5182:DF:85, March 85.

[25]   C. Su, K.G. Shin, Adaptive deadlock-free routing in multicomputers using one extra channel, *Proc. International Conference on Parallel Processing* Vol. 1, 1993, 175-182.

[26]   W.A. Whiteworth, Choice and Chance, [page 91], Cambridge University Press, 1901.

Routing in Wormhole-Switched Clustered Networks with Applications to Fault-Tolerance

Vivek Halwan and Füsun Özgüner
Department of Electrical Engineering
The Ohio State University
Columbus, OH 43210
{vhalwan,ozguner}@ee.eng.ohio-state.edu

Abstract

This paper presents a novel technique for routing in wormhole-switched clustered networks. The network model consists of a set of clusters interfaced through a common central network. First, a global routing algorithm is derived based on the local algorithms used for routing within clusters. This proposed algorithm is shown to be deadlock-free with two virtual channels. This method is then applied for fault-tolerant routing in meshes, without disabling any of the connected healthy nodes.

1 Introduction

The interest in routing in interconnection networks with irregular topology has been increasing lately, because irregular networks present greater flexibility and incremental scalability. *Wormhole switching* [1] is the prevalent switching technique in the current generation of message passing multiprocessors, such as the CRAY T3D and the Intel Paragon, and *networks of workstations* (NOWs) with wormhole switching, such as the ones using DEC Autonet, Servernet and Myrinet switches have also been recently introduced.

This paper considers a clustered network model composed of a collection of subnetworks of processing nodes, i.e. several *clusters* connected to a *central network*. No direct connection exists between nodes in different clusters, and messages are routed via the central network. It is assumed that each subnetwork uses an independent internal routing algorithm to transfer messages between its internal nodes. One of the main contributions in this paper is a global routing algorithm to allow the transfer of messages between any pair of nodes in the network, based on the existing routing algorithms in the subnetworks. The proposed global routing algorithm is deadlock-free using two sets of virtual channels.

The clustered network model has several practical applications. It can be used to interface existing networks with predefined routing algorithms to form a global network. It can also be used to incrementally scale a network with a new cluster of nodes without altering the routing algorithm of the existing network. Besides, this model can also be applied to enhance the fault-tolerance of existing routing algorithms for regular topologies. As multiprocessors scale in size, the likelihood of failures also increases, which should not keep the healthy nodes from being utilized. In the presence of faults, it is desirable not to redefine the routing method completely, but to alter it locally in a faulty neighborhood. The clustered network model can be used to isolate faulty neighborhoods in clusters, where routing can be redefined, while routing in the rest of the network is not affected by the faults.

The rest of this paper is organized as follows. Section 2 describes the clustered network model and a technique for routing in the network, based on the local routing algorithms in the subnetworks. Section 3 shows how the clustered network model can be applied for fault-tolerant routing in 2D meshes. In Section 4, extensions of the fault-tolerant routing approach to higher dimensional meshes and other topologies are discussed. Concluding remarks are presented in Section 5.

2 Routing in wormhole-switched clustered networks

2.1 The clustered network model

A common representation of a direct network is in the form of a graph, with vertices denoting processing nodes and edges representing bidirectional links, comprised of two unidirectional channels. A processing node may correspond to a single node in a direct network, or to a network switch and all its adjacent processors in a NOW. The following discussions can thus apply both to routing in wormhole-switched

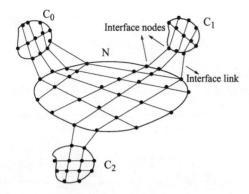

Figure 1: A clustered interconnection network.

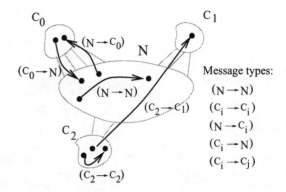

Figure 2: Five types of messages in the network.

direct networks and to routing among switches in a wormhole-switched NOW.

The network model considered here consists of clusters C_i connected to a central network N, as exemplified by the network in Figure 1, in which $i \in \{0, 1, 2\}$. The clusters and the central network are referred to as *subnetworks*. Each subnetwork is a connected network of processing nodes with arbitrary topology. No direct connection exists between nodes in separate clusters, so they must exchange messages through the central network N. An edge with an end node in N and another in a cluster C_i is an *interface link*, and its end nodes are the *interface nodes*. An interface node may have more than one interface link, and an interface node in N may be connected to interface nodes in different clusters. It is assumed that an interface node can identify which of its links are interface links, i.e. the boundaries between subnetworks are well defined. Note that this clustered network model is only partially hierarchical, since the central network does not simply transfer messages between clusters, but it also contains processing nodes, and many of them may not be interface nodes.

We assume that each subnetwork in the clustered model has a predefined deadlock-free routing algorithm for exchange of messages between its local nodes. The routing algorithm in a cluster C_i is denoted by R_{C_i} and the algorithm in N is referred to as R_N. A global routing algorithm R_G needs to be designed to allow the exchange of messages between any pair of nodes in the network.

2.2 A global routing method

Here we derive a global routing algorithm R_G, based on the routing algorithms in the individual subnetworks, i.e. R_N and R_{C_i}. The algorithm R_G should allow the transfer of messages between any pair of nodes in a deadlock-free manner. Five types of messages can be identified in the network, as illustrated

in Figure 2, based on the location of the source and the destination nodes.

Since each subnetwork has a predefined internal routing algorithm, $(N \to N)$ and $(C_i \to C_i)$ messages can be fully routed using the existing routing algorithm in N and C_i, i.e. R_N and R_{C_i}. All other types of messages need to access interface links during routing, and a logical solution is to use the existing routing algorithm at the location of the message header. With this approach, no new routing algorithm needs to be defined. A $(C_i \to C_j)$ message, for example, can first be routed using R_{C_i} to an interface node in C_i, and then request for any of the channels connected to network N. The message can then continue to be routed in N, using R_N, up to an interface node to the cluster C_j. Once the message enters cluster C_j, it can finally reach its destination node using R_{C_j}. The exchange of messages between N and a cluster C_i can be performed in a similar fashion, but only one subnetwork transition is necessary.

To guide a message during the routing process, the address field of the header is encoded with the address of up to two interface nodes, in addition to the final destination node. The header of a $(C_i \to C_j)$ message, for example, consists of the address of an interface node in C_i, followed by an interface node in N to the cluster C_j, and the address of the destination node in C_j. The choice of an interface node for each transition can be arbitrary, or based on some heuristic approach. As the message arrives at an interface node, its address is stripped from the header. The interface node then requests for any of the links connected to the next subnetwork. Algorithm R_G corresponds to a hybrid form of routing, partly source-based and partly based on distributed routing. Two methods for handling the transition of a message from one subnetwork into another can be considered:

1) *Absorb-and-retransmit*: With this method, a mes-

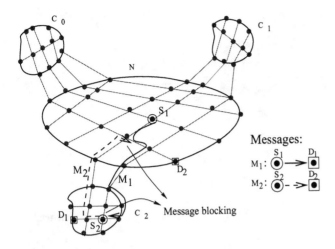

Figure 3: A potential deadlock involving M_1 and M_2.

Table 1: The three classes of messages in a cluster C_i, and the virtual channel assignment.

Message Class	Message Type	Channel Set
Incoming	$(N \to C_i)$, $(C_j \to C_i)$	vc_0
Outgoing	$(C_i \to N)$, $(C_i \to C_j)$	vc_1
Internal	$(C_i \to C_i)$	vc_0 or vc_1

Table 2: Summarized description of R_G.

Message Type	Routing
$(N \to N)$	R_N
$(C_i \to C_i)$	$R_{C_i}(vc_0)$ or $R_{C_i}(vc_1)$
$(N \to C_i)$	$R_N \to R_{C_i}(vc_0)$
$(C_i \to N)$	$R_{C_i}(vc_1) \to R_N$
$(C_i \to C_j)$	$R_{C_i}(vc_1) \to R_N \to R_{C_j}(vc_0)$

sage is fully received at an interface node before it is routed any further in the following subnetwork. In this case, the algorithm R_G will clearly be deadlock-free, since R_N and R_{C_i} are deadlock-free and no dependencies will exist between channels in different subnetworks. This method, however, creates additional communication latencies due to repeatedly storing and retransmitting the message at the interface nodes, which corresponds to the store-and-forward switching technique.

2) *Continuous-transfer*: This is an alternative method, in which the message header is immediately forwarded along an interface link as soon as it arrives at an interface node. This approach provides a seamless transition of the message header from one subnetwork to another, and only the routing algorithm applied to the header changes.

We select the continuous-transfer method for R_G, as it is likely to result in smaller message latencies, and it does not require additional buffering. However, it should be noted that cyclic dependencies may be introduced among channels in different subnetworks, which may ultimately lead to a deadlock, even if R_{C_i} and R_N are individually deadlock-free. A simple case of a cyclic dependency is illustrated in Figure 3, involving an $(N \to C_2)$ message M_1 and a $(C_2 \to N)$ message M_2. In this figure, the header of message M_1 is blocked in C_2 by M_2. Concurrently, the header of M_2 is also blocked in N by M_1. This dependency cycle cannot solely be prevented by R_{C_2} and R_N being deadlock-free.

For a deadlock-free implementation of R_G, we propose to use two virtual channel sets, vc_0 and vc_1, for each physical channel in a cluster C_i. A message

accessing physical channels in C_i can belong to one of three classes: *internal messages*, i.e. messages of type $(C_i \to C_i)$, *incoming messages* $((N \to C_i)$ and $(C_j \to C_i))$, or *outgoing messages* $((C_i \to N)$ and $(C_i \to C_j))$. These messages are multiplexed in C_i using vc_0 and vc_1, as described in Table 1. Internal messages are allowed to use either vc_0 or vc_1 channels, but a message must use the same type of virtual channel for the entire route. With this multiplexing of messages, the proposed routing algorithm R_G is summarized in Table 2. Theorem 1 below demonstrates that the algorithm R_G, as defined, is deadlock-free.

Theorem 1 - *If R_N and all R_{C_i} are deadlock-free, then R_G, as defined in Table 2, is also deadlock-free.*

Proof: During its routing process, a message using R_G can occupy channels in N and in at most two clusters. The proof that R_G is deadlock-free is derived by showing that no channel in the network can be part of a deadlock cycle, as follows:

(i) Incoming messages whose headers arrive at an interface node in the destination node cluster C_i will only request for vc_0 channels for the remaining route in C_i. These messages will only contend for vc_0 channels among themselves and with the internal messages that chose to use vc_0 channels. Since all these messages follow $R_{C_i}(vc_0)$, which is deadlock-free, they will all be successfully routed in C_i. Channels vc_0 in C_i cannot therefore be involved in a deadlock.

(ii) Only incoming messages in a cluster C_i request the interface channels directed from N to C_i, and once a message acquires such a directed channel, it is guaranteed to complete its routing in C_i, due to (i). Therefore, directed incoming interface channels cannot be part of a deadlock cycle.

116

(iii) Any message with its header being routed in network N, follows R_N, and is either addressed to a destination node in N or to an interface node connected to the destination node cluster. In the latter case, once a message reaches an interface node, it can successfully complete its routing, due to (i) and (ii). Therefore, since messages follow R_N up to a destination node or an interface node in N, and since R_N is deadlock-free, there cannot be a deadlock involving channels in N.

(iv) Only outgoing messages from a cluster C_i request for the interface channels directed from C_i to N, and once a message acquires such a directed channel, it is guaranteed to complete its routing, due to (i)–(iii). Therefore, directed outgoing interface channels cannot be part of a deadlock cycle.

(v) Outgoing messages from a cluster C_i, while in C_i, request for vc_1 channels only, and contend for vc_1 channels among themselves and with internal messages routed using vc_1 channels. Outgoing messages that reach an interface node in C_i will successfully be routed to their destinations, due to (i)–(iv). Therefore, since $R_{C_i}(vc_1)$ is deadlock-free, no deadlocks can involve vc_1 channels.

The five statements above show that none of the channels in the clustered network can be in a deadlock cycle. R_G is therefore deadlock-free. □

In addition to deadlocks, a routing algorithm should also avoid message livelocks. A livelocked message is not deadlocked, but is continuously misrouted, without ever reaching the destination. Theorem 2 below shows that R_G is livelock-free as long as R_N and R_{C_i} are livelock-free.

Theorem 2 - *If R_N and R_{C_i} are livelock-free, then algorithm R_G, as defined in Table 2, is also livelock-free.*

Proof: Considering that a message accesses physical channels in at most three subnetworks (two clusters and the central network) and that, within each subnetwork, a message is routed using a local routing algorithm that is livelock-free, it can be concluded that R_G is also livelock-free. □

It should be noted that two virtual channel sets in each cluster C_i are sufficient to avoid deadlocks, as long as the R_{C_i} algorithms do not require any virtual channels on their own. If a particular R_{C_i} requires at least v virtual channels for deadlock avoidance, then $2v$ virtual channels in C_i will be sufficient. Also note that no additional virtual channels are required in N

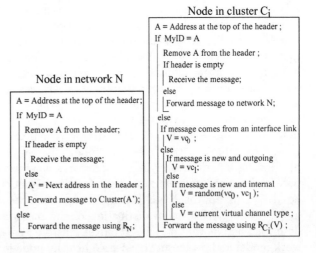

Figure 4: Implementation of R_G in N and C_i.

for R_G. For N, with R_G, messages to or from a cluster appear as messages consumed or injected by its interface nodes.

Limiting a message to up to two transitions of subnetworks serves two purposes: (a) it avoids unnecessarily long routes, by preventing a message from entering and exiting the same intermediate cluster network, and (b) it reduces the number of channel dependencies among clusters, which keeps the number of virtual channel requirements low. Minimal routing with R_G is possible, as long as R_N and R_{C_i} are minimal, and a source node can recognize which interface nodes are closest to the destination.

Figure 4 describes how R_G can be implemented in nodes in N and C_i. The implementation is straightforward, given that R_N and R_{C_i} are already defined in the subnetworks. To prepare the header of a message to a cluster C_j, a message source in N needs to know which interface nodes in N are connected to C_j. In addition, a message source in a cluster C_i also needs to know which nodes in C_i are the interface nodes. After the header is encoded, routing of the message can begin. In C_i, if the message is an outgoing message, it exits the source via a vc_1 channel. An incoming message that arrives at an interface node in C_i is forwarded via a vc_0 channel. At an intermediate node, the same virtual channel type as the input channel is also used for the output.

3 Fault-tolerant routing using the clustered network model

This section describes the use of the clustered network model for fault-tolerant routing in regular networks, such as cubes and meshes. Some routing algorithms, such as dimension-ordered routing and some adaptive routing methods [2], make use of the regular structure of meshes and cubes, which results in a simple and efficient implementation. Communication algorithms, such as for collective communication operations, are also optimized for these existing routing algorithms. In the presence of faults, however, meshes and cubes are no longer regular, and the existing routing algorithms may no longer be used, as they are not inherently fault-tolerant. It is desirable to enhance these algorithms so that messages follow these simple routing algorithms for regular networks wherever possible and get misrouted around faulty neighborhoods. This approach has been previously adopted in [3, 4, 5, 6]. The main distinction of the method described here is that it is based on the clustered network model and avoids any connected healthy node in the network from being disabled.

We initially consider 2D meshes only, but the results are later extended to other cases. Both node and link faults are considered, and a node fault is equivalent to all its attached links being faulty. It is assumed that no message originates from, or is addressed to a faulty node. The proposed method is described following a review of existing fault-tolerant algorithms.

3.1 Previous fault-tolerant methods

Boppana and Chalasani [3] proposed enhanced fault-tolerant versions, called *f-cube2* and *f-cube4*, for the well known X-Y routing algorithm in 2D meshes. They introduce the *block-fault* model, in which all faulty regions are enclosed in convex (rectangular) blocks, as illustrated in Figure 5. Healthy nodes surrounding a fault-block form a *fault-ring* (or a *fault-chain*, which is an incomplete fault-ring at a border of the mesh). A message essentially follows X-Y routing until it encounters a fault-block, and gets misrouted around fault-rings, along predefined directions [3]. Two basic examples of misrouting are shown in Figure 5. The f-cube2 method uses two virtual channels and tolerates non-overlapping fault-blocks, i.e. blocks whose fault-rings have no nodes in common. The f-cube4 method can tolerate overlapping fault-blocks, but with four virtual channels. In [4], the authors describe an improved version of f-cube4, called *f-cube3*, which tolerates the same types of faults but with only three virtual channels.

Su and Shin [5] proposed a fault-tolerant version of an adaptive routing algorithm [2] with two virtual channels. In this adaptive algorithm, two virtual networks (vn_0 and vn_1) are formed, and routing is X-Y in vn_0 and minimal and fully-adaptive in vn_1. The fault-tolerant version uses the same block-fault model described above, but the presentation in [5] consid-

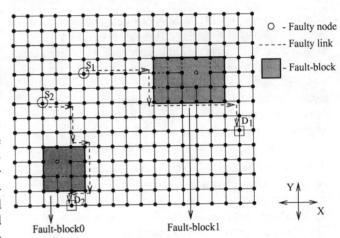

Figure 5: The block-fault model for misrouting in a fault-tolerant X-Y routing algorithm.

ers node faults only. Non-overlapping fault-blocks are tolerated with two virtual channels.

All the methods above use the block-fault model, and some are limited to non-overlapping fault-blocks. These restrictions, in practice, may require many healthy nodes in a faulty neighborhood to be disabled. More recently in [6], a fault-tolerant X-Y routing method was proposed with five virtual channels, which tolerates certain non-convex faulty regions, called *weakly convex* regions. Still, only certain types of non-convex faulty regions are tolerated. A logical consideration, therefore, is to verify whether an enhanced and fault-tolerant version of an existing routing algorithm can be designed, which does not require disabling healthy nodes, and which preserves the characteristics of the original routing method outside of faulty neighborhoods. In the next section, we propose a fault-tolerant routing method which attempts to provide these features.

3.2 A fault-tolerant method based on the clustered network model

Let R be the original routing algorithm for meshes with limited fault-tolerance, such as X-Y routing or the adaptive routing in [2]. The algorithm R_F, an enhanced fault-tolerant version of R, is derived by drawing an analogy between the block-fault model and the clustered network model described in Section 2.

Faulty regions in the block-fault model are enclosed by rectangular fault-blocks. The network outside the fault-blocks, including fault-rings and chains, is referred to as an *incomplete mesh*. Healthy nodes inside a fault-block that are either directly or indirectly connected to the incomplete mesh, form clusters of subnetworks in the fault-block. The incomplete mesh

Network N

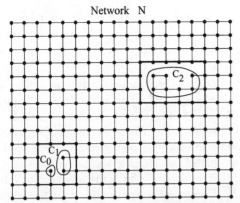

Figure 6: Analogy between the block-fault and the clustered network model.

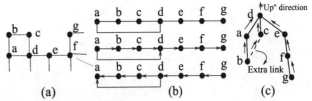

Figure 7: Methods for deriving routing algorithms in a cluster: (a) cluster C_2, (b) embedding a trail, (c) embedding a spanning tree.

can be considered analogous to the central network N in the clustered network model, and the clusters of healthy nodes appear as the clusters C_i attached to N. An illustrative example of this analogy is presented in Figure 6. Note that more than one cluster may exist inside a fault-block, since these clusters may not be directly connected, except through the incomplete mesh. The nodes in the clusters correspond to the nodes disabled in the algorithms reviewed in Section 3.1. Here, we attempt to preserve all the nodes in the clusters that are still connected to the incomplete mesh. Note that there may be clusters that are fully disconnected from the incomplete mesh. These clusters are treated as faulty regions in our model.

The algorithm R_F corresponds to the algorithm R_G (Table 2) in the case of a faulty mesh, and can be subdivided into R_N and R_{C_i}. The algorithm R_N in the incomplete mesh may correspond to any of the methods reviewed in Section 3.1, which consider the block-fault model. More specifically, R_N should correspond to the enhanced fault-tolerant version of the original routing algorithm R (X-Y routing or adaptive routing [2]), which only requires a slight modification of R [3, 4, 5]. Each cluster C_i is a connected irregular network, so R_{C_i} can be derived using any of the existing techniques for routing in irregular networks [7, 8, 9, 10]. Two basic approaches exist:

1) *Trail-based routing* [7, 8, 9]: This approach is based on embedding a trail in the network graph, which visits each node at least once. Two directed trails in opposite directions can be derived from the embedded trail, and short-cut channels are added to these directed graphs, as illustrated in Figure 7(b), for the fault-block in Figure 7(a). Each message uses channels in only one of the directed graphs, which avoids deadlocks. Embedding certain types of trails, such as Eulerian trails, and Hamiltonian or Pseudo-Hamiltonian

paths [9], allows deadlock-free routing without virtual channels. However, not all graphs have such trails and, in these cases, deadlock-free routing can be achieved with *skirt-based trails* [8], which require at most two virtual channels.

2) *Tree-based routing* [10]: This method is based on embedding a spanning tree in the network graph and assigning directions to the network links as, for example, in Figure 7(c). The "up" direction is towards the node closer to the root in the spanning tree. If both end nodes are at the same level, the direction is chosen by a tie-breaking criterion, such as the node ID. To prevent deadlocks, a route must traverse zero or more links in the "up" direction followed by zero or more links in the "down" direction. Routing is done via look-up tables, and does not require virtual channels to avoid deadlocks. Spanning trees always exist in connected graphs, and a distributed algorithm is presented in [10] to dynamically embed a spanning tree.

Either of the methods above can be used to derive a routing algorithm for C_i. The method based on embedding a spanning tree is practical because it does not require virtual channels and allows dynamic reconfiguration in the case of faults. The algorithm R_F is completely defined by R_N and R_{C_i} and the routing policy in Table 2. This proposed method can be used when the incomplete mesh is a connected network. It can also be extended for routing in each partition of an incomplete mesh, if it gets disconnected. Because of the analogy between faulty meshes and the clustered network model, Corollary 1 follows from Theorems 1 and 2 and the fact that R_N and R_{C_i} are deadlock- and livelock-free.

Corollary 1 - *If R_N and R_{C_i} are deadlock- and livelock-free, the fault-tolerant algorithm R_F based on the clustered network model is deadlock- and livelock-free, and can tolerate any fault distribution that does not disconnect the incomplete mesh.*

The minimum number of virtual channels needed to avoid deadlocks in R_F depends on the requirements for R_N and R_{C_i}. Some implementation methods for

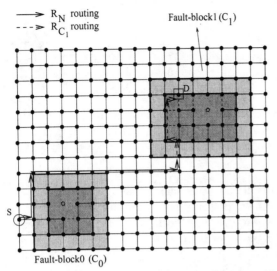

Fault-block0 (C_0)

Figure 8: R_F routing in a two-level block-fault model.

R_{C_i} require no virtual channels and, from Theorem 1, two virtual channels in the clusters are sufficient. The methods for R_N require at least two virtual channels in the incomplete mesh (Section 3.1).

The implementation of R_F is essentially the same as R_G in Figure 4, except, possibly, for the number of virtual channels used. In this current form, though, the implementation of R_F can be quite complex, as compared to the original algorithm R, because global knowledge of the fault distribution may be needed to locate the interface nodes to prepare the message header. The next section proposes a modified block-fault model, which results in a simplified implementation of R_F that only requires some limited knowledge of the fault distribution.

3.3 A simplified implementation of R_F

A modified block-fault model, called the *two-level block-fault model*, is proposed here, to simplify the implementation of R_F. In addition to the fault-ring or fault-chain in the original description of the block-fault model (referred to here as a *level-1 fault-ring* or *fault-chain*), a *level-2 fault-ring* (or *level-2 fault-chain*) is also defined, formed by the nodes in the incomplete mesh adjacent to the level-1 fault-ring, as illustrated in Figure 8. This modification essentially consists of increasing the size of the fault-block by one link along each direction. Henceforth, we use the term *ring* to refer to fault-rings and fault-chains in general.

With the two-level model, all nodes and links inside level-2 rings form clusters, and the nodes and links outside level-1 rings form the network N. Note that, due to the proximity to a border in the mesh, a level-1 fault-ring may be enclosed by a level-2 fault-chain,

instead of a fault-ring. Also, fewer fault-blocks may result with the two-level model, because previously disjoint fault-blocks may now be merged in a larger fault-block.

With the two-level model, only one cluster exists inside each fault-block. This is a result of the original ring (the level-1 ring) now being inside a fault-block; since all the other healthy nodes inside the fault-block are directly or indirectly connected to the level-1 ring, only one cluster, which includes the nodes in the level-1 ring, exists. Also, note that the links between level-1 and level-2 rings now form the interface links between N and C_i and, correspondingly, the interface nodes are nodes in the level-1 and level-2 rings. Note that only the nodes in a level-2 ring which are at the corners of the fault-block are not interface nodes.

With this modified model, the interface between the network N and each of the clusters C_i has a simple rectangular format, which can greatly simplify the implementation of R_F. The main advantages with the two-level model are the following:

a) The nodes in N that are not interface nodes need no knowledge of the fault distribution. An interface node in N only needs to know the defining coordinates of its adjacent rectangular fault-blocks, such as the coordinate of two diagonally opposite nodes in the rectangles. Nodes in a cluster C_i only need to identify the interface nodes in C_i, and no other cluster.

b) The header of a message originated in N only needs to contain the (X, Y) address of the final destination node. An outgoing message in C_i only needs two addresses, the address of an interface node in C_i and the final destination node. Thus, once this message exits the cluster, only the address of the final destination remains in the header.

The implementation of R_F in a cluster C_i is identical to the description for R_G in Figure 4. A message header in the network N contains only the address of the final destination node. The implementation of R_F in N has the simplified form presented in Figure 9. If a node in N is not an interface node, it either receives the message, if its ID matches the destination node address, or forwards it using R_N. Before forwarding a message using R_N, an interface node in N first checks whether the destination address belongs to an adjacent cluster. This can be done by simply checking to see whether the coordinates of the destination node are inside any adjacent rectangular fault-block. In this case, the message is forwarded to the corresponding cluster, instead of a node in N.

An illustration of R_F routing is shown in Figure 8

Node in network N

```
A = destination node address;

If MyID = A
    Receive the message;
else
    If A is in an adjacent cluster;
        Forward header to the interface link of the cluster;
    else
        Forward the message using R_N ;
```

Figure 9: Simplified implementation of R_F in N.

for an $(N \rightarrow C_i)$ message. This example considers R as the X-Y deterministic routing algorithm and R_N as its fault-tolerant version described in [3]. The message is initially routed according to R_N until it encounters the level-2 ring of fault-block0. Since the destination is not inside this block, the nodes at the level-2 ring continue to route the message according to R_N. Next, the message reaches the interface node in fault-block1, and is then forwarded to cluster C_1 and completes routing using R_{C_1}.

4 Generalizations of the fault-tolerant routing method

The authors in [3, 5] described extensions of the block-fault model to higher dimensional meshes. A faulty region, in this case, is enclosed by a block that is convex along each two-dimensional plane. A similar routing algorithm R_N can be used outside such fault-blocks. Likewise, clusters can be formed inside the fault-blocks, and the fault-tolerant method described above can be applied to any d-dimensional mesh.

It should be noted that the clustered network model makes no assumptions about the routing algorithm R_N. In general, any routing algorithm R can be made fault-tolerant if faulty neighborhoods can be enclosed by adequately shaped regions that allow a simple definition of an algorithm R_N from R. Healthy nodes inside the enclosed regions form clusters with routing algorithms defined internally. In addition, the analogy with the clustered model is not limited to the mesh topology. Similar approach for fault-tolerance in other topologies can also be considered.

5 Conclusions and future work

This paper presented a global routing algorithm for a clustered network configuration, based on the local routing algorithms in its subnetworks. The algorithm is shown to be deadlock-free with two virtual channel sets. This method was then applied for fault-tolerant routing in meshes, which only requires altering the existing routing algorithm in a faulty neighborhood.

A future task consists of implementing a distributed algorithm to dynamically construct level-1 and level-2 rings around fault-blocks in the presence of new faults. In addition, efficient ways for selecting an interface node for an outgoing message in a cluster need to be studied. Simulations will then be performed to assess the performance of this routing algorithm.

References

[1] L. Ni and P. McKinley, "A survey of wormhole routing techniques in direct networks," *IEEE Computer*, no. 2, pp. 62–76, 1993.

[2] J. Duato, "A new theory of deadlock-free adaptive routing in wormhole networks," *IEEE Transactions on Parallel and Distributed Systems*, vol. 4, no. 12, pp. 1320–1331, 1993.

[3] R. Boppana and S. Chalasani, "Fault-tolerant wormhole routing algorithms for mesh networks," *IEEE Transactions on Computers*, vol. 44, no. 7, pp. 848–864, 1995.

[4] P.-H. Sui and S.-D. Wang, "An improved algorithm for fault-tolerant wormhole routing in meshes," *IEEE Transactions on Computers*, vol. 46, no. 9, pp. 1040–1042, 1997.

[5] C. Su and K. G. Shin, "Adaptive fault-tolerant deadlock-free routing in meshes and hypercubes," *IEEE Transactions on Computers*, vol. 45, no. 6, pp. 666–683, 1996.

[6] W. Ho and Y. Cheung, "Fault-tolerant wormhole routing in mesh networks with non-rectangular fault regions," *Proceedings of the International Conference on Parallel and Distributed Computing Systems*, pp. 551–557, 1997.

[7] W. Qiao and L. Ni, "Adaptive routing in irregular networks using cut-through switches," *Proceedings of the 1996 International Conference on Parallel Processing*, vol. 1, pp. 52–60, 1996.

[8] Y. Tseng, D. Panda, and T. Lai, "A trip-based multicasting model in wormhole-routed networks with virtual channels," *IEEE Transactions on Parallel and Distributed Systems*, vol. 7, no. 2, pp. 138–150, 1996.

[9] R. Hadas, K. Watkins, and T. Hehre, "Fault-tolerant multicast routing in the mesh with no virtual channels," *Proceedings of the International Symposium on High-Performance Computer Architecture*, pp. 180–190, 1996.

[10] M. Schroeder, A. Birrell, et. al., "Autonet: a high-speed, self-configuring local area network using point-to-point links," *DEC Technical Report SRC 59*, 1990.

Routing Algorithms for Anycast Messages

Dong Xuan   Weijia Jia
Department of Computer Science
City University of Hong Kong
Kowloon, Hong Kong
Phone: +852 2788 9701
Email: wjia@cs.cityu.edu.hk

Wei Zhao
Department of Computer Science
Texas A & M University
College Station, TX77843-3112
Phone: 409-845-5098
Email: zhao@cs.tamu.edu

Abstract

In this paper, we propose and analyze three routing algorithms for anycast packets: i) source-destination based routing with weighted random selection (SD/WRS), ii) destination based routing with weighted random selection (D/WRS), and iii) the shortest shortest path first (SSPF) algorithms. The SSPF algorithm is a simple extension to the traditional SPF algorithm for routing unicast packets. The SD/WRS and D/WRS algorithms explicitly take into account characteristics of anycast message traffic and its recipient group. As a result, our simulation study shows that both the SD/WRS and D/WRS algorithms perform much better than SSPF in terms of average end-to-end packet delay. In particular, SD/WRS performs very close to a dynamic optimal algorithm in most cases. Our algorithms are simple, efficient, and compatible with the most of existing routing technologies. We also formally prove the loop free and correctness properties for our algorithms.

1. Introduction

In this paper, we address routing problems for *anycast* messages in packet switching networks. An anycast message is the one that should be delivered to one member in a group of designated recipients [PMM93]. Traditional unicast message is a special case of anycast message in that for an unicast message, the recipient group size is one.

Using anycast communication services may considerably simplify some applications. For example, it is much easier for a client to find an appropriate server when there are multiple servers for one kind of service in a network. In particular, without anycast service, a domain name resolver (client) has to be configured with the IP addresses of all the associated Domain Name Service (DNS) servers. However, with anycast service, a resolver will only need to send a query with a well-known DNS anycast address whenever the resolver wants the services from a domain name server. As another example of anycast service, multiple mirrored Web sites can share a single anycast address, and users could simply send a request with the anycast address in order to obtain information (e.g., weather and stock quotes).

Because more and more applications demand anycast services, in the latest version of IP specification, Ipv6,

anycast has been defined as a standard service [DH95]. Several studies have been done on communication with anycast messages since the notion was introduced in [PMM93]. Generally speaking, the problems pertaining to anycast can be divided in two classes: management methods at application layer for using anycast services, and procedures and protocols at network layer for routing and addressing anycast messages. In [HD95], it was determined that the anycast addresses are allocated from the unicast address space with any of the defined unicast address format. In [BAZSF97], the implication of an anycasting service supported at the application layer was explored. The internet draft [B96] addressed the issue relevant to notifying a client the address of a server which is initially accessed via an anycast address.

Little work has been done on routing anycast messages while extensive studies have been carried out for routing unicast and multicast messages [D88, E86, KJ83, SS80]. Routing in a network is concerned with determining a path for a message to travel from its source node to its destination node. There are two classes of routing approaches: *single path routing* and *multiple path routing*. With single path routing, the path of a given pair of source and destination hosts is unique. That is, the path for messages from the source to the destination is time invariant (unless, of course, the network topology changes). Single path routing is simple and easy to implement, and has been widely used in the internet. For example, the common routing protocol, RIP (Routing Information Protocol) uses the shortest path first (SPF) algorithm to select a single path that has the minimum value of an objective function. The objective function of a given path is usually defined by a numeric sum of the individual link parameters (e.g., number of hops, delay, bandwidth, etc.).

A problem associated with single path routing is that it may overload the selected path and hence cause traffic congestion [KZ89]. The multiple path routing approach addresses this problem. Generally speaking, a multiple path routing algorithm will split traffic into several different paths. Many analyses have shown that the multiple path routing algorithms can increase network throughput and decrease message delay [JG93, JL92].

Earlier studies and projects mostly addressed multiple path routing for unicast messages. A survey on the multiple path routing algorithms can be found in [GK97]. Some of the algorithms split traffic to multiple paths all the time. Heuristic [FC71, M93] and optimal methods [CG74, FCK73, G77, SC76, CR97] can be catalogued into these type of algorithms. Some algorithms do it only when the optimal path becomes inoperable [BZ92, SAN92, WC90]. For example, in [WC90], a SPF-EE algorithm is developed. With the algorithm, traffic is routed along the shortest-path under normal condition. Only in the presence of congestion and resource failures, the traffic is splitted to alternate paths.

The ideas of the multiple path routing algorithms are also used in recent versions of internet protocols. OSPF distributes traffic over paths, which have (almost) equal length [M94a]. IGRP goes even further: it quantifies the notion of "almost equality" by introducing variance coefficient of path lengths and uses it in route selection [H91]. PIM (protocol independent multicast) architecture supports both shared and source-specific (shortest-path) distribution trees [DEFJLW96].

In this study, we take a multiple path routing approach for anycast messages. The salient features of our routing algorithms are:

1. Our algorithms intend to take into account characteristics of anycast traffic and its recipient group. For example, the members of recipient group of an anycast message may be unevenly distributed in a network. The multiple paths from a source to the recipients do not converge as they do in the unicast case. Routing anycast messages must take these factors into account. As a result, the effectiveness of the routing algorithms can be improved.

2. Our algorithms aim at achieving a good balance between the complexity involved and the performance realized. A smarter routing decision could be made if more status information is collected and/or more complicated decision procedure is invoked. However, complexity has usually been a factor that limits the practical usage of an algorithm. We seek routing algorithms that are simple, efficient, and compatible with the most of existing routing technologies.

Within the domain of multiple path routing, we consider two classes of methods in making a routing decision in a router: source-destination based method and destination based method. The former selects a route based on both source address and destination address while the latter is based on the destination address only. The source-destination based method provides more routes to be selected but consumes more storage space. For each of the methods, we propose methods for loop elimination. This is necessary when we deal with multiple routes. We also propose a heuristic weighted random selection algorithm to choose one route from multiple routes that are available. Simulation data show that our proposed algorithms

perform much better than traditional shortest path first algorithm in terms of delay and throughput.

2. Models and Notations

The network we consider consists of a number of nodes. A node can be either a router or a host. Nodes are connected by physical links along which packets can be transmitted. Each link has an attribute called *distance*. The distance of a link is usually measured by delay, bandwidth, etc. As we will see, distance plays a critical role in route selection. See Figure 2-1 for a sample network where the numerical values associated with links are their distances.

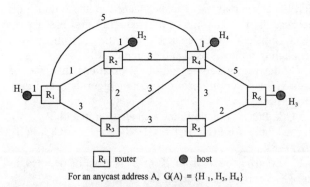

For an anycast address A, $G(A) = \{H_1, H_3, H_4\}$

Figure 2-1. A Sample Network

A packet is specified by addresses of its source and destination. A source is a host. The destination for an anycast packet can be any one in a group of pre-defined hosts. Let A be an anycast (destination) address. We denote G(A) to be the group of designated recipient hosts. That is, a packet with anycast address A can be sent to any host which is in G(A).

A node (say R) is a *next hop* of another node (say R') if R can receive a packet directly from R' without going through any other router.[1]

Routers in the network cooperatively decide a path for a packet and transmit the packet along the path. Formally, P(X, Y) denotes a *path* from X to Y where X and Y are nodes. Sometimes, we would like to list explicitly the sequence of nodes in a path. We will use terms route and path interchangeably.

D(P(X, Y)) denotes the *total distance* of links on path P(X, Y). It is usually defined by a numeric sum of the individual link distances.

A router typically has equal number of input ports and output ports, which in turn connect to input and output links, respectively. Each router has a number of *routing tables*. An entry in a routing table usually consists of fields for destination address, next hop, distance, etc. See Figure 2-2 for a sample entry in a routing table. For an incoming packet, the router locates an entry in a routing table such that the destination address of the packet matches the destination address of the entry. The *next hop field* defines

---

[1] Term "next hop" usually means a router. Here, we use it in a generalized sense. In this paper, a next hop can be either a router or a host. This simplies our discussion of the problems.

the next hop where the packet should be sent to. The *distance field* contains the value of the total distance of a path that leads to the destination address.

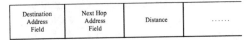

Destination Address Field	Next Hop Address Field	Distance	....

Figure 2-2. An Entry in Routing Table

In a router, once the next hop of a packet is determined, the packet will be transported to a proper output port where the packet will be transmitted into the associated output link, which in turn connects to the next hop. It is possible that a packet may have to be queued at the output port because the transmission of previous packet(s) has not yet been finished. We assume that the first-in-first-out scheduling policy is used at the output port.

Following are some additional notations that will be used in the descriptions of our routing algorithms and their properties.

$C(k, P(X, Y))$ denotes the *k-th element* in path $P(X, Y)$. For example, for $P(H_2, H_1) = <H_2, R_2, R_1, H_1>$, $C(3, P(H_2, H_1)) = R_1$.

A *shortest path* from X to Y is usually denoted as $P_{SPF}(X, Y)$. By definition, for any $P(X, Y)$,

$$D(P_{SPF}(X, Y)) \leq D(P(X, Y)) \qquad (2-1)$$

In the network shown in Figure 2-1, $P_{SPF}(H_2, R_6) = < H_2, R_2, R_3, R_5, R_6>$.

$P(X, Y, k)$ denotes a *sub-path* of $P(X, Y)$. $P(X, Y, k)$ starts from X and ends at the k-th node in $P(X, Y)$.

We make two assumptions when we describe our routing algorithms and analyze their properties. We assume that each host is *singly-homed* in the sense that a host only connects to one router which processes all the incoming and outgoing packets for the host. We assume that the network has *no faults*. Between any pair of nodes, there exists at least one functioning path. These two assumptions simplify the discussion of routing algorithms we are going to introduce. In Section 5, we will discuss how to extend our algorithms to the systems where these assumptions do not hold.

3. Routing Algorithms

3.1. Descriptions

In this paper, we consider two classes of methods in making a routing decision in a router: *source-destination based method* and *destination based method*.

1. With *the source-destination based routing*, a router maintains one table for each source. For an incoming packet, the router extracts the source and destination addresses from the packet header. Using the source address, a proper table is located. The router then looks up the table and locates an entry, which matches the destination address. Using this entry, the router determines the next hop to which the packet should be sent. Then, the router locates an output port that directly connects to the node defined by the field of next hop.

The packet is then sent to the output port and eventually transmitted out from this router to the next hop.

2. With *the destination based routing*, a router maintains only one table for all the sources. For an incoming packet, the router extracts the destination addresses from the packet header. The router then looks up the table and locates an entry, which matches the destination address. Using this entry, the router determines the next hop and the corresponding output port. The packet is then sent to the output port for transmission.

We propose to apply both source-destination based method and destination based method to routing anycast messages. Both methods have been used in routing unicast and multicast messages [M94a, M94b].

Each method has its own advantages and disadvantages. For example, the source-destination based method requires much more storage than the destination based one. On the other hand, however, for a given packet the source-destination based method can generally result in a better path than the destination based one. We will thoroughly compare and analyze both methods in Section 4.

Nevertheless, three issues have to be addressed in order to use both methods properly.

1. An entry in a routing table defines a mapping from a destination address to the output port (implied by the next hop field) at the associated router. There are many ways to define this mapping. For example, an entry may map a destination address to an output port which has the shortest waiting queue. The other method, that is used widely in many existing routers, is the shortest path first (SPF) method. With this protocol, an entry will map a destination address to an output port that leads to a path with the minimum value of an objective function.

We propose to use the SPF method to build entries in routing table. Note that while the mapping from a destination to the output port in the router is usually one-to-one for unicast address, it may be one-to-many for multicast and anycast addresses. Hence, we will have to have some modifications as discussed next.

2. As mentioned above, due to multiple destinations which an anycast packet may have, the routing table, established by the SPF method, may have multiple entries for a given anycast address. The semantics of anycast service requires that only one of those entries be used for a given packet. That is, the router should select one of the entries that matches the anycast address and then route the packet according to the entry. In this paper, we consider two ways to make the selection.

* Shortest shortest path first (SSPF). Recall that each entry maps an anycast address to an output port that will lead to one of the recipients with the shortest path. With the SSPF method, we will select an entry that has the minimum value of the objective function among all the eligible entries. In fact, the SSPF method is a simple extension to the traditional SPF algorithm for routing unicast packets.

* Weighted random selection (WRS). With this method, each entry is assigned a weight. An entry is randomly selected. The weight of an entry presents the probability that the entry is selected. We will discuss a weight assignment method in Section 3.3.

3. A route should not contain loop(s). A loop in a route implies wasting network resource and worsening packet delay. When we randomly select an entry in the routing table, care has to be taken. Otherwise, a route for an anycast message may contain loop(s). In Section 3.2, we will discuss methods that can eliminate any loop in routes for anycast message.

In brief, the routing algorithms in this paper can be classified as source-destination based and destination based. They each can be further classified according to the entry selection methods: the shortest shortest path first (SSPF) and the weighted random selection (WRS). However, as mentioned above, when the SSPF method is utilized, both source-destination and destination based methods result in the same route. Hence, we really deal with three algorithms: i) source-destination based with weighted random selection, denoted by SD/WRS; ii) destination based with weighted random selection, denoted by D/WRS, and iii) the SSPF method.

3.2. Loop Elimination Methods

We say that an entry in a routing table is *eligible* if the route resulting from using this entry is loop free. The objective of a loop elimination method is to determine which entries in a routing table are eligible. If an entry is not eligible, it should never be used.

A trivial loop elimination method would be to mark all the entries ineligible except the one that leads to the SSPF routing. In this way, it can be shown that there will be no loop in the routes. However, with this method we will not be able to share anycast traffic over multiple routes that are available from a source to the members in the recipient group. This may result in a poor delay and throughput performance (as we will demonstrate in Section 4). Hence, a good loop elimination method should allow as many entries as possible to be eligible while guaranteeing loop-free routing.

We need to introduce some notations which will help us to describe our loop elimination methods. In all the definitions introduced below, X and Y are nodes.

Definition 3-1. (Relation $>_{S,A}$). Let S be a source and A be an anycast address. $X >_{S,A} Y$ if for some $k \geq 0$ and $H \in G(A)$, $C(k, P_{SPF}(S, H)) = X$ and $C(k+1, P_{SPF}(S, H)) = Y$.

Informally, this definition implies that if X and Y are two adjunct elements in one of the shortest paths from source S to the members in G(A), then $X >_{S,A} Y$.

Definition 3-2. (Function min_d). Let A be an anycast address, min_d(X, A) is the minimum distance from X to

any member of the recipient group with anycast address A. That is,

$$\min\_d(X, A) = \min_{H \in G(A)} (D(P_{SPF}(X, H))) \cdot \qquad (3\text{-}1)$$

Definition 3-3. (Relation $>_A$). Let A be an anycast address. $X >_A Y$ if for some H in G(A) $C(2, P_{SPF}(X, H)) = Y$, and min_d(X, A) > min_d(Y, A).

Informally, this definition implies that if $X >_A Y$ if i) Y is a next hop of X, and ii) the minimum distance from Y to any member of the recipient group with anycast address A is less than the one of X.

Based on the notations defined above, our loop elimination methods can be described as follows:

1. *The case of source-destination based routing.* Let R be a router. In its routing table for source S, an entry for anycast address A is eligible if $R >_{S,A} R'$, and R' is the next hop field of the entry.

2. *The case of destination based routing.* Let R be a router. In its routing table an entry for anycast address A is eligible if $R >_A R'$, and R' is the next hop field of the entry.

Theorem 3-1. (loop-free routing). With the above loop elimination methods, there will be no loop in any route for anycast packets.

The proofs of the theorem and other theorems or lemmas are presented in [XJZ97].

3.3. Weight Assignment Method

When the weighted random selection method is used to choose an entry in the routing table, an anycast packet may be routed to different members in the recipient group. This effectively distributes the traffic over different routes, potentially improves the delay and throughput performance. To fully take advantage of this load sharing effect, we must carefully assign the weights to the eligible entries in a routing table.

Weight assignments for multiple path routing have been studied in the literature. For example, an optimal weight assignment was proposed in [G77] by which the average delay of messages can be minimized. We will take a heuristic approach. Our idea is to have a simple parameterized weight assignment formula that can cover a wide range of heuristics, which one may like to use in practice.

Without loss of generality, let us assume that there are K eligible entries in a routing table for a given anycast address. Let these entries be indexed by 1, 2, . . ., K; and their associated weights be denoted as $W_1, W_2, \ldots, W_K$, respectively.

From the information provided in the entries of a routing table, how should the weight of an entry be assigned? A rule of thumb is that the weight should be inversely proportional to the distance of the route that leads to a member in the recipient group. That is, for i = 1, 2, . . ., K,

$$W_i \propto 1/D_i \qquad (3\text{-}2)$$

where D_i is the value in the distance field of entry i. To normalize W_i to be a probability such that $\sum_{i=1}^{K} W_i = 1$, we should assign W_i as follows: for i = 1, 2, . . ., K,

$$W_i = (1/D_i) / \sum_{j=1}^{K} (1/D_j) \qquad (3\text{-}3)$$

However, we may further generalize (3-3) by raising the factor $1/D_i$ to a power of *r* where *r* is a non negative real number. That is, we propose, for i = 1, 2, . . ., K,

$$W_i = (1/D_i)^r / \sum_{j=1}^{K} (1/D_j)^r \qquad (3\text{-}4)$$

We would like to argue that (3-4) presents a spectrum of heuristics. We illustrate this by several special cases. First, if $r = 0$, then (3-4) becomes, for i = 1, 2, . . ., K,

$$W_i = 1/K \qquad (3\text{-}5)$$

This implies that all the eligible entries get the equal chance to be selected if $r = 0$.

Now consider the case when r approaches infinity. We have the following observations. Assume that $D_j < D_i$ for i = 1, 2, . . ., K and $i \neq j$. That is, entry j will route the anycast packets along the SSPF route. We can rewrite $1/D_i$ as β_i/D_j, where $0 < \beta_i < 1$. Note that $\lim_{r \to \infty} \beta_i^r = 0$. Substituting $1/D_i = \beta_i/D_j$ into (3-4), we obtain the weight for entry j as follows:

$$W_j = \lim_{r \to \infty} \frac{\left(\frac{1}{D_j}\right)^r}{\sum_{i=1}^{K}\left(\frac{1}{D_i}\right)^r} = \lim_{r \to \infty} \frac{\left(\frac{1}{D_j}\right)^r}{\left(\frac{1}{D_j}\right)^r (1 + \sum_{i=1, i \neq j}^{K} \beta_i^r)} = 1 \qquad (3\text{-}6)$$

For i = 1, 2, . . ., K and $i \neq j$,

$$W_i = \lim_{r \to \infty} \frac{\left(\frac{1}{D_j}\right)^r}{\sum_{h=1}^{K}\left(\frac{1}{D_h}\right)^r} = \lim_{r \to \infty} \frac{\left(\frac{1}{D_j}\right)^r \beta_i^r}{\left(\frac{1}{D_j}\right)^r (1 + \sum_{h=i, h \neq j}^{K} \beta_h^r)} = 0 \qquad (3\text{-}7)$$

That is, when r approaches infinity, our weight assignment algorithm will result in a performance equivalent to the SSPF algorithm.

As the third case, consider the situation when the network is heavily loaded. In [XJZ97], we demonstrate that under the assumption of heavy loading, an approximate analysis reveals that the proper weight assignment should be of the following form, for i = 1, 2, . . ., K,

$$W_i = (1/D_i) / \sum_{h=1}^{K} (1/D_h) \qquad (3\text{-}8)$$

This is a special case of (3-4) when $r = 1$.

Thus, (3-4) presents a wide range of heuristics for weight assignments. The question now is how to determine the value of r for a given router. For this, let us consider two special cases.

Case 1. If all the distances are almost equal, then all the weights should be almost equal. In other words, if the variance of the distances is small, then the variance of the weights should be small as well. As shown in (3-5),

when $r = 0$, all the weights are the same. Considering the fact that the variance of the weights is a continuous function of r, we conclude that when the variance of the distances is small, the value of r should be small as well.

Case 2. If the SSPF route (say, it is associated with entry j) is substantially shorter than all other routes, then W_j should be much larger than all others. In the extreme case, we may like to have W_j to be one and all other W_i ($i \neq j$) to be zero. From (3-6) and (3-7), we know that in this case, r should be infinity. This implies that when the variance of the distances is large, the value of r should be large as well.

The above two cases suggest that the value of r should be proportional to the variance of distances presented in the involved entries. Thus, we propose the following heuristic for selecting r:

$$r = \alpha \, \frac{\sqrt{E[(D - E[D])^2]}}{E[D]} \qquad (3\text{-}9)$$

where $E[D]$ is the mean value of distance values which is given by $\frac{1}{K} * \sum_{i=1}^{K} D_i$; $\sqrt{E[(D - E[D])^2]}$ is the standard deviation of distance values; and α is an adjustment factor. That is, r is the standard derivation normalized by the mean of distances. It measures the degree of variance of distances in comparison with the mean value. In the next section, we will show that our routing algorithms with a proper value of α will perform very well.

3.4. Correctness of the Routing Algorithms

The semantics of an anycast packet requires that one copy of an anycast packet must be delivered to one member in the recipient group. We say that a routing algorithm is correct if the semantics requirement of anycast can be satisfied. In this subsection, we will formally establish this *correctness* property for the routing algorithms introduced in this paper.

The correctness seems to be trivial. One would argue that if the network has no faults, all the routers and hosts are connected. Hence, there is always at least one path from a source to a member in the recipient group. A packet could always follow this path and hence be delivered.

While this is true for the SSPF method, the correctness property cannot be easily established for the source-destination based and destination based methods. This is because in order to eliminate loops, certain entries (hence, the corresponding links) have been marked to be ineligible. As a result, a path with this kind of links will not be used to deliver packets even if the links are physically functioning. We have to show that after marking the ineligibility of entries, there is still at least one path that connects a source to a member host in the recipient group.

We need the following lemmas [XJZ97] to prove the correctness property.

Lemma 3-1. Let S be a source host, A be an anycast address, and X be a router or host. If there is R such that R

126

$>_{S,A}$ X, then there is Y (Y is either a router or host) such that X $>_{S,A}$ Y unless X itself is in G(A).

Lemma 3-2. Let A be an anycast address. For any router R, there is X, where X is either a router or a host, such that R $>_A$ X.

Now, we are ready to prove the correctness property of our routing algorithms.

Theorem 3-2. (Correctness of the Algorithms). If the network has no fault, then with our routing algorithms any anycast packet from any source will eventually be delivered to one of the members in the recipient group.

Proof. The proof for the SSPF algorithm is trivial. We will concentrate on the SD/WRS and D/WRS algorithms. To prove the theorem, we should show that any router that can receive a packet must have some next hop to route the packet. Then, due to the fact that our methods are loop free, the packet will eventually be delivered.

First, consider the case of the source-destination based routing method. Let us say a router R' receives a packet from router R which is from source S with address A. Router R' can receive a packet from router R only if

$$R >_{S,A} R'. \qquad (3\text{-}10)$$

By Lemma 3-1, (3-10) implies that there is Y such that Y is a next hop of R' and

$$R' >_{S,A} Y. \qquad (3\text{-}11)$$

Consider the routing table for S in router R'. (3-11) means that the entry with the next hop field Y is eligible. That is, router R' can route an incoming packet to Y. Given that any path taken by our algorithm is loop free, this packet will eventually be delivered.

The case for D/WRS method can be similarly proved. by replacing Lemma 3-1, and $>_{SA}$ with Lemma 3-2 and $>_A$. We omit the details here due to the space limitation.

Q.E.D.

4. Performance Evaluation

4.1. Simulation Model

In this section, we will report performance results of the routing algorithms we introduced in this paper. We consider a network with its configuration similar to a sample network used in [M94a]. The configuration of the network is shown in Figure 4-1. We use a specific objective function to measure the distance of each link. For a link (say L), the value of its objective function is defined as

$$f(L) = 100 * 10^6 / B_L \qquad (4\text{-}1)$$

where B_L is the bandwidth of the link interface. By (4-1), the value of the objective function is the number of seconds taken to transmit 100 million bits over the interface. For example, if the links have their interface speeds as $10*10^6$, $25*10^6$, and $100*10^6$ bits per second, then their objective function values will be 10, 4, and 1, respectively.

To obtain the performance data, we use a discrete event simulation model to simulate the network. The simulation program is written in C programming language and runs in a SUN SPARC work station 20. We consider routers that use store-and-forward technique and always queue a waiting packet at output port (instead of input port). The

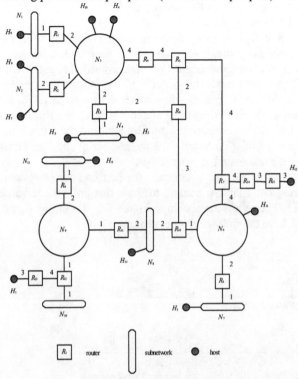

Figure 4-1. The Simulated Network

delay of a packet at a router is defined as the summation of the routing delay, the queuing delay, and the transmission delay. The end-to-end delay of a packet is the sum of the delays at all the routers through which the packet passes. For a given session, we are interested in the average end-to-end delay of all packets.

In order to obtain a lower bound on the average delay, we will also consider a dynamic optimal routing algorithm (DOR). For each packet, this algorithm will select a shortest path that results in the minimum end-to-end delay for the packet. The DOR algorithm achieves this by assuming that the complete dynamic system state information (e.g., queue length at each interface, current and future arrivals, etc.) is available without any delay or cost. Obviously, the performance of this algorithm is ideal but it is not realistic and cannot be implemented in practice. We use it as a baseline algorithm in order to obtain a lower bound on average delays.

We say that a system saturates at $\lambda = \lambda^*$ if any increase of λ value beyond λ^* will cause the system to become unstable[2]. We call λ^* as the *saturation rate*. In the simulation model, anycast packets arrive as a Possion process with rate λ where the value of λ is normalized by

---

[2] The instability of a system can be detected by observing the fact that during the simulation, the average delay of packets does not converge if the system is unstable.

the saturation rate of the DOR algorithm. That is, for the DOR algorithm, it is saturated at $\lambda^* = 1$.

4.2. Performance Observations

4.2.1. Sensitivity of r

Recall from (3-4) that r is the parameter used in the weight assignment. As discussed in Section 3.3, the value of r presents the degree of bias toward the paths with shorter distances. The larger r is, the bigger the weights will be for the entries with shorter distances. In (3-9), we propose a method that can adaptively select r values for a set of eligible entries in a routing table. In the simulation, the value of α is chosen to be the number of eligible entries for the associated anycast address.

We would like to compare the performance of systems using our adaptive method to those that use a fixed value of r. The results are shown in Figure 4-2. From this figure, we have the following observations:

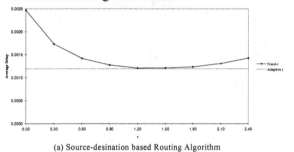

(a) Source-desination based Routing Algorithm

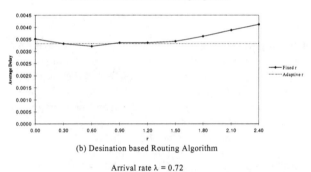

(b) Desination based Routing Algorithm

Arrival rate $\lambda = 0.72$

Figure 4-2. Effect of Parameter r

1. Consider the systems with fixed values of r. In both the cases shown in Figure 4-2 (a) and Figure 4-2 (b), the average end-to-end delay is indeed impacted by the value of r. For example, with the source-destination based method, the average delay at $r = 0.3$ is about 0.0018 second while at $r = 1.2$, it becomes 0.0012 second.

2. We note that generally when $r = 0$, the system will not result in the best performance in comparison when r takes other values. For example, in Figure 4-2 (a) when $r = 0$, the average delay is 0.0024 second, while when $r = 1.5$, the average delay is 0.0012 second. Recall that $r = 0$ implies to assign weights equally. Our data shows that generally this will not result in optimal performance.

3. The systems with adaptive r values perform

consistently better than those with fixed r values. Except when $r = 0.60$ and the destination based routing method is used, the average delay of the systems with adaptive r values is always no more than that with fixed r values. In most cases, the former substantially less than the latter.

44.2.2. Performance Comparison

In this section, we compare the delay performance of our algorithms introduced in this paper.

The simulation results for the SSPF, SD/WRS, D/WRS and DOR algorithms are shown in Figure 4-3. We have the following observations:

1. As expected, the dynamic optimal algorithm achieves the best performance in comparison with all others. This is simply because it uses much more state information which is not available to others.

2. When the system load is light, the delays of the

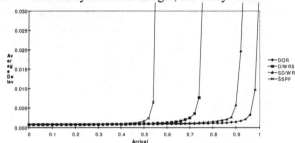

Arrival rates are normalized by the saturation rate of the DOR aglorithm

Figure 4-3 Comparision of Routing Algorithms

SSPF, SD/WRS, D/WRS algorithms are close to the dynamic optimal algorithm (DOR). This fact indicates that in the light load situation, it may be unnecessary to distribute anycast traffic over different paths.

3. When the system load increases, the performance difference among the algorithms becomes clearly visible. We observe that the SSPF algorithm performs poorer than other three. Its average delay is larger than others under medium and heavy load situations. The system with the SSPF algorithm saturates approximately at $\lambda^* = 0.55$, which is much smaller than other algorithms. The poor performance of the SSPF algorithm is due to the fact that it does not distribute traffic from a source into several different paths. As a result, the path that the SSPF algorithm uses quickly becomes overloaded when the overall load is large.

4. Under the medium and heavy load conditions, the SD/WRS algorithm performs better than the D/WRS algorithm. For example, when $\lambda = 0.7$, the average delay of the SD/WRS algorithm is 0.0012 second while the D/WRS algorithm yields 0.0025 second. For the system with the SD/WRS algorithm, the saturation occurs approximately at $\lambda^* = 0.92$, but with the D/WRS algorithm, it is around $\lambda^* = 0.75$. The performance difference between the SD/WRS and the D/WRS algorithms mainly comes from eligibility assignment of the routing entries. An entry is eligible with the D/WRS

algorithm entry only if a selection of the entry will not cause a loop for packets that come from *any* source. However, for the SD/WRS algorithm, an entry is eligible as long as it will not result in a loop for the packets that come from a *specific* source.

5. In all but the extremely heavily loaded situation ($\lambda >$ 0.85), the performance of the SD/WRS algorithm is very close to the dynamic optimal algorithm (DOR). The difference is usually within 15%. This justifies the approach of using static state information in routing anycast packets. Any algorithm that utilizes the dynamic state information may not bring additional performance benefit except when the load is extremely heavy.

5. Extensions

In this section, we discuss several directions to which our algorithms can be extended. We will briefly address the involved issues and possible solutions.

5.1. Networks with Faults

For the network with permanent faults (some links are broken and/or some routers stop functioning), if the permanent faults do not result in a partitioned network, then the fault state will eventually be reflected in the information exchanged between the routers. Consequently, the routing tables in routers will be modified accordingly. Our algorithms will be applicable to the modified routing tables.

Faults may make the network permanently partitioned into several subnetworks. In this case, our algorithms will still work as long as there is at least one member of G(A) in a subnetwork. The sources can send anycast packets with anycast address A if the routing tables of the routers in the subnetwork have been modified accordingly.

Sometimes, a network may have transient faults which will not cause permanent damage to the network but packets may be lost sporadically. To deal with transient faults, one may like to consider transmitting more than one copy of an anycast packet in the network. In this way, the chance that a packet loss can be reduced. In a router, the redundant copies of an anycast packet should be sent to different next hops whenever possible. This will minimize the packet loss probability. Note that this approach will have an impact on the network load and hence increase the packet delay. The number of redundant copies should also be properly chosen by balancing the loss probability and packet delay.

5.2. Multi-homed source hosts

We have assumed that all the source hosts are single-homed in the sense that each source host only connects to one router. It is possible that one host may be connected to multiple routers (say, in order to increase throughput and to improve fault tolerance capability). To deal with multi-homed source hosts, we may randomly select one router to send an anycast packet, just as we do in a router. The problem, however, is that a host may not have access to network (static) state information as a router does. As a result, it will be difficult for a host to make an intelligent selection. This can be overcome by letting the host exchange certain information with its routers. The tradeoff between performance benefit and algorithm complexity is worth investigating.

5.3. Dependent packets

The semantics of anycast communication services implies that packets with an anycast address are relatively independent [PMM93]. That is, any packet can be sent to any host in the recipient group without any correlation. Sometimes, anycast packets from a source may be dependent in terms of their destination. For example, some application may require that if the first packet from a flow of anycast packets is delivered to H, a member in the recipient group, all the consequent packets should also be delivered to the same member H. To deal with this situation, we need to use the flow id in the packet header [DH95]. When a router makes an entry selection for the first packet in the flow, the router should register the flow id with the entry selected. When the subsequent packets from the same flow arrive, they are routed according to the registered information, rather than going through new entry selections.

5.4. Hierarchical Routing

In the previous sections of this paper, we assumed that routers have all routing Information. This simplified the discussion. Nevertheless, our algorithm can be easily extended to the networks in which this assumption may not hold.

For example, consider a hierarchical network consisting a number of regions. The border routers of regions are connected by a backbone region. A router knows all routing information of its own region, but may not have complete information of others. A simple extension way of our algorithms is to designate the border routers of regions to act as proxies of anycast group members which locate outside regions. The similar idea can be applied to more complicated networks (say, with more than two layers).

One interesting observation is that in different regions and/or at different layers routing strategies may be not same. For example, a region may use SD/WRS but another uses SSPF. This is feasible as long as a proper protocol is used by the border routers to cooperate correctly. We address this issue in [XJZ98].

6. Final Remarks

In this paper, we have addressed the problem of routing anycast packets. We proposed and analyzed three routing algorithms: source-destination based routing with weighted random selection (SD/WRS), destination based routing with weighted random selection (D/WRS), and the shortest shortest path first (SSPF) algorithms. While the SSPF algorithm is a simple extension to the traditional SPF algorithm for routing unicast messages, the SD/WRS and D/WRS algorithms are designed to take into account the characteristics of anycast traffic. We proposed an adaptive heuristic algorithm to calculate weights (i.e., the probabilities that individual routing entries are selected). Loop free and correctness properties for these algorithms are formally proved. Results of simulation study show that both the SD/WRS and D/WRS algorithms perform much better than SSPF in terms of average end-to-end packet delay. Furthermore, we find that the SD/WRS algorithm performs very close to a dynamic optimal algorithm (DOR) in all except the extremely heavily loaded condition. The DOR algorithm provides a lower bound on average packet delay for any routing algorithm. Various extensions are discussed in order to deal with situations such as faulty networks, multi-homed hosts, dependent packets, and hierarchical routing.

It should be pointed out that our solutions are practical. Our algorithms are simple. The SD/WRS and D/WRS algorithms do not require extra information in comparison with algorithms which are currently used to route unicast and multicast packets. Hence, it should be relatively easy to realize our algorithms with current networking technology.

Acknowledgment

This work was partially sponsored by the Air Force Office of Scientific Research, Air Force Material Command, USAF, under grant (F49620-96-1-1076), by Texas Higher Education Coordinating Board under its Advanced technology Program with grant (999903-204), and by City University of Hong Kong under grants 700745 and 7000765. The U.S. Government is authorized to reproduce and distribute reprints for governmental purposes not withstanding any copyright notation thereon. The views and conclusions contained herein are those of the authors and should not be interpreted as necessarily representing the official polices or endorsements, either express or implied, of the Air Force Office of Scientific Research, the U.S Government, Texas State Government, Texas Higher Education Coordinating Board, Texas A & M University, or City University of Hong Kong.

References

[BAZSF97] S. Bhattacharjee, M.H. Ammar, E.W. Zegura, V. Shah and Z. Fei. Application-Layer Anycasting. *Proc. of IEEE INFOCOM*, 1997.

[BZ92] S. Bahk, M.El. Zarki. A Dynamic multi-Path Routing Algorithm for ATM Networks. *J. of High Speed Networks*, Vol. 1, No. 3, 1992.

[B96] J. Bound. Ipv6 Anycasting Service: Minimum Requirements for End Nodes. *draft-bound-anycast-00.txt*, June 1996.

[CG74] D. G. Cantor and M. Gerla. Optimal Routing in a Packet-Switched Computer Network, *IEEE trans. on Comp*, Vol. C-23, Oct. 1974.

[CR97] I. Cidon and R. Rom. Multi-Path Routing Combined with Resource Reservation. *Proc. of IEEE INFOCOM*, 1997.

[DH95] S. Deering and R. Hinden. Internet Protocol, Version 6, Specification. *RFC 1883*, December 1995.

[D59] E.W. Dijkstra. A Note on Two Problems in Connection with Graphs, *Numer. Math*. Vol. 1, 1959.

[D88] S. Deering. Multicast Routing in Internetworks and Extended LANs. *Proc. of SIGCOMM*, 1988.

[DEFJLW96] S. Deering, D. L. Estrin, D. Farinacci, V. Jacobson, C. Liu, and L. Wei. *The PIM Architecture for Wide-Area Multicast Routing*. IEEE/ACM Trans. on Networking, Vol. 4, No. 2, April 1996.

[E86] A. Ephremides. The Routing Problem in Computer Networks. I. Blake and H. Poor, eds., *Comm and Networks*, 1986.

[FCK73] L. Fratta, M. Cerla, and L. Kleinrock. The Flow Deviation Method: An Approach to Store-and-Forwad Communication Network Design. *Networks*, Vol 3, 1973.

[FC71] H. Frank and W. Chou. Routing in Computer Networks. *Networks*, Vol.1, 1971.

[GH85] D. Gross and C.M. Harris. *Fundamentals of Queueing Theory*. John Wiley & Sons, Inc. 1985.

[GK97] E. Gustafsson and G. Karlsson. A Literature Survey on Traffic Dispersion. *IEEE Network*, Vol. 11, No. 2, March/April 1997.

[G77] R.G. Gallager. A Minimum Delay Routing Algorithms Using Distributed Computation. *IEEE Trans on Comm*, Vol. COM-25, No. 1, January 1977.

[HD95] R. Hinden and S. Deering. IP Version 6 Addressing Architecture. *RFC 1884*, December 1995.

[H91] C.L. Hedricks. *An Introduction to IGRP*. Center for Computer and Information Services, Rutgers University, August, 1991.

[JG93] A. Jean-Marie and L. Gun. Parallel Queues with Resequencing. *J-ACM*, Vol 40, No. 5, November 1993.

[JL92] A. Jean-Marie and Z. Liu. A Stochastic Comparison for Queuing Models via Random Sums and Intervals. *Journal of Advanced Applied Probabilities*, No. 24, 1992.

[KJ83] K.B. Kumar and J. M. Jaffe. Routing to Multiple Destinations in Computer Networks. *IEEE Trans. on Comm*, COM-31, No.3, March 1983.

[KZ89] A. Khanna and J. Zinky. The Revised ARPANET Routing Metric. *Proc. of ACM SIGCOMM*, 1989.

[MTW93] J.E. Marsden and A.J. Tromba, A. Weinstein. *Basic Multivarible Calculus*. Springer-Verlag, Inc. 1993

[M93] N. F. Maxemchuk. Dispersity Routing in High-Speed Networks. *Computer Networks and ISDN System*, Vol. 25, No. 6, 1993.

[M94a] J. Moy. OSPF Version 2. *RFC1583*, March 1994.

[M94b] J. Moy. Multicast Extensions to OSPF. *RFC 1584*, March 1994.

[PMM93] C. Partridge, T. Mendez, and W. Milliken. Host Anycasting Service. *RFC1546*, November 1993.

[SAN92] D. Sidhu, S. Abdullah, and R. Nair. Congestion Control in high Speed networks via Alternate path Routing. *J. of High Speed networks*, Vol. 1, No. 2, 1992

[SC76] M. Schwartz and C.K. Cheung. The Gradient Projection Algorithm for Multiple Routing in Message-Switched Networks. *IEEE Trans. on Comm.*, Vol. COM-24, No. 4, April 1976.

[SS80] M. Schwartz and T. Stern. Routing Techniques Used in Computer Communications Networks. *IEEE Trans. on Comm.*, Vol. COM-28, No.4, April 1980.

[WC90] Z. Wang and J. Crowcroft. Shortest Path First with Emergency Exits. *Proc. of SIGCOMM*, 1990.

[XJZ97] D. Xuan, W. Jia, and W. Zhao. Formal Properties of Routing Algorithms for Anycast Messages, *Tech. Rep.*, CS Dept. City Univ. Hong Kong, July, 1997.

[XJZ98] D. Xuan, W. Jia and W. Zhao. Hierarchical Routing Algorithms for Anycast Messages, *Tech. Rep.*, CS Dept. Texas A&M Univ. College Station, May, 1998.

Session 3A
Fault-Tolerance

Chair: Füsun Özgüner
Ohio State University

Low-cost Fault-tolerance in Barrier Synchronizations

Sandeep S. Kulkarni   Anish Arora

Department of Computer and Information Science *
The Ohio State University
Columbus, OH 43210 USA

Abstract

In this paper, we show how fault-tolerance can be effectively added to several types of faults in program computations that use barrier synchronization. We divide the faults that occur in practice into two classes, *detectable* and *undetectable*, and design a fully distributed program that tolerates the faults in both classes. Our program guarantees that every barrier is executed correctly even if detectable faults occur, and that eventually every barrier is executed correctly even if undetectable faults occur. Via analytical as well as simulation results we show that the cost of adding fault-tolerance is low, in part by comparing the times required by our program with that required by the corresponding fault-intolerant counterpart.

Keywords: fault-tolerance, multitolerance, detectable and undetectable faults, synchronization, concurrency.

1 Introduction

In this paper, we show how to effectively add tolerance to several types of faults in program computations that use barrier synchronization. Barrier synchronization involves a collective communication between processes, in order to establish that all processes have reached a barrier before any process can compute beyond that barrier. We focus our attention on this form of synchronization because it is frequently used in implementing parallel algorithms on message passing, shared memory, and network of workstation systems.

Each of the above-mentioned systems is subject to various types of faults in practice. Examples of standard fault types include:

- *Communication faults* such as loss, corruption, duplication, reorder, and unexpected reception of messages; and failure and repair of channels.
- *Processor faults* such as fail-stop, repair, and rebooting of a processor.
- *Process faults* such as internal/design faults and "hanging" processes.
- *System faults* such as system reconfiguration, memory leaks, memory corruption, I/O faults, deadlocks, and non-availability of buffers or other resources.
- *Performance faults* such as network congestion and floating point errors.

Despite the existence of these multiple types of faults in practice and an extensive literature on barrier synchronization [1-7, to cite but a few], we are aware of little research

that has considered fault-tolerance in this context. Among the exceptions are [4], which deals with message loss and corruption only, and [7], which relies upon high atomicity shared memory access. We are therefore led to designing and analyzing a fully distributed program for barrier synchronization computations that provides tolerance to most of the faults discussed above.

Issues in dealing with multiple types of faults. When multiple types of faults are considered, it is possible that some "high" type of tolerance cannot be achieved with respect to each type of faults. On the other hand, even if some "low" type of tolerance can be achieved with respect to each fault type, this may yield unacceptable functionality or performance with respect to some fault type. It follows that one issue is to identify the potentially different types of tolerances that are respectively appropriate for the different fault types.

With this issue in mind, we classify the faults mentioned above into two: (i) the class of faults that can be masked, i.e., the faults in whose presence, it is possible to ensure that the program is executed correctly, and (ii) the class of faults that cannot be masked, i.e., the faults in whose presence, it is impossible to ensure that the program is executed correctly. We call these classes of faults *detectable* and *undetectable* respectively. While we give the formal description of what we mean by detectable and undetectable in the next section, we note that the former fault-class includes faults such as message loss, unexpected message reception, fail-stop, repair, and rebooting of a processor; and the latter includes faults such as internal/design errors, hanging processes, memory corruption, and memory leaks. (The interested reader is referred to [8] for heuristics for the selection of fault-classes.)

Goals of our design. Tolerance properties. As motivated above, we will ensure that in the presence of the detectable faults, the program is executed correctly. And, in the presence of the undetectable fault-class, we will ensure that even if the program reaches an arbitrary state, it eventually recovers to a state from where it is executed correctly. (Such a tolerance is denoted as *stabilizing* [9] tolerance.) Moreover, until the program recovers to such a state, the number of barriers executed incorrectly will be kept to a minimum.

Overhead of tolerances. We aim to keep the overhead due to the tolerances as small as possible, since parallel algorithm designers are unlikely to use barrier synchronization primitives where fault-tolerance comes at a significant cost.

Stepwise design. We will develop our program via a se-

⁰Email: {kulkarni,anish}@cis.ohio-state.edu; Web: http://www.cis.ohio-state.edu/{ kulkarni, anish }. Research supported in part by NSF Grant CCR-93-08640, OSU Grant 221506, and NSA MDA904-96-1-1011.

quence of refinement steps. More specifically, we will first start with a shared memory program wherein process actions can instantaneously access the state of all other processes. With this assumption, the program design and its proof of correctness can be simplified. Subsequently, we will relax this assumption in steps until the process actions can be implemented on a message passing system. In each step, we will verify that the program is a refinement of the program in the previous step, enabling a simple proof of correctness for the final program.

Outline of the paper. In Section 2, we formally specify the problem and the faults-classes. In Section 3, we present a solution for the problem which is coarse-grain in the sense that each process action can instantaneously communicate with all other processes and update its own state. In Section 4, we distribute this solution so that each process action can instantaneously communicate with only its neighboring processes and also update its own state. In Section 5, we further refine the granularity of process actions so that each action can instantaneously either communicate with one neighboring process or update its own state, but not both. In Section 6, we present analytical and simulation results for the performance of our program in the presence of detectable and undetectable faults, and quantify the overhead of fault-tolerance. Finally, we make concluding remarks in Section 7.

2 Problem Specification and Faults

Specification of barrier synchronization. Given is a system of processes, each of which consists of a cyclic sequence of n terminating phases, $[phase.0 \; ; \; phase.1 \; ; \; \ldots \; ; \; phase.(n{-}1)]$. The following two properties are required for each i, $0 \le i < n$:

  (*Safety*) Execution of $phase.(i{+}1)$ begins only after $phase.i$ is executed successfully,

  (*Progress*) Eventually $phase.i$ is executed successfully,

where $phase.n = phase.0$. Initially, $phase.(n{-}1)$ has executed successfully and each process is thus ready to execute $phase.0$. "Phase.i is executed successfully" is defined in the following terms.

Definition. An *instance of phase.i is executed* iff some process starts executing $phase.i$ and each process executes $phase.i$ at most once.

Note that when an instance of $phase.i$ is executed, some processes may execute $phase.i$ partially or not at all.

Definition. An *instance of phase.i is executed successfully* iff all processes execute $phase.i$ fully in that instance.

Definition. *Phase.i is executed successfully* iff one or more instances of $phase.i$ are executed in sequence, the last instance of which is executed successfully. □

From this specification, it follows that in a barrier synchronization program the processes execute the next phase only after all processes have completed execution of the previous phase. As described next, in the presence of faults, to execute $phase.i$, successfully, multiple instances of $phase.i$ may be executed (successfully or unsuccessfully)

in sequence. Of course, in the absence of faults, any reasonable implementation should execute $phase.i$ exactly once.

Faults. As discussed in the introduction, we classify the faults into two classes: detectable and undetectable.

Detectable faults. A fault is detectable if the state of the process where the fault occurs can be reset before any process accesses it. Faults such as message loss, detectable corruption, duplication, reorder; processor fail-stop, repair or reboot; I/O errors; exceptions such as floating point errors and access violations; and system reconfiguration are detectable faults. By way of explanation, a fault that reboots a processor is detectable because the state of the processes executing on that processor can be reset before restarting the processes.

Note that a reset after a fault may yield a state that is different from that before the fault. Therefore, in the presence of detectable faults, the local state of a process may be lost. Thus, information regarding the current phase being executed by that process may be lost. It follows that, in the presence of detectable faults, we cannot ensure that each process executes its current phase exactly once. However, we can still satisfy the specification of barrier synchronization by executing a new instance of the current phase successfully.[1] Note that, in order to satisfy Safety, this new instance must begin when no process is executing in the current instance.

Undetectable faults. A fault is undetectable if the state of the process where the fault occurs cannot be reset before any process accesses it. Faults such as internal/design errors, hanging processes, undetectable message corruption or reorder, memory leaks and transient state corruptions are undetectable faults. By way of explanation, a transient state corruption is undetectable as some processes may inadvertently access the corrupted state without detecting that it is in error. Sometimes, even if faults are detectable in principle, there may be factors that limit the ability of systems to detect them, e.g., the cost of detection [10]; such faults may instead be classified as undetectable.

In the presence of undetectable faults, the program may be perturbed to a state where processes are executing in different phases. It follows that the specification of barrier synchronization cannot be satisfied in the presence of such faults. Therefore, we ensure that even if the program is perturbed to an arbitrary state, it will eventually recover to a state from where the subsequent execution will satisfy the specification of barrier synchronization, and, the number of phases executed unsuccessfully in the interim is kept to a minimum.

Fault Assumptions. The following two assumptions apply to all faults:

1. Faults are eventually correctable, i.e., no part of the program is permanently affected by them. For example, if a processor fail-stops, one way to eventually correct is to restart all fail-stopped processes of that processor on some other processor—albeit with different

---

[1]This assumes that after a detectable fault occurs the identity of the current phase can be accessed from the state of some process. We will therefore treat the fault that corrupts the state of all processes detectably as an undetectable fault.

states. (We will discuss how to relax the assumption of eventual correctability in Section 7.)

2. Faults can occur at any time in any order and at any process. However, eventually they stop occurring. (Alternatively, they stop occurring for at least a sufficient duration so that the program makes progress.)

Programming notation. We write programs using a guarded command notation: Each process consists of a finite set of variables and a finite set of actions. Each action consists of two parts: a guard and a statement. For convenience, a unique name is associated with each action. Thus, each action has the following form:

$$\langle name \rangle :: \langle guard \rangle \longrightarrow \langle statement \rangle$$

The guard is a boolean expression over the variables of that and possibly other processes, and the statement updates zero or more variables of that process. An action is executed only if it is enabled, i.e., if its guard evaluates to true. To execute the action, its statement is executed atomically.

Each computation of the program is a fair interleaving of steps: In every step, some action that is enabled in the current state is chosen and its statement is executed atomically. Fairness of the interleaving means that each action that is continuously enabled is eventually chosen for execution in some step.

We represent each fault by an action. An undetectable fault assigns to variables of a process nondeterministically chosen values from their domains. A detectable fault assigns to variables of a process "reset" values from their domains. (Note that this reset would in practice be implemented in the process, but since the corrupted state of the process cannot be accessed by any process until the reset is complete, it is convenient to specify the reset as part of the fault action.)

3 Coarse-Grain Solution

In this section, we present a solution for the case where the graph of the processes is fully connected and the process actions can instantaneously communicate with the neighboring processes and update their own state. The resulting program recovers from detectable faults with no phase executed incorrectly and from undetectable faults that perturb processes into, say, m distinct phases with at most m phases executed incorrectly. For ease of exposition, we assume that the cyclic sequence of phases consists of at least two phases. The case where the cyclic sequence consists of a single phase is discussed in [11].

To synchronize the underlying computation, each process j maintains a control state, which we represent by the variable $cp.j$ (for control position of j). Clearly, there exists a $cp.j$ value, say $execute$, which denotes that j is executing its phase, and a value, say $success$, which denotes that j has completed its phase. We consider two additional control position values: $ready$, which denotes that j is ready to execute its phase, and $error$, which denotes that the control position of j is detectably corrupted. Also, to distinguish between the phases, each process j maintains a variable $ph.j$, whose value denotes the number of the phase that j is currently in.

Informally, the program works as follows (see Figure 1). In a start state, all processes are in the control position

$ready$ and in the same phase. In the absence of faults, processes first change their control position to $execute$, execute the current phase, and change their control position to $success$. They then increment their phase and change their control position to $ready$, thereby returning to a start state, from where the cycle repeats. In the presence of a detectable fault at a process, the control position of that process is changed to $error$. And if some process is in control position $error$, all processes are pulled back into the start state of the current phase, from where a new instance of the current phase is executed. In the presence of undetectable faults, the program recovers to some start state, from where the subsequent execution satisfies Safety and Progress.

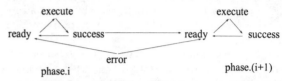

Figure 1: State transitions for program CB

The transition from $ready$ to $execute$ occurs only after some process checks that all processes are in control position $ready$. After the first process changes its control position thus from $ready$ to $execute$, the remaining processes can likewise change their control position by checking that some process is in control position $execute$.

The transition from $execute$ to $success$ occurs only after all processes start execution of their phases. This restriction is introduced to tolerate detectable faults. More specifically, if a process j changes its control position from $execute$ to $success$ while process k is in control position $ready$ *and* there is a detectable fault at k, then j cannot decide whether k has executed the current phase or not. (A detailed example of this scenario is discussed in [11].)

The transition from $success$ to $ready$ occurs only when no process is in the control position $execute$. This restriction is introduced to tolerate undetectable faults: It prevents the system from remaining forever in states where the control positions $ready$, $execute$, and $success$ all co-exist. The transition from $success$ to $ready$ also chooses the phase in which the process will execute next. For the first process that executes this transition in the current phase, if the control position of all processes is $success$ (i.e., all processes have completed the current phase successfully), its phase is incremented, thereby leading to the execution of the next phase; if, however, the control position of some process is $error$ (i.e., the instance of the current phase is not executed successfully), the phase is unchanged, thereby leading to a execution of a new instance of the current phase. After the first process executes transition to $ready$, other processes obtain their phase from any process whose control position is $ready$.

The transition from $error$ to $ready$ also occurs only when no process is in the control position $execute$. This restriction ensures that if any detectable corruption occurs during execution of a phase, execution of a new instance of that phase does not begin as long as some process is executing in that instance. This transition also obtains the phase in which the process will execute next. If there exists a pro-

134

cess that is in control position *ready*, the process obtains its control position from that process. Otherwise, it obtains the phase from some process that is control position *success*. If, however, there is no process in control position *ready*, i.e., the phase of all processes is corrupted, the phase is chosen arbitrarily.

Our barrier synchronization program, CB, consists of four actions, one for each transition discussed above(Let $(\underline{any}\ k : k \in X : ph.k)$ denote the phase of any process in the set X if X a nonempty set, and an arbitrary number in the set $\{0..n-1\}$ if X is the empty set):

$CB1 ::$ $cp.j = ready\ \land$
$\quad\quad ((\forall k :: cp.k = ready)\ \lor\ (\exists k :: cp.k = execute))$
$\quad \longrightarrow\ cp.j := execute$

$CB2 ::$ $cp.j = execute\ \land$
$\quad\quad ((\forall k :: cp.k \neq ready)\ \lor\ (\exists k :: cp.k = success))$
$\quad \longrightarrow\ cp.j := success$

$CB3 ::$ $cp.j = success\ \land\quad (\forall k :: cp.k \neq execute)$
$\quad \longrightarrow$ if $(\exists k :: cp.k = ready)$
$\quad\quad\quad ph.j := (\underline{any}\ k : cp.k = ready : ph.k)$
$\quad\quad$ elseif $(\forall k :: cp.k = success)\ \ ph.j := ph.j+1;$
$\quad\quad cp.j := ready$

$CB4 ::$ $cp.j = error\ \land\quad (\forall k :: cp.k \neq execute)$
$\quad \longrightarrow$ if $(\exists k :: cp.k = ready)$
$\quad\quad\quad ph.j := (\underline{any}\ k : cp.k = ready : ph.k)$
$\quad\quad$ elseif $(\forall k :: cp.k = success)$
$\quad\quad\quad ph.j := (\underline{any}\ k : cp.k = success : ph.k);$
$\quad\quad cp.j := ready$

Faults. The detectable and undetectable faults that affect the program are represented, respectively, as follows (Let ? denote any value from the domain (of $cp.j$ or $ph.j$)):

$\quad true\quad \longrightarrow\quad ph.j, cp.j := ?, error$
$\quad true\quad \longrightarrow\quad ph.j, cp.j := ?, ?,$

Proof of correctness: To prove Safety, we show (i) no two instances of *phase.i* overlap, and (ii) execution of an instance of *phase.(i+1)* is executed only after a successful instance of *phase.i*. (Observe that (i) is trivial in the absence of faults as only one instance is executed.)

To prove Progress, we show (i) after *phase.(i−1)* is executed successfully, in the absence of faults, any instance of *phase.i* is executed successfully, and (ii) in the presence of faults, eventually a new instance of *phase.i* is executed.

Theorem 3.1

- Program CB satisfies the specification of barrier synchronization in the absence of faults.
- Program CB is masking tolerant to detectable faults.
- Program CB is stabilizing tolerant to undetectable faults, and in the presence of undetectable faults, program CB executes minimum number of phases incorrectly.

For reasons of space, we relegate all proofs to the technical report version of this paper [11].

4   Accessing Neighbors Only

We now refine program CB so that instead of communicating with all processes, each process communicates with only one neighboring processes at a time. The refinement is based on the observation that in every phase execution the first process to change its control position to *ready* or to *execute* or to *success* necessarily detects the state of all other processes. So to refine CB, we let a distinguished process, say process 0, bear the responsibility of all of these detections. After 0 has detected the appropriate global condition, it changes its phase and control position, and the other processes then follow 0 one after another to change their phase and control position accordingly.

First, in Section 4.1, we refine CB for the case where the processes are organized in a ring. Then, in Section 4.2, we refine it for other topologies.

4.1   Ring Topology

We organize the processes, say $0..N$, in a ring and circulate a token around the ring. When 0 gets the token, it detects the global condition involving all processes, changes its phase and control position accordingly, and then forwards the token to its successor, process 1. Upon receiving the token, each non-0 process updates its phase and control position accordingly and then forwards the token to its successor. When 0 receives the token again, from N, it can detect the next global condition on the state of the processes, and the cycle repeats. To obtain the refined program, we superpose the refined barrier synchronization upon an underlying multitolerant token ring program, described next, which we have formally derived and proven correct elsewhere [8].

Underlying token ring program. Each process j maintains a sequence number, $sn.j$, which, in the absence of faults, is in the domain $\{0..K-1\}$ for some $K > N$. To handle detectable faults, two special values $\perp$ and $\top$ are added to the domain of the sequence number: when the sequence number is corrupted, it is set to $\perp$, and the sequence number $\top$ is used to detect whether a detectable fault has occurred at all processes. Process $j, j \neq N$, has the token iff $sn.j \neq sn.(j+1)$ and both $sn.j$ and $sn.(j+1)$ are different from $\perp$ and $\top$. Process N has the token iff $sn.N = sn.0$ and $sn.N$ and $sn.0$ are both different from $\perp$ and $\top$.

Notational remark. In the rest of the paper, our use of $+$ and $-$ is context sensitive: when used in connection with the process numbers, these operations are in modulo $N+1$ arithmetic, when used in connection with the sequence numbers, they are in modulo K arithmetic, and when used in connection with the phases of processes, they are in modulo n arithmetic. (End of remark.)

The token ring program has five actions. The first action lets process 0 receive the token, and the second action lets process j, $j \neq 0$, receive the token. The remaining three actions are used to detect if the state of all processes is corrupted. Formally, the actions are as follows:

$T1 :: (sn.j = sn.N \lor sn.j = \perp \lor sn.j = \top)\ \land$
$\quad\quad j = 0\ \land\ sn.N \neq \perp\ \land\ sn.N \neq \top \quad\quad \longrightarrow\ sn.j := sn.N+1$
$T2 :: sn.(j-1) \neq \perp\ \land\ sn.(j-1) \neq \top\ \land$
$\quad\quad j \neq 0\ \land\ sn.j \neq sn.(j-1) \quad\quad\quad\quad \longrightarrow\ sn.j := sn.(j-1)$
$T3 :: sn.N = \perp \quad\quad\quad\quad\quad\quad\quad\quad\quad\quad\quad \longrightarrow\ sn.N := \top$
$T4 :: j \neq N\ \land\ sn.j = \perp\ \land\ sn.(j+1) = \top \quad \longrightarrow\ sn.j := \top$
$T5 :: sn.0 = \top \quad\quad\quad\quad\quad\quad\quad\quad\quad\quad\quad\quad \longrightarrow\ sn.0 := 0$

This program has the following properties: In the absence of faults, it repeatedly circulates exactly one token around the ring. In the presence of detectable faults, (a) the ring contains at most one token but the program eventually reaches a state where the ring contains exactly one token; (b) each process can detect if it has been detectably corrupted by checking whether its sequence number is $\bot$ or $\top$; and (c) 0 never executes actions $T4$ and $T5$ (these are executed only in the case of undetectable faults, including the scenario when all processes are corrupted concurrently). Finally, in the presence of undetectable faults, the ring may contain any number of tokens but the program eventually reaches a state where the ring contains exactly one token.

Superposed program for updating cp and ph variables. Informally, the refined program works as follows. Each process updates its phase and control position whenever it receives a token, i.e., whenever it executes action $T1$ or $T2$. In a start state, all processes are in the same phase and in control position $ready$, and action $T1$ is enabled at process 0. Process 0 executes $T1$, increments its sequence number, and changes its control position to $execute$. This enables action $T2$ at process 1, which then updates $cp.1$ and $ph.1$ likewise, and so on until N updates $cp.N$ and $ph.N$ likewise. Subsequently, 0 changes its control position to $success$ and in the next circulation of the token around the ring, all processes change their control position to $success$. With this circulation of the token, 0 can detect whether some process had a detectable fault, by using a new control position, say $repeat$, as follows: If in this circulation the token reaches a process that had a detectable fault, that process changes its control position to $repeat$ (instead of $success$). The control position $repeat$ is propagated along with the token to process N. Therefore, if the state of some process is detectably corrupted, N will change its control position to $repeat$. In this situation, 0 decides to execute a new instance of the current phase. Else, if the control position of N is $success$ and $ph.0 = ph.N$, 0 detects that all processes have executed $ph.0$ and, hence, 0 decides to increment its phase.

Formally, the phase and the control position of j are updated as described below.

Updating $ph.0$ and $cp.0$ in process 0. When 0 receives the token (i.e., it executes action $T1$), it also executes the following statement in parallel with that of $T1$:

```
if      cp.0 = ready  ∧  cp.0 = cp.N  ∧  ph.0 = ph.N
then       cp.0 := execute
elseif  cp.0 = execute
then       cp.0 := success
elseif  cp.0 = success
then       if cp.0 = cp.N ∧ ph.0 = ph.N then ph.0 := ph.0 + 1;
           cp.0 := ready
elseif  cp.0 = error
then       ph.0 := ph.N ;  cp.0 := ready
```

Updating $ph.j$ and $cp.j$ in process j, $j \neq 0$. When j receives the token (i.e., it executes action $T2$), it also executes the following statement in parallel with that of $T2$:

```
ph.j := ph.(j−1) ;
if      cp.j = ready    ∧  cp.(j−1) = execute  then cp.j := execute
elseif  cp.j = execute  ∧  cp.(j−1) = success  then cp.j := success
elseif  cp.j ≠ execute  ∧  cp.(j−1) = ready    then cp.j := ready
elseif  cp.j = error    ∨  cp.(j−1) ≠ cp.j     then cp.j := repeat
```

Faults. The detectable and undetectable faults that affect the refined program are represented, respectively, as follows:

$$true \longrightarrow ph.j, cp.j, sn.j := ?, error, \bot$$
$$true \longrightarrow ph.j, cp.j, sn.j := ?, ?, ?$$

Theorem 4.1

- Program RB satisfies the specification of barrier synchronization in the absence of faults.
- Program RB is masking tolerant to detectable faults.
- Program RB is stabilizing tolerant to undetectable faults, and in the presence of undetectable faults, program RB executes minimum number of phases incorrectly.

4.2 Alternative Topologies

Due to the ring topology of program RB (see Figure 2 (a)), $O(N)$ time is required to detect that all processes have executed their phase successfully and to inform them to begin executing the next phase. We show how this detection and information dissemination can be reduced by parallelizing RB, next.

One alternative to a ring topology is to use two rings that intersect at process $0..j$, $j \geq 0$ (see Figure 2 (b)). The refined version of program CB for the two ring topology, RB' is obtained by changing RB as follows:

1. Process 0 checks that the sequence number 0 is the same as that of both N_1 and N_2 before executing $T1$. To update ph and cp, the condition $cp.0 = cp.N$ is replaced by $cp.0 = cp.N_1 = cp.N_2$ (and likewise for $ph.0 = ph.N$), and the assignment $ph.0 := ph.N$ is replaced by choosing $ph.N_1$ or $ph.N_2$.

2. Action $T3$ is executed by both N_1 and N_2.

3. Action $T4$ is executed by all processes other than N_1 and N_2: before executing this action, process j checks that the sequence numbers of all its successors are $\top$.

4. Actions T_2 and T_5 remain unchanged.

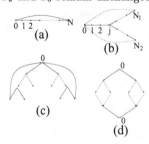

Figure 2: Refining RB for various topologies

Lemma 4.2.1 Program RB' is masking tolerant to detectable faults and stabilizing tolerant to undetectable faults. Moreover, in the presence of undetectable faults, the number of phases executed unsuccessfully by program RB' is kept to a minimum. □

By repetitively using Lemma 4.2.1, program CB can be refined for the topologies shown in Figure 2(c) and 2(d): in topology 2(c), the processes are organized in a tree and all the leaves are connected to the root, and topology 2(d), the processes are arranged in two trees such that every leaf is connected to at least one leaf in another tree. Note that in both these topologies, a process may occur more than once: for example, in 2(d), process 0 is the root of both trees. Thus, we have:

Proposition 4.2.2 If processes are organized in a tree as shown in Figure 2(c) (2(d) respectively), program CB can be refined while preserving its tolerance properties.

Observe that using the topology shown in Figure 2(c) (2(d) respectively), the time required to detect that all processes have executed their phase successfully and to inform all processors to begin executing the next phase is $O(h)$, where h is the height of the tree. It follows that if binary trees are used, the required time is $O(\log N)$.

5   Refining to Message Passing

The actions of program RB allow j to instantaneously access the state of one of its neighbors, $j-1$ or $j+1$, as well as update its own state. In this section, we refine the actions further so that they instantaneously either access the state of one of its neighbors or update its own state, but not both. As shown below, this program can be implemented on message passing systems.

To this end, the message passing program MB is obtained from RB as follows:

- The domain of all sn variables in augmented from $\{0..K-1\}$ where $K > N$ to $\{0..L-1\}$ where $L > 2N+1$.
- Process j additionally maintains a local copy of each of the variables $sn.(j-1)$, $cp.(j-1)$, $ph.(j-1)$ and $sn.(j+1)$.
- Actions $T1$, $T2$, and $T4$ are replaced with actions that instead of accessing the variables of the neighbors access the corresponding local copies.
- The local copy of $sn.(j-1)$ in j is updated only if $sn.(j-1)$ is different from $\perp$ and $\top$. Whenever this copy is updated, the local copies of $cp.(j-1)$ and $ph.(j-1)$ in j are also updated (from $cp.(j-1)$ and $ph.(j-1)$) by executing the same statement with which a non-0 process updates its phase and control position. Thus, the resulting local copy update action is identical to the superposed action $T2$ at a non-0 process.
- The local copy of $sn.(j+1)$ in j is updated only if $sn.(j+1)$ is $\top$.

Moreover, a fault action at j modifies the local copies of the phases and the control positions maintained at j in the same way as it affects $ph.j$ and $cp.j$ respectively.

Observe that in the resulting program no process other than j accesses the local copy variables in j. Also, j accesses only its local state when it updates a variable that is accessed by the other processes. It follows that the actions of j that update its local copy variables from the variables of a neighboring process need not be executed instantaneously and, hence, all program actions can be implemented using messages. It also follows that the concurrent execution of actions of neighboring processes can be equivalently represented by an interleaving of the action executions. Hence, for the purposes of the proof of correctness, we can "pretend" that the actions that update the local copies execute instantaneously.

6   Performance Analysis

In this section, we evaluate the time required for executing our barrier synchronization program, by analysis as well as by simulation.

The time required for executing the program depends upon (1) the communication latency, i.e., the time taken to send a message from one process to its neighbor, (2) the phase execution time, (3) the frequency of faults, and (4) the number of processes in the system. For simplicity, instead of considering (1) and (2) separately, we consider their ratio, c. For example, if the time required to execute a phase is $1ms$ and the communication latency is $10\mu s$, then c is

0.01. We assume that the probability that a fault occurs during the phase execution time is f, faults are uniformly distributed, and the graph of processes are organized on a tree (see Figure 2(c)) of height h. Also, based on the claim that the phase execution time dominates the synchronization time, we focus our attention on programs where the barrier synchronization time is at most one-half of the time required to execute a phase. Since in the absence of faults, barrier synchronization can be achieved in time $1+2hc$ time units, —one communication over the tree suffices to detect that all processes have completed execution of their phase and another to inform them to start the next phase—, we assume is that $2hc \leq 0.5$. (Thus, if h is 5, we will let the values of c range from 0 to 0.05.)

We evaluate our program for three cases: in the absence of faults, in the presence of detectable faults, and in the presence of undetectable faults. More specifically, in the absence of faults, barrier synchronization can be achieved with two communications over the tree. Our program, however, requires three communications over the tree. We, therefore, will evaluate the overhead of our fault-tolerant program.

In the presence of detectable faults, as claimed in Section 4, no phase is executed incorrectly, although some phases may be re-executed. Therefore, the time required for a successful execution of a phase increases. We, therefore, will evaluate the number of phases executed incorrectly and the extra time taken for a successful execution of a phase.

In the presence of undetectable faults, as claimed in Section 4, the number of phases executed incorrectly is kept to a minimum. However, the program does a wasteful computation until it recovers to a state from where further phases are executed correctly. We, therefore, will calculate the time taken by the program to recover from undetectable faults.

We now present our analytical model and the parameters used in our simulation. Then, we present our results for the case of detectable and undetectable faults. For brevity, we model the absence of faults by choosing the fault frequency to be zero. In both analytical and simulation results, we model true concurrency among processes via the maximum parallel semantics, i.e., time is computed in terms of steps, where in each step every process executes one of its enabled actions unless all its actions are disabled.

Analytical model.   As shown in Figure 1, to execute a phase successfully in the absence of faults, a process changes its control position thrice. During each such change of control position, a process receives a message from its predecessor. Thus, the communication time for barrier synchronization is $3hc$. Hence, the maximum time required for executing a phase successfully in the absence of faults is $1 + 3hc$, the probability that a fault does not occur during this time is $(1 - f)^{(1+3hc)}$, and the probability that a fault does occur during a phase is $1 - (1 - f)^{(1+3hc)}$.

To execute a phase successfully in the presence of detectable faults, exactly k instances of that phase are executed if detectable faults occur in each the first $k-1$ instances and no fault occurs in the kth instance. Therefore, the probability that a phase is executed exactly k times is $(f_{freq})^{k-1}(1 - f_{freq})$, where $f_{freq} = 1 - (1 - f)^{(1+3hc)}$.

Hence, the number of instances executed to execute a phase successfully in the presence of detectable faults is

$$\sum_{k=1}^{\infty} k(f_{freq})^{k-1}(1 - f_{freq})$$
$$= (1 - f_{freq}) \sum_{k=1}^{\infty} k(f_{freq})^{k-1}$$

137

$$= (1 - f_{freq})\frac{1}{(1-f_{freq})^2}$$
$$= \frac{1}{(1-f)^{(1+3hc)}}$$

It follows that the time required to execute a phase successfully in the presence of detectable faults is $\frac{1+3hc}{(1-f)^{(1+3hc)}}$.

Simulation parameters. We obtained simulation results using SIEFAST, a *Simulation and Implementation Environment for FAult-tolerant, Secure, and real-Time protocols* which we have developed at Ohio State (cf. http://www.cis.ohio-state.edu/siefast). SIEFAST models a program and its environments; the former by the guarded command notation discussed in Section 2, and the latter by actions that characterize faults, security intrusions, input traffics, etc. One advantage of using SIEFAST is that it uses the exact program discussed in this paper, and requires no further translation into another language such as C or C++.

We used program RB as the input to SIEFAST and selected the option that simulated the program under maximal parallelism semantics. For the purposes of the barrier synchronization simulation, we only modeled the fault environment. This fault environment specified the frequency of fault occurrence and the actions that capture how faults perturb the program.

Masking detectable faults. Effect on re-executions/phase. Figure 3 illustrates the effect of the fault-frequency on the number of phases executed incorrectly. We keep the number of processors fixed at 32, and vary the frequency of faults from $f = 0$ to $f = 0.1$. Figure 3 (a) gives the analytical results and Figure 3 (b) gives the simulation results. As expected, the number of re-executions of a phase increases as the frequency of the faults increases, and the analytical prediction matches the simulation results.

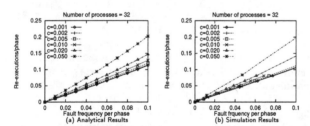

Figure 3: Effect on re-executions/phase

To give a more concrete interpretation of this evaluation, we will consider the following scenario: let the phase execution time be $1ms$. Then, $f = 0.01$ implies that 10 faults occur in every second, and $c = 0.01$ implies that the communication latency is $10\mu s$. We conclude that when the frequency of faults is low ($f \leq 0.01$), the percentage of phases executed incorrectly is lower than 1.6%.

Figure 3 (a) and (b) also illustrates the effect of communication latency on the number of instances executed in the presence of detectable faults. For a given fault-frequency, as the communication latency increases, there is a corresponding increase in the number of instances executed for a successful execution of phase. Observe that, even at high communication latency, $c = 0.05$, if the frequency of faults is low, say $f = 0.01$ (i.e., 10 faults per second), the probability that a phase is re-executed is as low as 1.7%. If the frequency of a fault is even lower, the number of re-executions is reduced further. (For subsequent results, we will use the the phase execution time to be $1ms$ while interpreting the

values of c and f.)

Effect on phase completion time. As mentioned above, if fault-tolerance is not an issue, barrier synchronization can be achieved in time $(1 + 2hc)$, whereas our program takes $\frac{(1+3hc)}{(1-f)^{(1+3hc)}}$ time. Figure 4 (a) and (b) illustrate the percentage increase in the time required for successful phase execution. Again, we consider 32 processes. If no fault occurs, the increase in the successful phase completion time is 4.5%. If $f = 0.01$ (10 faults in a second), there is a 5.7% increase, and even if the fault frequency is unreasonably high, $f = 0.05$ (50 faults in a second), the overhead is bounded by 10.8%. We conclude that the overhead for fault-tolerance is reasonably low.

The increase in the completion time of a phase in the simulated program is less than that predicated by analytical results. This is due to worst-case assumptions made in the analytical model. In particular, in the analytical model, we assume that if a detectable fault occurs during an instance of a phase, the time required for execution of that instance is still $1 + 3hc$. This is not the case if the fault occurs early on in the phase, in which case processes may complete an unsuccessful instance of the phase quickly.

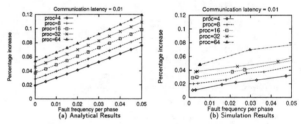

Figure 4: Effect on phase completion time

Recovery from undetectable faults. The program recovers from an arbitrary state in two stages: (i) the sn values of all processes are corrected, and (ii) subsequently the ph and cp values of all processes are corrected. Under the maximum parallel semantics, it is easy to show that the sn values are corrected in at most h communications steps. Thus, the first stage takes at most hc time.

After the sn values are corrected, 0 will get the token within hc time. Now, consider two cases: (a) 0 is in control position *ready*, and (b) 0 is not in control position *ready*. In case (a), it takes at most $2hc$ time for the program to reach a state from where further computation satisfies the specification of barrier synchronization. (See Lemma 4.1.3 of [11] for details.) In case (b), it takes at most $2hc$ time for the program to reach a state where the control position of 0 is *ready*. Moreover, when 0 changes its control position to *ready*, no process is in control position *execute*. (This follows from the fact that if 0 is in control position *success* when it sends the token to 1, each process will change its control position to either *success* or *repeat* in the circulation of that token.) Therefore, it takes at most hc time for the program to reach a state from where further computation satisfies the specification of barrier synchronization. Thus, the maximum time required in cases (a) and (b) is at most $3hc$ and, hence, the second stage takes at most $4hc$ time. It follows that within $5hc$ time the program recovers to a state from where further computation satisfies the specification of barrier synchronization. Moreover, under our assumption that $2hc$ is less than 0.5, the program recovers in at most 1.25 time units.

Since the recovery time is the time required for the program to reach a start state after faults stop occurring (at least long enough for the program to recover), it does not depend on the fault-frequency. Hence, we performed these simulations for various values of communication latency and various numbers of processes. As shown in Figure 5, the recovery time increases with the communication latency and the number of processes. However, the time required for recovery is small: for example, if the number of processors is 32 and c is 0.01 (10 μs), the recovery time is only 0.56 time units (560 ms). Also, if c is 0.05 and the number of processes is 128, the recovery time is less than one time unit. Note that due to the worst case assumptions made in the analytical results, the recovery time in the simulations is lower than that predicated by the analytical results.

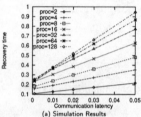

(a) Simulation Results

Figure 5: Recovery from undetectable faults

7 Concluding Remarks

In this paper, we presented barrier synchronization programs that tolerated two classes of faults, detectable and undetectable. We ensured that in the presence of detectable faults alone, the specification of barrier synchronization was always satisfied, and in the presence of undetectable faults, the program eventually reached a state from where the specification of barrier synchronization was (re)satisfied. Thus, our program was multitolerant [8] in that it provided appropriate tolerances with respect to multiple classes of faults. (The interested reader is referred to [8] for a formal method for the design of multitolerant programs.) We are not aware of work by others that has addressed multitolerance of barrier synchronization.

We also presented analytical and simulation results for the overhead incurred by our program in tolerating faults. As shown in Section 6, this overhead was low. In particular, the overhead was merely 3 to 4 percent when the frequency of faults was low (i.e., about 1 fault per second). Since faults occur relatively infrequently in modern day parallel systems, the program was optimized for the common case. Even if the frequency of faults were high (say, about 50 faults per second), the overhead was bounded by 10%.

In this paper, we assumed that faults are eventually correctable. While this assumption is true of many classes of faults, it is clearly not true of all types. (See Table 1 for a detailed classification.) If a fault is immediately correctable, i.e., it is possible to recover instantaneously from that fault, then we can pretend as if the fault does not not exist. Thus, masking tolerance can be trivially added to immediately correctable faults. If a fault is uncorrectable, it may be impossible to guarantee Progress. However, if the fault is detectable, it is possible to guarantee fail-safe tolerance where only Safety is guaranteed. Although, we only considered the middle row of Table 1 in this paper, our program can be extended to tolerate faults in the other two

rows. (See [11] for a discussion on how these faults can be tolerated.)

	Detectable	Undetectable
Immediately correctable	Trivially masking	
Eventually correctable	Masking[2]	Stabilizing
Uncorrectable	Fail-safe	Intolerant

Table 1 : Classification of faults and appropriate tolerances to them in barrier synchronization

Finally, we note that our program can be systematically extended to deal with fuzzy barriers [1]. In particular, the transition from *execute* to *success* is the same as entering the barrier, and the transition from *ready* to *execute* is the same as leaving the barrier. It is therefore possible to allow a process can perform useful work between these two state transitions, which captures the requirement of fuzzy barriers.

References

[1] R. Gupta and C. R. Hill. A scalable implementation of barrier synchronization using an adaptive combining tree. *International Journal of Parallel Programming*, 18(3), 1989.

[2] D. N. Jayasimha. Distributed synchronizers. *International Conference on Parallel Processing*, pages I 23–27, 1988.

[3] S. K. S. Gupta and D. N. Jayasimha. A generalized dynamic barrier synchronization scheme. *International Conference on Parallel Processing*, August 1992.

[4] R. Sivaram, C. B. Stunkel, and D. K. Panda. A reliable hardware barrier synchronization scheme. *International Parallel Processing Symposium*, pages 274–280, 1997.

[5] H. Xu, P.K. McKinley, and L. Ni. Efficient implementation of barrier synchronization in wormhole route hypercube multicomputers. *Journal of Parallel and Distributed Computing*, pages 172–184, 1992.

[6] D. Johnson, D. Lilja, J. Riedl, and J. Anderson. Low-cost, high-performance barrier synchronization on networks of workstations. *Journal of Parallel and Distributed Computing*, 40(1):131–137, January 1997.

[7] S. S. Kulkarni and A. Arora. Multitolerant barrier synchronization. *Information Processing Letters*, 64(1):29–36, October 1997.

[8] A. Arora and S. S. Kulkarni. Component based design of multitolerance. *IEEE Transactions on Software Engineering*, 24(1):63–78, January 1998.

[9] M. G. Gouda. The triumph and tribulation of system stabilization. In Jean-Michel Hélary and Michel Raynal, editors, *Distributed Algorithms, 9th International Workshop, WDAG '95*, volume 972 of *Lecture Notes in Computer Science*, pages 1–18, Le Mont-Saint-Michel, France,, 13–15 September 1995. Springer.

[10] MPI: A message-passing interface standard, June 1995. Version 1.1.

[11] S. S. Kulkarni and A. Arora. Low-cost fault-tolerance in barrier synchronizations. Technical Report OSU-CIS TR14, Ohio State University, May 1998.

---

[2] A further distinction can be made between faults that are detectable "immediately" versus those that are detectable "eventually" but not "immediately". Masking fault-tolerance is appropriate for the former but not the latter, assuming eventual correctability. Likewise, fail-safe tolerance is appropriate for the former but not the latter, assuming uncorrectability.

Embed Longest Rings onto Star Graphs with Vertex Faults

Sun-Yuan Hsieh, Gen-Huey Chen

Department of Computer Science and Information Engineering

National Taiwan University, Taipei, Taiwan, ROC

and

Chin-Wen Ho

Department of Computer Science and Information Engineering

National Central University, Taipei, Taiwan, ROC

Abstract

The star graph has been recognized as an attractive alternative to the hypercube. Let F_e and F_v be the sets of vertex faults and edge faults, respectively. Previously, Tseng et al. showed that an n-dimensional star graph can embed a ring of length n! if $|F_e| \leq n\text{-}3$ ($|F_v|=0$), and a ring of length at least $n!\text{-}4|F_v|$ if $|F_v| \leq n\text{-}3$ ($|F_e|=0$). Since an n-dimensional star graph is regular of degree n-1 and is bipartite with two partite sets of equal size, our result achieves optimality in the worst case.

1 Introduction

One crucial step on designing a large-scale multiprocessor system is to determine the topology of the interconnection network (network for short). In recent decades, a lot of networks have been proposed. The interested readers may refer to [4, 17] for extensive references. Among them, the star graph [1], which belongs to the class of Cayley graphs [2], has been recognized as an attractive alternative to the hypercube. It possesses many nice topological properties such as recursiveness, symmetry, maximal fault tolerance, sublogarithmic degree and diameter, and strong resilience, which are all desirable when we are building interconnection topologies for parallel and distributed systems. Besides, the star graph can embed rings [25], meshes [27], trees [3], and hypercubes [23]. Efficient communication algorithms for shortest-path routing [1], multiple-path routing [12], multicasting [16], broadcasting [31], gossiping [5], and scattering [16] have been proposed. Efficient algorithms for sorting [22], merging [25], selection [24], prefix sums [25], ranking [30], Fourier

transform [15], and computational geometry [26] have also been designed.

Since processor and/or link faults may happen when a network is put in use, it is practically meaningful to consider faulty networks. The problems of diameter [28], routing [14, 34], multicasting [21], broadcasting [33], gossiping [13], embedding [11, 29, 35], and fault-tolerant graphs [6-9, 19] have been solved on a variety of faulty networks. This paper is concerned with the problem of embedding a ring onto a faulty star graph. Throughout this paper, we use network and graph, processor and vertex, and link and edge, interchangeably.

Previously, embedding rings onto faulty star graphs has been studied in [20, 32]. In [20], Latifi and Bagherzadeh showed that an n-dimensional star graph with vertex faults can embed a ring of length $n!\text{-}m!$, where all vertex faults belong to an m-dimensional star graph and $m \leq n$ is minimal. Letting F_v and F_e denote the sets of vertex faults and edge faults, respectively, Tseng *et al.* [32] showed that an n-dimensional star graph can embed a ring of length $n!$ if $|F_e| \leq n\text{-}3$ ($|F_v|=0$), and a ring of length at least $n!\text{-}4|F_v|$ if $|F_v| \leq n\text{-}3$ ($|F_e|=0$). Since the n-dimensional star graph is regular of $n\text{-}1$ and contains $n!$ vertices, the former is optimal in the worst case. However, the latter is not optimal.

In this paper, we improve Tseng *et al.*'s latter result by lengthening the embedded ring from $n!\text{-}4|F_v|$ to $n!\text{-}2|F_v|$. We note that the star graph is bipartite and has two partite sets of equal size [18]. When $|F_v|$ vertex faults fall into the same partite set, an embedded ring has length not more than $n!\text{-}2|F_v|$. Hence, our result achieves optimality in the worst case.

2 Preliminaries

In this section the structure of the star graph is formally described. Some necessary notations and basic operations are also introduced. We use S_n to denote an n-dimensional star graph.

Definition 1. The vertex set of S_n is denoted by $\{a_1a_2...a_n \mid a_1a_2...a_n$ is a permutation of 1, 2, ..., $n\}$. Vertex adjacency is defined as follows: $a_1a_2...a_n$ is adjacent to $a_ia_2...a_{i-1}a_1a_{i+1}...a_n$ for all $2 \le i \le n$.

The vertices of S_n are $n!$ permutations of 1, 2, ..., n, and there is an edge between two vertices of S_n if and only if they can be obtained from each other by swapping the leftmost number with one of the other $n-1$ numbers. We refer to the position of a_i in $a_1a_2...a_n$ as the *ith dimension*, and the edge between $a_1a_2...a_n$ and $a_ia_2...a_{i-1}a_1a_{i+1}...a_n$ as the *ith-dimensional edge*. Clearly S_n is regular of degree $n-1$. Since S_1 is a vertex, S_2 is an edge, and S_3 forms a cycle of length 6, we consider S_n with $n \ge 4$ throughout this paper.

There are embedded S_r's contained in S_n, where $1 \le r \le n$. An embedded S_r can be conveniently represented by $<s_1s_2...s_n>_r$, where $s_1 = *$, $s_i \in \{*, 1, 2, ..., n\}$ for all $2 \le i \le n$, and exactly r of s_1, s_2, ..., s_n are * (* denotes a "don't care" symbol). For example, $<***3>_3$, which represents an embedded S_3 in S_4, contains six nodes 1243, 1423, 2143, 2413, 4123, and 4213. In terms of graph, $<***3>_3$ is a subgraph of S_4 induced by {1243, 1423, 2143, 2413, 4123, 4213}. When $r=n$, $<s_1s_2...s_n>_n$ represents S_n. Two basic operations on S_n are defined as follows.

Definition 2. An *i-partition on* $<s_1s_2...s_n>_r$ partitions $<s_1s_2...s_n>_r$ into r embedded S_{r-1}'s, denoted by $<s_1s_2...s_{i-1}qs_{i+1}...s_n>_{r-1}$, where $2 \le i \le n$, $s_i = *$, and $q \in \{1, 2, ..., n\} - \{s_1, s_2, ..., s_n\}$.

For example, executing a 3-partition on $<***15>_3$ produces three embedded S_2's, i.e., $<**215>_2$, $<**315>_2$, and $<**415>_2$.

Definition 3. An $(i_1, i_2, ..., i_m)$-partition on $<s_1s_2...s_n>_r$ performs an i_1-partition, an i_2-partition, ..., an i_m-partition, sequentially, on $<s_1s_2...s_n>_r$, where $i_1i_2...i_m$ is a permutation of m elements from $\{2, 3, ..., n\}$ and $s_{i_1} = s_{i_2} = \cdots = s_{i_m} = *$. After executing an $(i_1, i_2, ..., i_m)$-partition, $<s_1s_2...s_n>_r$ is partitioned into $r(r-1)\cdots(r-m+1)$ embedded S_{r-m}'s.

For example, when a (3, 2)-partition is applied to $<***15>_3$, a 3-partition is first executed on $<***15>_3$ to produce three embedded S_2's, i.e., $<**215>_2$, $<**315>_2$, and $<**415>_2$. Then, a 2-partition is executed on each of

these three S_2's to produce six embedded S_1's, i.e., $<*3215>_1$, $<*4215>_1$, $<*2315>_1$, $<*4315>_1$, $<*2415>_1$, and $<*3415>_1$.

Two embedded S_r's $<s_1s_2...s_n>_r$ and $<t_1t_2...t_n>_r$ are said to be *adjacent* if $s_j \ne *$, $t_j \ne *$, and $s_j \ne t_j$ for some $2 \le j \le n$, and $s_i = t_i$ for all $1 \le i \le n$ and $i \ne j$. Moreover, the position j is denoted by $dif(<s_1s_2...s_n>_r, <t_1t_2...t_n>_r)$. For example, $<**23>_2$ is adjacent to $<**13>_2$, and $dif(<**23>_2, <**13>_2)=3$.

In the rest of this paper, an embedded S_r is named an *r-vertex* when it is regarded as a supervertex. Imaginarily, there is a superedge, named an *r-edge*, between two adjacent *r-vertices*. Really, an *r-edge* in S_n comprises $(r-1)!$ edges. A 1-vertex in S_n is a vertex of S_n, and a 1-edge in S_n is an edge of S_n.

Definition 4. Suppose A_0, A_1, ..., $A_{n(n-1)(n-2)\cdots(r+1)-1}$ are $n(n-1)(n-2)\cdots(r+1)$ *r-vertices* that result from executing an $(i_1, i_2, ..., i_{n-r})$-partition on S_n, where $1 \le r \le n-1$. They form an *r-ring*, denoted by $R_r=[A_0, A_1, ..., A_{n(n-1)(n-2)\cdots(r+1)-1}]$, if A_i is adjacent to $A_{(i-1) \bmod n(n-1)(n-2)\cdots(r+1)}$ and $A_{(i+1) \bmod n(n-1)(n-2)\cdots(r+1)}$ for all $0 \le i \le n(n-1)(n-2)\cdots(r+1)-1$.

Definition 5. An *i-partition on an* $R_r=[A_0, A_1, ..., A_{n(n-1)(n-2)\cdots(r+1)-1}]$ performs an *i-partition* on A_0, A_1, ..., $A_{n(n-1)(n-2)\cdots(r+1)-1}$, where $2 \le i \le n$ and $r \ge 2$. An *i-partition on an* R_r is abbreviated to *a partition on an* R_r if the position i is "don't care".

After executing an *i-partition on an* $R_r=[A_0, A_1, ..., A_{n(n-1)(n-2)\cdots(r+1)-1}]$, each A_j is partitioned into r $(r-1)$-vertices, where $0 \le j \le n(n-1)(n-2)\cdots(r+1)-1$. Since every two of the r $(r-1)$-vertices are adjacent, each A_j can be viewed as a complete graph of r $(r-1)$-vertices. Throughout this paper, we use K_r^{r-1} to denote the complete graph.

Suppose $A_k=<s_1...s_{i-1}s_is_{i+1}...s_{j-1}xs_{j+1}...s_n>_r$ and $A_{(k+1) \bmod n(n-1)(n-2)\cdots(r+1)}=<s_1...s_{i-1}s_is_{i+1}...s_{j-1}ys_{j+1}...s_n>_r$ are two neighboring *r-vertices* in an R_r, where $r \ge 2$, $x \ne y$, and $s_i = *$. After an *i-partition*, they each are partitioned into r $(r-1)$-vertices. Among them, $r-1$ from A_k are adjacent to $r-1$ from $A_{(k+1) \bmod n(n-1)(n-2)\cdots(r+1)}$. The other two that are not adjacent are $<s_1...s_{i-1}ys_{i+1}...s_{j-1}xs_{j+1}...s_n>_{r-1}$ and $<s_1...s_{i-1}xs_{i+1}...s_{j-1}ys_{j+1}...s_n>_{r-1}$.

Suppose an $R_k=[A_0, A_1, ..., A_{n(n-1)(n-2)\cdots(k+1)-1}]$ is obtained in S_n, where $k \ge 4$. After executing a partition on the R_k, each A_i forms a K_k^{k-1}, where $0 \le i \le n(n-1)\cdots(k+1)-1$. There exist two $(k-1)$-vertices, say X_i and Y_i, in each A_i so that X_i and Y_i are adjacent to $Y_{(i-1) \bmod n(n-1)\cdots(k+1)}$ and $X_{(i+1) \bmod n(n-1)\cdots(k+1)}$, respectively. We refer to X_i and Y_i as the *entry (k-1)-vertex and exit (k-1)-vertex* of A_i, respectively, in subsequent discussion.

3 Embed a longest ring onto S_n with vertex faults

In this section we assume that S_n has $|F_v| \leq n-3$ vertex faults. We say that an i-vertex is *healthy* if it has no vertex fault, and *faulty* otherwise, where $1 \leq i \leq n$. Similarly, a ring (or a path) is *healthy* if it has no vertex fault. In this section we show that S_n with $n \geq 4$ can embed a healthy ring of length $n!-2|F_v|$. Since S_n is bipartite with two partite sets of equal size, the length $n!-2|F_v|$ is maximum in the worst case. Moreover, $|F_v|=n-3$ is also maximum in the worst case in order to embed a healthy ring of maximum length, because S_n is regular of $n-1$. Our method is first to determine an R_4 in S_n that owns the following three properties:

(P1) each 4-vertex of the R_4 has at most one vertex fault;

(P2) for every three consecutive 4-vertices $U=<u_1u_2...u_n>_4$, $V=<v_1v_2...v_n>_4$, and $W=<w_1w_2...w_n>_4$ in the R_4, $u_{dif(U,V)} \neq w_{dif(V,W)}$ holds;

(P3) both every two consecutive 4-vertices in the R_4 are not faulty.

Then, a healthy ring of length $n!-2|F_v|$ can be generated from the R_4.

Lemma 1. Suppose $U=<u_1u_2...u_n>_r$, $V=<v_1v_2...v_n>_r$, and $W=<w_1w_2...w_n>_r$ are arbitrary three consecutive r-vertices in an R_r, where $r \geq 2$. Let $p=dif(U, V)$ and $q=dif(V, W)$. If $u_p \neq w_q$, then after executing a partition on the R_r, each $(r-1)$-vertex of V is connected to U or W.

Proof. Without loss of generality, we assume that a j-partition is executed on the R_r, where $2 \leq j \leq n$. Hence, $u_j=v_j=w_j=*$. Since $p=dif(U, V) \neq 1$ and $q=dif(V, W) \neq 1$, we have $u_p \neq v_p$, $v_q \neq w_q$, $u_i=v_i$ for all $1 \leq i \leq n$ and $i \neq p$, and $v_i=w_i$ for all $1 \leq i \leq n$ and $i \neq q$. Suppose conversely that $u_p \neq w_q$ and there exists an $(r-1)$-vertex, say $V_1=<v_1v_2...v_{j-1}zv_{j+1}...v_n>_{r-1}$, of V, which is connected to neither of U and W. Thus, $z=u_p$, for otherwise V_1 is adjacent to some $(r-1)$-vertex of U. Similarly, $z=w_q$. Hence, $u_p=z=w_q$, which contradicts our assumption. Q.E.D.

The following lemma was shown in [32].

Lemma 2.[32] Suppose $|F_v| \leq n-3$. There exists a sequence $a_1, a_2, ..., a_{n-4}$ of positions so that after executing an $(a_1, a_2, ..., a_{n-4})$-partition on S_n, each resulting 4-vertex contains at most one vertex fault.

The positions $a_1, a_2, ..., a_{n-4}$ in Lemma 2 can be easily determined as follows. We let a_1 be a position where at least two vertices in F_v differ. For example, if $F_v=\{123456,$ 123654\}, a_1 is set to 4 or 6. An a_1-partition is then executed on S_n to produce n $(n-1)$-vertices, and F_v is partitioned accordingly. That is, two vertices in F_v fall into the same subset if and only if they belong to the same $(n-1)$-vertex. The position a_2 is determined similarly. We simply let a_2 be a position where at least two vertices in some subset differ. Then an a_2-partition is executed on the n $(n-1)$-vertices to produce $n(n-1)$ $(n-2)$-vertices, and every non-empty subset of F_v is partitioned accordingly. The process is repeated until every non-empty subset contains one vertex, when the remaining positions are determined arbitrarily.

A path in a graph G is said to be a *hamiltonian path* if it contains every vertex of G exactly once [10]. In the following discussion, a path between two vertices, say X and Y, are abbreviated to an X-Y path.

Lemma 3. Suppose $n \geq 6$ and $|F_v| \leq n-3$. An R_4 with properties (P1), (P2), and (P3) can be generated in S_n.

Proof. Suppose $a_1, a_2, ..., a_{n-4}$ are a sequence of positions that satisfy Lemma 2. We first construct an R_6 in S_n. When $n=6$, S_n is an R_6 with only one 6-vertex. For $n>6$, an R_6 can be obtained by executing an $(a_1, a_2, ..., a_{n-6})$-partition on S_n as follows. Initially, an a_1-partition is applied to S_n, and so a K_n^{n-1} results. An R_{n-1} can be easily generated from the K_n^{n-1}. Then, for $j=2, 3, ..., n-6$, an R_{n-j} can be generated from an R_{n-j+1} as explained below.

Suppose the $R_{n-j+1}=[A_{n-j+1,0}, A_{n-j+1,1}, ..., A_{n-j+1,n(n-1)\cdots(n-j+2)-1}]$. Each $A_{n-j+1,k}$ forms a K_{n-j+1}^{n-j} after an a_j-partition is executed on the R_{n-j+1}, where $0 \leq k \leq n(n-1)\cdots(n-j+2)-1$. Let X_k and Y_k denote a pair of distinct entry and exit $(n-j)$-vertices of $A_{n-j+1,k}$. It is easy to establish a hamiltonian X_k-Y_k path in each K_{n-j+1}^{n-j} formed by $A_{n-j+1,k}$. Then an R_{n-j} can be generated if all the hamiltonian paths are interleaved with $(n-j)$-edges $(Y_0, X_1), (Y_1, X_2), ..., (Y_{n(n-1)\cdots(n-j+2)-1}, X_0)$. When $j=n-6$, an $R_6=[A_{6,0}, A_{6,1}, ..., A_{6,n(n-1)\cdots7-1}]$ is obtained.

We continue to generate an R_5 from the R_6. When $n=6$, it is easy to generate an R_5 so that for arbitrary three consecutive 5-vertices $U=<u_1u_2...u_n>_5$, $V=<v_1v_2...v_n>_5$, and $W=<w_1w_2... w_n>_5$ in the R_5, $u_{dif(U,V)} \neq w_{dif(V,W)}$ holds. When $n>6$, each $A_{6,r}$ forms a K_6^5 after an a_{n-5}-partition is executed on the R_6, where $0 \leq r \leq n(n-1)\cdots7-1$. Let X_r and Y_r denote a pair of distinct entry and exit 5-vertices of $A_{6,r}$. It is easy to establish a hamiltonian X_r-Y_r path in the K_6^5 formed by $A_{6,r}$ whose first (last) two 5-vertices are connected to $A_{6,(r-1) \bmod n(n-1)\cdots7}$ ($A_{6,(r+1) \bmod n(n-1)\cdots7}$). All the hamiltonian paths interleaved with 5-edges $(Y_0, X_1), (Y_1,$

142

X_2), ..., $(Y_{n(n-1)\cdots7-1}, X_0)$ form an R_5. Besides, for arbitrary three consecutive 5-vertices $U=<u_1u_2...u_n>_5$, $V=<v_1v_2...v_n>_5$, and $W=<w_1w_2... w_n>_5$ in the R_5, $u_{dif(U,V)}\neq w_{dif(V,W)}$ holds. The reason is explained below.

Let $p=dif(U, V)$ and $q=dif(V, W)$. If $U=Y_i$ for some $0\leq i\leq n(n-1)(n-2)\cdots7-1$, then $V=X_{(i+1) \bmod n(n-1)\cdots7}$ and W is the second 5-vertex in the hamiltonian $X_{(i+1) \bmod n(n-1)\cdots7}$-$Y_{(i+1) \bmod n(n-1)\cdots7}$ path, which cause $p\neq a_{n-5}$ and $q=a_{n-5}$. Moreover, W is connected to $A_{6,i}$ according to the construction above. Recall that the 5-vertex of $A_{6,i}$ that are not connected to $A_{6,(i+1) \bmod n(n-1)\cdots7}$ is $<x_1...x_{q-1}y_px_{q+1}...x_n>_5$ and the 5-vertex of $A_{6,(i+1) \bmod n(n-1)\cdots7}$ that are not connected to $A_{6,i}$ is $<y_1...y_{q-1}x_py_{q+1}...y_n>_5$, where $x_q=y_p\neq x_p=y_q$ and $x_i=y_i$ for all $1\leq i\leq n$ and $i\notin\{p, q\}$. Hence, if $w_q=u_p$, then W is not connected to $A_{6,i}$, which is a contradiction. If $W=X_i$ for some $0\leq i\leq n(n-1)(n-2)\cdots7-1$, then $u_p\neq w_q$ can be shown similarly. Otherwise, if U, V, and W belong to the same 6-vertex, then $u_p\neq w_q$ because $p=q=a_{n-5}$.

We note that at most one 5-vertex in the R_5 contains two vertex faults and the others each contain at most one vertex fault. If there are two 5-vertices in the R_5 that each contain two or more vertex faults, then at most $n-5$ of the 5-vertices in the R_5 are faulty. This is a contradiction because the R_5, which results from executing an $(a_1, a_2, ..., a_{n-5})$-partition on S_n, contains at least $n-4$ faulty 5-vertices (see the paragraph after Lemma 2).

Next, we generate a desired R_4 from the R_5. Suppose the $R_5=[A_{5,0}, A_{5,1}, ..., A_{5,n(n-1)\cdots6-1}]$. Without loss of generality, we assume that one 5-vertex, say $A_{5,k}$ ($0\leq k\leq n(n-1)(n-2)\cdots6-1$), of the R_5 contains two vertex faults and the others each contain at most one vertex fault. An a_{n-4}-partition is executed on the R_5, and so each $A_{5,j}$ forms a K_5^4, where $0\leq j\leq n(n-1)\cdots6-1$. According to Lemma 1, each 4-vertex of $A_{5,k}$ is connected to $A_{5,(k-1) \bmod n(n-1)\cdots6}$ or $A_{5,(k+1) \bmod n(n-1)\cdots6}$. We further assume, without loss of generality, that $A_{5,k}$ contains two faulty 4-vertices, say C and E. A hamiltonian path in the K_5^4 formed by $A_{5,k}$ can be established according to the following three cases.

Case 1. Both of C and E are connected to both $A_{5,(k-1) \bmod n(n-1)\cdots6}$ and $A_{5,(k+1) \bmod n(n-1)\cdots6}$. Let B (F) be the 4-vertex in $A_{5,k}$ that is not connected to $A_{5,(k+1) \bmod n(n-1)\cdots6}$ ($A_{5,(k-1) \bmod n(n-1)\cdots6}$). A hamiltonian path is established as (B, C, D, E, F), where D is the other 4-vertex of $A_{5,k}$.

Case 2. One of C and E is connected to both $A_{5,(k-1) \bmod n(n-1)\cdots6}$ and $A_{5,(k+1) \bmod n(n-1)\cdots6}$, and the other is connected to one of $A_{5,(k-1) \bmod n(n-1)\cdots6}$ and $A_{5,(k+1) \bmod n(n-1)\cdots6}$. Without loss of generality, we assume C is connected to both $A_{5,(k-1) \bmod n(n-1)\cdots6}$ and $A_{5,(k+1) \bmod n(n-1)\cdots6}$. If E is connected to $A_{5,(k+1) \bmod n(n-1)\cdots6}$, a hamiltonian path is established as (B, C, D, E, F),

where B is the 4-vertex of $A_{5,k}$ that is not connected to $A_{5,(k+1) \bmod n(n-1)\cdots6}$, and D and F are the other two 4-vertices of $A_{5,k}$. If E is connected to $A_{5,(k-1) \bmod n(n-1)\cdots6}$, a hamiltonian path is established as (D, E, F, C, B), where B is the 4-vertex of $A_{5,k}$ that is not connected to $A_{5,(k-1) \bmod n(n-1)\cdots6}$, and D and F are the other two 4-vertices of $A_{5,k}$.

Case 3. One of C and E is not connected to $A_{5,(k-1) \bmod n(n-1)\cdots6}$, and the other is not connected to $A_{5,(k+1) \bmod n(n-1)\cdots6}$ (it is impossible that C and E are not connected to $A_{5,(k-1) \bmod n(n-1)\cdots6}$ or $A_{5,(k+1) \bmod n(n-1)\cdots6}$). Without loss of generality, we assume C is not connected to $A_{5,(k+1) \bmod n(n-1)\cdots6}$ and E is not connected to $A_{5,(k-1) \bmod n(n-1)\cdots6}$. A hamiltonian path is established as (B, C, D, E, F), where B, D, and F are the other three 4-vertices of $A_{5,k}$.

The first (last) 4-vertex in the hamiltonian paths above is the entry (exit) 4-vertex of $A_{5,k}$. Besides, the first (last) two 4-vertices are connected to $A_{5,(k-1) \bmod n(n-1)\cdots6}$ ($A_{5,(k+1) \bmod n(n-1)\cdots6}$). Then we determine the entry and exit 4-vertices of $A_{5,j}$, denoted by $X_{5,j}$ and $Y_{5,j}$, respectively, for all $0\leq j\leq n(n-1)(n-2)\cdots5-1$ and $j\neq k$ so that both $Y_{5,(j-1) \bmod n(n-1)\cdots6}$ and $X_{5,j}$ are not faulty and both $Y_{5,j}$ and $X_{5,(j+1) \bmod n(n-1)\cdots6}$ are not faulty. It is not difficult to establish a hamiltonian $X_{5,j}$-$Y_{5,j}$ path in the K_5^4 formed by each $A_{5,j}$ whose first (last) two 4-vertices are connected to $A_{5,(j-1) \bmod n(n-1)\cdots6}$ ($A_{5,(j+1) \bmod n(n-1)\cdots6}$).

All the hamiltonian paths interleaved with 4-edges constitute an R_4. Clearly the R_4 has properties (P1) and (P3). Recall that for arbitrary three consecutive 5-vertices $U=<u_1u_2...u_n>_5$, $V=<v_1v_2...v_n>_5$, and $W=<w_1w_2... w_n>_5$ in the R_5, $u_{dif(U,V)}\neq w_{dif(V,W)}$ holds. With similar arguments, the R_4 has property (P2). This completes the proof. Q.E.D.

Lemma 4. Suppose $|F_v|\leq1$. There is a healthy path of maximal length $4!-3$ between arbitrary two adjacent healthy vertices of S_4.

Proof. Suppose u and v are arbitrary two adjacent healthy vertices of S_4, and let $f=f_1f_2f_3f_4$ denote the faulty vertex. Since the star graph is edge symmetric [2], we assume $u=u_1u_2u_3u_4=1234$ and $v=v_1v_2v_3v_4=3214$ for illustration. We have $f_2\neq u_2=v_2$ or $f_4\neq u_4=v_4$, for otherwise $f=u$ or $f=v$, which is a contradiction. We assume $f_4\neq u_4=v_4=4$, without loss of generality. After executing a 4-partition on S_4, u and v belong to $<***4>_3$ and f belongs to $<***1>_3$ or $<***2>_3$ or $<***3>_3$.

If $f \in <***1>_3$, a healthy u-v path of length $4!-3$ can be constructed as follows:

(u=1234, 2134, 3124, 1324, 4321, 3421, 2431, 4231, 3241, 1243, 2143, 4123, 1423, 2413, 3412, 1432,

4132, 3142, 1342, 4312, 2314, 3214=v) if f=2341;

(u=1234, 4231, 3241, 2341, 4321, 3421, 1423, 2413, 4213, 1243, 2143, 3142, 1342, 4312, 3412, 1432, 4132, 2134, 3124, 1324, 2314, 3214=v) if f=2431;

(u=1234, 4231, 2431, 3421, 4321, 2341, 1342, 4312, 3412, 1432, 4132, 3142, 2143, 1243, 4213, 2413, 1423, 4123, 3124, 1324, 2314, 3214=v) if f=3241;

(u=1234, 2134, 3124, 4123, 1423, 2413, 4213, 1243, 2143, 3142, 1342, 4312, 3412, 1432, 2431, 4231, 3241, 2341, 4321, 1324, 2314, 3214=v) if f=3421;

(u=1234, 2134, 4132, 3142, 1342, 4312, 3412, 1432, 2431, 3421, 4321, 2431, 3241, 1243, 4213, 2413, 1423, 4123, 3124, 1324, 2314, 3214=v) if f=4231;

(u=1234, 2134, 3124, 4123, 2143, 1243, 4213, 2413, 1423, 3421, 2431, 4231, 3241, 2341, 1342, 3142, 4132, 1432, 3412, 4312, 2314, 3214=v) if f=2341.

If $f \in <***2>_3$ or $<***3>_3$, a healthy u-v path of length 4!-3 can be obtained similarly. Since the star graph is bipartite, the u-v path is the longest in the worst case. Q.E.D.

We note that S_3 forms a ring of length six. The following two lemmas were shown in [32].

Lemma 5.[32] Suppose U and V are two adjacent 3-vertices in S_n, and let (c_0, c_1, ..., c_5) denote the ring formed by U. Then, the vertices of U that are connected to V are c_j and $c_{(j+3) \mod 6}$ for some $0 \le j \le 5$.

Lemma 6.[32] Suppose U=$<u_1 u_2 ... u_n>_3$, V=$<v_1 v_2 ... v_n>_3$, and W=$<w_1 w_2 ... w_n>_3$ are three 3-vertices in S_n, and V is adjacent to both U and W. If $u_{dif(U,V)} \ne w_{dif(V,W)}$, then the two vertices of V that are connected to U are disjoint from the two vertices of V that are connected to W.

Lemma 7. Suppose $n \ge 5$ and $|F_v| \le n-3$. A healthy ring of maximal length $n!-2|F_v|$ can be generated from an R_4 in S_n that owns properties (P1), (P2), and (P3).

Proof. Suppose an R_4=[A_0, A_1, ..., $A_{(n-1) \cdots 5-1}$] with properties (P1), (P2), and (P3) is obtained after executing an (a_1, a_2, ..., a_{n-4})-partition on S_n. An a_{n-3}-partition is then executed on the R_4, and so each A_i is partitioned into four 3-vertices that form a K_4^3, where $a_{n-3} \in \{2, 3, ..., n\}$-$\{a_1, a_2, ..., a_{n-4}\}$ and $0 \le i \le n(n-1) \cdots 5-1$. According to Lemma 1, each 3-vertex of A_i is connected to $A_{(i-1) \mod n(n-1) \cdots 5}$ or $A_{(i+1) \mod n(n-1) \cdots 5}$ because of property (P2). Since three 3-vertices

of A_i are connected to $A_{(i-1) \mod n(n-1) \cdots 5}$ and three 3-vertices of A_i are connected to $A_{(i+1) \mod n(n-1) \cdots 5}$, two 3-vertices of A_i are connected to both $A_{(i-1) \mod n(n-1) \cdots 5}$ and $A_{(i+1) \mod n(n-1) \cdots 5}$.

We then determine the entry and exit 3-vertices of each A_i, denoted by X_i and Y_i, respectively, as follows. For each faulty A_i, we let X_i=Y_i=Q, where Q is a healthy 3-vertex of A_i that is connected to both $A_{(i-1) \mod n(n-1) \cdots 5}$ and $A_{(i+1) \mod n(n-1) \cdots 5}$. We note that A_i contains one vertex fault (property P(1)). Since $A_{(i-1) \mod n(n-1) \cdots 5}$ and $A_{(i+1) \mod n(n-1) \cdots 5}$ are healthy (property (P3)), $Y_{(i-1) \mod n(n-1) \cdots 5}$ and $X_{(i+1) \mod n(n-1) \cdots 5}$ are determined as the 3-vertex of $A_{(i-1) \mod n(n-1) \cdots 5}$ and the 3-vertex of $A_{(i+1) \mod n(n-1) \cdots 5}$, respectively, that are adjacent to Q. For every two consecutive healthy A_i and $A_{(i+1) \mod n(n-1) \cdots 5}$, Y_i and $X_{(i+1) \mod n(n-1) \cdots 5}$ are determined as two adjacent 3-vertices that belong to A_i and $A_{(i+1) \mod n(n-1) \cdots 5}$, respectively.

All X_i and Y_i thus determined are healthy. Moreover, when X_i=Y_i, $u_{dif(Y_{(i-1) \mod n(n-1) \cdots 5}, X_i)} \ne w_{dif(X_i, X_{(i+1) \mod n(n-1) \cdots 5})}$ holds, where $Y_{(i-1) \mod n(n-1) \cdots 5}$=$<u_1 u_2 ... u_n>_4$ and $X_{(i+1) \mod n(n-1) \cdots 5}$=$<w_1 w_2 ... w_n>_4$ are assumed. The reason is explained as follows. Suppose conversely $u_{dif(Y_{(i-1) \mod n(n-1) \cdots 5}, X_i)}$ = $w_{dif(X_i, X_{(i+1) \mod n(n-1) \cdots 5})}$. If $dif(Y_{(i-1) \mod n(n-1) \cdots 5}, X_i)$=$dif(X_i, X_{(i+1) \mod n(n-1) \cdots 5})$, then $Y_{(i-1) \mod n(n-1) \cdots 5}$=$X_{(i+1) \mod n(n-1) \cdots 5}$, which is a contradiction. If $dif(Y_{(i-1) \mod n(n-1) \cdots 5}, X_i) \ne dif(X_i, X_{(i+1) \mod n(n-1) \cdots 5})$, then there is a 3-vertex of A_i which is connected to neither of $A_{(i-1) \mod n(n-1) \cdots 5}$ and $A_{(i+1) \mod n(n-1) \cdots 5}$. This is again a contradiction because each 3-vertex of A_i is connected to $A_{(i-1) \mod n(n-1) \cdots 5}$ or $A_{(i+1) \mod n(n-1) \cdots 5}$.

Next we generate a healthy ring of length $n!-2|F_v|$ by establishing healthy paths in A_0, A_1, ..., $A_{(n-1) \cdots 5-1}$ in this sequence. First we construct a healthy path in A_0 as follows. Let x_0 be a healthy vertex of X_0 which is adjacent to a healthy vertex of $Y_{n(n-1) \cdots 5-1}$. When X_0=Y_0, $u_{dif(Y_{n(n-1) \cdots 5-1}, X_0)} \ne w_{dif(X_0, X_1)}$ holds for three consecutive 3-vertices $Y_{n(n-1) \cdots 5-1}$=$<u_1 u_2 ... u_n>_4$, $X_0(=Y_0)$, and X_1=$<w_1 w_2 ... w_n>_4$. According to Lemmas 5 and 6, there is a healthy vertex y_0 of $Y_0(=X_0)$ which is adjacent to both x_0 and x_1, where x_1 is a healthy vertex of X_1. If A_0 is healthy, it is not difficult to establish a healthy hamiltonian x_0-y_0 path in A_0. If A_0 is faulty, a healthy x_0-y_0 path of maximal length 4!-3 in A_0 can be established according to Lemma 4.

We then consider the situation of $X_0 \ne Y_0$. Let Q_0 (L_0) be the 3-vertex of A_0 that is not connected to A_1 ($A_{n(n-1) \cdots 5-1}$), where $Q_0 \ne Y_0$ ($L_0 \ne X_0$). A healthy hamiltonian X_0-Y_0 path for the K_4^3 formed by A_0 is established as (X_0, B, C, Y_0) if

144

$Q_0=X_0$ and $L_0=Y_0$, (X_0, Q_0, C, Y_0) if $Q_0 \neq X_0$ and $L_0=Y_0$, (X_0, B, L_0, Y_0) if $Q_0=X_0$ and $L_0 \neq Y_0$, and (X_0, Q_0, L_0, Y_0) if $Q_0 \neq X_0$ and $L_0 \neq Y_0$, where B and C are the other 3-vertices of A_0.

Without loss of generality, we assume (X_0, Q_0, L_0, Y_0) is the healthy hamiltonian X_0-Y_0 path. With the same arguments as the proof of Lemma 3, every three consecutive 3-vertices in $\{Y_{n(n-1)\cdots5-1}, X_0, Q_0, L_0, Y_0, X_1\}$ satisfy property (P2). Since A_0 is healthy, according to Lemmas 5 and 6 there are four pairs of distinct healthy vertices, denoted by $\{x_0, p\}$, $\{q, r\}$, $\{s, t\}$, and $\{z, y_0\}$, of X_0, Q_0, L_0, and Y_0, respectively, so that every two consecutive vertices in $\{x_0, p, q, r, s, t, z, y_0, x_1\}$ are adjacent, where x_1 is a healthy vertex of X_1. Clearly, there are healthy hamiltonian x_0-p, q-r, s-t, and z-y_0 paths in X_0, Q_0, L_0, and Y_0, respectively. These healthy hamiltonian paths interleaved with edges (p, q), (r, s), and (t, z) constitute a healthy hamiltonian x_0-y_0 path in A_0.

Then we construct healthy paths in A_1, A_2, …, $A_{n(n-1)\cdots5-2}$, sequentially. Suppose a healthy x_{j-1}-y_{j-1} path in A_{j-1} is obtained, where $1 \leq j \leq n(n-1)\cdots5-2$. Very similar to the situation of A_0, a healthy path in A_j can be constructed as follows. Let x_j be the (healthy) vertex of X_j that is adjacent to y_{j-1}. When $X_j=Y_j$, $u_{dif(Y_{j-1}, X_j)} \neq w_{dif(X_j, X_{j+1})}$ holds for three consecutive 3-vertices $Y_{j-1}=<u_1u_2\ldots u_n>_4$, $X_j(=Y_j)$, and $X_{j+1}=<w_1w_2\ldots w_n>_4$. According to Lemmas 5 and 6, there is a healthy vertex y_j of $Y_j(=X_j)$ which is adjacent to both x_j and a healthy vertex of X_{j+1}. If A_j is healthy, there is a healthy hamiltonian x_j-y_j path in A_j. If A_j is faulty, a healthy x_j-y_j path of maximal length 4!-3 in A_j can be established according to Lemma 4. When $X_j \neq Y_j$, a hamiltonian X_j-Y_j path for the K_4^3 formed by A_j is first established. Then a healthy hamiltonian x_j-y_j path in A_j can be obtained by concatenating healthy hamiltonian paths for the four 3-vertices of A_j, where y_j is a healthy vertex of Y_j and is adjacent to a healthy vertex of X_{j+1}.

Thus far we have established healthy paths in A_0, A_1, …, $A_{n(n-1)\cdots5-2}$. We continue to establish a healthy path in $A_{n(n-1)\cdots5-1}$. Let $x_{n(n-1)\cdots5-1}$ be the (healthy) vertex of $X_{n(n-1)\cdots5-1}$ that is adjacent to $y_{n(n-1)\cdots5-2}$, and $y_{n(n-1)\cdots5-1}$ be the (healthy) vertex of $Y_{n(n-1)\cdots5-1}$ that is adjacent to x_0. Without loss of generality, we use $(c_0, c_1, c_2, c_3, c_4, c_5)$ to represent $Y_{n(n-1)\cdots5-1}$, where $c_0=y_{n(n-1)\cdots5-1}$ is assumed. When $X_{n(n-1)\cdots5-1}=Y_{n(n-1)\cdots5-1}$, $u_{dif(Y_{n(n-1)\ldots5-2}, X_{n(n-1)\ldots5-1})} \neq w_{dif(X_{n(n-1)\ldots5-1}, X_0)}$ holds for three consecutive 3-vertices $Y_{n(n-1)\ldots5-2}=<u_1u_2\ldots u_n>_4$, $X_{n(n-1)\cdots5-1}(=Y_{n(n-1)\cdots5-1})$, and $X_0=<w_1w_2\ldots w_n>_4$. According to Lemmas 5 and 6, $x_{n(n-1)\cdots5-1}$ cannot be c_0 or c_3. Actually, $x_{n(n-1)\cdots5-1}=c_1$ or c_5 (i.e., $x_{n(n-1)\cdots5-1}$ and $y_{n(n-1)\cdots5-1}$ are adjacent) as explained below.

If $x_{n(n-1)\cdots5-1}=c_2$, a healthy path (c_2, c_1, c_0) in $Y_{n(n-1)\cdots5-1}$ together with all healthy paths that we have established in

A_0, A_1, …, $A_{n(n-1)\cdots5-2}$ form a ring of odd length in S_n. This is a contradiction because S_n is a bipartite graph in which every ring has even length. Similarly, there is a contradiction for $x_{n(n-1)\cdots5-1}=c_4$. Now that $x_{n(n-1)\cdots5-1}$ and $y_{n(n-1)\cdots5-1}$ are adjacent, there is a healthy hamiltonian $x_{n(n-1)\cdots5-1}$-$y_{n(n-1)\cdots5-1}$ path in $A_{n(n-1)\cdots5-1}$ if $A_{n(n-1)\cdots5-1}$ is healthy. If $A_{n(n-1)\cdots5-1}$ is faulty, there is a healthy $x_{n(n-1)\cdots5-1}$-$y_{n(n-1)\cdots5-1}$ path of maximal length 4!-3 in $A_{n(n-1)\cdots5-1}$ according to Lemma 4.

When $X_{n(n-1)\cdots5-1} \neq Y_{n(n-1)\cdots5-1}$, a healthy hamiltonian $X_{n(n-1)\cdots5-1}$-$Y_{n(n-1)\cdots5-1}$ path for the K_4^3 formed by $A_{n(n-1)\cdots5-1}$ is first established, similar to the situation of A_0. Without loss of generality, we assume $(X_{n(n-1)\cdots5-1}, D, E, Y_{n(n-1)\cdots5-1})$ is the healthy hamiltonian $X_{n(n-1)\cdots5-1}$-$Y_{n(n-1)\cdots5-1}$ path. There are three pairs of distinct healthy vertices, denoted by $\{x_{n(n-1)\cdots5-1}, a\}$, $\{b, c\}$, and $\{d, e\}$, in $X_{n(n-1)\cdots5-1}$, D, and E, respectively, so that every two consecutive vertices in $\{x_{n(n-1)\cdots5-1}, a, b, c, d, e, f\}$ are adjacent, where f is a healthy vertex of $Y_{n(n-1)\cdots5-1}$. Since $y_{n(n-1)\cdots5-1}=c_0$, f cannot be c_0 or c_3 according to Lemmas 5 and 6. Moreover, $f \in \{c_2, c_4\}$ will result in a ring of odd length in S_n, which is a contradiction. Hence, f is adjacent to $y_{n(n-1)\cdots5-1}$ (i.e., $f=c_1$ or c_5). It is easy to establish a healthy hamiltonian $x_{n(n-1)\cdots5-1}$-$y_{n(n-1)\cdots5-1}$ path in $A_{n(n-1)\cdots5-1}$.

Clearly, all the healthy paths that we have established in A_0, A_1, …, $A_{n(n-1)\cdots5-1}$ together with edges (y_0, x_1), (y_1, x_2), …, $(y_{n(n-1)\cdots5-1}, x_0)$ constitute a healthy ring of length $n!-2|F_v|$. Since S_n is bipartite with two partite sets of equal size, the ring is the longest in the worst case. Q.E.D.

Theorem 1. Suppose $n \geq 4$ and $|F_v| \leq n-3$. S_n can embed a healthy ring of maximal length $n!-2|F_v|$.

Proof. We show that S_n contains a healthy ring of maximal length $n!-2|F_v|$ according to different values of n. When $n=4$, $|F_v| \leq 1$. By the aid of Lemma 4, there is a healthy ring of maximal length $4!-2|F_v|$ in S_4.

When $n=5$, $|F_v| \leq 2$. Without loss of generality, we assume $|F_v|=2$. According to Lemma 2, the two vertex faults of S_5 will be distributed to two different 4-vertices after an a_1-partition is executed, where $2 \leq a_1 \leq 5$. Then an R_4 is established so that the two faulty 4-vertices are not adjacent in the R_4. Clearly the R_4 satisfies properties (P1) and (P3). Besides, it is not difficult to check that the R_4 also satisfies property (P2). By Lemma 7, a healthy ring of maximal length $5!-2|F_v|$ can be generated from the R_4.

When $n \geq 6$, an R_4 with properties (P1), (P2), and (P3) is first obtained by Lemma 3. Then, a healthy ring of maximal length $n!-2|F_v|$ can be generated by Lemma 7. Q.E.D.

4 Concluding remarks

In this paper, we have shown that a healthy ring of length $n!-2|F_v|$ can be embedded onto an n-dimensional star graph with $|F_v| \leq n-3$ vertex faults. This improves Tseng et al.'s result by lengthening the embedded ring from $n!-4|F_v|$ to $n!-2|F_v|$. Since the star graph is regular of degree $n-1$ and is bipartite with two partite sets of equal size, our result achieves optimality in the worst case.

In [32], Tseng et al. also showed that an n-dimensional star graph with $|F_v|$ vertex faults and $|F_e|$ edge faults can embed a healthy ring of length at least $n!-4|F_v|$ if $|F_v|+|F_e| \leq n-3$. With our result, the embedded ring can be lengthened from $n!-4|F_v|$ to $n!-2|F_v|$ as well.

References

[1]   S. B. Akers, D. Harel, and B. Krishnamurthy, "The star graph: an attractive alternative to the n-cube," *Proceedings of the International Conference on Parallel Processing*, 1986, pp. 216-223.

[2]   S. B. Akers, B. Krishnamurthy, "A Group-theoretic model for symmetric interconnection networks," *IEEE Transactions on Computers*, vol. 38, no. 4, pp. 555-566, 1989.

[3]   N. Bagherzadeh, M. Dowd, and N. Nassif, "Embedding an arbitrary tree into the star graph," *IEEE Transactions on Computers*, vol. 45, no. 4, pp. 475-481, 1996.

[4]   J. C. Bermond, Ed., *Interconnection Networks*, a special issue of *Discrete Applied Mathematics*, vol. 37+38, 1992.

[5]   P. Berthome, A. Ferreira, and S. Perennes, "Optimal information dissemination in star and pancake networks," *IEEE Transaction on Parallel and Distributed Systems*, vol. 7, no. 12, pp. 1292-1300, 1996.

[6]   J. Bruck, R. Cypher, and C. T. Ho, "Fault-tolerant meshes and hypercubes with minimal numbers of spares," *IEEE Transaction on Computers*, vol. 42, no. 9, pp. 1089-1104, 1993.

[7]   J. Bruck, R. Cypher, and C. T. Ho, "Fault-tolerant de Bruijn and shuffle-exchange networks," *IEEE Transaction on Parallel and Distributed Systems*, vol. 5, no. 5, pp. 548-553, 1994.

[8]   J. Bruck, R. Cypher, and C. T. Ho, "On the construction of fault-tolerant cube-connected cycles networks," *Journal of Parallel and Distributed Computing*, vol. 25, pp. 98-106, 1995

[9]   J. Bruck, R. Cypher, and C. T. Ho, "Wildcard dimensions, coding theory and fault-tolerant meshes and hypercubes," *IEEE Transaction on Computers*, vol. 44, no. 1, pp. 150-155, 1995.

[10]   F. Buckley and F. Harary, *Distance in Graphs*, Addition-Wesley, 1989.

[11]   M. Y. Chan, F. Y. L. Chin, and C. K. Poon, "Optimal simulation of full binary trees on faulty hypercubes," *IEEE Transaction on Parallel and Distributed Systems*, vol. 6, no. 3, pp. 269-286, 1995.

[12]   K. Day and A. Tripathi, "A comparative study of topological properties of hypercubes and star graphs," *IEEE Transactions on Parallel and Distributed Systems*, vol. 5, no. 1, pp. 31-38, 1994.

[13]   K. Diks and A. Pele, "Efficient gossiping by packets in networks with random faults," *SIAM Journal on Discrete Mathematics*, vol. 9, no. 1, pp. 7-18, 1996.

[14]   A. H. Esfahanian and S. L. Hakimi, "Fault-tolerant routing in de Bruijn communication networks," *IEEE Transactions on Computers*, vol. C-34, no. 9, pp. 777-788, 1985.

[15]   P. Fragopoulou and S. G. Akl, "A parallel algorithm for computing Fourier transforms on the star graph," *IEEE Transactions on Parallel and Distributed Systems*, vol. 5, no. 5, pp. 525-531, 1994.

[16]   P. Fragopoulou and S. G. Akl, "Optimal communication algorithms on star graphs using spanning tree constructions," *Journal of Parallel and Distributed Computing*, vol. 24, pp. 55-71, 1995.

[17]   D. F. Hsu, *Interconnection Networks and Algorithms*, a special issue of *Networks*, vol. 23, no. 4, 1993.

[18]   J. S. Jwo, S. Lakshmivarahan, and S. K. Dhall, "Embedding of cycles and grids in star graphs," *Journal of Circuits, Systems, and Computers*, vol. 1, no. 1, pp. 43-74, 1991.

[19]   H. K. Ku and J. P. Hayes, "Optimally edge fault-tolerant trees," *Networks*, vol. 27, pp. 203-214, 1996.

[20]   S. Latifi and N. Bagherzadeh, "Hamiltonicity of the Clustered-star graph with embedding applications," *Proceedings of the International Conference on Parallel and Distributed Processing Techniques and Applications*, 1996, pp. 734-744.

[21]   A. C. Liang, S. Bhattacharya, and W. T. Tsai, "Fault-tolerant multicasting on hypercubes," *Journal of Parallel and Distributed Computing*, vol. 23, pp. 418-428, 1994.

[22]   A. Mann and A. K. Somani, "An efficient sorting algorithm for the star graph interconnection network," *Proceedings of the International Conference on Parallel Processing*, vol. III, 1990, pp. 1-8.

[23]   Z. Miller, D. Pritikin, and I. H. Sudborough, "Near embeddings of hypercubes into Caley graphs on the

146

symmetric group," *IEEE Transactions on Computers*, vol. 43, no. 1, pp. 13-22, 1994.

[24] K. Qiu and S. G. Akl, "Load balancing and selection on the star and pancake interconnection networks," *Proceedings of the 26th Annual Hawaii International Conference on System Sciences*, 1993, pp. 235-242.

[25] K. Qiu, S. G. Akl, and H. Meijer, "On some properties and algorithms for the star and pancake interconnection networks," *Journal of Parallel and Distributed Computing*, vol. 12, pp. 16-25, 1994.

[26] K. Qiu, S. G. Akl, and I. Stojmenovic, "Data communication and computational geometry on the star and pancake networks," *Proceedings of the IEEE Symposium on Parallel and Distributed Processing*, 1991, pp. 415-422.

[27] S. Ranka, J. C. Wang, and N. Yeh, "Embedding meshes on the star graph," *Journal of Parallel and Distributed Computing*, vol. 19, pp. 131-135, 1993.

[28] Y. Rouskov, S. Latifi, and P. K. Srimani, "Conditional fault diameter of star graph networks," *Journal of Parallel and Distributed Computing*, vol. 33, pp. 91-97, 1996.

[29] R. A. Rowley and B. Bose, "Distributed ring embedding in faulty De Bruijn networks," *IEEE Transaction on Computers*, vol. 46, no. 2, pp. 187-190, 1997.

[30] D. K. Saikia and R. K. Sen, "Two ranking schemes for efficient computation on the star interconnection network," *IEEE Transactions on Parallel and Distributed Systems*, vol. 7, no. 4, pp. 321-327, 1996.

[31] J. P. Sheu, C. T. Wu and T. S. Chen, "An optimal broadcasting algorithm without message redundancy in star graphs," *IEEE Transactions on Parallel and Distributed Systems*, vol. 6, no. 6, pp. 653-658, 1995.

[32] Y. C. Tseng, S. H. Chang, and J. P. Sheu, "Fault-tolerant ring embedding in star graphs," *IEEE Transactions on Parallel and Distributed Systems*, to appear.

[33] J. Wu, "Safety levels-an efficient mechanism for achieving reliable broadcasting in hypercubes," *IEEE Transaction on Computers*, vol. 44, no. 5, pp. 702-706, 1995.

[34] J. Wu, "Reliable unicasting in faulty hypercubes using safety levels," *IEEE Transaction on Computers*, vol. 46, no. 2, pp. 241-247, 1997.

[35] P. J. Yang, S. B. Tien, and C. S. Raghavendra, "Embedding of rings and meshes onto faulty hypercubes using free dimensions," *IEEE Transaction on Computers*, vol. C-43, no. 5, pp. 608-613, 1994.

Cluster Fault Tolerant Routing in Hypercubes

Qian-Ping Gu and Shietung Peng
Department of Computer Software, The University of Aizu
Aizu-Wakamatsu, Fukushima, Japan 965-8580
qian@u-aizu.ac.jp, s-peng@u-aizu.ac.jp

Abstract: *We say a network (graph) can tolerate l faulty nodes for a specific routing problem if after removing at most l arbitrary nodes from the graph, the routing paths exist for the routing problem. However, the bound l is usually a worst-case measure and it is interesting, both practical and theoretical, to find the routing paths when more than l faulty nodes present. Cluster fault tolerant (CFT) routing has been proposed as an approach for this purpose. In CFT routing we try to reduce the number of "faults" that a routing problem has to deal with using subgraphs to cover the faulty nodes. In particular, we consider the number and the size (diameter) of faulty subgraphs rather than the number of faulty nodes that a graph can tolerate. We show the necessary and sufficient conditions on the number and the size of faulty subgraphs that the hypercube can tolerate for the following routing problems: find a path from a source node s to a target node t; and find k node-disjoint paths from s to k nodes $t_1, ..., t_k$. Our results imply that the hypercube can tolerate far more faulty nodes than the worst-case measures for these routing problems when the faulty nodes can be covered by certain subgraphs. We also give algorithms for finding the routing paths for the above routing problems.*

1 Introduction

With the rapid progress in VLSI and optic fiber technologies, the size of computer and communication networks has increased tremendously. As a result fault tolerant routing has become one of the central issues in the study of those networks [11, 10, 1, 2]. In this paper, we study node-fault tolerant routing problems. For a specific routing problem, we say a graph can tolerate l faulty nodes if after deleting at most l arbitrary nodes from the graph, the required routing paths exist for the routing problem. However the bound l is usually the worst-case measure that is unlikely to happen in practice. What are the sufficient conditions that guarantee the existence of the routing paths when more than l faulty nodes present? Several approaches such as *forbidden set* [5, 12, 17] and cluster fault tolerant routing (CFT routing) [9, 7] have been developed for this purpose. It has been observed that for several fundamental routing problems in the interconnection networks with regular structures like hypercube, star graphs, and so on, if multiple faulty nodes can be covered by a subgraph of small diameter, then those faulty nodes can be viewed as a single "fault" rather than several arbitrary ones. On the other hand, nodes of a network often "fail" in a cluster-like manner. For example, one of the most important operations in a network is to establish routing paths without disturbing the existing ones. The nodes in the existing paths can be covered by much less number of clusters. Motivated by the above observation, the CFT routing has been proposed to reduce the number of faulty nodes that the routing has to deal with using subgraphs of small diameters to cover the faulty nodes. A cluster of a graph is a connected subgraph of the graph. A cluster is *faulty* if all its nodes are faulty. In CFT routing we consider the number and the size (diameter) of faulty clusters that a graph can tolerate for certain routing problems. It is previously known that for some fundamental routing problems, a faulty cluster of diameter one in the hypercube and a faulty cluster of diameter two in star graphs can be viewed as a single "fault" [9, 7].

The hypercube is one of the most studied topologies of interconnection networks and has been adopted for a number of times in practice. Numerous works have been done on fault tolerant routing in the hypercube [3, 4, 13, 15, 17, 16]. Especially, several fundamental routing problems have been studied on hypercubes in a restricted CFT routing model in which the diameter of the faulty clusters is at most one [9, 6, 8]. In this paper, we show the necessary and sufficient conditions on the number and the size of arbitrary faulty clusters that an n-dimensional hypercube H_n can tolerate for the following routing problems:

1. find a path from a source node s to a target node t (node-to-node routing); and

2. find k ($2 \leq k \leq n$) node-disjoint paths from a source node s to a set of target nodes $T = \{t_1, ..., t_k\}$ (node-to-set routing).

Since H_n is n-connected, from Menger's theorem H_n can tolerate $n-1$ arbitrary faulty nodes for node-to-node routing and $n-k$ arbitrary faulty nodes for node-to-set routing [14]. Recently, it was shown that H_n can tolerate $n-2$ faulty cluster of diameter one plus one faulty node for node-to-node

0190-3918/98 $10.00 © 1998 IEEE

routing and $n - k$ faulty clusters of diameter one for node-to-set routing [8, 6].

In this paper, we prove that H_n can be disconnected by one faulty cluster of diameter four. This implies that the diameter of faulty clusters that H_n can tolerate is at most three for the above routing problems. For the clusters with diameter at most three, we show that the sum of the diameters of the clusters is a key parameter for the routing problems in H_n. For a faulty cluster C, define $\delta(C) = d(C)$ if $d(C) \geq 1$, where $d(C)$ is the diameter of C, otherwise $\delta(C) = 1$. Roughly speaking, $\delta(C)$ is the diameter of C but we view the diameter of a single faulty node as one. Let $\mathcal{F}$ be a set of faulty clusters and $\Delta(\mathcal{F})$ be the sum of "diameters" of clusters in $\mathcal{F}$, i.e., $\Delta(\mathcal{F}) = \sum_{C \in \mathcal{F}} \delta(C)$. Then the following conditions are keys for the routing problems in H_n:

C1 $\delta(C) \leq 3$ for $C \in \mathcal{F}$.

C2 $\Delta(\mathcal{F}) \leq n - 1$.

C3 $\Delta(\mathcal{F}) = n - 1$ implies $\exists C \in \mathcal{F}$ such that $d(C) \neq 1$.

C4 $\Delta(\mathcal{F}) \leq n - k$.

Especially, we prove that for $n \geq 3$ conditions C1, C2, and C3 are necessary and sufficient conditions on $\mathcal{F}$ that H_n can tolerate for node-to-node routing. For node-to-set routing, we show that for $n \geq 3$ conditions C1 and C4 are necessary and sufficient conditions on $\mathcal{F}$ that H_n can tolerate.

The above results can be interpreted as that if H_n can tolerate l arbitrary faulty nodes then H_n can tolerate a set of faulty clusters with the sum of the diameters bounded by l. In other words, a faulty cluster C can be viewed as only $\delta(C)$ arbitrary faulty nodes, although the number of nodes in C may be much larger than the "diameter" of C. Since a cluster of diameter two or three in H_n may have as many as $O(n)$ nodes, the above results imply that H_n can tolerate $O(nl)$ faulty nodes if they can be covered by certain clusters. This is in contrast with l arbitrary faulty nodes given by the worst case measure.

We also propose algorithms for finding the routing paths for the above routing problems. For node-to-node routing, we show that if the conditions C1, C2, and C3 are satisfied then a nonfaulty path of length $d(s,t) + O(\log n)$ can be found in $O(n + |F|)$ optimal time, where $|F|$ is the total number of faulty nodes in $\mathcal{F}$; and a nonfaulty path of optimal length $\min\{d(s,t) + 4, n + 2\}$ can be found in $O(n^2)$ time. For node-to-set routing, if the conditions C1 and C4 are satisfied then the k nonfaulty node-disjoint paths of length at most $n + O(\log n)$ can be found in $O(kn + |F|)$ optimal time (using the optimal time node-to-node algorithm as a subroutine); and the k paths of length at most $n + 2$ (which is optimal) can be found in $O(kn^2)$ time (using the optimal length node-to-node algorithm as a subroutine).

In the next section, we give preliminaries of this paper. Section 3 shows the necessary conditions on $\mathcal{F}$ that H_n can tolerate. The sufficient conditions on $\mathcal{F}$ that H_n can tolerate for node-to-node routing and node-to-set routing are proved in Sections 4 and 5, respectively. The final section concludes the paper.

2 Preliminaries

A path in a graph G is a sequence of edges of the form $(s_1, s_2)(s_2, s_3) \ldots (s_{k-1}, s_k)$, $s_i \in V(G)$, $1 \leq i \leq k$, and $s_i \neq s_j$, $i \neq j$. The length of a path is the number of edges in the path. We sometimes denote the path from s_1 to s_k by $s_1 \rightarrow s_k$. For a path $P = (s_1, s_2) \ldots (s_{k-1}, s_k)$, we also use P to denote the set $\{s_1, \ldots, s_k\}$ of nodes that appear in path P, if no confusion arises. A path P is called *nonfaulty* if all nodes in P are nonfaulty. Paths P and Q are disjoint if $P \cap Q = \emptyset$. Two paths P and Q that share a common end node s are called disjoint if $(P \setminus \{s\}) \cap (Q \setminus \{s\}) = \emptyset$. For any two nodes $s, t \in G$, $d(s, t)$ denotes the distance between s and t, i.e., the length of the shortest path connecting s and t. The diameter of G is defined as $d(G) = \max\{d(s,t)|s, t \in G\}$. The *eccentricity* of $s \in G$ is $e(s) = \max\{d(s,t)|t \in G\}$ and the *radius* of G is $r(G) = \min\{e(s)|s \in G\}$. The *center node* of a graph G is the node $s \in G$ such that $e(s) \leq r(G)$.

The n-dimensional hypercube H_n, called n-cube sometimes, is an undirected graph on the node set $H_n = \{0,1\}^n$ such that there is an edge between $u \in H_n$ and $v \in H_n$ if and only if u and v differ exactly in one bit position. H_n is n-connected, has 2^n nodes, and has diameter $d(H_n) = n$. For $n \geq 1$, the 0-subcube of H_n on dimension i, denoted as $H_{n-1}^{i=0}$, is defined to be the subgraph of H_n induced by the set of nodes whose ith bit is 0. Define similarly the 1-subcube $H_{n-1}^{i=1}$. $H_{n-1}^{i=0}$ and $H_{n-1}^{i=1}$ are both isomorphic to H_{n-1} and are connected to each other by edges in dimension i of H_n. H_n can be partitioned into two subcubes on any dimension i. For two distinct nodes $s = a_1 a_2 \ldots a_n$ and $t = b_1 b_2 \ldots b_n$, s and t are in different subcubes $H_{n-1}^{i=0}$ and $H_{n-1}^{i=1}$ for any $i \in \{j | a_j \neq b_j\}$. We say that s and t are separated by the partition on the dimension $i \in \{j | a_j \neq b_j\}$. We will denote $H_{n-1}^{i=0}$ and $H_{n-1}^{i=1}$ by H_{n-1}^0 and H_{n-1}^1, respectively, when the dimension i is not important in the content. Given a set $\mathcal{F}$ of clusters, define $\mathcal{F}_b = \{C \cap H_{n-1}^b | C \in \mathcal{F}\}$, $b = 0, 1$. For the set F of the faulty nodes of $\mathcal{F}$, define $F_b = F \cap H_{n-1}^b$, $b = 0, 1$.

For a node $s = a_1 a_2 \ldots a_n \in H_n$, $s^{(i)}$, $1 \leq i \leq n$, denotes the node $a_1 \ldots a_{i-1} \bar{a}_i a_{i+1} \ldots a_n$, where $\bar{a}_i$ is the logical negation of a_i. Similarly, $s^{(i_1, \ldots, i_k)}$ denotes the node $b_1 \ldots b_n$, where $b_i = \bar{a}_i$ for $i \in \{i_1, \ldots, i_k\}$ and $b_j = a_j$ for $j \in <n> \setminus \{i_1, \ldots, i_k\}$. In this paper, $<n>$ denotes the set $\{1, 2, \ldots, n\}$, and $<n> \setminus \{i_1, \ldots, i_k\} = \{j | j \in <n>, j \notin \{i_1, \ldots, i_k\}\}$.

We will view H_n as a graph and assume that each node of H_n can be identified in $O(1)$ time. The following properties

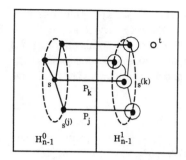

Figure 1: The n paths from s in H_{n-1}^0 to n nodes in H_{n-1}^1.

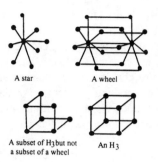

Figure 2: The star and wheel.

of H_n are important in this paper.

Proposition 1 *Let H_{n-1}^0 be the 0-subcube and H_{n-1}^1 be the 1-subcube of H_n on an arbitrary dimension k. For any node $s \in H_{n-1}^0$ (resp. $s \in H_{n-1}^1$), there are n disjoint paths of length at most 2 that connect s to n distinct nodes in H_{n-1}^1 (resp. H_{n-1}^0).*

For $s \in H_{n-1}^0$, the n paths are $P_k : s \rightarrow s^{(k)} \in H_{n-1}^1$ (of length 1), and $P_j : s \rightarrow s^{(j)} \rightarrow s^{(j,k)} \in H_{n-1}^1$ (of length 2), $1 \leq j \leq n, j \neq i$. (see Figure 1).

3 The necessary conditions

In this section, we prove that if any of the three conditions C1, C2, and C3 is not satisfied then we may not be able to find the path for node-to-node routing in H_n. Similarly, if any of the conditions C1 and C4 is not satisfied then we may not be able to find the k paths for node-to-set routing.

Lemma 2 *For $n \geq 3$, H_n can be disconnected by a faulty cluster C of diameter 4, or $n - 1$ faulty clusters of diameter 1, or n faulty nodes.*

Proof: For a node s and a dimension j, let $C = \{s^{(j)}, s^{(i)}, s^{(i,j)} | 1 \leq i \leq n, i \neq j\}$. Then $d(C) = 4$ and s is disconnected from the other nodes of H_n by the cluster C. Remove the node $s^{(j)}$ from C, we get $n - 1$ clusters $\{s^{(i)}, s^{(i,j)}\}$ of diameter 1, and nodes s and $s^{(j)}$ are isolated from the other nodes of H_n by the $n - 1$ clusters. Obviously, a node s is disconnected from the other nodes of H_n by its n neighbors. $\square$

From this lemma, the node s can be isolated by a cluster of diameter 4 and thus, $\delta(C) \leq 3$ (condition C1) for $C \in \mathcal{F}$ is a necessary condition on $\mathcal{F}$ that H_n can tolerate for the two routing problems. Similarly, $\Delta(\mathcal{F}) \leq n - 1$ (condition C2) and $\Delta(\mathcal{F}) = n - 1$ implies $\exists C \in \mathcal{F}$ such that $d(C) \neq 1$ (condition C3) are necessary conditions on $\mathcal{F}$ that H_n can tolerate for node-to-node routing.

We now show that $\Delta(\mathcal{F}) \leq n - k$ (condition C4) is a necessary condition on $\mathcal{F}$ that H_n can tolerate for node-to-set

routing. Let $\mathcal{F}$ be the set of $n - k + 1$ clusters each of which is a neighbor node of s. Then s has at most $k - 1$ nonfaulty neighbors. Obviously, there do not exist k nonfaulty disjoint paths from s to k nodes of T in this case.

4 Node-to-node routing

We call a set of faulty clusters $\mathcal{F}$ an *admissible set* on H_n for node-to-node routing if $\mathcal{F}$ satisfies conditions C1, C2, and C3. To show the conditions C1, C2, and C3 are sufficient conditions on $\mathcal{F}$ for node-to-node routing, we prove that given an admissible set $\mathcal{F}$ and any two nonfaulty nodes s and t in H_n, a nonfaulty path $s \rightarrow t$ can be found. In finding the path $s \rightarrow t$, we partition H_n into subcubes and reduce the problem in H_n into a subproblem in one of the two subcubes. To reduce the problem, we will often need to connect the node s (or t) in one subcube to a node s' (or t') in the opposite subcube. To connect s to s', the n disjoint paths for s given in Proposition 1 play a key role. We need to know how many of the n paths can be blocked by a faulty cluster of diameter at most 3.

We first show some properties of a cluster of diameter at most 3. A cluster C of H_n is called a star if $C = \{u\} \cup \{v | v = u^{(i)}, 1 \leq i \leq n\}$. A cluster C is called a wheel if $C = \{u, u^{(j)}\} \cup \{u^{(i)}, u^{(j,i)} 1 \leq i \leq n, i \neq j\}$. Obviously, a star is a cluster of diameter 2 and a wheel is a cluster of diameter 3 (see Figure 2). We will denote a star by V and a wheel by W.

Lemma 3 *Let C be a cluster of H_n. (1) If $d(C) = 2$ then $C \subseteq V$ or $C = H_2$. (2) If $d(C) = 3$ then $C \subseteq W$ or $C \subseteq H_3$*

We call a center c of a cluster C an *essential center* if the *radius* of C is less than the *diameter* of C, i.e., $r(C) < d(C)$. Notice that a star V has an unique essential center, a wheel W has two essential centers, and a subcube H_i has no essential center. For a node $s \in H_{n-1}^0$, if $s^{(k)} \in H_{n-1}^1$ is the essential center of a cluster C then C may block all the n disjoint paths for s (see Figure 1). However, if $s^{(k)}$ is not an essential center of a cluster C then the number of the n paths for s that

C can block is much smaller. The following lemmas show the number of the n paths that a cluster can block.

Lemma 4 *A cluster C with $\delta(C) \leq 3$ can block at most $\delta(C)$ neighbors of a node $s \notin C$.*

Lemma 5 *Given $s \in H_{n-1}^0$ and a cluster C with $s \notin C$ and $\delta(C) \leq 3$, if $s^{(k)}$ is not an essential center of C then C can block at most $\delta(C)$ paths P_j of length 2 for s.*

Lemma 6 *Let C be a cluster with $\delta(C) = \delta(C \cap H_{n-1}^0) \leq 3$. (1) For a node $s \in H_{n-1}^0$ with $s \notin C$, C does not block the path of length 1 for s. (2) $|C \cap H_{n-1}^1| \leq \delta(C) - 1$ if $d(C) \neq 1$ otherwise $|C \cap H_{n-1}^1| \leq d(C)$.*

Notice that a cluster C may block $\delta(C)$ of the $n - 1$ paths of length 2 and the path of length 1 for s even if $s^{(k)}$ is not an essential center of C (e.g., C is the $H_2 = \{s^{(k)}, s^{(k,i)}, s^{(k,j)}, s^{(k,i,j)}\}$).

Lemma 7 *Given an admissible set $\mathcal{F}$ of faulty clusters in H_n and a nonfaulty node s in one of the subcube of H_n, we can find a nonfaulty path of length at most 3 which connects s to a node s' in the opposite subcube.*

Proof: Assume that $s \in H_{n-1}^0$. If one of the n paths of length at most 2 for s is nonfaulty then we have done. So, we assume that all the n paths for s are blocked by the faulty clusters. From Lemma 4, $\mathcal{F}$ admissible, and the neighbor $s^{(k)} \in H_{n-1}^1$ of s faulty, s has a nonfaulty neighbor $u = s^{(i)} \in H_{n-1}^0$. We show that a nonfaulty path $u \to u' \in H_{n-1}^1$ of length 2 and thus, a nonfaulty path $s \to u'$ of length 3 can be found. The proof is divided into two cases.

Case 1: $s^{(k)}$ is an essential center of a cluster C'.
We first find a nonfaulty neighbor $s^{(j)} (j \neq k)$ of s such that $s^{(j,k)}$ is not an essential center of any faulty cluster. For a neighbor $s^{(j)}$ with $j \neq k$, assume that $s^{(j,k)}$ is an essential center of a cluster C_i. Since $d(s^{(j,k)}, s^{(l)}) = 3$ for $l \neq j, k$ and $\delta(C_i) \leq 3$, C_i does not block any $s^{(l)}$ and $s^{(l,k)}$ is not an essential center of C_i. Notice that C_i may block $s^{(j)}$. That is, C_i can block at most one neighbor $s^{(j)}$ of s with $j \neq k$. Let $C_1, ... C_x$ be the clusters of $\mathcal{F}$ such that one essential center of C_i ($1 \leq i \leq x$) is the node $s^{(j_i, k)}$. Then $\delta(C_i) \geq 2$ and C_i ($1 \leq i \leq x$) do not block any node of $S = \{s^{(j)}, 1 \leq j \leq n, j \neq k\} \setminus \{s^{(j_1)}, ..., s^{(j_x)}\}$. The set S has $(n - 1) - x$ nodes and $\sum_{C \in \mathcal{F} \setminus \{C_1, ..., C_x\}} \delta(C) \leq (n - 1) - 2x$. From Lemma 4, at most $(n - 1) - 2x$ nodes of S can be blocked by the clusters in $\mathcal{F} \setminus \{C_1, ..., C_x\}$. Therefore, we can find a nonfaulty neighbor $s^{(j)}$ of s such that $s^{(j,k)}$ is not an essential center of any cluster.

Let C' be the cluster with an essential center $s^{(k)}$. Then C' blocks only one of the $n - 1$ paths of length 2 for $s^{(j)}$ (otherwise $s^{(j,k)}$ becomes an essential center of C'). From Lemma 5, the clusters of $\mathcal{F} \setminus \{C'\}$ can block at most $\Delta(\mathcal{F}) - \delta(C') \leq n - 3$ of the $n - 1$ paths of length 2 for $s^{(j)}$. Thus, at

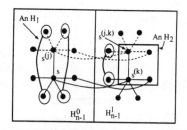

Figure 3: H_2 blocks 2 paths of s and 2 paths of $s^{(j)}$.

least one of the $n - 1$ paths of length 2 for $s^{(j)}$ is nonfaulty.

Case 2: $s^{(k)}$ is not an essential center of any cluster $C \in \mathcal{F}$.
Since all the n paths for s are faulty, from Lemma 5 we have that $\Delta(\mathcal{F}) = n - 1$, a cluster $C \in \mathcal{F}$ blocks $\delta(C)$ paths of length 2 and the path of length 1, and each of other clusters $C' \in \mathcal{F}$ blocks $\delta(C')$ paths of length 2. From Lemma 4, there is a nonfaulty neighbor $s^{(j)}$ with $j \neq k$ of s. If one of the n paths for $s^{(j)}$ is nonfaulty then we have done. So, we assume that all the n paths for $s^{(j)}$ are faulty as well.

From the argument of Case 1, $s^{(j,k)}$ is not an essential center of any cluster C as well, otherwise one of the n paths for s is nonfaulty. Therefore, for any cluster $C \in \mathcal{F}$ which blocks $\delta(C)$ paths of length 2 for s, C also blocks $\delta(C)$ paths of length 2 for $s^{(j)}$. From this, all the clusters in $\mathcal{F}$ are subcubes H_i with $1 \leq i \leq 3$. Since $\mathcal{F}$ is an admissible set and $\Delta(\mathcal{F}) = n - 1$, $\mathcal{F}$ has at least one subcube H_i with $2 \leq i \leq 3$. This H_i blocks i paths of length 2 for s and i paths of length 2 for $s^{(j)}$. This could happen only if H_i is a subset of H_{n-1}^1 since s and $s^{(j)}$ are nonfaulty (Figure 3 shows the case of H_2). So, H_i does not block any neighbor of s other than $s^{(k)}$. Therefore, we can find another nonfaulty neighbor $s^{(j_1)}$ of s, $j_1 \neq j, k$. Since an H_1 which blocks the paths of length 2 for s and $s^{(j)}$ does not block any path of length 2 for $s^{(j_1)}$, at least one of the n paths for $s^{(j_1)}$ is nonfaulty. $\square$

Lemma 8 *Given an admissible set $\mathcal{F}$ of faulty clusters in H_n, if $\mathcal{F}_1$ (resp. $\mathcal{F}_0$) is not admissible on H_{n-1}^1 (resp. on H_{n-1}^0) then H_{n-1}^0 (resp. H_{n-1}^1) has at most $\max\{n - 2, 2\}$ faulty nodes.*

Proof: Since $\mathcal{F}$ is admissible, for any $C \in \mathcal{F}$, $\delta(C \cap H_{n-1}^1) \leq \delta(C) \leq 3$. Therefore, to make $\mathcal{F}_1$ not admissible on H_{n-1}^1, we may only violate conditions C2 or C3. Assume that $\Delta(\mathcal{F}_1) = n - 1$. This implies that $\Delta(\mathcal{F}) = n - 1$ and for any $C \in \mathcal{F}$, $\delta(C \cap H_{n-1}^1) = \delta(C)$. Since $\mathcal{F}$ is admissible, $\mathcal{F}$ has at least one cluster C with $d(C) \neq 1$. From Lemma 6, $|C \cap H_{n-1}^0| \leq \delta(C) - 1$ and H_{n-1}^0 has at most $\Delta(\mathcal{F}) - 1 \leq n - 2$ faulty nodes.

Assume that $\Delta(\mathcal{F}_1) = n - 2$ and the diameter of clusters in $\mathcal{F}_1$ is one. Then at most one cluster $C' \in \mathcal{F}$ satisfies

151

$\delta(C') - 1 = \delta(C' \cap H_{n-1}^1)$, and for any $C \in \mathcal{F} \setminus \{C'\}$, $\delta(C \cap H_{n-1}^1) = \delta(C)$. From $d(C \cap H_{n-1}^1) = 1$ (the assumption) and $\delta(C \cap H_{n-1}^1) = \delta(C)$, C has no node in H_{n-1}^0. For the C' with $\delta(C') - 1 = \delta(C' \cap H_{n-1}^1)$, either $C' \cap H_{n-1}^1 = \emptyset$ or $d(C' \cap H_{n-1}^1) = 1$. Therefore, either C' is a single node or $C' \subseteq H_2$. Thus, H_{n-1}^0 has either 0 faulty nodes or 2 faulty nodes (these two nodes are connected). $\square$

Now, we prove that the conditions C1, C2, and C3 are sufficient conditions on $\mathcal{F}$ for node-to-node routing in H_n. We prove the above statement by finding the routing path between nonfaulty nodes s and t in the presence of an admissible set $\mathcal{F}$ of faulty clusters. In particular, we find the routing path by two different approaches. These approaches yield two algorithms for finding the routing path as well.

The first approach works like this: First partition H_n such that s and t are separated, say $s \in H_{n-1}^0$ and $t \in H_{n-1}^1$. Then we choose a subcube which contains at most half of the faulty nodes of $\mathcal{F}$. Assume that H_{n-1}^1 is chosen. Then we connect s to a node $s' \in H_{n-1}^1$ by a nonfaulty path of length at most 3. Finally, s' and t is connected recursively in H_{n-1}^1. An advantage of this approach is that the routing path can be found in optimal time. However, the length of the found path is not optimal, because when we find the path $s \rightarrow s'$ in each recursion, we can not guarantee that $s \rightarrow s'$ is a segment of an optimal path.

To find a routing path of optimal length, the second approach is proposed. In this approach, there are two schemes, one for $d(s,t) < n$ and the other for $d(s,t) = n$. For $d(s,t) < n$, partition H_n such that s and t are in the same subcube, say H_{n-1}^1. If $\mathcal{F}_1$ is admissible on H_{n-1}^1 then s and t are connected in H_{n-1}^1 recursively. Otherwise, we connect s and t to s' and t' in H_{n-1}^0 and then connect s' and t' there (H_{n-1}^0 has at most $\max\{n-2, 2\}$ faulty nodes by Lemma 8).

For $d(s,t) = n$, we partition H_n to separate s and t and connect e.g., s to s' as we did in the first approach. Notice that if $d(s,t) = n$ then the path $s \rightarrow s'$ must be a segment of an optimal path. If $d(s',t) < n - 1$ then s' and t are connected by the scheme for $d(s,t) < n$ otherwise by that for $d(s,t) = n$.

Theorem 9 *Given an admissible set $\mathcal{F}$ of faulty clusters and nonfaulty nodes s and t in H_n ($n \geq 2$), a nonfaulty path $s \rightarrow t$ of length $d(s,t) + O(\log n)$ can be found in $O(|F| + n)$ time, where F is the set of all faulty nodes in $\mathcal{F}$.*

Proof: Obviously, the theorem is true for $n \leq 3$. Assume $n \geq 4$. Partition H_n such that $s \in H_{n-1}^0$ and $t \in H_{n-1}^1$. Assume that $|F_0| \geq |F_1|$. We connect s to $s' \in H_{n-1}^1$ by a nonfaulty path of length at most 3 (Lemma 7) and then connect s' to t in H_{n-1}^1 recursively. Lemma 8 and $|F_0| \geq |F_1|$ guarantee that $\mathcal{F}_1$ is admissible on H_{n-1}^1 and thus, the recursion can be done.

In each recursion, at least half of the faulty nodes are removed. Assume that in each recursion, node s is connected

to the opposite subcube. Then after $r = \lceil \log |F| \rceil$ recursions, s is connected to a node s^* by a nonfaulty path, s^* and t are in the same $(n-r)$-dimensional subcube H_{n-r}, and H_{n-r} has no faulty node. Finally, s^* and t can be connected in H_{n-r} by a path of length $d(s^*, t)$.

The above proof implies an algorithm for finding a nonfaulty path $s \rightarrow t$. The time for connecting s or t to the opposite subcube in the ith ($1 \leq i \leq r$) resursion is $O(f_i)$, where f_i be the number of faulty nodes involved in the ith recursion, $f_1 = |F|$, and $f_i \leq f_{i-1}/2$ for $i > 1$. The total time for finding the path $s \rightarrow t$ is

$$T(n) = O(|F|) + O\left(\sum_{1 \leq i \leq r} \frac{|F|}{2^i}\right) = O(n + |F|).$$

In each recursion, a path $s \rightarrow s'$ of length at most 3 is found. From this and $r = O(\log |F|)$, the length of $s \rightarrow s^*$ is $O(\log |F|)$ and $d(s^*, t) = d(s, t) + O(\log |F|)$. Since a cluster of $\mathcal{F}$ has $O(n)$ faulty nodes, $|F| = O(n^2)$. Thus, the algorithm finds a nonfaulty path $s \rightarrow t$ of length $d(s,t) + O(\log n)$. $\square$

It needs to check all the faulty nodes (which takes $|F|$ time) to find the path $s \rightarrow t$ in the worst case and the length of $s \rightarrow t$ can be n (it takes n time to construct). Thus, the time complexity $O(|F| + n)$ in Theorem 9 is optimal. A lower bound on the length of the path $s \rightarrow t$ is $\min\{d(s,t) + 4, n + 2\}$ [8]. We now prove that the path $s \rightarrow t$ of optimal length $\min\{d(s,t) + 4, n + 2\}$ can be found.

Theorem 10 *Given an admissible set $\mathcal{F}$ of faulty clusters and nonfaulty nodes s and t in H_n ($n \geq 2$), a nonfaulty path $s \rightarrow t$ of length $\min\{d(s,t) + 4, n + 2\}$ can be found in $O(n^2)$ time.*

Proof: For $n \leq 3$, the theorem can be verified by an enumeration argument. We now prove the theorem for $n \geq 4$. Assume $s = a_1 a_2 ... a_n$ and $t = b_1 b_2 ... b_n$. Let $D = \{i | a_i \neq b_i\}$ ($|D| = d(s,t)$). We partitioning H_n on a dimension $i \notin D$ if $|D| < n$ (s and t are in the same subcube) otherwise on a dimension $i \in D$ (s and t are separated). For $|D| = n$, we connect s or t to the opposite subcube as shown in Theorem 9. Assume a nonfaulty path $s \rightarrow s' \in H_{n-1}^1$ of length at most 3 is found. Then we connect s' and t in H_{n-1}^1 recursively. Since every bit a_i of s is different with the bit b_i of t, $d(s', t) = d(s, t) - L(s \rightarrow s')$, where $L(s \rightarrow s')$ is the length of $s \rightarrow s'$. Thus, if we find a path $s' \rightarrow t$ of length $d(s', t) + c$ then we get a path $s \rightarrow t$ of length $d(s, t) + c$.

For $|D| < n$, assume that $s, t \in H_{n-1}^1$. If $\mathcal{F}_1$ is admissible on H_{n-1}^1 then we connect s and t in H_{n-1}^1 recursively. When the recursion goes down to an H_3, s and t can be connected by a path of length at most $d(s,t) + 2$.

Assume that $\mathcal{F}_1$ is not admissible. In this case, we find nonfaulty paths $s \rightarrow s' \in H_{n-1}^0$ and $t \rightarrow t' \in H_{n-1}^0$ and then connect s' and t' in H_{n-1}^0. As shown in the proof of

Lemma 8, at most one $C' \in \mathcal{F}$ has the property that $\delta(C') - 1 = \delta(C' \cap H^1_{n-1})$, and for any $C \in \mathcal{F} \setminus \{C'\}$, $\delta(C \cap H^1_{n-1}) = \delta(C)$. From Lemma 6, C can block at most $\delta(C)$ of the $n-1$ paths of length 2 and does not block the path of length 1 for s. For the cluster C', if C' is a single node then C' can block the path of length 1 for s, otherwise C' can block at most one of the $n-1$ paths of length 2 and does not block the path of length 1 for s. Therefore, at least one of the n paths for s is nonfaulty. If the path of length 1 for s is blocked then H^0_{n-1} has only one faulty node and the path of length 1 for t is nonfaulty. In this case, s' and t' can be connected by a nonfaulty path of length $d(s', t')$. From $d(s', t') \leq d(s, t) + 1$,

$$
\begin{aligned}
L(s \to t) &= L(s \to s') + L(s' \to t') + L(t \to t') \\
&= 2 + d(s', t') + 1 \leq d(s, t) + 4.
\end{aligned}
$$

Assume that both the paths of length 1 for s and t are nonfaulty. From Lemma 8, H^0_{n-1} has at most $n-2$ faulty nodes. Therefore, s' and t' can be connected by a nonfaulty path of length at most $d(s', t') + 2$ in H^0_{n-1} (see [8], for example). Since $d(s', t') = d(s, t)$ in this case, we can find a nonfaulty path $s \to t$ of length at most $d(s, t) + 4$.

Finally, we analyze the time complexity of the algorithm, $T(n)$. In the beginning, we find the essential center of each star and wheel in $\mathcal{F}$. This takes $|F| = O(n^2)$ time. Then, each recursive step can be done in $O(n)$ time. Therefore, $T(n)$ satisfies the inequality $T(n) \leq T(n-1) + O(n)$. From this, we conclude $T(n) = O(n^2)$. $\square$

5 Node-to-set routing

A set $\mathcal{F}$ of faulty clusters is called an admissible set on H_n for node-to-set routing if for $2 \leq k \leq n$ $\mathcal{F}$ satisfies conditions C1 and C4. To show C1 and C4 are sufficient conditions on $\mathcal{F}$ for node-to-set routing, we prove that given an admissible $\mathcal{F}$ and nonfaulty nodes s and $T = \{t_1, ..., t_k\}$, k nonfaulty disjoint paths $s \to t_i$ can be found.

We follow a divide-and-conquer approach to find the k paths. We partition H_n into subcubes such that s and its nonfaulty neighbor $s^{(r)}$ are separated (say $s \in H^0_{n-1}$ and $s^{(r)} \in H^1_{n-1}$) and reduce the problem of connecting s to T into two subproblems of connecting s to $T_0 = T \cap H^0_{n-1}$ and connecting $s^{(r)}$ to $T_1 = T \cap H^1_{n-1}$. The subproblem in H^1_{n-1} is first solved recursively. Assume that the paths $s^{(r)} \to s^{(r,j_i)} \to t_i$ have been found in H^1_{n-1} for $t_i \in T_1$. We replace the path $s^{(r)} \to s^{(r,j_i)} \to t_i$ by the path $s^{(j_i)} \to s^{(r,j_i)} \to t_i$ for $|T_1| - 1$ nodes in T_1 (t_i is connected to s via $s^{(j_i)}$). One node of T_1 is connected to s via $s^{(r)}$. After this, we mark $s^{(j_i)}$ faulty and solve the subproblem in H^0_{n-1} recursively. Figure 4 shows the connection from s to T_1.

As the recursion goes down, the problem is finally reduced to node-to-node routing problem and the results in the previous section are used. Since we partition H_n based on s and $s^{(r)}$, we can not guarantee that $T_0 \neq \emptyset$ and $T_1 \neq \emptyset$. We

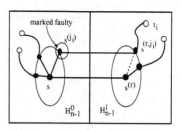

Figure 4: Connecting s to T_1.

solve the problem as a special case if one of the two sets T_0 and T_1 is empty.

Theorem 11 *For $2 \leq k \leq n$, given an admissible set $\mathcal{F}$, a nonfaulty node and a set $T = \{t_1, ..., t_k\}$ of nonfaulty nodes in H_n, k nonfaulty disjoint paths $s \to t_i$, $1 \leq i \leq k$, of length at most $n + 2$ (resp. $n + O(\log n)$) can be found in $O(kn^2)$ (resp. $O(kn + |F|)$) time.*

Proof: It is easy check that the theorem is true for $n \leq 3$. Assume that $n \geq 4$. From Lemma 4, at least k neighbors of s are nonfaulty. Let $s^{(r)}$ be one of the nonfaulty neighbors of s. Partition H_n on the dimension r (s and $s^{(r)}$ are separated) and assume $s \in H^0_{n-1}$ and $s^{(r)} \in H^1_{n-1}$. The proof is divided into two cases.

Case 1: $|T_0| = 0$ or $|T_1| = 0$.

We only prove the case of $|T_0| = 0$ (the other case can be done similarly). The details of the proof is further divided into two cases.

Assume that $\exists C \in \mathcal{F}$ such that $\delta(C \cap H^1_{n-1}) \leq \delta(C) - 1$. In this case, we first find the k nonfaulty disjoint paths $s^{(r)} \to s^{(r,j_i)} \to t_i$ in H^1_{n-1} for all $t_i \in T_1$ and then replace $k - 1$ of the k paths $s^{(r)} \to s^{(r,j_i)} \to t_i$ by $s^{(j_i)} \to s^{(r,j_i)} \to t_i$. That is, we connect $k - 1$ nodes of T_1 to s via $s^{(j_i)}$. The rest node is connected to s via $s^{(r)}$. To realize the above, we need to connect at least $k - 1$ nodes t_i of T_1 to $s^{(r)}$ via such $s^{(r,j_i)}$ that $s^{(j_i)}$ are nonfaulty. Let $S = \{s^{(r,j)} | s^{(j)}$ is faulty and $s^{(r,j)}$ is nonfaulty.$\}$. We mark $|S| - 1$ nodes of S faulty. After this, if the nodes of T_1 can be connected to $s^{(r)}$ by nonfaulty disjoint paths in H^1_{n-1} then the nodes of T_1 can be connected to s.

Now, we prove that the nodes of T_1 can be connected to $s^{(r)}$ in H^1_{n-1} after the marking. The key of the proof is to show that the set $\mathcal{F}'_1$ of faulty clusters in H^1_{n-1} is admissible for node-to-set routing on H_{n-1} after the marking ($\Delta(\mathcal{F}'_1)$ may be larger than $\Delta(\mathcal{F}_1)$ due to the marking). If $|S| \leq 1$ then no node in H^1_{n-1} is marked faulty and $\mathcal{F}'_1 = \mathcal{F}_1$. From the assumption that $\exists C \in \mathcal{F}$ such that $\delta(C \cap H^1_{n-1}) \leq \delta(C) - 1$,

$$
\Delta(\mathcal{F}'_1) \leq \Delta(\mathcal{F}) - 1 \leq (n-1) - k.
$$

153

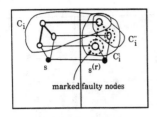

Figure 5: Clusters C_i, C_i', and C_i''.

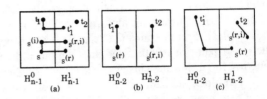

Figure 6: Connecting t_1', t_2 to $s^{(r)}$, $s^{(r,i)}$ in H_{n-1}^1.

Assume that $|S| \geq 2$. Let $C_1, ..., C_r$ be the clusters each of which contains at least one node of S. From Lemma 4, each C_i ($1 \leq i \leq r$) can have at most $\delta(C_i)$ nodes of S. If $C_i \cap H_{n-1}^1 = \emptyset$ then $\sum_{s^{(j)} \in C_i} \delta(\{s^{(r,j)}\}) \leq \delta(C_i)$. If $C_i \cap H_{n-1}^1 \neq \emptyset$ then $\delta(C_i) \geq 2$. Assume that $\delta(C_i) = 2$. Then C_i is a subset of a star ($C_i \subseteq V$) and C_i has a single node in H_{n-1}^1. The set $(C_i \cap H_{n-1}^1) \cup \{\{s^{(r,j)}\}|s^{(j)} \in C_i\}$ forms a cluster C_i' (see Figure 5). If C_i has two nodes of S then C_i' has three nodes and $\delta(C_i') = 2$, otherwise $\delta(C_i') = 1$. Removing any marked node from C_i' will result in a cluster C_i'' with $\delta(C_i'') = 1$. Similarly, it is easy to check that for $\delta(C_i) = 3$, the set $(C_i \cap H_{n-1}^1) \cup \{\{s^{(r,j)}\}|s^{(j)} \in C_i\}$ forms a cluster C_i' with $\delta(C_i') \leq \delta(C_i)$ and removing any node $s^{(r,j)}$ from C_i' will result in a cluster C_i'' with $\delta(C_i'') < \delta(C_i)$. Concluding the above, after marking $|S| - 1$ nodes of S faulty, the marked faulty nodes and the nodes of $C_i \cap H_{n-1}^1$ ($1 \leq i \leq r$) form a set $\mathcal{F}'$ of faulty clusters with $\Delta(\mathcal{F}') < \sum_{1 \leq i \leq r} \delta(C_i)$. From this, $\mathcal{F}_1' = \mathcal{F}' \cup \{C|C \in (\mathcal{F}_1 \setminus \{C_1, ..., C_r\})\}$ and

$$\Delta(\mathcal{F}_1') \leq \Delta(\mathcal{F}') + \Delta(\mathcal{F}_1) - \sum_{1 \leq i \leq r} \delta(C_i)$$
$$\leq \Delta(\mathcal{F}) - 1 \leq (n-1) - k.$$

Thus, $\mathcal{F}_1'$ is admissible on H_{n-1}^1 for connecting $s^{(r)}$ to T_1 and the k paths from $s^{(r)}$ to T_1 can be found in H_{n-1}^1.

Assume that for each $C \in \mathcal{F}$, $\delta(C) = \delta(C \cap H_{n-1}^1)$. In this case, $\Delta(\mathcal{F}_1)$ may be as large as $n - k = (n-1) - k + 1$ and we may not be able to connect the k nodes of T_1 to s in H_{n-1}^1. From Lemma 6, H_{n-1}^0 has at most $n - k$ faulty nodes and for any nonfaulty node $u \in H_{n-1}^1$ the node $u^{(r)} \in H_{n-1}^0$ is nonfaulty. We will make use of this property to connect $k - 1$ nodes of T_1 to $s^{(r)}$ in H_{n-1}^1 and connect one node t of T_1 to a node $t' \in H_{n-1}^0$. Node t' is then connected to s in H_{n-1}^0. Pick up an arbitrary node t_i and connect $s^{(r)}$ to $T_1 \setminus \{t_i\}$ ($\mathcal{F}_1$ is admissible for connecting $s^{(r)}$ to $k - 1$ nodes of T_1). If t_i is included in a path $s^{(r)} \to t_j$ ($t_j \in T_1 \setminus \{t_i\}$) then we discard the segment of $t_i \to t_j$, connect $s^{(r)}$ to t_i, and connect t_j to $t_j^{(r)} \in H_{n-1}^0$ by the path of length 1, otherwise connect t_i to $t_i^{(r)} \in H_{n-1}^0$. After this, $k - 2$ of the $k - 1$ paths $t_i \to s^{(r,j_i)} \to s^{(r)}$ are replaced

by $t_i \to s^{(r,j_i)} \to s^{(j_i)}$ ($k - 2$ nodes of T_1 are connected to s via $s^{(j_i)}$), one node of T_1 is connected to s via $s^{(r)}$. Consider the nodes $s^{(j_i)}$ as faulty nodes, H_{n-1}^0 has at most $n - k + (k - 2) = n - 2$ faulty nodes. Thus, t_j' can be connected to s in H_{n-1}^0 by a nonfaulty path.

Case 2: $|T_0| \geq 1$ and $|T_1| \geq 1$.

Assume $k = 2$ ($|T_0| = 1$ and $|T_1| = 1$). If $\mathcal{F}_b$ is admissible on H_{n-1}^b, $b = 0, 1$ then the node of T_0 can be connected to s in H_{n-1}^0 and the node of T_1 can be connected to $s^{(r)}$ in H_{n-1}^1. If $\mathcal{F}_0$ is not admissible then $\Delta(\mathcal{F}_0) = n - 2$ and $d(C) = 1$ for all $C \in \mathcal{F}_0$. From $\Delta(\mathcal{F}_0) = n - 2$ and $\Delta(\mathcal{F}) \leq n - 2, \forall C \in \mathcal{F}, \delta(C) = \delta(C \cap H_{n-1}^0)$. Therefore, $\forall C \in \mathcal{F}, C \cap H_{n-1}^1 = \emptyset$, i.e., H_{n-1}^1 has no faulty node. For the node $t_1 \in T_0$ we can find a path $t_1 \to t_1' \in H_{n-1}^1$ of length at most 2 that has no faulty node or the node $t_2 \in T_1$. Notice that s has at least one nonfaulty neighbor $s^{(i)}$ ($i \neq r$) in H_{n-1}^0. We connect the nodes t_1' and t_2 to $s^{(r)}$ and $s^{(r,i)}$ in H_{n-1}^1 (Figure 6 (a)). To do so, we further partition H_{n-1}^1 into H_{n-2}^0 and H_{n-2}^1 such that $t_1' \in H_{n-2}^0$ and $t_2 \in H_{n-2}^1$. If $s^{(r)}$ and $s(r, i)$ are separated then the connection is done as shown in Figure 6 (b); otherwise in Figure 6 (c). The length of paths $s \to t_1$ and $s \to t_2$ is at most $2 + (n-2) + 2 = n + 2$. The time complexity of finding the two paths is $O(n)$. The case that $\mathcal{F}_1$ is not admissible can be shown similarly.

Assume $k \geq 3$. We first connect the nodes of T_1 and then the nodes of T_0 to s. To connect the nodes t_i of T_1 to s, we first find the nonfaulty paths $s^{(r)} \to s^{(r,j_i)} \to t_i$ in H_{n-1}^1 and then replace $|T_1| - 1$ of the $|T_1|$ paths $s^{(r)} \to s^{(r,j_i)} \to t_i$ by $s^{(j_i)} \to s^{(r,j_i)} \to t_i$. The rest node is connected to s via $s^{(r)}$. Let $S = \{s^{(r,j)}|s^{(j)} \text{ is faulty and } s^{(r,j)} \text{ is nonfaulty.}\}$. We mark $|S| - 1$ nodes of S faulty. After this, if we can connect the nodes of T_1 to $s^{(r)}$ by nonfaulty disjoint paths in H_{n-1}^1 then the nodes of T_1 can be connected to s. Let $\mathcal{F}_1'$ be the set of faulty clusters in H_{n-1}^1 after the marking. By a similar argument as that in Case 1, if $|S| \geq 2$ then

$$\Delta(\mathcal{F}_1') \leq (n-1) - k < (n-1) - |T_1|,$$

otherwise

$$\Delta(\mathcal{F}_1') \leq \Delta(\mathcal{F}_1) \leq n - k \leq (n-1) - |T_1|.$$

From $k \geq 3$, $\mathcal{F}_1'$ is admissible on H_{n-1}^1 for connecting $s^{(r)}$ to T_1.

154

To connect the nodes of T_0 to s, we first mark the nodes $s^{(j_i)}$ which has been used by a path from T_1 to s faulty. Let $\mathcal{F}'_0 = \mathcal{F}_0 \cup \{s^{(j_i)}\}$. Then $\Delta(\mathcal{F}'_0) \leq n - k + (|T_1| - 1) = (n-1) - |T_0|$. If $|T_1| \geq 2$ then at least one cluster of $\mathcal{F}'_0$ is a single node. If $|T_1| = 1$ then $|T_0| \geq 2$. Therefore, $\mathcal{F}'_0$ is admissible and s and T_0 can be connected in H^0_{n-1} recursively.

Let $L(k, n)$ be the length of the longest path in the k paths from s to $T = \{t_1, ..., t_k\}$. $L(1, n) \leq n + 2$ if Theorem 10 is used, and $L(1, n) = n + O(\log n)$ if Theorem 9 is used. $L(2, n) \leq \max\{n + 2, L(1, n-1) + 1\} \leq \max\{n + 2, L(1, n)\}$. For $k \geq 3$, it is easy to see that $L(k, n) \leq \max\{L(k_0, n-1), L(k_1, n-1) + 1\} \leq L(2, n)$, where $0 \leq k_0, k_1 \leq k$ and $k_0 + k_1 = k$. Thus, the length of the paths $s \to t_i \in T$ are bounded by $n + O(\log n)$ (Theorem 9) or $n + 2$ (Theorem 10).

Let $T(k, n)$ be the time complexity of finding the k paths from s to T in H_n. $T(1, n) = O(|F| + n)$ if Theorem 9 is used, and $T(1, n) = O(n^2)$ if Theorem 10 is used. It is easy to check that $T(k, n) = T(k_0, n-1) + T(k_1, n-1)$, where $0 \leq k_0, k_1 \leq k$ and $k_0 + k_1 = k$. Thus, the time complexity is $O(kn + |F|)$ (Theorem 9) or $O(kn^2)$ (Theorem 10). $\square$

It needs to check all the faulty nodes to find the k disjoint paths in the worst case and the sum of the lengths of the k paths can be $\Omega(kn)$. Thus, the time complexity $O(kn + |F|)$ for finding the k paths is optimal. From the lower bound $\min\{d(s, t) + 4, n + 2\}$ on the length of the path for node-to-node routing, it is easy to get that $n + 2$ is a lower bound on the length of the longest one in the k paths for node-to-set routing. Thus, the upper bound $n + 2$ on the length of the k paths is optimal as well.

6 Conclusional Remarks

In this paper, we proved the necessary and sufficient conditions on the $\mathcal{F}$ of faulty clusters that the hypercube can tolerate for node-to-node and node-to-set routings. For these routing problems, a faulty cluster of diameter d ($1 \leq d \leq 3$) can be viewed as d "faults." Since a cluster of diameter two or three in H_n may have as many as $O(n)$ nodes, the above results imply that H_n can tolerate $O(nl)$ faulty nodes if they can be covered by the clusters, where l is the worst case measure. It is interesting to study other routing problems in H_n on the CFT routing model. Investigating CFT routing properties and designing efficient CFT routing algorithms for other interconnection networks are certainly worth further research attention.

References

[1] J. C. Bermond. Interconnection networks. *Discrete Applied Math.*, Special issue (Edited), 1992.

[2] J. C. Bermond, N. Homobono, and C. Peyrat. Large fault-tolerant interconnection networks. *Graphs and Combinatorics*, 5, 1989.

[3] J. Bruck, R. Cypher, and D. Soroker. Tolerant faults in hypercubes using subcube partitioning. *IEEE Trans. on Computers*, pages 599–605, 1992.

[4] M.S. Chen and K.G. Shin. Depth-first search approach for fault-tolerant routing in hypercube multiprocessors. *IEEE Trans. on Parallel and Distributed Systems*, pages 152–159, 1990.

[5] A. H. Esfahanian. Generalized measures of fault tolerance with application to n-cube networks. *IEEE Trans. on Computers*, 38(11):1586–1591, 1989.

[6] Q. Gu and S. Peng. Advanced fault tolerant routing in hypercubes. In *Proc. of the International Symposium on Parallel Architectures, Algorithms and Networks (ISPAN'94)*, pages 189–196, 1994.

[7] Q. Gu and S. Peng. Node-to-node cluster fault tolerant routing in star graphs. *Information Processing Letters*, 56:29–35, 1995.

[8] Q. Gu and S. Peng. Optimal algorithms for node-to-node fault tolerant routing in hypercubes. *The Computer Journal*, 39(7):626–629, 1996.

[9] Q. Gu and S. Peng. k-pairwise cluster fault tolerant routing in hypercubes. *IEEE Trans. on Computers*, 46(9):1042–1049, 1997.

[10] D. F. Hsu. Interconnection networks and algorithms. *Networks*, Special issue 23(4), 1993.

[11] D. F. Hsu. On container with width and length in graphs, groups, and networks. *IEICE Trans. on Fundamental of Electronics, Information, and Computer Sciences*, E77-A(4):668–680, 1994.

[12] S. Latifi, M. Hedge, and M. Naraghi-Pour. Conditional connectivity measures for large multiprocessor systems. *IEEE Trans. on Computers*, 43(2):218–222, 1994.

[13] T.C. Lee and J.P. Hayes. A fault-tolerant communication scheme for hypercube computers. *IEEE Trans. on Computers*, pages 1242–1256, 1992.

[14] J. McHugh. *Algorithmic Graph Theory*. Prentice-Hall Inc., 1990.

[15] M. Peercy and P. Banerjee. Optimal distributed deadlock-free algorithms for routing and broadcasting in arbitrarily faulty hypercubes. In *Proc. of the 20th International Symposium on Fault-Tolerant Computing*, 1990.

[16] C.S. Raghavendra, P.J. Yang, and S.B. Tien. Free dimensions—an efficient approach to archieving fault tolerance in hypercube. *IEEE Trans. on Computers*, Vol. 44:1152–1157, 1995.

[17] S.B. Tien and C.S. Raghavendra. Algorithms and bounds for shortest paths and diameter in faulty hypercubes. *IEEE Trans. on Parallel and Distributed Systems*, pages 713–718, 1993.

Fault-Tolerant Multicasting in Multistage Interconnection Networks

Jinsoo Kim*
Seoul Telecommunication O & M Research Center,
Korea Telecom,
17, Woomyeon-Dong, Seocho-Gu, Seoul 137-792, Korea
jinsoo@dambi.kotel.co.kr

Jaehyung Park
Department of Computer Science,
Purdue University, West Lafayette, IN, 47907
hyeoung@cs.purdue.edu

Jung Wan Cho and Hyunsoo Yoon
Department of Computer Science,
Korea Advanced Institute of Science and Technology
373-1, Kusong-Dong, Yusung-Gu, Taejon 305-701, Korea
{jwcho,hyoon}@camars.kaist.ac.kr

Abstract

In this paper, we study fault-tolerant multicasting in multistage interconnection networks (MINs) for constructing large-scale multicomputers. In addition to point-to-point routing among processor nodes, efficient multicasting is critical to the performance of multicomputers. This paper presents a new approach to provide fault-tolerance multicasting, which employs the restricted header encoding schemes. The proposed approach is based on a recursive scheme in order to send a multicast packet to the desired destinations detouring faulty element(s). In the proposed fault-tolerant multicasting, a multicast packet is routed to its own destinations in only two passes through the MIN having a number of faulty elements by exploiting its nonblocking property.

1. Introduction

Multistage interconnection networks (MINs) are popular and efficient interconnection for large-scale multicomputers, such as IBM SP1/SP2 [12] and NEC Cenju-3 [5]. Many of them are a class of networks which consist of $\log_2 N$ stages of 2×2 switching elements connecting N input ports to

N output ports. These networks have the property of full access capability that any output can be reachable from any input in a single pass through the network. In addition, there exist a unique path between any pair of input and output in these networks. The unique path property helps the use of a simple and efficient routing algorithm for setting up connections.

However, any single fault on a link or a switching element (SE) of these networks may cause to destroy the full access property. Interconnection networks have the feature of *fault-tolerance* if they can sustain to provide connection in spite of having faulty components. Fault-tolerance criterion for networks in this paper is preserving full access capability [2, 13].

To achieve fault-tolerance in MIN-based multicomputers, there are two alternative approaches. The first is to add SEs and/or links in the network [1, 10], which provide multiple paths to detour faulty elements. In this scheme, the failure of SE(s) and/or link(s) in the network causes reconfiguration of the network in order to preserve full access capability. The reconfigured network by such scheme has the same communication capability as the original network. However, this scheme renders an enormous waste of resources [13] or the modification of its original routing algorithm. In addition, extra logics to tolerate faults may cause irregularity in designing the internal structure; this results in decreasing the modularity of its structure for

---

This author is also currently working in Department of Computer Science, Korea Advanced Institute of Science and Technology.

multicomputers.

Instead of augmenting additional elements, the second is to expense routing overhead in order to minimize the loss of resources [6, 13]. Thus, the influence of the faulty SE(s) and/or link(s) can be decreased by allowing multiple passes through the network. The network is known to possess *dynamic full access capability* if every output can be reachable from every input in a finite number of passes, as routing the packet through intermediate outputs if necessary [13]. Even though a single fault destroys the full access capability, some faults do not destroy the dynamic full access capability. A routing algorithm is known as *recursive scheme*, which allow routing through intermediate destinations and recycling through the network. Without loss of resources, in this scheme, a destination can be reachable from its source detouring faulty element(s).

In this paper, we propose fault-tolerant multicasting in MIN-based multicomputers. While unicasting means that a source node delivers a packet to only one destination node. multicasting means that the same packet is delivered from a source to an arbitrary number of destinations. In many multicomputer systems, it is important to provide multicasting as well as unicasting [8, 9]. The proposed multicasting employs the restricted header encoding schemes in order to specify packet's destinations and is based on the recursive scheme which allows a packet recycle at the output to its input in order to send its own destination. The proposed fault-tolerant multicasting exploits the intrinsic nonblocking property of the MIN. Hence, a multicast packet is routed to its own destinations in only two passes in the MIN having certain fault sets which satisfy some conditions.

The structure of this paper is organized as follows. The next section describes the MIN topology, its intrinsic properties, and the restricted header encoding schemes as a system model. Section 3 describes the fault model and terminologies used in this paper. In Section 4 a fault-tolerant multicasting is proposed under certain fault-set environment, which is based on the recursive scheme. Section 5 concludes the paper.

2. System Model

This section describes the MIN topology of multicomputers, its intrinsic properties, and the restricted header encoding scheme.

2.1. Basic Architecture

The MIN is an $N \times N$ interconnection network with $n = \log_2 N$ stages. Each stage contains $N/2$ (2×2) switching elements (SEs). The stages are labeled in a sequence from $(n-1)$ to 0 with $(n-1)$ for the first stage. The N input/output ports at each stage are labeled using n binary digits $(a_{n-1}a_{n-2}\cdots a_0)$, within each stage starting from the top. And the SEs at each stage are labeled using $(n-1)$ binary digits $(a_{n-1}a_{n-2}\cdots a_1)$ starting from the top.

The MIN that we consider in this paper has butterfly interconnection patterns between stages, and a perfect shuffle interconnection pattern between input controllers and stage $(n-1)$, as shown in Figure 1. In MIN-based multicomputers, output links at the final stage are connected to processing nodes through external links, hence packets can be recycled through the MIN.

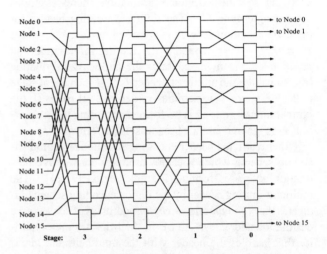

Figure 1. A MIN-based multicomputers

The MIN has the following property on account of its interconnection patterns.

Property 1 Let the source and destination of a packet be $a = a_{n-1}a_{n-2}\cdots a_0$ and $b = b_{n-1}b_{n-2}\cdots b_0$, respectively. In stage i, the SE $b_{n-1}\cdots b_{i+1}a_{i-1}\cdots a_1a_0$ is used for the packet, the b_ith output port of the SE is selected.

2.2. Nonblocking Properties

The MIN considered in this paper is topologically equivalent to the *omega network* [14]. We can easily analogize the following two nonblocking properties from the results of omega network [3]. We represent the source and destination of a packet p_i as s_i and d_i, respectively.

Property 2 Assume that $s_i > s_j$ and $d_i > d_j$. If the difference between two source addresses is not greater than the difference between two destination addresses, that is, $s_i - s_j \leq d_i - d_j$, then two packets cannot induce any blocking in the MIN.

Definition 1 $S_{msb}(a, b)$ is the number of bits which are identical from $n - 1$ to 0 in the binary expansions of a and b, and $S_{lsb}(a, b)$ is the number of bits which are identical from 0 to $n - 1$.

Property 3 Two packets p_i and p_j cannot induce any blocking in the MIN if and only if $S_{lsb}(s_i, s_j) + S_{msb}(d_i, d_j) < n$.

2.3. Restricted Header Encoding Scheme

The restricted header encoding scheme constructs a multicast routing header from reachable destinations which are restricted into a single cube or a single region in the MINs.

As one of the restricted header encoding scheme, a cube encoding specifies arbitrary destination addresses forming a single cube C. The multicast routing header for the cube encoding scheme is specified by $\{R, M\}$, where $R = r_{n-1} \cdots r_1 r_0$ contains the routing information and $M = m_{n-1} \cdots m_1 m_0$ contains the multicast information [4]. To handle the multicast header $\{R, M\}$, an SE at stage i ($0 \le i \le n-1$) examines r_i and m_i. If m_i is 0, the normal unicast routing is performed according to r_i. If m_i is 1, r_i is ignored and the broadcast is performed.

Other restricted header encoding scheme is a region encoding scheme which specifies arbitrary consecutive destination addresses forming a single region [7, 11]. The multicast routing header by the region encoding scheme indicates the *minimum* and *maximum* addresses of consecutive destination addresses. An SE in the MIN has the capability that handles the header with the minimum and maximum addresses. Suppose that an SE at stage i received a packet with the header containing the two addresses: $min_{i+1} = m_{n-1} \cdots m_1 m_0$ and $max_{i+1} = M_{n-1} \cdots M_1 M_0$, where the argument $(i+1)$ denotes an SE in stage $(i+1)$ from where the packet came to stage i. The decision for packet routing and replication is described as follows:

1. If $m_i = M_i = 0$ or $m_i = M_i = 1$, then send the packet out on port 0 or 1, respectively.

2. If $m_i = 0$ and $M_i = 1$, then replicate the packet, modify the headers, and send both packets out on both ports.

These rules that $m_{i'} = M_{i'}, i < i' \le n-1$ hold for every packet which arrives at stage $i, 0 \le i \le n-1$. The modification of a packet header is done according to the following recursion :

- $\left. \begin{array}{l} min_i = min_{i+1} = m_{n-1} \cdots m_1 m_0, \\ max_i = M_{n-1} \cdots M_{i+1} 01 \cdots 1 \end{array} \right\}$

for the packet sent out on port 0, and

- $\left. \begin{array}{l} min_i = m_{n-1} \cdots m_{i+1} 10 \cdots 0, \\ max_i = max_{i+1} = M_{n-1} \cdots M_1 M_0 \end{array} \right\}$

for the packet sent out on port 1, at stage i.

3. The Faulty Model and Terminologies

We assume that SEs in stage $(n-1)$ or 0 cannot be faulty, otherwise packets with some sources and destinations alway cannot be routed. We also assume that the mean time to repair faults is quite large.

The *destination group* is a set of destinations such as a region or a cube. The *group packet* is the packet routed to a destination group from a source.

Definition 2 The *binary relation* $<_D$ is defined between two destination groups D_1 and D_2 as follows:
$D_1 <_D D_2$ if and only if $d_1 < d_2$ for all d_1 and d_2 such that $d_1 \in D_1$ and $d_2 \in D_2$.

$M(\alpha)$ and $L(\beta)$ are a set of addresses whose most significant bits are α, and a set of addresses whose least significant bits are β, respectively. Thus, $M(0)$ and $M(1)$ are disjoint groups. Similarly, $L(0)$ and $L(1)$ are also disjoint groups.

Definition 3 D^α is defined as a set of destination groups Ds such that at least one destination in D is an element of the set $M(\alpha_{n-1})$. $D^{\bar{\alpha}}$ is defined as a set of destination groups Ds such that any destinations in D are not in $M(\alpha_{n-1})$.

Let $A = \{s_1, \ldots, s_m\}$ be a set of source addresses satisfying that $s_1 < s_2 < \cdots < s_m$, and $B = \{D_1, \ldots, D_n\}$ be a set of destination groups, satisfying that $D_1 <_D D_2 <_D \cdots <_D D_n$. The notation $A \Rightarrow^k B$ means that each packet is routed from a source s_i to a destination group D_i, for all $i, 1 \le i \le k$, where $1 \le k \le m$ and $1 \le k \le n$.

A faulty SE at stage i is represented by $f = \alpha\beta$ or $\alpha_{n-1} \cdots \alpha_{i+1} \beta_{i-1} \cdots \beta_0$. Therefore, each packet whose source is in $L(\beta)$ and destination is in $M(\alpha)$ always passes the faulty SE $\alpha\beta$ in banyan network, according to Property 1. Consequently, if such packets are excluded, the faulty SE cannot induce any problem in routing.

4. Fault-Tolerant Multicasting in MINs

In this section, we propose fault-tolerant multicasting in MIN-based multicomputers with certain fault set.

4.1. On Region Encoding Scheme

Definition 4 Let R_1 and R_2 be two regions satisfying that $R_1 <_D R_2$. $R_2 - R_1$, is defined the value of $d_{min2} - d_{max1}$ where d_{min2} and d_{max1} are the minimum destination in R_2 and the maximum destination in R_1.

For example, if $R_1 = [0000, 0010]$, $R_2 = [0100, 0100]$, then $R_2 - R_1 = 0100 - 0010 = 2$.

Fault-Tolerant Multicasting I (FTM-I)
Phase 1: Copy from the source to $2k$ consecutive intermediate destinations SR through the MIN, where $k = max(|D^\alpha|, |D^{\bar{\alpha}}|)$. The start address is randomly selected within the restriction that all the consecutive intermediate destinations are in $M(\alpha_{n-1}^-)$ if the source is in $L(\beta)$.
Phase 2: Route the recycled copies from SR to the regions as follows :

158

- Case 1 : $A_1 \Rightarrow^{|D^\alpha|} D^\alpha$ if $A_1 = \{a|a \in SR$ and $a \in L(\bar{\beta}_0)\}$.

- Case 2 : $A_2 \Rightarrow^{|D^{\tilde{\alpha}}|} D^{\tilde{\alpha}}$ if $A_2 = \{a|a \in SR$ and $a \in L(\beta_0)\}$.

In Figure 2, an example of the second phase is shown, where source 0 sends a multicast packet to destinations $\{1, 3, 4, 7, 8, 10, 11, 14\}$ in a banyan network with a faulty SE 000 at stage 2. Thus, α is 0 and β is 00. Therefore, $D^\alpha = \{[0001, 0001], [0011, 0100], [0111, 1000]\}$ and $D^{\tilde{\alpha}} = \{[1010, 1011], [1110, 1110]\}$. $|D^\alpha| = 3$, $|D^{\tilde{\alpha}}| = 2$, and $k = 3$. During the first phase, source 0 sends a copy to 6 intermediate destinations $SR = \{8, 9, 10, 11, 12, 13\}$. Although the source 0 is in $L(\beta)$ or $L(00)$, destinations are not in $M(0)$ and then the packet does not pass the faulty SE. In this case, the start address 8 is randomly selected. In the second phase, $A_1 = \{9, 11, 13\}$ and $A_2 = \{8, 10, 12\}$. The thick solid lines of Figure 2 shows the case 1 in which the recycled sources 9, 11, and 13 in A_1 send their own copies of the multicast packet to destination groups $[0001, 0001]$, $[0011, 0100]$, and $[0111, 1000]$ in $|D^\alpha|$, respectively. The dotted lines shows the case 2 in which the recycled sources 8 and 10 in A_2 send copies to destination groups $[1010, 1011]$ and $[1110, 1110]$ in $|D^{\tilde{\alpha}}|$, respectively. Note that the recycled source 12 of the first phase discards its packet.

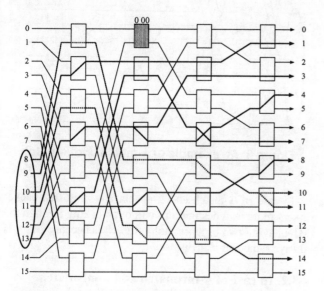

Figure 2. An example of the routing phase in FTM-I

Lemma 1 Let s_i and s_j be the source addresses of two group packets, and R_i and R_j be their destination regions, respectively. Assume that $s(i) < s(j)$ and $R_i <_D R_j$. If $s_j - s_i \leq R_j - R_i$, then two group packets cannot induce any blocking.

Proof : By Definition 4, it is clear that $s_j - s_i \leq R_j - R_i \leq d_j - d_i$ for all d_1 and d_2 such that $d_i \in R_i$ and $d_j \in R_j$. Therefore, two group packets cannot induce any blocking according to Property 2, if $s_j - s_i \leq R_j - R_i$. ∎

Lemma 2 Blocking cannot occur between any two group packets whose sources are in $L(0)$ and $L(1)$ respectively, if their destination groups D_1 and D_2 are disjoint.

Proof : We consider it for any two packets whose destinations are $d_1 = d_{n-1}^1 \cdots d_0^1 \in D_1$ and $d_2 = d_{n-1}^2 \cdots d_0^2 \in D_2$. Based on Property 1, two packets cannot pass the same SE in stage j, $n - 1 \geq j \geq 1$. If $d_j^1 = d_j^2$, $n - 1 \geq j \geq 1$, they encounter the same SE $d_{n-1}^1 \cdots d_1^1$ in stage 0. Since D_1 and D_2 are disjoint, $d_1 \neq d_2$. Hence, two packets are routed to different output ports d_0^1 and d_0^2 at the SE. Therefore, two packets cannot induce any blocking in all stages. ∎

Lemma 3 The total number of regions that can be composed of k bit destinations is less than or equal to 2^{k-1}.

Proof of Lemma 3 is trivial.

Theorem 1 Algorithm FTM-I with the region encoding scheme can route a multicast packet with any arbitrary set of destination groups in two phases across the MIN having a single faulty SE at stage i, $n - 2 \geq i \geq 1$.

Proof : We first consider the routing possibility of any arbitrary set of destination groups. The maximum number of consecutive destinations in the first phase are guaranteed to be 2^{n-1} at the worst case that the source is in $L(\beta)$. Besides, both $|D^\alpha|$ and $|D^{\tilde{\alpha}}|$ are less than or equal to 2^{n-2} respectively, according to Lemma 3. Thus, $|A_1| \geq |D^\alpha|$ in the case 1 and $|A_2| \geq |D^{\tilde{\alpha}}|$ in the case 2. Therefore, FTM-I can route any arbitrary set of destination groups if routing problems do not occur.

Routing problems that may occur in the faulty MIN are the blocking and the packet passing the fault. We prove that such problems cannot occur in two phases. In the first phase, sources in $L(\beta)$ cannot allowed to send a copy to any destination in $M(\alpha_{n-1})$. Thus, packets that such sources send do not pass any SE $\alpha_{n-1}\gamma\beta$, including the faulty SE, at stage i where $|\gamma| = n - i - 2$. Obviously, packets whose sources are not in $L(\beta)$ don't pass the faulty SE at stage i. Moreover, it is clear that a single group packet does not induce any blocking.

In the second phase, all the packets cannot pass the faulty SE, since the SE that can be used in routing at any stage is $\alpha_{n-1}\gamma\bar{\beta}_0$, $\bar{\alpha}_{n-1}\gamma\bar{\beta}_0$, or $\bar{\alpha}_{n-1}\gamma\beta_0$, where $|\gamma| = n - 3$. There is no blocking between any two group packets in the case 1 and the case 2 respectively according to Lemma 2. Let the active sources and the regions of group packets in the case 1 be two ordered sets as $\{s_1, s_2, \ldots, s_x\}$ and $\{R_1, R_2, \ldots, R_x\}$, respectively. It is clear that $s_{j+1} - s_j = 2$ and $R_{j+1} - R_j \geq 2$ for any j such that $1 \leq j < x$. Consequently, $s_k - s_j \leq R_k - R_j$, $1 \leq j < k \leq x$, since the number of destinations in each region is greater than or equal to 1. Therefore, blocking cannot occur among the group packets in the case 1. It can be analogized that there is no blocking in the case 2 by similar arguments to the case 1. ∎

4.2. On Cube Encoding Scheme

A set of regions that represent all the destinations of a multicast packet satisfies the relation $<_D$ between adjacent regions. However, any arbitrary set of cubes does not so and may cause routing to be more complex. The cube $C = c_{n-1}c_{n-2}\cdots c_0$, where $c_j \in \{0, 1, *\}, n-1 \geq j \geq 0$ satisfying the following condition is called the *least significant bit ordered (LSBO) cube*.

- If $c_j = *$, then $c_k = *$, for all k such that $j > k \geq 0$

For example, $00***$ is LSBO cube, but $00*0*$ is not. Let $S = \{C_1, C_2, \ldots C_m\}$ be an ordered set of LSBO cubes that represent any arbitrary multicast destinations. It is clear that $C_j <_D C_k$ for j, k such that $1 \leq j < k \leq m$.

Fault-Tolerant Multicasting II (FTM-II)
Assume that a set of LSBO cubes represents multicast destinations.
Phase 1: Copy from the source to a single cube SC with $2k$ consecutive intermediate destinations through the MIN, where k is the maximum number of $2^{\lceil \log_2 |D^\alpha| \rceil}$ and $2^{\lceil \log_2 |D^{\bar\alpha}| \rceil}$. The cube SC is randomly selected within the same restriction as that of FTM-I.
Phase 2: Route the recycled copy from SC to the LSBO cubes with the appropriate routing headers as follows :

- Case 1 : $A_1 \Rightarrow^{|D^\alpha|} D^\alpha$ if $A_1 = \{a | a \in SC$ and $a \in L(\bar\beta_0)\}$.

- Case 2 : $A_2 \Rightarrow^{|D^{\bar\alpha}|} D^{\bar\alpha}$ if $A_2 = \{a | a \in SC$ and $a \in L(\beta_0)\}$.

The remaining $(2k - |D^\alpha| - |D^{\bar\alpha}|)$ destinations in SC discard their packets.

4.3. Under Certain Fault Set

We consider fault-tolerant multicasting in the MIN with certain fault set.

Definition 5   Let f^1 and f^2 be any two faulty SEs, which they are represented as $\alpha^1_{n-1}\cdots\alpha^1_{i+1}\beta^1_{i-1}\cdots\beta^1_0$ and $\alpha^2_{n-1}\cdots\alpha^2_{i+1}\beta^2_{i-1}\cdots\beta^2_0$. α-match is defined if $S_{msb} > 0$ and α-mismatch is otherwise. Also, β-match is defined if $S_{lsb} > 0$ and β-mismatch is otherwise.

Using the previous approaches FTM-I and FTM-II, any multicast packet is sent to its own destinations without blocking through the MIN having a certain fault set.

4.3.1. In case of α-match and β-match

In Figure 3, an example of the second phase is shown, where source 0 sends a multicast packet to destinations $\{1, 2, 3, 7, 8, 10, 11, 14\}$ in a MIN with a faulty SE 000 at stage 1 and 010 at stage 2. Thus, α_{n-1} is 0 and β_{n-1} is 0. Therefore, $D^\alpha = \{0001, 001*, 0111\}$ and $D^{\bar\alpha} = \{1000, 101*, 1110\}$. $|D^\alpha| = 3$, $|D^{\bar\alpha}| = 3$, and $k = max(2^{\lceil\log_2 3\rceil}, 2^{\lceil\log_2 3\rceil}) = 4$. During the first phase, source 0 sends a copy to a single cube $1***$ with 8 destinations. In the second phase, the recycled source $9, 11$, and 13 in A_1 send their own recycled copies of the multicast packet to destination groups $0001, 001*$, and 0111 in D^α, respectively. the recycled source $8, 10$, and 12 in A_2 send their own recycled copies to destination groups $1000, 101*$, and 1110 in $D^{\bar\alpha}$, respectively. While the recycled sources 14 and 15 discard their packets.

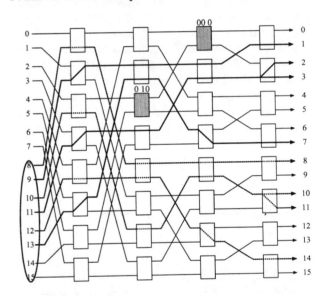

Figure 3. An example of α-match and β-match

In case of α-match and β-match, any multicast packet is sent to its own destinations without blocking through the MIN having two or more faulty SEs. It is because α_{n-1} is always same and β_{n-1} is, too.

4.3.2. In case of α-mismatch and β-mismatch

In the first phase, the source s sends a multicast packet to $M(f^k_{n-1})$ such that $s_0 \neq f^k_0$, where k is 1 or 2. In Figure 4, an example of the first phase is shown, where source 1 sends a multicast packet to destinations $\{1, 2, 3, 7, 8, 10, 11, 14\}$ in a MIN with a faulty SEs 001 and 100 at stage 2.

In the second phase, the destinations $8, 10, 12, 9, 11, 13$ send their own recycled copies of the multicast packet to $0001, 001*, 0111, 1000, 101*, 1110$, respectively.

160

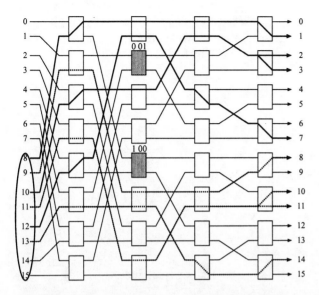

Figure 4. An example of α-mismatch and β-mismatch

Lemma 4 Let MC_k be the number of cubes that can be composed of k bit destinations. Then, $MC_k \leq 2^{k-1}$.

Proof : It can be proved by induction on k. It is clear that the property is true for $k = 1$, since $MC_1 = 1$. Assume that it is true for $k - 1$. Let C_k^0 and C_k^1 be two sets of cubes of which k bit destinations are in $M(0)$ and $M(1)$ respectively. By the assumption, $|C_k^0| \leq 2^{k-2}$ and $|C_k^1| \leq 2^{k-2}$. If there are two cubes $C_a = 0a_1a_2\cdots a_{k-1} \in C_k^0$ and $C_b = 1b_1b_2\cdots b_{k-1} \in C_k^1$ where $a_j, b_j \in \{0, 1, *\}$ and $a_j = b_j$, for all j such that $1 \leq j \leq k - 1$, then such cubes are merged into a single cube $*a_1a_2\cdots a_{k-1}$. Therefore, $MC_k \leq |C_k^0| + |C_k^1| \leq 2^{k-1}$. ∎

Lemma 5 Let a and b be two n-bit numbers such that $a < b$. Then, $S_{lsb}(a, b) \leq \log(b - a)$.

Proof : Let $k = S_{lsb}(a, b)$. Then, a and b can be represented by $a_{n-1}a_{n-2}\cdots a_k c_{k-1}\cdots c_0$ and $b_{n-1}b_{n-2}\cdots b_k c_{k-1}\cdots c_0$ respectively. Thus, $b - a \geq 2^k$, and accordingly $S_{lsb}(a, b) = k \leq \log(b - a)$ ∎

Lemma 6 Let $S = \{C_1, C_2, \ldots, C_m\}$ be an ordered set of LSBO cubes. $S_{msb}(C_a, C_b) \leq n - \log(b - a + 1) - 1$, if $b > a$.

Proof : Let $k = S_{msb}(C_a, C_b)$. Since $C_a <_D C_j <_D C_b$, $S_{msb}(C_a, C_j) \geq k$, for all j such that $a < j < b$. Thus, the most significant k bits of the cubes $C_j, a \leq j \leq b$ are identical. Considering the remaining $n - k$ bits, the number of such cubes, that is $b - a + 1$, must be less than or equal to the maximum number of cubes that composed of addresses with $n - k$ bits. By Lemma 4, $b - a + 1 \leq 2^{(n-k)-1}$. Consequently, $S_{msb}(C_a, C_b) = k \leq n - \log(b - a + 1) - 1$. ∎

Theorem 2 FTM-I and FTM-II can route a multicast packet with any arbitrary set of destination groups in two phases across the MIN having some faulty SEs.

Proof : By the similar argument to Theorem 1, the following facts can be proved.

- $2^{n-2} \geq |A_1| \geq |D^\alpha|$ in the case 1 and $2^{n-2} \geq |A_2| \geq |D^\alpha|$ in the case 2.

- Any packet cannot pass the faulty SE in the first and the second phases.

- There is no blocking in the first phase.

- Any two group packets in the case 1 and the case 2 respectively, do not induce any blocking.

We consider blocking problems among the group packets in the case 1 of the second phase, those in case 2 are similar. Let the active sources and the cubes of group packets in the case 1 be two ordered sets as $\{s_1, s_2, \ldots, s_{|D^\alpha|}\}$ and $SC = \{C_1, C_2, \ldots, C_{|D^\alpha|}\}$, respectively. Assume that $1 \leq j < k \leq |D^\alpha|$. By Lemma 5, $S_{lsb}(s_j, s_k) \leq \log(s_k - s_j) = \log(2(k - j))$. $S_{msb}(C_j, C_k) \leq n - \log(k - j + 1) - 1$ by Lemma 6. Consequently, $S_{lsb}(s_j, s_k) + S_{msb}(C_j, C_k) < n$. According to Property 3, blocking cannot occur among the group packets in the case 1. ∎

5. Conclusions

In this paper, we proposed fault-tolerant multicasting in the wrap-around MIN for large-scale multicomputers. The proposed algorithms can employs both region and cube encoding schemes as the header encoding scheme. They are based on a recursive scheme in order to send a multicast packet to the desired destinations. A multicast packet is routed to its own destinations in only two passes on the MIN having a certain fault set. It has been proved that these algorithms can route any arbitrary multicast destinations without any blocking, by exploiting well-known nonblocking properties of MIN. The proposed approach can be easily applied to wormhole or virtual cut-through routed MINs for multicomputers.

Acknowledgement

This work is supported in part by KOSEF(Korea Science and Engineering Foundation) through *Center for Artificial Intelligence Research* at Korea Advanced Institute of Science and Technology.

References

[1] G. B. Adams III, D. P. Agrawal, and H. J. Siegel. A Survey and Comparison of Fault-Tolerant Multistage

Interconnection Networks. *IEEE Computer*, 20:14–27, 1987.

[2] S. Chalasani, C. S. Raghavendra, and A. Varma. Fault-Tolerant Routing in MIN-Based Supercomputers. *Journal of Parallel and Distributed Computing*, 22(2):154–167, Aug. 1994.

[3] V. Chandramouli and C. S. Raghavendra. Nonblocking Properties of Interconnection Switching Networks. *IEEE Transactions on Communications*, 43(2/3/4):1793–1799, Feb./Mar./Arp. 1995.

[4] X. Chen and V. Kumar. Multicast Routing in Self-Routing Multistage Networks. In *Proc. of IEEE Infocom*, pages 306–314, Apr. 1994.

[5] N. Koike. NEC Cenju-3: A Microprocessor-Based Parallel Computer. In *Proc. of the Int'l Parallel Processing Symposium*, pages 396–401, Apr. 1994.

[6] V. P. Kumar and S. J. Wang. Dynamic Full Access in Fault Tolerant Multistage Interconnection Network. In *Proc. of the Int'l Conf. on Parallel Processing*, pages 621–630, 1990.

[7] T. T. Lee. Nonblocking Copy Networks for Multicast Packet Switching. *IEEE Journal on Selected Areas in Communications*, 6(9):1455–1467, Dec. 1988.

[8] P. K. McKinley, Y. Tsai, and D. F. Robinson. Collective Communication in Wormhole-Routed Massively Parallel Computers. *IEEE Computer*, 28(12):39–50, Dec. 1995.

[9] D. K. Panda. Issues in Designing Efficient and Practical Algorithms for Collective Communication Wormhole-Routed Systems. In *Proc. of the Int'l Conf. on Parallel Processing*, pages 8–15, Aug. 1995.

[10] J. Park and H. Lee. Ring Banyan Network: A Fault-Tolerant Multistage Interconnection Network and Its Fault Diagnosis. In *Lecture Notes in Computer Science*, volume 852, pages 511–528. Springer-Verlag, 1994.

[11] C. S. Raghavendra, X. Chen, and V. P. Kumar. A Two Phase Multicast Routing Algorithm in Self-Routing Multistage Networks. In *Proc. of Int'l Conference on Communications*, pages 1612–1618, Jun. 1995.

[12] C. B. Stunkel and *et al.* The SP2 Communication Subsystem. Technical report, IBM Thomas J. Watson Research Center, Aug. 1994.

[13] A. Varma and C. S. Raghavendra. Fault-Tolerant Routing in Multistage Interconnection Networks. *IEEE Transactions on Computers*, 38(3):385–393, Mar. 1989.

[14] C. L. Wu and T.-Y. Feng. On a Class of Multistage Interconnection Networks. *IEEE Transactions on Computers*, C-29(8):694–702, Aug. 1980.

Session 3B
Compiler I: Reducing
Communication Overhead

Chair: Chris Newburn
Intel

Schemes for Reducing Communication Latency
in Regular Computations on DSM Multiprocessors

Masaru Takesue

Dept. Electronics and Information Engr., Hosei University

Kajino-cho 3-7-2, Koganei 184-8584 Japan

takesue@ami.ei.hosei.ac.jp

Abstract

This paper proposes two schemes for reducing the communication latency in the computations with local and regular communication patterns. The primary scheme is the local protocol *for enhancing spatial locality of the coherence actions, and the second is for the communication via stream data. The local protocol is a subsidiary of a traditional coherence protocol and activated on a memory-block basis. If activated on a memory block, the domain of coherence actions is confined into the caches that are currently sharing that block. Otherwise, the domain involves the memory as well as those caches. It is easy to efficiently communicate via stream data in the local coherence domain. Our experimental results show that one of the three proposed local protocols, the tampering protocol, significantly improves the performance as compared with the conventional protocol. The communication via stream data contributes to a further performance improvement.*

1. Introduction

Many important applications are amenable to parallel computing since those have local and regular communication patterns such as the mesh and tree [1]. The computations with or without such communication patterns are referred to as being regular or irregular. Even the regular computation is, however, not practical on large-scale cache-coherent multiprocessors: Despite a unit distance, the latency of communication between adjacent nodes is very large since the coherence actions are performed in a spatially global domain that involves the memory as well as the caches. We refer to this type of protocols as *global* protocols; the traditional protocol is global.

This paper focuses on the regular computations and proposes two schemes for reducing the great communication latency assuming multiprocessors with distributed shared memory (DSM) and write-invalidate cache. The goal is to make the regular computations practical on the large-scale multiprocessor. The first proposed scheme is a *local protocol* that is a subsidiary protocol of the global protocol. The second scheme is a support for efficient communication through a stream type of data; this scheme is based on the first.

The local protocol is activated on a memory-block basis, and confines the domain of coherence actions into the caches currently sharing the memory block; then the memory is not involved in the domain. Thus the communication latency, especially between adjacent or nearby nodes, is reduced. Three alternative local protocols are proposed in the paper; the *sharing, migrating,* and *tampering* local protocols.

The local protocol freezes the write copy of the memory block into an agency cache in the coherence domain. Depending on the sort of local protocols, the copies, only the write copy, and no copy of the *agent's frozen copy* can respectively be cached into the other caches of the domain; the frozen copy is directly accessed on a word basis with no coherence actions in the domain of tampering protocol.

The communication via stream data is in general effective to reduce the latency. With the tampering protocol, the data structures such as the queue for implementing stream can be frozen on the cache. Then the traffic of stream access is restricted into the spatially local domain of tampering, so the communication via frozen stream data can further reduce the latency achieved by the tampering protocol alone.

Related work: The data mapping technique is effective for the reduction of memory latency [2]. By the data mapping, data blocks are allocated to the nodes so that the coherence domain is spatially localized. The latency reduction with this technique is, however, limited by the speed of memory since the domain is still global, that is, involves the memory. Moreover when the virtual memory is supported, page migration [3] or page allocation is needed for the spatial locality of memory accesses. On the other side, the local protocol needs no static data mapping; the freezing of the write copy into the agency cache can be considered as a dynamic data mapping. In the system with virtual memory, the local protocol requires neither the allocation nor migration of pages.

Several techniques for hiding memory latency have been studied; those include the relaxed memory consistency models [4, 5], data prefetching [6], and multithreading [7]. Those techniques are orthogonal to the local protocol, so combining them will be more effective. Although many cache coherence protocols have been reported, no protocol supports the subsidiary and local protocol [8]–[13].

Block-data transfer is frequently used in the operating system and important applications such as data base, so a few research shared-memory multiprocessors are integrating block transfer with cache coherence [14, 15]. Block transfer can be integrated with global coherence [15] or local coherence [14], that restricts the caching of source and target buffers to their respective local nodes. We integrate block transfer into the tampering protocol [17, 18]. Then no coherence action is required, and no restriction is put on the caching location of source and target.

The idea of the tampering protocol has been published in [16]–[18], and the communication via stream data in [16, 18]. The implementation of the stream described in [16] is different from those presented in this paper and [18]; the latter two are the same.

The rest of the paper is organized as follows: Section 2 presents three alternative local protocols. Section 3 describes the scheme for communication via steam data. Section 4 outlines the architecture of our multiprocessor. Section 5 shows the performance data obtained with the local protocols and the communication via stream data. The evaluation is performed by an RTL simulator of our multiprocessor with up to 256 nodes. Section 6 concludes the paper.

2. Local protocols

This section introduces the principle of local protocols, and presents three local protocols.

2.1. Principle

The local protocol is enabled and disabled respectively by an FRZ (freeze) and a DFR (defrost) instructions both on a memory-block basis. The freezing and defrosting of a memory block and its copies induce no memory reference in the coherence domain of local protocol are performed as follows: When a process issues the FRZ for freezing a memory block, the cache sends a block-freezing request to the memory. Then the memory freezes the requested block, saves the address of the requesting cache into the block, and returns the write copy of the block to the requesting cache.

The cache that issues the FRZ is referred to as the *agent* for the block. For simplicity, the write copy of frozen block that the agent receives from the memory is referred to as the *proxy block* (or *proxy*, for short). The proxy is maintained in the agent until the frozen block is defrosted by the DFR.

When received a read or write request for the frozen block, the memory returns the agent pointer saved in the block to the requesting cache. The requesting cache saves the received pointer in the line for the block. The cache that has the agent pointer is referred to as a *client* of that agent. Similar to the proxy in the agent, the agent pointer in the client is not invalidated unless the block is defrosted by the DFR. So the client always hit on (the line that has) the agent pointer to redirect the request to the agent.

The agent can maintain the coherence of *copies of the proxy* since it is a single exclusive copy of the frozen block in the system. The domain of coherence actions for the (copies of) proxy is confined into the caches, i.e., the agent and clients. Note that the agent can be a client of the own. For a request from the client, a copy of the proxy is returned or the requested *word* is read from or written into the proxy (if it is a tampering request) depending on the type of local protocol as described in **2.2** to **2.3**.

The local protocol maintains the coherence of copies of frozen blocks (strictly, the copies of proxy blocks) in the local memory systems each organized on geometrically local nodes, while the global protocol the coherence of copies of nonfrozen blocks in the base memory system. The protocol for a memory block switches from global to local when the block is frozen, and in reverse when it is defrosted. Thus a total of the global and local protocols is a cache coherence protocol.

Freezing for spatial locality: The local protocol by itself cannot assure spatial locality of the coherence domain. To obtain the spatial locality, the processes that will frequently communicate with each other must be allocated on adjacent or nearby nodes. With this prerequisite, the rules for freezing are as follows:

The data that are frequently read-write shared by processes must be frozen, while the data for which the sharing frequency is not so high should be frozen if the communication latency can be reduced by the local protocol. Local data of the processes, global read-only data, and instructions need not be frozen since those are cached by the global protocol.

One of the writers of shared data freezes and defrosts the memory blocks for the data, so that the FRZ and DFR are inserted respectively at the beginning and just before the RETURN instruction of the writer's code. By this freezing, the writer's cache becomes the agent for the blocks, and the caches of both the readers and the other writers become the clients of that agent.

2.2. Sharing local protocol

The state transition of an integrated global and local protocol is shown Fig. 1. The global protocol shown here is commonly used for embedding each of the local protocols. The local protocol shown in Fig. 1 is referred to as a sharing (SHR, for short) local protocol. Of the six states, the `invalid`, `read`, and `write` states are for the global protocol, and the rest are for the SHR protocol. Read and write misses are denoted by RD and WT. The solid and dotted lines stand for the transitions caused respectively by a local and a remote caches.

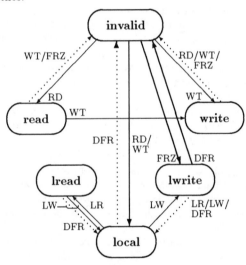

Fig. 1. State transition of the sharing (SHR) local protocol.

The global protocol: A simple global protocol is used here since it is out of scope of the paper. Only the portion of the protocol relating to the local protocol is described below. It is assumed that a memory block takes one of the four states; Valid, Read, Write, and Frozen.

When a request for freezing a block reaches the memory, the current copies of the block are invalidated

if it is not Valid. The state of the block moves to the Frozen, and the write copy of the block is returned to the requesting cache. When received the copy, the cache becomes the agent of the block, and the state of the copy (i.e., proxy) moves to the `lwrite` state.

For a request to the Frozen block, the memory returns the agent pointer to the requesting cache. Then the cache saves the received pointer in the line for the block, and becomes a client of the agent pointed to by the pointer. The line that has the agent pointer moves to the `local` state. Once the domain of the agent and clients are organized for a memory block, the coherence actions for the block are performed in the domain according to the local protocol unless the DFR is executed for the block.

The SHR local protocol: The client's line in the `local` state has no data but the agent pointer, and the client always hits on that line. We refer to this hit as a *local miss* since it entails the coherence actions local to the agent and clients. The proxy block takes one of the three states; Pvalid, Pwrite, and Pread.

In the Pvalid state, the consistent proxy is in the agent. The Pwrite is the state that the copy (of the proxy) in the `lwrite` state resides in a single client, whereas the Pread means that the copies in the `lread` state are in the clients. The client sends a request for the proxy to the agent when a local read-miss or write-miss (denoted LR or LW in Fig. 1) occurs.

If the proxy is in the Pvalid state when received the request, its copy in the `lread` or `lwrite` state (depending on the request type) is returned immediately to the requesting client. Otherwise, for the read request, a copy of the `lread` state is returned immediately or after invalidating the current copy depending on whether the proxy is in the Pread or Pwrite state. For the write request, the copy in the `lwrite` state is returned after invalidating the current copies. A client's copy in the `lread` or `lwrite` state returns to the `local` state if it is locally invalidated, that is, invalidated under the local protocol. Then the copy is written back to the agent if it is the `lwrite` copy.

When performing the DFR, the agent takes the `lwrite` copy of proxy back from the clients by issuing a write request for the proxy. Then the proxy is updated and written back to the memory, that defrosts the frozen block and returns the invalidation signal to the agent. The defrosted block moves to the Valid state. On receiving the signal, the agent globally invalidates (that is, invalidates under the global protocol) the lines for the own and clients if those are in the directory. Otherwise, the clients are invalidated as described below. The globally invalidated lines return to the `invalid` state, when the defrosting operation completes.

Control for correctness: It is necessary to guarantee that the requests from clients never reach the agent before it becomes the agent and after it is invalidated. The first condition is satisfied by the memory: When performing the FRZ on a block, the memory does not accept the subsequent requests for the block unless the proxy block reaches the agent.

The second condition is satisfied by the agent: After received the `lwrite` copy when performing the DFR, the agent accepts no subsequent requests from the clients. Then the clients in the directory are globally invalidated as mentioned above, while the other clients are invalidated when those clients receive a special (no-agent) signal in reply to the requests to the (ex-)agent. Thus the client lines returns to the `invalid` state, so that no requests effectively reach the agent after the DFR.

In the replacement, the `lread` or `lwrite` copy in the client is invalidated locally and next globally. Then the replaced `lwrite` copy is written back to the agent but not to the memory. The operation for replacing the proxy in the agent is similar to the DFR operation. Thus once a memory block is frozen, it is not updated until the block is defrosted or the proxy is replaced.

2.3. Migrating and tampering protocols

The migrating (MGR, for short) local protocol is the same as the SHR protocol except that read-copies are not allowed but only the write-copy of the proxy migrates among the clients. The state transition graph of this protocol is omitted since it is easily obtained from Fig. 1 by removing the `lread` state and the transitions incident to that state, and by adding a transition on LR from the `local` to `lwrite` states.

The tampering (TMP, for short) local protocol organizes the local memory system that has no cache, thus cache coherence problems never occur with this protocol: The client sends a request for a *word* of the proxy to the agent, that writes the received word into the proxy if it is a write request or returns the requested word to the client otherwise.

The state transition graph of the TMP protocol is also omitted; it is obtained from Fig. 1 if the `lread` state, the transitions incident to that state, and all the transitions between the `local` and `lwrite` states are removed. Thus the `local` and `lwrite` states are respectively the only states that the client and agent can take.

2.4. Implementation

The local directory for the SHR protocol is implemented by a doubly-linked list. The cache-line format (except of the `state` and `data` fields) for the local directory is shown in Fig. 2. The fields `lck` (lock), `head`, `tail`, and `ctl1` (control 1) are for the agent, and the rest for the client. The agent and client can share no fields since the agent can be a client. The `head` and `tail` are the pointers to the head and tail elements (clients) in the directory. The `ctl1` are used when performing the DFR.

(3)	(10)	(10)	(2)	(10)	(10)	(10)	(3)
lck	head	tail	ctl1	agent	next	prev	ctl2

Fig. 2. The cache line format for the SHR protocol.

The local coherence actions is performed as follows: If the local miss occurs, the client sends a request for the proxy to the agent, that forwards the request to the tail client. So the requesting client receives a copy of the proxy from the tail client. A problem of the chained directory is the race conditions that are induced by the concurrent requests for removing elements from the list; appending an element to the tail and deleting the tail from the list must also be serialized. Two bits of the `lck` are used as a two-bit lock variable for the mutual exclusion of those requests, and indicates which of a nontail client, the tail client, and the agent (when executing the DFR) has acquired the lock. The other bit is a flag for indicating that a local invalidation is outstanding.

The `agent`, `next`, and `prev` are the pointers respectively to the agent, the next client, and the previous client in the directory. The `ctl2` is used as the flags for indicating that the request forwarded from the agent (and hence, originated in the next client) reaches the current client during it is waiting for the copy from the previous client.

The line format for the MGR protocol is very simple (omitted for space) as compared with that of the SHR protocol since only the single write-copy migrates among the clients. The `head` and `prev` fields for the SHR protocol are not needed for this protocol, so that a singly-linked list is used as the directory structure. In addition, the control becomes simple; no `lck` and smaller `ctl1` and `ctl2` fields are needed.

The TMP protocol needs no local directory. The agent pointer is saved in the data field of the client since it never have the copy of proxy. Note that the agent has the proxy but needs no agent pointer. Thus the line format is the same as that of the global protocol except that the state field must be enlarged so as to accommodate additional two states, local and lwrite.

3. Communication via stream data

This section presents a scheme for the communication through a stream type of data. It is well known that the communication through stream data is efficient. This is because not only no separate synchronization variable is needed for the stream but also a request for a stream element can wait for a successful synchronization in the association mechanism for the stream. Moreover, those contribute to a lighter traffic in the network.

Although a hardware association mechanism is effective to reduce the communication latency, it is costly [16]. For a cheaper stream, we implemented the mechanism by the data structure that is frozen in the agency cache by the TMP protocol. The data structure (see Fig. 3) comprises an element queue EQ, a request queue RQ, and several control variables.

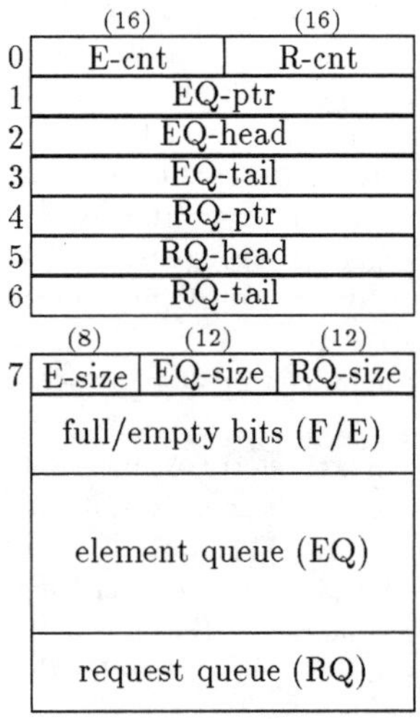

	(16)	(16)
0	E-cnt	R-cnt
1	EQ-ptr	
2	EQ-head	
3	EQ-tail	
4	RQ-ptr	
5	RQ-head	
6	RQ-tail	

	(8)	(12)	(12)
7	E-size	EQ-size	RQ-size

full/empty bits (F/E)

element queue (EQ)

request queue (RQ)

Fig. 3. Data structure for the stream.

For the element of the single-word size, an STS (store stream) instruction for producing a stream element and an LDS (load stream) instruction for consuming the element are prepared. The STS puts an element into the EQ if no request for the element is waiting in the RQ, while the LDS puts a request into the RQ if the requested element is not in the EQ. If an element reaches the stream when the RQ has the request for the element, or if the request for an element arrives at the stream when the EQ has the element, the element is returned to the requesting LDS and removed. For the instructions prepared for larger sizes of stream elements, see Reference [18].

4. Architecture

This section outlines the architecture of our shared-memory multiprocessor, named LoRe (after Local Reference), with up to 1024 processing nodes interconnected by the hypercube. The node is composed of a processor (PE), a cache, a DSM unit, an MCC (memory and communication control unit), and a PFI (packet fetch and issue unit). The parameters of LoRe architecture are listed in Table 1. For a more detail, see Reference [18].

Table 1   The LoRe architecture

Items	Description
PE	extended DLX [19]
Cache	unified and blocking, 64k bytes 32-byte line, set-associative
Network	hypercube 8 bits/cycle, wormhole routing
Cycle time	PE, Cache, Network: 1 clock DSM: 10 clocks

5. Evaluation

This section shows the performance of regular computations with the local protocols. An RTL simulator of LoRe was coded by C, and the evaluations were performed by the simulator with up to 256 nodes. To simulate a greater number of nodes, a rather small cache of 8K bytes was used. The other parameters of the simulated architecture are the same as those presented in the previous section.

5.1. Benchmarks

The benchmark programs and virtual networks (shown in the parentheses) are listed in Table 2. A virtual network refers to a topology desirable for executing the benchmark, and it is embedded in the base hypercube. The problem size and the number N of nodes are the same. For instance in the reduction on 256 nodes, 256 integers are reduced by the same number of nodes. The programs were coded by an assembly language as we are currently designing the compiler.

Table 2   Benchmark Programs

Program	Description (Network)
distance	Communication between two nodes (hypercube)
one2one	Simultaneous one-to-one communication (hypercube)
one2all	Broadcast (binary tree)
reduction	Parallel reduction (hypercube)
label	Two-phase component labelling (mesh)
closure	$\sqrt{N}$-phase transitive closure (mesh)
radix	Radix sorting of 32-bit integers (hypercube)

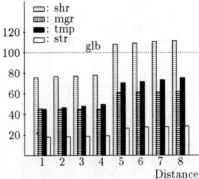

Fig. 4. Distance.

The first four benchmarks are for the primitive communication operations, and each iterates the operation a hundred times. The last three benchmarks are small but typical examples of regular computations. In the **label** and **closure**, the number of iterations depends on the problem size. The **radix** finishes after 32 iterations independent of the problem size. The producer-consumer type of sharing is dominant in the benchmarks; the number of consumers varies from one to eight depending on the benchmarks. Note that the **radix** exhibits a migratory sharing pattern in the compacting phase of each iteration; this induces an irregular communication pattern.

A benchmark program is denoted by **glb** when performed with the global protocol alone, and by **shr**, **mgr**, and **tmp** when performed with the same global protocol embedding respectively the SHR, MGR, and TMP protocols. The **tmp** that communicates via stream data is denoted by **str**.

The **glb** induces a heavy memory contention [17, 18]. To reduce the contention, a static data mapping is exploited for the **glb**. Suppose that a shared block is frozen into an agent node when the benchmark executes with the local protocols. Then for the **glb**, the block is mapped onto the same node as the agent node. The other blocks of the **glb** are not distributed but loaded contiguously from address 0. The **shr**, **mgr**, and **tmp** need no static data mapping, so those programs are loaded from address 0.

5.2. Results and analyses

Execution time: Normalized execution time of the benchmark programs is shown in Figs. 4 and 5, where the normalized execution time is the execution time relative to that of the **glb**.

Benchmark **distance** (see Fig. 4) induces neither memory contention nor traffic congestion in the network, so that the spatial locality of coherence actions and the complexity of each protocol straightforwardly affect the execution time of this benchmark. The effect of communication through frozen stream data is significant as can be seen in the **str**. Although the **tmp** is slower than the **mgr**, this is not the case in the other benchmarks. The weak point of TMP protocol — no prefetching of a copy of the block — is disclosed in this benchmark. This weak point can be remedied by the block transfer with the TMP protocol as reported in [18].

In all the benchmarks, the **str** and **tmp** are faster than the **glb** respectively by a factor of about 1.3 to 6.1 and by a factor of about 1.2 to 3.7. The **str** improves performance over the **tmp** by a factor of about 1.0 to 2.7. The reasons for those results are as follows:

A shared memory block is allocated or frozen in the same node in all the programs as mentioned in **5.1**. Although the spatial locality of coherence actions in the **glb** and **tmp** are then the same in the node level, the cache is faster than the memory and the **tmp** needs no coherence actions. So the **tmp** outperform the **glb**. The **str** waits for a successful synchronization in the queue for stream, so that both the latency of synchronization and network traffic are reduced. This improves the performance of **str** over **tmp**.

The MGR and SHR protocols are implemented by the chained directories as described in Section 2. So the miss penalty, especially in the SHR protocol, is rather great (shown shortly), though the domain of coherence actions with those protocols are restricted in the caches. The **shr**'s performance is lower than that of the **glb** in almost all cases. The **mgr**, however, improves the performance of **glb** in many cases since the

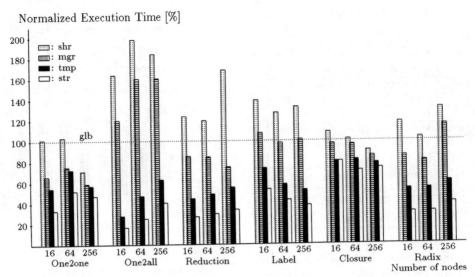

Fig. 5. Normalized execution time.

MGR protocol is simple.

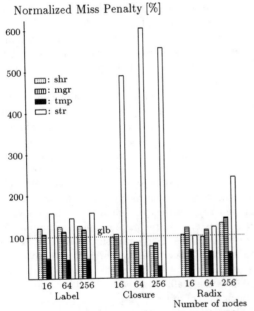

Fig. 6. Normalized data-miss penalties.

Miss penalty: We refer to the penalty when a local miss (see **2.2**) occurs as a *local* miss penalty to distinguish from the (global) miss penalty with the global protocol. Normalized global and local data-miss penal-

ties of the last three benchmarks as measured by the number of clocks are shown in Fig. 6, where the normalization is performed relative to the penalty in `glb`.

A point that may look like strange is that the penalty in `str` is much greater than that in `tmp`. This is, however, reasonable since the penalty in `tmp` is the time during one round trip between the client and agent, whereas the `str`'s penalty involves the time waiting for a success of synchronization in the queue in addition to the round-trip time. For a successful synchronization, the `str` stalls during the time equal to the miss penalty shown in Fig. 6, while the `tmp` stalls during the time equal to multiple miss penalties.

Except of the point mentioned above, the data-miss penalty has a tendency similar to that observed in the execution time. The penalty in the `tmp` is about a half or one-third the global penalty. For the `closure` and `radix`, the penalty in the `mgr` is slightly greater than that in the `shr`. This is because the miss penalty in `mgr` are all for write blocks.

6. Conclusions

We have proposed three alternative local protocols; the tampering, migrating, and sharing protocols. The local protocol can reduce communication latency in DSM multiprocessors because of its enhanced spatial locality and simple coherence actions. To further reduce the latency, the communication via stream data is effective.

The tampering protocol needs no coherence actions and hence, it induces no false sharing. Thus this protocol improves the performance with the global protocol by a factor of 1.2 to 3.7. The migrating and sharing local protocols are currently implemented by the chained directories. So those protocols are respectively slightly faster and significantly slower than the global protocol. The communication via stream data improves the performance with tampering protocol by a factor of about 1.0 to 2.7, and the performance with global protocol by a factor about 1.3 to 6.1.

We are designing a tree type of directory to improve the performance of migrating and sharing protocols. For irregular computations, the local protocols are being extended so as to allow multiple agents for a memory block.

References

[1] F. T. Leighton, *Introduction to Parallel Algorithms and Architectures: Arrays · Trees · Hypercubes*, Morgan Kaufmann Publishers, 1992.

[2] V. Kumar, A. Grama, A. Gupta, and G. Karypis, *Introduction to Parallel Computing: Design and Analysis of Algorithms*, Benjamin/Cummings Publishing, 1994.

[3] A. L. Cox and R. J. Fowler, "The Implementation of a Coherent Memory Abstraction on a NUMA Multiprocessor: Experiences with Platinum," *Proc. the 12th ACM Symp. on Operating System Principles*, Dec. 1989, pp. 32-43.

[4] K. Gharachorloo, A. Gupta, and J. Hennessy, "Performance Evaluation of Memory Consistency Models for Shared-Memory Multiprocessors," *Proc. the 4th Int. Conf. on Architectural Support for Programming Languages and Operating Systems*, Apr. 1991, pp. 245-257.

[5] R. N. Zucker and J.-L. Baer, "A Performance Study of Memory Consistency Models", *Proc. the 19th Annu. Int. Symp. on Computer Architecture*, May 1992, pp. 2-12.

[6] T. Mowry and A. Gupta, "Tolerating Latency through Software-Controlled Prefetching in Shared-Memory Multiprocessors," *Jour. Parallel and Distributed Computing*, Vol. 12, No. 2, pp. 87-106, Jun. 1991.

[7] A. Agarwal, "Performance Tradeoffs in Multithreaded Processors," *IEEE Trans. on Parallel and Distributed Systems*, Vol. 3, No. 5, pp. 525-539, Sep. 1992.

[8] P. Stenström, "A Survey of Cache Coherence Schemes for Multiprocessors," *IEEE Computer Mag.*, No. 23, Vol. 6, pp. 12-24, Jun. 1990.

[9] D. Lenoski, J. Laudon, K. Gharachorloo, A. Guputa, and J. Hennessy, "The Directory-Based Cache Coherence Protocol for the DASH multiprocessor," *Proc. the 17th Annu. Int. Symp. on Computer Architecture*, Aug. 1990, pp. 312-321.

[10] D. Chaiken, J. Kubiatowicz, and A. Agarwal, "LimitLESS Directories: A Scalable Cache Coherence Scheme," *Proc. the 4th Int. Conf. on Architectural Support for Programming Languages and Operating Systems*, Apr. 1991, pp. 224-234.

[11] A. L. Cox and R. J. Fowler, "Adaptive Cache Coherency for Detecting Migratory Shared Data," *Proc. the 20th Annu. Int. Symp. on Computer Architecture*, May 1993, pp. 98-108.

[12] H. Cheong and A. V. Veidenbaum, "Compiler-Directed Cache Management in Multiprocessors," *IEEE Computer Mag.*, No. 23, Vol. 6, pp. 39-47, Jun. 1990.

[13] H. Grahn, and P. Stenström, "Efficient Strategies for Software-Only Directory Protocols in Shared-Memory", *Proc. the 22th Annu. Int. Symp. on Computer Architecture*, Jun. 1995, pp. 38-47.

[14] A. Agarwal, R. Bianchini, D. Chaiken, K. L. Johnson, D. Kranz, J. Kubiatowicz, B.-H. Lim, K. Mackenzie, and D. Yeung, "The MIT Alewife Machine: Architecture and Performance," *Proc. the 22nd Annu. Int. Symp. on Computer Architecture*, June 1995, pp. 2-13.

[15] J. Heinlein, R. P. Bosch, Jr., K. Gharachorloo, M. Rosenblum, and A. Gupta, "Coherent Block Data Transfer in the FLASH Multiprocessor," *Proc. the 11th Int. Parallel Processing Symp.*, Apr. 1997, pp. 18-27.

[16] M. Takesue, "Virtual Network Schemes for Shared-Memory Multiprocessors," *Technical Report of IEICE*, CPCY96-51, Aug. 1996.

[17] M. Takesue, "Tampering Cache: A Scheme for Virtual Networks on Shared-Memory Multiprocessors," *Proc. 1997 Joint Symp. on Parallel Processing*, IPSJ, May 1997, pp. 249-256.

[18] M. Takesue, "A Tampering Protocol for Reducing the Coherence Transactions in Regular Computation," *Proc. 1997 Int. Symp. on Parallel Architectures, Algorithms, and Networks*, Dec. 1997, pp. 465-471.

[19] J. L. Hennessy and D. A. Patterson, *Computer Architecture: A Quantitative Approach*, Morgan Kaufmann Publishers, 1990.

Optimal Task Scheduling to Minimize Inter-Tile Latencies *

Fabrice Rastello
LIP, Ecole Normale
Supérieure de Lyon
46 allée d'Italie
69364 Lyon Cedex 07, France
fabrice.rastello@ens-lyon.fr

Amit Rao
PO Box 210030
Dept. of ECECS
University of Cincinnati,
Cincinnati, OH 45221
arao@ececs.uc.edu

Santosh Pande
PO Box 210030
Dept. of ECECS
University of Cincinnati,
Cincinnati, OH 45221
santosh@ececs.uc.edu

Abstract

This work addresses the issue of exploiting intra-tile parallelism by overlapping communication with computation removing the restriction of atomicity of tiles. The effectiveness of tiling is then critically dependent on the execution order of tasks within a tile. In this paper we present a theoretical framework based on equivalence classes that provides an optimal task ordering under assumptions of constant and different permutations of tasks in individual tiles. Our framework is able to handle constant but compile-time unknown dependences by generating optimal task permutations at run-time and results in significantly lower loop completion times. Our solution is an improvement over previous approaches [2, 6] and is optimal for all problem instances. We also propose efficient algorithms that provide the optimal solution. The framework has been implemented as an optimization pass in the SUIF compiler and has been tested on a distributed memory system using a message passing model. We show that the performance improvement over previous results is substantial.

1. Introduction

Loop tiling is one of the most popular techniques to partition uniform loop nests and map tasks to processors in a multicomputer. The notion of loop tiling was introduced by Wolfe [11] and the issue of legality of tiling was formalized by Irigoin and Triolet [7]. Usually tiles are considered to be atomic *i.e.*, inter-processor communication is considered to take place only after the end of computation in each tile. Atomic tile considerations are justified when the cache size is small since tile size is chosen to fit the underlying data in the cache. However, the assumption of atomic tiles leads to loss of potential parallelism when targeting parallel machines such as distributed shared memory systems (DSMs) that are capable of overlapping communication with computation. In fact, intra-tile optimizations, given that computation and communication can overlap, open opportunities for exploiting more parallelism.

Hollander [5] extracts parallelism in nested loops by identifying and labeling independent subsets of iterations using unimodular transformations. However, this work is not suited to DSMs as it involves complex data partitioning and assignment of iterations to processors. Tiling is more attractive in such situations where data and iteration space partitioning can be kept simple and efficient. Many approaches [1, 3, 8, 10] use the assumption of atomic tiles to derive the optimal tile size and shape. These approaches involve re-distribution of data among processors in order to improve data locality thereby addressing the issue of memory to tile latencies. On the other hand, we perform loop tiling and attempt to minimize inter-tile latencies by re-ordering individual tasks within a tile.

Previous approaches by Chou & Kung [2] and Dion et al [6] to the problem of finding an optimal task ordering within loop tiles have relied on heuristics that do not yield the optimal solution for all instances of the problem even in one dimension. Thus, finding the optimal solution in one dimension is still an open issue. The central contribution of this work is the development of a new formulation of this problem along with a framework based on equivalence classes to derive optimal permutations. Using this framework we also develop efficient algorithms that result in an optimal solution for all problem instances in one dimension. Further, we take into account the possibility of having different task permutations in each tile and give the optimal solution for this case too.

The remainder of the paper is organized as follows. Section 2 presents the problem statement. Section 3 introduces definitions and notations used in this paper. Section 4 discusses previous work. Section 5 formulates the problem based on equivalence classes. In section 6 we develop the theoretical framework and show optimality results. Section 7 presents the proposed constant permutation algorithm. Section 8 discusses the solution when different task permutations are considered in each tile. In section 9, we present and discuss our performance evaluation. Finally, section 10 provides concluding remarks.

2. Statement of the problem

Consider a loop of N iterations that carries a dependence of distance l. Assume that the loop is tiled with tile size n and mapped on to P processors. The N tasks are partitioned into

*This work is supported in part by the National Science Foundation through grant no. CCR-9696129; by the CNRS–ENS Lyon–INRIA project *ReMaP*; and by the Eureka Project *EuroTOPS*

$\lceil \frac{N}{n} \rceil$ tiles such that for $0 \le i < \lceil \frac{N}{n} \rceil - 1$, the tasks contained in tile T_i are $\{t_{ni}, t_{ni+1}, ..., t_{n(i+1)-1}\}$ and $T_{\lceil \frac{N}{n} \rceil - 1} = \{t_{n(\lceil \frac{N}{n} \rceil-1)}, ..., t_{N-1}\}$. Tile T_i is executed on processor P_i for every i. The problem is to find an optimal ordering (σ) of tasks in a tile, so as to minimize the overall completion time (T_{tot}) of the loop respecting the dependences imposed. Since tiling the loop and mapping the tiles are dictated by different considerations, the number of processors and tiles need not be the same.

We now present some of the definitions and notations used in the paper.

3. Terms and Definitions

Definition 1 *Let us denote* $\tau = \{t_0, t_1, ..., t_{N-1}\}$ *as the task space. Each element of τ is a task to be executed.*

Definition 2 *The iteration space is mapped onto the tile space. Each tile contains n tasks ; more precisely, a tile is a set $T_j = \{t_{nj}, t_{nj+1}, t_{nj+2}, ..., t_{nj+n-1}\} \cap \tau$ with $j \in \{0, ..., \lceil \frac{N}{n} \rceil - 1\}$. All the tasks of one tile are to be executed on one processor only.*

Let τ_{calc} be the time to perform one task with one processor, and let τ_{comm} be the time for one communication between two adjacent processors. The g.c.d of n and l is denoted by $n \wedge l$. P denotes the number of processors. k denotes n mod l while p denotes $\lfloor \frac{n}{l} \rfloor$. Finally,

$$x \equiv y[l] \iff x \bmod l = y \bmod l$$

Definition 3 *T is called the period of ordering such that for each i, tile T_i is executed from time iT to time $iT + n\tau_{calc}$.*

Since, the total loop completion time depends linearly on the value of T, the problem reduces to minimizing T.
In each tile, the permutation of tasks is modulo n. Let σ_0 denote the permutation of tasks in tile T_0.

$$\{0, 1, ..., n\} \xrightarrow{\sigma_0} \{0, 1, ..., n\}$$

Definition 4 *A constant task permutation is one in which for all $i \in \{0, 1, ..., N-1\}$, t_i is executed by the processor $j = \lfloor \frac{i}{n} \rfloor$ between time $\tau_i = jT + \sigma_0(i - nj)\tau_{calc}$ and the time $\tau_i + \tau_{calc}$.*

Definition 5 *A non-constant task permutation is one in which for all $i \in \{0, 1, ..., N-1\}$, t_i is executed by the processor $j = \lfloor \frac{i}{n} \rfloor$ between time $\tau_i = jT + \sigma_j(i - nj)\tau_{calc}$ and the time $\tau_i + \tau_{calc}$.*

Definition 6 *For a given n, and a given l, and τ_{calc} and τ_{comm} being fixed, the minimum period of ordering T_{min} is the smallest reachable value of T satisfying the above constraints with an appropriate permutation within a tile.*

4. Previous Work

The problem of determining optimal permutations of tasks within a tile to reduce inter-tile latencies and thereby minimize loop completion time has been attempted by Chou & Kung [2] and by Dion et. al. [6].

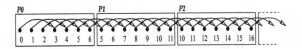

Case n=7, l=3 & T=5tcalc+tcom

Figure 1. Chou & Kung's solution for the case $n = 7$ and $l = 3, T = 5$ (numbers below tasks represent times at which they are executed, considering $\tau_{calc} = 1$ & $\tau_{comm} = 0$).

4.1. Chou & Kung's Solution

Chou and Kung propose the following ordering of tasks on each tile (processor),
For all $i \in \{0, .., N-1\}$, $j = \lfloor \frac{i}{n} \rfloor$ (we have $nj \le i \le nj+n-1$), t_i is executed by processor P_j between time $\tau_i = (i-nj) \times \tau_{calc} + j \times T$ and $\tau_i + \tau_{calc}$. The period of ordering is given by,

$$T = (n - l + 1) \times \tau_{calc} + \tau_{comm}$$

Hence, for all i, the processor P_i starts working at time $i \times T$ and ends working at time $i \times T + n \times \tau_{calc}$. Chou & Kung's solution for the case $n = 7$ and $l = 3$ is presented in Figure 1. As one can see their approach is non-optimal. Dion improved over Chou and Kung's solution by considering a better ordering of tasks within each tile so as to decrease the period (T) of ordering.

4.2. Dion's solution

First Dion et al. show the following results,

Lemma 1 *The best local permutation that permits reaching the minimum period T_{min} is independent of the values of τ_{calc} and τ_{comm}. Moreover, if $T_{min}^{1,0}$ is the minimum period for $\tau_{calc} = 1$ and $\tau_{comm} = 0$ then $T_{min}^{\tau_{calc}, \tau_{comm}} = T_{min}^{1,0} \times \tau_{calc} + \tau_{comm}$.*

Lemma 2 *If $n \wedge l \ne 1$, the problem is equivalent to a smaller problem with $n' = \frac{n}{n \wedge l}$ and $l' = \frac{l}{n \wedge l}$.*

Hence, from now on we can choose n and l such that $n \wedge l = 1$, τ_{calc} will be equal to 1, and τ_{comm} will be 0, so that the discussion is simplified.

Dion et al's permutation leads to a smaller period of ordering than Chou & Kung's solution. In fact, their solution is optimal for the special case $l = 2$. For example, for the case $n = 9$ and $l = 2$ Dion et al's solution leads to $T = 7$ which is the optimal solution, while Chou and Kung's solution leads to $T = 8$. Larger the value of n, greater will be the difference between the two solutions and thus, the loop completion times. The solutions are presented in Figure 2.

The following theorem summarizes Dion et al's contribution for the special case $l = 2$,

Theorem 1 *For $n = 2k + 1$, $k > 0$ and $l = 2$, the optimal ordering has a period of ordering,*

$$T_{opt} = \lceil \frac{3n - 1}{4} \rceil$$

173

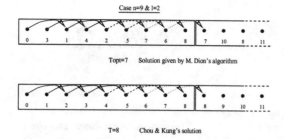

Case n=9 & l=2

0 3 1 4 2 5 7 6 8   7 10 8 11

Topt=7   Solution given by M. Dion's algorithm

0 1 2 3 4 5 6 7 8   8 9 10 11

T=8   Chou & Kung's solution

Figure 2. Comparison of Dion et al's solution and Chou & Kung's solution for $n = 9$ and $l = 2$.

For $l \geq 3$, Dion et al. give an algorithm called a *cyclic* algorithm that gives a correct permutation or schedule with $T = 2\lfloor \frac{n}{l} \rfloor + 2$. However, this is not an optimal solution. This is one of the major limitations of their solution. The other limitation is that they have used the simplifying assumption of a constant permutation in every processor similar to Chou and Kung's work. In later sections we show that the solution can be greatly improved if we remove this restriction.

However, determining the optimal solution for both constant and non-constant permutations is a non-trivial combinatorial problem. We propose a suitable framework that determines optimal task permutations in $O(n)$. Our framework derives the optimal period of ordering T_{min}, for all cases of l, in terms of n, k and l, where $n = lp + k$ & $0 \leq k < l$. The framework also leads to efficient algorithms that always reach the optimal period of ordering (T_{min}).

5. Formulation of the Problem using Equivalence Classes

We introduce the following notations and definitions for our subsequent discussion,

1. The set of tasks of the first tile is given by $\Omega = \{t_0, t_1, ..., t_{n-1}\}$. Further, we say that $t_i \equiv t_j$ iff $i \equiv j[l]$. Hence, by using a simplified notation, we denote task t_i by the integer i.

2. The operator $\equiv$ is an equivalence relation that defines equivalence classes within $\{0, 1, ..., n - 1\}$. This equivalence relation defines l components or equivalence classes, $X_0, X_1, ..., X_{l-1}$. We denote the set of equivalence classes by $\Psi = \{X_0, X_1, ..., X_{l-1}\}$.

3. We say that, $X \rightarrow Y$ if,

$$\exists (x, y) \in (X, Y) \cdot x \equiv y + n[l]$$

4. The indices for the equivalence classes are chosen in a manner such that,

   - $X_0 = \{i \in \Omega \cdot i \equiv 0[l]\}$
   - $X_0 \rightarrow X_1 \rightarrow X_2 \rightarrow \cdots \rightarrow X_{l-1} \rightarrow X_0$

From the following definitions we have,

$$\forall X_i \in \Psi, p \leq |X_i| \leq p + 1$$

Moreover, there are k classes of size $(p + 1)$ & $(l - k)$ classes of size p.

Definition 7 *For all i in $\{0, 1, \cdots, l-1\}$, we define $\lambda_i = |X_i| - p$. In other words, if $|X_i| = p + 1$ then $\lambda_i = 1$, else $|X_i| = p$ and $\lambda_i = 0$.*

Definition 8 *For all $i \geq l$, $\lambda_i = \lambda_{i \bmod l}$*

Therefore, the λ−string can be extended to an infinite string (periodic with period l).
Example 2 : Consider $n = 7$ and $l = 3$. We have,

$$X_0 = \{0, 3, 6\}, \lambda_0 = 1$$
$$X_1 = \{2, 5\}, \lambda_1 = 0$$
$$X_2 = \{1, 4\}, \lambda_2 = 0$$

The task permutation and therefore the period of ordering depends on the relative values of λ_i *i.e.,* the property of the string $\lambda_0 \lambda_1 \lambda_2 \cdots \lambda_{l-1} \cdots$. We derive the optimal solution in the next section.

6. Optimal Solution

As shown in last section, the size of an equivalence class X_i is $p + \lambda_i$, with $p = \lfloor \frac{n}{l} \rfloor$. We claim that the optimum period of ordering depends on the relative values of λ_i, more specifically λ_i and λ_{i+1}. We, thus, first quantify the property of the string in theorem 2 and then use it to determine the optimum period of ordering in theorem 3. Specifically, theorem 2 analyzes the property of the string $\lambda_0, \lambda_1, ..., \lambda_{l-1}.....$ in terms of the tile size (n) and the dependence distance (l). This relationship is quantified in terms of Λ presented below.

Theorem 2 *If $l \geq 3, n \wedge l = 1$ and $\Lambda = \min_{i \in \mathbb{N}} [\max_{i+1 \leq j, j+1 \leq i+l-1} (\lambda_j + \lambda_{j+1})]$, then*

- *If $l = 4$ & $k = 3$ then*

$$\Lambda = \max_{2 \leq j, j+1 \leq 4} (\lambda_j + \lambda_{j+1}) = 1$$

- *Else*

$$\Lambda = \max_{1 \leq j, j+1 \leq l-1} (\lambda_j + \lambda_{j+1}) = \begin{vmatrix} 0 & if \, k = 1 \\ 1 & if \, 1 < k \leq \lceil \frac{l}{2} \rceil \\ 2 & if \, k > \lceil \frac{l}{2} \rceil \end{vmatrix}$$

□

As seen above, the definition of Λ is a min-max definition. The above theorem gives the values of Λ for all cases of tile size and dependence distance.

We now illustrate the result of theorem 2 through some examples.

Example 3 : Consider $n = 7$, $l = 3$ ($k = 1$)
$\lambda -$ string $= \mathbf{1}00\mathbf{1}00\mathbf{1}00...$
$\Lambda = 0$.

Example 4 : Consider $n = 7$, $l = 4$ ($k = 3$)
$\lambda -$ string $= 11\mathbf{1}0\mathbf{11}10...$
$\Lambda = 1$

174

Example 5 : Consider $n = 7$, $l = 5$ ($k = 2 < \lceil \frac{5}{2} \rceil$)
$$\lambda - \text{string} = \mathbf{1010}010100...$$
$$\Lambda = 1$$
Example 6 : Consider $n = 9$, $l = 5$ ($k = 4 > \lceil \frac{5}{2} \rceil$)
$$\lambda - \text{string} = \mathbf{11110}11110...$$
$$\Lambda = 2$$

The Λ values calculated above for different tile sizes and dependence distances allow us to determine the optimal period of ordering as per theorem 3. In order to prove theorem 2 we need a few results.

Lemma 3 gives us a working definition for X_i.

Lemma 3 *If* $X_i' = \{x \in \Omega \mid \exists \alpha \in I\!N \cdot (x \equiv \alpha l[n]) \wedge (in \le \alpha l < (i+1)n)\}$, *then* $\forall i$, $X_i' = X_i$.

Proof Refer [9].

The next lemma states the condition that the tile size and the dependence distance should satisfy in order to have a sub-string 11 within the λ-string.

Lemma 4

$$\exists i \in \{1, ..., l-1\} \mid \lambda_i \lambda_{i+1} = 11 \iff 2k > l+1$$
$$\iff k > \frac{l}{2}$$

Proof Refer [9].

In order to prove theorem 2, we have to differentiate between the cases $\Lambda = 1$ and $\Lambda = 2$ (the case $\Lambda = 0$ is trivial). To achieve this task we need to discuss whether there exists i in $\{2, \cdots, l-1\}$ such that $\lambda_i \lambda_{i+1} = 11$ or not. Indeed, we will see that if $k > \lceil \frac{l}{2} \rceil$ then $\lambda_0 \lambda_1 = 11$ and that $\lambda_{l-1} = 0$.

To formalize it, we need to introduce a new concept - the property of a string to be well balanced.

Let $\sum = \{0, 1\}$ be the alphabet of the λ-string.

Definition 9 (sub-string) *v is said to be a sub-string of u, if there exist two strings* α *&* β, *such that* $u = \alpha v \beta$.

Definition 10 (length) *The length of a string* $u = u_1 u_2 u_3 .... u_n$ *is the integer n denoted by* $|u|$.

Definition 11 (weight) *Let* $\alpha \in \sum$. *If* $u = u_1 u_2 ..... u_n \in \sum^*$ *is a string of length n, then* $|u|_\alpha = |\{i \in \{1, ..., n\}, u_i = \alpha\}|$.

Definition 12 (well-balanced) *Let* $u \in \sum^*$. *u is said to be well-balanced if for any pair of sub-strings of u,* (v, v'),

$$|v| = |v'| \implies ||v|_1 - |v'|_1| \le 1$$

Lemma 5 *The infinite string* $\lambda = \lambda_0 \lambda_1 \lambda_2 .....$ *is well-balanced.*

Proof Refer [9].
Now we can easily prove *theorem 2*,
Theorem 2 proof: First, note that $\lambda_0 = 1$. We have,
$|X_0| = |X_0'| = |\{\alpha \in I\!N, 0 \le \alpha l < n\}| = p+1$.
Also $\lambda_{l-1} = 0$.

$$
\begin{aligned}
|X_{l-1}| &= |\{\alpha \in I\!N, (l-1)n \le \alpha l < ln\}| \\
&= |\{\alpha \in I\!N, (l-1)n \le \alpha l \le ln\}| - 1 \\
&\le (p+1) - 1
\end{aligned}
$$

1. Case $k = 1$:

   - As $k = |\lambda_0 \lambda_1 .... \lambda_{l-1}|_1 = 1$
     & $\lambda_0 = 1$ therefore,
     $\Lambda \le \max_{1 \le p, p+1 \le l-1}(\lambda_p + \lambda_{p+1}) = 0$
   - Consequently, $\Lambda = 0$.

2. Case $1 < k \le \lceil \frac{l}{2} \rceil$:

   - $\forall i, |\lambda_i \lambda_{i+1} .... \lambda_{i+l-1}| = k \ge 2$, therefore,
     $\forall i, \exists p \in \{i, ..., l+i-2\} \mid \lambda_p = 1$
     Hence, $\Lambda \ge 1$.
   - From the proof of *lemma 4*, we have

     $$\Lambda \le \min_{1 \le p, p+1 \le l-1} \lambda_p + \lambda_{p+1} \le 1$$

   - Consequently, $\Lambda = 1$.

3. $l > k > \lceil \frac{l}{2} \rceil$:

   - We have $2n = 2pl + 2k \ge (2p+1)l + 1$. Therefore,

     $$
     \begin{aligned}
     |X_0'| + |X_1'| &= |\{\alpha \in I\!N, 0 \le \alpha l < 2n\}| \\
     &= 2p + 2
     \end{aligned}
     $$

     Hence, $\lambda_0 \lambda_1 = 11$

   - Suppose that *there exists i in* $\{2, 3, ..., l-1\}$ such that $\lambda_i \lambda_{i+1} = 11$. Since $i \ne l-1$ this will lead to $\Lambda = 2$.

   - Suppose that *there does not exist* $i \in \{2, 3, ..., l-1\}$ such that $\lambda_i \lambda_{i+1} = 11$.
     Then $\lambda_{l-1} \lambda_0 \lambda_1 \lambda_2 = 0111$ ($\lambda_2 = 0$ violates $k > \lceil \frac{l}{2} \rceil$).
     Hence, $l \ge 4$. Let $l > 4$.
     From *lemma 5* we have, $\lambda_0 \lambda_1 ..... \lambda_{l-1}$ does not contain the substring 00.
     So, l is necessarily even ($l \ge 6$)

     $$
     \begin{aligned}
     \lambda_0 \lambda_1 .... \lambda_{l-1} &= 111(01)^{\frac{l-4}{2}} 0 \\
     &= 111010(10)^{\frac{l-6}{2}}
     \end{aligned}
     $$

     But this violates *lemma 5*, because of the sub-strings 111 & 010.
     Finally, $l = 4$ & $k = 3$ gives
     $\lambda_0 \lambda_1 \lambda_2 \lambda_3 \lambda_4 \lambda_5 \lambda_6 \lambda_7 = 11101110$,
     and $\Lambda = \max_{2 \le p, p+1 \le 4} \lambda_p + \lambda_{p+1} = 1$

$\square$

We now state the theorem that determines the lower bound on the period of ordering in case of constant task permutations in tiles.

Theorem 3 *For constant task permutations in tiles and* $l > 2$, $T \ge 2p + \Lambda$. $\square$

Proof Refer [9].

175

7. Constant Permutation Algorithm

7.1. Case $n \wedge l = 1$

Using the framework developed in the previous section we are now able to devise an algorithm that will compute the optimal ordering of tasks under the assumption that the ordering is the same in every tile. *Algorithm 1* gives us a correct permutation of tasks with period of ordering $(T) = 2p + \Lambda$. Recall that $l \geq 3$ and $n \wedge l = 1$.

Algorithm 1

procedure *ComputeOrderingCst* $(n,\ l)$
Input: n (tile size)
           l (dependence distance)
Precondition: $l \geq 3$
              $n \wedge l = 1$
Output: $permutation[0 : n - 1]$ (task ordering)
{ Initialize variables p and k }
  $p := \lfloor \frac{n}{l} \rfloor$
  $k := n \bmod l$
{ Assign the first task f to be executed }
  if ($l = 4$ **and** $k = 3$) **then**
    $f := l - k$ { because $0 = (f + n)[l]$ }
  else $f := 0$
{ Execute the first p tasks of X_f }
  $t := f$
  for $i := 0$ **to** $p - 1$ **do**
    $permutation[i] := t$
    $t := t + l$
  endfor
{ Equivalence classes are executed in the
  opposite order to $(\longrightarrow)$ }
  $t := (t + n) \bmod l$
  while $t \neq f$
    repeat
      $permutation[i] := t$
      $t := t + l$
      $i := i + 1$
    until $t \geq n$
    $t := (t + n) \bmod l$
  endwhile
{ Execute the last task of X_f }
  $permutation[i] := f + p \times l$
end *ComputeOrderingCst*

The permutation given by this algorithm clearly obeys the constraints of dependences in the tile. Algorithm 1 has time complexity $O(n)$. Please refer to [9] for the proof that the permutation given by algorithm 1 gives the minimum period of ordering, $T_{min} = 2p + \Lambda$.

7.2. General Case

We illustrate how our approach finds an optimal task permutation when we have a single constant dependence vector (l) and $n \wedge l = d \geq 1$.

		Case $n = 14$ & $l = 6$													
Tile 0	Tasks	0	1	2	3	4	5	6	7	8	9	10	11	12	13
	Times	0	7	2	9	4	11	1	8	3	10	5	12	6	13
Tile 1	Tasks	14	15	16	17	18	19	20	21	22	23	24	25	26	27
	Times	4	11	6	13	8	15	5	12	7	14	9	16	10	17
Tile 2	Tasks	28	29	30	31	32	33	34	35	36	37	38	39	40	41
	Times	8	15	10	17	12	19	9	16	11	18	13	20	14	21

Table 1. Optimal ordering with constant permutation in each tile ($n = 14, l = 6$).

Let us consider a correct ordering with T as the period. Consider the sub-set of tasks $(t'_i)_{i \in [0, n-1]}$ such that $\forall i, t'_i = t_{id}$. Let us call the tile consisting of the tasks (t'_i) a derived tile. The length of the derived tile is $n' = \frac{n}{d}$. The derived dependence distance is $l' = \frac{l}{d}$. We assume that the derived permutations in each tile are constant (constant permutation).

Hence, according to the last part $T \geq T_{min}(n', l')$.

Now, let us show that $T_{min}(n, l) = 2\lfloor \frac{n'}{l'} \rfloor + \Lambda(n', l')$

Let $\sigma' : \{0, \cdots, n' - 1\} \to \{0, \cdots, n' - 1\}$ be the permutation of tasks that gives the period T'_{min}.

Then, consider $\forall v \in \{0, \cdots, d - 1\}, \forall i \in \{0, \cdots, n' - 1\}\ \sigma(v + id) = v + \sigma'(i)d$

Clearly, this permutation permits to reach the period $T = T'_{min}$. Thus, algorithm 1 generates the optimal permutation for this case also simply by using n' and l' as inputs instead of n and l.

The task execution times given by our algorithm for $n = 14$ and $l = 6$ is shown in Table 1. Since $n \wedge l = 2$, tile 0 has two components *viz.*, $\{0,2,4,6,8,10,12\}$ and $\{1,3,5,7,9,11,13\}$. Each of them form derived tiles with $n' = 7$ and $l' = 3$. The first component has equivalence classes $X_0 = \{0, 6, 12\}$, $X_1 = \{4, 10\}$, $X_2 = \{2, 8\}$. First, p tasks of X_0 are executed followed by all the tasks of X_2 and X_1 in that order. Finally the last task of X_0 is executed. The second component is then executed with a similar task ordering.

The period of ordering reached by our algorithm is 4 while that reached by Dion's algorithm is 6.

8. Optimal Solution with Non-constant Permutations

We can further optimize the solution if we relax the constraint of maintaining a constant permutation in every tile. We also show that computing the optimal permutation in every tile does not result in any overhead because the optimal permutation in each tile is a simple shift of the permutation in the previous tile. By removing the constraint, we can reach the optimal period of ordering which is half smaller than that in the case of constant permutation.

Let $n \wedge l = d \geq 1$. Recall that from section 5, we have $X_0 \to X_1 \to \cdots \to X_{l-1} \to X_0$. The algorithm computes task ordering such that it leads to the following execution order. The first processor executes tasks belonging to X_0 then X_1, X_2 and finally X_{l-1}. The second processor starts working $|X_0|\tau_{calc} + \tau_{comm}$ units of time after the first one, and executes the tasks of X_1 then $X_2, X_3 \cdots X_{l-1}$ and finally X_0. The third processor starts working $|X_1|\tau_{calc} + \tau_{comm}$ units of time after the second one, and executes the tasks of X_2 then $X_3, X_4 \cdots X_0$ and finally

X_1. Clearly, we can see that all dependences are satisfied. This leads to the following algorithm.

Algorithm 2

procedure *ComputeOrderingNoncstGen* (n, l, i)
Input: n (tile size)
  l (dependence distance)
  i (tile number)
Output: $permutation[0 : n - 1]$ (task ordering)
{ Initialize variables d, n_d and l_d }
  $d := \gcd(n, l)$
  $n_d := \frac{n}{d}$
  $l_d := \frac{l}{d}$
{ Initialize variables m and f }
  $m := \lceil \frac{n_d i}{l_d} \rceil$
  $f := (ml_d) \bmod n_d$
  for $i_d := 0$ **to** $d - 1$ **do**
{ Assign the first task f to be executed }
    $x := 0$
    $permutation[x] := fd + i_d$
{ Execute each equivalence class in the
  order of $(\longrightarrow)$}
    $j := (f + l_d) \bmod n_d$
    while $j \neq f$ **do**
      $x := x + 1$
      $permutation[x] := jd + i_d$
      $j := (j + l_d) \bmod n_d$
    endwhile
  endfor
end *ComputeOrderingNoncstGen*

In the above algorithm we have,

- i is the ordinal of the tile being executed.
- i_d is the ordinal of the derived tile being executed.
- m is the smallest integer where $n_d i \leq m l_d < n_d(i + 1)$.
- f is the first task of the derived tile i_d to be executed.

The time offset O_i for each tile is the number of time units between the start of execution of tile i and tile $i + 1$. The offset O_i as opposed to the period of ordering need not be the same for every tile. The offset O_i (in computational-time units) corresponds to the cardinality of the following set,

$$X_i = \{m \in N, in \leq ml < (i + 1)n\}$$

Hence,

$$O_i = \lceil \frac{n(i + 1) - \lceil \frac{ni}{l} \rceil l}{l} \rceil \tau_{calc} + \tau_{comm}$$

Consider the example $n = 5$ and $l = 3$. We have the following times when tasks are executed.

```
0  2  4  1  3 | 5  2  4  6  3 | 5  7  4  6  8 ⋯
•  ○  ×  •  ○ | ×  •  ○  ×  • | ○  ×  •  ○  × ⋯
```

Table 2[1] illustrates that the ordering in each tile is a circular shift of the ordering in the previous tile.

It is easy to show that the period of ordering reached by algorithm 2 is optimal. Consider two tiles T_j and T_{j+1}. Suppose

---
[1]The subscripts of tasks are modulo n.

Case $n = 5$ & $l = 3$	
Tile 0	Order 0 3 1 4 2
	Offset 2
Tile 1	Order 1 4 2 0 3
	Offset 2
Tile 2	Order 2 0 3 1 4
	Offset 1

Table 2. Optimal ordering with non-constant permutation in each tile ($n = 5, l = 3$).

that equivalence class X_i starts executing on T_j at $t = t_0$. Since $X_i \rightarrow X_{i+1}$ the earliest time at which X_{i+1} can start execution on T_{j+1} is $t = t_0 + |X_i|$. This is precisely the time offset between two consecutive tiles obtained through *algorithm 2*. Thus, latency between two tiles using non constant permutations is $\approx p$.

9   Results

9.1   Performance Evaluation

The performance evaluation of the proposed methods was carried out using several signal processing applications consisting of matrix transformations. We tested our proposed algorithms using a sample test routine shown below,

```
Do i: 0 -> N
   Task(i)
EndDo
```

In the above loop, `Task()` exhibits a compile-time unknown dependence distance l in the outermost loop. In general, `Task()` can represent a loop nest or a function call or a group of statements. We tiled the above loop using the tiling transformation provided by the *SUIF* compiler. Since the dependence distance is a compile-time unknown in the above loop, the code must be generated which computes the task permutation at run time. In order to enforce synchronization between tiles imposed by the dependence relation, data is passed between left and right processing elements (PEs) using message passing library (MPI) calls. The complete framework has been incorporated in the *SUIF* compiler as an optimization pass.

The code generated by the compiler's optimization pass is sketched in figure 3. In case of constant permutations (figure 3(a)), permutations are generated at the entry point of the tile loop (i_tile). In case of non-constant permutations (figure 3(b)), permutations are generated at the entry point of the element loop (i). The element loop is executed following the owner computes rule. At run time `permute_tile` will generate an optimal task permutation in each tile using the appropriate algorithm (1 or 2). This permutation is saved in the array `perm` which is used to order the task execution. The final transformed code was targeted on Cray T3E.

We performed experiments by varying the tile size (n) and the dependence distance (l). The metric used to evaluate the performance of our algorithms in comparison to previous algorithms was

177

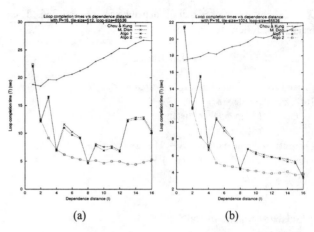

(a)   (b)

Figure 5. Loop completion time v/s dependence distance on Cray T3E for (a) P = 16, n = 512 and N = 65536 and (b) P = 16, n = 1024 and N = 65536.

l	Time (micro-sec)		
	Dion	Algo 1	Algo 2
3	11937	17153	19451
5	13108	18352	19546
7	13923	18422	19711
9	14966	18783	19627

Table 3. Permutation generation times ($N = 256, n = 64, P = 4$).

One can see that although Dion's algorithm is more time efficient, better loop completion times result from algorithm 1 & 2 due to superior task permutations. Thus, it is clear that the overhead of generating more complex task permutations does not nullify the performance gain achieved by those permutations. The results indicate the following *performance hierarchy* of the algorithms proposed in this paper. For $gcd(n, l) \neq l$,

Algorithm 2 > Algorithm 1 > Dion's algorithm

Algorithm 2 is also the most natural and efficient algorithm. For all tile sizes the results indicate that Algorithm 2 yields the best solution which is superior to solutions obtained by all constant permutation algorithms.

9.2 Effect of tile size

An interesting issue is to study the effect of variation of tile size on performance. In case of the multi-dimensional tiling problem $n_1 \times n_2 \times \cdots \times n_d$, the gain of our method using Algorithm 1 over Dion's algorithm will be proportional to $\prod_{i=1}^{d-1} n_i$.

Desprez et al [4] have addressed the issue of finding the optimal grain size that minimizes the execution time by improving pipeline communications on parallel computers. The following discussion presents the effect of tile size (n) on the total loop completion time (T_{tot}) in light of the framework developed in this paper.

Using Algorithm 2, we obtain the following period of ordering,

$$T \approx \frac{n}{l}\tau_{calc} + \tau_{comm}$$

```
permute_tile(n,l); <generates permutation
                      using algo 1>
Do i_tile: 0 -> N by n
  if i_tile maps onto PE then
    Do i: i_tile -> min(N,i_tile+n-1)
    <If needed, receive data from left PE>
      Task(perm[i]);
    <If needed, send data to right PE>
    EndDo
  endif
EndDo
```

```
Do i_tile: 0 -> N by n
  if i_tile maps onto PE then
    permute_tile(n,1,i_tile); <generates
                       permutation using algo 2>
    Do i: i_tile -> min(N,i_tile+n-1)
    <If needed, receive data from left PE>
      Task(perm[i]);
    <If needed, send data to right PE>
    EndDo
  endif
EndDo
```

(a)   (b)

Figure 3. (a) Code generating constant permutations (b) Code generating non-constant permutations.

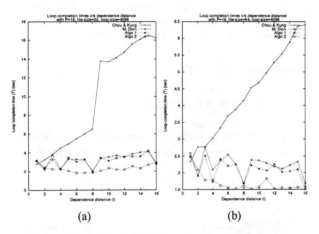

(a)   (b)

Figure 4. Loop completion time v/s dependence distance on Cray T3E for (a) P = 16, n = 32 and N = 4096 and (b) P = 16, n = 64 and N = 4096.

the total loop completion time. The tests were carried out using 16 processing elements with a cyclic distribution of tiles on processors. Figure 4 compares the performance of the final transformed code using the proposed algorithms (Algorithm 1 and 2 presented in sections 7 and 8) in comparison to previous approaches on the Cray T3E for small tile sizes. Figure 5 presents results obtained on the Cray T3E for larger tile sizes.

As seen in Figures 4 and 5 the performance obtained by using the two proposed algorithms is superior to that obtained by using algorithms proposed by Dion and Chou & Kung. This is true in the case of small tile sizes as well as large tile sizes.

Figures 4 and 5 show that when $gcd(n, l)$ is l, Dion's algorithm and the proposed algorithms yield very similar results. This is because in this case l' is 1 causing all three algorithms to generate identical permutations.

Since task permutations are generated at run-time we need to investigate the execution efficiency of the proposed algorithms in comparison to previous approaches. Table 3 presents the times taken by the code that generates task permutations using our and Dion's algorithms indicating the following hierarchy in the permutation generation times.

Dion's algorithm < Algorithm 1 < Algorithm 2

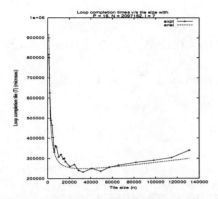

Figure 6. Loop completion time v/s tile size on SGI Power Challenge for P = 16, l = 7 and N = 2097152.

The total loop completion time is given by,

$$
\begin{aligned}
T_{tot} &\approx \frac{N}{n}T + n\tau_{calc} \\
&= \frac{N\tau_{calc}}{l} + n\tau_{calc} + \frac{N\tau_{comm}}{n} \\
&= A + Bn + \frac{C}{n}
\end{aligned}
$$

Minimizing the above expression we get,

$$
n_{opt} = \sqrt{\frac{C}{B}} = \sqrt{\frac{N\tau_{comm}}{\tau_{calc}}}
$$

Let $\frac{\tau_{comm}}{\tau_{calc}} = c$. Therefore,

$$
n_{opt} \approx \sqrt{cN}
$$

Also we have,

$$
\frac{n}{l}\tau_{calc} > \tau_{comm}
$$

This leads to,

$$
n > lc
$$

In order to compare the above analytical solution with experimental results we observed the total loop completion time (T_{tot}) varying the tile size (n) keeping P fixed. Figure 6 presents this comparison for $N = 2097152$ and $l = 7$. Figure 6 shows that the analytical expression derived for the loop completion time closely matches the experimental results. The knee of the analytical solution curve corresponds to the optimum tile size that yields the minimum loop completion time.

10. Conclusions

The effectiveness of loop tiling is critically dependent on the execution order of tasks within a tile. In this work, we have addressed the problem of finding an optimal ordering of tasks within tiles executed on multicomputers for constant but compile-time unknown dependences. We remove the restriction of atomicity on tiles and exploit the internal parallelism within each tile by overlapping computation with communication. We have formulated the problem and developed a new framework based on equivalence classes and show optimality results for single dimensional tiles with single constant dependences. Using the framework we have also developed two efficient algorithms that provide the optimal solution in both cases,

1. Same (constant) task ordering in tiles,
2. Different (non-constant) task ordering in tiles.

We have shown that the two proposed algorithms yield superior results to the previous approaches when tested on distributed memory systems. We also show that the non-constant permutations in our approach significantly reduce the loop completion time unlike the constant permutations in previous approaches. Finally, we have investigated the relationship between tile size and the loop completion time and developed a methodology to obtain optimal tile size given our framework.

References

[1] A. Agarwal, D. Kranz, and V. Natrajan. Automatic Partitioning of Parallel Loops and Data Arrays for Distributed Shared-Memory Multiprocessors. *IEEE Transactions on Parallel and Distributed Systems*, 6(9):943–962, Sept. 1995.

[2] W. Chou and S. Kung. Scheduling Partitioned Algorithms on Processor Arrays with Limited Communication Supports. In *Proceedings of the International Conference on Application Specific Array Processors (ASAP)*, pages 53–64, 1993.

[3] F. Desprez et al. Scheduling Block-Cyclic Array Redistribution. In *Parallel Computing '97 (ParCo97)*. North-Holland, September 1997.

[4] F. Desprez, P. Ramet, and J. Roman. Optimal Grain Size Computation for Pipelined Algorithms. In *Europar '96 Parallel Processing*, volume 1123 of *Lecture Notes in Computer Science*, pages 165–172. Springer Verlag, August 1996.

[5] E. D'Hollander. Partitioning and Labeling of Loops by Unimodular Transformations. *IEEE Transactions on Parallel and Distributed Systems*, 3(4):465–476, July 1992.

[6] M. Dion, T. Risset, and Y. Robert. Resource-constrained Scheduling of Partitioned Algorithms on Processor Arrays. In *Proceedings of Euromicro Workshop on Parallel and Distributed Processing*, pages 571–580, 1995.

[7] F. Irigoin and R. Triolet. Supernode Partitioning. In *15th Symposium on Principles of Programming Languages (POPL XV)*, pages 319–329, 1988.

[8] J. Ramanujam and P. Sadayappan. Tiling Multidimensional Iteration Spaces for Multicomputers. *Journal of Parallel and Distributed Computing*, 16:108–120, 1992.

[9] F. Rastello, A. Rao, and S. Pande. Optimal Task Ordering in Linear Tiles for Minimizing Loop Completion Time. Technical Report TR 213/02/98/ECECS, University of Cincinnati, Jan. 1998. http://www.ececs.uc.edu/~compiler.

[10] M. Wolf and M. Lam. A Data Locality Optimizing Algorithm. In *Proceedings of the ACM SIGPLAN '91 Conference on Programming Language Design and Implementation*, pages 30–44, June 1991.

[11] M. Wolfe. Iteration Space Tiling for Memory Hierarchies. In *Proceedings of the 3rd SIAM Conf. on Parallel Processing for Scientific Computing*, pages 357–361, 1987.

Minimizing Data and Synchronization Costs in One-Way Communication

M. Kandemir*†   N. Shenoy‡†   P. Banerjee‡§   J. Ramanujam¶   A. Choudhary‡†

Abstract

In contrast to the conventional send/receive model, the one-way communication model—using Put and Synch—allows the decoupling of message transmission from synchronization. This opens up new opportunities not only to further optimize communication but also to reduce synchronization overhead. In this paper, we present a general technique which uses a global dataflow framework to optimize communication and synchronization in the context of the one-way communication model. Our approach works with the most general data alignments and distributions in languages like HPF, and is more powerful than other current solutions for eliminating redundant synchronization messages. Preliminary results on several scientific benchmarks demonstrate that our approach is successful in minimizing the number of data and synchronization messages.

1 Introduction

Most of the current compilers for distributed memory machines rely on the send and recv primitives to implement communication. The impact of this approach is twofold. First, this technique combines synchronization with communication in the sense that data messages also carry implicit synchronization information. While this relieves the compiler of the job of inserting synchronization messages to maintain data integrity, separating synchronization messages from data messages may actually improve the performance of some programs. Second, the compiler has the difficult task of matching send and recv operations in order to guarantee correct execution.

In this paper, we focus on compilation of programs annotated by HPF-like directives with one-way communication operations Put and Synch, introduced by Gupta and Schonberg [6] and Hinrichs [8]. Let us consider Figure 1(a); here, a consumer processor sends a Synch message to the producer informing that the producer can *put* data in a buffer physically located in the consumer's memory. After receiving the Synch message, the producer deposits the data in that buffer. We note that the Synch operation is necessary for the repetition of this communication; that is, when the producer wants to deposit new data into the buffer, it must know that the consumer has indeed consumed the old data in the buffer.

After briefly discussing the fundamental concepts used in this paper in Section 2, in Section 3 we show how the communica-

tion sets as well as the producers and the consumers manipulated by the Put operation can be implemented on top of the existing send/recv type of communication framework in our compiler [3]. Having determined those, the next issue is to minimize the number of Put communications as well as the communication volume. Section 4 presents an algorithm to achieve this goal. Our algorithm can take arbitrary control flow (excluding *goto* statements) into account and can optimize programs with all types of HPF-like alignments and distributions, including block-cyclic distributions. It is based on a linear algebra framework introduced by Ancourt et al. [2]; in addition, our approach is quite general in the sense that several current solutions to the problem can be derived by a suitable definition of associated predicates.

Clearly, in a compilation framework based on the Put operation, the correct ordering of memory accesses has to be imposed by the compiler using the synchronization primitives. A straightforward approach inserts a Synch operation just before each Put operation as shown in Figure 1(a). The next question to be addressed then is whether or not every Synch operation inserted that way is always necessary. The answer is no, and Section 5 proposes an algorithm to eliminate redundant synchronization messages. We refer to a Synch operation as *redundant* if its functionality can be fulfilled by other data communications or other Synch operations occurring in the program. The basic idea is to use another message in the reverse direction between the same pair of processors in place of the Synch call as shown in Figure 1(b). In such a situation, we say that the communication t_j kills the synchronization requirement of communication i. We show that our algorithm is very fast and more powerful than the previous work in synchronization elimination. This is because (1) it is very accurate in eliminating redundant synchronization, since it works at the granularity of a processor-pair using the Omega library [11]; (2) it can eliminate a synchronization message by using several data messages; (3) it handles block, cyclic, and block-cyclic distributions in a unified manner, whereas the previous approaches either work on virtual processor grids only or use an extension of regular section descriptors which are inherently inaccurate; and (4) it is preceded by a global communication optimization algorithm which itself eliminates a lot of synchronization messages. To show the idea behind the algorithm, we consider Figure 2(a), where eight processors (numbered 0 thru 7) are involved in a Put communication that repeats itself (as in a loop); processor i deposits data in the memory of processor $i - 1$ for $1 \leq i \leq 7$; the arrows indicate the direction of communication. Figure 2(b) shows the Synch messages required for the repetitions of this communication. Suppose that between successive repetitions of the communication pattern in Figure 2(a), subsets of processors are involved in communication patterns using Put shown in Figures 2(c) and 2(d). Our synchronization elimination algorithm can detect that the communications given in Figures 2(c) and 2(d), *together*, kill the synchronization requirement of the first communication, i.e., kill the Synch messages shown in Figure 2(b).

In Section 6, we give preliminary results on several benchmark

---

*Elec. Engr. & Comp. Sci. Dept., Syracuse University, Syracuse, NY 13244. e-mail: mtk@ece.nwu.edu

†Supported in part by NSF Young Investigator Award CCR-9357840 and NSF grant CCR-9509143

‡Elec. & Comp. Engr. Dept., Northwestern University, Evanston, IL 60208. e-mail: {nagaraj,banerjee,choudhar}@ece.nwu.edu

§Supported in part by NSF under grant CCR-9526325 and in part by DARPA under contract DABT-63-97-C-0035.

¶Elec. & Comp. Engr. Dept., Louisiana State University, Baton Rouge, LA 70803. e-mail: jxr@ee.lsu.edu. Supported in part by NSF Young Investigator Award CCR-9457768 and NSF grant CCR-9210422.

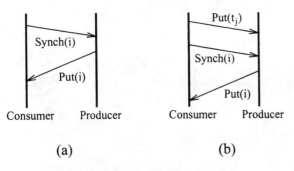

(a)　　　　　　　　(b)

Figure 1: (a) one-way communication with Put operation. (b) elimination of a Synch message.

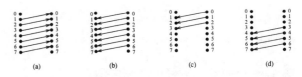

Figure 2: Communication and synchronization messages for the first loop of the program in Figure 6(a).

programs. Our experiments show that we are able to reduce data messages on the average by 37% and synchronization messages by 96%. We believe that these are also the first results from a comprehensive evaluation of synchronization elimination in one-way communication. We discuss related work in Section 7 and conclude the paper with a summary in Section 8.

2 Preliminaries

We focus on structured programs with conditional statements and nested loops but without arbitrary goto statements. A *basic block* is a sequence of consecutive statements in which the flow of control enters at the beginning and leaves at the end without the possibility of branching except perhaps at the end [1]. A *control flow graph* (CFG) is a directed graph constructed by basic blocks and represents the flow-of-control information of the program. For the purpose of this paper, the CFG can be thought of as a directed graph $\mathcal{G} = (\mathcal{V}, \mathcal{E})$ where each $v \in \mathcal{V}$ represents either a basic block or a (reduced) interval that represents a loop, and each $e \in \mathcal{E}$ represents an edge between blocks. In this paper, depending on the context, we use the term *node* interchangeably for a statement, a block or an interval. Two unique nodes s and t denote the start and terminal nodes respectively of a CFG. One might think of these nodes as dummy statements. We define the sets of all successors and predecessors of a node n as $succ(n) = \{m \mid (n,m) \in \mathcal{E}\}$ and $pred(n) = \{m \mid (m,n) \in \mathcal{E}\}$, respectively. Node i *dominates* node j in the CFG (written as $j \in dom(i)$), if every path from s to j goes through i. We assume that prior to communication analysis, any edge that goes directly from a node with more than one successor to a node with more than one predecessor is split by introducing a dummy node. Our technique for minimizing the communication volume and the number of messages is based on *interval analysis* [1]. Interval analysis consists of a *contraction* phase and an *expansion* phase. For programs written in a structured language, an interval corresponds to a loop. The contraction phase collects information about what is generated and what is killed inside each interval. Then the interval is reduced to a single node and annotated with the information collected. This is a recursive procedure and stops when the reduced CFG contains no more cycles. In each step of the expansion phase, a node (reduced interval) is expanded, and the information regarding the nodes in that interval is computed.

3 Producers and Consumers

We assume that all loop bounds and subscript expressions are affine functions of enclosing loop indices and symbolic variables. Under this condition, a loop nest, an array and a processor grid can all be represented as bounded polyhedra. Our compiler currently uses the owner-computes rule [9], which assigns each computation to the processor that owns the data being computed.

Consider the generic single loop i shown in Figure 3(a). Let $\mathcal{R}_{\mathcal{L}}(i) = \mathtt{X}(\gamma_L * i + \theta_L)$ and $\mathcal{R}_{\mathcal{R}}(i) = \mathtt{Y}(\gamma_R * i + \theta_R)$. Let p and q denote two processors. We define several sets shown in Figure 3(b) where S is the communication statement and $\vee$ and $\wedge$ are logical 'or' and 'and' operations respectively. The set Own(X,p) refers to the elements of array X mapped onto processor p through compiler directives. Similar Own sets are defined for other arrays as well. The sets Producers(S) and Consumers(S) denote, respectively, the processors that produce and consume data communicated in S. For a specific processor, ProducersFor and ConsumersFor give the set of processors that send data to and receive data from that processor respectively. PutSet(S,p,q) is the set of elements that should be put (written) by processor q to memory of processor p. SendSet(S) is set of pairs (q', p') such that q' sends data to (write data in the memory of) p'. Finally, Pending(S) is the inverse of SendSet(S), and gives set of pairs (p', q') such that p' should send a Synch message to q' for the repetitions of the communication (in each iteration of the time-step loop t) occurring in S. For a communication occurring in i, the set Pending(i) represents a list of individual Synch messages that should be sent for the safe repetition of the data communication in i. That is, a Synch message is between just a pair of processors. For an i and a Synch, we say whether or not Synch $\in$ Pending(i).

In fact, by using appropriate projection functions all of those sets can be obtained from a single set called CommSet(S) containing triples (p', q', d) meaning that element d should be communicated from q' to p' in S. The CommSet(S) is currently used in our compiler's communication generation portion to generate send and recv commands. The necessary projection functions can be implemented by using the Omega library [11], and are shown in Figure 3(c). For instance, ConsumersFor(S, q) is obtained from CommSet(S) by projecting out d and substituting q for q'; that is, q is a parameter and ConsumersFor(S, q) enumerates p' values in terms of q.

By taking into account the alignment and distribution information, we can define the Own set more formally as

$$\begin{aligned}
\mathtt{Own}(\mathtt{Y}, q) = {} & \{d \mid \exists t, c, l \text{ s. t. } (t = \alpha d + \beta = \mathcal{C}Pc + \mathcal{C}q + l) \\
& \wedge\ (y_l \leq d \leq y_u) \wedge (p_l \leq q \leq p_u) \wedge (t_l \leq t \leq t_u) \\
& \wedge\ (0 \leq l \leq \mathcal{C} - 1)\},
\end{aligned}$$

where $P = p_u - p_l + 1$. In this formulation, $t = \alpha d + \beta$ represents alignment information and $t = \mathcal{C}Pc + \mathcal{C}q + l$ denotes distribution information. In other words, each array element d is mapped onto a point in a two-dimensional array. This point can be represented by a

181

```
        REAL X(x_l:x_u), Y(y_l:y_u)
        !HPF$ TEMPLATE T(t_l:t_u)
        !HPF$ PROCESSORS PROC(p_l:p_u)
        !HPF$ ALIGN X(j), Y(j) WITH T(α*j+β)
        !HPF$ DISTRIBUTE T(CYCLIC(C)) ON TO PROC

        DO t = 1, TIMES /* time-step loop */
          ...
          < synchronization for Y using Synch operations >
        S: < communication for Y using Put operations >
          DO i = i_l, i_u
            ...
            X(γ_L*i+θ_L) = ... Y(γ_R*i+θ_R) ...
            ...
          END DO
          ...
        END DO

            (a)
```

SET	PROJECTION FUNCTION
Producers(S)	$[p', q', d] \mapsto [q']$
Consumers(S)	$[p', q', d] \mapsto [p']$
ProducersFor(S, p)	$[p, q', d] \mapsto [q']$
ConsumersFor(S, q)	$[p', q, d] \mapsto [p']$
PutSet(S, p, q)	$[p, q, d] \mapsto [d]$
SendSet(S)	$[p', q', d] \mapsto [q', p']$
Pending(S)	$[p', q', d] \mapsto [p', q']$

(c)

$$
\begin{aligned}
\texttt{Own}(X,q) &= \{d \mid d \in X \wedge \text{ is owned by } q\} \\
\texttt{Producers}(S) &= \{q' \mid \exists i, p' \text{ s. t. } \mathcal{R_R}(i) \in \texttt{Own}(Y,q') \wedge \mathcal{R_L}(i) \in \texttt{Own}(X,p') \wedge i_l \le i \le i_u \wedge q' \ne p'\} \\
\texttt{Consumers}(S) &= \{p' \mid \exists i, q' \text{ s. t. } \mathcal{R_R}(i) \in \texttt{Own}(Y,q') \wedge \mathcal{R_L}(i) \in \texttt{Own}(X,p') \wedge i_l \le i \le i_u \wedge q' \ne p'\} \\
\texttt{ProducersFor}(S,p) &= \{q' \mid \exists i \text{ s. t. } \mathcal{R_R}(i) \in \texttt{Own}(Y,q') \wedge \mathcal{R_L}(i) \in \texttt{Own}(X,p) \wedge i_l \le i \le i_u \wedge q' \ne p\} \\
\texttt{ConsumersFor}(S,q) &= \{p' \mid q \in \texttt{ProducersFor}(S,p')\} \\
\texttt{PutSet}(S,p,q) &= \{d \mid \exists i \text{ s. t. } d = \mathcal{R_R}(i) \in \texttt{Own}(Y,q) \wedge \mathcal{R_L}(i) \in \texttt{Own}(X,p) \wedge i_l \le i \le i_u \wedge q \ne p\} \\
\texttt{SendSet}(S) &= \{(q',p') \mid \exists d \text{ s. t. } d \in \texttt{PutSet}(S,p',q')\} \\
\texttt{Pending}(S) &= \{(p',q') \mid (q',p') \in \texttt{SendSet}(S)\}.
\end{aligned}
$$

(b)

Figure 3: (a) Generic loop. (b) Several sets. (c) Projection functions to manipulate sets (p and q are symbolic names).

---

pair (c, l) and gives the local address of the data item in a processor. Simple BLOCK and CYCLIC(1) distributions can be handled within this framework by setting $c = 0$ and $l = 0$, respectively. The formulation given here can be generalized to multi-dimensional loops, arrays and processor grids [2]. Consider the first i-loop in Figure 6(b). Figure 4(a) shows the sets for this loop assuming that in the transformed program array bounds start from 0. Notice that a processor q is in the Producers set if there exists a processor p such that $q \ne p$ and q puts data in p's memory. Similarly, a processor p is in the Consumers set if there exists a processor q such that $p \ne q$ and q puts data in p's memory. For this example, if distribution directive for the arrays is changed to CYCLIC(4), then we have the sets shown in Figure 4(b). All of these sets can easily be represented and manipulated by the Omega library [11]. Notice that using the Omega sets to represent producer-consumer information, we are able to accommodate any kind of HPF-like alignment and distribution data in our framework through Own sets.

Let $\{\vec{d} \mid \mathcal{P}(\vec{d})\}$ and $\{\vec{d} \mid \mathcal{Q}(\vec{d})\}$ be two PutSets for a same multi-dimensional array where $\mathcal{P}(.)$ and $\mathcal{Q}(.)$ denote two predicates and $\vec{d}$ refers to an array element. We define three operations, $\vee_c$, $-_c$, and $\wedge_c$ on these PutSets as shown in Figure 4(c). In the remainder of this paper, $\bigvee$ and $\bigwedge$ symbols will also be used for $\vee_c$ and $\wedge_c$, respectively, when there is no confusion.

4 Optimizing Communication

The objective of our global communication optimization framework is to determine $\texttt{PutSet}(i, p, q)$ for each node i in the program globally; that is, by taking into account all the nodes in the CFG that are involved in communication.

Local (Intra-Interval) Analysis The local analysis part of our framework computes Kill, Gen and Post_Gen sets defined below for each interval. Then the interval is reduced to a single node and annotated with these sets. With reference to Figure 3(a),

$$
\begin{aligned}
\texttt{Kill}(i,q) &= \{(\vec{d} \mid \vec{d} \in \texttt{Own}(X,q)) \wedge (\exists \vec{i} \text{ s. t.} \\
&\quad (\vec{d} = \mathcal{R_L}(\vec{i})) \wedge (\vec{i_l} \le \vec{i} \le \vec{i_u}))\}, \\
\texttt{Modified}(i,q) &= [\bigvee_{j \in pred(i)} \texttt{Modified}(j,q)] \vee_c \texttt{Kill}(i,q).
\end{aligned}
$$

assuming $\texttt{Modified}(\texttt{pred}(\texttt{first}(i)), q) = \emptyset$ where first(i) is the first node in i.

Kill(i, q) is the set of elements owned and written (killed) by processor q locally in i, and Modified(i, q) is the set of elements that may be killed along any path from the beginning of the interval to (and including) i. The computation of the Kill set proceeds in the forward direction; that is, the nodes within the interval are traversed in topological sort order. If last(i) is the last node in i, then

$$
\texttt{Kill}(i,q) = \texttt{Modified}(\texttt{last}(i), q)
$$

This last equation is used to reduce an interval into a node. The reduced interval is then annotated by its Kill set.

Gen(i, p, q) is the set of elements to be written by q into p's memory to satisfy the communication in i. The computation of the Gen proceeds in the backward direction, i.e., the nodes within each interval are traversed in reverse topological sort order. The elements that can be written by q into p's memory at the beginning of a node in the CFG are the elements required by p due to a RHS reference in the node except the ones that are written locally (killed) by q before being referenced by p.

182

$$\text{Producers}(2) = \{q \mid 1 \le q \le 7\}$$
$$\text{Consumers}(2) = \{p \mid 0 \le p \le 6\}$$
$$\text{ProducersFor}(2, p) = \{q \mid (q = p + 1) \wedge (0 \le p \le 6)\}$$
$$\text{ConsumersFor}(2, q) = \{p \mid (p = q - 1) \wedge (1 \le q \le 7)\}$$
$$\text{PutSet}(2, p, q) = \{d \mid (d = 16q) \wedge (p + 1 = q) \wedge (1 \le q \le 7)\}$$
$$\text{SendSet}(2) = \{(q, q - 1) \mid 1 \le q \le 7\}$$
$$\text{Pending}(2) = \{(p, p + 1) \mid 0 \le p \le 6\}$$

(a)

$$\text{Producers}(2) = \{q \mid 0 \le q \le 7\}$$
$$\text{Consumers}(2) = \{q \mid 0 \le q \le 7\}$$
$$\text{ProducersFor}(2, p) = \{q \mid q = 0 \wedge p = 7\}$$
$$\qquad \cup \{q \mid (q = p + 1) \wedge (0 \le p \le 6)\}$$
$$\text{ConsumersFor}(2, q) = \{p \mid p = 7 \wedge q = 0\}$$
$$\qquad \cup \{p \mid (p = q - 1) \wedge (1 \le q \le 7)\}$$
$$\text{PutSet}(2, p, q) = \{d \mid \exists \alpha \text{ such that } (d = 32\alpha) \wedge (q = 0) \wedge (p = 7)$$
$$\qquad \wedge (32 \le d \le 128)\} \cup$$
$$\qquad \{d \mid \exists \alpha \text{ s. t. } (d = 4 + 4p + 32\alpha) \wedge (q = p + 1)$$
$$\qquad \wedge (0 \le p \le 6) \wedge (4p + 4 \le d \le 4p + 100)\}$$
$$\text{SendSet}(2) = \{(0, 7)\} \cup \{(q, q - 1) \mid 1 \le q \le 7\}$$
$$\text{Pending}(2) = \{(p, p + 1) \mid 0 \le p \le 6\} \cup \{(7, 0)\}$$

(b)

$$\{\vec{d} \mid \mathcal{P}(\vec{d})\} \vee_c \{\vec{d} \mid \mathcal{Q}(\vec{d})\} = \{\vec{d} \mid \mathcal{P}(\vec{d}) \vee \mathcal{Q}(\vec{d})\}$$
$$\{\vec{d} \mid \mathcal{P}(\vec{d})\} -_c \{\vec{d} \mid \mathcal{Q}(\vec{d})\} = \{\vec{d} \mid \mathcal{P}(\vec{d}) \wedge \neg(\mathcal{Q}(\vec{d}))\}$$
$$\{\vec{d} \mid \mathcal{P}(\vec{d})\} \wedge_c \{\vec{d} \mid \mathcal{Q}(\vec{d})\} = \{\vec{d} \mid \mathcal{P}(\vec{d}) \wedge \mathcal{Q}(\vec{d})\}$$

(c)

$$\text{PENDING\_IN}(i) = \bigsqcup_{j \in pred(i)} \text{PENDING\_OUT}(j)$$
$$\text{PENDING\_OUT}(i) = \mathcal{F}_i(\text{PENDING\_IN}(i))$$

(d)

Figure 4: (a) Sets for the first loop in Figure 6(b) for BLOCK distribution. (b) Sets for the first loop in Figure 6(b) for CYCLIC(4) distribution. (c) Operations on PutSets. (d) Dataflow equations for optimizing synchronization messages.

Assuming $\vec{\imath} = (\imath_1, ..., \imath_n)$ and $\vec{\imath'} = (\imath_1', ..., \imath_n')$, let $\vec{\imath'} \prec \vec{\imath}$ mean that $\vec{\imath'}$ is lexicographically less than or equal to $\vec{\imath}$; and $\vec{\imath'} \prec_k \vec{\imath}$ mean that $\imath_j' = \imath_j$ for all $j < k$, and $(\imath_k', ..., \imath_n') \prec (\imath_k, ..., \imath_n)$. Let $\text{Comm}(\mathtt{i}, p, q)$ be the set of elements that may be communicated at the beginning of interval $\mathtt{i}$ to satisfy communication requirements from the beginning of $\mathtt{i}$ to the last node of $\mathtt{i}$. Then, from Figure 3(a), assuming that $\text{Comm}(\mathtt{succ(last(i))}, q) = \emptyset$, we have

$$\text{Gen}(\mathtt{i}, p, q) = \{\vec{d} \mid \exists \vec{\imath} \text{ s. t. } (\vec{\imath_l} \le \vec{\imath} \le \vec{\imath_u}) \wedge$$
$$(\vec{d} = \mathcal{R}_\mathcal{R}(\vec{\imath}) \in \text{Own(Y}, q)) \wedge (\mathcal{R}_\mathcal{L}(\vec{\imath}) \in \text{Own(X}, p))$$
$$\wedge \neg(\exists \vec{\jmath}, \mathcal{R}_\mathcal{L}' \text{ s. t. } (\vec{\imath_l} \le \vec{\jmath} \le \vec{\imath_u}) \wedge (\vec{d} = \mathcal{R}_\mathcal{L}'(\vec{\jmath})$$
$$\wedge (\vec{\jmath} \prec_{\mathtt{level(i)}} \vec{\imath}))\},$$
$$\text{Comm}(\mathtt{i}, p, q) = [\bigwedge_{s \in succ(\mathtt{i})} \text{Comm}(\mathtt{s}, p, q)] \vee_c \text{Gen}(\mathtt{i}, p, q).$$

The negated condition eliminates all the elements written by q locally in an earlier iteration than the one in which p requires them. In addition, we use the following equation to reduce an interval into a single node

$$\text{Gen}(\mathtt{i}, p, q) = \text{Comm}(\mathtt{First(i)}, p, q).$$

In the definition of Gen, $\mathcal{R}_\mathcal{R}$ denotes the RHS reference, and $\mathcal{R}_\mathcal{L}$ denotes the LHS reference of the same statement. $\mathcal{R}_\mathcal{L}'$, on the other hand, refers to any LHS reference within the same interval. Notice that while $\mathcal{R}_\mathcal{L}'$ is a reference to the same array as $\mathcal{R}_\mathcal{R}$, in general $\mathcal{R}_\mathcal{L}$ can be a reference to any array. level(i) gives the nesting level of the interval (loop), 1 corresponding to the outermost loop in the nest.

After the interval is reduced, the Gen set for it is recorded, and an operator $\mathcal{N}$ is applied to the last part of this Gen set to propagate it to the outer interval:

$$\mathcal{N}(\vec{\jmath} \prec_k \vec{\imath}) = \vec{\jmath} \prec_{(k-1)} \vec{\imath}.$$

It should be emphasized that computation of Gen sets gives us all the communication that can be vectorized above a loop nest; that is, our analysis easily handles message vectorization [9]. A naive implementation may set $\text{Put\_Set}(\mathtt{i}, p, q)$ to $\text{Gen}(\mathtt{i}, p, q)$ for every $\mathtt{i}$, p and q. But such an approach often retains redundant communication which would otherwise be eliminated.

Finally, $\text{Post\_Gen}(\mathtt{i}, p, q)$ is the set of elements to be written by q into memory of p at node $\mathtt{i}$ with no subsequent local write to them by q:

$$\text{Post\_Gen}(\mathtt{i}, p, q) = \{\vec{d} \mid \exists \vec{\imath} \text{ s. t. } (\vec{\imath_l} \le \vec{\imath} \le \vec{\imath_u}) \wedge$$
$$(\vec{d} = \mathcal{R}_\mathcal{R}(\vec{\imath}) \in \text{Own(Y}, q)) \wedge (\mathcal{R}_\mathcal{L}(\vec{\imath}) \in \text{Own(X}, p))$$
$$\wedge \neg(\exists \vec{\jmath}, \mathcal{R}_\mathcal{L}' \text{ s. t. } (\vec{\imath_l} \le \vec{\jmath} \le \vec{\imath_u}) \wedge (\vec{d} = \mathcal{R}_\mathcal{L}'(\vec{\jmath})$$
$$\wedge (\vec{\imath} \prec_{\mathtt{level(i)}} \vec{\jmath}))\}.$$

The computation of $\text{Post\_Gen}(\mathtt{i}, p, q)$ proceeds in the forward direction. Its computation is very similar to those of Kill and Gen sets, so we do not discuss it further.

Dataflow Equations In our framework, one-way communication calls are placed at the beginning of nodes in the CFG. Our dataflow analysis consists of a backward and a forward pass. In the backward pass, the compiler determines sets of data elements that can safely be communicated at specific points. The forward pass, on the other hand, eliminates redundant communication and determines the final set of elements that should be communicated (written by q into p's memory) at the beginning of each node $\mathtt{i}$. The input for the equations consists of the Gen, Kill and Post_Gen sets.

The dataflow equations for the backward analysis are given by Equations (1) and (2) in Figure 5. Basically, they are used to combine and hoist communication. The sets Safe_In(i, p, q) and Safe_Out(i, p, q) consist of elements that *can* safely be communicated at the beginning and end of node i, respectively. Equation (1) says that an element should be communicated at a point if and only if it will be used in all of the following paths in the CFG. Equation (2), on the other hand, gives the set of elements that can safely be communicated at the beginning of i. Intuitively, an element can be written by q into p's memory at the beginning of i if and only if it is either required by p in i or it reaches at the end of i (in the backward analysis) and is not overwritten (killed) by the owner (q) in it. The predicate $\mathcal{P}(i)$ is used to control communication hoisting. If $\mathcal{P}(i)$ is true, communication is not hoisted to the beginning of i. $\mathcal{P}(i)=false$ implies aggressive communication combining and hoisting. An algorithm can also put a condition which tests the compatibility between Gen(i,p,q) and Safe_Out(i,p,q) (e.g. two left-shift communications are compatible whereas a left-shift and a right-shift are not) [4].

The task of the forward analysis phase, which makes use of Equations (3), (4) and (5) in Figure 5, is to eliminate redundant communication by observing that (1) a node in the CFG should not have a non-local datum which is exclusively needed by a successor unless it dominates that successor; and (2) a successor should ignore what a predecessor has so far unless that predecessor dominates it. Put_In(i, p, q) and Put_Out(i, p, q) denote the set of elements that *have been* written so far (at the beginning and end of node i respectively) by q into memory of p. Equation (3) conservatively says that the communication set arriving in a join node can be found by intersecting the sets for all the joining paths. Equation (4) is used to compute the PutSet set which corresponds to the elements that can be communicated at the beginning of the node except the ones that have already been communicated (Put_In). The elements that have been communicated at the end of node i (that is, Put_Out set) are simply the union of the elements communicated up to the beginning of i (that is, Put_In set), the elements communicated at the beginning of i (that is, PutSet(i,p,q) set) (except the ones which have been killed in i) and the elements communicated in i and not killed subsequently (Post_Gen).

Interval Analysis Our approach starts by computing the Gen, Kill and Post_Gen sets for each node. Then the contraction phase reduces the intervals from the innermost loop to the outermost loop and annotates them with Gen, Kill and Post_Gen sets. When a reduced CFG with no cycles is reached, the expansion phase starts and PutSets for each node is computed from the outermost loop to the innermost loop. There is one important point to note: before starting to process the next graph in the expansion phase, the Put_In set of the first node in this graph is set to the PutSet of the interval that contains it to avoid redundant communication. More formally, in the expansion phase, we set Put_In$(i,p,q)^{k^{th} pass}$ = PutSet$(i,p,q)^{(k-1)^{th} pass}$. This assignment then triggers the next pass in the expansion phase. Before the expansion phase starts Put_In$(i, p, q)^{1^{st} pass}$ is set to the empty set. Note that the whole dataflow procedure operates on sets of equalities and inequalities which can be manipulated by the Omega library [11] or a similar tool.

Example Consider the synthetic benchmark given in Figure 6(a). In this example, communication occurs for three arrays: B, D and F. A communication optimization scheme based on message vector-

ization alone, can place communications and associated synchronizations as shown in Figure 6(b) before the loop bounds reduction. Note that a Synch message in that figure in fact represents a number of point-to-point synchronization messages. An application of our global communication optimization method generates the program shown in Figure 6(c). As compared with the message vectorized version, there is a 50% reduction (from 28 to 14) in the number of messages and 40% in the communication volume (from 35 to 21) across all processors. We note that we can optimize this program even the distribution directive is changed to CYCLIC(K) for any K. When the distribution directive is CYCLIC(4), we have a 50% reduction (from 48 to 24) in the number of messages and 32% reduction (from 139 to 94) in the communication volume across all processors. Note that our approach here reduces the original number of synchronization messages as well (from 28 to 14 for the BLOCK distribution and from 48 to 24 for the CYCLIC(4) case).

5 Optimizing Synchronization

In this section, we assume that the compiler has conducted the dataflow analysis described in Section 4 and determined the optimal communication points and communication sets. Assuming that these communications will be implemented by Put operations, we present a dataflow analysis to minimize the number of Synch messages. We assume that communication patterns (i.e. producer-consumer relationships) are *identical* for each repetition of a communication. For example, in Figure 6(c), the producer-consumer pattern for the communication occurring in 1 is identical for every repetition of time-step loop t.

Our approach first makes a single pass over the current interval and determines some synchronizations that cannot be eliminated by the analysis to be described. We call the set of synchronizations (associated with a node i) that cannot be eliminated SynchFix(i). We refer the reader to [10] for the definition of SynchFix(i).

The dataflow technique described here starts with the deepest loops and works its way through loops in a bottom up manner, handling one loop at a time. It then reduces the loop to a node and annotates it with its final synchronization requirements that cannot be eliminated. The procedure works on an augmented CFG, where each communication loop is represented by a single node. In the following, the symbol i refers to such a node.

For a given i, we can define the set SynchSet as a set of processor pairs that should be synchronized after our analysis. In a straightforward implementation, SynchSet(i) = Pending(i) for each i. We would like to reduce the cardinality of SynchSet(i) for each i. We say that no synchronization is required for a communication i, if SynchSet(i) happens to be empty after our dataflow analysis.

If the compiler wants to eliminate a Synch message for communication i from p to q, it needs to find a message t_j for another communication from p to q and use it as synchronization. Such a message should occur *between* repetitions of i and *after* the data value communicated at i is consumed. Suppose that a specific producer q and a consumer p are involved in a communication in i. Consider all k communications t_j $(1 \leq j \leq k)$ occurring after the value communicated in i is consumed by p and before the next repetition of i. Then, if the following holds, the Synch message from p to q can be eliminated:

$$(\exists j \mid (1 \leq j \leq k) \wedge q \in \texttt{ConsumersFor}(t_j, p))$$

An interesting case occurs when all the Synch messages contained in the Pending(i) set for a specific i are eliminated. We can formalize this condition as

$$\forall p \forall q (((p, q) \in \texttt{Pending}(i)) \ \Rightarrow \ \exists j ((p, q) \in \texttt{SendSet}(t_j))) \ (6)$$

184

$$\text{Safe\_Out}(i,p,q) \;=\; \bigwedge_{s \in succ(i)} \text{Safe\_In}(s,p,q) \tag{1}$$

$$\text{Safe\_In}(i,p,q) \;=\; \begin{cases} \text{Gen}(i,p,q) & \text{if } \mathcal{P}(i) \\ (\text{Safe\_Out}(i,p,q) -_c \text{Kill}(i,q)) \vee_c \text{Gen}(i,p,q) & \text{otherwise} \end{cases} \tag{2}$$

Forward Analysis:

$$\text{Put\_In}(i,p,q) \;=\; \bigwedge_{j \in pred(i)} \text{Put\_Out}(j,p,q) \tag{3}$$

$$\text{PutSet}(i,p,q) \;=\; \begin{cases} \text{Gen}(i,p,q) -_c \text{Put\_In}(i,p,q) & \text{if } \exists k \text{ s.t. } k \in succ(i) \text{ and } k \notin dom(i) \\ \text{Safe\_In}(i,p,q) -_c \text{Put\_In}(i,p,q) & \text{otherwise} \end{cases} \tag{4}$$

$$\text{Put\_Out}(i,p,q) \;=\; \begin{cases} \text{Put\_In}(i,p,q) -_c \text{Kill}(i,q) & \text{if } \exists k \text{ s.t. } k \in succ(i) \text{ and } k \notin dom(i) \\ ((\text{PutSet}(i,p,q) +_c \text{Put\_In}(i,p,q)) -_c \text{Kill}(i,q)) +_c \text{Post\_Gen}(i,p,q) & \text{otherwise} \end{cases} \tag{5}$$

Figure 5: Dataflow equations for optimizing communication.

```
REAL A(128), B(128), C(128)
     D(128), E(128), F(128)
!HPF$ PROCESSORS PROC(0:7)
!HPF$ DISTRIBUTE BLOCK ON TO
      PROC ::  A, B, C, D, E

    DO t = 1, TIMES
      DO i = 1, 127
S:      A(i) = B(i+1)
      END DO
      DO i = 1, 126
        D(i) = A(i) + 1
        A(i) = B(i+1) + B(i+2)
      END DO
      IF (A(1).EQ.B(1))
        DO i = 2, 64
          C(i) = D(i-1)
        END DO
      ELSE
        DO i = 2, 64
          A(i) = C(i) + D(i-1)
        END DO
      END IF
      DO i = 1, 127
        F(i) = A(i) - 1
        B(i) = A(i) * A(i)
      END DO
      DO i = 65, 128
        E(i) = F(i-1)
      END DO
    END DO
          (a)
```

```
     REAL A(128), B(128), C(128)
          D(128), E(128), F(128)
     !HPF$ PROCESSORS PROC(0:7)
     !HPF$ DISTRIBUTE BLOCK ON TO
           PROC ::  A, B, C, D, E

1  DO t = 1, TIMES
2    | Synch; put{B}; |
3    DO i = 1, 127
4      A(i) = B(i+1)
5    END DO
6    | Synch; put{B}; |
7    | Synch; put{B}; |
8    DO i = 1, 126
9      D(i) = A(i) + 1
10     A(i) = B(i+1) + B(i+2)
11   END DO
12   IF (A(1).EQ.B(1))
13     | Synch; put{D}; |
14     DO i = 2, 64
15       C(i) = D(i-1)
16     END DO
17   ELSE
18     | Synch; put{D}; |
19     DO i = 2, 64
20       A(i) = C(i) + D(i-1)
21     END DO
22   END IF
23   DO i = 1, 127
24     F(i) = A(i) - 1
25     B(i) = A(i) * A(i)
26   END DO
27   | Synch; put{F}; |
28   DO i = 65, 128
29     E(i) = F(i-1)
30   END DO
31 END DO
          (b)
```

```
     REAL A(128), B(128), C(128)
          D(128), E(128), F(128)
     !HPF$ PROCESSORS PROC(0:7)
     !HPF$ DISTRIBUTE BLOCK ON TO
           PROC ::  A, B, C, D, E

    DO t = 1, TIMES
1:    | Synch; put{B}; |
      DO i = 1, 127
        A(i) = B(i+1)
      END DO
      DO i = 1, 126
        D(i) = A(i) + 1
        A(i) = B(i+1) + B(i+2)
      END DO
2:    | Synch; put{D}; |
      IF (A(1).EQ.B(1))
        DO i = 2, 64
          C(i) = D(i-1)
        END DO
      ELSE
        DO i = 2, 64
          A(i) = C(i) + D(i-1)
        END DO
      END IF
      DO i = 1, 127
        F(i) = A(i) - 1
        B(i) = A(i) * A(i)
      END DO
3:    | Synch; put{F}; |
      DO i = 65, 128
        E(i) = F(i-1)
      END DO
    END DO
          (c)
```

Figure 6: (a) A synthetic benchmark. (b) Message vectorized translation. (c) Global communication optimization.

assuming $1 \leq j \leq k$. Notice that j values can be different for each q. If we additionally stipulate that all j values should be the same for all q values, then we obtain

$$\forall p \forall q \exists j (((p,q) \in \texttt{Pending(i)}) \quad \Rightarrow \quad ((p,q) \in \texttt{SendSet}(\texttt{t}_j))) \quad (7)$$

We note that the condition (7) implies the algorithms offered by [6] and [8].

Claim: The synchronizations eliminated by (7) are a subset of the synchronizations that can be eliminated by (6) (see [10] for the proof).

Even if a `Pending(i)` set cannot be totally eliminated we can reduce its cardinality by eliminating as many `Synch` messages as possible from it. That is, after our analysis, for every `i`,

$$\texttt{SynchSet(i)} \quad = \quad \texttt{Pending(i)} -_c \{(p,q) \mid \exists j \text{ s. t.} \quad (8)$$
$$q \in \texttt{ConsumersFor}(\texttt{t}_j, p)\} \vee_c \texttt{SynchFix(i)} \quad (9)$$

As an example, let us consider the program shown in Figure 6(c). In this program, communication occurs at three points: 1, 2 and 3. A straightforward implementation inserts three (sets of) `Synch` operations, corresponding to 1, 2 and 3 as shown in that figure. Let us now focus on the communication in 1. Figure 2(a) shows the messages sent (`Put` operations) for this communication. Figure 2(b), on the other hand, shows the required synchronization messages for the repetitions of this communication. Finally, Figures 2(c) and 2(d) show the communication messages in 2 and 3 respectively. Notice that, by using the condition given in (6), the synchronization requirements for 1 can be eliminated; that is, the communications occurring in 2 and 3 together kill the synchronization requirements of the communication in 1. If we consider Figure 2(c) and Figure 2(d) separately for the condition given by (7), however, none of them individually can eliminate the synchronization for 1. By a similar argument, it can be concluded that the communications in 2 and 3 do not need any synchronization either, as their synchronization requirements are killed by communication in 1.

Dataflow Analysis: Our data flow equations are shown in Figure 4(d). Our analysis consists of iterative forward passes on the CFG. We first concentrate on the second equation and explain the functionality of $\mathcal{F}_i$. Here `PENDING_IN(i)` represents the synchronization requirements of all the communications traversed so far up to the beginning of `i`. `PENDING_OUT(i)` is defined analogously for the end of `i`. Assuming that P_k is the synchronization requirement (in terms of pairs of processors) for node `k` up to `i` in the analysis and `PENDING_IN(i)` $= \{P_1, ..., P_{i-1}, P_i, P_{i+1}, ..., P_m\}$, we can define $\mathcal{F}_i$ as

$$\mathcal{F}_i(\texttt{PENDING\_IN(i)}) = \{f_i(P_1), ..., f_i(P_{i-1}), P_i, f_i(P_{i+1}), ..., f_i(P_m)\}$$

where $f_i(P_k) = P_k -_c \texttt{SendSet(i)}$. That is, when a node `i` is visited, the synchronization requirements for all other communications are checked to see whether or not any synchronization can be eliminated by using the communication occurring at `i`. Prior to the analysis, P_i is set to `Pending(i)` for the *first* node. After a fixed state is reached, the `PENDING_OUT` set of the *last* node gives the synchronization requirements to be satisfied. The resulting `PENDING_OUT` set, which is in fact a set of sets, is then reduced to a single set and used to represent the synchronization requirements of this loop to the next upper level.

We now consider the first equation of Figure 4(d) and explain the $\bigsqcup$ operator appearing there. In the join nodes, the compiler takes a conservative approach by unioning the synchronization requirements for the same communication. Suppose that for each $j \in pred(i)$, `PENDING_OUT(j)` $= \{P_{j1}, P_{j2}, ..., P_{jm}\}$, where P_{jk}

is the synchronization requirement of communication k up to the end of `j`. Assuming then that the resulting `PENDING_IN(i)` $= \{P_1, P_2, ..., P_m\}$, each $P_l \in$ `PENDING_IN(i)` can be computed as $P_l = \vee_c P_{jl}$ where $\vee_c$ is performed over the j values. We note that this algorithm is more accurate and faster than those proposed in [8] and [6].

Claim: The dataflow procedure defined by equations given in Figure 4(d) can reach a steady state in at most after two iterations (see [10] for the proof).

Example The upper part of Table 1 shows the sets `SendSet` and `Pending` (in an open form rather than in terms of equalities and inequalities) for the program shown in Figure 6(c). Note that the sets `SendSet(1)` and `Pending(1)` are computed from the `SendSet` and `Pending` sets respectively given in Figure 4(a). The sets for 2 and 3 are computed similarly. Before the dataflow analysis starts, `PENDING_IN(1)` is initialized as follows:

```
PENDING_IN(1) = {{Pending(1)},{Pending(2)},{Pending(3)}}
            = {(0,1),(1,2),(2,3),(3,4),(4,5),(5,6),(6,7),
               (1,0),(2,1),(3,2),(4,3),(5,4),(6,5),(7,6)}
```

The lower part of Table 1 demonstrates application of our dataflow algorithm to this example. After the fixed state is reached, an examination of `PENDING_OUT(3)` reveals that the program can be executed without any synchronization.

6 Preliminary Results

The applications used in our study and their characteristics are listed in Table 2. We experimented with `BLOCK`, `B-CYC` (block-cyclic) and `CYCLIC` distributions on 8 and 32 processors to measure the static improvements. We refer to a version of program which is optimized by message vectorization alone as `base`. Table 3 presents the communication volume and the number of data messages (that is also the number of `Synch` messages) across all processors in the `base` programs.

For these applications, we first applied our global communication optimization algorithm. The percentage improvements are listed in Table 4. It should be noted that in block-cyclic distributions where most of the previous approaches fail, we have, on the average, a 29% reduction in communication volume and 40% reduction in number of messages across all processors.

We then applied our synchronization elimination scheme to the `base` version as well as the globally optimized version (`C-opt`) for each program. The results shown in Table 5 reveal that the algorithm is surprisingly successful in eliminating the redundant `Synch` messages. Except for two programs, the algorithm eliminates all synchronization messages from the `base` programs. When we look at the results for the programs that are optimized for communication prior to synchronization analysis, however, the picture somewhat changes. In `C-Opt` versions of `Jacobi` and `stfrg`, since the communication loop is reduced to one, no synchronization messages can be eliminated.

To sum up, our communication optimization algorithm eliminates 37.3% of the data messages and synchronization messages and reduces communication volume across all processors by 26%. Our synchronization elimination algorithm eliminates 96.8% of the synchronization messages in the message vectorized programs and 74% of the synchronization messages in the globally optimized programs.

186

Table 1: Dataflow sets and PENDING_OUT sets for the example in Figure 6(c).

communication in	SendSet	Pending
1	$\{(1,0),(2,1),(3,2),(4,3),(5,4),(6,5),(7,6)\}$	$\{(0,1),(1,2),(2,3),(3,4),(4,5),(5,6),(6,7)\}$
2	$\{(0,1),(1,2),(2,3)\}$	$\{(1,0),(2,1),(3,2)\}$
3	$\{(3,4),(4,5),(5,6),(6,7)\}$	$\{(4,3),(5,4),(6,5),(7,6)\}$

PENDING_OUT for	iteration 1	iteration 2
1	$\{\{(0,1),(1,2),(2,3),(3,4),(4,5),(5,6),(6,7)\},\{\emptyset\},\{\emptyset\}\}$	$\{\{\emptyset\},\{\emptyset\},\{\emptyset\}\}$
2	$\{\{(3,4),(4,5),(5,6),(6,7)\},\{\emptyset\},\{\emptyset\}\}$	$\{\{\emptyset\},\{\emptyset\},\{\emptyset\}\}$
3	$\{\{\emptyset\},\{\emptyset\},\{\emptyset\}\}$	$\{\{\emptyset\},\{\emptyset\},\{\emptyset\}\}$

7 Related Work

Previously several methods have been presented to optimize the communication on distributed-memory message-passing machines. Most of the efforts considered communication optimization at loop (or array assignment statement) level. Although each approach has its own unique features, the general idea is to apply an appropriate combination of message vectorization, message coalescing and message aggregation [9, 3]. Recently some researchers have proposed techniques for optimizing communication across multiple loop nests. The works in [5], [7], [12], [4], and [14] present similar frameworks to optimize send/recv communication globally and use variants of Regular Section Descriptors (RSD). Although this representation is convenient for simple array sections such as those found in block distributions, it is hard to embed alignment and general distribution information into it. Apart from this, working with section descriptors may result in overestimation of the communication sets. Instead, our approach is based on a linear algebra framework, and can represent all HPF-like alignment and distribution information accurately.

The approaches given in [6] and [8] examine the problem of eliminating redundant synchronization operations by piggy-backing them on data messages. Our approach is superior to both of these in eliminating synchronization as explained in the paper. Tseng [13] focuses on synchronization elimination problem. There is an important difference between our work and his. He eliminates synchronizations which are introduced by the insufficient communication analysis performed by the shared memory compilers. A compiler approach based on a distributed memory paradigm (like ours) does not insert those synchronizations in the first place. In our case, we start with an unoptimized program in which those types of artificial synchronizations are non-existent anyway. We rather focus on elimination of synchronizations that are caused by mandatory data communications. Such types of synchronization are not eliminated by Tseng's solution [13].

8 Summary

We presented dataflow algorithms to reduce number of data messages, communication volume and number of synchronization messages. Our experimental results revealed that our approach is quite successful in practice reducing on average 37.3% of data messages and 96.8% of synchronization messages in the message vectorized programs. We are working on compiling data-parallel programs with Get primitives, and elimination of synchronizations and possible deadlocks from programs compiled under hybrid approaches which employ both Put/Get and send/recv primitives.

References

[1] A. V. Aho, R. Sethi, and J. Ullman. *Compilers: Principles, techniques, and tools.* Addison-Wesley, 1986.

[2] A. Ancourt, F. Coelho, F. Irigoin, and R. Keryell. A linear algebra framework for static HPF code distribution. *Scientific Programming,* 6(1):3–28, Spring 1997.

[3] P. Banerjee, J. Chandy, M. Gupta, E. Hodges, J. Holm, A. Lain, D. Palermo, S. Ramaswamy, and E. Su. The PARADIGM compiler for distributed-memory multicomputers. *IEEE Computer,* 28(10):37–47, October 1995.

[4] S. Chakrabarti, M. Gupta, and J.-D. Choi. Global communication analysis and optimization. In *Proc. ACM SIGPLAN Conference on Programming Language Design and Implementation,* pages 68–78, Philadelphia, PA, May 1996.

[5] C. Gong, R. Gupta, and R. Melhem. Compilation techniques for optimizing communication on distributed-memory systems. In *Proc. International Conference on Parallel Processing,* Volume II, pages 39–46, St. Charles, IL, August 1993.

[6] M. Gupta, and E. Schonberg. Static analysis to reduce synchronization costs in data-parallel programs. In *Proc. ACM Conference on Principles of Programming Languages,* pages 322–332, St. Petersburg, FL, 1996.

[7] M. Gupta, E. Schonberg, and H. Srinivasan. A unified data-flow framework for optimizing communication. In *Languages and Compilers for Parallel Computing,* K. Pingali et al. (Eds.), Lecture Notes in Computer Science, Volume 892, pages 266–282, 1995.

[8] S. Hinrichs. Synchronization elimination in the deposit model. In *Proc. 1996 International Conference on Parallel Processing,* pages 87–94, St. Charles, IL, 1996.

[9] S. Hiranandani, K. Kennedy, and C. Tseng. Compiling Fortran D for MIMD distributed-memory machines. In *Communications of the ACM,* 35(8):66–80, August 1992.

[10] M. Kandemir, P. Banerjee, A. Choudhary, J. Ramanujam, and N. Shenoy. A combined communication and synchronization optimization algorithm for one-way communication. Technical Report, CPDC-TR-97-03, Northwestern University, October 1997.

[11] W. Kelly, V. Maslov, W. Pugh, E. Rosser, T. Shpeisman, and D. Wonnacott. The Omega Library interface guide. Technical Report CS-TR-3445, CS Dept., University of Maryland, College Park, March 1995.

[12] K. Kennedy, and A. Sethi. A constrained-based communication placement framework, Technical Report CRPC-TR95515-S, CRPC, Rice University, 1995.

[13] C.-W. Tseng. Compiler optimizations for eliminating barrier synchronization. In *Proc. the 5th ACM Symposium on Principles and Practice of Parallel programming (PPOPP'95),* Santa Barbara, CA, July 1995.

[14] X. Yuan, R. Gupta, and R. Melhem. Demand-driven data flow analysis for communication optimization. *Parallel Processing Letters,* 7(4):359–370, December 1997.

Table 2: Programs in our experiment set and their characteristics (+ = block, block-cyclic(4) or cyclic; * = not distributed).

PROGRAM	SUITE	LINES	ARRAYS	SIZE	DISTRIBUTION	DESCRIPTION
Jacobi	—	25	$2 \times 2D$	1024×1024	(+,*)	Jacobi iteration
2D hydro	Livermore 18	38	$9 \times 2D$	512×512	(+,*)	2D hydrodynamics
ADI	Livermore 8	30	$3 \times 3D, 3 \times 1D$	$256 \times 256 \times 2$	(+,*,*)	ADI fragment
vpenta	Spec92/NAS	147	$2 \times 3D, 7 \times 2D$	$128 \times 128 \times 3$	(*,+,*)	pentadiagonal inversion
SOR	—	25	$2 \times 2D$	256×256	(+,*)	successive over-relaxation
stfrg	Livermore 7	17	$1 \times 1D$	1024	(+)	state fragment equation
tomcatv	Spec95	190	$7 \times 2D, 2 \times 1D$	512×512	(+,*)	2D mesh generation
swim256	Spec95	428	$14 \times 2D$	512×512	(+,*)	shallow water eqn. solver

Table 3: Communication volume and number of data messages in the base (message vectorized) programs for a single iteration of the time-step loop.

PROGRAM	comm. volume (in thousand elements)						no. of data messages (Synch messages)					
	No. of Processors = 8			No. of Processors = 32			No. of Processors = 8			No. of Processors = 32		
	BLOCK	B-CYC	CYCLIC	BLOCK	B-CYC	CYCLIC	BLOCK	B-CYC	CYCLIC	BLOCK	B-CYC	CYCLIC
Jacobi	14.4	522.2	2088.9	63.3	522.2	2088.9	14	16	16	62	64	64
2D hydro	57.1	1036.3	4169.8	252.9	1036.3	4169.8	112	128	128	496	512	512
ADI	10.7	96.8	387.1	47.2	96.8	387.1	42	48	48	186	192	192
vpenta	343.2	343.2	343.2	1519.7	1519.7	1519.7	784	784	784	13888	13888	13888
SOR	21.3	193.5	774.2	94.5	193.5	774.2	84	96	96	372	384	384
stfrg	0.2	4.6	6.1	0.7	4.6	6.1	42	64	48	186	256	192
tomcatv	57.1	1040	8323.2	252.9	2072.6	8323.2	112	128	128	496	1024	1024
swim256	57.6	914.4	3649.1	229	914.4	3649.1	128	142	142	464	478	478

Table 4: Percentage (%) improvement over base (message vectorized) in communication volume and number of data messages.

PROGRAM	% improvement in comm. volume						% improvement in no. of data messages					
	No. of Processors = 8			No. of Processors = 32			No. of Processors = 8			No. of Processors = 32		
	BLOCK	B-CYC	CYCLIC	BLOCK	B-CYC	CYCLIC	BLOCK	B-CYC	CYCLIC	BLOCK	B-CYC	CYCLIC
Jacobi	0%	0%	0%	0%	0%	0%	0%	0%	0%	0%	0%	0%
2D hydro	50%	50%	50%	50%	50%	50%	50%	51%	50%	50%	50%	51%
ADI	0%	0%	0%	0%	0%	0%	0%	0%	0%	0%	0%	0%
vpenta	1%	1%	1%	1%	1%	1%	79%	78%	78%	78%	78%	78%
SOR	0%	0%	0%	0%	0%	0%	0%	0%	0%	0%	0%	0%
stfrg	71%	64%	0%	71%	64%	0%	83%	74%	0%	81%	73%	0%
tomcatv	74%	74%	75%	75%	75%	75%	74%	74%	75%	75%	75%	74%
swim256	37%	41%	43%	41%	41%	43%	44%	42%	42%	43%	41%	43%
average	29%	29%	21%	30%	29%	21%	41%	40%	31%	41%	40%	31%

Table 5: Percentage (%) improvement in number of synchronization messages obtained by our approach over the message vectorized (base) and globally optimized (C-Opt) versions.

PROGRAM	No. of processors = 8						No. of Processors = 32					
	BLOCK		B-CYC		CYCLIC		BLOCK		B-CYC		CYCLIC	
	Base	C-Opt	Base	C-Opt	Base	C-Opt	Base	C-Opt	Base	C-Opt	Base	C-Opt
Jacobi	100%	0%	100%	0%	100%	0%	100%	0%	100%	0%	100%	0%
2D hydro	100%	100%	100%	100%	100%	100%	100%	100%	100%	100%	100%	100%
ADI	100%	100%	100%	100%	100%	100%	100%	100%	100%	100%	100%	100%
vpenta	100%	100%	100%	100%	100%	100%	100%	100%	100%	100%	100%	100%
SOR	100%	100%	100%	100%	100%	100%	100%	100%	100%	100%	100%	100%
stfrg	83%	0%	75%	0%	83%	0%	83%	0%	75%	0%	83%	0%
tomcatv	100%	100%	100%	100%	100%	100%	100%	100%	100%	100%	100%	100%
swim256	94%	89%	93%	89%	93%	89%	93%	88%	93%	88%	93%	88%
average	97%	74%	96%	74%	97%	74%	97%	74%	96%	74%	98%	74%

A Memory-layout Oriented Run-time Technique for Locality Optimization on SMPs*

Yong Yan
HAL Computer Systems, Inc.
1315 Dell Avenue
Campbell, CA 95008

Xiaodong Zhang   Zhao Zhang
Computer Science Department
College of William & Mary
Williamsburg, VA 23187-8709

Abstract

Exploiting locality at run-time is a complementary approach to a compiler approach for those applications with dynamic memory access patterns. This paper proposes a memory-layout oriented approach to exploit cache locality for parallel loops at run-time on Symmetric Multi-Processor (SMP) systems. Guided by application-dependent hints and the targeted cache architecture, it reorganizes and partitions a parallel loop through shrinking and partitioning the memory-access space of the loop at run-time. In the generated task partitions, the data sharing among partitions is minimized and the data reuse in a partition is maximized. The execution of tasks in partitions is scheduled in an adaptive and locality-preserved way to achieve balanced execution, for minimizing the execution time of applications by trading off load balance and locality.

Based on simulation and measurement, we show our run-time approach can achieve comparable performance with the compiler optimizations for two applications, whose load balance and cache locality can be well optimized by the tiling and other program transformations. However, our experimental results also show that our approach is able to significantly improve the memory performance for the applications with dynamic memory access patterns. This type of programs are usually hard to be optimized by compilers.

1. Introduction

The increasing speed gap between the processor and the memory system makes techniques of latency hiding and reduction very important for both uniprocessor systems and multiprocessor systems. Recently, Symmetric Multi-Processor (SMP) systems have emerged as a major class of high-performance platforms, such as HP/Convex Exemplar S-class [1], Sun SPARCcenter 2000 [4], SGI Challenge [8], and DEC AlphaServer [18]. SMPs dominate the server market for commercial applications and are used as desktops for scientific computing. They are also important building blocks for large-scale systems. Because the access latency of a processor to the shared memory in a SMP is usually tens of times of that to a cache, improving the memory performance of applications on SMPs is crucial to the successful use of SMP systems.

The techniques for reducing the effect of long memory latency have been intensively investigated by researchers from application designers to hardware architects. The proposed techniques, so far, fall into two categories: *latency avoidance* and *latency tolerance* [9]. The latency tolerance techniques [7] are aimed at hiding the effect of memory-access latencies by overlapping computations with communications or by aggregating communications. Most of these techniques, while reducing the impact of contention-less access latencies, do so at the cost of increasing a program's bandwidth requirements [3]. The latency avoidance techniques, also called locality optimization techniques, are aimed at reducing low-level memory accesses using software and hardware approaches. In a SMP system, reducing the total number of accesses at low levels of the memory hierarchy is a substantial solution to reduce cache coherence overhead, memory contention, and network contention. Optimizing the locality of parallel computations is more demanding than tolerating their memory latency, which is the goal of this paper.

1.1. The problem

Locality optimization has been paid attention by many researchers for several years. The majority of the existing work focuses on compiler-based optimizations [6, 10,

*This research has been supported by the National Science Foundation under grants CCR-9400719, the Air Force Office of Scientific Research under grant AFOSR-95-1-0215 and by the Office of Naval Research under grant ONR-95-1-1239.

11, 12, 14, 15]. Because a compiler can exploit detailed information of applications using comprehensive analysis techniques, compiler-based locality optimization techniques have been shown to be very effective in improving the performance of those applications to which they can be applied (see e.g. [6, 10, 11, 12, 14]). Unfortunately, many of the applications in the real world possess dynamic data-access patterns which cannot be analyzed at compiler time.

```
double A[X], B[Y], C[M][M];
int Arow[M+1], Acol[X], Bcol[M+1], Brow[Y];

sparse-mm()
{    int i, j, k, r, start, end;
     register double d;
     for (i=0; i<M; i++)
        for (j=0; j<M; j++){
            d = 0;
            start = Bcol[j]; end = Bcol[j+1];
            for (k=Arow[i]; k<Arow[i+1]; k++)
                for (r=start; r<end; r++)
                    if (Acol[k] == Brow[r]){          ----> task t(i, j)
                        d += A[k]*B[r];
                        start = r+1;
                        break;
                    }
            C[i][j] = d;
        }
}
```

Figure 1. A Sparse Matrix Multiplication (SMM) which has a dynamic data-access pattern and an irregular computation pattern.

In Figure 1, we present a sparse matrix multiplication algorithm where two sparse source matrices have dense representations. In the innermost loop, the two elements to be multiplied, A[k] and B[r], are indirectly determined by the data in arrays Arow, Acol, Bcol and Brow. At compiler-time, because a compiler does not know what kind of data the program is going to process, it cannot determine how the program accesses its data. The data-access pattern of this program can only be determined at run-time when input data has been obtained. However, on a SMP system, the design of a run-time locality optimization technique is challenged by low overhead requirement and the complexities of minimizing data sharing among caches, maximizing data reuses in the cache, and trading off locality and the other performance factors.

1.2. Our solution and contributions

Because most data reuses of an application occur in loop structures [15] and the parallel loop is a major program structure in scientific applications [13, 14, 16, 22], we propose a run-time technique to improve the memory performance of parallel loops with dynamic data-access patterns.

In our run-time technique, the memory-access patterns of parallel tasks in a program are captured at run-time using a multi-dimensional memory-access space based on simple application-dependent hints. Based on the abstracted memory-access space and the cache architecture, the locality of a program is optimized through two types of space-based transformations: space shrinking and space partitioning. Then, tasks are adaptively scheduled to trade off locality and load imbalance, aiming at minimizing the parallel computing time. The proposed information abstraction and transformations can be efficiently implemented at acceptable overhead. Finally, with respect to three applications with different data-access patterns, the effectiveness of the proposed technique is evaluated in detail on an event-driven simulator and two commercial SMP systems,

1.3. Comparisons with related work

Exploiting cache locality at run-time has been paid attention by some previous work. References [13, 22] present dynamic loop scheduling algorithms that consider the affinity of loop iterations to processors. Although significant performance improvement can be acquired for some applications, the type of affinity exploited by this approach is not very popular and the relations between memory references of different iterations are not considered. The proposed technique in this paper not only takes into consideration the affinity of parallel tasks to processors, it also uses information on the underlying cache architecture and memory reference patterns of tasks to minimize cache misses and false sharing.

In the design of the COOL language [5], the locality exploitation issue is addressed by using language mechanisms and a run-time system. Both task affinity and data affinity are specified by users and then are implemented by the run-time system. A major limit with this approach is that the quality of locality optimizations totally depends on a programmer. For complicated applications, such as the example in Figure 1, it is difficult for a user to specify affinity. Our proposed technique uses a simple programming interface for a user or compiler to specify simple information about data, not about complicated affinity relations. Regarding the run-time locality optimization of sequential programs, reference [16] proposes a memory-layout oriented method. It reorganizes the computation of a loop based on some simple hints about the memory reference patterns of loops and cache architectural information. Compared with a uniprocessor system, a cache coherent shared memory system has more complicated factors that should be considered for locality exploitation, such as data sharing and load imbalance.

More recently, reference [2] uses a run-time system to color the virtual pages of a program based on both machine-specific parameters and a summary of the array access patterns generated by the high-level compiler. This approach still depends on the compiler-time static analysis on data-access patterns

1.4. Organization of this paper

The remaining of this paper contains four sections. The next section describes our run-time optimization technique in detail. Section 3 presents our performance evaluation method and performance results. In Section 4, we conclude our work.

2. A memory-layout oriented optimization technique

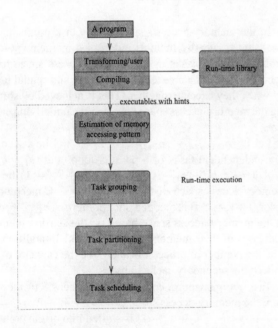

Figure 2. Framework of the run-time technique.

Our run-time technique has been implemented as a set of library functions. Figure 2 presents a framework for our run-time optimization. A given sequential application program is first transformed by a compiler or rewritten by a user to insert run-time functions. The generated executable file is encoded with application-dependent hints. At run-time, the encoded run-time functions are executed to fulfill the following functionalities: estimating the memory-access pattern of a program, reorganizing tasks into cache affinity groups where the tasks in a group are expected to heavily reuse their data in the cache, partitioning task-affinity groups onto multiple processors so that data sharing

among multiple processors are is minimized, and then adaptively scheduling the execution of tasks.

In order to minimize run-time overhead, a multi-dimensional hash table is internally built to manage a set of task-affinity groups. Meanwhile, a set of hash functions are given to map into an appropriate task-affinity group in the hash table. Locality oriented task reorganization and partitioning are integratedly finished in the task mapping. This section describes our information estimation method, the design of the hash table and hash functions along with task reorganization and partitioning, and our task scheduling algorithm.

2.1. Memory-access pattern estimation

In a loop structure, referenced data are usually structured as arrays. Let $A_1, A_2, \cdots, A_n$ be the n arrays accessed in the loop body of a nested data-independent loop. Each array is usually laid out in a contiguous memory region, independent of the other arrays. In rare cases, an array may be laid out across several uncontiguous memory pages. Although our run-time system may not handle these rare cases efficiently, the system works well for most memory layout cases in practice. Visualizing an array in an independent dimension, the memory regions of the n arrays can be integratedly abstracted as an n-dimensional memory-access space, expressed as $(A_1, A_2, \cdots, A_n)$ where arrays are arranged in any selected order by a user. This n-dimensional memory-access space actually contains all the memory addresses that are accessed by a loop. This abstract is similar to that used in [16].

In order for the run-time system to precisely capture this memory space information, the following three hints must be provided by the interface.

Hint 1. n, *the number of arrays accessed by tasks.*

Hint 2. The *size* in bytes of each array. Based on this, the run-time system maintains a Memory-access Space Size vector $(s_1, s_2, \cdots, s_n)$, denoted the MSS vector, where s_i is the size of i-th array $(i = 1, 2, \cdots, n)$.

Hint 3. The *starting memory address* of each array. From this, the underlying run-time system constructs a starting address vector $(b_1, b_2, \cdots, b_n)$, denoted the SA vector, where $b_i(i = 1, 2, \cdots, n)$ is the starting memory address of i-th array.

Here **Hint 1** is a static information. The array size may be static if the size is known at compiler-time or dynamic if the size is determined by run-time data and the hint should tell how to calculate the size at run-time. The starting addresses are dynamic because memory addresses can only be determined at run-time. **Hint 3** tells how to determine the starting addresses at run-time.

After determining the global memory-access space of a loop, we need to determine how each parallel iteration accesses the global memory-access space so that we can reorganize them to improve memory performance. Here, we abstract each instance of a loop body of a parallel loop as a parallel task. The access region of a task in an array is simply represented by the starting address of its access region. So, the following hint should be provided by interface functions.

Hint 4: *A memory-access vector of task t_j*:

$$(a_{j1}, a_{j2}, \cdots, a_{jn})$$

where a_{ji} is the starting address of the referenced region on i-th array by t_j ($i = 1, 2, \cdots, n$). In some loop structures, a parallel iteration may not contiguously access an array so that the access region may not be precisely abstracted by the starting address. In this case, the loop iteration should be further split into smaller iterations so that each iteration accesses a contiguous region on each array. In addition, the following hint also should be provided to assist task partitioning.

Hint 5: *The number of processors, p.*

(a) hints on memory layouts of two accessed arrays.

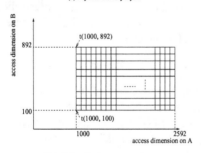

(b) Physical memory layout

(c) An 2-dimensional memory-accessing space.

Figure 3. Memory-access space representation.

Based on the above hints, the memory-access space of the loop is abstracted as a n-dimensional memory-access space:

$$(b_1 : b_1 + s_1 - 1, b_2 : b_2 + s_2 - 1, \cdots, b_n : b_n + s_n - 1).$$

Task t_j is abstracted as point $(a_{j1}, a_{j2}, \cdots, a_{jn})$ in the memory-access space based on the estimation on its memory-access pattern. Figure 3 presents an example of the abstract representation of the memory accesses based on the physical memory layout of arrays A and B in the SMM given in Figure 1. Figure 3(a) gives the hints on the memory-access space. Figure 3(b) illustrates the memory layout of two arrays where B and A are laid out at starting address 100 and 1000 respectively. Each array element has size of 8 bytes. The memory space of arrays A and B is the whole memory space accessed by tasks. Then, the memory-access space is represented as a 2-dimensional space as shown in Figure 3(c) where each point gives a pair of possible starting memory-access addresses on A and B respectively by a task. For example, t(1000, 100) means task t will access array A at starting memory address 1000, and access array B at starting physical address 100.

2.2. Task reorganization

In the memory-access space, nearby task points access the same or nearby memory addresses in memory. So, grouping nearby tasks in the memory access space has a good change to enhance temporal locality and spatial locality when they execute together. This is achieved by shrinking the memory-access space based on the underlying cache size.

Let $\{t_i(a_{i1}, a_{i2}, \cdots, a_{in}) | i = 1, 2, \cdots, m\}$ be a set of m data-independent tasks of a parallel loop, and $(b_1 : b_1 + s_1 - 1, b_2 : b_2 + s_2 - 1, \cdots, b_n : b_n + s_n - 1)$ be the memory-access space of the parallel loop. Conceptually, task t_i ($i=1, \cdots, n$) is mapped onto point $(a_{i1}, a_{i2}, \cdots, a_{in})$ in the memory-access space based on the starting memory addresses of their memory-access regions. In addition, let p be the number of processors and C be the capacity of the underlying secondary cache in bytes.

Task reorganization consists of two steps. In the first step, the memory-access space $(b_1 : b_1 + s_1 - 1, b_2 : b_2 + s_2 - 1, \cdots, b_n : b_n + s_n - 1)$ is shifted into origin point $(0, \cdots, 0)$ by subtracting $(b_1, b_2, \cdots, b_n)$ from the coordinates of all task points. In the second step, we use *equal-shrinking* method to shrink each dimension of the shifted memory by fC/n. The n-dimensional space resulted from shrinking is called a n-dimensional bin space. Here, f is a weight constant in $(0, 1]$. In the bin space, each point is associated with a task bin to hold all the tasks that are mapped into the task bin.

In Figure 4, the shrinking procedure of the memory-access space is exemplified by the 2-dimensional memory-access space given in Figure 3. Before shrinking, the original memory-access space is shifted to origin point $(0,0)$ (see Figure 4(b)). The shifting function is shown in Figure 4(b). Then each dimension of the shifted memory-access space is shrunk by C/2 into a new 2-dimensional bin space in Figure 4(c). The tasks in the shadow square in Figure 4(b)

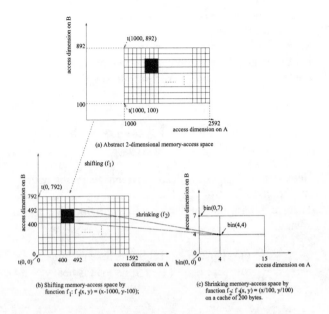

(a) Abstract 2-dimensional memory-access space

shifting (f_1)

(b) Shifting memory-access space by
function f_1: $f_1(x, y) = (x-1000, y-100)$;

shrinking (f_2)

(c) Shrinking memory-access space by
function f_2: $f_2(x, y) = (x/100, y/100)$
on a cache of 200 bytes.

Figure 4. Equally shrinking a memory-access space.

would not access more space than the cache size, and are mapped onto one point in the bin space so that they can be grouped together to execute.

2.3. Task partitioning

After shrinking an n-dimensional memory-access space, tasks have been grouped based on locality affinity information in an n-dimensional bin space. Task partitioning is aimed at partitioning the n-dimensional bin space into p partitions (p is the number of processors and each partition is an n-dimensional polyhedron) so that

1. *the data sharing degree among partitions is minimized*, which is measured by the volume of boundary spaces among partitions.

2. *p partitions are balanced*, where the balance refers to partitions with the same volume.

The major function of partitioning an n-dimensional bin space $B^n(0{:}L_1, 0{:}L_2, \cdots, 0{:}L_n)$ is to find a partitioning vector $\vec{k}(k_1, k_2, \cdots, k_n)$ so that the above conditions are satisfied. Because finding an optimal partition vector is a NP-complete problem, we propose a heuristic algorithm based on the following partitioning rules. Detailed proofs can be found in [21].

Theorem 1 Ordering Rule
For a given partitioning vector $\vec{k}(k_1, k_2, \cdots, k_n)$ not in decreasing order, the partitioning vector resulting by sorting

$\vec{k}$ *in decreasing order is at least as good as $\vec{k}$ in terms of the sharing degree.*

Theorem 2 Increment Rule 1
For an n-dimensional bin space B^n, and partitioning vectors $\vec{k}(k_1, k_2, \cdots, k_i, k_{i+1} \times q, 1, \cdots, 1)$ and $\vec{k}'(k_1, k_2, \cdots, k_i \times q, k_{i+1}, 1, 1, \cdots, 1)$, where $q > 1$, $\vec{k}$ is better than $\vec{k}'$ in terms of the sharing degree if and only if

$$k_i \times L_{i+1} > k_{i+1} \times L_i.$$

Corollary 1 Increment Rule 2
For an n-dimensional bin space B^n, and partitioning vectors $\vec{k}(k_1, k_2, \cdots, k_i, k_{i+1}, 1, \cdots, 1)$ and $\vec{k}'(k_1, k_2, \cdots, k_i \times k_{i+1}, 1, 1, \cdots, 1)$, where $k_{i+1} > 1$, $\vec{k}$ is better than $\vec{k}'$ in terms of the sharing degree if and only if

$$k_i \times L_{i+1} > \times L_i.$$

Based on the above three rules, we design an efficient heuristic algorithm as follows.

1. Factor p, the number of processors, to generate all the prime factors of p in decreasing order. Assume that there are q prime factors: $r_1 \geq r_2 \geq \cdots \geq r_q$. Initially, the n-dimensional partitioning vector $\vec{k}$, stored in $k[1:n]$, is $(1, 1, \cdots, 1)$ for the bin space $B^n(0 : L_1, 0 : L_2, \cdots, 0 : L_n)$.

2. Let $last$ index the position in $k[1:n]$ where $k[i] > 1$ for $i < last$ and $k[i] = 1$ for $i \geq last$. Initially, $last = 1$. For each prime factor r_j where j increases from 1 to q, do the following:

   (a) When ($last \leq n$), use the increment rule 2 to determine whether r_j should be put in $k[last]$. Based on the ordering rule, the best place to put r_j must be in $k[1 : last]$. So, we use increment rules to find a better place in $k[1 : last]$. If so, $last$ is increased by 1 and go back; otherwise, use the increment rule 1 to put r_j together with $k[last-1]$ or $k[last-2]$, then reorder $k[1 : last-1]$ in decreasing order and go back.

   (b) Otherwise: use the increment rule 1 to put r_j together with $k[last-1]$ or $k[last-2]$, then reorder $k[1 : last - 1]$ in decreasing order and go back.

The above algorithm has a computational complexity $O(n+\sqrt{p})$. After the determination of a partitioning vector, the bin space is partitioned into multiple independent spaces that are further reconstructed in a $(n + 1)$-dimensional space. This procedure is shown in Figure 5 where the bin space produced in Figure 4 is partitioned by vector (2, 2). The partitions in Figure 5(a) are first transformed into four independent spaces in Figure 5(b), which are further transformed into a 3-dimensional space shown in in Figure 5(c).

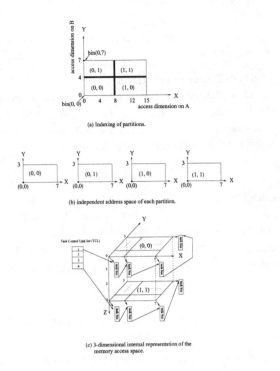

(a) Indexing of partitions.

(b) independent address space of each partition.

(c) 3-dimensional internal representation of the memory access space.

Figure 5. Partitioning: the bin space is evenly divided into 4 partitions from X and Y dimensions.

The 3-dimensional space in Figure 5(c) is implemented as a 3-dimensional hash table where task bins in each partition are chained together to be pointed by a record in a Task Control Linked (TCL) list. The hashing of tasks into the hash table is finished by the space transformation functions (details are presented in [21]).

2.4. Task scheduling

In order to minimize the parallel computing time of partitioned tasks, we present a Locality-preserved Adaptive Scheduling (LAS) algorithm by extending our linearly adaptive algorithm proposed in [22].

Initially, the i-th task group chain in the TCL list is considered to be the local task chain of processor i, for $i = 1, 2, \cdots, p$ (p is the total number of processors). Each task chain has a head and a tail. The initial allocation maintains the minimized data sharing achieved in the task reorganization step among processors. The number of current tasks in the local chain of processor i is recorded by a TCL counter, denoted C_i, which is used in the LAS algorithm to estimate load imbalance. In addition, each processor has a chunking control variable of initial value of p, denoted K_i for processor i, to determine how many tasks to be executed at each scheduling step.

The scheduling algorithm still works in two phases: the local scheduling phase and the global scheduling phase. All the processors start at the local scheduling phase. In the local scheduling phase, processor i calculates its load status relative to the other processors as follows:

$$
\begin{array}{lll}
\text{heavy} & \text{if } C_i > \sum_{j=1}^{p} C_j/p + \alpha & (1) \\
\text{light} & \text{if } C_i < \sum_{j=1}^{p} C_j/p - \alpha & (2) \\
\text{normal} & \text{otherwise} & (3)
\end{array}
$$

Here, α is $\lceil \sum_{j=1}^{p} C_j/p)/(2p) \rceil$, which decreases with the execution to control the load distribution more closely. Then, it adjusts its chunking control variable, K_i, as following:

$$
K_i = \begin{cases}
\max\{p/2, K_i - 1\} & \text{if its load is light} \\
\min\{2p, K_i + 1\} & \text{if its load is heavy} \\
K_i & \text{otherwise}
\end{cases} \quad (4)
$$

Finally, processor i gets $1/K_i$ of remaining tasks from the head of its local task chain to execute. The varying range $[p/2, 2p]$ for the chunking control variables has been shown to be safe for balancing load [13, 22].

When processor i finishes its local tasks, it sets its chunking control variable, K_i, to p, then enters the global scheduling phase where it will get $1/K_i$ of remaining tasks on the most heavily load processor from the tail of the task chain.

3. Performance evaluation

3.1. Evaluation method

We implemented our locality optimization technique as three simple run-time library functions. Performance evaluation is based on simulation and measurement. Simulation was conducted on an event-driven simulator for bus-based shared memory systems, which was built on the MINT, a MIPS interpreter [19]. Measurements were conducted on two commercial systems: HP/Convex S-class which is a crossbar-based cache coherent SMP system with 16 processors, and Sun Ultr-SPRACstation-20 which is a bus-based cache coherent SMP system with 4 processors.

The selected applications are: (1) dense matrix multiplication, denoted as DMM, that has a regular computation pattern and a static data-access pattern, adjoint convolution, denoted as AC, that has a irregular computation pattern and a static data-access pattern, and sparse matrix multiplication with 30% non-zero elements, denoted as SMM, that has a irregular computation pattern and a dynamic data-access pattern. Their optimized versions by exploiting locality using our runtime library are denoted as DMM_LO, AC_LO, and SMM_LO respectively. For comparison, the three benchmarks are parallelized respectively using the

194

best existing techniques as follows. (1) For the DMM application, we parallelized the blocked matrix multiplication algorithm given by Wolf and Lam [20]. This program is denoted as DMM_WL. (2) For the AC application, we first used loop split, loop reverse, and loop fusion transformations to get a balanced outer loop, which is then equally partitioned across processors. This program is denoted as AC_BF. (3) For the SMM application, we used the linearly adaptive scheduling technique proposed in [22] to schedule the executions of parallel iterations in SMM. This program is denoted as SMM_A. The detailed description about these programs are given in [21].

3.2. Performance results

Processors	Miss rate					
	DMM application		AC application		SMM application	
	DMM_WL	DMM_LO	AC_BF	AC_LO	SMM_A	SMM_LO
2	0.006	0.008	0.051	0.043	0.025	0.011
4	0.006	0.008	0.051	0.044	0.025	0.011
8	0.005	0.007	0.052	0.044	0.025	0.012

Table 1. Cache miss-rate based comparison where experiments were conducted under shrinking factor $f = 1$.

Table 1 presents the miss rates of the six benchmark programs on 2 processors to 8 processors. Regarding regular application DMM, the locality-optimized version (DMM_LO) using the run-time technique is 9% to 14% higher than the well-tuned version (DMM_WL) in the number of cache misses (Table 1). AC_LO, a locality optimized program of AC using the run-time technique, is shown to achieve slightly better cache performance than AC_BF, a well-tuned program. Regarding the application SMM, the run-time locality technique is shown to be very effective in reducing cache misses. The cache miss rate was reduced for more than 50% as shown in Table 1.

program	size	On HP S-class				size	On SUN SPARC	
		processors					processors	
		2	4	8	16		2	4
DMM_WL	1024	11	5.7	3.0	1.8	1024	108	57
DMM_LO	1024	13	6.6	3.9	2.2	1024	115	63
AC_BF	400	180	102	65	39	256	763	390
AC_LO	400	144	91	60	38	256	698	349
SMM_A	1024	4.1	2.5	1.4	0.8	1024	37	20
SMM_LO	1024	2.2	1.3	0.5	0.5	1024	23	12

Table 2. Measured time (in seconds) based comparison. ($f = 1$).

Table 2 presents execution comparisons on two SMP systems. Measured load balance is presented in Table 3. Regarding the DMM program, DMM_WL consistently performed a little bit better than DMM_LO, not larger than 20% on both SMP systems. The better load balance in

program	size	On HP S-class				size	On SUN SPARC	
		processors					processors	
		2	4	8	16		2	4
DMM_WL	1024	0.0026	0.0052	0.0095	0.010	1024	0.01	0.02
DMM_LO	1024	0.024	0.021	0.038	0.040	1024	0.06	0.03
AC_BF	400	0.0007	0.001	0.0018	0.0031	256	0.002	0.003
AC_LO	400	0.003	0.004	0.006	0.010	256	0.003	0.005
SMM_A	1024	0.02	0.03	0.04	0.06	1024	0.012	0.022
SMM_LO	1024	0.03	0.05	0.06	0.06	1024	0.035	0.038

Table 3. Measured load imbalance in terms of the rate of the time deviation to the mean time. ($f = 1$).

DMM_WL is a reason for this. This shows that the run-time optimization can also achieve a comparable performance with the compiler-based optimization for regular applications. For program AC, AC_LO performed better than AC_BF on two processors on both SMP systems. When more processors were applied, the execution times were close. But, AC_BF always balanced load better due to its perfect initial partition. But, the load imbalance occurred in the AL_LO was no larger than 1%. This shows that the run-time optimization has chance to outperform compiler-based optimization for applications with irregular computation pattern. For SMM, SMM_LO had achieved a much better performance improvement over the SMM_A. About 50% reduction in execution time was observed for all test cases on both SMP systems. This confirms the effectiveness of the run-time technique in improving the performance of applications with dynamic memory-access patterns

Table 4 presents run-time overhead measurements. On both SMP systems, the run-time overhead is not larger than 10% of the execution time in all cases except one. This shows the effectiveness of using hash table and hash functions to integrate locality optimizations at run-time.

program	size	On HP S-class				size	On SUN SPARC	
		processors					processors	
		2	4	8	16		2	4
DMM_LO	1024	6	8	9	10	1024	9	10
AC_LO	400	0.3	0.25	0.3	0.3	256	0.1	0.2
SMM_LO	1024	5	8	16	2	1024	9	10

Table 4. Run-time overhead in percentage of total time. ($f = 1$).

In Table 5, we show the effects of selecting different shrinking factors for f. The change in f does affect the execution times of benchmark programs. But, this effect is not very big. So, we recommend to use $f=1$ for programming ease.

4. Conclusion

In this paper, we have presented a run-time locality optimization technique and have shown its effectiveness for

Application	Machine	value of f			
		1	0.5	0.25	0.125
DMM_LO (N=1024)	S-class	6.6	6.1	5.8	5.8
DMM_LO (N=1024)	HyperSPARC	63	64	58	59
AC_LO (N=400)	S-class	91	90	91	90
AC_LO (N=256)	HyperSPARC	349	347	352	373
SMM_LO (N=1024)	S-class	1.3	1.3	1.4	1.5
SMM_LO (N=1024)	HyperSPARC	12	13	14.6	14.2

Table 5. The effects of different values of f on execution time (in seconds) using 4 processors.

optimizing the memory performance of applications with dynamic memory-access pattern. For those applications whose memory performance can be optimized well by current compiler-based optimizations, the presented run-time technique can achieve comparable performance. Using the hash table and hash functions has been shown to be an effective way to reduce run-time overhead.

Our work does have some limits that need to be studied further. (1) The access-pattern of a task on an array is estimated only by a starting address. When a task accesses several non-contiguous regions on an array, multiple starting addresses should be used or the task should be split into several small tasks. Further investigation is needed for this case. (2) In space shrinking, we only use an equal-shrinking approach. When tasks accesses different arrays in different ways, a non-equal shrinking approach should be used. But, the difficulty is how to estimate array-access patterns at low cost. (3) The program structure should be extended to consider data-dependence. By combining our run-time locality optimization technique with the run-time parallelization technique given in [17], more general program structures can be handled.

ACKNOWLEDGEMENT: We thank Dr. C. C. Douglas for sending us their thread library. We are grateful to Dr. Greg Astfalk for his constructive suggestions and help in using the HP/Convex S-class. Finally, we appreciate Neal Wagner's careful reading of the manuscript and constructive comments.

References

[1] G. Astfalk and T. Brewer. An overview of the HP/convex exemplar hardware. Technical report, Hewlett-Packard Inc., System Technology Division, 1997.

[2] E. Bugnion, J. M. Anderson, T. C. Mowry, M. Rosenblum, and M. S. Lam. Compiler-directed page coloring for multiprocessors. *Proceedings of ASPLOS'96*, pages 244–255, Oct. 1996.

[3] D. Burger, J. R. Goodman, and A. Kagi. Limited bandwidth to affect processor design. *IEEE Micro*, pages 55–62, November/December 1997.

[4] M. Cekleov and et al. SPARCcenter 2000: Multiprocessing for the 90's. *IEEE COMPCON*, pages 345–353, February 1993.

[5] R. Chandra, A. Gupta, and J. L. Hennessy. Data locality and load balancing in cool. *Proceedings of PPOPP'93*, pages 249–259, May 1993.

[6] S. Coleman and K. S. Mckinley. Tile size selection using cache organization and data layout. *Proceedings of PLDI'95*, pages 279–289, June 1995.

[7] D. Culler, J. P. Singh, and A. Gupta. *Parallel Computer Architecture: A Hardware/Software Approach*. Morgan Kaufmann Publishers, Inc., U. S. A., 1997.

[8] M. Galles and E. Williams. Performance optimizations, implementation, and verification of the sgi challenge multiprocessor. *Proceedings of the Twenty-Seventh Hawaii International Conference on System Sciences*, pages 134–143, Jan. 1994.

[9] J. L. Hennessy and D. A. Patterson. *Computer Architecture: A Quantitative Approach*. Morgan Kaufmann Publishers, Inc., U. S. A., 1996.

[10] T. E. Jeremiassen and S. J. Eggers. Reducing false sharing on shared memory multiprocessors through compile time data transformations. *Proceedings of PPOPP'95*, pages 179–188, July 1995.

[11] I. Kodukula, N. Ahmed, and K. Pingali. Data-centric multilevel blocking. *Proceedings of PLDI'97*, pages 346–357, May 1997.

[12] M. S. Lam, E. E. Rothberg, and M. E. Wolf. The cache performance and optimizations of blocked algorithms. *Proceedings of ASPLOS'91*, pages 63–74, April 1991.

[13] E. P. Markatos and T. J. Leblanc. Using processor affinity in loop scheduling scheme on shared-memory multiprocessors. *IEEE Trans. Para. & Dist. Syst.*, 5(4):379–400, April 1994.

[14] K. S. McKinley, S. Carr, and C. W. Tseng. Improving data locality with loop transformations. *ACM Trans. Prog. Lang. Syst.*, 18(4):424–453, July 1996.

[15] K. S. Mckinley and O. Teman. A quantitative analysis of loop nest locality. *The Proceedings of ASPLOS'96*, pages 94–104, Oct. 1996.

[16] J. E. Philbin, O. J. Anshus, C. C. Douglas, and K. Li. Thread scheduling for cache locality. *Proceedings of ASPLOS'96*, pages 60–71, Oct. 1996.

[17] J. H. Saltz and R. Mirchandaney. Run-time parallelization and scheduling of loops. *IEEE Trans. Comput.*, pages 603–612, May 1991.

[18] M. B. Steinman, G. J. Harris, A. Kocev, V. C. Lamere, and R. D. Pannell. The alphaserver 4100 cached processor module architecture and design. *Digital Technical Journal*, 8(4):21–37, 1996.

[19] J. E. Veenstra and R. J. Fowler. Mint: A front end for efficient simulation of shared-memory multiprocessors. *Proceedings of MASCOTS'94*, pages 201–207, Jan. 1994.

[20] M. E. Wolf and M. Lam. A data locality optimizing algorithm. *Proceedings of PLDI'91*, pages 30–44, June 1991.

[21] Y. Yan. *Exploiting Cache Locality at Run-time*. PhD thesis, Computer Science Department, College of William & Mary, May 1998.

[22] Y. Yan, C. M. Jin, and X. Zhang. Adaptively scheduling parallel loops in distributed shared-memory systems. *IEEE Trans. Para. & Dist. Syst.*, 8(1):70–81, Jan. 1997.

Session 3C
Distributed Shared Memory

Chair: Dhabaleswar Panda
Ohio State University

Binding Time in Distributed Shared Memory Architectures

Jinseok Kong
Dept. of Computer Science and Engineering
University of Minnesota
Minneapolis, MN 55455-0159, USA
jkong@cs.umn.edu

Gyungho Lee
Division of Engineering
University of Texas
San Antonio, TX 78249-0665, USA
glee@voyager1.eng.utsa.edu

Abstract

This paper revisits three distributed shared memory (DSM) architectures to clarify them with their binding times for new addresses at the local memory: page fault time, node miss time, and cache miss time. The DSM architectures which have different binding times arrange data in different ways with different overheads at an event of reference. Since a large number of cache misses can occur in a large (relative to the cache size) working set, binding at the page fault time alone cannot efficiently utilize locality of reference at the local memory. In a small working set, most of the addresses bound to the local memory at a node miss time are not effective due to the low cache miss rate. This paper shows that binding at the cache miss time can improve system performance.

1 Introduction

When a processor makes a reference to memory, there are two necessary conditions: *data integrity* and *data consistency*. The referenced data must exist in the memory and should be supplied to the processor to satisfy the data integrity condition. Also, the supplied data should be valid for data consistency. The next consideration is to speed up the execution of a program. Since the processor can issue a large number of memory references, reduction of accumulated memory reference time is more important than that of a specific reference time. If there are several locations of memory, memory reference time will vary with the relative distances of memory locations from the processor. Also, patterns of references are changed dynamically over the time. Therefore, *how to arrange data in the memory locations at a moment of time* is a critical factor that affects system performance.

Every datum has a name, called *address*. When an address is found missing at a memory location, we have two choices; binding the address to the location or not. *Bind-*

ing time for the location is the time when the new address is assigned to the location. At that time, an existing address may be unbound due to limited space. For data integrity, the unbound address may need to be bound to some other memory location. This may in turn induce another displacement, leading to a new arrangement of data in the memory locations. Generally, a valid datum is saved in the location at the binding time. The datum at the location could be updated or invalidated before its address is unbound from the location. Bindings can create extra overhead. For each binding, at least two memory accesses and one use of datapath are incurred. Although the extra overhead can be hidden from the critical path of a data access, it can still make other data accesses longer due to possible contentions

Most memory architectures bind a new address to the processor cache at the time of a cache miss. Utilizing memory local to a node is as important as utilizing the processor cache especially when the working set of a program does not fit in the processor cache. A message-passing architecture [9, 20] supports the scheduled binding times by using special instructions. A distributed shared memory (DSM) architecture uses the event of a memory reference as the binding time for the local memory [1, 3, 13, 17].

The references at the local memory may not be as highly localized as at the processor cache. Also, unlike in conventional caches, the replaced data from a local memory can cause side effects on locality of data in a remote memory. The question we address in this paper is what is the proper binding time for the local memory when a page fault, a node miss, or a cache miss occurs. Using the variation in binding time, we could completely characterize the DSM architectures, and understand their performance.

Section 2 describes the events of references which could trigger the bindings. Section 3 qualitatively analyzes the relative performance of three DSM architectures which have different binding times. For the quantitative evaluation, some possible DSM machines are designed in Section 4. In Section 5, the machines are simulated using real benchmark programs. Section 6 offers a conclusion.

2   Reference Events

When a memory reference is issued by the processor in a node, the event can be characterized with three aspects; locations of data, states of data, and the reference type (read or write). Depending on the relative location of a valid data referenced by the processor, the event is called a cache hit, a node hit, a node miss, or a page fault. The data related to the event can be shared by several nodes. The data can have ownership among the shared copies. The data could be invalid. Although there are a great number of other possible states, the states can also be restricted to a small number in a machine for practical reasons. The number of occurrences of a specific event can also be considered as a type of event [4, 6, 14].

Any fresh address can be bound to any locations at any events of reference. However, to exploit program locality, most DSM architectures attempt to bind recently referenced address to the memory location close to the processor. Generally, no bindings are made on a cache hit, and a cache miss causes the referenced data to be saved to the processor cache. The missing data is retrieved to the node at a node miss. Also, a page fault initiates the load of a new page into main memory.

Although one can devise a memory architecture which allows the bindings for the local memory on different reference events [5], this paper focuses on the memory architecture which commits the bindings on the same typical event. Cache-Coherent Nonuniform Memory Architecture (CC-NUMA), such as the Stanford DASH [13], maps a data address to the local memory on a page fault. Cache Only Memory Architecture (COMA) [2, 7, 8, 14, 16, 23], such as the Kendall Square Research KSR-1 [3], has the bindings to the local memory on a node miss. Another DSM architecture, called Dynamic Memory Architecture (DYMA) [10], permits the bindings on a cache miss.

3   Reference Patterns

To see how the different binding times can help to predict reference patterns to reduce the memory access time with different overheads, consider the simple configuration shown in Figure 1. In the figure, the cache and the local memory (LM) have two and four frames respectively, and they are direct-mapped. A, a and a' in Figure 1 respectively represent an owner, a non-owner, and an invalid data line with the same address A. Initially, A, B, C and D are in Node$_i$'s LM, and a and d are in Node$_i$'s cache. E, F and G are in Node$_j$'s LM, and e and f are in Node$_j$'s cache. Here, we assume a directory-based, write-invalidation scheme in following discussions.

When processor P_i in Node$_i$ reads line E at time t_1, it will trigger a node miss, and e is brought to Node$_i$.

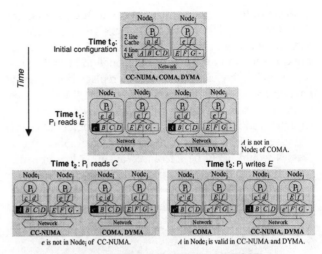

Figure 1. Arranging Data in DSM.

To utilize locality in the processor cache, every architecture, including CC-NUMA, COMA and DYMA, binds e to Node$_i$'s cache. The difference among these architectures happens in the LM. Since the replaced a from Node$_i$'s cache is neither updated nor new to the LM, no more overheads are required both in CC-NUMA and DYMA. Since e is new to Node$_i$'s LM, COMA binds e to the LM. For this, an access to the LM is needed. Also, if A is the last copy in the system, it should be relocated to a remote memory. In this case, two more LM accesses, some use of network bandwidth, and directory processing are needed. Furthermore, if A is relocated at Node$_j$, the copies of E are unbound from Node$_j$ due to the inclusion property enforced between the cache and the LM. This can reduce P_j's cache and LM hit rates. The same data arrangement of CC-NUMA and DYMA can cause higher node hit rate than that of COMA since A is not in Node$_i$ of COMA.

If processor P_i reads address C at time t_2 (a cache miss), e will be displaced from Node$_i$ in CC-NUMA even though address E is more recently referenced than address A. Since e already exists in the LM of COMA, no write-back occurs. DYMA binds e to the LM at this time since e is fresh to the LM. The configuration of DYMA becomes that of COMA. Unlike COMA, DYMA needs an extra access to Node$_i$'s cache to have a copy of e, but can relocate A to Node$_j$'s LM without removing e from Node$_j$'s cache. Under the new data arrangement, higher LM hit rate may compensate COMA and DYMA for the extra overhead at time t_1 and t_2.

Before e is removed from Node$_i$'s cache, if processor P_j writes to address E at time t'_2 (a cache write hit on shared data), every shared copy whose address is E should be invalidated. Although no bindings are needed at this event, the states of data are changed. In COMA, the access to Node$_i$'s LM tag to invalidate e is extra. Nothing can compensate for the extra overhead incurred at time t_1 and t'_2.

In the following subsections, we will discuss each architecture in depth with emphasis on the general reference patterns which give them strengths or weaknesses. If the working set of a program is small enough to fit in the processor cache, few cache lines will be replaced, and hardly referenced again after being unbound from the processor cache. However, if the processor cache does not match well with the working set of a program, a large number of cache addresses will be unbound, and most of the unbound addresses would likely be referenced again. Also, in some patterns, some shared addresses are extensively referenced by several processors. In some other patterns, most of cache lines are not modified when they are unbound.

3.1 CC-NUMA

When a new page is brought into main memory from a disk due to a page fault, all of the lines in the page are bound to some local memories in CC-NUMA, and the memory locations for the lines are not changed until the page is replaced from main memory at another page fault time. Thus, the address set of the lines bound to the processor cache is a subset of the address set of the lines in main memory. The inclusion property enables CC-NUMA to have no replacements from the local memory at different events of reference. The reference patterns would change dynamically during the sojourn time of the page. Therefore, the data missing in the processor cache is usually in the remote memory. A replaced copy from the processor cache at a cache miss is normally written back to a remote memory. Even though the write-back increases the number of valid copies in the remote memory, it seems to be hard to reduce the number of node misses in the remote node. If the working set of an application is large, a large number of data accesses and replacements have to go to a remote memory through the underlying network. Thus, CC-NUMA may suffer from seriously long memory reference time if the network service time is long and the network bandwidth is not wide enough to support the overheads. If the working set is small, CC-NUMA may perform well since less network traffic is generated and there are no extra bindings to the local memory for the temporarily used data at the processor cache.

3.2 COMA

COMA binds a new address to the local memory, called attraction memory (AM), at a node miss. The newly bound address will be unbound from the AM at another node miss. Thus, COMA has the inclusion property between the processor cache and the AM. The overhead at a cache miss (and a node hit) can be reduced since no replaced copies consume network bandwidth. The new data arrangement

can also reduce the node miss rate compared to CC-NUMA since the replaced lines are kept in the AM. However, the AM binding at a node miss can create extra overhead which does not occur in CC-NUMA. At this time, CC-NUMA requires at most two accesses to the local memory. COMA requires at least two accesses to the AM. A scheme to check whether the missing line is in the memory location or not is required as well. If a replaced AM line is the last valid copy in the system, two more accesses to the AM are needed. The probability of selecting the last valid copy is high under tight *memory pressure* $(= \frac{\text{data size}}{\text{memory size}})$ [8]. All of the nodes which share a line can have two copies of the line in COMA, while in CC-NUMA only the home node can have two copies. Thus, the number of accesses to the local memory for invalidation in COMA can be larger than in CC-NUMA.

The new data arrangement at a node miss does not alway have positive aspects. The address newly bound to its local AM would more likely be referenced again than the other existing addresses in the AM. However, the address bound to a remote AM may not be recently referenced by the remote node. Furthermore, the inclusion property in COMA can cause negative effects on the locality of data in the cache of the remote node [10]. Therefore, if the patterns of reference at the AM are not highly localized, it may be hard for COMA to offer performance advantages over CC-NUMA mainly due to the extra overhead and the side effects of affecting locality of data in a remote node at the binding time. A large working set can improve the locality of reference at the AM and can make the side effects frivolous. Here, we can expect a synergy of the AM miss rate between the actions of saving the newly referenced line in an AM and relocating the replaced line into an AM. Higher AM miss rate increases the number of replacements, and hence the AM miss rate further.

COMA has another drawback of limiting the number of addresses simultaneously shared by system nodes given memory pressure. Thus, if some shared addresses are actively referenced by several processors, COMA with high memory pressure can suffer from high node miss rate and frequent replacements. To minimize the extra overhead and the negative effects, one may want to lower memory pressure in COMA. However, low memory pressure makes caching space of main memory for the data in disk small. This contradicts the philosophy of COMA, accommodating a large working set with the local memories.

3.3 DYMA

DYMA binds a new address to the local memory, called dynamic memory (DM), on a cache miss. Since a node miss involves a cache miss, the binding to the DM can happen on a node miss as well. However, the address missing in

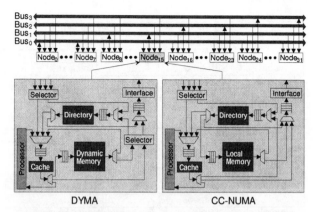

Figure 2. Datapath block diagrams for DYMA and CC-NUMA.

the node is bound only to the processor cache like in CC-NUMA. The processor cache keeps the address as long as the address is persistently referenced. The longer the sojourn time of the line in the processor cache is, the higher the possibility of the line being invalidated or updated by a write reference is. On a cache miss, if the cache line selected for replacement is valid and new to the DM, a binding occurs. If the new line is updated by a local write reference, copying the line from the processor cache and saving it into the DM are not additional overhead. If the new line is not modified, copying the line from the processor cache is extra overhead since the other architectures merely overwrite on the line. Since no inclusion property is enforced between any two memory locations in DYMA, the replaced DM line can be saved in a remote DM without purging a cache copy from the node. Thus, no side effects are found in a remote cache, and the overhead can be less than in COMA. By delaying the binding to the DM, the DM line which would have been discarded from the node in COMA can be referenced again in DYMA. If the selected cache copy is not new but updated, it is written back into the DM like in COMA. DYMA allows a large number of addresses to be replicated to nodes even under 100% of memory pressure.

The data configuration of DYMA becomes similar to that of CC-NUMA in a small working set, which is desirable. If the efforts of binding a new address to the local memory for higher local memory hit rate are not easily nullified by the side effects of replacements in a large working set, DYMA can have the advantage of reducing data access latency over CC-NUMA. However, if the new address cache copies are neither updated nor invalidated when they are unbound, and if few of the replaced copies are referenced again, DYMA can cause an unwanted arrangement of data with higher overhead than the others.

4 Machine Design

Figure 2 shows possible datapath block diagrams for a DYMA and a CC-NUMA machine. The control mechanism described in this section allows each system resource to function independently.

4.1 Data states and requests

In order to prevent a request from being generated at every write and to keep data from becoming inconsistent, the state of a line should have *privateness* and *validity*. Also, to avoid loss of a memory line and to minimize the attempts of relocating a replaced copy, *ownership* should be included in the state of a line. If all of the lines discarded from the processor cache attempt to be relocated in the DM of DYMA, extra overhead can occur. Thus, the state of a cache copy has *inclusiveness* which indicates whether the same address copy is in its DM or not.

Since all write accesses to the clean cache copies generate invalidation requests in CC-NUMA, we do not have to differentiate the two clean states, Exclusive and Shared states, in the MOESI model [19]. Generally, the *dirty bit* corresponding to a local memory frame is used both for indicating validity of the copy in the frame and for representing ownership of the copy. In COMA, since a remote access can get a copy of an updated line from a remote cache without writing the copy back to the remote AM under our assumption, all five states in the MOESI model are required for each cache copy. The AM in COMA has four states since the private state copy in the AM has ownership as well. DYMA has 12 and 4 states for the cache and the DM respectively. A state transition in the processor cache and the DM of DYMA can be found in [10].

The processor cache of DYMA has the largest number of states for additional functions. However, since the additional functions can be done with just one tag access and happen for replacement, we assume the service time for a request at the processor cache is the same in the three machines. Also, for modulization, DYMA sacrifices some replacement overhead. Although the modulization is hard to accomplish in COMA, we assume that probing the processor cache for the requests to the AM can be done simultaneously without adding penalty.

A *requester node* is the node that contains the processor originating a given request, while a *home node* is the node containing the directory information of the requested address. Each memory address has an invariant home node [18]. A *remote node* is any node that is not the requester. An *owner node* is the node which has the ownership copy among the copies of the requested address. If processor's *data request* is not satisfied in the requester node, the request is delivered to the owner node via the directory in

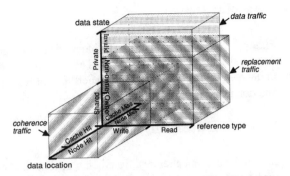

Figure 3. A view of network traffic at a reference event.

Unit	Parameters	Default values
cache	size per node	16K bytes
	access time	1 cycle
	fill time	4 cycles
	associativity	4-way
	replacement	random selection
memory	mem. pr.	73.0~94.9%
	access time	24 cycles
	tag access time	8 cycles
	associativity	8-way
	replacement	priority selection
directory	size	less than 7% of local memory
	processing time	8 × (# of DRAM acc.) cycles
	protocol	non-blocking
network	type	multibus (4 buses)
	service time	10/30 cycles w/o data
32 processors, 64 byte line, 4K byte page		

Table 1. Machine parameters.

the home node. The owner node is responsible for replying to the request. When an ownership or non-inclusive copy needs to be replaced from the processor cache or the local memory, a *relocation request* is generated to relocate the copy to a different memory. If a non-ownership copy is replaced from the processor cache in CC-NUMA or from the local memory in COMA and DYMA, a *replacement-hint request* is initiated to maintain correct directory information at the home node. When a processor writes to a shared line, all shared copies in remote nodes should be invalidated by generating *invalidation requests*.

4.2 Directory and network

Storage requirement of the directory in each machine is minimized without running short of free pointers [11] by using the directory structure proposed in [10]. For fast data access latency, the directory supports a non-blocking directory scheme [12]. This means that all subsequent requests to the same line can proceed beyond the directory. The interconnection network is designed with a multibus. One bus serves the network requests generated from a part of system nodes, while all of the nodes can get the requests directly from the bus. In fact, the protocol used in our organization works correctly for any type of network as long as the network routing is static.

Figure 3 depicts a view of network traffic at an event of reference in the machines. The axis of the data location tells us the position of the line requested by the processor. The axis of the data state has two aspects: (private and shared) states of the requested line and (invalid, non-owner, and owner) states of the replaced copy from a node. The three boxes in the figure represent the types of network traffic: data, replacement, and coherence traffic. Data traffic is the movements of data requests on the network. Replacement traffic is the transactions of relocation and replacement-hint requests on the network. Invalidation requests on the network are considered as coherence traffic.

5 Simulation

We developed a program-driven simulator for the machines designed in the previous section using the Splash-2 programs [22] as workloads. The default parameters are shown in Table 1. The working sets of applications continue to grow, and there are hundreds of applications whose working sets are too large to be supported even with main memory. Correspondingly, the processor cache is ever increasing while covering larger number of applications. In order to reflect the various working set sizes (relative to the processor cache size) in our simulation, the default cache size (16K bytes) is scaled down so as to fit between the first and the second important working sets of the Splash-2 programs. The cache hit access time is the unit of our simulation clock cycle. Four cycles are assumed for the cache fill time. By default, four-way set associativity for the processor cache is assumed. The line for replacement is randomly selected.

To remove an anomaly in COMA and to make DYMA work correctly, we choose the number of the local memory sets to be a multiple of the number of the cache sets. The memory data and tag access times are 24 and 8 cycles respectively. The tag of the memory is assumed to be slow DRAM to minimize the memory cost. In the local memories of COMA and DYMA, each set has 8-way associativity by default. For replacement, a valid copy is selected with following priority sequence; a shared non-owner copy, a shared owner copy, and a private owner copy.

DRAM is utilized for the directory information in the three DSM machines except one case. The directory information for the cache copies in CC-NUMA is saved in fast SRAM. The size overhead is less than 7% of the local memory. The number of DRAM accesses is counted

Program	Problem Size	Footprint	Parallelism
Barnes	16K particles	≈ 3.5 Mb	≈ 91 %
FMM	16K particles	≈ 29.5 Mb	≈ 73 %
Ocean	258×258 ocean	≈ 16.0 Mb	≈ 99 %
Radiosity	room	≈ 29.4 Kb	≈ 55 %
Radix	1 M integers	≈ 10.2 Kb	≈ 98 %
Water-Nsqr	1000 molecules	≈ 3.7 Kb	≈ 77 %

Table 2. Characteristics of the traces.

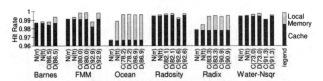

Figure 4. Node hit rates.

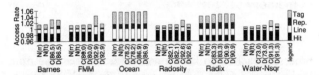

Figure 5. Number of accesses to the processor cache per reference.

for the processing time at the directory. Eight cycles for each DRAM access are assumed. Four network buses are used in our simulation. The service time for a network request with/without data takes 30/10 cycles, and the size is assumed to be 68/4 bytes. We use a 32 processor configuration organized with one processor per node. The size of a line is 64 bytes, and the page size is 4K bytes.

Some characteristics of the Splash-2 programs are illustrated in Table 2 including parallelism and the footprint in main memory. We acquire the parallelism and the footprint by simulating the machines with the default machine parameters. The formula we use for calculating parallelism of a program is as follow:

$$\left(\frac{\sum_{i=0}^{p-1} I_i}{\max(I_0, I_1, ..., I_{p-1})} - 1 \right)\left(\frac{1}{p-1}\right), \qquad (1)$$

where p is the number of processors and I_i is the number of instructions executed at the ith processor. We applied the formula once at the end of the program execution with the number of references instead of the number of instructions. Although some of kernel programs are not shown in the table due to their low parallelism, they can be applied to an application for high parallelism since their long serial sections can be just for the initialization.

We use MINT [21] as a front end part of our simulator. At the back end part of our simulator, we modeled the contention through FIFO queue buffers at each system resource. No request for the use of resources is rejected due to the lack of buffers. We also assume that the references to instructions always hit in an instruction cache. Each non-memory instruction completes in a single cycle as assumed in MINT. The page fault cost is assumed to be zero while all of the lines in a page are initially loaded at the same node.

5.1 Simulation results

Since a node hit substitutes a local data access with a remote data access, it makes memory reference time short. Further, it changes the amount of network bandwidth usage, the number of accesses to the processor cache and the local memory, and the processing overhead at the directory. Thus, the node hit rate of a machine is a solid predictor of

how well the machine will perform. Figure 4 shows the average node hit rates per reference. In the figure, N, C, and D denotes CC-NUMA, COMA, and DYMA machines respectively. CC-NUMA(rr) places the missing page of the application data into a node in round-robin (rr) fashion. In CC-NUMA(ft), a page is allocated on the node which causes the page fault (ft). The memory pressures in COMA and DYMA are represented by the values (%) in the parentheses.

Since different binding times arrange data differently, there is diversity in the node hit rates as shown in Figure 4. Since the size of the AM in COMA is slightly larger than the size of the cache in some programs such as Barnes and Water-Nsqr, COMA has slightly higher or even lower node hit rates than CC-NUMA. Further, the inclusion property in COMA is negative to the cache hit rate while the cache hit rate of DYMA is almost equal to that of CC-NUMA. The relocation from the cache to the DM in DYMA do not weaken locality of data at the DM. Since high memory pressure makes caching space small and the possibility of replacements high, the node hit rates of COMA and DYMA drop as the memory pressure rises. However, the amount of degradation is different. The degradation in COMA is greater due to the lower cache hit rate. The local memory hit rate of CC-NUMA(ft) is higher than that of CC-NUMA(rr) but smaller than that of DYMA. This suggests that a careful page placement at first time can increase node hit rates, and that few programs have strong patterns of reference where most of the lines are not referenced again after being replaced from the processor cache. The local memory hit rates in COMA and DYMA are not as high as the cache hit rates especially when the cache hit rates are high.

The average number of accesses to the processor cache per reference is shown in Figure 5. We divide the accesses into four different cases; hit, line, replacement, and tag accesses. The hit access happens when a reference hits at the

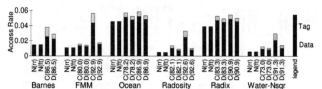

Figure 6. Number of accesses to the local memory per reference.

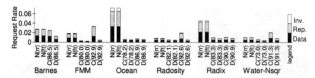

Figure 7. Number of requests to the directory per reference.

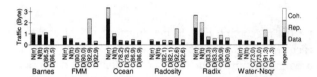

Figure 8. Amount of network traffic per reference.

processor cache. To have a copy of a replaced line from the processor cache for replacement, the replacement access is used. All other types of access for the cache line are considered as the line access. If an access searches just the tag of the cache, it is classified into the tag access. As can be seen in the figure, DYMA usually has the largest replacement access rate (particularly in Barnes). This is because DYMA additionally needs the access to the processor cache to have a copy of the clean line for the binding to the DM and to modulize the control of data states at the cache. The tag and the line access rates in COMA and DYMA are generally larger than in CC-NUMA. Some of the overheads such as replacement accesses can be hidden from the critical path of data access, and some of the overheads such as remote cache accesses can make the data access fast. Thus, the increased number of accesses to the processor cache in COMA and DYMA does not always indicate that the performance of COMA and DYMA is worse than that of CC-NUMA.

In Figure 5, the increment of the line access rate in COMA with high memory pressure is much higher than what we expect, especially in FMM. This suggests that the number of remote cache hits increases in those programs. One possible reference pattern which could cause this irregularity is the pattern which actively shares some memory addresses.

Figure 6 shows the number of accesses to the local memory per reference. In the figure, the accesses for data fetch and save are counted in the data access rate. The accesses for the unsuccessful data or relocation requests, and the accesses for invalidation requests are categorized as tag accesses. Since the dirty bits for memory copies are in the directory of CC-NUMA, no accesses to the tag of the local memory are found. As we expected, CC-NUMA allows the smallest accesses to the local memory. COMA has the largest number of local memory accesses while DYMA is in the midst of those two extremes.

The directory overhead is illustrated in Figure 7. We divide the requests to the directory into three categories; data, replacement, and invalidation requests. Since all requests at a cache miss are delivered to the directory in CC-NUMA, CC-NUMA has higher request rate than DYMA. Due to the analogous cache hit rates, the number of direc-

tory requests is almost the same both in CC-NUMA(rr) and CC-NUMA(ft). Since the node hit rates of COMA in some programs are lower than the cache hit rates of CC-NUMA, COMA does not always have lower request rates than CC-NUMA. The number of invalidation requests are not related to the size of caching space but related to the node miss rate.

The results in Figure 8 are the amount of bytes needed for network communication per reference. The ratio of the replacement traffic rate to the whole network traffic rate is small in CC-NUMA compared to the ratios in COMA and DYMA. Even though CC-NUMA has the smallest cache and local memory access rates, the amount of network traffic is higher than the others except some cases of COMA. Also, CC-NUMA(rr) has higher traffic rate than CC-NUMA(ft) while both have almost the same cache and local memory access, and directory request rates. COMA fails to reduce network traffic in the small data size programs. Furthermore, COMA increases the amount of network traffic much higher than CC-NUMA in the programs where some lines are vigorously shared by several nodes. The amount of network traffic is small in most of the cases in DYMA.

The average waiting time per request at each system resource is exhibited in Figure 9. The average waiting time in CC-NUMA(rr) is shorter than in CC-NUMA(ft) in most of cases although CC-NUMA(ft) has lower network traffic rate and almost the same rates in the other resources. This is because the loads on the system resources are centralized to the master node ($Node_0$). Thus, the page placement policy in CC-NUMA(ft) seems to be not preferable in the perspective of load balancing.

The average data access latency per reference shown in Figure 10 consists of four different cases; local-cache hit, local-memory hit, remote-cache hit, and remote-memory

204

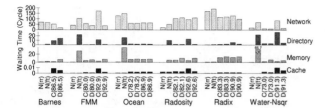

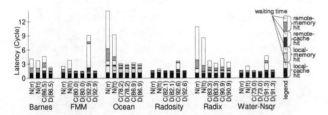

Figure 9. Waiting time per request at the system resources.

Figure 10. Average data access latency including the waiting time.

hit. The average waiting time caused by contention at the system resources is also included in the latency. The average latency of DYMA is shorter than the others in most of the programs. CC-NUMA(ft) has longer waiting time in some of the programs compared to CC-NUMA(rr) due to the intensive contention. COMA tries in vain to reduce the number of long remote accesses and their waiting time in several programs. The remote-cache hit latency of COMA with high memory pressure is significantly long especially in FMM due to the intensive reference patterns of shared lines. The waiting times of CC-NUMA(rr) in Ocean and Radix are extraordinarily long compared with the others. The reason for this is the frequent write hits on a clean cache copy.

Figure 11 depicts the speedup based on CC-NUMA(rr), i.e., $\frac{\text{exec. time in N(rr)}}{\text{exec. time of a machine}}$. A processor which arrives at a synchronization point (wait(), barrier(), lock(S), etc) is blocked until the blocking event is released. The maximum blocking time accumulated among the processors is pre-

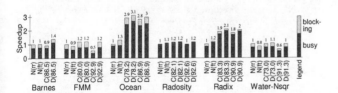

Figure 11. Speedup: the ratio of a program execution time to the case of CC-NUMA(rr).

sented in Figure 11. DYMA is faster than the others except one special case; CC-NUMA(rr) in Water-Nsqr. Since there are almost no local memory hits in those cases, few long remote accesses are replaced by the short local accesses in DYMA. In our simulator, when a new page is loaded into main memory, the page is saved in the local memory without generating any replacements in CC-NUMA, while in DYMA the binding of the page creates replacements of DM copies if necessary due to the limited amount of the local memory. There is no winner between CC-NUMA(rr) and CC-NUMA(ft). COMA has the biggest variation of performance. COMA performs worse than CC-NUMA when the working set size is small. The situation is reversed when the working set size of an application is large enough to create serious network bottleneck in CC-NUMA. The performance degradation in DYMA with high memory pressure is small.

We also studied performance sensitivity to the set associativities of the processor cache and the local memory. Interestingly, the node hit rates of COMA tend to tilt downward as the cache associativity rises due to the synergy of the AM miss rates. Also, the cache hit rate of COMA has higher sensitivity to the local memory set associativity than that of DYMA. Finally, we found that the performance gap between DYMA and CC-NUMA is usually narrowing as the cache size and the number of network buses increase, while the gap is widening as the working set size and the number of the nodes increase.

6 Conclusion

New addresses might need to be bound to memory locations at its *binding time* to improve performance. Also, the displaced data may need to be bound to some other memory location, leading to a new arrangement of data. The bound data can be updated or invalidated. Committing the bindings is desirable only when the extra overhead caused by the bindings can be amortized by shorter memory reference time with the new arrangement of data.

DSM architectures try to bind a recently referenced address to memory local to a node. However, we need to carefully decide the binding time because references to the local memory are not as highly localized as references to the processor cache. In general, the higher the cache hit rate is, the lower the local memory hit rate is. Also, unlike in traditional caches, the displaced data from the local memory can have side effects of affecting the locality of a remote memory.

This paper focuses on the three typical binding times for the local memory. CC-NUMA determines data locations at a page fault. COMA varies locations of data at a node miss. DYMA allows dynamic change of the addresses of the local memory at a cache miss. This paper shows that the three binding schemes arrange data in different ways with different overheads under the same pattern of references. There is no oracle scheme that achieves the best performance across different reference patterns. Instead, we have to choose a memory architecture which performs well under the patterns of references common in applications. The working sets of applications continue to grow, and there are applications whose working sets are too large to be captured even within main memory. For general purpose, a memory architecture should support a wide rage of working set sizes.

Our simulation results confirm that CC-NUMA suffers from seriously long memory access latency when the processor cache does not match well with the working set of a program. To support a large working set, COMA tries to reduce the remote data accesses while sacrificing the number of accesses to the processor cache and the local memory. However, if references to the local memory are not strongly localized, the negative effects of binding a new address to a remote memory becomes higher than the positive effects of saving missing data in the local memory. Although large unallocated memory space in COMA can reduce the negative effects, it can reduce the caching space of main memory for the data from disk.

When a program has a small working set, DYMA performs like CC-NUMA. For a large working set, by holding locality of references at the local memory, DYMA has the advantage even over COMA in reducing data access latency because of its lower overhead and better data arrangement at the binding time. Therefore, DYMA can improve performance for a large number of applications.

Acknowledgments. We thank the anonymous referees for their helpful comments on the manuscript. We express thanks to Prof. Pen-Chung Yew, Prof. David Lilja, and Sangyeun Cho at the University of Minnesota for proofreading and their valuable comments.

References

[1] A. Agarwal, R. Bianchini, D. Chaiken, K. L. Johnson, D. Kranz, J. Kubiatowicz, B. H. Lim, K. Mackenzie, D. Yeung, "The MIT Alewife Machine: Architecture and Performance," *Proc. of the 22nd Annual Int'l Sym. on Comp. Archi.*, 1995.

[2] S. Basu, J. Torrellas, "Enhancing Memory Use in Simple Coma: Multiplexed Simple Coma," *Proc. of the 4st IEEE Symp. on High Perform. Comp. Archi.*, 1998.

[3] H. Burkhardt III, S. Frank, B. Knobe, J. Rothnie, "Overview of the KSR-1 Computer System," Technical Report KSR-TR-9202001, Kendall Square Research Corp., Feb. 1992.

[4] R. Chandra, S. Devine, B. Verghese, A. Gupta, M. Rosenblum, "Scheduling and Page Migration for Multiprocessor Computer Servers," *Proc. of the 6th ASPLOS-VI*, Oct. 1994.

[5] F. Dahlgren, A. Landin, "Reducing the Replacement Overhead in Bus-Based COMA Multiprocessors," *Proc. of the 3rd Int'l Sym. on High-Perform. Comp. Archi.*, 1997.

[6] B. Falsafi and D. A. Wood, "Reactive NUMA: A Design for Unifying S-COMA and CC-NUMA," *Proc. of the 24th Annual Int'l Sym. on Comp. Archi.*, 1997.

[7] E. Hagersten, S. Haridi, A. Landin, "DDM - A Cache-Only Memory Architecture," *IEEE Computer*, pp 44-54, Sep. 1992.

[8] T. Joe, J. Hennessy, "Evaluating the Memory Overhead Required for COMA Architectures," *Proc. of the 21st Annual Int'l Sym. on Comp. Archi.*, 1994.

[9] A. Klaiber, H. Levy, "A Comparison of Message Passing and Shared Memory Architectures for Data Parallel Programs," *Proc. of the 21st Annual Int'l Sym. on Comp. Archi.*, 1994.

[10] J. Kong, G. Lee, "Relaxing the Inclusion Property in Cache Only Memory Architecture," *Proc. of Euro-Par '96 Parallel Processing*, Lyon, France, vol. II, pp 435-444, Aug. 1996.

[11] J. Kong, P.-C. Yew, G. Lee, "Minimizing the Size of Directory for Large-Scale Multiprocessors," in preparation.

[12] J. Kong, P.-C. Yew, G. Lee, "A Non-blocking Directory Protocol for Large-Scale Multiprocessors," in preparation.

[13] D. E. Lenoski, J. Laudon, K. Gharachorloo, A. Gupta, J. Hennessy, "The Directory-Based Cache Coherence Protocol for DASH multiprocessor," *Proc. of the 17th Annual Int'l Sym. on Comp. Archi.*, pp 148-159, 1990.

[14] A. Moga, M. Dubois, "The Effectiveness of SRAM Network Caches in Cluster DSMs," *Proc. of the 4th IEEE Symp. on High Perform. Comp. Archi.*, 1998.

[15] X. Qiu, M. Dubois, "Options for Dynamic Address Translation in COMAs," *Proc. of the 25th Annual Int'l Sym. on Comp. Archi.*, 1998.

[16] A. Saulsbury, T. Wilkinson, J. Carter, A. Landin, "An Argument for Simple COMA," *Proc. of the 1st IEEE Symp. on High Perform. Comp. Archi.*, 1995.

[17] V. Soundararajan, M. Heinrich, B. Verghese, K. Gharachorloo, A. Gupta, J. Hennessy, "Flexible Use of Memory for Replication/Migration in Cache-Coherent DSM Multiprocessors," *Proc. of the 25th Annual Int'l Sym. on Comp. Archi.*, 1998.

[18] P. Stenström, T. Joe, A. Gupta, "Comparative Performance Evaluation of Cache-Coherent NUMA and COMA Architectures," *Proc. of the 19th Annual Int'l Sym. on Comp. Archi.*, pp 80-91, 1992.

[19] P. Sweazey, A.J. Smith, "A Class of Compatible Cache Consistency Protocols and their Support by the IEEE Futurebus," *Proc. of the 13th Annual Int'l Sym. on Comp. Archi.*, 1986.

[20] Thinking Machines Corp., *CM-5 Technical Summary*, 1991.

[21] J. Veenstra, R. Fowler, "Mint: A Front-End for Efficient Simulation of Shared-Memory Multiprocessors," *Proc. of 2nd MASCOTS*, Jan.-Feb., 1994.

[22] S. C. Woo, M. Ohara, E. Torrie, J. P. Singh, A. Gupta, "The SPLASH-2 Programs: Characterization and Methodological Considerations," *Proc. of the 22nd Annual Int'l Sym. on Comp. Archi.*, 1995.

[23] Z. Zhang, J. Torrellas, "Reducing Remote Conflict Misses: NUMA with Remote Cache versus COMA," *Proc. of the 3rd IEEE Symp. on High Perform. Comp. Archi.*, 1997.

ASCOMA : An Adaptive Hybrid Shared Memory Architecture

Chen-Chi Kuo, John Carter, Ravindra Kuramkote, and Mark Swanson*

Department of Computer Science
University of Utah
Salt Lake City, UT 84112

E-mail: {chenchi,retrac,kuramkot,swanson}@cs.utah.edu

Abstract

Scalable shared memory multiprocessors traditionally use either a cache coherent non-uniform memory access (CC-NUMA) or simple cache-only memory architecture (S-COMA) memory architecture. Recently, hybrid architectures that combine aspects of both CC-NUMA and S-COMA have emerged. In this paper, we present two improvements over other hybrid architectures. The first improvement is a page allocation algorithm that prefers S-COMA pages at low memory pressures. Once the local free page pool is drained, additional pages are mapped in CC-NUMA mode until they suffer sufficient remote misses to warrant upgrading to S-COMA mode. The second improvement is a page replacement algorithm that dynamically backs off the rate of page remappings from CC-NUMA to S-COMA mode at high memory pressure. This design dramatically reduces the amount of kernel overhead and the number of induced cold misses caused by needless thrashing of the page cache. The resulting hybrid architecture is called adaptive S-COMA (AS-COMA). AS-COMA exploits the best of S-COMA and CC-NUMA, performing like an S-COMA machine at low memory pressure and like a CC-NUMA machine at high memory pressure. AS-COMA outperforms CC-NUMA under almost all conditions, and outperforms other hybrid architectures by up to 17% at low memory pressure and up to 90% at high memory pressure.

---

*Mark Swanson is now at Intel Corporation. Current email addresses: Mark_R_Swanson@ccm.dp.intel.com

This research was supported in part by the Space and Naval Warfare Systems Command (SPAWAR) and the Advanced Research Projects Agency (ARPA), under SPAWAR contract No.#N0039-95-C-0018 and ARPA Order No.#B990. The views and conclusions contained herein are those of the authors and should not be interpreted as necessarily representing the official policies or endorsements, either expressed or implied, of DARPA, the Air Force Research Laboratory, or the US Government.

1. Introduction

Scalable hardware distributed shared memory (DSM) architectures have become increasingly popular as high-end compute servers. One of the purported advantages of shared memory multiprocessors compared to message passing multiprocessors is that they are easier to program, because programmers are not forced to track the location of every piece of data that might be needed. However, naive exploitation of the shared memory abstraction can cause performance problems, because the performance of DSM multiprocessors is often limited by the amount of time spent waiting for remote memory accesses to be satisfied. When the overhead associated with accessing remote memory impacts performance, programmers are forced to spend significant effort managing data placement, migration, and replication – the very problem that shared memory is designed to eliminate. Therefore, it is important to develop memory architectures that reduce the overhead of remote memory access.

Remote memory overhead is governed by three issues: (i) the number of cycles required to satisfy each remote memory request, (ii) the frequency with which remote memory accesses occur, and (iii) the software overhead of managing the memory hierarchy. The designers of high-end commercial DSM systems such as the SUN UE10000 [12] and SGI Origin 2000 [5] have put considerable effort into reducing the remote memory latency by developing specialized high speed interconnects. These efforts can reduce the ratio of remote to local memory latency to as low as 2:1, but they require expensive hardware available only on high-end servers costing hundreds of thousands of dollars. In this paper, we concentrate on the second and third issues, namely reducing the frequency of remote memory accesses while ensuring that the software overhead required to do this remains modest. Previous studies have tended to ignore the impact of software overhead [3, 9, 10], but our findings indicate that the effect of this factor can be dramatic.

Scalable shared memory multiprocessors traditionally use either a *cache coherent non-uniform memory access* (CC-NUMA) architecture [5, 6, 12] or a *simple cache-only memory architecture* (S-COMA) [10]. In a CC-NUMA, the amount of remote shared data that can be replicated on a node is limited by the size of a node's processor cache(s) and *remote access cache* (RAC) [6]. S-COMA architectures employ any unused DRAM on a node as a cache for remote data [10]. However, the performance of pure S-COMA machines is heavily dependent on the *memory pressure* of a particular application. Put simply, memory pressure is a measure of the amount of physical memory in a machine required to hold an application's instructions and data. A 20% memory pressure indicates that 20% of a machine's pages must be used to hold the initial (home) copy of the application's instructions and data. Although this ability to cache remote data in local memory can dramatically reduce the number of remote memory operations, page management can be expensive.

Recently, hybrid architectures that combine aspects of both CC-NUMA and S-COMA have emerged, such as the Wisconsin *reactive CC-NUMA* (R-NUMA) [3] and the USC *victim cache NUMA* (VC-NUMA) [9]. Intuitively, these hybrid systems attempt to map the remote pages for which there are the highest number of conflict misses to local S-COMA pages, so-called *hot* pages, thereby eliminating the greatest number of expensive remote operations. All other remote pages are mapped in CC-NUMA mode. Ideally, such systems would exploit unused available DRAM for caching without penalty but the proposed implementations fail to achieve this goal under certain conditions.

In this paper, we present two improvements over R-NUMA and VC-NUMA. The first improvement is a page allocation algorithm the prefers S-COMA pages at low memory pressures. Once the local free page pool is drained, additional pages are initially mapped in CC-NUMA mode until they suffer sufficient remote misses to warrant upgrading to S-COMA mode. The second improvement is a page replacement algorithm that dynamically backs off the rate of page remappings between CC-NUMA and S-COMA mode at high memory pressure. This design dramatically reduces the amount of kernel overhead and the number of induced cold misses caused by needless thrashing of the page cache. The resulting hybrid architecture is called *adaptive S-COMA* (AS-COMA).

We used detailed execution-driven simulation to evaluate a number of AS-COMA design tradeoffs and then compared the resulting AS-COMA design against CC-NUMA, pure S-COMA, R-NUMA, and VC-NUMA. We found that AS-COMA's hybrid design provides the best behavior of both CC-NUMA and S-COMA. At low memory pressures, AS-COMA acts like S-COMA and outperforms other hybrid architectures by up to 17%. At high memory pressures, AS-COMA avoids the performance dropoff induced by thrashing and aggressively converges to CC-NUMA performance, thereby outperforming the other hybrid architectures by up to 90%. In addition, AS-COMA outperforms CC-NUMA under almost all conditions, and at its worst only underperforms CC-NUMA by 5%.

The remainder of this paper is organized as follows. In Section 2 we describe the basics of all scalable shared memory architectures, followed by an in-depth description of existing DSM models. Section 3 presents the design of our proposed AS-COMA architecture. We describe our simulation environment, test applications, and experiments in Section 4, and present the results of these experiments in Section 5. Finally, we draw conclusions in Section 6.

2. Background

In this section, we discuss the organization of the existing DSM architectures: CC-NUMA, S-COMA, R-NUMA, and VC-NUMA.

2.1. Directory-based DSM Architectures

All of the shared memory architectures that we consider share a common basic design, as described below. Individual nodes are composed of one or more commodity microprocessors with private caches connected to a coherent split-transaction memory bus. Also on the memory bus is a main memory controller with shared main memory and a distributed shared memory controller connected to a node interconnect. The aggregate main memory of the machine is distributed across all nodes. The processor, main memory controller, and DSM controller all snoop the coherent memory bus, looking for memory transactions to which they must respond.

The internals of a typical DSM controller consist of a memory bus snooper, a control unit that manages locally cached shared memory (*cache controller*), a control unit that retains state associated with shared memory whose "home" is the local main memory (*directory controller*), a network interface, and some local storage. In all of the design alternatives that we explore, the local storage contains DRAM that is used to store directory state.

The remote access overhead of these architectures can be represented as: $(N_{pagecache} * T_{pagecache}) + (N_{remote} * T_{remote}) + (N_{cold} * T_{remote}) + T_{overhead}$. $N_{pagecache}$ and N_{remote} represent the number of conflict misses that were satisfied by the page cache or remote memory, respectively. N_{cold} represents the number of cold misses induced by flushing and remapping pages, and thus is zero only in the CC-NUMA model. $T_{pagecache}$ and T_{remote} represent the latency of fetching a line from the local page cache or remote memory, respectively. $T_{overhead}$ represents the software overheads of the S-COMA and the hybrid models to support page remapping.

2.2. CC-NUMA

In CC-NUMA [5, 6, 12], the first page access on each node to a particular page causes a page fault, at which time the local TLB and page table are loaded with a page translation to the appropriate *global* physical page. The home node of each page can be determined from its physical address. When the local processor suffers a cache miss to a line in a remote page, the DSM controller forwards the memory request to the memory's home node, incurring a significant access delay. Remote data can only be cached in the processor cache(s) or an optional remote access cache (RAC) on the DSM controller. Applications that suffer a large number of conflict misses to remote data, e.g., due to the limited amount of caching of remote data, perform poorly on CC-NUMAs [3]. Unfortunately, these applications are fairly common [3, 10]. Careful page allocation [1, 7], migration [13], or replication [13] can alleviate this problem by selecting or modifying the choice of home node for a given page of data, but these techniques have to date only been successful for read-only or non-shared pages.

The conflict miss cost in the CC-NUMA model is represented by $(N_{remote} * T_{remote})$, that is, all misses to shared memory with a remote home must be remote misses. To reduce this overhead, designers of some such systems have adopted high speed interconnects to reduce T_{remote} [5, 12].

2.3. S-COMA

In the S-COMA model [10], the DSM controller and operating system cooperate to provide access to remotely homed data. S-COMA's aggressive use of local memory to replicate remote shared data can completely eliminate N_{remote} when the memory pressure on a node is low. However, pure S-COMA's performance degrades rapidly for some applications as memory pressure increases. Because *all* remote data *must* be mapped to a local physical page before it can be accessed, there can be heavy contention if the number of local physical pages available for S-COMA page replication is small. Under these circumstances, thrashing occurs, not unlike thrashing in a conventional VM system. Given the high cost of page replacement, this can lead to dismal performance.

In the S-COMA model, the conflict miss cost is represented by $(N_{pagecache} * T_{pagecache}) + (N_{cold} * T_{remote}) + T_{overhead}$. When memory pressure is low enough that all of the remote data a node needs can be cached locally, page remapping does not occur and both N_{cold} and $T_{overhead}$ are zero. As the memory pressure increases, and thus more remote pages are accessed by a node than can be cached locally, N_{cold} and $T_{overhead}$ increase due to remapping. N_{cold} increases because the contents of any pages that are replaced from the local page cache must be flushed from the processor cache(s). Subsequent accesses to these pages will suffer cold misses in addition to the cost of remapping. An even worse problem is that as memory pressure approaches 100%, the time spent in the kernel flushing and remapping pages ($T_{overhead}$) skyrockets. Sources of this overhead include the time spent context switching between the user application and the pageout daemon, flushing blocks from the victim page(s), and remapping pages.

2.4. Hybrid DSM Architectures

Two hybrid CC-NUMA/S-COMA architectures have been proposed: R-NUMA [3] and VC-NUMA [9]. We describe these architectures in this section.

The basic architecture of an R-NUMA machine [3] is that of a CC-NUMA machine. However, unlike CC-NUMA, which "wastes" local physical memory not required to hold home pages, R-NUMA uses this otherwise unused storage to cache frequently accessed remote pages, as in S-COMA. This mechanism requires a number of modest modifications to a conventional CC-NUMA's DSM engine and operating system, as described below.

In addition to its normal CC-NUMA operation, the directory controller in an R-NUMA machine maintains an array of counters that tracks for each page the number of times that each processor has refetched a line from that page, as follows. Whenever a directory controller receives a request for a cache line from a node, it checks to see if that node is already in the copyset of nodes for that line. If it is, this request is a *refetch* caused by a conflict miss, and not a coherence or cold miss, and the node's refetch counter for this page is incremented. The per-page/per-node counter is used to determine which CC-NUMA pages are generating frequent remote refetches, and thus are good candidates to be mapped to an S-COMA page on the accessing node. When a refetch counter crosses a configurable threshold (e.g., 64), the directory controller piggybacks an indication of this event with the data response. This causes the DSM engine on the requesting node to interrupt the processor with an indication that a particular page should be remapped to a local S-COMA page. In a recent study [3], R-NUMA's flexibility and intelligent selection of pages to map in S-COMA mode caused it to outperform the best of pure CC-NUMA and pure S-COMA by up to 37% on some applications.

Although R-NUMA frequently outperforms both CC-NUMA and S-COMA, it was also observed to perform as much as 57% worse on some applications [3]. This poor performance can be attributed to two problems. First, R-

NUMA initially maps all pages in CC-NUMA mode, and only upgrades them to S-COMA mode after some number of remote refetches occur, which introduces needless remote refetches when memory pressure is low. Second, R-NUMA always upgrades pages to S-COMA mode when their refetch threshold is exceeded, even if it must evict another hot page to do so. When memory pressure is high, and the number of hot pages exceeds the number of free pages available for caching them, this behavior results in frequent expensive page remappings for little value. This leads to performance worse than CC-NUMA, which never remaps pages.

VC-NUMA [9] treats its RAC as a victim cache for the processor cache(s). However, this solution requires significant modifications to the processor cache controller and bus protocol. The designers of VC-NUMA also noticed the tendency of hybrid models to thrash at high memory pressure and suggested a thrashing detection scheme to address the problem. Their scheme requires a local refetch counter per S-COMA page, a programmable *break even* number that depends on the network latency and overhead of relocating pages, and an *evaluation threshold* that depends on the total number of free S-COMA pages in the page cache. Although VC-NUMA frequently outperforms R-NUMA, the study did not isolate the benefit of the thrashing detection scheme from that of the integrated victim cache.

In these hybrid models, the conflict miss cost is represented by $(N_{pagecache} * T_{pagecache}) + (N_{remote} * T_{remote}) + (N_{cold} * T_{remote}) + T_{overhead}$. $N_{pagecache}$ and N_{remote} closely depend on the relocation mechanisms. Remappings between CC-NUMA and S-COMA modes account for the increased cold miss rate (N_{cold}), as described earlier. $T_{overhead}$ is the software overhead required for the kernel to handle interrupts, flush pages, and remap pages.

When there are plentiful free local pages, the difference between the hybrid models and S-COMA is that S-COMA does not suffer from as many initial conflict misses, nor does it pay for page remapping. In such a case, the relative costs between the two models can be represented as:

$$N_{remote.hybrid} + N_{cold.hybrid} \gg N_{cold.scoma} \approx 0, \quad (1)$$

$$T_{overhead.hybrid} > T_{overhead.scoma} \approx 0, \quad (2)$$

$$N_{pagecache.scoma} > N_{pagecache.hybrid} \quad (3)$$

As the memory pressure increases, R-NUMA and VC-NUMA suffer from the same problems as pure S-COMA, although to a lesser degree. Even hot pages already in the page cache begin to be remapped. In a worst case, the relative cost between the hybrid models and CC-NUMA under high memory pressure can be represented as:

$$N_{remote.hybrid} + N_{cold.hybrid} > N_{remote.ccnuma}, \quad (4)$$

$$T_{overhead.hybrid} \gg T_{overhead.ccnuma} \approx 0. \quad (5)$$

Relations (1), (2) and (3) suggest that one way to improve the hybrid models at low memory pressure is to accelerate their convergence to S-COMA. Likewise, relations (4) and (5) suggest that performance can be improved by throttling CC-NUMA $\leftrightarrow$ S-COMA transitions at high memory pressure. Unlike S-COMA, in which remapping is required for the architecture to operate correctly, the hybrid architectures can choose to stop remapping and leave pages in CC-NUMA mode.

In summary, the performance of hybrid S-COMA/CC-NUMA architectures is significantly influenced by the memory pressure induced by a particular application. Since it is common for users to run the largest applications they can on their hardware, the performance of an architecture at high memory pressures is particularly important. Therefore, it is crucial to conduct performance studies of S-COMA or hybrid architectures across a broad spectrum of memory pressures. An improved hybrid architecture, motivated by the analysis above, that performs well regardless of memory pressure is discussed in the following section.

3. Adaptive S-COMA

At low memory pressure, S-COMA outperforms CC-NUMA, but the converse is true at high memory pressure [10]. Thus, our goal when designing AS-COMA was to develop a memory architecture that performed like pure S-COMA when memory for page caching was plentiful, and like CC-NUMA when it is not.

To exploit S-COMA's superior performance at low memory pressures, AS-COMA initially maps pages in S-COMA mode. Thus, when memory pressure is low, AS-COMA will suffer no remote conflict or capacity misses, nor will it pay the high cost of remapping (i.e., cache flushing, page table remapping, TLB refill, and induced cold misses). Only when the page cache becomes empty does AS-COMA begin remapping.

Like the previous hybrid architectures, AS-COMA reacts to increasing memory pressure by evicting "cold" pages from, and remapping "hot" pages to, the local page cache. However, what sets AS-COMA apart from the other hybrid architectures is its ability to adapt to differing memory pressures to fully utilize the large page cache at low memory pressures and to avoid thrashing at high memory pressures. It does so by dynamically adjusting the *refetch threshold* that triggers remapping, increasing it when it notices that memory pressure is high.

AS-COMA uses the kernel's VM system to detect thrashing, as follows. The kernel maintains a pool of free local pages that it can use to satisfy allocation or relocation requests. The pageout daemon attempts to keep the size of this pool between *free_target* and *free_min* pages. Whenever the size of the free page pool falls below *free_min* pages, the pageout daemon attempts to evict enough "cold" pages to refill the free page pool to *free_target* pages. Only S-COMA pages are considered for replacement. To replace a page, its valid blocks are flushed from the processor cache, and then its corresponding global virtual address is remapped to its home physical address. *Cold* pages are detected using a *second chance* algorithm: the TLB reference bit associated with each S-COMA page is reset each time it is considered for eviction by the pageout daemon. If the reference bit is zero when the pageout daemon next runs, the page is considered cold.

Under low to moderate memory pressure, allocation or relocation requests can be performed immediately because there will be pages in the free page pool. However, at heavy memory pressure, the pageout daemon will be unable to find sufficient cold pages to refill the free page pool. Whenever the pageout daemon is unable to reclaim at least *free_target* free pages, AS-COMA begins allocating pages in CC-NUMA mode under the assumption that local memory can not accommodate the application's entire working set. In addition, it raises the refetch threshold by a fixed amount to reduce the rate at which "equally-hot" pages in the page cache replace each other. It also increases the time between successive invocations of the pageout daemon. Should the number of hot pages drop, e.g., because of a phase change in the program that causes a number of hot pages to grow cold, the pageout daemon will detect it by seeing an increase in the number of cold pages. At this point, it can reduce the refetch threshold.

Using this backoff scheme, the rate at which destructive flushing and remapping occurs is decreased, as is the number of cold misses induced by remapping. In addition, the frequency at which the pageout daemon is invoked is reduced, which eliminates context switches and pageout daemon execution time. Overall, we found this back pressure on the replacement mechanism to be extremely important. As will be shown in Section 5, it alleviates the performance slowdowns experienced by R-NUMA or VC-NUMA when memory pressure is high.

AS-COMA's conflict miss cost is identical to SCOMA's when there are enough local free pages to accommodate the application's working set. In such cases, the remote refetch cost of AS-COMA will be close to ($N_{pagecache} * T_{pagecache}$). Until memory pressure gets high, N_{remote} will grow slowly. Eventually the page cache will no longer be large enough to hold all hot pages. Ideally AS-COMA's performance would simply degrade smoothly to that of CC-NUMA, ($N_{remote} * T_{remote}$), as memory pressure approaches 100%. Realizable AS-COMA models will fare somewhat worse due to the extra kernel overhead incurred before the system stabilizes. Nevertheless, AS-COMA is able to converge rapidly to either S-COMA or CC-NUMA mode, depending on the memory pressure.

4. Performance Evaluation

4.1. Experimental Setup

All experiments were performed using an execution-driven simulation of the HP PA-RISC architecture called Paint (PA-interpreter)[11]. Our simulation environment includes detailed simulation modules for a first level cache, system bus, memory controller, and DSM engine. Note that our network model only accounts for input and output ports contention. The simulation environment also provides a multiprogrammed process model with support for operating system code, so the effects of OS/user code interactions are modeled. It includes a kernel based on 4.4BSD that provides scheduling, interrupt handling, memory management, and limited system call capabilities. The modeled physical page size is 4 kilobytes. All three hybrid architectures we study adopt BSD4.4's page allocation mechanism and paging policy [8] with minor modifications. *Free_min* and *free_target* (see Section 3) were set to 5% and 7% of total memory, respectively. We extended the first touch allocation algorithm [7] to distribute home pages equally.

The modeled processor and DSM engine are clocked at 120MHz. The system bus modeled is HP's Runway bus, which is also clocked at 120MHz. All cycle counts reported herein are with respect to this clock. The characteristics of the L1 cache, RACs, and network that we modeled are shown in Table 1.

For most of the SPLASH2 applications we studied, the data sets provided have a primary working set that fits in an 8-kbyte cache[14]. We, therefore, model a single 8-kilobyte direct-mapped processor cache to compensate for the small size of the data sets, which is consistent with previous studies of hybrid architectures[3, 9].

We modeled a 4-bank main memory controller that can supply data from local memory in 58 cycles. The size of main memory and the amount of free memory used for page caching was varied to test the different models under varying memory pressures.

We used a sequentially-consistent write-invalidate consistency protocol with a coherence unit of 128 bytes (4 lines). Our CC-NUMA and hybrid models are not "pure," as we employ a 128-byte RAC containing the last remote data received as part of performing a 4-line fetch. An initial relocation threshold of 32, the number of remote refetches required to initiate a page remapping, is used in all three hybrid architectures. The relocation thresholds were incremented by 8 whenever thrashing is detected by AS-COMA's software scheme or by VC-NUMA's hardware scheme. VC-NUMA uses a breakeven number of 16 for its thrashing detection mechanism. We did not simulate VC-NUMA's victim-cache behavior, because we considered the use of non-commodity processors or busses to be beyond the scope

Component	Characteristics
L1 Cache	Size: 8-kilobytes. 32 byte lines, direct-mapped, virtually indexed, physically tagged, non-blocking, up to one outstanding miss, write back, 1-cycle hit latency
RAC	128 byte lines, direct-mapped, non-inclusive, non-blocking, up to one outstanding miss, 23-cycle hit latency.
Networks	1 cycle propagation, 2X2 switch topology, port contention (only) modeled Fall through delay: 4 cycles (local and remote memory access latencies - 58 and 147 cycles)

Table 1. Cache and Network Characteristics

of this study. Thus, the results reported for VC-NUMA are only relevant for evaluating its relocation strategy, and not the value of treating the RAC as a victim cache[9].

4.2. Benchmark Programs

We used six programs to conduct our study: barnes, fft, lu, ocean, and radix from the SPLASH-2 benchmark suite [14] and em3d from a shared memory implementation of the Split-C benchmark [2]. Table 2 shows the inputs used for each test program. The column labeled *Total Home pages* indicates the total number of shared data pages initially allocated at all nodes. These numbers indicate that each node manages from 0.5 megabytes (barnes) to 2 megabytes (lu, em3d, and ocean) of home data.

The *Total Remote Pages* column indicates the maximum number of remote pages that are accessed by all nodes for each application, which gives an indication of the size of the application's global working set. The *Ideal pressure* column is the memory pressure below which S-COMA and AS-COMA machines act like a "perfect" S-COMA, meaning that every node has enough free memory to cache all remote pages that it will ever access. Below this memory pressure, S-COMA and AS-COMA never experience a conflict miss to remote data, nor will they suffer any kernel or page daemon overhead to remap pages.

Due to its small default problem size and long execution time, lu was run on just 4 nodes - all other applications were run on 8 nodes.

5. Results

Figure 1 shows the performance of CC-NUMA, S-COMA, and three hybrid CC-NUMA/S-COMA architectures (AS-COMA, VC-NUMA, R-NUMA) on the six applications. Each graph displays the execution time of the various architectures relative to CC-NUMA, and indicates where this time was spent by each program[1]. More performance statistics, e.g., where cache misses to shared data

were satisfied, can be found in the technical report version of this paper [4]. We simulated the applications across a range of memory pressures between 10% and 90%. Only one result is shown for CC-NUMA, since it is not affected by memory pressure. As can be seen in the graphs, the relative performance of the different architectures can vary dramatically as memory pressures change. All results include only the parallel phase of the various programs.

5.1. Initial Allocation Schemes

We will first focus on the effect of the initial allocation policies. As shown in Table 2, the "ideal" memory pressure for the six applications ranged from 16% to 57%. Below this memory pressure, the local page cache is large enough to store the entire working set of a node. To isolate the impact of initially allocating pages in S-COMA, we simulated S-COMA and the hybrid architectures at a memory pressure of 10%, when no page remappings beyond any initial ones will occur. Table 2 shows the percentage of remote pages that are refetched at least 32 times (*Relocated Pages*), and thus will be remapped from CC-NUMA to S-COMA mode in R-NUMA or VC-NUMA, the total number of remote pages accessed (*Total Remote Pages*), and the percentage of remote pages eligible for relocation (*% of Relocated Pages*). This percentage ranges from under 1% in fft to over 95% in lu and radix.

First, to illustrate the importance of employing a hybrid memory architecture over a vanilla CC-NUMA architecture, examine Figure 1 at 10% memory pressures. At this low memory pressure, AS-COMA, like S-COMA, outperforms CC-NUMA by 20-35% for four of the applications (lu, radix, barnes, and em3d). Looking at the hybrid architectures in isolation, we can see that for radix, AS-COMA outperforms R-NUMA and VC-NUMA by 17%. In radix, the percentage and total number of remote pages that need to be remapped are both quite high, 98% and 10236 respectively. In the other applications, the initial page allocation policy had little impact on performance. There is no strong correlation between the number of pages

---

[1] *U-SH-MEM*: stalled on shared memory. *K-BASE*: performing essential kernel operations (i.e., those required by all architectures). *K-OVERHD*: performing architecture-specific kernel operations, such as remapping pages and handling relocation interrupts. *U-INSTR* and *U-LC-*

MEM: performing user-level instructions or non-shared (local) memory operations. *SYNC*: performing synchronization operations.

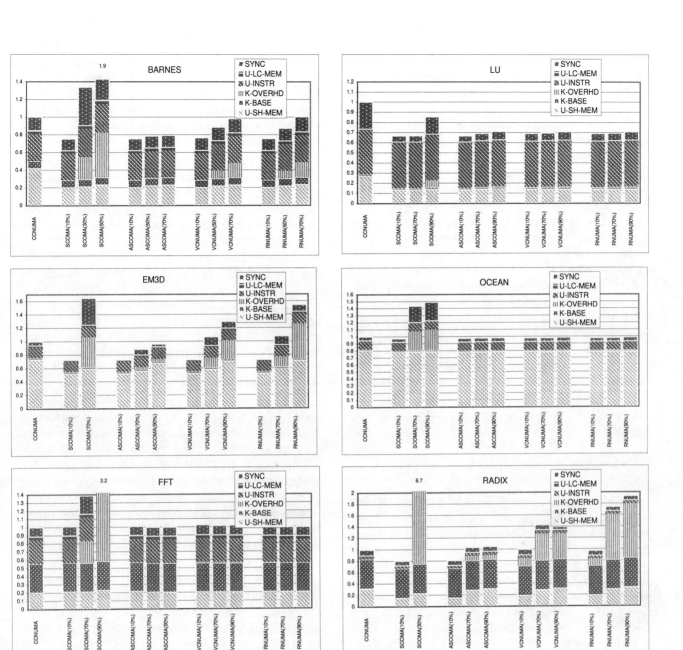

Figure 1. Relative Execution Time for barnes, em3d, fft, lu, ocean, **and** radix.

Program	Input parameters	Total Home Page	Total Remote Pages	Ideal Pressure	Relocated Pages	% of Relocated Pages
barnes	16K particles	816	4416	16%	3498	80%
em3d	40K nodes,15%remote,20 iters	3928	6224	39%	1868	29%
FFT	256K points	3120	10032	24%	5	0.05%
LU	1024x1024 matrix,16x16 blocks	2056	1620	56%	1606	99%
ocean	258x258 ocean	3784	2848	57%	569	20%
radix	1M Keys, Radix = 1024	2072	10448	17%	10236	98%

Table 2. Programs and Problem Sizes Used in Experiments and Their Shared Memory Pages Statistics

that need to be remapped and performance. We can observe a 5% performance benefit in lu, where the percentage of relocated remote pages is very high (99%), but the total number is fairly small (1606).

There are two primary reasons why the initial allocation policy did not have a stronger impact on performance. First, our interrupt and relocation operations are highly optimized, requiring only 2000 and 6000 cycles, respectively, to perform. Thus, the impact of the unnecessary remappings and flushes is overwhelmed by other factors. Second, as an artifact of our experimental setup, the initial remappings for several applications were not included in the performance results, as they took place before the parallel phase when our measurements are taken. This was the case for barnes and em3d. The final two applications, fft and ocean, only access a small number of remote pages enough times to warrant remapping, and thus the impact of initially mapping pages in S-COMA mode is negligible.

In summary, if memory pressure is low and local pages for replication are abundant, an S-COMA-preferred initial allocation policy can improve the performance hybrid architectures moderately by accelerating their convergence to pure S-COMA behavior. However, the performance boost is modest.

5.2. Thrashing Detection and Backoff Schemes

The performance of hybrid DSM architectures depends heavily on the memory pressure. Performance seriously degrades when the page cache cannot hold all "hot" pages and those pages start to evict one another. Intuitively, when this begins to occur, the memory system should simply treat the page cache as a place to store a *reasonable* set of hot pages, and stop trying to fine tune its contents since this tuning adds significant overhead. Previous studies have not considered the kernel overhead ($T_{overhead}$), but we found it to be very significant at high memory pressures. Once the page cache holds only hot pages, further attempts to refine its contents lead to thrashing, which involves unnecessary flushing of hot data, cache flushes, and induced cold misses. Since one hot page is replacing another, the benefit of this remapping is likely to be minimal compared to the cost of the remapping itself. As a result, the performance of a hybrid architecture will quickly drop below that of CC-NUMA if a mechanism is not put in place to avoid thrashing. As described in Section 3, the pageout daemon in AS-COMA detects thrashing when it cannot find cold pages to replace, at which point it reduces the rate of page remappings, going so far as to stop it completely if necessary. As can be seen in Figure 1, this can lead to significant performance improvements compared to R-NUMA and VC-NUMA under heavy memory pressure.

We can divide the six applications into two groups:

(i) applications where there are sufficient remote conflict misses that handling thrashing effectively can lead to large performance gains (barnes, em3d, and radix), and (ii) applications in which minimal efforts to avoid thrashing are sufficient for handling high memory pressure (fft, ocean, and lu).

The behavior of em3d shows the danger of focusing solely on reducing remote conflict misses [4] when designing a memory architecture. As shown in Figure 1, the performance of em3d on the hybrid architectures is quite sensitive to memory pressure. R-NUMA outperforms CC-NUMA until memory pressure approaches 70%, after which time its performance drops quickly. CC-NUMA outperforms R-NUMA by 5% at 70% memory pressure and by 50% at 90%. Looking at the detailed breakdown of where time is spent, we can see that increasing kernel overhead is the culprit. In em3d, approximately 29% of remote pages, i.e., 230 pages, are eligible for relocation (see Table 2), but at 70% memory pressure there are only 210 free local pages. It turns out that for em3d, most of the remote pages ever accessed are in the node's working set, i.e., they are "hot" pages. Thus, above 70% memory pressure, R-NUMA begins to thrash and its performance degrades badly. This performance dropoff occurs even though there are significantly fewer remote conflict misses in R-NUMA than in CC-NUMA or AS-COMA [4]. The cost of constantly remapping pages between CC-NUMA and S-COMA mode and the increase in remote cold misses overwhelms the benefit of the reduced number of remote conflict misses. This behavior emphasizes the importance of detecting thrashing and reducing the rate of remappings when it occurs.

Recognizing this problem, VC-NUMA uses extra hardware to detect thrashing. However, its mechanism is not as effective as AS-COMA's. VC-NUMA starts to underperform CC-NUMA at the same memory pressure that R-NUMA does, 70%. While VC-NUMA outperforms R-NUMA by 22% at 90% memory pressure, it underperforms CC-NUMA by 27% and AS-COMA by 31%. In contrast, AS-COMA outperforms CC-NUMA even at 90% memory pressure, when the other hybrid architectures are thrashing. It does so by dynamically turning off relocation as it determines that this relocation has no benefits because it is simply replacing hot pages with other hot pages. This results in more remote conflict/capacity misses than the other hybrid architectures, but it reduces the number of cold misses caused by flushing pages during remapping and the kernel overhead associated with handling interrupts and remapping [4]. As a result, AS-COMA outperforms VC-NUMA by 31% and R-NUMA by 53% at 90% memory pressure. Moreover, despite having only a small page cache available to it and a remote working set larger than this cache, AS-COMA outperforms CC-NUMA.

Barnes exhibits very high spatial locality. It accesses large dense regions of remote memory, and thus can make good use of a local S-COMA page cache[2]. As shown in in Table 2, barnes's ideal memory pressure is 16%. Like em3d, most of the remote pages that are accessed are part of the working set and "hot" for long periods of execution. We observed that thrashing begins to occur at 50% memory pressure. As in em3d, R-NUMA reduces the number of remote conflict/capacity misses at high memory pressures, at the cost of increasing kernel overhead and remote cold misses. As a result, it is able to outperform CC-NUMA at low memory pressure, but is only able to break even by the time memory pressure reaches 70%. Similarly, VC-NUMA's backoff mechanism is not sufficiently aggressive at moderate memory pressures to stop the increase in kernel overhead or cold misses. In particular, VC-NUMA only checks its backoff indicator when an average of two replacements per cached page have occurred, which is not sufficiently often to avoid thrashing. As shown in the previous study [9], VC-NUMA does not significantly outperform R-NUMA until memory pressure exceeds 87.5%. Once again, AS-COMA's adaptive replacement algorithm detects thrashing as soon as it starts to occur, and the resulting backoff mechanism causes performance to degrade only slightly as memory pressure increases. As a result, it consistently outperforms CC-NUMA by 20% across all ranges of memory pressures, and outperforms the other hybrid architectures by a similar margin at high memory pressures.

Unlike barnes, radix exhibits almost no spatial locality. Every node accesses every page of shared data at some time during execution. As such, it is an extreme example of an application where fine tuning of the S-COMA page cache will backfire - each page is roughly as "hot" as any other, so the page cache should simply be loaded with some reasonable set of "hot" pages and left alone. With an ideal memory pressure of 17% and low spatial locality, the performance of pure S-COMA is 6.7 times worse than CC-NUMA's at memory pressures as low as 30%. Although the performance of both R-NUMA and VC-NUMA are significantly more stable than that of S-COMA, they too suffer from thrashing by the time memory pressure reaches 70%. The source of this performance degradation is the same as in em3d and barnes - increasing kernel overhead and (to a lesser degree) induced cold misses. Once again, R-NUMA induces fewer remote accesses than CC-NUMA [4], but the kernel overhead required to support page relocation is such that R-NUMA underperforms CC-NUMA by 75% at 70% memory pressure and by almost a factor of two at

90% memory pressure. Once again, VC-NUMA's backoff algorithm proves to be more effective than R-NUMA's, but it still underperforms CC-NUMA by roughly 40% at high memory pressures. AS-COMA, on the other hand, deposits a reasonable subset of "hot" pages into the page cache and then backs off from replacing further pages once it detects thrashing. As a result, even for a program with almost no spatial locality, AS-COMA is able to converge to CC-NUMA-like performance (or better) across all memory pressures. At 90% memory pressure, AS-COMA outperforms VC-NUMA by 35% and R-NUMA by 90% at high memory pressures, and it remains within 5% of CC-NUMA's performance. The slight degradation compared to CC-NUMA is due to the short period of thrashing that occurs before AS-COMA can detect it and completely stop relocations.

Applications in the second category (fft, ocean, and lu) exhibit good page-grained locality. All three applications only have a small set of "hot" pages, which can be easily replicated using a small page cache, or references to remote pages are so localized that the small (128-byte) RAC in our simulation was able to satisfy a high percentage of remote accesses [4]. As a result, thrashing never occurs and the various backoff schemes are not invoked. Thus, the performance of the three hybrid algorithms is almost identical.

In summary, for applications that do not suffer frequent remote cache misses or for which the active working set of remote pages is small at any given time, all of the hybrid architectures perform quite well, often outperforming CC-NUMA. However, for applications with less spatial locality or larger working sets, the more aggressive remapping backoff mechanism used by AS-COMA is crucial to achieving good performance. In such applications, AS-COMA outperformed the other hybrid architectures by 20% to 90%, and either outperformed or broke even with CC-NUMA even at extreme memory pressures. Given programmers' desire to run the largest problem size that they can on their machines, this stability of AS-COMA at high memory pressures could prove to be an important factor in getting hybrid architectures adopted.

6. Conclusions

The performance of hardware distributed shared memory is governed by three factors: (i) remote memory latency, (ii) the number of remote misses, and (iii) the software overhead of managing the memory hierarchy. In this paper, we evaluated the performance of five DSM architectures (CC-NUMA, S-COMA, R-NUMA, VC-NUMA, and AS-COMA) with special attention to the third factor, system software overhead. Furthermore, since users of SMPs tend to run the largest applications possible on their hardware, we paid special attention to how well each architec-

---

[2]Note that barnes is very compute-intensive, and a problem size that can be simulated in a reasonable amount of time requires only approximately 100 home pages per node of data. Since there are only about 50 free pages per node available for page replication at 70% memory pressure, we did not simulate barnes at higher memory pressures since the results would be heavily skewed by small sample size effects.

ture performed under high *memory pressure*.

We found that at low memory pressure, architectures that were most aggressive about mapping remote pages into the local page cache (S-COMA and AS-COMA) performed best. In our study, S-COMA and AS-COMA outperformed the other architectures by up to 17% at low memory pressures. As memory pressure increased, however, it became increasingly important to reduce the rate at which remote pages were remapped into the local page cache. S-COMA's performance usually dropped dramatically at high memory pressures due to thrashing. The performance of VC-NUMA and R-NUMA also dropped at high memory pressures, albeit not as severely as S-COMA. This thrashing phenomenom has been largely ignored in previous studies, but we found that it had a significant impact on performance, especially at the high memory pressures likely to be preferred by power users.

In contrast, AS-COMA's software-based scheme to detect thrashing and reduce the rate of page remappings caused it to outperform VC-NUMA and R-NUMA by up to 90% at high memory pressures. AS-COMA is able to fully utilize even a small page cache by mapping a subset of "hot" pages locally, and then backing off further remapping. This mechanism caused AS-COMA to outperform even CC-NUMA in five out of the six applications we studied, and only underperform CC-NUMA by 5% in the sixth.

Consequently, we believe that hybrid CC-NUMA/S-COMA architectures can be made to perform effectively at all ranges of memory pressures. At low memory pressures, aggressive use of available DRAM can eliminate most remote conflict misses. At high memory pressures, reducing the rate of page remappings and keeping only a subset of "hot" pages in the small local page cache can lead to performance close to or better than CC-NUMA. To achieve this level of performance, the overhead of system software must be carefully considered, and careful attention must given to avoiding needless system overhead. AS-COMA achieves these goals.

7 Acknowledgements

We would like to thank Leigh Stoller who supported the simulator environment, the anonymous reviewers, and the members of *Avalanche* project at the University of Utah for their helpful comments on drafts of this paper.

References

[1] W. Bolosky, R. Fitzgerald, and M. Scott. Simple but effective techniques for NUMA memory management. In *Proceedings of the 12th ACM Symposium on Operating Systems Principles*, pages 19–31, Dec. 1989.

[2] S. Chandra, J. Larus, and A. Rogers. Where is time spent in message-passing and shared-memory programs? In *Proceedings of the 6th Symposium on Architectural Support for Programming Languages and Operating Systems*, pages 61–73, Oct. 1994.

[3] B. Falsafi and D. Wood. Reactive NUMA: A design for unifying S-COMA and CC-NUMA. In *Proceedings of the 24th Annual International Symposium on Computer Architecture*, pages 229–240, June 1997.

[4] C.-C. Kuo, J. Carter, R. Kuramkote, and M. Swanson. AS-COMA: An adaptive hybrid shared memory architecture. Technical report, University of Utah - Computer Science Department, March 1998.

[5] J. Laudon and D. Lenoski. The SGI Origin: A ccNUMA highly scalable server. In *SIGARCH97*, pages 241–251, June 1997.

[6] D. Lenoski, J. Laudon, K. Gharachorloo, W.-D. Weber, A. Gupta, J. Hennessy, M. Horowitz, and M. S. Lam. The Stanford DASH multiprocessor. *IEEE Computer*, 25(3):63–79, Mar. 1992.

[7] M. Marchetti, L. Kontothonassis, R. Bianchini, and M. Scott. Using simple page placement policies to reduce the code of cache fills in coherent shared-memory systems. In *Proceedings of the Ninth ACM/IEEE International Parallel Processing Symposium (IPPS)*, Apr. 1995.

[8] M. Mckusick, K. Bostic, M. Karels, and J. Quarterman. *The Design and Implementation of the 4.4BSD operating system*, chapter 5 Memory Management, pages 117–190. Addison-Wesley Publishing Company Inc, 1996.

[9] A. Moga and M. Dubois. The effectiveness of SRAM network caches in clustered DSMs. In *Proceedings of the Fourth Annual Symposium on High Performance Computer Architecture*, 1998.

[10] A. Saulsbury, T. Wilkinson, J. Carter, and A. Landin. An argument for Simple COMA. In *Proceedings of the First Annual Symposium on High Performance Computer Architecture*, pages 276–285, Jan. 1995.

[11] L. Stoller, R. Kuramkote, and M. Swanson. PAINT- PA instruction set interpreter. Technical Report UUCS-96-009, University of Utah - Computer Science Department, Sept. 1996.

[12] Sun Microsystems. Ultra Enterprise 10000 System Overview. http://www.sun.com/servers/datacenter/products/starfire.

[13] B. Verghese, S. Devine, A. Gupta, and M. Rosenblum. Operating system support for improving data locality on CC-NUMA compute servers. In *Proceedings of the 7th Symposium on Architectural Support for Programming Languages and Operating Systems*, Oct. 1996.

[14] S. Woo, M. Ohara, E. Torrie, J. Singh, and A. Gupta. The SPLASH-2 programs: Characterization and methodological considerations. In *Proceedings of the 22nd Annual International Symposium on Computer Architecture*, pages 24–36, June 1995.

The Effect of Using State–Based Priority Information in a Shared–Memory Multiprocessor Cache Replacement Policy

Farnaz Mounes–Toussi
IBM AS/400 Division
3605 Highway 52 North
Rochester, MN 55901
fmt@vnet.ibm.com

David J. Lilja
Department of Electrical
and Computer Engineering
University of Minnesota
Minneapolis, MN 55455
lilja@ece.umn.edu

Abstract

The cache replacement policy is one of the factors that determines the effectiveness of cache memories. In this paper, we study the impact of incorporating the cache block coherence state information in the Random *replacement policy in a shared–memory multiprocessor. We assign replacement priority to each cache block within a set based on its state. To reduce the probability of replacing a recently accessed block and to adapt to the program's access patterns, we also associate with each set an MRU (Most Recently Used)– state. The MRU–state causes the lowest replacement priority to be assigned to the blocks in the same state as the MRU–state. Our evaluations indicate that, with the appropriate priority assignment and a set associativity size less than 16, the proposed policy can outperform the* Random *and* Random & Invalid *policies and, in some cases, can even outperform the LRU policy.*

1. Introduction

Most general–purpose processors use a cache memory to reduce the average memory delay and thereby reduce the total program execution time. Three primary factors that characterize cache memories are: the write policy, the line (or block) placement policy, and the block replacement policy. The *write policy* determines whether or not data should be forwarded to the memory on every write operation and whether or not the cache blocks are allocated on write misses. The *placement policy* determines how a memory block is mapped to a cache block. Placement policies vary from direct–mapped to set–associative to fully associative. A direct–mapped cache maps each memory block to a unique cache block whether or not the cache block is empty. A fully associative cache, on the other hand, allows a memory block to be mapped to any of the empty cache blocks, if one exists. If there is no empty cache block, a *replacement policy* is used to select one of the cache blocks for replacement. A set–associative cache is a compromise between the direct–mapped and fully–associative placement policies. A set–associative cache divides the cache into sets and allows a memory block to be mapped to any of the empty cache blocks within the set, if an empty cache block exists. Otherwise, similar to a fully associative cache, one of the cache blocks within the set is selected for replacement.

Several cache replacement mechanisms have been proposed and studied [2, 3, 6, 7]. The LRU (Least Recently Used) policy uses a program's memory access patterns to guess that the block that is least likely to be accessed in the near future is the one that has been accessed least recently. This mechanism requires a number of status bits to track when each block is accessed. The number of these bits increases as the set associativity size increases. To reduce the cost and complexity of the LRU policy, the Random policy can be used, but potentially at the expense of performance. Unlike the LRU policy, the Random replacement policy ignores the program's memory access patterns, but it can be implemented as a single counter, for instance.

Several researchers and processor designers have considered both the LRU and Random mechanisms as too extreme either in terms of implementation cost or performance impact, respectively. As alternatives, various PLRU (Partial Least Recently Used) mechanisms have been proposed [2, 3, 7]. A PLRU mechanism reduces the hardware cost and complexity by approximating the LRU mechanism. For instance, in the scheme proposed by So and Rechtschaffen [7], each

217

set is associated with 1 bit which points to the most recently used half of the set. A block is randomly selected for replacement from the least recently used half of the set. This study shows that a 1–bit PLRU policy performs worse than the LRU policy when the set associativity exceeds 8 blocks/set. They conclude that the number of bits used to approximate the LRU algorithm must be proportional to the set size. Deville [2] also presents a replacement policy that keeps the implementation simpler than the complete LRU policy while its performance is held between those of the FIFO and LRU policies.

While these PLRU schemes rely entirely on the hardware, the Priority Data Cache [3] uses both run–time and compile–time information to select a block for replacement. The PDC associates a data priority bit with each cache block. Priorities are assigned by the compiler through two additional bits associated with each memory access instruction. These two bits indicate whether the data priority bit should be set and the priority of the block, i.e. low or high. The cache block with the lowest priority is the one to be replaced. Note that if there is more than one block within a set with low priority, or if the compiler cannot determine whether or not the data priority bit should be set, a standard hardware replacement mechanism is used.

While the LRU and PLRU schemes, and the Priority Data Cache, require some additional hardware and/or software support to capture the program's access patterns, they ignore the cache block state information which is also indicative of the program's characteristics. In this paper, we study the effect of incorporating the state information into one of the existing replacement policies. In particular, we attempt to improve the performance of the Random replacement policy in a shared–memory multiprocessor by prioritizing the cache blocks for replacement based on the state information associated with each cache block within a set. To reduce the probability of replacing a recently accessed block, and to adapt to the program's access patterns, we also associate each set with an MRU (Most Recently Used)–state. The MRU–state causes the lowest replacement priority to be assigned to the blocks in the same state as the MRU–state. Section 2 describes the proposed replacement algorithm in more detail. Sections 3 and 4 then present the simulation methodology and the test programs used in our evaluations. Section 5 presents our simulation results and Section 6 concludes the paper.

2. The replacement algorithm

The basic idea behind the proposed replacement algorithm is to incorporate the additional information about a program's characteristics, which is available in the form of the cache block states, in a replacement algorithm such as Random, LRU, or PLRU to thereby improve performance. Note that the basic algorithm can be applied to either a single processor or a multiprocessor independent of a particular coherence protocol. For simplicity of presentation, however, the following subsection describes a State–Based priority random replacement policy under the following assumptions:

- We assume a shared–memory multiprocessor in which each processor is associated with a private data cache. The processor and the shared–memory communicate through a single shared bus. Each cache block can be in one of the following four states [4].

  - *Invalid* : not present in cache.
  - *Shared* : multiple copies of the block exist and the memory copy is up–to–date.
  - *Exclusive* : only one processor has a copy of the block, and the memory copy is up–to–date.
  - *Modified* : the processor has the only valid copy of the block and the memory copy is stale.

- Cache coherence is maintained by snooping on the shared bus and taking one of the following actions for each different type of memory transaction.

  - **Read hit**: On a read hit the cache can satisfy the processor's request and no additional action is required.
  - **Read miss**: On a read miss, a read–miss request is sent to the bus. Either the memory or one of the caches with a valid copy of the block supplies the block to the requester. Note that there will be a *Modified* to *Shared* state transition if there is a *Modified* cached copy of the block already in the system.
  - **Write miss**: On a write miss, all caches with a valid copy of the block, if any, are invalidated and either the memory or one of the processors supplies the block to the requesting processor. The state of the cached block is set to *modified* as a result of this write miss.

– **Write hit**: A write hit is handled in a fashion similar to a write miss in that all other copies are invalidated. The only difference is that in this case the requester already has a valid copy. If the cached block is in the *Shared* state, the processor sends an invalidate request to get *exclusive* access to the cached block.

2.1. The State–Based priority random replacement policy

Figure 1 shows a flow chart of the proposed replacement policy. As this figure shows, a block in the *Invalid* state is the first choice for replacement. When there is no *Invalid* block within a set, however, a block that is not in the same state as the MRU–state should be chosen for replacement. The MRU–state keeps track of the state of the most recently accessed block within the set and it can be *Shared*, *Exclusive*, or *modified*.

Assuming the replacement priority assignments (from high to low) are *Shared*, *Exclusive*, *Modified*, a block is chosen for replacement in the following manner.

- If there is a block in the *Shared* state such that the state is not equal to the MRU–state, then a block in the *Shared* state is randomly selected.

- Otherwise, if there is a block in the *Exclusive* state such that the state is not equal to the MRU–state, then a block in the *Exclusive* state is randomly selected.

- Otherwise, if there is a block in the *Modified* state such that the state is not equal to the MRU–state, then a block in the *Modified* state is randomly selected.

- Otherwise, a block in the MRU–state is randomly selected.

Note that the MRU–state reduces the priority of the most recently accessed block to decrease the probability of replacing a recently used block. It should also be noted that the priority assignment described above is effective as long as the following program characteristics are true:

- Blocks in the *Shared* state exhibit lower locality than *Modified* or *Exclusive* blocks.

- *Modified* blocks exhibit higher locality than the *Exclusive* blocks.

Since programs' characteristics are different, and so may require different priority assignments, we assume that the priority assignment is programmable. Either the compiler or the programmer determines the appropriate state priority assignment before running the program.

2.2. Implementation of the State–Based random policy

The State–Based random policy associates a bit vector with each set to keep track of the MRU–state. The storage cost associated with the MRU–state is proportional to the number of valid cache block states. Some additional cache controller selection logic is also required for grouping blocks within the accessed set based on their state and for selecting the block with the highest priority. Thus, given the same number of sets, the storage cost of the State–Based random policy is independent of the set associativity size. Although the cache controller selection logic is more complicated than that required for a typical PLRU scheme, our study [5] indicates that the delay through the selection logics are comparable.

3. Evaluation methodology

We use an execution–driven simulator to evaluate the effectiveness of the proposed replacement policy. The simulator consists of a front–end called MINT which was developed at the University of Rochester [8], plus an architecture simulator. MINT executes each instruction in one simulation cycle and sends the events generated by memory operations (read and write) to the architecture simulator. The architecture simulator then performs the operations necessary to simulate the system architecture, including the proposed replacement policy.

The architecture simulator models a 4–processor shared–memory multiprocessor. Each processor includes a set–associative write–back data cache. The cache size varies from 16 to 64 Kbytes with associativities of 2, 4, 8, 16, and 32. The two different cache sizes are used to determine whether or not the test programs' working set fit in the cache. The cache block size is 64 bytes and the coherence protocol is the same as the one described in Section 2.

Using this simulator, we compare the performance effects of the following replacement policies:

- *Random*: randomly selects a block for replacement.

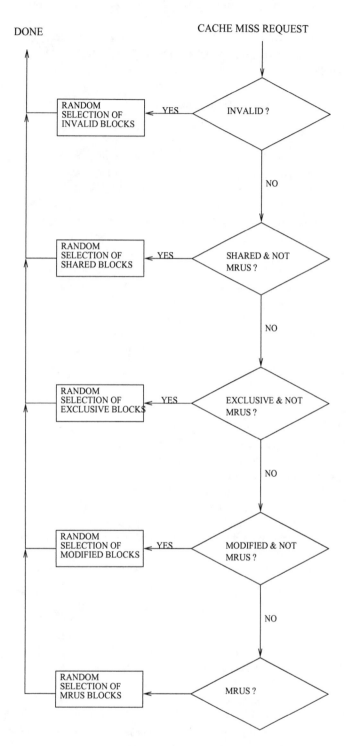

DONE   CACHE MISS REQUEST

Figure 1. The State–Based priority Random replacement algorithm flow chart.

- *Random & Invalid*: selects an *Invalid* block for replacement, if there is one. Otherwise, randomly selects one of the valid blocks.

- *LRU*: Selects the least recently used block for replacement.

- Variations of the State–Based priority policy in which the priority ordering of the states is changed:

  - SEM: 1) *Invalid* (highest priority for replacement), 2) *Shared*, 3) *Exclusive*, 4) *Modified* (lowest priority).

  - SME: 1) *Invalid*, 2) *Shared*, 3) *Modified*, 4) *Exclusive*.

  - MSE: 1) *Invalid*, 2) *Modified*, 3) *Shared*, 4) *Exclusive*.

  - MES: 1) *Invalid*, 2) *Modified*, 3) *Exclusive*, 4) *Shared*.

  - EMS: 1) *Invalid*, 2) *Exclusive*, 3) *Modified*, 4) *Shared*.

  - ESM: 1) *Invalid*, 2) *Exclusive*, 3) *Shared*, 4) *Modified*.

These variations allow us to determine the importance of the priority ordering for the different cache states.

In this study, we use the global system miss ratio, $r_{miss} = n_{miss} / n_{refs}$, as the primary performance metric where n_{miss} is the total number of cache misses in all of the processors and n_{refs} is the total number of read and write references issued by all of the processors.

4. The test programs

Using the *Power Fortran* automatic parallelizing compiler available on the Silicon Graphics Challenge multiprocessor, we created parallel versions of three programs from the NAS Parallel Benchmarks [1]. The Multigrid benchmark (MGRID) solves a 3-D Poisson PDE. The Conjugate Gradient benchmark (CGM) computes an approximation to the smallest eigenvalue of a matrix. The Integer Sort benchmark (BUK) tests a sorting operation which is similar to particle–in–cell applications used in many physics computations. In addition, we used three programs from the SPLASH2 benchmarks [9], RADIX, LU (two versions), and FFT. The FFT algorithm is optimized to minimize interprocessor communication. The RADIX program is an iterative integer sorting algorithm. The LU program factors a matrix into the product of a lower triangular and upper triangular matrix. One version of the

LU program, referred to as LUC, enhances data locality properties by continuous allocation of the memory blocks while the other version, referred to as LU, does not.

5. Results

Figures 2 through 4 show how the *Random & Invalid* policy, and the different variations of the *State–Based priority* policy compare to the traditional *Random* replacement policy. The x–axis is the set associativity size and the y–axis is the percentage of miss ratio improvement or degradation with respect to the *Random* replacement policy. That is, the improvement factor is $(r_{miss-Random} - r_{miss-i}) * 100 / r_{miss-Random}$, where r_{miss-i} can be the *Random & Invalid* policy or one of the *State–Based priority* variations. From these figures we conclude the following:

- The *Random* and *Random & Invalid* policies perform similarly for all of the seven test programs. Thus, giving only invalid blocks priority to be replaced does little to improve performance compared to a completely random policy. This result likely occurs since there are relatively few blocks marked as invalid when a replacement is needed.

- Among the different variations of the State–Based priority policy, the ESM priority ordering performs reasonably well for six out of the seven test programs. That is, except for LUC, the LU program with 16K cache and an associativity of 32, the FFT with 64K cache and associativity sizes of 16 and 32, and MGRID with 16K cache and associativity sizes of 16 and 32, the ESM priority ordering performs up to 34 percent better than the *Random* and the *Random & Invalid* policies.

- Increasing the cache size from 16K to 64K improves the performance impact of the State–Based priority policy with respect to the set associativity size. Increasing the cache size reduces the probability of block replacements, and thus, reduces any positive or negative performance impact of the replacement policy. For instance, with FFT and LU, ESM performs similar to the *Random* and *Random & Invalid* policies with a 16K 8–way set associative cache. With a 64K 8–way set associative cache, on the other hand, the ESM miss ratio is improved by about 2 percent for FFT while for LU it shows about 28 percent improvement. The CGM program, on the other hand, indicates up to 34 percent improvement over the

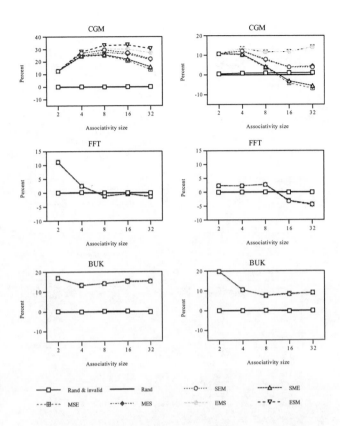

Figure 2. A comparison of the *Random & Invalid,* **the different variations of the** *State–Based priority,* **and the** *Random* **replacement policies with cache sizes of 16 Kbytes on the left and 64 Kbytes on the right.**

Random and *Random & Invalid* policies with a 16K cache and up to 14 percent improvement with a 64K cache.

- A comparison of the LU and LUC programs indicates that the memory allocation can significantly affect the performance of the State–Based priority policy. As Figure 4 shows, in general, any of the priority orderings are preferred over the ESM and SEM priority orderings, which are more likely to replace a shared or exclusive block than a modified block. It appears that the memory allocation has changed the LU program's characteristics so that the modified blocks have lower locality than the shared or exclusive blocks.

Nevertheless, in six out of the seven test programs, the ESM policy performs reasonably well, and, thus, we choose the ESM policy to represent the State–Based priority policy in Figures 5 through 7. These figures show that, in general, the following results hold:

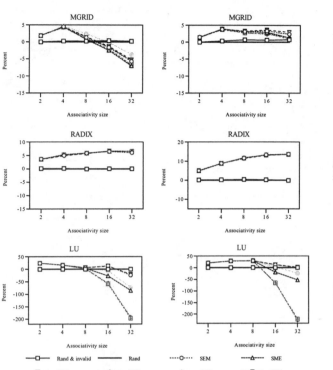

Figure 3. A comparison of the *Random & Invalid*, **the different variations of the** *State–Based priority*, **and the** *Random* **replacement policies with cache sizes of 16 Kbytes on the left and 64 Kbytes on the right.**

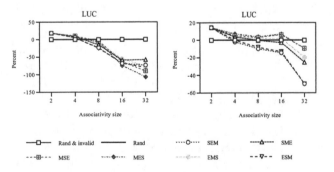

Figure 4. A comparison of the *Random & Invalid*, **the different variations of the** *State–Based priority*, **and the** *Random* **replacement policies with cache sizes of 16 Kbytes on the left and 64 Kbytes on the right.**

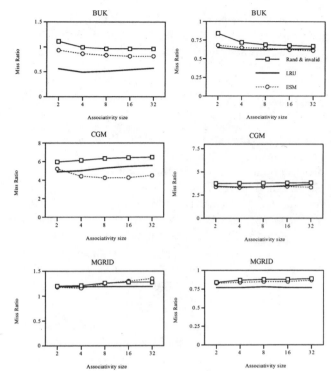

Figure 5. A comparison of the *Random & Invalid*, **the** *ESM* **variation of the** *State–Based priority*, **and the** *LRU* **policies with cache sizes of 16 Kbytes on the left and 64 Kbytes on the right.**

- For RADIX, CGM, BUK, and LU (except for the associativity size of 32 with a 16K cache), the *ESM* policy outperforms the *Random & Invalid* policy by up to 34 percent. Compared to the LRU policy, the ESM miss ratio is within -15 and +48 percent of the LRU miss ratio.

- For FFT and MGRID, the ESM miss ratio is approximately within +5 and -6 percent of the miss ratio generated by the *Random & Invalid* policy. Note that the 6 percent increase in the ESM miss ratio occurs with set associativity sizes greater than 16. As So and Rechtschaffen [7] have shown, increasing the set size requires a more accurate replacement scheme. The ESM policy appears not to be accurate for the two programs FFT and MGRID with set sizes greater than 16.

We conclude that, at least for the limited applications used in this study, with the appropriate priority assignment and a set associativity size less than 16, the State–Based priority policy can outperform the

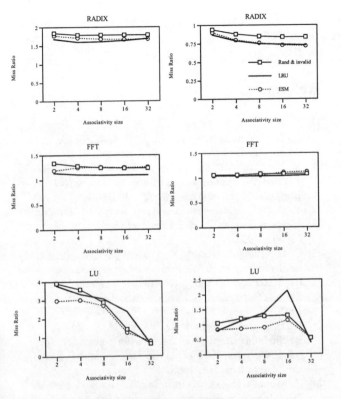

Figure 6. A comparison of the *Random & Invalid*, **the** *ESM* **variation of the** *State-Based priority*, **and the** *LRU* **policies with cache sizes of 16 Kbytes on the left and 64 Kbytes on the right.**

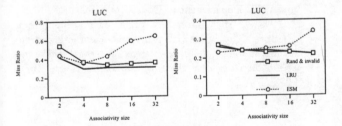

Figure 7. A comparison of the *Random & Invalid*, **the** *ESM* **variation of the** *State-Based priority*, **and the** *LRU* **policies with cache sizes of 16 Kbytes on the left and 64 Kbytes on the right.**

Random and *Random & Invalid* policies and, in some cases, can even outperform the LRU policy.

5.1. The effect of MRU–state

To determine the effect of the MRU–state we consider the State–Based priority random policy with and without the ESM ordering in this section. Figures 8 and 9 show the effect of discarding the ESM ordering and using only the MRU–state to choose a block for replacement. As these figures show for only two of the programs, CGM and LU, the ESM ordering improves the miss ratio by up to 8 percent. With CGM and LU programs the access patterns are such that blocks with different states reside in the same set, and thus, the priority assignment affects performance. With the other four programs, BUK, FFT, MGRID, and RADIX, however, variation of the block states within a set does not appear to be significant enough to cause a performance difference when the ESM ordering is included.

With the LUC program, discarding the ESM ordering and using only the MRU–state improves the miss ratio by up to 27 percent. As pointed out previously, the ESM ordering is not an ideal priority ordering for this program. Although not shown in the figures, the MSE and MES orderings are better for the LUC program and they improve miss ratio of the MRU–state only case by up to 7 percent. Therefore, with the test programs used in our study we can conclude that the MRU–state effect is significant and one may choose to use only the MRU–state to select a block for replacement.

6. Summary

This paper studied the effect of prioritizing cache blocks for replacement based on the state information associated with each cache block within a set. The proposed mechanism keeps track of the state of the most recently accessed block by associating an *MRU-state* with each set. The MRU–state prevents the replacement of a block that is likely to be accessed in the near future. During a cache block replacement, the algorithm selects a non–*MRU-state* block with the highest priority. Our performance evaluations indicate that with the appropriate cache associativity and state priority assignment, the proposed mechanism can outperform the *Random* and *Random & Invalid* policies, and in some cases, can even outperform the LRU replacement policy.

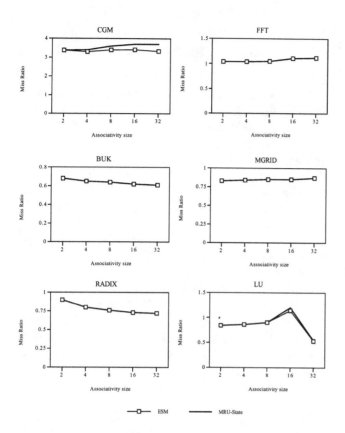

Figure 8. A comparison of the *State–Based priority* **policy with and without the ESM priority assignment and a cache size of 64 Kbytes.**

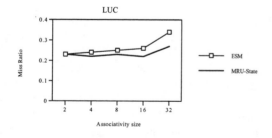

Figure 9. A comparison of the *State–Based priority* **policy with and without the ESM priority assignment and a cache size of 64 Kbytes.**

Acknowledgments

We would like to thank Jack Veenstra for access to the MINT simulator. This work was supported in part by IBM Corporation.

References

[1] D. H. Bailey, E. Barszcz, J. T. Barton, D. S. Browning, R. L. Carter, L. Dagum, R. A. Fatoohi, P. O. Frederickson, T. A. Lasinski, R. S. Schreiber, H. D. Simon, V. Venkatakrishnan, and S. K. Weeratunga. The NAS Parallel Benchmarks. *International Journal of Supercomputer Applications*, 5(3):63–73, 1991.

[2] Y. Deville. A low–cost–based replacement algorithm for cache memories. *Computer Architecture News*, pages 52–58, 1990.

[3] E. D. Granston and A. V. Veidenbaum. An integrated hardware/software solution for effective management of local storage in high–performance systems. *International Conference on Parallel Processing*, pages 83–90, 1991.

[4] R. H. Katz, S. Eggers, D. Wood, C. L. Perkins, and R. Sheldon. Implementing a cache consistency protocol. *International Symposium on Computer Architecture*, pages 276–283, 1985.

[5] F. Mounes-Toussi, K. Imming, D. Krolak, and D. J. Lilja. The implementation impact of state-based priority information in a shared-memory cache replacement policy. Technical Report HPPC-98-05, University of Minnesota, May 1998. High–Performance Parallel Computing Research Group.

[6] A. J. Smith. Cache memories. *ACM Computing Surveys*, 14:473–530, September 1982.

[7] K. So and R. N. Rechtschaffen. Cache operations by MRU change. *IEEE Transactions on Computers*, 37(6):700–707, June 1988.

[8] J. E. Veenstra and R. J. Fowler. MINT tutorial and user manual. Technical Report 452, University of Rochester, June 1993. Department of Computer Science.

[9] S. C. Woo, M. Ohara, E. Torrie, J. P. Singh, and A. Gupta. The SPLASH2 programs: Characterization and methodological considerations. *International Symposium on Computer Architecture*, pages 24–36, June 1995.

Supporting Software Distributed Shared Memory
with an Optimizing Compiler

Tatsushi Inagaki*   Junpei Niwa   Takashi Matsumoto   Kei Hiraki
Department of Information Science, Faculty of Science, University of Tokyo
7-3-1 Hongo, Bunkyo-ku, Tokyo 113 Japan
{ inagaki, niwa, tm, hiraki }@is.s.u-tokyo.ac.jp

Abstract

To execute a shared memory program efficiently, we have to manage memory consistency with low overheads, and have to utilize communication bandwidth of the platform as much as possible. A software distributed shared memory (DSM) can solve these problems via proper support by an optimizing compiler. The optimizing compiler can detect shared write operations, using interprocedural points-to analysis. It also coalesces shared write commitments onto contiguous regions, and removes redundant write commitments, using interprocedural redundancy elimination. A page-based target software DSM system can utilize communication bandwidth, owing to coalescing optimization. We have implemented the above optimizing compiler and a runtime software DSM on AP1000+. We have obtained a high speed-up ratio with the SPLASH-2 benchmark suite. The result shows that using an optimizing compiler to assist a software DSM is a promising approach to obtain a good performance. It also shows that the appropriate protocol selection at a write commitment is an effective optimization.

1. Introduction

Applications using software distributed shared memory (DSM) can run without troubles of unnecessary memory copy and address translation which happen with the inspector/executor mechanism[22]. Most of existing software DSM systems are designed on the assumption of using sequential compilers[23, 20, 19]. An executable object made by a sequential compiler only issues a shared memory access as the ordinary memory access(load/store). To utilize bandwidth, a runtime system has to buffer the remote memory access. There is another approach where a programmer can specify optimal granularity, protocol, and association

between synchronization and shared data[3, 30]. However, with this approach, existing shared memory applications require rewriting.

Our idea is that an optimizing compiler directly analyses shared memory source programs, and optimizes communication and consistency management for software DSM execution[28]. Our target is a page-based software DSM, asymmetric distributed shared memory (ADSM)[26, 25]. ADSM uses a virtual memory mechanism for shared read, and uses explicit user-level consistency management code sequences for shared write. This enables static optimization of shared write operations. Static optimizing information about them can reduce the overhead of the runtime system. Shasta[29] is another software DSM system assuming optimizing compiler support. Since Shasta compiler analyzes objects generated by sequential compilers, it only performs limited local optimizations. Our compiler analyzes a source program directly. Therefore, it performs array data-flow analysis interprocedurally.

Here we have to solve the following three problems in order to show that our approach is effective. First, the compiler must perform sufficient optimization in reasonable compilation time. We have applied interprocedural points-to analysis[14, 31], and implemented interprocedural write set calculation, to detect and optimize shared write operations. We have found out that the above powerful analysis is done in reasonable time. Second, the runtime system also must work efficiently. We had been using a history-based runtime system of lazy release consistency[28]. But when the compiler can not optimize, the system introduces a large runtime overhead and causes the growth of synchronization costs. Therefore, we have implemented a new page-based runtime system with delayed invalidate release consistency (DIRC) model[12] to overcome these problems. We have made sure that the new system is more efficient than the history-based runtime system. Third, we have to provide an interface such that users can give information which the compiler can not extract statically. Memory access patterns of irregular applications depend on input parameters. It is

---

*Presently with Tokyo Research Laboratory, IBM Japan, Ltd.

difficult for a compiler to optimize copy management protocols statically. We have examined the effect of manual protocol selection on the bottleneck shared write operations of the program.

We have evaluated the performances with the SPLASH-2 benchmark suite[32]. SPLASH-2 is not only the most frequently used benchmark to evaluate shared memory systems, but also a benchmark suite with in detailed algorithmic information about each program. We have manually optimized shared write protocols using these descriptions. We do not consider SPLASH-2 as "dusty deck". Our target is to investigate what information from a user or a compiler is required for the efficient execution about shared memory programs on software DSM.

Section 2 describes a process of compilation and optimization. Section 3 describes the implementation of the runtime software DSM. Section 4 describes performance evaluation with SPLASH-2. Section 5 describes related work about a combination of optimizing compiler and software DSM. Section 6 gives a summary.

2. Compilation Process

Figure 1 describes the overall compilation process. The input is a shared memory program written in C extended with PARMACS[4]. PARMACS provides the primitives for task creation, shared memory allocation, and synchronization (barrier, lock, and pause). The consistency of shared memory follows lazy release consistency (LRC) model[20]. Our compiler inserts consistency management code sequences for software DSM into a given shared memory program. The backend sequential compiler compiles the instrumented source program and links it with a runtime library.

To inform the runtime system that a write happened onto a contiguous shared block, we use a pair found by the initial address and the size of of the block. We call this pair a *(shared) write commitment*. Besides the start address and the size, a write commitment also requires the written contents of the block. Therefore, we place a write commitment after the corresponding shared write operations. The single write commitment can represent a lot of shared writes onto a large contiguous region. When there are succeeding write commitments with the same parameters, we can eliminate them but the last one.

2.1. Shared Write Detection

The goal of our optimizing compiler is to insert valid write commitments and to decrease the number of write commitments as much as possible. First we have to enumerate all shared memory access in a given shared memory program. Since the input program is written in C, a shared

address may be contained in a pointer variable and may be passed across procedure calls.

We have applied interprocedural points-to analysis[14, 31] to shared write detection. Interprocedural points-to analysis calculates symbolic locations where variables may point to. Variables and heap locations are represented with a *location set*, a tuple of a symbolic base address, an offset, and a stride. The compiler interprocedurally calculates points-to relations among location sets using a depth-first traversal of the call graph. We track the return values of shared memory allocation primitive (G_MALLOC). We insert a write commitment after a write operation using shared address values.

We adopted interprocedural points-to analysis because of the following merits:

- succeeding optimization passes can perform code motion using pointer information, and

- precise shared pointer information can decrease the costs of the redundancy elimination pass.

Points-to analysis represents all variables as memory locations. This is a conservative assumption in C. When an input program contains unions or type-castings, they may generate false alias information, which takes many iterations to converge. We assume that an input program is type-safe about pointer values, that is pointer values are not conveyed through non-pointer locations. In points-to analysis, we only record pointer assignments into pointer type locations. This assumption prevents generating false alias relations in a program with complex structures.

2.2. Redundancy Elimination

In release consistency model, a shared write is not transmitted to other nodes until the node which had issued the shared write reaches a synchronization. Therefore, it is valid that we place a write commitment everywhere from the corresponding shared write to the first synchronization thereafter. We use this flexibility to remove redundant write commitments.

For example, let us look the following code sequence from LU:

```
a[ii][jj] = ((double) lrand48())/MAXRAND;
if (i == j)
  a[ii][jj] *= 10;
```

Suppose that a[ii][jj] is shared. It is valid that we insert write commitments after both assignments. However, if we delay the first write commitment after the conditional, the write commitment within the conditional is redundant. When we denote a write commitment as WC,

226

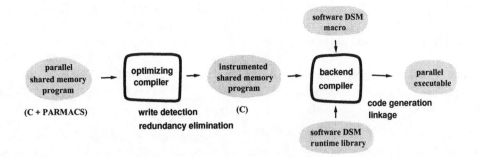

Figure 1. Overall compilation process

```
a[ii][jj] = ((double) lrand48())/MAXRAND;
if (i == j)
  a[ii][jj] *= 10;
WC (&a[ii][jj], 1);
```

Note that this holds if the order between the assignment and the conditional is opposite.

This optimization can be formalized as redundancy elimination[8, 27] of write commitment. Here we represent a statement in a procedure as i. We can consider that i is a node of a control flow graph (CFG) of the procedure. For simplicity, we fix a write commitment with the same address and the same size. From the result of points-to analysis, we obtain the following logical constants about each statement i:

COMP(i)   the statement i issues the shared write

TRANS(i)   the statement i propagates information about the shared write

TRANS(i) is false when the statement i is a synchronization primitive or the statement i modifies the parameters of the write commitment. We can calculate the following logical dataflow variables from these constants:

Availability In all paths which precede the statement i, the shared write is issued

Anticipatability In all paths which succeed the statement i, the shared write is issued

To minimize the number of write commitments, we place write commitments only where,

- the shared write is available,

- the shared write is not available in one of the succeeding paths, and

- the shared write is not anticipatable.

We represent availability before and after execution of the statement i as AVIN(i) and AVOUT(i). Similarly, we represent anticipatability as ANTIN(i) and ANTOUT(i). INSERT(i) is a variable which means we actually place the write commitment after the statement i. Variables are calculated under dataflow equations in Figure 2. Primitives pred(i) and succ(i) represent sets of statements preceding and succeeding the statement i.

$$AVIN(i) = \prod_{p \in pred(i)} AVOUT(p)$$

$$AVOUT(i) = COMP(i) + TRANS(i) \cdot AVIN(i)$$

$$ANTOUT(i) = \prod_{s \in succ(i)} ANTIN(s)$$

$$ANTIN(i) = COMP(i) + TRANS(i) \cdot ANTOUT(i)$$

$$INSERT(i) = AVOUT(i) \cdot \neg \left(\prod_{s \in succ(i)} AVOUT(s) \right)$$
$$\cdot \neg ANTOUT(i)$$

Figure 2. Dataflow equation to remove redundant write commitments

To compute interprocedurally, we reflect AVOUT at the exit of the callee procedure to the COMP at the call site of the caller procedure. When the availability of the callee can not be propagated to the caller, we insert write commitments at the exit of the callee. We call a procedure which is called recursively or called through function pointers, as *open* procedure[7]. An open procedure does not inform availability to the call sites. Therefore, we can consider the call graph is acyclic. The compiler simply calculates interprocedural availability with bottom-up traversal of the call graph. If we want more precise elimination, the compiler also can traverse the call graph in depth-first manner, which is not implemented yet.

2.3. Merging Multiple Write Commitments

A write commitment can handle shared write operations onto a contiguous region. For example, let us look the following code sequence in LU:

```
for (i = 0; i<n; i++)
  a[i] += alpha * b[i];
```

Suppose that a is a shared pointer. Instead of inserting a write commitment into the innermost loop, we can generate:

```
for (i = 0; i<n; i++)
  a[i] += alpha * b[i];
WC (a, n);
```

This code generation has two merits. First, a consistency management overhead is reduced because the write commitment is hoisted out from the loop. Second, the runtime system can utilize the size information for message vectorization.

To combine multiple write commitments, it is convenient to represent a sequence of write commitments as *(shared) write set*. A write set $W = (f, s, C)$ is a tuple, such that f is a start address of a write commitment, s is a size, and C is a set of inequalities which generate write commitments. Inequalities C represent induction variables of enclosing loops around the write commitment.

A dataflow variable takes a set of write sets. The logical operations in the above dataflow equations are considered as set operations. Just after points-to analysis, each write set includes only one write commitment, i.e., $s = 1, C = \emptyset$. We use interval analysis[9, 5] to calculate dataflow equations. In interval analysis, CFG is represented hierarchically with interval (i.e. loop) structures. When a summary of interval is propagated outward, inequalities which represent induction variables are added to C.

We describe optimizing methods to combine multiple write commitments using write set.

Coalescing This is applicable when write commitments onto contiguous locations are issued in a loop. Suppose a write set $W = (f(i), s, C(i))$ and the induction variable i has a increment value c. If $f(i+c) - f(i) = s$, we can replace i with the initial value of i, multiply s by the number of iterations, and remove inequalities about i from C. For the above example,

$$W = (\&a[i], 1, \{0 \le i < n\}) \rightarrow W' = (a, n, \emptyset).$$

Coalescing is applicable when the index variable is only *continuous*. For example, let us look the following code sequence in Radix:

```
for (i=key_start; i<key_stop; i++) {
  this_key = key_from[i] & bb;
  this_key = this_key >> shiftnum;
  tmp = rank_ff_mynum[this_key];
  key_to[tmp] = key_from[i];
  rank_ff_mynum[this_key]++;
} /* i */
```

Suppose key_to points to shared addresses. Variables rank_ff_mynum[this_key] are incremented by one when key_to[tmp] is written. Therefore, we can coalesce write commitments using initial values and final values of rank_ff_mynum[this_key].

Fusion We can also merge write commitments originating in different statements in the program. We represent this operation as a binary operator "∘". For example, let us look the following code sequence in FFT:

```
for (i = 0; i<n1; i++) {
  x[2*i] /= N; x[2*i+1] /= N;
}
```

Suppose x points to shared address,

$$W = (\&x[2 * i], 1, \emptyset), \qquad W' = (\&x[2 * i + 1], 1, \emptyset),$$

$$W \circ W' \rightarrow W'' = (\&x[2 * i], 2, \emptyset)$$

Redundant index elimination When the start address of a write commitment is a constant, we can delegate the write commitment with the maximal size. If we can detect the maximum, this index variable is redundant. We can eliminate redundant indexes using Fourier-Motzkin elimination[11]. Fourier-Motzkin elimination is also applicable to nonlinear but monotonous expressions. For example, in the following write set in FFT,

$$W = (x, 2 * 2^q * (N/2^q), \{1 \le q \le M\}),$$

we can eliminate q, using monotonicity of 2^q and $Q * (N/Q)$, and obtain

$$W \rightarrow W' = (x, 4 * (N/2), \emptyset).$$

The names coalescing and fusion come from the similarity to loop transformations. When a dimension of inequalities in C is decreased, the dimension of generated loop of write commitments is decreased.

When the summary of an interval is computed, we apply coalescing and redundant index elimination to write sets. Fusion is applied to the computation of set union in dataflow equations. When a write set is propagated outward from a loop without coalescing or index elimination, we add inequalities about loop indexes into C. This corresponds to *fission*(or distribution) in loop transformations. Fission does not reduce the number of issued write commitments but improves memory access locality. Along dataflow computation in interval analysis, the compiler repeatedly applies Fourier-Motzkin elimination to the expressions in innermost loops. We use *memorization*[1] technique which stores and reuses the results computed before.

3. Target Software DSM

We implemented a runtime library of ADSM on a Fujitsu AP1000+. The AP1000+ has dedicated hardware which executes remote block transfer operation (put/get interface[18]). We assume that point-to-point message order is preserved.

Formerly, we had been using a history-based runtime system of lazy release consistency[28]. This implementation stores write commitments as a write history. When a synchronization primitive is issued, the page contents are written back to the page-home. This corresponds to a software emulation of automatic update release consistency (AURC)[19]. Diff based implementation compares whole page contents[20]. History based implementation can avoid this when the compiler successfully eliminates and coalesces the write commitments. However, the following two problems exist:

- When the compiler can not optimize, history management introduces a large runtime overhead.

- We handle logical timestamps between each synchronization like LRC and AURC. Frequent synchronization causes long synchronization messages and the growth of synchronization costs.

This time, we have implemented a new page-based runtime system. The basic design is similar to that of SoftFLASH[15] with delayed invalidate release consistency (DIRC) model[12]. We use a write commitment for message vectorization.

3.1. Basic Design

Shared memory is managed by pages. Each page has a page-home node and the user can specify which it is. Each node manages the following bit tables with the size of the number of shared pages.

Valid bit table indicates that the page contents are valid.

Dirty bit table indicates that the node has written into the page with the current synchronization interval[20].

Each node also manages the following bit table with the size of the number of nodes.

Acknowledge table indicates that the node had written into the page of the corresponding page-home node.

Synchronization tags of locks and pauses are handled by specified synchronization-home(i.e., lock-home or pause-home) nodes. Each lock and pause has its own dirty bit table. We describe the behaviors of the runtime system for each primitive.

When a write commitment is issued, the written memory contents are sent to the page-home node with a put operation. The size parameter of the write commitment corresponds to the length of the block transfer. The page-home node is recorded in the acknowledge table.

At an acquire operation, the node receives the dirty bit table from the lock-home processor. The obtained dirty bit table is applied to the valid bit table. The size of synchronization messages are limited by the dirty bit table size because the time information is not utilized at synchronization. However, if a node acquires the same lock again, a page may be invalidated even when the page is not written between lock acquisitions.

In a release operation, the node sends the nodes recorded in the acknowledge table and confirms that all sent messages have arrived to the destinations. Then, the node sends the dirty bit table to the lock-home node.

When a page fault occurs, the page contents are copied from the page-home by a get operation.

At a barrier operation, the following steps are executed:

1. Each node confirms whether all the preceding page-home updates are completed.

2. All nodes send their own dirt bit tables to the master node.

3. The master merges the sent dirty bit tables and broadcasts the merged one.

4. All nodes invalidate their copies using the sent dirty bit table.

5. Each node clears its dirty bit table and the dirty bit table of synchronization tags which it manages.

Communications at page faults and write commitments are handled asynchronously. Acquire and release operations are serialized by sending explicit messages to the synchronization-home nodes. Currently we use CellOS on AP1000+. CellOS does not provide a signal mechanism to users. Therefore, shared memory accesses are not handled by the virtual memory mechanism. But they are executed by code sequences which check valid bit tables. The optimizing compiler inserts this code sequence before each shared memory access. The compiler also inserts message polling[29].

3.2. Protocol Selection at Write Commitment

The above runtime system provides a write-invalidate protocol. We can simulate two other protocols

By modifying behavior at a write commitment, we can select two other protocols[26, 25] at each write commitment.

Broadcast At a write commitment, the writing node sends written contents to all nodes. The node does not set the dirty bit table entry.

Home Only The writer updates the page-home without making a copy. This is achieved by omitting the valid bit table checking of the corresponding shared write.

The broadcast protocol can reduce the communication latency and alleviate false sharing. Broadcast is also useful to efficiently execute a program which is not properly labeled[16]. At the release operation after broadcasting, the sender node must wait for acknowledgments from all nodes. Home only protocol can reduce page fault traffic at fetch-on-write. The contents of the page and the state of the valid bit table entry are temporarily inconsistent until the succeeding synchronization. When a home only write and ordinary page accesses occur in the same page, this may cause incorrect page contents. We introduce the *home only acknowledge table* which records the page-home node for home only write commitments. When a page fault occurs, the node checks this table and waits for an acknowledgment from the page-home node.

To perform the protocol optimization, we have manually specified the type of write commitments in the bottleneck part of a generated source program. When we implement the home only protocol using a virtual memory mechanism, we have to explicitly check the valid bit table at conflicting writes to avoid frequent page faults.

4. Performance Study with SPLASH-2

We used three kernels (LU-Contig, Radix, FFT) and five applications (Barnes, Raytrace, Water-Nsq, Water-Sp, Ocean) from SPLASH-2.

4.1. Compilation Time

At redundancy elimination, we calculated availability with bottom up traversal of the call graph, and calculated ancitipatability intraprocedurally. We show the compilation time of each program in Figure 1. The compiler is run on Sun SPARCstation 20 (with 50MHz SuperSPARC) + SunOS4.1.3. "Scalar dataflow" represents the time to detect induction variables. Without type-safe assumption, points-to analysis takes from 1.4 to 4.2 times longer time for

Table 2. Input problem size and sequential execution time (in seconds)

program	problem size	sequential
LU-Contig	1024^2 doubles	115.67
Radix	1M integer keys	4.32
FFT	64K complex doubles	2.10
Barnes	16K bodies	54.68
Raytrace	balls4, 128^2 pixels	349.38
Water-Nsq	4096 molecules	800.08
Water-Sp	4096 molecules	88.37
Ocean	130^2 ocean	7.09

programs with structures containing pointers (Barnes, Raytrace, and Water-Sp) and for a program with pointer casting (Ocean).

4.2. Runtime System

We show the problem size of each program and the sequential execution time on one node. Each node of the AP1000+ consists of 50MHz SuperSPARC (20KB I-cache and 16KB D-cache) and 16MB memory. The nodes are linked by 2D torus network whose bandwidth is 25MB/s per link. The small problem size of Ocean is caused because of the limit of physical memory size.

The page table checking is implemented by software. If we use a virtual memory mechanism, there is no checking overhead when the page is valid. Coalescing and redundancy elimination are also applicable to the software page table checking. We manually applied redundancy elimination to checking codes using a similar interprocedural algorithm to that of write commitments. We selected 4KB page size for kernels, and 1KB for applications. We used gcc 2.7.2 (the optimizing level is -O2) as the backend compiler.

We modified the source codes of FFT and Raytrace. The transpose operation of the original FFT is written so that a receiver reads the parts of the array. But their page-home nodes are not receivers but senders. This causes a severe false sharing. We rewrote the procedure `Transpose` so that a sender writes to the page-home of receivers. In the original Raytrace, lock acquisition for ray ID is a bottleneck for the execution. This ID is not used for any actual computation. We removed this lock operation. For each program, we specified a page-home and a synchronization-home according to optimization hints of SPLASH-2. We applied protocol optimization to Radix, FFT, Barnes, and Raytrace.

In Figure 3, we show effects of compiler optimization on 32 nodes execution. The left bar of each program is the

Table 1. Compilation time of SPLASH-2 (in seconds)

program	number of lines	type checking	points-to analysis w/ assumption	points-to analysis conservative	scalar dataflow	write set calculation
LU-Contig	980	0.77	4.77	4.78	0.90	0.85
Radix	816	0.56	2.78	3.47	0.66	0.33
FFT	992	0.69	1.23	1.27	0.68	2.26
Barnes	3,052	6.44	16.69	25.31	3.28	1.31
Raytrace	10,910	33.23	18.38	71.26	4.06	2.84
Water-Nsq	2,080	1.64	6.05	6.17	2.44	1.04
Water-Sp	2,748	2.41	30.14	42.70	3.91	3.22
Ocean	4,847	10.70	207.46	897.04	22.84	21.20

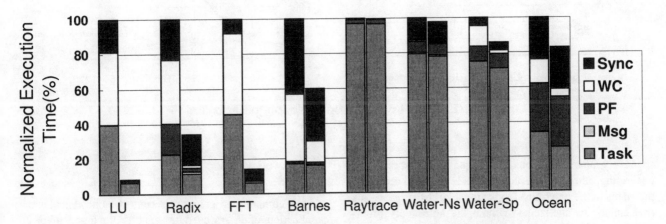

Figure 3. Effects of compiler optimization (executed on 32 nodes)

execution time without compiler optimization (base time). The right bar is that with the optimization. The base run of Radix and FFT use the protocol optimization. Execution time is normalized by the base time. "Sync" means waiting time for synchronization. "WC" means time for write commitment. "PF" means waiting time for page fault. "Msg" is message handling time for synchronization. "Task" is time for the original computation. In LU-Contig, shared writes into each block are coalesced into one write commitment. In Radix, we can apply the previously described coalescing for a continuous variable. In FFT, a write commitment is issued for each column of the block decomposed array. Since LU-Contig, Radix, and FFT contain regular memory accesses in the innermost loops, coalescing reduces from 60% to 90% the total execution time. A write commitment in a innermost loop introduces an overhead of procedure call and reduces memory access locality. Since these overheads are included in task time, optimization also reduces task time. In Radix, the response time of page fault is im-

proved because the traffic of network is reduced by coalescing. In Barnes, the compiler coalesces the write commitments for each record of the structure. Raytrace and Water-Ns have high task ratio and the reduction of execution time is less than 3%. In Ocean, overheads of synchronization and page fault are dominant because of the small problem size. The effect of optimization is confined to 17%.

FFT and Radix are challenging applications for a shared memory system because they potentially require high communication bandwidth because of false sharing[15]. We show effects of protocol optimization to Radix and FFT in Figure 4. In Radix, write operations for the sorted array cause severe false sharing. Since all of the contents of the target array are written at the previous iteration, this traffic can not be reduced by the diff mechanism of LRC. We selected a home only protocol for this write operation. We also selected a broadcast protocol for the array radix which is used by all nodes. The left figure shows speedup ratio of Radix. "w/o BC", "w/o CO", and "w/o HO" re-

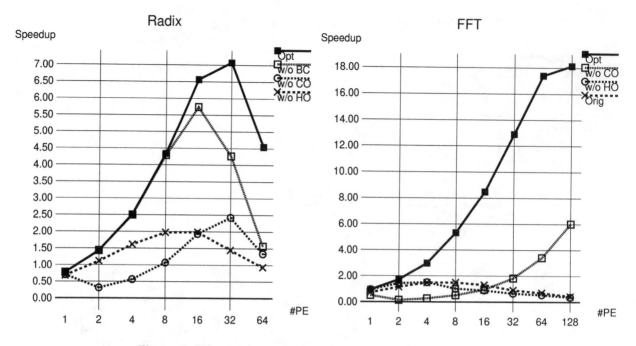

Figure 4. Effects of protocol optimization to Radix and FFT

spectively mean executions without the broadcast protocol, coalescing, and the home only protocol. Though write commitments in the innermost loop cause a large overhead, this part can be parallelized. Without the home only protocol, the performance is saturated over 16 nodes because of heavy traffic. The broadcast protocol is effective also over 16 nodes. The right figure shows the speedup ratio of FFT. "Orig" means the execution of the original SPLASH-2 code. In FFT, the code restructuring of `Transpose` and protocol selection raise the maximal speedup ratio from 1.49 to 18.1.

In Figure 5, we show speedup ratio of the programs with compiler optimization and protocol selection. Because of the low overheads of our runtime system and the utilization of the communication bandwidth, Raytrace, LU-Contig, Water-Ns, and Water-Sp show high speedup ratios and a good scalability. Both in Radix and FFT, an appropriate protocol selection is crucial for scalability. The performance of Barnes is saturated over 32 nodes. In Radix and Barnes, the principal overhead is synchronization because of the problem decomposition. Only Ocean slows down owing to the page fault handling which is an overhead of the runtime system. This is mainly because of the small size of the problem. As a whole, both compiler optimization and appropriate protocol specification are essential for scalability of the input problem.

5. Related Work

The computation power of recent machines enables the application of interprocedural analysis to practical problems (e.g. interprocedural points-to analysis[14, 31], interprocedural array dataflow analysis[17], and interprocedural partial redundancy elimination[2]). So far, these advanced analyses have not been used for explicit parallel shared memory programs.

Existing research about cooperation between optimizing compilers and software DSM can be divided in three kinds. The first is that a parallelizing compiler targets software DSM[21, 13, 24]. For parallelizable programs, the compiler can use precise communication information. Message vectorization is applicable to regular communication. The compiler can use code generation techniques for inspector/executor mechanism. Software DSM does not require complex code generation for multi-level indirection. The runtime library has the benefit of message vectorization, synchronization messages, and support for sender initiated communication. However, this policy is only applicable to automatically parallelizable programs.

The second is that a programmer declares shared data and association between data and synchronization[3, 10, 30, 6]. The programmer can select appropriate protocols for each data. The runtime system can utilize application specific information. Since this model hides a memory model from users, the system does not suffer from false sharing.

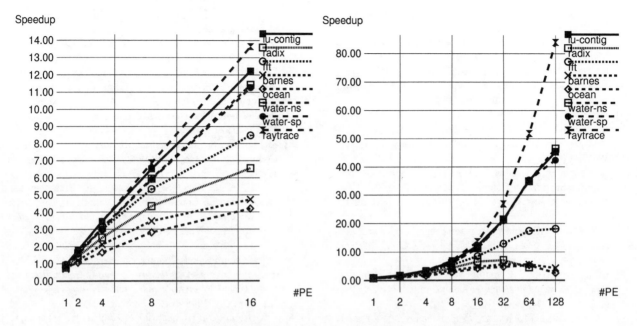

Figure 5. Speedup ratio up to 16 nodes (left) and up to 128 nodes (right)

However, the message packing/unpacking mechanism must be implemented efficiently. Users also have to adjust parallel programs to the provided programming model.

The third is that a compiler directly analyzes a shared memory program. Our system and Shasta[29] are classified in this kind. The Shasta compiler uses two optimizing techniques to reduce software overheads. One is a special flag value which indicates that the content is invalid. If the loaded value is not equal to the flag value, we know that the content is valid without using the page table checking. The other is batching to combine multiple checking for the same entry of the directory. These optimizations are intraprocedural. Since they do not perform loop level optimization, their system requires both high network bandwidth and low latency.

6. Summary

We have shown that compiler support enables efficient software DSM which can utilize communication bandwidth as much as possible. We designed an interface between a shared memory program and a runtime library, and established a coalescing and redundancy elimination problem of write commitments. Our framework enabled applying interprocedural optimizations to a shared memory program. We have described the interprocedural optimization scheme and an efficient implementation of the runtime system. We have shown that the appropriate write protocol selection is one

important application specific information for the efficient software DSM.

The redundancy elimination scheme in this paper decreases the number of write commitment as much as possible and makes the size of the write commitment as large as possible. Therefore, it issues write commitments as late as possible. This policy is suitable for the runtime system on AP1000+, since AP1000+ has a fast communication network. However, this is not always optimal, especially on machines with slower communication facilities. Our future work is to reflect this tradeoff of the platform into dataflow equations.

Acknowledgments

We would like to thank the referees for their valuable comments and aadvice. This work is partly supported by Advanced Information Technology Program (AITP) of Information-technology Promotion Agency (IPA) Japan.

References

[1] H. Abelson, G. J. Sussman, and J. Sussman. *Structure and Interpretation of Computer Programs*. The MIT Press, Cambridge, MA, 1985.

[2] G. Agrawal, J. Saltz, and R. Das. Interprocedural Partial Redundancy Elimination and its Application to Distributed

Memory Compilation. In *Proc. of '95 Conf. on PLDI*, pages 258–269, June 1995.

[3] B. N. Bershad, M. J. Zekauskas, and W. A. Sawdon. The Midway Distributed Shared Memory System. In *Proc. of the 1993 CompCon Conf.*, pages 528–537, Feb. 1993.

[4] J. Boyle et al. *Portable Programs for Parallel Processors*. Holt, Rinehart and Winston, Inc., 1987.

[5] M. Burke. An Interval-Based Approach to Exhaustive and Incremental Interprocedural Data-Flow Analysis. *ACM Trans. on Programming Languages and Systems*, 12(3):341–395, July 1990.

[6] C. Chang, A. Sussman, and J. Saltz. Object-Oriented Runtime Support for Complex Distributed Data Structures. Technical Report CS-TR-3428, University of Maryland, Mar. 1995.

[7] F. C. Chow. Minimizing Register Usage Penalty at Procedure Calls. In *Proc. of the SIGPLAN '88 Conf. on PLDI*, pages 85–94, June 1988.

[8] J. Cocke. Global Common Subexpression Elimination. *Proc. of a Symp. on Compiler Optimization, SIGPLAN Notices*, 5(7):20–24, July 1970.

[9] J. Cocke and J. T. Schwartz. *Programming Languages and Their Compiler*. New York University Press, 2nd edition, Apr. 1970.

[10] D. E. Culler et al. Parallel Programming in Split-C. In *Proc. of Supercomputing '93*, pages 262–273, Nov. 1993.

[11] G. B. Dantzig and B. C. Evans. Fourier-Motzkin Elimination and Its Dual. *Journal of Combinatorial Theory*, A(14):288–297, 1973.

[12] M. Dubois. *Scalable Shared Memory Multiprocessors*, chapter 11, Delayed Consistency, pages 207–218. Kluwer Academic Publishers, MA, 1992.

[13] S. Dwarkadas, A. L. Cox, and W. Zwaenepoel. An Integrated Compile-Time/Run-Time Software Distributed Shared Memory System. In *Proc. of the ASPLOS-VII*, Oct. 1996.

[14] M. Emami, R. Ghiya, and L. J. Hendren. Context-Sensitive Interprocedural Points-to Analysis in the Presence of Function Pointers. In *Proc. of '94 Conf. on PLDI*, pages 242–256, June 1994.

[15] A. Erlichson, N. Nuckolls, G. Chesson, and J. Hennessy. SoftFLASH: Analyzing the Performance of Clusterd Distributed Virtutal Shared Memory. In *Proc. of ASPLOS-VII*, pages 210–220, Oct. 1996.

[16] K. Gharachorloo, D. Lenoski, J. Laudon, P. Gibbons, A. Gupta, and J. Hennessy. Memory Consistency and Event Ordering in Scalable Shared-Memory Multiprocessors. In *Proc. of the 17th ISCA*, pages 15–26, May 1990.

[17] M. W. Hall, B. R. Murphy, S. P. Amarasinghe, S. Liao, and M. S. Lam. Interprocedural Analysis for Parallelization. In *Proc. of the 8th Int. Workshop on LCPC*. Springer-Verlag, Aug. 1995.

[18] K. Hayashi et al. AP1000+: Architectural Support for Parallelizing Compilers and Parallel Programs. In *Proc. of the 3rd Parallel Computing Workshop*, pages P1–F–1 – P1–F–9, Nov. 1994.

[19] L. Iftode, C. Dubnicki, E. W. Felten, and K. Li. Improving Release-Consistent Shared Virtual Memory using Automatic Update. In *Proc. of the 2nd HPCA*, Feb. 1996.

[20] P. Keleher, A. L. Cox, and W. Zwaenepoel. Lazy Release Consistency for Software Distributed Shared Memory. In *Proc. of the 19th ISCA*, pages 13–21, May 1992.

[21] P. Keleher and C. Tseng. Enhancing Software DSM for Compiler-Parallelized Applications. In *Proc. of the 11th International Parallel Processing Symp.*, Mar. 1996.

[22] C. Koelbel and P. Mehrotra. Compiling Global Name-Space Parallel Loops for Distributed Execution. *IEEE Trans. on Parallel and Distributed Systems*, 2(4):440–451, Oct. 1991.

[23] K. Li. IVY: A Shared Virtual Memory System for Parallel Computing. In *Proc. of the 1988 ICPP*, pages 94–101, Aug. 1988.

[24] H. Lu, A. L. Cox, S. Dwarkadas, R. Rajamony, and W. Zwaenepoel. Compiler and Software Distributed Shared Memory Support for Irregular Applications. In *Proc. of the Symp. on PPoPP*, pages 48–56, 1997.

[25] T. Matsumoto and K. Hiraki. Memory-Based Communication Facilities and Asymmetric Distributed Shared Memory. In *Innovative Architecture for Future Generation High-Performance Processors and Systems*, pages 30–39, Los Alamitos, CA, 1998. IEEE Computer Society.

[26] T. Matsumoto, T. Komaarashi, S. Uzuhara, S. Takeoka, and K. Hiraki. A General-Purpose Massively-Parallel Operating System: SSS-CORE – Implementation Methods for Network of Workstations –. In *IPSJ SIG Notes*, volume 96-OS-73, pages 115–120, Aug. 1996. (in Japanese).

[27] E. Morel and C. Renvoise. Global Optimization by Suppression of Partial Redundancies. *CACM*, 22(2):96–103, Feb. 1979.

[28] J. Niwa, T. Inagaki, T. Matsumoto, and K. Hiraki. Efficient Implementation of Software Release Consistency on Asymmetric Distributed Shared Memory. In *Proc. of the 1997 ISPAN*, pages 198–201, Dec. 1997.

[29] D. J. Scales, K. Gharachorloo, and C. A. Thekkath. Shasta: A Low Overhead, Software-Only Approach for Supporting Fine-Grain Shared Memory. In *Proc. of ASPLOS-VII*, pages 174–185, Oct. 1996.

[30] D. J. Scales and M. S. Lam. The Design and Evaluation of a Shared Object System for Distributed Memory Machines. In *Proc. of the 1st OSDI*, Nov. 1994.

[31] R. P. Wilson and M. S. Lam. Efficient Context-Sensitive Pointer Analysis for C Programs. In *Proc. of '95 Conf. on PLDI*, pages 1–12, June 1995.

[32] S. C. Woo, M. Ohara, E. Torrie, J. P. Singh, and A. Gupta. The SPLASH-2 Programs: Characterization and Methodological Considerations. In *Proc. of the 22nd ISCA*, pages 24–36, June 1995.

Keynote Address
Implementing Parallelism on Silicon

Speaker: C.L. Wu
National Chiao Tung University

Session 4A
Applications and Algorithms II

Chair: Sandeep Gupta
Colorado State University

Parallel Formulations of Decision-Tree Classification Algorithms*

Anurag Srivastava
Information Technology Lab
Hitachi America, Ltd.
anurags@hitachi.com

Eui-Hong (Sam) Han
Dept. of Computer Science
Army HPC Research Center
University of Minnesota
han@cs.umn.edu

Vipin Kumar
Dept. of Computer Science
Army HPC Research Center
University of Minnesota
kumar@cs.umn.edu

Vineet Singh
Information Technology Lab
Hitachi America, Ltd.
vsingh@hitachi.com

Abstract

Classification decision tree algorithms are used extensively for data mining in many domains such as retail target marketing, fraud detection, etc. Highly parallel algorithms for constructing classification decision trees are desirable for dealing with large data sets in reasonable amount of time. Algorithms for building classification decision trees have a natural concurrency, but are difficult to parallelize due to the inherent dynamic nature of the computation. In this paper, we present parallel formulations of classification decision tree learning algorithm based on induction. We describe two basic parallel formulations. One is based on Synchronous Tree Construction Approach and the other is based on Partitioned Tree Construction Approach. We discuss the advantages and disadvantages of using these methods and propose a hybrid method that employs the good features of these methods. Experimental results on an IBM SP-2 demonstrate excellent speedups and scalability.

1. Introduction

Classification is an important data mining problem. A classification problem has an input dataset called the training set which consists of a number of examples each having a number of attributes. The attributes are either *continuous*, when the attribute values are ordered, or *categorical*, when the attribute values are unordered. One of the categorical attributes is called the *class label* or the *classifying attribute*. The objective is to use the training dataset to build a model of the class label based on the other attributes such that the model can be used to classify new data not from the training dataset. Application domains include retail target marketing, fraud detection, and design of telecommunication service plans. Several classification models like neural networks [11], genetic algorithms [7], and decision trees [13] have been proposed. Decision trees are probably the most popular since they obtain reasonable accuracy [6] and they are relatively inexpensive to compute. Most current classification algorithms such as *C4.5* [13], and *SLIQ* [12] are based on the *ID3* classification decision tree algorithm [13].

In the data mining domain, the data to be processed tends to be very large. Hence, it is highly desirable to design computationally efficient as well as scalable algorithms. One way to reduce the computational complexity of building a decision tree classifier using large training datasets is to use only a small sample of the training data. Such methods do not yield the same classification accuracy as a decision tree classifier that uses the entire data set [4, 5]. In order to get reasonable accuracy in a reasonable amount of time, parallel algorithms may be required.

Classification decision tree construction algorithms have natural concurrency, as once a node is generated, all of its children in the classification tree can be generated concurrently. Furthermore, the computation for generating successors of a classification tree node can also be decomposed by performing data decomposition on the training data. Nevertheless, parallelization of the algorithms for construction the classification tree is challenging for the following reasons.

*A significant part of this work was done while Anurag Srivastava and Vineet Singh were at IBM TJ Watson Research Center. This work was supported by NSF grant ASC-9634719, Army Research Office contract DA/DAAH04-95-1-0538, Cray Research Inc. Fellowship, and IBM partnership award, the content of which does not necessarily reflect the policy of the government, and no official endorsement should be inferred. Access to computing facilities was provided by AHPCRC, Minnesota Supercomputer Institute, Cray Research Inc., and NSF grant CDA-9414015.

First, the shape of the tree is highly irregular and is determined only at runtime. Furthermore, the amount of work associated with each node also varies, and is data dependent. Hence any static allocation scheme is likely to suffer from major load imbalance. Second, even though the successors of a node can be processed concurrently, they all use the training data associated with the parent node. If this data is dynamically partitioned and allocated to different processors that perform computation for different nodes, then there is a high cost for data movements. If the data is not partitioned appropriately, then performance can be bad due to the loss of locality.

In this paper, we present parallel formulations of classification decision tree learning algorithm based on induction. We describe two basic parallel formulations. One is based on *Synchronous Tree Construction Approach* and the other is based on *Partitioned Tree Construction Approach*. We discuss the advantages and disadvantages of using these methods and propose a hybrid method that employs the good features of these methods. Experimental results on an IBM SP-2 demonstrate excellent speedups and scalability.

2. Sequential Classification Rule Learning Algorithms

Most of the existing induction–based algorithms like *C4.5* [13], *CDP* [1], *SLIQ* [12], and *SPRINT* [14] use Hunt's method [13] as the basic algorithm. Here is a recursive description of Hunt's method for constructing a decision tree from a set T of training cases with classes denoted $\{C_1, C_2, \ldots, C_k\}$.

Case 1 T contains cases all belonging to a single class C_j. The decision tree for T is a leaf identifying class C_j.

Case 2 T contains cases that belong to a mixture of classes. A test is chosen, based on a single attribute, that has one or more mutually exclusive outcomes $\{O_1, O_2, \ldots, O_n\}$. Note that in many implementations, n is chosen to be 2 and this leads to a binary decision tree. T is partitioned into subsets $T_1, T_2, \ldots, T_n$, where T_i contains all the cases in T that have outcome O_i of the chosen test. The decision tree for T consists of a decision node identifying the test, and one branch for each possible outcome. The same tree building machinery is applied recursively to each subset of training cases.

Case 3 T contains no cases. The decision tree for T is a leaf, but the class to be associated with the leaf must be determined from information other than T. For example, *C4.5* chooses this to be the most frequent class at the parent of this node.

The *C4.5* algorithm generates a classification–decision tree for the given training data set by recursively partitioning the data. The decision tree is grown using depth–first strategy. The algorithm considers all the possible tests that can split the data set and selects a test that gives the best information gain. For each discrete attribute, one test with outcomes as many as the number of distinct values of the attribute is considered. For each continuous attribute, binary tests involving every distinct value of the attribute are considered. In order to gather the entropy gain of all these binary tests efficiently, the training data set belonging to the node in consideration is sorted for the values of the continuous attribute and the entropy gains of the binary cut based on each distinct values are calculated in one scan of the sorted data. This process is repeated for each continuous attribute.

Recently proposed classification algorithms *SLIQ* [12] and *SPRINT* [14] avoid costly sorting at each node by presorting continuous attributes once in the beginning. In *SPRINT*, each continuous attribute is maintained in a sorted attribute list. In this list, each entry contains a value of the attribute and its corresponding record id. Once the best attribute to split a node in a classification tree is determined, each attribute list has to be split according to the split decision. A hash table, of the same order as the number of training cases, has the mapping between record ids and where each record belongs according to the split decision. Each entry in the attribute list is moved to a classification tree node according to the information retrieved by probing the hash table. The sorted order is maintained as the entries are moved in pre-sorted order.

Decision trees are usually built in two steps. First, an initial tree is built till the leaf nodes belong to a single class only. Second, pruning is done to remove any *overfitting* to the training data. Typically, the time spent on pruning for a large dataset is a small fraction, less than 1% of the initial tree generation. Therefore, in this paper, we focus on the initial tree generation only and not on the pruning part of the computation.

3. Parallel Formulations

In this section, we give two basic parallel formulations for the classification decision tree construction and a hybrid scheme that combines good features of both of these approaches. We focus our presentation for discrete attributes only. The handling of continuous attributes is discussed in Section 3.4. In all parallel formulations, we assume that N training cases are randomly distributed to P processors initially such that each processor has N/P cases.

3.1. Synchronous Tree Construction Approach

In this approach, all processors construct a decision tree synchronously by sending and receiving class distribution information of local data. Major steps for the approach are shown below:

1. Select a node to expand according to a decision tree expansion strategy (eg. Depth-First or Breadth-First), and call that node as the current node. At the beginning, root node is selected as the current node.

2. For each data attribute, collect class distribution information of the local data at the current node.

3. Exchange the local class distribution information using global reduction [10] among processors.

4. Simultaneously compute the entropy gains of each attribute at each processor and select the best attribute for child node expansion.

5. Depending on the branching factor of the tree desired, create child nodes for the same number of partitions of attribute values, and split training cases accordingly.

6. Repeat above steps (1–5) until no more nodes are available for the expansion.

The advantage of this approach is that it does not require any movement of the training data items. However, this algorithm suffers from high communication cost and load imbalance. For each node in the decision tree, after collecting the class distribution information, all the processors need to synchronize and exchange the distribution information. At the nodes of shallow depth, the communication overhead is relatively small, because the number of training data items to be processed is relatively large. But as the decision tree grows and deepens, the number of training set items at the nodes decreases and as a consequence, the computation of the class distribution information for each of the nodes decreases. If the average branching factor of the decision tree is k, then the number of data items in a child node is on the average $\frac{1}{k}$th of the number of data items in the parent. However, the size of communication does not decrease as much, as the number of attributes to be considered goes down only by one. Hence, as the tree deepens, the communication overhead dominates the overall processing time.

The other problem is due to load imbalance. Even though each processor started out with the same number of the training data items, the number of items belonging to the same node of the decision tree can vary substantially among processors. For example, processor 1 might have all the data items on leaf node A and none on leaf node B, while processor 2 might have all the data items on node B and none on node A. When node A is selected as the current node, processor 2 does not have any work to do and similarly when node B is selected as the current node, processor 1 has no work to do.

This load imbalance can be reduced if all the nodes on the frontier are expanded simultaneously, i.e. one pass of all the data at each processor is used to compute the class distribution information for all nodes on the frontier. Note that this improvement also reduces the number of times communications are done and reduces the message start–up overhead, but it does not reduce the overall volume of communications.

In the rest of the paper, we will assume that in the synchronous tree construction algorithm, the classification tree is expanded breadth-first manner and all the nodes at a level will be processed at the same time. The level of the tree being processed at a particular time is referred as the current frontier of the tree.

3.2. Partitioned Tree Construction Approach

In this approach, whenever feasible, different processors work on different parts of the classification tree. In particular, if more than one processors cooperate to expand a node, then these processors are partitioned to expand the successors of this node. Consider the case in which a group of processors P_n cooperate to expand node n. The algorithm consists of following steps:

Step 1 Processors in P_n cooperate to expand node n using the method described in Section 3.1.

Step 2 Once the node n is expanded in to successor nodes, $n_1, n_2, \ldots, n_k$, then the processor group P_n is also partitioned, and the successor nodes are assigned to processors as follows:

Case 1: If the number of successor nodes is greater than $|P_n|$,

1. Partition the successor nodes into $|P_n|$ groups such that the total number of training cases corresponding to each node group is roughly equal. Assign each processor to one node group.

2. Shuffle the training data such that each processor has data items that belong to the nodes it is responsible for.

3. Now the expansion of the subtrees rooted at a node group proceeds completely independently at each processor as in the serial algorithm.

Case 2: Otherwise (if the number of successor nodes is less than $|P_n|$),

1. Assign a subset of processors to each node such that number of processors assigned to a node is proportional to the number of the training cases corresponding to the node.

2. Shuffle the training cases such that each subset of processors has training cases that belong to the nodes it is responsible for.

3. Processor subsets assigned to different nodes develop subtrees independently. Processor subsets that contain only one processor use the sequential algorithm to expand the part of the classification tree rooted at the node assigned to them. Processor subsets that contain more than one processor proceed by following the above steps recursively.

At the beginning, all processors work together to expand the root node of the classification tree. At the end, the whole classification tree is constructed by combining subtrees of each processor.

Figure 1 shows an example. First (at the top of the figure), all four processors cooperate to expand the root node just like they do in the synchronous tree construction approach. Next (in the middle of the figure), the set of four processors is partitioned in three parts. The leftmost child is assigned to processors 0 and 1, while the other nodes are assigned to processors 2 and 3, respectively. Now these sets of processors proceed independently to expand these assigned nodes. In particular, processors 2 and processor 3 proceed to expand their part of the tree using the serial algorithm. The group containing processors 0 and 1 splits the leftmost child node into three nodes. These three new nodes are partitioned in two parts (shown in the bottom of the figure); the leftmost node is assigned to processor 0, while the other two are assigned to processor 1. From now on, processors 0 and 1 also independently work on their respective subtrees.

The advantage of this approach is that once a processor becomes solely responsible for a node, it can develop a subtree of the classification tree independently without any communication overhead. However, there are a number of disadvantages of this approach. The first disadvantage is that it requires data movement after each node expansion until one processor becomes responsible for an entire subtree. The communication cost is particularly expensive in the expansion of the upper part of the classification tree. (Note that once the number of nodes in the frontier exceeds the number of processors, then the communication cost becomes zero.) The second disadvantage is poor load balancing inherent in the algorithm. Assignment of nodes to processors is done based on the number of training cases in the successor nodes. However, the number of training cases associated with a node does not necessarily correspond to the amount of work needed to process the subtree rooted at the node. For example, if all training cases associated with a node happen to have the same class label, then no further expansion is needed.

3.3. Hybrid Parallel Formulation

Our hybrid parallel formulation has elements of both schemes. The *Synchronous Tree Construction Approach* in Section 3.1 incurs high communication overhead as the

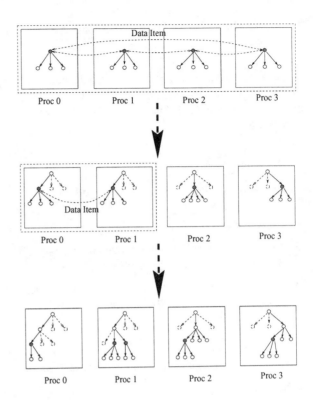

Figure 1. Partitioned Tree Construction Approach

frontier gets larger. The *Partitioned Tree Construction Approach* of Section 3.2 incurs cost of load balancing after each step. The hybrid scheme keeps continuing with the first approach as long as the communication cost incurred by the first formulation is not too high. Once this cost becomes high, the processors as well as the current frontier of the classification tree are partitioned into two parts.

Our description assumes that the number of processors is a power of 2, and that these processors are connected in a hypercube configuration. The algorithm can be appropriately modified if P is not a power of 2. Also this algorithm can be mapped on to any parallel architecture by simply embedding a virtual hypercube in the architecture. More precisely the hybrid formulation works as follows.

- The database of training cases is split equally among P processors. Thus, if N is the total number of training cases, each processor has N/P training cases locally. At the beginning, all processors are assigned to one partition. The root node of the classification tree is allocated to the partition.

- All the nodes at the frontier of the tree that belong to one partition are processed together using the synchronous tree construction approach of Section 3.1.

- As the depth of the tree within a partition increases, the volume of statistics gathered at each level also in-

240

creases as discussed in Section 3.1. At some point, a level is reached when communication cost become prohibitive. At this point, the processors in the partition are divided into two partitions, and the current set of frontier nodes are split and allocated to these partitions in such a way that the number of training cases in each partition is roughly equal. This load balancing is done as described as follows:

- On a hypercube, each of the two partitions naturally correspond to a sub-cube. First, corresponding processors within the two sub-cubes exchange relevant training cases to be transferred to the other sub-cube. After this exchange, processors within each sub-cube collectively have all the training cases for their partition, but the number of training cases at each processor can vary between 0 to $\frac{2*N}{P}$. Now, a load balancing step is done within each sub-cube so that each processor has an equal number of data items.

- Now, further processing within each partition proceeds asynchronously. The above steps are now repeated in each one of these partitions for the particular subtrees. This process is repeated until a complete classification tree is grown.

- If a group of processors in a partition become idle, then this partition joins up with any other partition that has work and has the same number of processors. This can be done by simply giving half of the training cases located at each processor in the donor partition to a processor in the receiving partition.

A key element of the algorithm is the criterion that triggers the partitioning of the current set of processors (and the corresponding frontier of the classification tree). If partitioning is done too frequently, then the hybrid scheme will approximate the partitioned tree construction approach, and thus will incur too much data movement cost. If the partitioning is done too late, then it will suffer from high cost for communicating statistics generated for each node of the frontier, like the synchronized tree construction approach. One possibility is to do splitting when the accumulated cost of communication becomes equal to the cost of moving records around in the splitting phase. More precisely, splitting is done when

$$\sum (\text{Communication Cost}) \geq \text{Moving Cost} + \text{Load Balancing}$$

3.4. Handling Continuous Attributes

Note that handling continuous attributes requires sorting. If each processor contains N/P training cases, then one approach for handling continuous attributes is to perform a parallel sorting step for each such attribute at each node of the decision tree being constructed. Once this parallel sorting is completed, each processor can compute the best local value for the split, and then a simple global communication among all processors can determine the globally best

splitting value. However, the step of parallel sorting would require substantial data exchange among processors. The exchange of this information is of similar nature as the exchange of class distribution information, except that it is of much higher volume. Hence even in this case, it will be useful to use a scheme similar to the hybrid approach discussed in Section 3.3.

A more efficient way of handling continuous attributes without incurring the high cost of repeated sorting is to use the pre-sorting technique used in algorithms *SLIQ* [12], *SPRINT* [14], and *ScalParC* [9]. These algorithms require only one pre-sorting step, but need to construct a hash table at each level of the classification tree. In the parallel formulations of these algorithms, the content of this hash table needs to be available globally, requiring communication among processors. Existing parallel formulations of these schemes [14, 9] perform communication that is similar in nature to that of our synchronous tree construction approach discussed in Section 3.1. Once again, communication in these formulations [14, 9] can be reduced using the hybrid scheme of Section 3.3.

Another completely different way of handling continuous attributes is to discretize them once as a preprocessing step [8]. In this case, the parallel formulations as presented in the previous subsections are directly applicable without any modification.

Another approach towards discretization is to discretize at every node in the tree. There are two examples of this approach. The first example can be found in [3] where quantiles [2] are used to discretize continuous attributes. The second example of this approach to discretize at each node is *SPEC* [15] where a clustering technique is used. *SPEC* has been shown to be very efficient in terms of runtime and has also been shown to perform essentially identical to several other widely used tree classifiers in terms of classification accuracy [15]. Parallelization of the discretization at every node of the tree is similar in nature to the parallelization of the computation of entropy gain for discrete attributes, because both of these methods of discretization require some global communication among all the processors that are responsible for a node. In particular, parallel formulations of the clustering step in *SPEC* is essentially identical to the parallel formulations for the discrete case discussed in the previous subsections [15].

4. Experimental Results

We have implemented the three parallel formulations using the MPI programming library. We use binary splitting at each decision tree node and grow the tree in breadth first manner. For generating large datasets, we have used the widely used synthetic dataset proposed in the *SLIQ* paper [12] for all our experiments. Ten classification functions were also proposed in [12] for these datasets. We have used the function 2 dataset for our algorithms. In this dataset, there are two class labels and each record consists of 9 attributes having 3 categoric and 6 continuous attributes. The same dataset was also used by the *SPRINT* algorithm [14] for evaluating its performance. Experiments were done on an IBM SP2. The results for comparing speedup of the three parallel formulations are reported for parallel runs on 1, 2, 4, 8, and 16 processors. More experiments for the hybrid approach are reported for up to 128 processors. Each processor has a clock speed of 66.7 MHz with 256 MB real memory. The operating system is AIX version 4 and the processors communicate through a high performance switch (hps). In our implementation, we keep the "attribute lists" on disk and use the memory only for storing program specific data structures, the class histograms and the clustering structures.

First, we present results of our schemes in the context of discrete attributes only. We compare the performance of the three parallel formulations on up to 16 processor IBM SP2. For these results, we discretized 6 continuous attributes uniformly. Specifically, we discretized the continuous attribute *salary* to have 13, *commission* to have 14, *age* to have 6, *hvalue* to have 11, *hyears* to have 10, and *loan* to have 20 equal intervals. For measuring the speedups, we worked with different sized datasets of 0.8 million training cases and 1.6 million training cases. We increased the processors from 1 to 16. The results in Figure 2 show the speedup comparison of the three parallel algorithms proposed in this paper. The graph on the left shows the speedup with 0.8 million examples in the training set and the other graph shows the speedup with 1.6 million examples.

The results show that the synchronous tree construction approach has a good speedup for 2 processors, but it has a very poor speedup for 4 or more processors. There are two reasons for this. First, the synchronous tree construction approach incurs high communication cost, while processing lower levels of the tree. Second, a synchronization has to be done among different processors as soon as their communication buffer fills up. The communication buffer has the histograms of all the discrete variables for each node. Thus, the contribution of each node is independent of its tuples count, the tuple count at a node being proportional to the computation to process that node. While processing lower levels of the tree, this synchronization is done many times at each level (after every 100 nodes for our experiments). The distribution of tuples for each decision tree node becomes quite different lower down in the tree. Therefore, the processors wait for each other during synchronization, and thus, contribute to poor speedups.

The partitioned tree construction approach has a better speedup than the synchronous tree construction approach. However, its efficiency decreases as the number of processors increases to 8 and 16. The partitioned tree construction approach suffers from load imbalance. Even though nodes are partitioned so that each processor gets equal number of tuples, there is no simple way of predicting the size of the subtree for that particular node. This load imbalance leads to the runtime being determined by the most heavily loaded processor. The partitioned tree construction approach also suffers from the high data movement during each partitioning phase, the partitioning phase taking place at higher levels of the tree. As more processors are involved, it takes longer to reach the point where all the processors work on their local data only. We have observed in our experiments that load imbalance and higher communication, in that order, are the major cause for the poor performance of the partitioned tree construction approach as the number of processors increase.

The hybrid approach has a superior speedup compared to the partitioned tree approach as its speedup keeps increasing with increasing number of processors. As discussed in Section 3.3, the hybrid controls the communication cost and data movement cost by adopting the advantages of the two basic parallel formulations. The hybrid strategy also waits long enough for splitting, until there are large number of decision tree nodes for splitting among processors. Due to the allocation of decision tree nodes to each processor being randomized to a large extent, good load balancing is possible. The results confirmed that the proposed hybrid approach based on these two basic parallel formulations is effective.

We have also performed experiments to verify that our splitting criterion of the hybrid algorithm is correct. Figure 3 shows the runtime of the hybrid algorithm with different ratio of communication cost and the sum of moving cost and load balancing cost, i.e.,

$$ratio = \frac{\sum(\text{Communication Cost})}{\text{Moving Cost} + \text{Load Balancing}}.$$

The graph on the left shows the result with 0.8 million examples on 8 processors and the other graph shows the result with 1.6 million examples on 16 processors. We proposed that splitting when this ratio is 1.0 would be the optimal time. The results verified our hypothesis as the runtime is the lowest when the ratio is around 1.0. The graph on the right with 1.6 million examples shows more clearly why the splitting choice is critical for obtaining a good performance. As the splitting decision is made farther away from the optimal point proposed, the runtime increases significantly.

The experiments on 16 processors clearly demonstrated that the hybrid approach gives a much better performance and the splitting criterion used in the hybrid approach is close to optimal. We then performed experiments of running the hybrid approach on more number of processors with different sized datasets to study the speedup and scalability. For these experiments, we used the original data set with continuous attributes and used a clustering technique to dis-

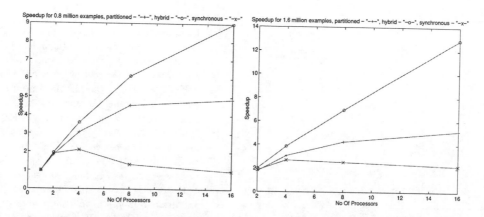

Figure 2. Speedup comparison of the three parallel algorithms.

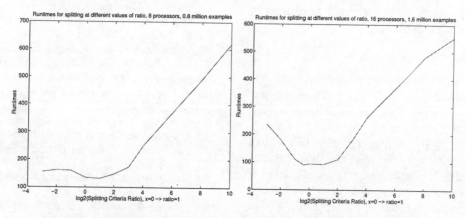

Figure 3. Splitting criterion verification in the hybrid algorithm.

cretize continuous attributes at each decision tree node [15]. Note that the parallel formulation gives *almost identical* performance as the serial algorithm in terms of accuracy and classification tree size [15]. The results in Figure 4 show the speedup of the hybrid approach. The results confirm that the hybrid approach is indeed very effective.

5. Concluding Remarks

In this paper, we proposed three parallel formulations of inductive-classification learning algorithm. The *Synchronous Tree Construction Approach* performs well if the classification tree remains skinny, having few nodes at any level, throughout. For such trees, there are relatively large number of training cases at the nodes at any level; and thus the communication overhead is relatively small. Load imbalance is avoided by processing all nodes at a level, before synchronization among the processors. However, as the tree becomes bushy, having a large number of nodes at a level, the number of training data items at each node decrease. Frequent synchronization is done due to limited communication buffer size, which forces communication after pro-

cessing a fixed number of nodes. These nodes at lower depths of the tree, which have few tuples assigned to them, may have highly variable distribution of tuples over the processors, leading to load imbalance. Hence, this approach suffers from high communication overhead and load imbalance for bushy trees. The *Partitioned Tree Construction Approach* works better than *Synchronous Tree Construction Approach* if the tree is bushy. But this approach pays a big communication overhead in the higher levels of the tree as it has to shuffle lots of training data items to different processors. Once every node is solely assigned to a single processor, each processor can construct the partial classification tree independently without any communication with other processors. However, the load imbalance problem is still present after the shuffling of the training data items, since the partitioning of the data was done statically.

The hybrid approach combines the good features of these two approaches to reduce communication overhead and load imbalance. This approach uses the *Synchronous Tree Construction Approach* for the upper parts of the classification tree. Since there are few nodes and relatively large number of the training cases associated with the nodes in the upper

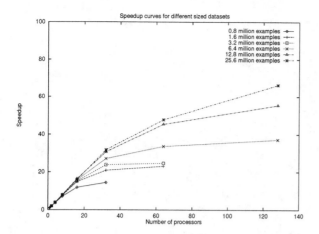

Figure 4. Speedup of the hybrid approach with different size datasets.

part of the tree, the communication overhead is small. As soon as the accumulated communication overhead is greater than the cost of partitioning of data and load balancing, this approach shifts to the *Partitioned Tree Construction Approach* incrementally. The partitioning takes place when a reasonable number of nodes are present at a level. This partitioning is gradual and performs randomized allocation of classification tree nodes, resulting in a better load balance. Any load imbalance at the lower levels of the tree, when a processor group has finished processing its assigned subtree, is handled by allowing an idle processor group to join busy processor groups.

The size and shape of the classification tree varies a lot depending on the application domain and training data set. Some classification trees might be shallow and the others might be deep. Some classification trees could be skinny others could be bushy. Some classification trees might be uniform in depth while other trees might be skewed in one part of the tree. The hybrid approach adapts well to all types of classification trees. If the decision tree is skinny, the hybrid approach will just stay with the *Synchronous Tree Construction Approach*. On the other hand, it will shift to the *Partitioned Tree Construction Approach* as soon as the tree becomes bushy. If the tree has a big variance in depth, the hybrid approach will perform dynamic load balancing with processor groups to reduce processor idling.

References

[1] R. Agrawal, T. Imielinski, and A. Swami. Database mining: A performance perspective. *IEEE Transactions on Knowledge and Data Eng.*, 5(6):914–925, December 1993.

[2] K. Alsabti, S. Ranka, and V. Singh. A one-pass algorithm for accurately estimating quantiles for disk-resident data. In *Proc. of the 23rd VLDB Conference*, 1997.

[3] K. Alsabti, S. Ranka, and V. Singh. CLOUDS: Classification for large or out-of-core datasets. *http://www.cise.ufl.edu/~ranka/dm.html*, 1998.

[4] J. Catlett. *Megainduction: Machine Learning on Very Large Databases. PhD thesis.* University of Sydney, 1991.

[5] P. K. Chan and S. J. Stolfo. Metalearning for multistrategy learning and parallel learning. In *Proc. Second Intl. Conference on Multistrategy Learning*, pages 150–165, 1993.

[6] D. S. D. Michie and C. Taylor. *Machine Learning, Neural and Statistical Classification.* Ellis Horwood, 1994.

[7] D. E. Goldberg. *Genetic Algorithms in Search, Optimizations and Machine Learning.* Morgan-Kaufman, 1989.

[8] S. Hong. Use of contextual information for feature ranking and discretization. *IEEE Transactions on Knowledge and Data Eng.*, 9(5):718–730, September/October 1997.

[9] M. Joshi, G. Karypis, and V. Kumar. ScalParC: A new scalable and efficient parallel classification algorithm for mining large datasets. In *Proc. of the International Parallel Processing Symposium*, 1998.

[10] V. Kumar, A. Grama, A. Gupta, and G. Karypis. *Introduction to Parallel Computing: Algorithm Design and Analysis.* Benjamin Cummings/ Addison Wesley, Redwod City, 1994.

[11] R. Lippmann. An introduction to computing with neural nets. *IEEE ASSP Magazine*, 4(22), April 1987.

[12] M. Mehta, R. Agrawal, and J. Rissanen. SLIQ: A fast scalable classifier for data mining. In *Proc. of the Fifth Int'l Conference on Extending Database Technology*, Avignon, France, 1996.

[13] J. R. Quinlan. *C4.5: Programs for Machine Learning.* Morgan Kaufmann, San Mateo, CA, 1993.

[14] J. Shafer, R. Agrawal, and M. Mehta. SPRINT: A scalable parallel classifier for data mining. In *Proc. of the 22nd VLDB Conference*, 1996.

[15] A. Srivastava, V. Singh, E.-H. Han, and V. Kumar. An efficient, scalable, parallel classifier for data mining. Technical Report TR-97-010,http://www.cs.umn.edu/~kumar, Department of Computer Science, University of Minnesota, Minneapolis, 1997.

Inter-Iteration Optimization of Parallel EM Algorithm on Message-Passing Multicomputers

Wei-Min Jeng and Shou-Hsuan Stephen Huang
Department of Computer Science
University of Houston
Houston, Texas 77204
{wjeng, shuang} @cs.uh.edu

Abstract

Estimation of the parameters of a probability distribution function is a complicated problem that is frequently encountered in many instances of real world problems. The Expectation Maximization (EM) algorithm often can be employed when there is a many-to-one mapping from all possible distribution patterns to the distribution governing the outcome. With its Maximum Likelihood (ML) formulation, optimal estimate can be made for the unknown variables after iterations until convergence. A variety of parallel methods have been proposed to boost its performance because of the complexity involved in the algorithm. Despite the efforts, the ML algorithm could not be easily adopted in practice primarily due to both intra- and inter-iteration data dependence problems resulting from the iterative nature of the algorithm. This research builds upon experimentation that demonstrated promising results in speeding up the algorithm in and between iterations using distributed-memory message-passing architecture.

1. Introduction

A common problem in many application areas has to deal with either incomplete or missing data necessary in estimating the unknown parameters. The EM [1] algorithm formalizes many of the previous ad hoc ideas for approximating the missing data with maximum likelihood. The algorithm has been widely used in clinical, signal processing, genetic, and even sociological studies that have unknown parameters governing the observations [2, 3]. It is a technique which consists of two major steps, expectation and maximization, in each iteration. A sequence of iterations are performed until convergence to estimate the unknown information. To manage the complexity involved in the algorithm, parallel methods [4, 5] have been employed to speed up the iterative operations. However, the precedence relations of the algorithm remain unsolved and hinder the efficiency of these parallelization implementations. Distributed-memory message-passing architecture is chosen in this study for both of its scalability to massive number of processors and data coherence. The fact that the performance of this type of machine is strongly connected to the communication overhead requires appropriate message passing patterns. In this paper, we propose a new algorithm intended to boost the performance with both intra- and inter-iteration speedup. Performance model is established as well as the experimental results.

Section 2 briefly introduce the steps of the original EM algorithm and its application in Positron Emission Tomography (PET) [6] image reconstruction. Section 3 describes the optimization strategy in parallelizing the problem aiming at precedence constraints. Section 4 defines the performance metrics of our model for prediction of performance. Section 5 shows both the experimental environment and the performance results collected from actual runs of our Message Passing Interface (MPI) [7] implementation. Section 6 summarizes about this research and addresses issues on some possible future works.

2. Expectation Maximization Algorithm

2.1. Introduction to EM Algorithm

In many situations, the direct access to the data necessary to estimate the parameters is impossible. The EM algorithm is well suited to this category of problems to generate the parameter estimates by maximizing the incomplete-data likelihood with observed data. Let Y denote the sample space of the observations, and let $\mathbf{y}$ denote an observation from Y. Let X denote the underlying space and let $\mathbf{x}$ be an outcome from X, with an associated probability density function $f(\mathbf{x}|\theta)$, where θ is the set of parameters of the density. The complete data $\mathbf{x}$ is not observed directly, instead, it is observed by means of $\mathbf{y}$, where $\mathbf{y}=\mathbf{y}(\mathbf{x})$ and that $\mathbf{x}$ is known only to lie in $X(\mathbf{y})$. The probability density function of the incomplete data given observed data can be defined as $g(\mathbf{y}|\theta)$. The complete data specification is related to its corresponding incomplete data specification by

$$L(\mathbf{y},\theta) = g(\mathbf{y}|\theta) = \int_{X(y)} f(\mathbf{x}|\theta)\, d\mathbf{x}.$$

The goal of the algorithm is to estimate θ by maximizing the incomplete data likelihood function, denoted by $L(\mathbf{y},\theta)$. Since the logarithm is monotonically increasing, maximizing the log-likelihood function $l(\mathbf{y},\theta)$ is equivalent to maximizing the likelihood and be defined as follows,

$$l(\mathbf{y},\theta) = \log L(\mathbf{y},\theta) = \log g(\mathbf{y}|\theta)$$

with respect to θ for fixed $\mathbf{y}$.

Since the information of complete-data $\mathbf{x}$ is unknown to us, the expectation of likelihood function $g(\mathbf{y}, \theta)$ is maximized instead given both the observation $\mathbf{y}$ and the current estimate of θ. The algorithm uses both the expectation of the likelihood function L given the observed data $\mathbf{y}$ and the estimate of θ iteratively until its convergence. Let $\theta^{[r]}$ represent the current estimate of the unknown parameters at the rth iteration. It was shown that the repeated iterations lead to value $\theta^{[r]}$ of θ that maximizes $l(\mathbf{y},\theta)$. The two steps of the EM algorithm can be described as follows:

In the Expectation Step, we define function Q which computes the expected likelihood given both the observed data $\mathbf{y}$ and current parameter estimate $\theta^{[r]}$.

$$Q(\theta|\theta^{[r]}) = \mathrm{E}[\log f(\mathbf{x}|\theta)|\mathbf{y}, \theta^{[r]}).$$

and in the Maximization Step, choose $\theta^{[r+1]}$ which can maximize the Q function

$$\theta^{[r+1]} = \max Q(\theta|\theta^{[r]})$$

with respect to the first argument θ. The change from $\theta^{[r]}$ to $\theta^{[r+1]}$ increases the likelihood and its proof can be found at [1].

2.2. EM Algorithm for PET

PET machine, a system of detectors, captures the gamma rays emitting from the radiopharmaceuticals within the tissues of patient's body. Coincidence results if two detectors on opposite sides of the body both detect the double photon along the path of detector pair. Such events are registered and all the counts are collected in a profile which becomes the input to the reconstruction process. Each slice of the target image volume can be viewed as a 2-D grid of boxes (or image pixels when they are brought to display). The commonly used image reconstruction technique in PET industry is the Filtered

BackProjection (FBP) algorithm based on Fourier Transform. Despite of its fastness, the deterministic nature of the FBP algorithm does not account for statistical fluctuations in its measurement thus results in noticeable artifacts [8]. Instead, EM is employed to determine the amount of photons for better results.

The number of photons emitted from each box is denoted by $\mathbf{n}(b)$, b=1,2,...,B. The number of photons detected in each detector pair is denoted by $\mathbf{y}(d)$, d=1,2,...,D. It is assumed that the generated photons with mean $\lambda(b)$ is a Poisson variable with the distribution,

$$f(\mathbf{n}(b)=k|\lambda(b)) = P(\mathbf{n}(b)=k) = e^{-\lambda(b)} \lambda(b)^{k}/k!,$$
$$b = 1, 2,...,B.$$

The detector variable $\mathbf{y}(d)$ is Poisson distributed with the following function

$$f(\mathbf{y}(d)=k|\lambda(d)) = P(\mathbf{y}(d)=k) = e^{-\lambda(d)} \lambda(d)^{n}/n!,$$
$$d = 1, 2,...,D.$$

In the discrete reconstruction, $\mathbf{n}(d)$ is a random variable with the means

$$\lambda(d) = \sum_{b=1}^{B} \lambda(b)P(b,d), \qquad d=1, 2,..., D.$$

Let $\mathbf{x}(b, d)$ denote the number of emissions in b detected by detector d, there exists a mapping from $\mathbf{x}(b, d)$ to $\mathbf{y}(d)$. The variable of $\mathbf{x}(b, d)$ is Poisson with mean

$$\lambda(b, d) = \lambda(b)P(b, d),$$

where P(b, d) is the probability that a photon emission in box b detected in detector d. It is assumed that both $\mathbf{y}(d)$ and $\lambda(b)$ are Poisson variables that operated independently, the likelihood of the observed data $\mathbf{y}(d)$ can be defined by the likelihood function as

$$L(\mathbf{y}, \lambda) = f(\mathbf{y}|\lambda) = \prod_{\substack{b=1,...,B \\ d=1,...,D}} e^{-\lambda(b,d)} \frac{\lambda(b,d)^{x(b,d)}}{x(b,d)}.$$

Intermediate computation and storage can be eliminated by substitution to obtain its ML estimate solution [6]

$$\lambda^{\text{new}}(b) = \lambda^{\text{old}}(b) \sum_{d=1}^{D} \frac{y(d)p(b,d)}{\sum_{b'=1}^{B} \lambda^{\text{old}}(b')p(b',d)},$$

or stated as the four separate steps in each iteration

Step 1) $\mathbf{t} = P^{T} \times \lambda$,

Step 2) $\Phi_d = \mathbf{y}_d / \mathbf{t}_d$ for d = 1, 2, ...,D,

Step 3) $\mathbf{r} = P \times \Phi$, and

Step 4) $\lambda^{\text{new}} = \lambda^{\text{old}} \cdot \mathbf{r}$,

where

$\mathbf{y}_d$: vector containing the number of photons detected by detector pair d, for d=1,2,...,D.

Φ_d: vector containing the ratio between the measured and theoretical counts, for d=1,2,...,D.

t_d: vector containing the theoretical counts, for d=1,2,...,D.

r_b: vector containing the correcting factor for intensity levels, for b=1,2,...,B.

With the geometry information (P matrix), actual count profile (y vector), and initial estimates of intensity λ, the problem of reconstruction is to approximate the actual value of λ iteratively until its convergence.

3. Problem Parallelization

3.1. Problem Analysis

First we divide the problem data into small pieces of approximately equal size and distribute them into local memories on each processor. A number of tasks are formed using the partitioning strategy each of which has both decomposed data and associated computations on the data. The above algorithm represents an inherently sequential problem in terms of the multiple dependencies that exist in successive steps. In the original form of EM algorithm, Steps 1 and 3 take the majority amount of time because of the size of the P matrix. There exists two kinds of dependencies in the intrinsically sequential algorithm. First. All four of the steps have to be executed in sequence without violating the read-after-write rule, in other words, elements need to be computed first from the preceding step before they can be put in use. Secondly, there exists an inter-iteration dependence because each iteration represents a refining operation and generates the input for the immediately following iteration.

The core of the partition problem is how to divide the huge matrix P (B×D) into individual processors in a way that the operation can proceed with minimum overhead. Due to the nature of the algorithm, both P and its transposed one are employed in Steps 1 and 3 multiplication operation therefore it is inevitable to exchange the data once in one iteration. For instance, if P is divided by its detector dimension, Step 1 will have all the data it needs to perform the operation at the cost of exchanging the partial results of Step 3 in the same iteration. The design consideration is to find the maximum parallelism with minimize communication overhead caused by both these precedence relations and specific partitions.

There are generally two different phases for most of the parallel algorithms, local computation and global synchronization. The synchronization phase usually come in the form of either global communication and/or computation depending on different natures of the algorithm. The transport of information causes significant cost on most of the machines and thus becomes the major concern in improving the overall performance. Overlapping computation and communication [9] is one of the most important techniques that have been commonly used to overcome this problem. Jeng and Huang [10] investigated additional level of parallelism and proposed early communication strategy for the EM problem that took advantage of the total exchange collective communication operations. Operations in Step 3 assigned to each processing node can be further divided into finer grains and the partial results can be sent across the network without waiting for the completion of the remaining computations. However, the performance gain is limited to be within the same iteration.

3.2. Optimization within Iteration

Multiple dependencies occur when one aspect of data partially, along with other aspects of data, determine another. Our first technique is to overlap portions of Steps 3 and 4 of the original algorithm so that some of the parameter updating operations in Step 4 can start as soon as the information is available from Step 3. The resulting smaller vector is then sent across the network to exchange the information with other processing nodes for the reduction operation. Depending on the type and status of the communication network, the updating factors should arrive at different times for parameter refining, which is independent from one box location to another. Jeng and Huang [10] found the optimal number to divide the transmitted messages to be two. For example, the matrix-vector multiplication in Step 3 is split into two; therefore, there will be two non-blocking *Allreduction()* total exchange function invocations. The detailed parallel scheme of intra-iteration optimization per iteration can be represented as follows:

Algorithm EM   (intra-iteration optimization)
Input: partitioned probability matrix and observed counts of emissions.
Output: estimate of unknown vector λ with non-decreasing likelihood.

```
/* N denotes the number of nodes */
for all I, 0 <= I < N do in parallel
   Initialize λ to arbitrary values;
   /* Step 1: t = Pᵀ · λ */
   d = 0;
   while (d < D) do
      b = 0;
      while (b < B) do
         t[d] += Pᵢ[b][d] * λ[b];
         b = b + 1;
      endwhile
      d = d + 1;
   endwhile
   /* Step 2: Φd = yd / td */
```

```
         d = 0;
         while (d < D) do
             Φ[d] = y[d] / t[d];
             d = d + 1;
         endwhile
         /* Step 3: r = P · Φ*/
         b = 0;
         while (b < B/2) do
             d = 0;
             while (d < D) do
                 r[b]=r[b]+P[b][d]*Φ[d];
                 d = d + 1;
             endwhile
             b = b + 1;
         endwhile
         /* first Reduction operation on
         first half of r */
         Allreduction (r1);
         while (b < B) do
             d = 0;
             while (d < D) do
                 r[b]=r[b]+P[b][d]* Φ[d];
                 d = d + 1;
             endwhile
             b = b + 1;
         endwhile
         /* second Reduction operation on
         second half of r */
         Allreduction (r2);
         Wait(r1); /* for r1 */
         /* Step 4.1: λ_b^new = λ_b^old · r_b */
         b = 0;
         while (b < B/2) do
             λ[b] = λ[b] * r[b]
             b = b + 1;
         endwhile
         Wait(r2); /* for r2 */
         /* step 4.2: λ_b^new = λ_b^old · r_b */
         while (b < B) do
             λ[b] = λ[b] * r[b]
             b = b + 1;
         endwhile
endfor
```

3.3. Optimization between Iterations

Step 1 of the EM algorithm represents the expectation operation which requires the estimate from the prior iteration. To be precise, the value of λ vector has to be available from Step 4 of the immediately preceding iteration before Step 1 of the current iteration can begin. Continuing the improvement made from the last section, λ vector can be similarly divided into two or more smaller vectors for early computation as soon as the they are available. In

light of the amount of computation needed in Step 3, the leading smaller vector **r** should be generated after the end of the total Step 3 computation. Therefore, there is virtually no elapsed time for Step 4 to use the smaller vector λ as an updated parameter. Step 1 can then start its first half of the computation without any wait. Importantly, Step 4 was also split into several smaller sub-steps and interleaved with Step 1 of the next iteration and its wait functions corresponded to the non-blocking reduction operations of Step 3. Due to the amount of computation needed in Step 1, the next smaller vector λ will arrive for another expectation step operation again with virtually no wait. Both intra- and inter-iteration optimizations can be combined into the following:

Algorithm EM (with intra- and inter-iteration optimization)
Input: partitioned probability matrix and observed counts of emissions.
Output: estimate of unknown vector λ with non-decreasing likelihood.

```
    /* N denotes the number of process-
ing nodes used */
for all I, 0 <= I < N    do in parallel
    /* initialization */
    Initialize λ to arbitrary values;
    /* Step 1.1: t = P^T · λ */
    d = 0;
    while (d < D) do
        b = 0;
        while (b < B/2) do
            t[d] += P[b][d] * λ[b];
            b = b + 1;
        endwhile
        d = d + 1;
    endwhile
    /* perform the following block
    except for first iteration */
    if (iteration_num != 1) do
    /* wait for r2 from second reduction
    operation completion from previous
    iteration */
        Wait (r2);
    /* Step 4.2: λ_b^new = λ_b^old · r_b */
        while (b < B) do
            λ[b] = λ[b] * r[b]
            b = b + 1;
        endwhile
    endif
    /* Step 1.2: t = P^T · λ */
    d = 0;
    while (d < D) do
        b = B / 2;
        while (b < B) do
```

248

```
        t[d]+=P[b][d] * λ[b];
        b = b + 1;
      endwhile
      d = d + 1;
    endwhile
    /* Step 2: Φ_d = y_d / t_d */
    d = 0;
    while (d < D) do
        Φ[d] = y[d] / t[d];
        d = d + 1;
    endwhile
    /* Step 3.1: r = P · Φ*/
    b = 0;
    while (b < B/2) do
      d = 0;
      while (d < D) do
        r[b] += (P[b][d] * Φ[d]);
        d = d + 1;
      endwhile
      b = b + 1;
    endwhile
    /* non-blocking reduction operation
    on first half of r */
    Allreduction(r1);
    /* Step 3.2: r = P · Φ*/
    b = B/2;
    while (b < B) do
      d = 0;
      while (d < D) do
        r[b]+=(P[b][d]*Φ[d]);
        d = d + 1;
      endwhile
      b = b + 1;
    endwhile
    /* second non-blocking reduction
    operation on r */
    Allreduction(r2);
    /* wait for r1 from first reduction
    operation completion */
    Wait (r1);
    /* Step 4.1: λ_b^new = λ_b^old · r_b */
    b = 0;
    while (b < B/2) do
      λ[b] = λ[b] * r[b]
      b = b + 1;
    endwhile
endfor
```

4. Performance Metrics

4.1. Functions and Parameters

Assuming a communication group is formed to perform the collective operations by a number of processes distributed across the parallel system, with one process per proc-

essor. Consider the following two collective operations with their definitions:

Reduction: A function which aggregates a group of data by one controlling process, each from every process in the communication group, into a global value.

Broadcast: A function which sends its local data by one process to all processes.

Also let the following definitions denote the system parameters used by the model:

- n_i represents the number of substeps of ith step in one iteration, ($i=1,\ldots,m$, $n_i=1,\ldots$)
- S_i^j represents the jth substep of computation of ith step in one iteration, ($j \in n_i$)
- C_i^j represents the incurred communication overhead from jth substep of ith step of one iteration, ($j \in n_i$)
- *COMP* represent the total computational time needed locally on each processor to perform one iteration,

$$(COMP = \sum_{i=1}^{m} (\sum_{j=1}^{n_i} S_i^j))$$

- *COMM* represent the communication overhead needed to finish *all_reduction* (equivalent to *reduction + broadcast*) collective operation including both *reduction* and *broadcast* operations in one iteration. Currently, the synchronization only happens at the third step of the algorithm. (e.g., $COMM = C_3^1 + C_3^2$ in our scheme), and
- let τ represent the software overhead incurred to invoke the *all_reduction* function for one divided message. It is assumed that the overhead is approximately the same for each invocation under the same configuration.

4.2. Performance Model

The total execution time per iteration for EM algorithm without overlapping can be estimated by the sum of following three terms, computation time, communication time, and communication software overhead as

$$T = COMP + COMM + 2\tau.$$

Depending on the optimizations schemes used, the patterns of the overlapping can be illustrated as follows:

Scheme 1: Intra-iteration Optimization

According to the EM algorithm, the amount of computation in step 4 is negligible compared to the total computation time. A little more than half of the communication overhead for the transmitted messages can be hidden therefore the execution time can be defined as

$$T = COMP - S_4^1 + \frac{COMM}{2} + 2\tau$$

$$\approx COMP + \frac{COMM}{2} + 2\,\tau. \tag{1}$$

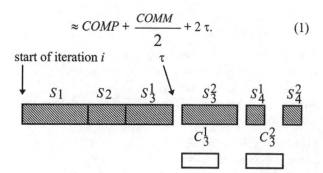

Figure 1: Layout of timing diagram for intra-iteration optimization scheme with 2 messages.

Scheme 2: Inter-iteration Optimization
As explained in Section 3, all of the communication overhead except the startup cost can be hidden with the inter-iteration scheme. Figure 2 illustrates how the steps from neighboring iterations are unrolled and rescheduled to achieve the inter-iteration optimization. In particular, Step 4 is divided into two sub-steps and its second part moves to the code block of next iteration. Similarly, first part of Step 1 starts early as its input data becomes available.

$$T = COMP + 2\,\tau. \tag{2}$$

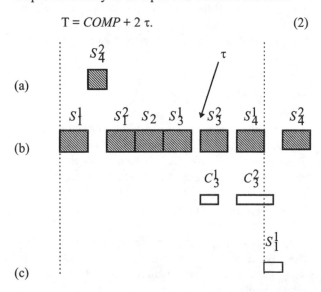

Figure 2: Layout of unrolled timing diagram for inter-iteration optimization scheme with 2 messages where (a), (b), and (c) represent iterations *i*-1, *i*, and *i*+1 respectively.

It is assumed that:
1. Each processing node communicates with all others, using *allreduction* collective operations with two split messages,
2. The size of communication messages per iteration per processor is M bytes,
3. There are N processing nodes used in running the parallel EM algorithm,

4. W is the total work load in terms of the problem space in Mbytes, and
5. B is the process bandwidth in Mflops/sec.

The timing formula for the total exchange collective communication has been curve fitted for both latency and asymptotic bandwidth [11]. Its aggregated communication overhead [12] can be represented by

Startup overhead = $40 \cdot \log N$

$$\text{Transmission Latency} = \frac{(0.037 \log N) * M}{2D}$$

Collective Reduction Cost = $(45 \cdot \log N + 15) * 10^3$

$$\text{Total Cost} = 40 \cdot \log N + \frac{(0.037 \log N) * M}{2D} +$$
$$(45 \cdot \log N + 15) * 10^3 \tag{3}$$

where time is represented by microsecond.

Using the performance parameters that we have defined, execution time can be predicted by applying the specific problem size data into the model. The measured time data from SP2 machine was used to curve fit and derive the timing formula for *COMP* with the size of W equals to 1 Mbytes.

$$COMP = \frac{W}{N * B} \approx 31.12 \frac{1}{N} \tag{4}$$

The resulting non-blocking *reduction* operation overhead τ, a function of both partitioned problem size P and number of early communication messages D, can be estimated as

$$\tau\,(P,D) = 165\,D \qquad \text{if } (P <= 64 \text{ Mbytes}) \tag{5}$$

From Equations (1) - (5), the execution time complexity for intra- and inter-iteration schemes, T_{intra} and T_{inter} respectively, can be derived as a function of M and N as follows:

$$T_{intra} = 31.12 \frac{1}{N} + 40 \cdot \log N + \frac{(0.037 \log N) * M}{2}$$
$$+ (45 \cdot \log N + 15) * 10^3 + 165 * 2$$

$$T_{inter} = 31.12 \frac{1}{N} + 40 \cdot \log N.$$

5. Experiment results

5.1. Distributed-memory architecture

The migration of high-performance computing environment from single-processor machines to multiprocessor systems that run in parallel raises the performance issues of communications activities. In a distributed-

250

memory architecture, the system memory is distributed into its local processors to ease the access of local memory. Access to remote memory has to be done via transmitted messages over the network for sharing of information or serving other synchronization needs. Due to the fact that each processor can only directly access its own local memory of the system, sharing of global data among processors requires additional mechanism. The method for exchanging data to program under a distributed-memory machine is called message passing. Both point-to-point and collective communication primitives can be used to perform the communication need for a group of processors. The overall implementation is not effective if the distributed system spends too much time in moving data around the communication network.

5.2. Results

Different sizes of the problem data sets are selected to test their performance characteristics for both intra- and inter-iteration optimization schemes. 2, 4, …,to 64 processing nodes of SP2 machine are employed to conduct the experiments and the data are collected and analyzed. User Space (US) of communication mode is used to ensure the exclusive access to the communication switch of the network for best performance. EM reconstruction is set up to run for 50 iterations per study case to obtain the average of the some of the measurements. Figures 3 and 4 illustrate the average execution time per iteration for various problem size (BxD=1024×1024 and 4096×4096 respectively) by applying two different parallelization schemes and compare them with the naïve one without any overlapping. The inter-iteration method outperforms others in every test scenario for its superiority in hiding the communication overhead. Even with shared data across the network, the inter-iteration method results in zero-wait.

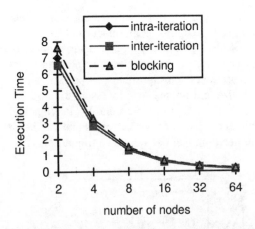

Figure 4: Execution time for blocking, intra-, and inter-iteration schemes. (B=4096, D=4096)

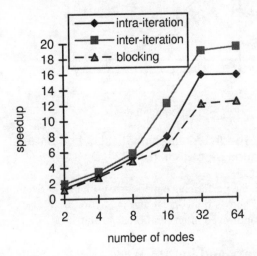

Figure 5: Speedup values for blocking, intra-, and inter-iteration schemes. (B=1024, D=1024)

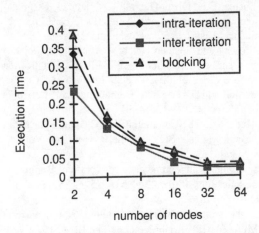

Figure 3: Execution time for blocking, intra-, and inter-iteration schemes. (B=1024, D=1024)

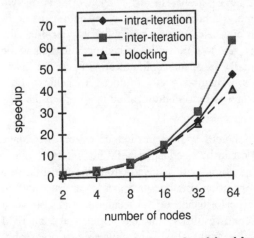

Figure 6: Speedup values for blocking, intra-, and inter-iteration schemes. (B=4096, D=4096)

Figures 5 and 6 alternatively present the speedup values for the same test setup to help understand the cost-effectiveness of the algorithms with increasing number of processors. The close-to-linear speedup values are obtained which promises the algorithms to be scalable in both problem size and number of processors dimensions. The cost-effective solution can be found by looking into the exact efficiency values of the test cases and can be of great help for deciding the best system configuration.

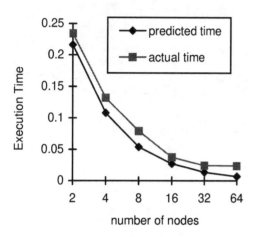

Figure 7: Predicted and actual execution time for inter-iteration algorithm. (B=1024, D=1024)

To validate the performance model we establish in Section 4, Figure 7 shows both actual and prediction time of execution for optimized inter-iteration algorithm.

6. Summary and Future Work

As an iterative type of algorithm, EM has been useful in solving the unknown information and frequently used in many fields of study. In our study, we focus on two issues, namely iteration dependency and hiding of communication overhead. Better scheduling by unrolling the iterations is used to remove the precedence relations while hiding virtually all of the communication overhead. New parallelization method was introduced to achieve both intra- and inter-iteration optimization to speed up the performance.

In our scheme, a great portion of expectation stage computation can be overlapped with the collective maximization operation with the help from the non-blocking reduction operation. Performance metrics are modeled to predict the performance of the technique and compared with the actual results. Although implemented on IBM SP2, the same approach still is applicable to other platforms such as networks of workstations as well. Communication activities, particularly on a heterogeneous net-

work environment, can be further investigated to better help design and use of the message passing software and its applications. New programming paradigm can be looked into by optimizing the performance for parallel applications without imposing the designers for explicit message passing setup.

Reference

[1] A. P. Dempster, N. M. Laird, and D. B. Rubin, "Maximization Likelihood from Incomplete Data via the EM Algorithm," J. Royal Statistical Soc., Ser. B, Vol. 39, No. 1, pp. 1-38, 1977.

[2] R. Little and D. Rubin, "On Jointly Estimating Parameters and Missing Data by Maximizing the Complete-Data Likelihood," Am. Statistn., Vol. 37, No. 3, pp. 218-200, 1983.

[3] R. Streit and T. Luginbuh, "ML Training of Probabilistic Neural Networks," IEEE Trans. Neural Net., Vol. 5, No. 5, pp. 764-783, 1994.

[4] Chung-Ming Chen and Soo-Young Lee, "On Parallelizing the EM Algorithm for PET Image Reconstruction," IEEE Transactions on Parallel and Distributed Systems, Vol. 5, No. 8, pp. 260-273, August 1994.

[5] T.M. Guerrero, S.R. Cherry, M. Dahlbom, et al, "Fast Implementations of 3D PET Reconstruction Using Vector and Parallel Programming Techniques," IEEE Transactions on Nuclear Science, Vol. 40, No. 4, pp. 1082-1086, 1993.

[6] L. A. Shepp and Y. Vardi, "Maximum Likelihood Reconstruction for Emission Tomography," IEEE Transactions on Medical Imaging, Vol. 1, pp. 113-122, Oct. 1982.

[7] MPI Forum. "The MPI Message Passing Interface Standard," Http://www.mcs.anl.gov/mpi/mpi-report/mpi-report.html, November 1995.

[8] J. Llacer, E. Veklerov, L.R. Baxter, et al, "Results of a Clinical Receiver Operating Characteristic Study Comparing Filtered Backprojection and Maximum Likelihood Estimator Images in FDG PET Studies," Journal of Nuclear Medicine, Vol. 34, No. 7, pp. 1198-1203, 1993.

[9] Alvaro Suarez, C.N. Ojeda-Guerra, "Overlapping Computations and Communications in Torus Networks," IEEE Proceedings of Parallel and Distributed Processing, pp. 162-169, 1996.

[10] Wei-Min Jeng and Stephen Huang, "Efficient Parallel EM Image Reconstruction Algorithm: An Early Communication Approach," Proceedings of the IASTED International Conference on Parallel and Distributed Computing and Networks (PDCN), Acta Press, pp. 123-126, 1997.

[11] R. W. Hockney, "The Communication Challenge for MPP: Intel Paragon and Meiko CS-2," Parallel Computing, Vol. 20, pp. 389-398, March 1994.

[12] Gordon Bell, "Ultracomputers: A Teraflop Before Its Time," Communications of the ACM, Vol. 35, No. 8, pp. 27-47, August 1992.

[13] Zhiwei Xu and Kai Hwang, "Modeling Communication Overhead: MPI and MPL Performance on the IBM SP2," IEEE Parallel & Distributed Technology, pp. 9-23, Spring 1993.

On Computing the Upper Envelope of Segments in Parallel

Wei Chen,* Koichi Wada
Department of Electrical and Computer Engineering
Nagoya Institute of Technology
Showa, Nagoya 466, Japan.
E-mail: (chen, wada)@elcom.nitech.ac.jp

Abstract

Given a collection of segments in the plane that intersect pairwise at most k times, regarding the segments as opaque barriers, their upper envelope consists of the portions of the segments visible from point $(0, +\infty)$. In this paper, we give efficient parallel methods for finding the upper envelope of k-intersecting segments for any integer $k \geq 0$, in the weakest shared-memory model, the EREW PRAM. We show that the upper envelope of n k-intersecting segments can be found in $O(\log^{1+\epsilon} n)$ time using $O(\lambda_{k+1}(n)/\log^\epsilon n)$ processors for any $\epsilon > 0$, where $\lambda_{k+2}(n)$ [1] is the size of the upper envelope. In particular, for line segments we show the following optimal algorithms: the upper envelope of n line segments can be found in $O(\log n)$ time using $O(n)$ processors, and if the line segments are nonintersecting and sorted, the envelope can be found in $O(\log n)$ time using $O(n/\log n)$ processors. We also show that our methods imply a fast sequential result: the upper envelope of n sorted line segments can be found in $O(n \log \log n)$ time sequentially, which improves the known lowest upper bound $O(n \log n)$.

1. Introduction

Let S be a set of n segments in the plane. Considering the segments as opaque barriers, the upper envelope of S, denoted as $UE(S)$, is made of the portions of the segments visible from point $(0, +\infty)$. The upper envelope of segments is an important concept in computational geometry which has a host applications in visibility, motion planning, convex hulls, Voronoi diagrams, ray-shooting data structures, hidden surface elimination, the construction of arrangements, and polygon containment [2, 5, 11, 16].

First we restrict the problem to line segments. When the segments of S are nonintersecting, the complexity of $UE(S)$ (the number of distinct pieces of segments that appear on the upper envelope) is linear in n. In this case, $UE(S)$ can be computed optimally in $O(n \log n)$ time, and it needs only $O(n)$ time if the segment endpoints are sorted in x-coordinate [2]. Now let the segments of S be possibly-intersecting. The complexity of $UE(S)$ is $(n\alpha(n))$, where $\alpha(n)$ is the functional inverse of Ackermann's function and grows extremely slowly [12, 19]. A straightforward divide-and-conquer algorithm computes $UE(S)$ in $O(n\alpha(n) \log n)$ time [3, 12]. Hershberger reorganizes the divide-and-conquer to run in optimal $O(n \log n)$ time [13]. His algorithm can be easily implemented in the EREW PRAM in $O(\log^2 n)$ time using $O(n/\log n)$ processors. The PRAM (Parallel Random Access Machine) is a synchronous parallel computational model employing a number of processors which share a common memory. There are three versions of the PRAM model: the EREW (Exclusive Reading Exclusive Writing) PRAM, the CREW (Concurrent Reading Exclusive Writing) PRAM, and CRCW (Concurrent Reading Concurrent Writing) PRAM, where the EREW PRAM is weakest and the CRCW PRAM is strongest. A great effort has been made for finding $UE(S)$ in the PRAM. Boxer and Miller find $UE(S)$ in $O(\log^2 n)$ time using $O(n)$ processors in the CREW PRAM [4]. Goodrich uses some approximation parallel methods to construct $UE(S)$ with high probability in $O(\log n \log^* n)$ time using $O(n/\log^* n)$ processors in a randomized CRCW PRAM [11]. MacKenzie and Stout consider the visibility problem of S in hypercube network [17], and if their algorithm were correct, by simulating the algorithm in the PRAM EREW, $UE(S)$ would be computable in $O(\log n \log \log n)$ time using $O(n/\log \log n)$ processors, however some errors were found in their algorithm (from the personal communication among D. Z. Chen, P. D. MacKenzie, W. Chen and K. Wada). It was also claimed that $UE(S)$ can be constructed optimally in $O(\log n)$ time using $O(n)$ processors in CREW PRAM, but the paper was withdrawn soon [5]. The intersting reader can also find some other

*Supported by the telecommunications Advancement Foundation (1997), Japan

[1] $\lambda_k(n) = O(n)$, $(n\alpha(n))$, and $O(n\alpha(n)^{\alpha(n)^{k-3}})$ for $k = 1, 2$, $k = 3$ and $k > 3$, respectively, where $\alpha(n)$ is the extremely slowly growing functional inverse of Ackermann's function.

related work [10, 14]. By so far finding $UE(S)$ optimally in the PRAM is still an open problem.

In this paper, we show the following optimal results in the EREW PRAM: (1) the upper envelope of n possibly-intersecting line segments in the plane can be found in $O(\log n)$ time using $O(n)$ processors, and (2) if the segments are nonintersecting and their endpoints are sorted in x-coordinate, the upper envelope can be found in $O(\log n)$ time using $O(n/\log n)$ processors. As a by-product our parallel methods imply a sequential result: the upper envelope of n possibly-intersecting line segments can be found in $O(n \log \log n)$ time sequentially if the segments and their endpoints are sorted in slope and x-coordinate, respectively, however, it needs $(n \log n)$ time if using the previous algorithms.

We also consider the upper envelope problem for generalized segments. A curved line in the plane is defined by a function: $R \to R$. Two curved lines or two segments (of curved lines) are k-*intersecting*, if the number of the intersections between them is bounded by a constant k. Let C and S be the sets of n k-intersecting curved lines and n k-intersecting segments of (curved lines), respectively. It is known that the complexity of $UE(C)$ is bounded by $\lambda_k(n)$, where $\lambda_k(n)$ is the function related to the complexity of a class of strings known as Davenport-Schinzel sequences and equal to $O(n)$, $(n\alpha(n))$, and $O(n\alpha(n)^{\alpha(n)^{k-3}})$ for $k = 1$, 2, $k = 3$ and $k > 3$, respectively. The complexity of $UE(S)$ is slightly higher which is bounded by $\lambda_{k+2}(n)$ [12, 13]. For any positive k, $\lambda_k(n) = O(n \log^* n)$. In general, Hershberger's algorithm finds $UE(S)$ in $O(\lambda_{k+1}(n) \log n)$ time sequentially, and it can be easily implemented in $O(\log^2 n)$ time using $O(\lambda_{k+1}(n)/\log n)$ processors in the EREW PRAM. Boxer and Miller's algorithm and Goodrich's algorithm construct $UE(C)$ in $O(\log^2 n)$ time using $O(\lambda_k(n))$ processors in the CREW PRAM, and in $O(\log n \log^* n)$ time using $O(\lambda_k(n)/\log^* n)$ processors in a randomized CRCW PRAM with high probability, respectively. They can be also used to find $UE(S)$, but the numbers of processors in both algorithms increase to $O(\lambda_{k+2}(n))$ and $O(\lambda_{k+2}(n)/\log^* n)$, respectively. In this paper, we show a more efficient parallel algorithm which constructs $UE(S)$ in $O(\log^{1+\epsilon} n)$ time using $O(\lambda_{k+1}(n)/\log^\epsilon n)$ processors in the EREW PRAM for any constant $\epsilon > 0$.

Some simple but effective techniques are used in our algorithms. The main method is *multi-level divide-and-conquer* which is similar to an ordinary divide-and-conquer except containing more than one division steps [9]. In the upper envelope algorithms for line segments, we combine multi-level divide-and-conquer with a *prune technique* which makes the results optimal. These techniques have broad senses and can be expected to improve a large class of parallel algorithms.

A set of segments in the plane has a *left (or right) base* if all the segments start from (or end at) a same vertical line. The problem of finding the upper envelope of the segments which have a base is substantial in our algorithms. In Section 2, we improve Hershberger's algorithm to show that if the upper envelope of the segments which have a base can be found, the upper envelope of the segments without a base can be found easily. In Section 3 and Section 4, we describe the main part of our algorithms: finding the upper envelope for the segments which have a base.

2. Improved Hershberger's Algorithm

Let $UE(S)$ be represented by the sequence of the subsegments of S that appear on the upper envelope in the left-to-right order. Generally, $UE(S)$ has $O(n\alpha(n))$ segments, but if S has a left (right) base, $UE(S)$ contains at most $2n - 1$ segments, since in this case any two segments of S may contribute an $a \ldots b \ldots a$ subsequence to the Davenport-Schinzel sequence corresponding to an upper envelope, but they cannot contribute an $a \ldots b \ldots a \ldots b$ subsequence [13]. By using this property, Hershberger's algorithm finds $UE(S)$ in $O(\log^2 n)$ time using $O(n/\log n)$ processors in the EREW PRAM. The outline of the algorithm is as follows: (1) construct an interval tree of S which divides S into the subsets of each with a left (right) base, (2) find the upper envelope of each subset, and (3) merge these upper envelopes. We prove that each step except step (2) can be easily improved.

2.1. Interval Tree of Line Segments

Sort the endpoints of the segments in S in increasing x-coordinate order. Partition the x-axis by the x-coordinates of the endpoints into $2n + 1$ intervals, and add a reference point at the midpoint of each interval. Number the endpoints and the reference points from 1 to $4n - 1$ in the left-to-right order, and let x_i be the x-coordinate of the ith point. The domain of each segment $s \in S$ can be represented by an integer interval (i, j) such that x_i and x_j are the x-coordinates of the left and right endpoints of s, respectively. The interval tree of S, denoted as $IT(S)$ is built as follows: (i) construct a complete binary tree with $2n$ leaves (if n is not the power of 2, add some dummy leaves), (ii) label the nodes in symmetric order from 1 to $4n - 1$, and (iii) with each node i ($1 \le i \le 4n - 1$) associate the x-coordinate x_i, and with each internal node $2i$ ($1 \le i \le 2n - 1$) associate a set $S[2i]$ of segments, where a segment $s \in S$ is included in $S[2i]$ if the x-coordinates of its endpoints are associated with the leaves a and b and the lowest common ancestor (LCA) of a and b is $2i$ (Fig. 1) ($2i$ is also called the LCA of segment $s = ab$). The endpoints of S can be sorted in $O(\log n)$ using n processors. Steps (i) and (ii) can be easily executed in $O(\log n)$ time using $O(n/\log n)$ processors. The LCA of two nodes in a symmetric ordered complete binary tree can be determined in $O(1)$ time [15]. $S[2i]$ for all i can be found by computing the LCA for each segment of S and then sort all the segments of S by their LCAs. Thus, step (iii) can be done in $O(\log n)$ time using $O(n)$.

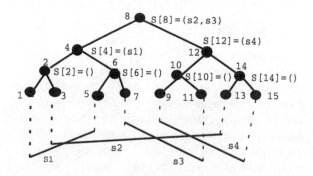

8 $S[8]=(s2,s3)$
$S[12]=(s4)$
4 $S[4]=(s1)$
12
2
$S[2]=()$ 6 $S[6]=()$ 10 14
$S[10]=()$ $S[14]=()$
1 3 5 7 9 11 13 15
s2 s4
s1 s3

Figure 1. Interval tree $IT(S)$

Lemma 1 *The interval tree of n line segments in the plane can be constructed in $O(\log n)$ time using $O(n)$ processors in the EREW PRAM.* ∎

Two sets of segments in the plane are *separated* if there is a straight line such that the sets locate on each side of the line. Without loss of generality, we assume that the separating line is vertical.

Property 1 *[13] The interval tree of S divides set S into subsets $S[2], S[4], \ldots, S[4n-2]$ which satisfy the following properties: (1) for any two node $2i$ and $2j$ in the same level, $S[2i]$ and $S[2j]$ are separated, and (2) $UE(S[2i])$ has at most $2|S[2i]| - 1$ segments.* ∎

Lemma 2 *The interval tree of n line segments in the plane can be constructed in $O(\log n)$ time using $O(n/\log n)$ processors in the EREW PRAM if the endpoints of the segments are sorted in x-coordinates.*

(Proof) Except $S[2i]$ $(1 \le i \le 2n-1)$ the other parts of constructing $IT(S)$ are executed in $O(\log n)$ time using $O(n/\log n)$ processors. >From the condition, the segments of S can be easily listed in the left-to-right order of their left endpoints in $O(\log n)$ time using $O(n/\log n)$ processors. Let S^j $(2 \le j \le \log n + 1)$ be the subset of S such that the LCAs of its segments locate on level j of $IT(S)$ and let X^j be the set of the x-coordinates associated on the nodes of level j. Compute S^j for all j as follows: assign each segment of S with a mark j if its LCA locates on level j, and then sort S by the marks. The marks are valued from 2 to $\log n + 1$, therefore, the sorting can be done in $O(\log n)$ time using $O(n/\log n)$ processors by stable integer sorting [18]. From Property 1 and the fact that the segments of S are

sorted in increasing x-coordinate order of the left endpoints, after stably sorting the segments of $S[2i]$ list contiguously in S^j for each node i of level j. Finally, $S[2i]$ for all i $(1 \le i \le 2n-1)$ can be found by merging the the x-coordinates of the segment endpoints of S^j with X^{j-1} for each j in $O(\log n)$ time using $O(n/\log n)$ processors. ∎

2.2. An improved Algorithm

Hershberger's algorithm is based on Property 1 and its parallel version is as follows.

Hershberger's Algorithm

(Input) A set S of n segments.
(Output) $UE(S)$, the upper envelope of S.
[Step 1] Construct the interval tree $IT(S)$.
[Step 2] Let $S[2i]$ and x_{2i} be the subset and the x-coordinate associated with node $2i$ $(1 \le i \le 2n-1)$ of $IT(S)$. Find $UE(S[2i])$ for each i as follows.
(i) For each i, partition $S[2i]$ by the vertical line $l(i)$: $y = x_{2i}$ into two part $S_1[2i]$ and $S_2[2i]$ (therefore, $l(i)$ is the right base and the left base of $S_1[2i]$ and $S_2[2i]$, respectively).
(ii) Find $UE(S_1[2i])$ and $UE(S_2[2i])$, respectively,
(iii) Concatenate $UE(S_1[2i])$ and $UE(S_2[2i])$.
[Step 3] Let UE^k $(2 \le k \le \log n + 1)$ be the upper envelope of the segments assigned in level k of $IT(S)$. Construct UE^k by concatenating $UE(S[i_1])$, $UE(S[i_2])$, $\ldots$, where $i_1, i_2, \ldots$ are the nodes of level k listing in the left-to-right order.
[Step 4] Merge the upper envlopes of all levels. ∎

Hershberger's Algorithm can be executed in $O(\log^2 n)$ time using $O(n/\log n)$ processors in the EREW PRAM [13]. We show that except Step 2 each step can be improved. Step 1 has been considered in Section 2.1. Step 3 can be executed in $O(\log n)$ time using $O(n/\log n)$ processors by prefix sum computing. In the following, we improve Step 4. Instead of merging $\log n$ upper envelopes UE_2, UE_3, $\ldots$, $UE_{\log n+1}$ directly, we cut them into $O(n/\log n)$ separate parts with $O(\log n)$ segments each by a set of vertical lines, find the upper envelope of each part, and then concatenate the upper envelopes from the left to right. Let $X(p)$ and $X(l)$ denote the x-coordinates of point p and vertical line l, respectively, and let $S[l_1, l_2]$ and $UE(S)[l_1, l_2]$ denote the sets of the segments (subsegments) of S and $UE(S)$ locating between vertical lines l_1 and l_2, respectively. A convex polygon is upper if all its vertices locate above the straight line which passes through its leftmost and rightmost vertices. Obviously, the upper envelope of line segments is an upper convex polygon.

Lemma 3 *Let E_i $(1 \le i \le k)$ be an upper convex polygon and $E = \cup_{i=1}^{k} E_i$ have $O(n)$ segments. E can be divided* *by $n/k + 1$ vertical lines into (n/k) separated parts with (k) segments each in $O(\log n)$ time using $O(n/\log n)$ processors in the EREW PRAM.*

(Proof) (1) Determine the separating lines: (i) Let set U_i consist of the endpoints of E_i in the left-to-right order and let $U = \cup_{i=1}^{k} U_i$. Partition U into $m = |U|/k$ subsets D_1, $D_2, \ldots, D_m$ with size k each such that for any two indices i and j with $1 \le i < j \le m$, the x-coordinate of each point in D_i is not bigger than that of any point in D_j. (ii) Compute the leftmost point of every D_i with $1 \le i \le m$ in parallel. Let l_i be the vertical line passing through the leftmost point of D_i and let l_{m+1} be the vertical line passing through the rightmost point of the last point set D_m. (2) Compute $E[l_i, l_{i+1}]$, the part of E between separating lines l_i and l_{i+1}, for each i ($1 \le i \le m$).

The parallel partition in phase (1)(i) can be done in $O(\log n)$ time using $O(n/\log n)$ processors [6] (In [6], E_i contains only $O(n/k)$ elements, therefore, if $|E_i| > n/k$, divide E_i into $|E_i|k/n$ subsets in advance). Phase (1)(ii) can be done in $O(\log n)$ time using $O(n/\log n)$ processors by the minimum computation. In phase (2), $E[l_i, l_{i+1}]$ ($1 \le i \le m$) can be found by computing the intersection of E_j and l_i for any i and j (one should make k copies of lines $l_1, l_2, \ldots, l_{m+1}$ to avoid concurrent reading), and then for every j compute the intersections of E_j with $l_1, l_2, \ldots, l_{m+1}$ by merging the endpoints of the segments of U_j with $l_1, l_2, \ldots, l_{m+1}$ by their x-coordinates, in $O(\log n)$ time using $O(n/\log n)$ processors [15]. Obviously, $|E[l_i, l_{i+1}]| = (k)$. ∎

(Improved Step 4 of Hershberger's Algorithm)

(A) Divide the upper envelopes $UE_2, UE_3, \ldots, UE_{\log n+1}$ into m ($= O(n/\log n)$) separated subsets $E_1, E_2, \ldots, E_m$ with $O(\log n)$ segments each.
(B) For each i, compute $UE(E_i)$ in parallel.
(C) Concatenate $UE(E_i)$ from $i = 1$ to $i = m$. ∎

Phase (A) can be done in $O(\log n)$ time using $O(n/\log n)$ processors by Lemma 3. E_i has only $O(\log n)$ segments, therefore, $UE(E_i)$ can be found by Hershberger's algorithm in $O((\log \log n)^2)$ time using $O(\log n/\log \log n)$ processors, and if the segments are nonintersecting, it can be found in $O(\log n)$ time sequentially [2]. Therefore, Phase (B) can be executed in $O(\log n)$ time using $O(n \log \log n/\log n)$ processors, or in $O(\log n)$ time using $O(n/\log n)$ processors if the segments are nonintersecting. Phase (C) can be executed in $O(\log n)$ time using $O(n/\log n)$ processors by computing prefix sum. Adding the complexity of Step 1 and Step 3 of the algorithm, we have the following lemma.

Lemma 4 *Each step except Step 2 of Hershberger's algorithm can be improved to execute in the EREW PRAM (i) in $O(\log n)$ time using $O(n)$ processors, (ii) in $O(\log n)$ time using $O(n \log \log n/\log n)$ processors if the segment endpoints of S are sorted in x-coordinate, and (iii) in $O(\log n)$*

time using $O(n/\log n)$ processors if the segments of S are nonintersecting and the segment endpoints are sorted in x-coordinate. ∎

3. Upper Envelope of the Line Segments with A Base

In this section, we discuss the upper envelope problem for a set S of n line segments which has a left or right base. Without loss of generality, let S have a left base. If the segments of S are nonintersecting, $UE(S)$ can be found easily as follows: Let P be the sequence consisting of the right endpoints of the segments of S in decreasing x-coordinate order. Let $Y(P)$ be the sequence whose ith element is the y-coordinate of the ith point of P. For any segment of S, only the subsegment which contains the right endpoint can appear on $UE(S)$. The ith point of P appears on $UE(S)$ *iff* its y-coordinate is the maximum of the first i elements of $Y(P)$. The prefix maxima computation of $Y(P)$ can be done in $O(\log n)$ time using $O(n/\log n)$ processors[15]. Adding the conclusion of Lemma 4(iii), we have the following theorem.

Theorem 1 *The upper envelope of n nonintersecting line segments in the plane can be found in $O(\log n)$ time using $O(n/\log n)$ processors in the EREW PRAM if the endpoints of the segments are sorted in x-coordinate.* ∎

In the following, let the segments of S be possibly-intersecting. From the duality of points and lines, the upper envelope problem of lines can be reduced to that of points. Therefore, the upper envelope of n lines can be optimally found in $O(\log n)$ time using $O(n)$ processors in the EREW PRAM, and in $O(\log n)$ time using $O(n/\log n)$ processors if the lines are sorted in slope [1, 7, 8]. We introduce a *prune technique*: as it is shown below, some segments of S can be treated as lines whose upper envelope can be obtained directly by using the above optimal algorithms, and this enables us to reduce the size of the segments.

The *extension* of S, denoted as $L(S)$, is a set of the lines obtained by lengthening each line segment of S in both directions into infinity. Let S' be a set of subsegments of S. For any two segments $s \in S$ and $s' \in S'$, s is called the origin of s' if s' is a subsegment of s. Let $Ori(S', S)$ be a set consisting of all the origins of S' in S. The following lemma reveals the relation of lines and line segments.

Property 2 *Let T be a set of line segments. If T has a left base l_1 and a right base l_2, then $UE(T) = UE(L(T))[l_1, l_2]$, where $L(T)$ is the extension of T (Fig. 2(a)).* ∎

Given two vertical lines l_1 and l_2 with $X(l_1) < X(l_2)$ and a set T of line segments, $T' = T[l_1, l_2]$ can be divided

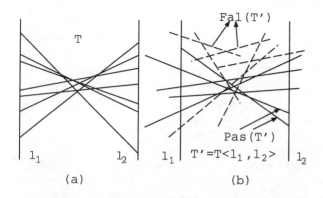

T   Fal(T')
                    Pas(T')
l_1 l_2 l_1 $T'=T<l_1,l_2>$ l_2

(a)   (b)

Figure 2. Prune technique: some segments can be considered as lines

into two subsets: *passing-through-segment set* $Pas(T')$ and *falling-in-segment set* $Fal(T')$ (Fig. 2(b)), where $t' \in Pas(T')$ if t' begins from l_1 and ends at l_2 and $t' \in Fal(T')$ if at least one x-coordinate of two endpoints of t' belongs to the open interval $(X(l_1), X(l_2))$. It is easily seen that $UE(T') = UE(UE(Pas(T')) \cup UE(Fal(T')))$.

We compute $UE(S)$ as follows: (1) separate S by a set of vertical lines $l_0, l_1, \ldots, l_k$ into $S[l_0, l_2]$, $S[l_1, l_2]$, ..., $S[l_{k-1}, l_k]$, where $X(l_0) < X(l_1) < \ldots < X(l_k)$, l_0 is the left base of S and l_k passes through the endpoint of the rightmost segment of S, (2) recursively find $UE(S[l_i, l_{i+1}])$ for each i, and (3) concatenate the upper envelopes from the left to right. Since $UE(S[l_i, l_{i+1}]) = UE(UE(Pas(S[l_i, l_{i+1}])) \cup UE(Fal(S[l_i, l_{i+1}])))$ and $UE(Pas(S[l_i, l_{i+1}]))$ can be computed directly by the upper envelope algorithm for lines from Property 2, we prune $Pas(S[l_i, l_{i+1}])$ from $S[l_i, l_{i+1}]$ in the recursive step and compute only $UE(Fal(S[l_i, l_{i+1}]))$ recursively.

There is still one problem to solve: separating S by k vertical lines may cut one line segment to many subsegments. In the worst case it causes (kn) segments. To avoid of increasing the complexity of the problem, we use two-level divide-and-conquer technique. We add one more division step before the above algorithm: divide S into n/k equally-sized subsets such that each subset contains k segments of S (note that here we divide the segments S without cutting them) and then compute the upper envelope of each subset. After doing this division step, we find the upper envelope of these n/k upper envelopes. Separating n/k upper envelopes by k vertical lines increases only $O(n)$ subsegments since one line intersects one upper envelope at most at one place. In the following, we give the details of computing $UE(S)$. Let $P(S)$ be the set of the right endpoints of the segments in S. We first sort S in increasing slope and sort $P(S)$ in increasing x-coordinate in $O(\log n)$ time using $O(n)$ pro-

cessors in the EREW PRAM [15].

Algorithm **UEWithBase**(S)

(Input) S and $P(S)$, where S is a set of n possibly-intersecting line segments with a left base and $P(S)$ is a set of the points which are the right endpoints of the segments in S. S is sorted in increasing slope and $P(S)$ is sorted in increasing x-coordinate.

(Output) $UE(S)$, the upper envelope of S.

(Base Phase)

[Step 1] If $n = 1$, $UE(S) = S$. This completes the algorithm.

(First division phase)

[Step 2] (1) Divide $P(S)$ into $n^{1/2}$ equally-sized sequences $P_1, P_2, \ldots, P_{n^{1/2}}$ such that P_i $(1 \le i \le n^{1/2})$ contains the $((i-1)n^{1/2}+1)$th to the $(in^{1/2})$th points of $P(S)$. Divide S into $n^{1/2}$ subsets $S_1, S_2, \ldots, S_{n^{1/2}}$ such that S_i consists of the segments whose right endpoints belong to P_i, that is, $P(S_i) = P_i$. (2) For each i, sort S_i in increasing slope.

[Step 3] For each i, recursively construct $UE(S_i)$ in parallel.

(Second division phase)

[Step 4] Let l_i $(1 \le i \le n^{1/2})$ be the vertical line passing through the rightmost point of P_i.

(1) Separate the segments of $\overline{S} = \cup_{i=1}^{n^{1/2}} UE(S_i)$ by lines $l_0, l_1, \ldots, l_{n^{1/2}}$ into $n^{1/2}$ parts $\overline{S}[l_0, l_1]$, $\overline{S}[l_1, l_2]$, ..., $\overline{S}[l_{n^{1/2}-1}, l_{n^{1/2}}]$ such that each part contains $O(n^{1/2})$ segments, where l_0 is the left base of $\overline{S}$.

(2) For each i, divide $\overline{S}[l_{i-1}, l_i]$ into $Pas(\overline{S}[l_{i-1}, l_i])$ and $Fal(\overline{S}[l_{i-1}, l_i])$.

[Step 5] For each i, compute $UE(Pas(\overline{S}[l_{i-1}, l_i]))$ in parallel.

[Step 6] For each i, compute $UE(Fal(\overline{S}[l_{i-1}, l_i]))$ in parallel.

[Step 7] For each i, merge $UE(Pas(\overline{S}[l_{i-1}, l_i]))$ and $UE(Fal(\overline{S}[l_{i-1}, l_i]))$ in parallel.

(Merge step)

[Step 8] Concatenate $UE(\overline{S}[l_{i-1}, l_i])$ from $i = 1$ to $i = n^{1/2}$ in the increasing order of i. ∎

Now, we analyse the algorithm in the EREW PRAM. Meanwhile, we give an attention to its sequential behavior. Let $T(n)$ be the running time and $P(n)$ be the number of the using processors. Step 2(1) can be easily done in $O(1)$ time using $O(n)$ processors. Step 2(2) sorts S_i for each i which can be executed in $O(\log n)$ time using $O(n)$ processors (it needs only $O(n)$ time if we implement it sequentially as follows: assign the segments of S_i $(1 \le i \le n^{1/2})$ with a mark i and use the stable integer sorting to sort all the segments of S in the increasing order of their marks in $O(n)$ time. Since S is sorted in the slopes, after the stable integer sorting, the segments of each S_i are sorted in the slopes). Step 3 recursively constructs $UE(S_i)$ for each i. Since S_i and P_i satisfy the conditions for the inputs of the algorithm: S_i has the left base and is sorted in increasing slope, and P_i ($= P(S_i)$) is sorted in increasing x-coordinate. Step 3 can be executed in $T(n^{1/2})$ time using $n^{1/2}P(n^{1/2})$ processors. Step 4(1) can be executed in $O(\log n)$ time using $O(n/\log n)$ processors by the method used in Lemma 3. Step 4(2) can be done in $O(1)$ time using $O(n)$ processors. >From Property 2, Step 5 can be executed in $O(\log n)$ time using $O(n)$ pocessors by the upper envelope algorithm for lines (it can be executed sequentially in only $O(n)$ time as follows: for each i sort the segments of $Pas(\overline{S}[l_i, l_{i+1}])$ in their slops in $O(n)$ time by using the stable integer sorting, and then find the upper envelope of $Pas(\overline{S}[l_i, l_{i+1}])$ which can be do in linear time). Let us consider Step 6. From the definitions of S_i and $Fal(\overline{S}[l_i, l_{i+1}])$, $Ori(Fal(\overline{S}[l_i, l_{i+1}]), S)$ $= S_i$. Therefore, $UE(Fal(\overline{S}[l_i, l_{i+1}])) = UE(S_i)[l_i, l_{i+1}]$. $UE(S_i)$ has been found in Step 3, therefore Step 6 can be done in $O(1)$ time using $O(n)$ processors. Step 7 can be executed in $O(\log n)$ time using $O(n/\log n)$ processors by merging the endpoints of the segments of two upper envelopes based on their x-coordinates. Step 8 concatenates $n^{1/2}$ upper envelopes which can be done in $O(\log n)$ time using $O(n/\log n)$ processors by computing prefix sum. Therefore, we get $T(n) \le T(n^{1/2}) + O(\log n)$ and $P(n) \le \max\{n^{1/2}P(n^{1/2}), n\}$. Thus, $T(n) = O(\log n)$ and $P(n) = n$. Adding the result of Lemma 4(i), we have the following theorem.

Theorem 2 *The upper envelope of n possibly-intersecting line segments in the plane can be found in $O(\log n)$ time using $O(n)$ processors in the EREW PRAM.* ∎

In the above analysis, we also show that if the segments of S are sorted in slope and their endpoints are sorted in x-coordinate, each step except the recursive part (i.e., Step 3) can be executed in $O(n)$ time sequentially. Let $T'(n)$ be the sequential running time of the algorithm. We get $T'(n) = n^{1/2}T'(n^{1/2}) + O(n)$. Thus, $T'(n) = O(n \log \log n)$. Adding the result of Lemma 4(ii), we have the following theorem.

Theorem 3 *The upper envelope of n possibly-intersecting line segments in the plane can be found in $O(n \log \log n)$ time sequentially if the segments are sorted in slope and the segment endpoints are sorted in x-coordinate.* ∎

4. Upper Envelope of Generalized Segments

Let S be a set of n k-intersecting segments in the plane, where k is a constant. In general, the complexity of $UE(S)$ is $\lambda_{k+2}(n)$, but if S has a left or right base, the complexity

of $UE(S)$ is $\lambda_{k+1}(n)$ [13]. Given two upper envelopes f_1 and f_2 of k-intersecting segments, the upper envelope of f_1 and f_2 can be found by merging the segment endpoints of f_1 and f_2. The merging procedure and other operations for line segments can be used for k-intersecting segments without change if the following queries can be answered in constant time [11, 13]: (1) given a segment s, return the x-coordinates of its left and right endpoints, (2) given an x-coordinate $\pitchfork$ and two segments s_1 and s_2 whose intervals include $\pitchfork$, tell which of s_1 and s_2 is uppermost at $x = \pitchfork$, or return "equal" if the segments intersect at $x = \pitchfork$, and (3) given an x-coordinate $\pitchfork$ and two segments s_1 and s_2, return the x-coordinate of the next intersection of s_1 and s_2 that lies strictly to right of $\pitchfork$, if any such intersection exists.

Hershberger's algorithm compute the upper envelope of n k-intersecting segments in $O(\log^2 n)$ time using $O(\lambda_{k+1}(n)$ $/ \log n)$ processors in the EREW PRAM. We give a more efficient algorithm. Replacing the word "line segment" with "k-intersecting segment", the improved Hershberger's algorithm in Section 2 can be used to find $UE(S)$. We can prove (like we did in Section 2) that each step of the algorithm expect Step 2 (finding the upper envelope of k-intersecting segments with a bases) can be executed in $O(\log n)$ time using $\lambda_{k+1}(n)$ processors in the EREW PRAM. In the rest of the section, we let S has a left base. We show that two-level divide-and-conquer technique is also effective to general segments. The following algorithm constructs $UE(\hat{S})$, where $\hat{S}$ has m ($\le n$) segments. In the algorithm, $d_h(n) = 2^{\log^{h/(h+1)} n}$ and $h \ge 0$.

Algorithm G-UEWithBase($\hat{S}, h + 1$)

(Input) a set $\hat{S}$ of m k-intersecting segments with a left base, and an integer $h \ge 0$.

(Output) the upper envelope of $\hat{S}$.

(Base Step)

[Phase 1] If $h = 0$ compute $UE(\hat{S})$ by Hershberger's algorithm else if $m \le d_h(n)$ use algorithm G-UEWithBase($\hat{S}, h$) to compute $UE(\hat{S})$. This completes the algorithm. Else do the following steps.

(First division step)

[Phase 2] Divide $\hat{S}$ into $d_h(n)$ equally-sized subsets $S_1, S_2, \ldots, S_{d_h(n)}$ such that S_i has $m/d_h(n)$ segments of S. For each i, recursively construct $UE(S_i)$ in parallel.

(Second division step)

[Phase 3] Let $T = \cup_{i=1}^{d_h(n)} UE(S_i)$. Notice that $|T| \le \lambda_{k+1}(m)$. Divide T into $\lambda_{k+1}/(d_h(n))$ separated parts T_1 $T_2, \ldots, T_{\lambda_{k+1}/(d_h(n))}$ by vertical lines such that each part has $O(d_h(n))$ subsegments of T.

[Phase 4] For each i ($1 \le i \le \lambda_{k+1}(m)/d_h(n)$), compute $UE(T_i)$ by algorithm G-UEWithBase(T_i, h) in parallel.

(Merge step)

258

[Phase 5] Concatenate the upper envelopes $UH(T_i)$ for all i in the increasing order of i. ∎

Lemma 5 *Let S be a set of n k-intersecting segments with a left base. If algorithm G-UEWithBase(S,h) ($h \geq 1$) computes $UE(S)$ in $O(\log^{1+1/h} n)$ time using $O(\frac{\lambda_{k+1}(n)}{\log^{1/h} n})$ processors in the EREW PRAM, then algorithm G-UEWithBase(S, $h + 1$) computes $UE(S)$ in $O(\log^{1+1/(h+1)} n)$ time using $O(\frac{\lambda_{k+1}(n)}{\log^{1/(h+1)} n})$ processors in the EREW PRAM.*

(Proof) Let $T(m)$ be the running time and $P(m)$ be the number of the processors used for the algorithm. Notice that $\log(\lambda_k(m)) = O(\log m)$ for any $k \geq 0$. By the assumption of the lemma, Phase 1 can be done in $O(\log^{1+1/h} m)$ time using $O(\frac{\lambda_{k+1}(m)}{\log^{1/h} m})$ processors. Since $m \leq d_h(n)$ in Phase 1, it can be done in $O(\log^{1+1/h} d_h(n)) = O(\log n)$ time using $O(\frac{\lambda_{k+1}(m)}{\log^{1/h} d_h(n)}) = O(\frac{\lambda_{k+1}(m)}{\log^{1/(h+1)} n})$ processors. Similarly Phase 4 can be done in $O(\log n)$ time using $O(\frac{\lambda_{k+1}(n)}{\log^{1/(h+1)} n})$ processors. Phase 2 can be done in $T(m/d_h(n))$ time using $d_h(n)P(m/d_h(n))$ processors. Phase 3 can be done in $O(\log m)$ time using $O(\frac{\lambda_{k+1}(m)}{\log m})$ processors by Lemma 3. The other steps of the algorithm can be easily done in $O(\log m)$ time using $O(\frac{\lambda_{k+1}(m)}{\log m})$ processors. Therefore, each step except the recursive step can be done in $O(\log n)$ time using $O(\frac{\lambda_{k+1}(m)}{\log^{1/(h+1)} n})$ processors. We have the following recurrences.

$$T(m) \leq \begin{cases} T(m/d_h(n)) + O(\log n), & if\ m > d_h(n) \\ O(\log n), & if\ m \leq d_h(n) \end{cases}$$

$$P(m) \leq \begin{cases} \max\{d_h(n)P(\frac{m}{d_h(n)}), \frac{\lambda_{k+1}(m)}{\log^{1/(h+1)} n}\}, \\ \quad if\ m > d_h(n) \\ O(\frac{\lambda_{k+1}(m)}{\log^{1/(h+1)} n}), & if\ m \leq d_h(n) \end{cases}$$

From the recurrence of $T(n)$, we get $T(n) = O(\log^{1+\frac{1}{(h+1)}} n)$. From the recurrence of $P(n)$ and the property $\lambda_{k+1}(m_1)/m_1 \leq \lambda_{k+1}(m_2)/m_2$ for any $0 \leq m_1 \leq m_2$, we get $P(n) = O(\frac{\lambda_{k+1}(n)}{\log^{1/(h+1)} n})$. ∎

Theorem 4 *Let S be a set of n k-intersecting segments in the plane. The upper envelope of S can be found in $O(\log^{(1+\epsilon)} n)$ time using $O(\frac{\lambda_{k+1}(n)}{\log^{\epsilon} n})$ processors for any constant $\epsilon > 0$ in the EREW PRAM.*

(Proof) For any given constant $\epsilon > 0$, let $N > 0$ be the smallest integer such that $1/N \leq \epsilon$. Algorithm G-UEWithBase(S, 1) computes $UE(S)$ by Hershberger's algorithm in $O(\log^2 n)$ time using $O(\frac{\lambda_{k+1}(n)}{\log n})$ processors. In general, let algorithm G-UEWithBase(S, h) find $UE(S)$ in

$O(\log^{(1+1/h)} n)$ time using $O(\frac{\lambda_{k+1}(n)}{\log^{1/h} n})$ processors for $h \geq 1$. By Lemma 5, algorithm G-UEWithBase(S,h + 1) finds $UE(S)$ in $O(\log^{(1+1/(h+1))} n)$ time using $O(\frac{\lambda_{k+1}(n)}{\log^{1/(h+1)} n})$ processors. Therefore, algorithm G-UEWithBase(S,N) finds $UE(S)$ in $O(\log^{(1+1/N)} n)$ time using $O(\frac{\lambda_{k+1}(n)}{\log^{1/N} n})$ processors. ∎

5. Conclusions

We have described the efficient upper envelope algorithms for segments in the plane in the EREW PRAM. There still some open problems. First, contrast with the known sequential results we would like to find the following parallel algorithms in the EREW PRAM: (1) given n k-intersecting segments, construct the upper envelope in $O(\log n)$ time using $O(\lambda_{k+1}(n))$, and (2) given n possibly-intersecting line setments which are sorted in the slops and whose endpoints are sorted in the left-to-right order, construct the upper envelope in $O(\log n)$ time using $O(n \log \log n / \log n)$ processors. Next, contrast with the complexity of the upper envelopes, we would like to know the answers for the following questions: (1) given n possibly-intersecting line setments which are sorted in some way, is it possible to find the upper envelope in $O(n\alpha(n))$ time (we have improved the upper bound from $O(n \log n)$ to $O(n \log \log n)$), and (2) in general, since $\lambda_k(n) = O(n \log^* n)$ for any positive integer k, is it possible to find the upper envelope of n k-intersecting segments in $O(n \log n^*)$ time, and furthermore, in the time of its lower bound $(\lambda_{k+2}(n))$?

References

[1] A. Aggarwal, B. Chazelle, L. Guibas, C. O'Dunlaing and C. Yap. Parallel computational geometry. *Algorithmica*, No.3, pp.293-327, 1988.

[2] Ta. Asano, Te. Asano, L. Guibas, H, Hershberger and H. Imai. Visibility of disjoint polygons. *Algorithmica*, No.1, pp.49-63, 1986.

[3] M. Atallah. Some dynamic computational geometry problems. *Comput. Math. Appl.*. Vol.11, No.12, pp.1171-1181, 1985.

[4] L. Boxer and R. Miller. Parallel dynamic computational geometry. *TR 87-11, SUNY-Buffalo*, 1987.

[5] L. Boxer and R. Miller. Common intersections of polygons. *Information Processing Letters*, Vol.33, No.5, pp.249-254, 1988 & Vol.35, No.1, p.53, 1990.

[6] D. Z. Chen, W. Chen, K. Wada and K. Kawaguchi. Parallel algorithms for partitioning sorted sets and re-

lated problems. *Lecture Notes in Computer Science*, Vol.1136, pp.234-245, 1996.

[7] D. Z. Chen. Efficient geometric algorithms on the EREW PRAM. *IEEE Transactions on Parallel and Distributed Systems*, No.6, pp.41-47, 1995.

[8] W. Chen, K. Nakano, T. Masuzawa and N. Tokura. Optimal parallel algorithms for finding the convex hull of a sorted point set. *IEICE Trans.*, Vol.J74-D-I, No.12, pp.814-825, 1991.

[9] W. Chen, K. Wada and K. Kawaguchi. A parallel method for finding the convex hull of discs. *IEEE First International Conference on Algorithm and Architectures for Parallel Processing*, pp. 274-281, 1995.

[10] F. Dehne, C. Kenyon and A. Fabri, "Scalable and architecture independent parallel geometric algorithms with high probability optimal algorithm," *Proc. Sixth IEEE Symposium on Parallel and Distributed Processing*, 586-593 (1994).

[11] M. T. Goodrich. Using approximation algorithms to design parallel algorithms that may ignore processors allocation. *Proc. 34nd Annual Symposium on Foundations of Computer Science*, pp.711-722, 1991.

[12] D. Hart and M. Sharir. Nonlinearity of Davenport-Schinzel sequences and of generalized path compression schemes. *Combinatorica*, No.6, pp.151-177, 1989.

[13] J. Hershberger. Finding the upper envelope of n line segments in $O(n \log n)$ time. *Information Processing Letters*, Vol.33, No.4, pp.169-174, 1989.

[14] J. Hershberger, "Upper envelope onion peeling," *Comput. Geom. Theory Appl.*, Vol.2, No.2 (1989), pp.93-110.

[15] J. JaJa. *An Introduction to Parallel algorithms*. Addison Wesley Publishing Company, 1992.

[16] K. Kedem, and M. Sharir. An efficient motion-planning algorithm for a convex polygonal object in two-dimensional polygonal space. *Discrete Comput. Geometry*, Vol.5, No.1, pp.43-755, 1990.

[17] P. D. MacKenzie and Q. Stout. Asymptotically efficient hypercube algorithms for computational geometry. *Proc. 3rd Symp. on the Frontiers of Massively Parallel Computation*, pp.8-11, 1990.

[18] J. H. Reif. An optimal parallel algorithm fo integer sorting. *Proc. 26th Annual Symposium on Foundations of Computer Science*, pp.496-504, 1985.

[19] M. Sharir and P. K. Agarwal. *Davenport-Schinzel Sequences and Their Geometric Applications*. Cambridge University Press, 1995.

Session 4B
Memory/Storage Management

Chair: Xiaodong Zhang
College of William and Mary

Optimizing Dynamic Memory Management in a Multithreaded Application Executing on a Multiprocessor

Daniel Häggander
Ericsson Software Technology AB
S-371 23 Karlskrona, Sweden
Daniel.Haggander@epk.ericsson.se

Lars Lundberg
University of Karlskrona/Ronneby
S-372 25 Ronneby, Sweden
Lars.Lundberg.ide.hk-r.se

Abstract

The Billing Gateway (BGw) is a large multithreaded object oriented C++ application running on Sun Solaris. Due to frequent allocation and deallocation of dynamic memory, the initial implementation of this system suffered from poor performance when executed on a multiprocessor.

In this paper we compare two approaches for improving the performance of BGw. First we replace the standard Solaris heap with a parallel heap. In the second approach we optimize the application code by removing a number of heap allocations/deallocations. In order to do this, we introduce memory pools for commonly used object types and replace some heap variables with stack variables.

The parallel heap approach resulted in a dramatic speedup improvement. The optimization of the application code did also result in a dramatic speedup improvement. For this approach the performance using a single-processor computer was also increased by a factor of eight. The optimizations took approximately one week to implement.

1. Introduction

Today, multiprocessors are used in a number of applications. Multithreaded programing makes it possible to write parallel applications which benefit from the processing capacity of multiprocessors. However, some parallel applications suffer from large run-time overhead and serialization problems when using multiprocessors. The speedup for multithreaded applications is usually good when the first processors are added. When more processors are added, the speedup curve increases more slowly. In some cases the speedup can actually start to decrease when we add more processors.

One serialization problem is sequential dynamic memory management. Moreover, most dynamic memory handlers are implemented without any consideration of multiprocessing specific problems, e.g. false memory sharing [2].

Object-orientation helps the programmer to develop large and maintainable software. Unfortunately, this use of object-orientation often results in an more intensive use of dynamic memory, making the dynamic memory performance problem worse.

The standard implementation of dynamic memory is often rather inefficient. A number of more efficient implementations have been developed, e.g. SmartHeap [4] and Heap++ [5]. The most common strategy is to use different allocation algorithms depending on the size of the requested memory. QuickHeap is a typical example [7].

An optimized heap often results in better performance for none-parallel applications. However, a performance evaluation of a weather forecast model [3] showed that a heap implementation which was efficient on a single-processor caused performance problems on a multiprocessor.

For multiprocessor systems ptmalloc [6] can be efficient. ptmalloc is a heap implementation which can perform several allocations and deallocations in parallel. The ptmalloc implementation is a version of Doug Lea's malloc implementation that was adapted for multiple threads by Volfram Gloger, while trying to avoid lock contention as much as possible.

The Billing Gateway (BGw) is a system for collecting billing information about calls from mobile phones. The system is a commercial product and it has been developed by the Ericsson telecommunication company. BGw is written in C++ [11] (approximately 100,000 lines of code) using object-oriented design, and the parallel execution has been implemented using Solaris threads. The system architecture is parallel and we therefore expected good speedup when using a multiprocessor. However, the actual speedup of BGw was very disappointing.

By using the BGw as an example, we explain why dynamic memory management can cause poor speedup when using a multiprocessor, particularly for object oriented programs. We also describe and evaluate two methods which dramatically improved the speedup of the BGw using a Sun multiprocessor with eight processors. These two methods are: using a parallel heap implementation and redesigning memory usage within the application code, respectively.

The rest of the report is structured in following way: Section 2 describes the BGw and its speedup problem. Section 3 describes the dynamic memory performance problem in detail. In section 4 a parallel heap implementation is investigated. Section 5 describes a redesign which reduces the number of heap allocations. Section 6 concludes the paper.

2. Billing Gateway (BGw)

2.1. Overview

BGw transfers, filters and translates raw billing information from Network Elements (NE), such as switching centers and voice mail centers, in the telecommunication network to billing systems and other Post Processing Systems (PPS). Customer bills are then issued from the billing systems (see figure 1). The raw billing information consists of Call Data Records (CDRs). A CDR contains information about a call (in certain rare cases information about a call may be split up into several CDRs, e.g. when the call is very long). Each CDR is 175-225 bytes long. The CDRs are continuously stored in files in the network elements. With certain time intervals or when the files have reached a certain size, these files are sent to the billing gateway.

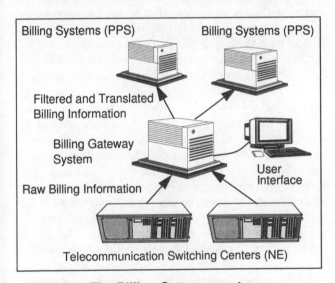

Figure 1. The Billing Gateway system.

There is a graphical user interface connected to the gateway system. In this interface the different streams of information going through the gateway are visualized as a directed graph, i.e. each billing application is represented as a graph. There are four major types of nodes in the application graphs.

Network element (NE) and post processing system (PPS) nodes represent external systems which communicate with the gateway, e.g. each switching center is represented as a NE node and each billing system is represented as a PPS node. There may be any number of NE and PPS nodes in an application.

The information streams in an application start in a NE node. An information stream always ends at a PPS node. Using a Filter node, it is possible to filter out some records in the information streams. In some cases the record format in the information streams has to be changed, e.g. when the post processing systems do not use the same record format as the network elements. Formatter nodes make it possible to perform such reformatting.

Figure 2 shows an application where there are two network elements producing billing information (the two leftmost nodes). These are called "MSC - New York" and "MSC - Boston" (MSC = Mobile Switching Center). The CDRs from these two MSCs are sent to a filter called "isBillable". There is a function associated with each filter, and in this case the filter function evaluates to true for CDRs which contain proper information about billable services. CDRs which do not contain information about billable services are simply filtered out. The other CDRs are sent to another filter called "isRoaming". In this case, there are two stream going out from the filter.

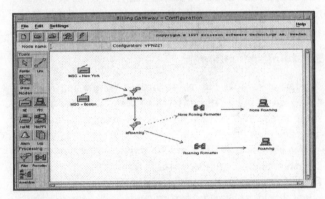

Figure 2. BGw configuration window.

The function associated with "isRoaming" evaluates to true if the CDR contains information about a roaming call (a roaming call occurs when a customer is using a network operator other than his own, e.g when travelling in another country). In this case, the record is forwarded to a formatter, and then to a billing system for roaming calls. If the filter function evaluates to false, the record is sent to a formatter and billing system for non-roaming calls. The billing systems are represented as PPS nodes.

The record format used by the billing systems differs from the record format produced by the MSCs. This is why the CDRs coming out of the last filter have to be translated into the record format used by the billing system before they can be sent from the gateway system to the billing systems.

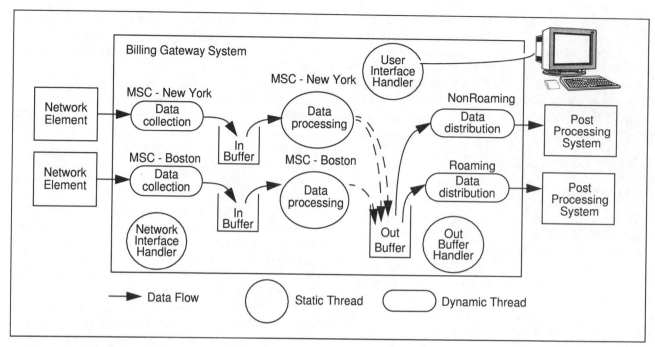

Figure 3. The thread structure of Billing Gateway.

The graph shown in figure 2 is only one example of how billing applications can be configured. The system can handle a large number of combinations of network elements, filters, formatters and post processing systems.

2.2. Implementation

Figure 3 shows the major threads for the application shown in figure 2. In order not to complicate the figure, some threads which monitor disk and memory usage etc. have been left out.

When there is no flow of data through the gateway, the system contains a number of static threads. When there is a flow of information going through the system, some additional threads are created dynamically.

When a network element wants to send a billing file to the gateway it starts by sending a connect message. This message is handled by the Network Interface Handler thread. This thread checks if the message is valid and determines the identity of the requesting network element. If the message is valid, a data collection thread is created. This thread reads the file from the network element and stores it on disk. When the complete file has been stored the data collection thread notifies the thread that shall process the data, and then the data collection thread terminates.

The data processing, i.e. the part of BGw that does the actual filtering and formatting, is implemented in a different way. When a configuration is activated, BGw creates one data processing thread for each NE node within the configuration (see figure 3). Every thread is bound to a certain NE,

i.e a data processing thread can only process files which have been collected by the corresponding NE.

For the application in figure 2 each file of billing information from the network elements may generate a transmission of either zero, one or two files of billing information to the post processing systems. If all CDRs are filtered out as unbillable, no file is generated by the data processing thread. If all billable CDRs are either roaming or non-roaming, one file is generated for the billing system for roaming or non-roaming calls. If the MSC file contains billable CDRs for both roaming and non-roaming calls, one file is generated for each of the two billing systems. The files generated by the data processing threads are put into an out-buffer. When a file has been generated, the data processing thread notifies the Out Buffer Handler thread. The data processing thread then starts to process the next file in its In Buffer. If the In Buffer is empty, the thread waits until the next files has been collected.

The Out Buffer Handler is notified that a new file has been put into its buffer and a data distribution thread is created. This thread sends the file to the corresponding post processing system. The data distribution thread terminates when the file has been transmitted.

2.3. Performance

Billing Gateway versions 1 and 2 have been evaluated, using a Sun Sparc Center 2000 and a Sun Enterprise 4000 with eight processors [10]. These evaluations showed that a good speedup was achieved when the first processors were added. When more processors were added, the speedup curve started to fall off. The speedup curves for BGw 1 and BGw 2 can be seen in figure 4. The configuration is the same as in figure 2 with the exception that there are eight network elements (MSCs) instead of two.

BGw 3 is the latest version of the Billing Gateway. This version has some new features. The most significant one is a new language which makes is possible to define more complex filters and formatters. The new language is of "C" style with sub-functions and local variables. The new language makes it easier to adapt BGw to new environments and configurations. However, the speedup of BGw 3 was extremely poor (see figure 4).

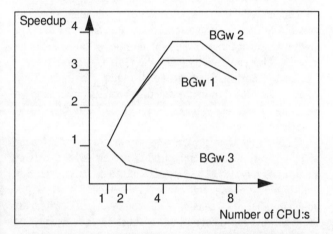

Figure 4. The speedup of the 3 BGw releases.

Previous investigations [3] have shown that dynamic memory can cause performance problems for multithreaded applications executing on multiprocessors. To find out if the dynamic memory caused the performance problem in BGw 3, an additional test was made.

One of the new features in BGw 3 which uses dynamic memory very frequently is the run-time interpreter of the filter- and formatter-language. The implementation of the language interpreter uses memory from the heap to store the local variables. The design of the application is made in such a way that at least one sub-function call was done when a CDR was processed by a filter or a formatter. This design led to a very intensive use of the heap, even for small configurations.

Another feature which uses dynamic memory frequently is the CDR decoder. More exactly, the decoding of CDRs containing dynamic structures of information. The implementation of the decoding algorithm is (more or less) the same in BGw 1, 2 and 3.

In order to test if dynamic memory management caused the speedup problems, the problematic CDRs were removed from the test files. Also, the filters and formatters used in the test was redefined in such a way that the number of sub-function calls and the use of local variables was minimized. The speedup of the adapted configuration and the new work-load was almost linear, i.e. almost optimal. Consequently, dynamic memory management caused most of the speedup problems in BGw 3.

In the next section we will discuss why dynamic memory management causes such large performance problems.

3. Dynamic memory management

Some features within the C++ language, such as dynamic binding [11] make it possible to implement a more maintainable software design. This type of design often use dynamic memory to become as general as possible. Reuse issues, such as class libraries and object oriented frameworks [9], advocate a general design and implementation, often resulting in very frequent allocation and deallocation of dynamic memory.

In C++, dynamic memory is allocated via the operator new. The operator returns a pointer to an allocated memory area The memory is then deallocated by the operator delete. Most compilers simply map these operators directly to the malloc() and free() functions of the standard C library. Consequently, C++ applications which have been developed to be general and reusable, use the malloc() and the free() functions very frequently. Figure 5 shows examples of memory management in C and C++ respectively.

In a multithreaded application, all threads use the same memory [8][13]. This means that all threads use the same heap for dynamic memory allocations. Therefore, the allocation- and deallocation-functions should be reentrant. Otherwise, they have to be protected against simultaneous usage. The C library functions malloc() and free() are usually not reentrant and must therefore be protected. In the Solaris implementation the heap is protected by a global mutex. The mutex is locked on entrance and unlock before returning, making sure that only one allocation or deallocation can be performed at the same time.

A major problem for a multithreaded application running on a multiprocessor, is that only one thread can allocate or deallocation memory at the same time. According to Amdahl's Law, no application can run faster than the total execution time of its sequential parts. For applications where dynamic memory is allocated and deallocated frequently, the dynamic memory management significantly decreases the speedup.

However, even if an application spends all its time allocating and deallocating memory, i.e in malloc() and free(), the speedup should never be less than one, which was the case for BGw 3 (see figure 4). Consequently, there must be some additional explanation.

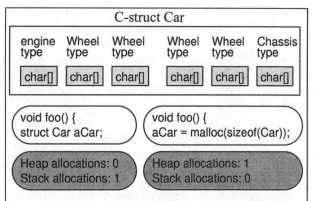

The C programer makes a "struct", in which all the information about the four wheels, the engine and the chassis are stored.

If the car-struct is defined as a local variable, no heap allocation is made. Even if the programer chooses to make a global car, i.e uses the heap, only one heap allocation is necessary.

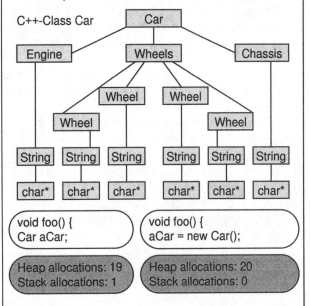

The C++ programmer often chooses to define a number of sub-objects (this technique improves the reusability). These sub-objects are combined into a car. The programer may also use a class library to handle the names of items, i.e the String object in the figure above. In the constructor of the car object, four wheels, one engine and one chassis are created via the operator new.

Even if the car object is defined as a local variable, at least 19 heap allocations are needed. One for each car item and one for each item name. Only the first object, the car object, use stack memory.

Figure 5. Data distribution in C and C++ respectively.

To lock and unlock a free mutex is fast in Solaris. On a single-processor, only one thread can execute at the same time. It is, therefore, rare that a thread tries to lock the heap mutex while another thread is holding it.

On a multiprocessor, several threads can execute at the same time. It is, therefore, more likely that two threads want to allocate or deallocate dynamic memory at the same time. In that case, one of the threads will fail to lock the mutex which protects the heap. In these cases, a queue of blocked threads is created. When the global mutex is unlocked, all the blocked threads in the queue try to complete their locks. It is common that an allocation is followed by a deallocation or a new allocation, i.e the thread which unlocks the mutex is often the one which succeeds in locking it again.

The many lock attempts generated produce large system overhead. The time in system mode increases and the time in user mode decreases when the number of failed locks increases. This can seen by using the Unix command time.

The system overhead produced when locking and unlocking the global mutex protecting heap, is one reason for speedup figures less than one (see figure 4). Another reason is false memory sharing.

Cache memories consist of a number of blocks (cache lines). The size of the cache line is system dependent. Sun computers have a cache line size on 16-64 bytes [1]. Sun multiprocessors have one cache for each CPU. It is possible that a number of threads have allocated variables which are stored in the same cache line. If these threads execute on different CPUs, false memory sharing will appear. When one thread changes its variable, the other copies of the cache line are invalidated. When the copies are invalidated, the other threads which are accessing data in the same cache line have to update the caches on their CPUs. The overhead costs of constantly updating the caches can be large.

The Solaris dynamic memory implementation has an alignment of 16 bytes and a minimum allocation size of 16 bytes. If the multiprocessor uses caches with a cache line size of 64 bytes (Enterprise 4000), up to 4 CPUs can share the same cache line (16 bytes x 4 is 64 bytes).

By overloading the malloc() function in libc (se figure 6), we were able to monitor the physical placement of the allocated memory. The malloc() function was overloaded with a new function which called the original malloc(), stored the address value returned from it and finally evaluated the possibility of false memory sharing. An allocation which shared a cache line with a memory area of another thread was identified as a false memory sharing candidate. Tests on Billing Gateway show that 50% of all dynamic memory allocations are such candidates.

4. A parallel heap implementation - ptmalloc

Two main problems with the standard malloc() and free() functions are that they can not be executed in parallel and the large overhead caused by the global mutex protecting the heap. These two problems would be solved if malloc() and free() were re-written in a way which made it possible for threads to allocate and deallocate memory in parallel.

It is rather simple to replace the standard heap implementation in existing applications. The heap can either be inserted when the application is linked or the heap library can be preloaded before the application is started, using dynamic libraries [12] (see figure 6).

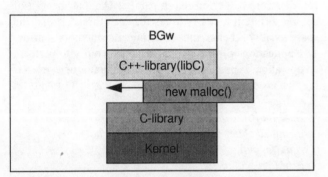

Figure 6. Overload the standard heap implementation.

A straight forward solution to implement a parallel heap is to have one heap area for each thread within an application. However, each heap area must be protected with a mutex even in this case. This is to make sure that no other thread currently uses it for deallocation. However, the mutex protection would probably not cause any major performance problems. Allocating memory from one thread and then deallocating it from another is not that common.

Many applications use a very large number of threads, and having a very large number of heap areas results in bad memory utilization. Most applications also create and delete threads dynamically. To create a new heap area each time a thread is created would generate large overhead for such applications.

A better idea is to have one heap area for each simultaneous allocation, i.e one heap area for each processor. The number of processors is low and static. However, to identify the processor currently used, is very costly. In Solaris, this operation requires a system call.

Most operating systems try to schedule a thread on the same processor as much as possible. Consequently, when a thread allocates dynamic memory, it is often executing on the same processor as it was when it made the previous allocation To use the same heap area as the last time can therefore be a good approximation.

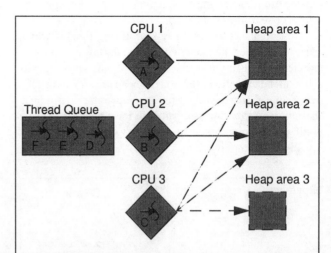

An application has 6 threads and executes on a multiprocessor with 3 processors. On CPU 1, thread A is currently allocating memory from heap area 1.
When thread B, which is running on CPU 2, wants to allocate memory it first tests heap area 1. This heap is locked. Thread B then tests heap area 2. This heap is free and thread B can therefore lock and use this area.
Thread C is scheduled on CPU 3 and tries to allocate memory. Thread C tests heap areas 1 and 2, which are both locked. Thread C therefore creates a new heap (heap area 3), which is locked and used.

Figure 7. One heap for each simultaneous allocation.

If one heap area is occupied, e.g if a thread is scheduled up on a new processor, the thread will try to find a new heap area using trylock (se figure 7). With the trylock function a thread can test the status of a mutex without blocking the thread. A trylock locks the mutex if it is free, otherwise it returns an error status. The heap areas can in this way be tested one by one until a free area is found. The new area found will be used for further allocations, i.e. the thread will start the next allocation by looking at this heap area.

If no free heap area is found, a new heap area is created (see figure 7). In this way the number of heap areas will be dynamically adjusted to the number of processors.

The implementation discussed so far is basically the implementation of ptmalloc. In order to test how often a thread has to choose a new heap area, the source code of ptmalloc was modified. An alarm was raised every time a thread changed heap area. Tests made on BGw showed that the number of times a thread had to change heap area was very limited.

ptmalloc has the same interface as the C library functions and provides the same functionality. ptmalloc can therefore replace the standard implementation without changing the source code of the application.

ptmalloc also reduces the risk of having threads which share the same cache block. The reason for this is that a certain heap area is often shared by a small number of threads and a thread can often use the same heap area for long periods of time. Consequently, ptmalloc reduces the risk of false sharing. However, the problem with false memory sharing is still not completely solved, e.g ptmalloc has a static memory alignment of 8 byte.

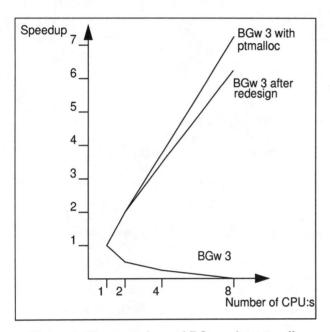

Figure 8. The speed-up of BGw using ptmalloc.

5. Redesign of BGw

There are, at least, three different aspects of dynamic memory management which affects performance negatively. First, the sequential nature of most implementations causes a serialization bottleneck. This problem was successfully removed by using a parallel heap implementation like ptmalloc. The second problem is false memory sharing due to the fact that variables from different threads, executing on different processors, often share the same cache line. This problem was reduced by using ptmalloc. The third problem is that it is relatively costly to allocate and deallocate memory from the heap. This problem affects not only the speedup, but also the performance on a single-processor computer. Replacing the standard heap implementation with ptmalloc did not affect the performance on a single-processor computer.

In order to improve also the single-processor performance we introduced memory pools for commonly used object types. Instead of deallocating an object, the object is returned to the pool and when a new object of the same type is needed it can be reclaimed from the pool. These pools are managed by the application code, thus reducing the number of heap allocations and deallocations. We also replaced a number of heap variables with variables on the stack. After doing these optimizations, the speedup was more or less the same when using the standard heap implementation compared to ptmalloc, i.e. the heap was no longer a serialization bottleneck.

The simple stack functionality offers faster allocations and deallocation of memory compared to the more complex heap. The stack memory is also thread specific, i.e each thread has its own stack. The allocations and deallocations can therefore be performed in parallel. Another benefit of having different memory areas for each thread is that the space locality is better, thus reducing false memory sharing.

Applications often need temporary memory to perform an operation. A bad habit is to use the operator new, even if the size is constant.

```
readAndPrint(int fd) {
unsigned char* buff = new unsigned char[16];
read(fd, buff, 16);
printf("%s",buff);
delete buff;}
```

An alternative implementation is to use memory from the stack.

```
readAndPrint(int fd) {
char buff [16];
read(fd, buff, 16);
printf("%s",buff);}
```

The typical situation were dynamic memory is used are when the size of the allocated memory has to be decided in run-time. In this cases the C library function, alloca() can be used instead of the operator new. The function allocates a dynamic number of bytes from the stack.

The designers used approximately one week to replace a number of heap allocations with stack allocations and implement memory pools for commonly used objects (BGw 3 consists of more than 100,000 lines of C++ code). The redesign improved the speedup significantly (see figure 9). Figure 9 also shows that the design changes did not only improve the speedup. They also improve the performance of the application when it executes on a single-processor with a factor of eight. Better single-processor performance is one of the benefits of redesigning the application code compared to using a parallel heap implementation.

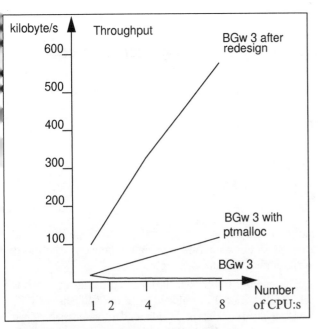

Figure 9. The new throughput of BGw.

6. Conclusions

Object oriented design, reusability and maintainability aspects all encourage the use of dynamic memory. The Billing Gateway (BGw 3) was developed using object oriented design, and reusability and maintainability were important aspects.

This study shows that for BGw 3, and similar multi-threaded object oriented applications, dynamic memory can cause severe performance problems when using a multiprocessor. In the first version of BGw 3, the sequential implementation of dynamic memory allocation/deallocation and false memory sharing resulted in a performance degradation when using more than one processor.

Using a parallel dynamic memory handler, such as pt-malloc, is the easiest solution to the performance problem. The speedup improvement when using ptmalloc was dramatic. In fact, the speedup was almost linear, i.e. almost optimal. Consequently, the performance problems in BGw 3 were caused entirely by dynamic memory management, i.e. there were no other overhead problems or serialization bottlenecks. We expect that most multiprocessor manufactures will offer implementations similar to ptmalloc in the future. However, ptmalloc is not a commercial product, and the use of non-commercial products is often restricted at professional software companies.

An alternative solution to the dynamic memory performance problem, is to modify the application code in such a way that the number of heap allocations/deallocations is reduced. We were able to reduce the number of heap allocations/deallocations by introducing memory pools for commonly used object types and by replacing some heap variables with stack variables. It turned out that this approach did not only result in almost linear speedup; the performance using a single-processor computer was also improved by a factor of eight (see figure 9). The redesign reduced the number of heap allocations/deallocations significantly, thus making it possible to use the standard heap implementation without suffering from any serialization problems. The time for redesigning BGw in this way was one week. Consequently, the performance improvement was extremely good considering the limited effort.

Object oriented techniques make it possible to build large and complex systems, which are reusable and maintainable. However, if not carefully designed, object oriented programs may run into serious performance problems when using a multiprocessor. The poor performance due to dynamic memory management is not isolated to BGw. A number of related products have similar problems.

References

[1] Adrian Cockcroft, "SUN Performance and Tuning", Prentice Hall, 1995.

[2] M. Dubois, J. Skeppstedt, and P. Stenström, "Essential Misses and Data Traffic in Coherence Protocols", J. Parallel and Distributed Computing 29(2):108-125, October 1995.

[3] R. Ford, D. Snelling and A. Dickinson, "Dynamic Memory Control in a Parallel Implementation of an Operational Weather Forecast Model, in Proceedings of the 7:th SIAM Conference on parallel processing for scientific computing, 1995.

[4] http://www.microquill.com

[5] http://www.rougewave.com

[6] http://www.cs.colorado.edu/~zorn/Malloc.html

[7] Nick Lethaby and Ken Black, "Memory Management Strategies for C++", Embedded Systems Programming, San Francisco, June, 1993.

[8] B. Lewis, "Threads Primer", Prentice Hall, 1996.

[9] T. Lewis, L. Rosenstein, W. Pree, A. Weinand, E. Gamma, P. Calder, G. Anderst, J. Vlissides, and K. Schmucker, "Object Oriented Application Frameworks", Manning Publication Co, 1995.

[10] L. Lundberg and D. Häggander, "Multiprocessor Performance Evaluation of Billing Gateway Systems for Telecommunication Applications", in Proceedings of the ISCA 9th International Conference in Industry and Engineering, December, Orlando 1996.

[11] B. Stroustrup, "The C++ Programming Language", Addison-Wesley, 1986.

[12] Microsystems, Inc., "Linker And Libraries", 1994.

[13] Soft, "Solaris Multithreaded Programming Guide", Prentice Hall, 1995.

Improving Parallel-Disk Buffer Management using Randomized Writeback[*]

Mahesh Kallahalla   Peter J. Varman

Deptartment of Electrical and Computer Engineering
Rice University
Houston TX 77251
E-mail: {kalla,pjv}@rice.edu

Abstract

We address the problems of I/O scheduling and buffer management for general reference strings in a parallel I/O system. Using the standard parallel disk model with D disks and a shared I/O buffer of size M, we study the performance of on-line algorithms that use bounded global M-block lookahead. We introduce the concept of write-back whereby blocks are dynamically relocated between disks during the course of the computation. Write-back allows the layout to be altered to suit different access patterns in different parts of the reference string. We show that any bounded-lookahead on-line algorithm that uses purely deterministic policies must have a competitive ratio of $\Omega(D)$. We show how to improve the performance by using randomization, and present a novel algorithm, RAND-WB, using a randomized write-back scheme. RAND-WB has a competitive ratio of $\Theta(\sqrt{D})$, which is the best achievable by any on-line algorithm with only global M-block lookahead. If the initial layout of data on the disks is uniformly random, RAND-WB has a competitive ratio of $\Theta(\log D)$.

1. Introduction

Continuing advances in processor architecture and technology have resulted in the I/O subsystem becoming the bottleneck in many applications. The problem is exacerbated by the advent of multiprocessing systems which can harness the power of hundreds of processors in speeding up computation. Improvements in I/O technology are unlikely to keep pace with processor-memory speeds, causing many applications to choke on I/O. The increasing availability of cost-effective multiple-disk storage systems [7] provides an opportunity to improve the I/O performance through the use of parallelism. However it remains a challenging problem to effectively use the increased disk bandwidth to reduce

the I/O latency of an application. Effective use of I/O parallelism requires careful coordination between data placement, prefetching and caching policies.

The parallel I/O system is modeled using the intuitive parallel disk model introduced by Vitter and Shriver [18]: the I/O system consists of D independently-accessible disks and an associated I/O buffer with a capacity of M blocks that is shared by all the disks. The data for the computation is stored on the disks in blocks; a block is the unit of access from a disk. In each parallel I/O up to D blocks, at most one from each disk, can be read (written) from (to) the I/O subsystem. From the viewpoint of the I/O, the computation is characterized by a *reference string* consisting of the ordered sequence of blocks that the computation accesses. A block should be present in the I/O buffer before it can be accessed by the computation. Serving the reference string requires performing I/O operations to provide the computation with blocks in the order specified by the reference string. In this model the measure of performance of the system is the number of parallel I/Os required to service a given reference string.

Classical buffer management has been studied extensively in a sequential I/O model [1, 4, 5, 6, 8, 16]. These works primarily deal with developing efficient buffer management algorithms for a single-disk system by optimizing decisions regarding the blocks to be evicted from the buffer. The use of information regarding future accesses, *lookahead*, to improve the eviction decisions made by on-line algorithms for single-disk systems was studied in [1] and [5] using different models of lookahead. The overlap of cpu and I/O operations using prefetching in a single-disk system was addressed in [6], and off-line approximation algorithms were presented and analyzed. In the context of parallel I/O studied in this paper, several new issues (discussed in Section 2) arise precluding any straightforward extensions of the algorithms for single-disk systems to the parallel situation. In [3] the question of designing on-line prefetching algorithms for a parallel I/O system using bounded lookahead was addressed. Fundamental bounds on the performance of

---

[*]Supported in part by the National Science Foundation under grant CCR-9704562 and a grant from the Schlumberger Foundation.

algorithms were presented for an important class of reference strings called read-once reference strings. However, the problem of general reference strings in which blocks can be repeatedly accessed, called read-many reference strings, was not considered. For read-many reference strings an optimal off-line buffer management and scheduling algorithm was presented in [17] for a distributed-buffer parallel I/O model in which each disk has its own private buffer. In an alternative stall model of parallel I/O, a generalization of the sequential model of [6] to multiple disks and a shared buffer, an approximate off-line algorithm for I/O scheduling and buffer management was presented in [10]. However, so far the question of devising an on-line algorithm with bounded lookahead for general read-many reference strings in a parallel I/O model has not been addressed.

In this paper we study the on-line I/O scheduling problem for read-many reference strings in the framework of competitive analysis. We use the competitive ratio (defined formally in Section 2.1) as the measure of performance of an on-line algorithm . Informally, this ratio measures how well a given on-line algorithm compares with the optimal off-line algorithm; the off-line algorithm has access to the entire reference string and constructs its schedule using some off-line optimization strategy. We introduce the concept of *write-back*, whereby blocks are dynamically relocated between disks during the course of the computation. We show that buffer management algorithms which perform no write-back can pay a significant I/O penalty when compared to algorithms that do. However deciding which blocks to relocate and how to move them is non-trivial to do in an online manner. We show that *any* scheduling algorithm with bounded lookahead that uses deterministic rather than randomized buffer management and I/O scheduling policies can in the worst case require $\Theta(D)$ times as many I/Os as the optimal off-line algorithm.

We use *randomization* to improve the performance of buffer management and scheduling decisions. In particular, we design an on-line buffer management and scheduling algorithm, RAND-WB, whose competitive ratio matches that of the *best on-line* algorithm that uses the same amount of lookahead. For worst case reference strings, the expected number of I/Os performed by RAND-WB is shown to be within $\Theta(\sqrt{D})$ times the number of I/Os done by the optimal off-line algorithm. This is significantly better than the $\Theta(D)$ competitive ratio of deterministic methods.

The rest of the paper is organized as follows. Issues in parallel I/O and basic definitions are presented in Section 2. In Section 3 we introduce the concept of write-back and derive a lower bound of $\Omega(D)$ on the competitive ratio of any deterministic algorithm using global M-block lookahead. An algorithm using randomized write-back that achieves a competitive ratio of $\Theta(\sqrt{D})$ is presented in Section 4.

2. Performance Issues in Parallel I/O

In the sequential I/O model, the measure of performance is the total number of blocks accessed from the disk. However, for parallel I/O a better measure is the number of parallel I/Os performed, as more than one block can be fetched in a single I/O operation. The potential for overlapped accesses raises new issues that make the problem of optimizing the number of parallel I/Os challenging.

Prefetching: It is well known that early fetching cannot reduce the number of I/Os needed[1] in the single-disk model [16]. In a parallel I/O system fetching a block only when it is requested by the computation is wasteful of the available I/O bandwidth, since only one block will be fetched in any I/O operation. Disk parallelism can be obtained by prefetching blocks from disks that would otherwise idle, concurrently with a demand I/O. In order to prefetch accurately, the computation must therefore be able to look ahead in the reference string, beyond the last referenced block. Prefetching for multiple disks for specific applications has been studied in [2, 11, 12, 13, 14], for example.

Choice of blocks to fetch on an I/O: In the sequential model blocks are always fetched strictly in order of the reference string. In the parallel model fetching blocks in order of their appearance in the reference string can be inefficient. For instance, consider the example of Figure 1 which assumes $D = 3$ and $M = 6$. Assume that blocks labeled A_i (respectively B_i, C_i) are placed on disk 1 (respectively 2, 3), and that the reference string $\Sigma = A_1A_2A_3A_4B_1C_1A_5B_2C_2A_6B_3C_3A_7B_4C_4C_5C_6C_7$. Figure 1 (a) shows the I/O schedule obtained by always fetching in the order of the reference string. At step 1, blocks

Disk 1	A_1	A_2	A_3	A_4	A_5	A_6	A_7		
Disk 2	B_1	B_2	B_3		B_4				
Disk 3	C_1	C_2			C_3	C_4	C_5	C_6	C_7

(a)

Disk 1	A_1	A_2	A_3	A_4	A_5	A_6	A_7
Disk 2	B_1				B_2	B_3	B_4
Disk 3	C_1	C_2	C_3	C_4	C_5	C_6	C_7

(b)

Figure 1. Schedules for reference string Σ.

B_1 and C_1 are prefetched along with the demand block A_1. At step 2, B_2 and C_2 are prefetched along with A_2. At step 3, there is buffer space for just 1 additional block besides A_3, and the choice is between fetching B_3, C_3 or neither. Fetching in the order of Σ means that we fetch B_3; continuing in this manner we obtain a schedule of length 9. In Fig-

---
[1]Prefetching may however help in overlapping cpu and I/O operations [6].

ure 1 (b), at step 2 disk 2 is idle (even though there is buffer space) and C_2 that occurs later than B_2 in Σ is prefetched; similarly, at step 3, C_3 that occurs even later than B_2 is prefetched. However, the overall length of the schedule is 7, better than the schedule that fetched in the order of Σ.

Replacement Policy: In the parallel I/O model, choosing a block to evict is complicated because of two reasons: the need for parallelism and the use of prefetching. It is well known that the replacement policy that evicts the block whose next reference is the farthest (known as the MIN algorithm [4]) minimizes the total number of I/Os done in the sequential model. In a parallel system this is not sufficient. The eviction decision is influenced by the potential parallelism with which blocks can be read again; that is, it may be better to evict a block even though it increases the total number of blocks fetched, if it permits greater parallelism. Secondly, there is a tension between the need to increase parallelism by prefetching and the desire to delay the fetch as late as possible to obtain the best possible candidate for eviction. For illustration, consider the following example with $D = 3$ and $M = 6$, where blocks A_i (respectively B_i, C_i) are placed on disk 1 (respectively 2, 3). Suppose that at some point the buffer contains $A_1, A_2, A_3, B_1, B_2, C_1$; and the remainder of the reference string consists of the subsequence: $\Sigma^* = A_4 B_3 C_2 A_4 B_3 B_2 B_1 C_1 A_1 A_2 A_3$. Figure 2(a) shows the I/O schedule obtained by using the same policy as MIN (known to be optimal for a single-disk) to determine evictions. To fetch A_4 the algorithm evicts A_3 that

Disk 1	A_4	A_1	A_2	A_3
Disk 2	B_3			
Disk 3	C_2			

(a)

Disk 1	A_4	A_1
Disk 2	B_3	B_1
Disk 3	C_2	C_1

(b)

Figure 2. Schedules for reference string Σ^*.

is referenced later than all the other blocks in buffer. B_3 and C_2 are prefetched along with A_4, evicting blocks A_2 and A_1[2]. The buffer now has blocks $A_4 B_3 C_2 B_1 B_2 C_1$, and the computation proceeds till block A_1 is referenced. Three more I/Os, fetching blocks A_1, A_2 and A_3 respectively, are required to complete the schedule. In contrast Figure 2(b) shows a schedule that takes only 2 rather than 4 steps. This is obtained by evicting blocks A_1, B_1 and C_1 (instead of A_1, A_2 and A_3) at the first step. When the computation references B_1 these blocks are read back in just one I/O.

---

[2]Note that even if we did not prefetch B_3 or C_2 but fetched them on demand on the next 2 I/Os, the same eviction decisions would be made, so any difference in performance in this example is not due to suboptimal decisions caused by prefetching.

2.1. Definitions

We use the Parallel Disk Model [18] of a parallel I/O system. This model consists of D independently accessible disks and an associated I/O buffer capable of holding M ($M \geq 2D$) data blocks. In one parallel I/O step up to D accesses, at most one on any disk, can proceed in parallel. The measure of performance is the number of parallel I/Os performed to service a given sequence of I/O requests. This model uses the I/O time as the measure, and looks to the overlap of operations on different disks as the primary method of performance improvement, rather than overlap of cpu and I/O operations. In the rest of the paper we shall use I/O to mean a *parallel I/O*.

Reference strings, introduced informally in the previous section, model the sequence of I/O accesses. In this paper we consider read-many reference strings where there is no restriction on the blocks referenced. This is contrast to *read-once* reference strings [3], where all the requests are to distinct blocks.

Definition 1. The sequence of read I/O requests is called the *reference string*. In a *read-once* reference string all the references are to distinct blocks. In a *read-many* reference string any two references can be to the same data block.

In order to perform accurate rather than speculative prefetching it is necessary to have some knowledge of the future requests to be made to the I/O system, beyond the current reference. This window of future accesses embodies the notion of lookahead. In sequential I/O systems lookahead helps in the eviction decisions of the buffer management algorithm [1, 5]. In parallel systems lookahead is needed for making prefetching decisions [3] independent of its use in aiding evictions. Our algorithms use global M-block lookahead defined below for read-many reference strings. Such a lookahead is called M-block strong lookahead in the model of [1]. There has been substantial interest in obtaining such lookahead information for prefetching from applications using combinations of programmer hints and program analysis [15]. Intuitively, global M-block lookahead gives the next buffer-load of distinct requests to the buffer management algorithm. This information can aid both prefetching and caching.

Definition 2. An I/O scheduling algorithm has *global M-block lookahead* if it knows the portion of the reference string containing the next M distinct blocks.

Definition 3. An online parallel prefetching algorithm A has a competitive ratio of C_A if for any reference string the number of I/Os required by A is within a factor C_A of the number of I/Os required by the optimal off-line algorithm to serve the same reference string. If A is a randomized algorithm then the expected number of I/Os done by A is considered.

3. Lower Bound on Deterministic Algorithms

In a read-many reference string, data blocks can be requested more than once by the computation. Hence a situation may arise wherein a particular data layout strategy may be favorable for data accesses occurring in one section of the reference string but unfavorable for accesses in other sections. One way to tackle this problem is to relocate data blocks dynamically so as to have a favorable data placement during the next set of accesses. The underlying intuition is to rearrange the layout so that blocks which are evicted may be fetched in parallel with other blocks in the future. Of course, writing a block out to a different disk, other than the one on which it currently resides, incurs the cost of writing out a block. But the gain in I/O parallelism as a result of this relocation can be used to offset the extra cost in performing the write. We refer to this action of writing an evicted block to a disk, different from the one it was fetched from, as *write-back*. Write-back allows the location of a data block to be dynamically altered. However, there is only one copy of the block on the disks at any time.

We next introduce the notion of simple deterministic algorithms that captures the determinism inherent in most existing buffer management algorithms. An algorithm is said to be a *simple deterministic algorithm* (SDA) if at any instant the set of blocks that it prefetches, the set of blocks that it evicts from the buffer and the disks to which it writes back these evicted blocks is a deterministic function of the reference string till that instant, the lookahead, and the contents of the buffer. The central idea in the above characterization is that a SDA uses *deterministic* policies. This determinism can be exploited by an adversary to generate reference strings which require a SDA to unnecessarily make a large number of I/Os.

As a simple illustration, consider a reference string that consists of accesses to an $M \times D$ matrix of blocks. The blocks are first accessed in row-major order and then in column-major order. Assume that the matrix is laid out in block row-major order, striped across all disks. An algorithm with only global M-block lookahead, that does not perform any write-back will significantly serialize the I/Os while accessing the columns. A better strategy would be to relocate the blocks while accessing the rows so that the accesses for the columns can also be parallelized. In this case the writes too can proceed with full parallelism and drastically reduce the number of I/Os required.

Even in a more general case, when a deterministic algorithm uses an arbitrary write-back policy along with more sophisticated prefetching and block replacement heuristics, there are reference strings for which the algorithm must serialize significantly. This intuition is formalized in Theorem 1 which gives a lower bound of $\Omega(D)$ on the competitive ratio of any simple deterministic algorithm.

3.1. Proof of Lower Bound

Let $\mathcal{A}$ be an arbitrary SDA with global M-block lookahead. Based on the behavior of $\mathcal{A}$ we construct a reference string for which $\mathcal{A}$ requires $\Omega(MD)$ I/Os (Lemma 2). We then show an alternative off-line schedule which services the same reference string in $\Theta(M)$ I/Os (Lemma 3), thereby showing that the ratio between the two is $\Omega(D)$. The detailed proofs follow.

Theorem 1 *Every simple deterministic algorithm with only global M-block lookahead has a competitive ratio of $\Omega(D)$.*

To aid in the analysis it is useful to define the notion of a *phase*, which is a sub-sequence of the reference string.

Definition 4. The reference string is partitioned into substrings called *phases* such that each phase (a) is of maximal length and (b) contains references to exactly M distinct blocks. The ith phase, $i \geq 1$, is denoted by $phase(i)$.

The *end of a phase* refers to the instant when the last block of a phase has been serviced. The following definitions will be useful in characterizing the set of blocks which are accessed in a phase.

Definition 5. The set of *clean blocks* in $phase(i)$ is the set of blocks in $phase(i)$ not requested in $phase(i-1)$. The set of *stale blocks* in $phase(i)$ is the set of blocks in $phase(i)$ requested in $phase(i-1)$. The set of *new blocks* in $phase(i)$ is the set of blocks in $phase(i)$ not requested in any, $phase(j)$, $1 \leq j < i$. The set of *reuse blocks* in $phase(i)$ is the set of clean blocks in $phase(i)$ that have been requested in some $phase(j)$, $j < i - 1$.

Let us now construct a reference string η, consisting of $M(3D+1)$ references, which will be used to give a lower bound on the performance of $\mathcal{A}$. Reference strings of arbitrary length for which the proofs will follow can be constructed by repeating η. The details of the construction are presented in Figure 3. Figure 4 illustrates the structure of the constructed reference string as seen by algorithm $\mathcal{A}$.

With respect of the construction of Figure 3, we note the following. By counting the number of blocks which have been referenced exactly once till $phase(2i + D + 1)$, and using the fact that there are at most M blocks in the buffer, we can show that at the end of $phase(2i + D + 1)$ at least $M/2$ blocks, requested exactly once and not present in the buffer, reside on some disk. This will ensure that Λ_{2i+D+1} is well defined for all $0 \leq i < D$ thereby allowing the construction of the sequence η.

Lemma 1 *With respect to algorithm $\mathcal{A}$ and the reference string η, $height(2i + D + 1) \geq M/2$, for $0 \leq i < D$.*

Lemma 2 *Algorithm $\mathcal{A}$ performs $\Omega(MD)$ I/Os to service reference string η.*

1. The first $D+1$ phases of the reference string η, consists of $M(D+1)$ references to new blocks which are striped across all disks. Let F denote this set of $M(D+1)$ blocks.

2. The last $2D$ phases are constructed in sets of two phases. The ith, $0 \leq i < D$, set is constructed as follows:

   - The first phase of the set, $phase(2i+D+2)$, consists of M new blocks striped across all disks.
   - The next phase, $phase(2i+D+3)$, is made of two parts. The first part consists of $M/2$ new blocks striped across all disks. The second part is given by the sequence Λ_{2i+D+1}, determined as follows.
     Let $k = 2i+D+1$. Let F_k denote the set of all blocks from F which have been referenced exactly once till the end $phase(k)$. Let $A_{k,j}$, be the set of blocks from F_k, residing on disk j at the end of $phase(k)$; let $B_{k,j}$, subset of $A_{k,j}$, be the set of all such blocks in the buffer. Then $height(k) = \max_j\{|A_{k,j} - B_{k,j}|\}$, is the maximum number of blocks from F_k, residing on the same disk and not in the buffer. Let d denote the disk with the maximum number of blocks from F_k not in the buffer. The sequence Λ_k, is defined as the ordered sequence of $M/2$ earliest referenced blocks in $A_{k,d} - B_{k,d}$.

Figure 3. Construction of reference string η

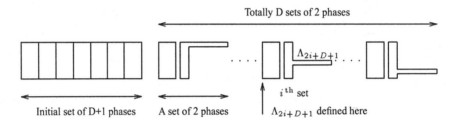

Figure 4. Structure of a worst case reference string for $\mathcal{A}$

Proof : To service the first $M(D+1)$ requests algorithm $\mathcal{A}$ performs at least $M(D+1)/D$ I/Os. By construction no block referenced in $phase(2i+D+3)$ is present in algorithm $\mathcal{A}$'s buffer at the end of $phase(2i+D+1)$. In addition, $M/2$ blocks in $phase(2i+D+3)$ are referenced from a single disk. In order to service these requests algorithm $\mathcal{A}$ must perform at least a total of $M/2$ I/Os in phases $phase(2i+D+2)$ and $phase(2i+D+3)$ combined, for each $0 \leq i < D$. Hence the total number of I/Os performed by algorithm $\mathcal{A}$ to service η, is $\Omega(MD)$. □

In contrast, if all the blocks of the last $2D$ phases are written out striped across all disks the number of I/Os performed in each of these phases can be reduced to $O(M/D)$. This approach is used in Lemma 3 to develop a scheme which can service η in $\Theta(M)$ I/Os.

Lemma 3 *η can be serviced in $\Theta(M)$ I/Os.*

Proof : Let us consider an I/O schedule to service η based on the following two rules (a) within a phase I/Os are initiated only on demand; in parallel prefetch as many of the next D requests as allowed by buffer space (b) let Γ be the set of all blocks occurring in some Λ_{2k+D+1}, $0 \leq k < D$. At the end of $phase(D+1)$, I/Os are performed to relocate all blocks in Γ such that the M/2 blocks in each Λ_{2k+D+1} are uniformly distributed on all disks.

This schedule performs $(D+1)M/D$ read I/Os till the end of $phase(D+1)$. In each of the subsequent phases only M/D reads are required, as the blocks are uniformly distributed across all disks following the relocation. If $M \geq D^2$, the relocation can be performed in M reads and writes of Γ by reading blocks with full parallelism and writing out one stripe whenever D blocks are got from any set Λ_{2i+D+1}, $0 \leq i < D$. Interestingly, relocation can be done in $\Theta(M)$ I/Os even if $M \geq D$ by reducing it to an off-line load-balancing problem which can be solved using bipartite graph matching. □

A special case, when the SDA does not do any write-back is representative of buffer management algorithms normally used in practice. In this case it is easy to see that the same proof with a simpler construction suffices (the last $2MD$ requests can be constructed from the initial data layout). Hence in the worst case such algorithms are ineffective in exploiting the latent I/O parallelism even when substantial lookahead – one memory load – is provided to them.

Algorithm RAND-WB uses global M-block lookahead. Initially unmark all blocks in the buffer.
On a request for a data block the following actions are taken.

1. If the requested block is present in the buffer the request is serviced without any further action.
2. If the requested block is not present in the buffer a parallel I/O needs to be initiated for all blocks in the set L. Some action is required, to create the necessary space for these blocks.
   (a) Choose any $|L|$ unmarked blocks from the buffer, giving priority to blocks that have already been relocated. Of these write-back those blocks which have not been relocated as described in (b), after flagging them as relocated.
   (b) To perform the write-back, stripe the blocks in a round robin fashion across all the disks starting the stripe from a randomly (uniform probability) chosen disk.
   (c) Read in the blocks of L in one parallel I/O.

Figure 5. Algorithm RAND-WB

4. RAND-WB: A Randomized Algorithm

From the preceding discussion, *determinism* in the I/O scheduling algorithm results in poor performance. We address this problem through the use of randomization and present an on-line algorithm, RAND-WB, which uses randomized write-back in an attempt to parallelize repeated accesses to blocks. By doing so we show that its competitive ratio can be improved to $\Theta(\sqrt{D})$. In perspective, this is the best competitive ratio that is achievable by algorithms which have global M-block lookahead and a fixed initial layout of blocks on disks [3].

A block in the buffer is called *marked* if it is referenced in the current phase; else it is called *unmarked*. To specify the blocks to be prefetched in an I/O consider, for each disk, the next block not present in the buffer that is referenced in the same phase. Let L denote the set of these blocks. Let $\mathcal{B}$ denote the set of all blocks in the buffer. Intuitively, RAND-WB works as follows. If the I/O request is a hit in the buffer it can be serviced without any I/O. If it is a miss, an I/O is initiated and prefetches issued in parallel. However some buffer space needs to be freed to complete these I/Os. Since we prefetch blocks only in the current phase (size M) there will be at least $|L|$ blocks in the buffer which are not marked; these are candidates for eviction. As we do not need to write-back blocks that have been relocated previously, we try to choose such blocks whenever possible. The randomization in the choice of the first disk to start a stripe guarantees that each block is effectively relocated to a randomly chosen disk. The specifics of algorithm RAND-WB are presented in Figure 5. In the next section we analyze the performance of RAND-WB.

4.1. Analysis of RAND-WB

Let OPT denote the optimal off-line algorithm. First note that any I/O schedule can be transformed into another schedule of the same or smaller length in which a block is never evicted before it has been referenced at least once since the last time it was fetched. Hence we implicitly assume this property for OPT. We shall now prove that the competitive ratio of RAND-WB is $\Theta(\sqrt{D})$.

The following terms are defined with respect to the schedule created by OPT. We shall say that a block is *prefetched for* $phase(i)$ if the earliest future reference of that block is in $phase(i)$. Similarly a block is said to be *from disk* j if it was last fetched from disk j.

Definition 6. Let the set of new blocks in $phase(i)$ be N_i.

- At some instant let the blocks in the buffer be $\mathcal{B}$. The *residual height* of $phase(i)$ at that time is the maximum number of blocks residing on a single disk in the set $N_i - \mathcal{B}$.
- The number of *useful blocks* prefetched in $phase(j)$ for $phase(i)$ is the difference between the residual heights of $phase(i)$ at the start and end of $phase(j)$.

If at the start of a phase, there are U useful blocks in the buffer for that phase, at least U I/Os need to have been done in the past to fetch them since at least U blocks need to have been fetched from a single disk. Of course, the I/Os to fetch useful blocks for different phases can be overlapped. Let $I_{\text{OPT}}(i)$ and $I_{\text{RAND-WB}}(i)$ be the number of I/Os done by OPT and RAND-WB, respectively, in the ith phase. Let T_{OPT} be the total number of I/Os done by OPT.

Claim 1 *In a phase no I/O is done by RAND-WB to fetch stale blocks, and any block is read in at most once.*

This follows from the marking nature of RAND-WB. Hence, if at the start of a phase there are a maximum of

b blocks from some disk referenced in that phase and not present in the buffer, then the number of read I/Os performed by RAND-WB in that phase is b. We next show that the analysis can be decoupled into counting the number of I/Os done by the algorithm in servicing the new blocks and reuse blocks. Let H_i^n (H_i^r) denote the maximum number of new (reuse) blocks of $phase(i)$ on a single disk, at the start of $phase(i)$.

Lemma 4 *The number of read I/Os done by RAND-WB in* $phase(i)$ *is at most* $I_{RAND-WB}(i) \leq H_i^n + H_i^r$.

Proof : From Claim 1 no I/O is done by RAND-WB to fetch the stale blocks in $phase(i)$. Hence, the total number of I/Os done by RAND-WB in $phase(i)$ is equal to the maximum number of clean blocks on any single disk in $phase(i)$. By definition, the number of clean blocks in $phase(i)$ is the sum of the number of new and reuse blocks in that phase; hence the maximum number of clean blocks on any disk in $phase(i)$ is at most $H_i^n + H_i^r$. □

Algorithm RAND-WB randomly relocates blocks that are evicted from the buffer. Therefore, we can bound the number of I/Os that algorithm RAND-WB requires to fetch the reuse blocks in any phase, by relating it to the classical occupancy problem [9]. *Suppose that m balls are randomly (uniform distribution) thrown into n urns, what is the expected maximum number of balls in any urn?* Let $\mathcal{C}(m, n)$ denote the expected maximal occupancy when m balls are thrown into n urns. Let the number of reuse blocks in $phase(i)$ be r_i.

Lemma 5 *The expected value of the maximum number of reuse blocks from any disk that RAND-WB needs to fetch in* $phase(i)$ *is at most* $\mathcal{C}(r_i, D) = O(r_i \log D / D)$.

It can be noted that the total number of writes performed by RAND-WB is bounded by the number of reads. Hence it is enough to only count reads performed by RAND-WB. Thus, from Lemmas 4 and 5, if $\sum_p$ indicates the sum over all i such that $phase(i)$ is in the reference string, we get:

Lemma 6 *If the total number of useful blocks prefetched by OPT is U,*

$$\sum_p I_{RAND-WB}(i) \leq 2(\sum_p I_{OPT}(i) + U + \sum_p \mathcal{C}(r_i, D))$$

Theorem 2 *The competitive ratio of RAND-WB is $\Theta(\sqrt{D})$.*

Proof : We shall prove the theorem by deriving a lower bound on the number of I/Os performed by OPT. Let the number of useful blocks prefetched by OPT in $phase(i)$ for n other phases be γ_i. Let the number of I/Os done by OPT in $phase(i)$ to prefetch these blocks be I_i. Let $phase(i_k)$, be the kth phase for which a useful block is prefetched by

OPT in $phase(i)$. Let β_k be the number of useful blocks prefetched by OPT in $phase(i)$ for $phase(i_k)$. During one I/O by OPT in $phase(i)$ at most one useful block could have been prefetched for $phase(i_k)$: the number of I/Os done by OPT to fetch useful blocks in $phase(i)$ is $I_i \geq \beta_k$, $1 \leq i \leq n$.

The number of useful blocks prefetched in $phase(i)$ for phases prior to and including $phase(i_k)$ is $\sum_{l=1}^{k} \beta_l$. This implies that the number of (useful) blocks occupying space in the buffer during $phase(i_k)$ is at least $\gamma_i - \sum_{l=1}^{k} \beta_l$. Hence at least these many blocks, referenced in $phase(i_k)$, are not present in the buffer at the start of $phase(i_k)$. Due to this at least $(\gamma_i - \sum_{l=1}^{k} \beta_l)/D$ I/Os need to be done by OPT in $phase(i_k)$.

The total number of useful blocks prefetched in $phase(i)$ for other phases is $\gamma_i = \sum_{l=1}^{n} \beta_l$. Then the total number of I/Os caused by the reduced buffer space due to prefetched blocks is at least

$$T_{\text{OPT}} \geq \sum_p \sum_{k=1}^{n} (\gamma_i - \sum_{l=1}^{k} \beta_l)/D$$

$$= \sum_p \left(\sum_{k=1}^{n} k\beta_k/D - \gamma_i/D \right)$$

We know that $\sum_{k=1}^{n} \beta_k = \gamma_i$ and also $\beta_k \leq I_i$. Then $\sum_{k=1}^{n} k\beta_k$ is minimized when $\beta_r \geq \beta_s$ whenever $r < s$. Therefore each β_k is set to its maximum value: I_i.

$$\sum_{k=1}^{n} k\beta_k \geq \sum_{k=1}^{\gamma_i/I_i - 1} kI_i \geq \frac{\gamma_i^2}{2I_i} - \frac{\gamma_i}{2}$$

Hence the total number of I/Os caused by prefetching and consuming useful blocks can be bounded as follows.

$$T_{\text{OPT}} \geq \sum_p \left(\frac{\gamma_i^2}{2I_i D} - \frac{3\gamma_i}{2D} \right)$$

The total number of I/Os performed by OPT is at least the sum of the number of I/Os to fetch useful blocks:

$$T_{\text{OPT}} \geq \sum_p I_i$$

Since a total of γ_i (useful) blocks are fetched in $phase(i)$, the number of I/Os performed must be at least

$$T_{\text{OPT}} \geq \sum_p \gamma_i/D$$

Combining the three bounds on T_{OPT}

$$T_{\text{OPT}} \geq \max(\sum_p I_i, \sum_p \left(\frac{\gamma_i^2}{2I_i D} - \frac{3\gamma_i}{2D} \right), \sum_p \frac{\gamma_i}{D})$$

$$\geq \sum_p (I_i + \frac{\gamma_i^2}{2I_i D} - \frac{3\gamma_i}{2D} + \frac{\gamma_i}{D})/3$$

Noting that $I_i \geq \gamma_i/D$ we get

$$I_i + \frac{\gamma_i^2}{2I_iD} - \frac{\gamma_i}{2D} \geq \frac{I_i}{2} + \frac{\gamma_i^2}{2I_iD} \geq \gamma_i/\sqrt{D}$$

Hence if a total of U useful blocks are prefetched by OPT: $\sum_p \gamma_i \geq U$. Hence, $T_{\text{OPT}} \geq U/3\sqrt{D}$.

Now, by definition, a block which is a reuse block in $phase(i)$ is not referenced in $phase(i-1)$. Hence it can be argued in a fashion similar to that of the useful blocks that at least $\sum_p r_i/D$ I/Os is performed by OPT due to the reuse blocks – either they are in the buffer during $phase(i-1)$, in which case they occupy buffer space, or are fetched in $phase(i)$ with full parallelism. Hence the total number of I/Os done by OPT, is at least

$$T_{\text{OPT}} \geq \max(U/3\sqrt{D}, \textstyle\sum_p r_i/D)$$

By Lemma 6 and the preceding bound on T_{OPT},

$$T_{\text{RAND-WB}}/T_{\text{OPT}} = O(\sqrt{D})$$

By adapting a result in [3] a read-once reference string can be constructed, for which RAND-WB performs at least $\Omega(\sqrt{D})$ times more I/Os than OPT. This therefore implies that the competitive ratio of RAND-WB is $\Theta(\sqrt{D})$. □

Corollary 1 *If the initial data distribution is such that each block independently has probability $1/D$ of being on any disk then the competitive ratio of RAND-WB is $\Theta(\log D)$.*

The proof follows from the fact that if the initial data layout is random, then the number of I/Os required to fetch the new blocks in any phase parallels that required for reuse blocks. In fact, in this situation RAND-WB does not need to rewrite evicted blocks, since the placement for the reuse blocks is already randomized.

5. Conclusions

In this paper we studied the I/O scheduling problem for general read-many reference strings in a parallel I/O system. We introduced the concept of *write-back* whereby blocks are dynamically relocated between disks during the course of the computation. We showed that any algorithm with bounded lookahead, that uses deterministic write-back and buffer management policies must have a competitive ratio of $\Omega(D)$. That is, any strategy that is based solely on the bounded lookahead and the past behavior of the algorithm, can in the worst case significantly serialize its disk accesses.

Using *randomization* we improved the performance of scheduling decisions. We presented a randomized algorithm, RAND-WB, that uses a novel randomized write-back scheme, and attains the lowest possible competitive ratio of $\Theta(\sqrt{D})$. As a corollary, if initially all the data blocks are randomly placed on disks, the competitive ratio of RAND-WB is $\Theta(\log D)$.

References

[1] S. Albers. The Influence of Lookahead in Competitive Paging Algorithms. In *Proc. of ESA '93*, volume 726, pages 1–12, *LNCS*, Springer Verlag, 1993.

[2] R. D. Barve, E. F. Grove, and J. S. Vitter. Simple Randomized Mergesort on Parallel Disks. *Parallel Computing*, 23(4):601–631, June 1996.

[3] R. D. Barve, M. Kallahalla, P. J. Varman, and J. S. Vitter. Competitive Parallel Disk Prefetching and Buffer Management. In *Proc. of IOPADS '97*, pages 47–56. ACM, 1997.

[4] L. A. Belady. A Study of Replacement Algorithms for a Virtual Storage Computer. *IBM Systems Journal*, 5(2):78–101, 1966.

[5] D. Breslauer. On Competitive On-Line Paging with Lookahead. In *Proc. of STOC '96*, volume 1046, *LNCS*, pages 593–603. Springer Verlag, Feb. 1996.

[6] P. Cao, E. W. Felten, A. R. Karlin, and K. Li. A Study of Integrated Prefetching and Caching Strategies. In *Proc. of the Joint Int. Conf. on Measurement and Modeling of Comp. Sys.*, pages 188–197. ACM, May 1995.

[7] P. M. Chen, E. K. Lee, G. A. Gibson, R. H. Katz, and D. A. Patterson. RAID: High Performance Reliable Secondary Storage. *ACM Computing Surveys*, 26(2):145–185, 1994.

[8] A. Fiat, R. Karp, M. Luby, L. McGeoch, D. D. Sleator, and N. E. Young. Competitive Paging Algorithms. *Journal of Algorithms*, 12(4):685–699, Dec. 1991.

[9] N. L. Johnson and S. Kotz. *Urn Models and Their Application: an Approach to Modern Discrete Probability Theory.* Wiley, New York, 1977.

[10] T. Kimbrel and A. R. Karlin. Near-Optimal Parallel Prefetching and Caching. In *Proc. of FOCS '96*, pages 540–549. IEEE, Oct. 1996.

[11] D. Kotz and C. S. Ellis. Practical Prefetching Techniques for Multiprocessor File Systems. *Journal of Distributed and Parallel Databases*, 1(1):33–51, 1999.

[12] K. K. Lee, M. Kallahalla, B. S. Lee, and P. J. Varman. Performance Comparison of Sequential Prefetch and Forecasting Using Parallel I/O. In *Proc. of PDCN '97*, Apr. 1997.

[13] K.-K. Lee and P. J. Varman. Prefetching and I/O Parallelism in Multiple Disk Systems. In *Proc. of ICPP '95*, pages III:160–163, Aug. 1995.

[14] V. S. Pai, A. A. Schäffer, and P. J. Varman. Markov Analysis of Multiple-Disk Prefetching Strategies for External Merging. *Theoretical Computer Science*, 128(1–2):211–239, June 1994.

[15] R. H. Patterson, G. Gibson, E. Ginting, D. Stodolsky, and J. Zelenka. Informed Prefetching and Caching. In *Proc. of ASPLOS '95s*, pages 79–95, Dec. 1995.

[16] D. D. Sleator and R. E. Tarjan. Amortized Efficiency of List Update and Paging Rules. *Communications of the ACM*, 28(2):202–208, Feb. 1985.

[17] P. J. Varman and R. M. Verma. Tight Bounds for Prefetching and Buffer Management Algorithms for Parallel I/O Systems. In *Proc. of FSTTCS '96*, volume 16, *LNCS*, Springer Verlag, Dec. 1996.

[18] J. S. Vitter and E. A. M. Shriver. Optimal Algorithms for Parallel Memory, I: Two-Level Memories. *Algorithmica*, 12(2–3):110–147, 1994.

An Evaluation of Storage Systems based on Network-attached Disks *

Gang Ma   A. L. Narasimha Reddy

Dept. of Computer Science,   Dept. of Electrical Engineering,

Texas A & M University

College Station, TX 77843-3128

Abstract: *The emergence of network-attached disks provides the possibility of transferring data between the storage system and the client directly. This offers new possibilities in building a distributed storage system. In this paper, we examine different storage organizations based on network-attached disks and compare the performance of these systems to a traditional system. Trace-driven simulations are used to measure the average response times of the client requests in two different workloads. The results indicate that it is possible to reduce the workload on the file manager and improve performance in some workloads. However, in other workloads, reduced cache hit ratios may offset the gains of distributing the network processing workload.*

1 Introduction

With the increasing processor speeds and increasing use of I/O intensive applications such as video retrieval, distributed and parallel storage organizations have received considerable attention recently. However, it has been observed that even as parallelism is being exploited in data retrieval, the file manager managing the data remains a bottleneck. In a traditional file system, file server has to be involved intensively in order to satisfy a client's request. With the rapid growth of the number of network users and the number of requests, demands on the file server continue to increase. It has become imperative to find ways to reduce workload on the file servers(for example through client caching) and to increase the throughput capacity of the servers(for example, through parallel and distributed systems).

Earlier work has been done in AFS [1] to reduce the file server load. AFS clients use the local disk as a cache to store the files that have been accessed before and will probably be needed in the future. While client caching can significantly reduce the requests going to

the file server, the load on the file server could still be too high due to a large number of misses in the client cache caused by file sharing and increasing file sizes.

NetServer of Auspex exploits a unique functional multiprocessor architecture by coupling storage devices to network as directly as possible [2] to improve file system scalability. Server level striping is shown to be effective in improving data throughput in ZEBRA [3] and in SWIFT [4]. NCSA HTTP server [5] employs an AFS based organization to distribute the workload at the file server to multiple HTTP servers. Cooperative caching scheme [6]in xFS file system utilizes the idle client's cache to obtain higher global hit ratio.

With the introduction of network-attached disks, the workload of file server could be reduced by transferring data directly between clients and the storage system. Fibre Channel attached disks [7] and Servernet-attached disks [8] are examples of such an approach. The file server may need to set up a session between a client's request and the disk controller. After that data can be transferred directly between the client and the disk without going through the file server. This can reduce the server load and thus can potentially improve the overall performance. Several organizations for a file system based on network-attached disks are studied in [9]. The authors measured the workload in the file server under the the proposed NetSCSI and NASD architecture and showed that the server load could be reduced by a factor of up to ten in NFS and five in AFS. However, the average response time of the client requests, an important factor of overall performance was not measured.

In this paper, we study several issues in organizing a storage system based on network-attached disks. In a regular file system, file server manages the file name space, allocates physical disk space and supports user's requests for file service. A file server typically uses memory caching to improve response time for user requests. Without extensive modifications of the file system, only a few of these functions can be delegated to other components in the system in order to reduce the load at the file server. Network-attached disks, by

*This work is supported in part by an NSF Career grant and by a grant from Texas Higher Education Board

their ability to supply data directly to the user, can reduce the network precessing overhead on the server. This is one of the main perceived advantages of a storage system based on network-attached disks. Then how much impact does this make on user's response time? If the network precessing work is to be done at the disks, how much processing capacity do the disks require to offload this work from the server system? Typically disks have a small cache on the disk read-write arm. The size of this cache is in the range of 512k-2MB. Is this cache sufficient for providing better response time than a traditional system that employs server caching? These are some of the issues that will be studied in this paper.

In order to answer the above questions, we use trace-driven simulations to compare storage systems based on network-attached disks with a traditional file system? We use the average response time of client requests as the primary measure of evaluation.

The rest of this paper is organized as follows. Section 2 describes the system organizations we will study in this paper. In section 3, we discuss the simulations performed. In section 4, we present and analyze the simulation results. Section 5 describes related work in this area. Section 6 provides a summary of the results and directions for future work.

2 Storage System Organizations

In the following subsections, we discuss two organizations for a storage system.

2.1 Server-disk: Regular storage system with server-attached disks

This storage organization is used by the current distributed file systems. The disks are attached to the file server via a private bus(typically SCSI bus). Clients access the file server through a public network(typically a LAN). All the client requests are sent to the file server first. The file server is responsible for handling and interpreting the requests. File servers typically employing caching to reduce the load on the disks at the server and to improve response time for client requests. If a miss occurs in the server cache, file server will issue a request to the disk, which in turn accesses the data and sends it back to the file server. Finally file server will satisfy the client request by sending the data to the client. In this situation, file server is intensively involved in handling every request from the clients. Fig. 1 shows the sequence of operations that take place to serve a user's request in this organization.

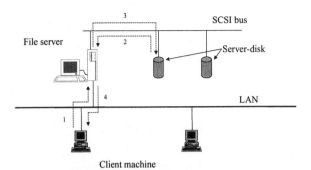

1. Client sends request to file server.
2. File server forwards the request to disk if necessary.
3. Disk accesses the data and sends reply to file server.
4. File server replies to client.

Figure 1: Server-disk: Regular server-attached disk.

2.2 Net-disk: Storage System based on Network-attached disks

In this system, the disks are attached to the file server via a private network. Disks are also directly connected to the LAN which connects clients and the file server together. Clients still send requests to the file server first. The file server processes the requests and forwards them to the disks via the private network if necessary. Rather than sending the data back to the file server again, the disks send the desired data directly to the client via the LAN. Since the file server is no longer involved in block data transfer, the load on it will possibly be less than in a regular server-disk system. On the other hand, to offload network processing work to disks, the file server does not employ data caching. Then how does the performance of this organization compare to regular server-disk organization? If we allow the server to continue to cache and reply data to the client, the network processing can not be offloaded to the network-attached disks on cache hits. Then the network-attached disks can reply data to clients only on cache misses at the server. Fig. 2 describes the sequence of operations that take place to serve a user's request in this organization.

Net-disk and server-disk organizations employ caching at different places in the system. A single large cache space in the file manager in server-disk enables efficient utilization of cache space across all the data sets in the system. The smaller caches at each disk in net-disk organizations can lead to inefficiencies if disks are accessed non-uniformly. Our assumption of system-wide disk striping [10] however reduces this disadvantage. We assume that the file manager caches metadata in both the organizations and replies directly

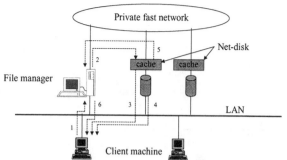

1. Client sends request to file server.
2. File server forwards the request to disk if necessary.
3. Disk controller accesses the data from disk cache if hits,
   then transfers to client directly.
4. Or accesses the block data from disk if misses, and
   directly transfers to client.
5. Disk sends completion status to file manager.
6. File manager sends request completion code to client.

Figure 2: Net-disk:Storage system based on Network-attached disks.

to clients on metadata related requests. However, the file data caching is performed differently in different organizations. Server-disk caches file data in the file manager cache while net-disk organization caches file data at the disk.

We are also interested in other issues in organizing the storage system. For example, how powerful should the disk processor be in a net-disk system? How large a cache should disks have in order to maintain comparably high hit ratios? How will the overall performance change if we vary the number of disk nodes? We also want to identify which component among file server, network and disks is the bottleneck that impacts the system performance in these different approaches.

3 Simulations

In order to measure the overall system performance under the different storage system organizations, we performed a set of trace-driven simulations.

In each organization, the simulated system consists of a file manager and a set of disks. The file manager and the disks are interconnected differently in the different organizations. In the server-disk, the disks are attached to the file manager through a SCSI bus and in the net-disk case, the disks are attached to the file manager through a private fast network. In both the cases, cost of control messages to talk to disk is assumed to be 50us.

In both organizations, we assume that the file manager caches the metadata of the file system. In the server-disk case, the file manager also caches the

block data. The size of the file manager cache is varied from 128MB to 2GB. We vary the size of the disk cache from 4MB to 128MB in the network-attached disk. We assume LRU is used as the replacement policy for the caches both at the file managers and at the disks. We assume that the caches are organized on a 4KB block basis.

It is assumed that data is striped across the disks in order to distribute the load evenly among the disks. The data will be stored in all available disks in a stripe size of 16 blocks(64KB). In our system, the first chunk (64KB) of each file is stored on a random starting disk, s. Subsequent chunks of that file are consecutively stored on disks $(s+1)mod\ n$, $(s+2)mod\ n$, ..., where n is the number of disks. Equal number of disks are employed in both the organizations.

The simulations are written in CSIM. All the requests are sent to the file server first via regular network(LAN), and then processed in separate ways depending on the organization as shown in figures 1 and 2. The file manager processor is assumed to have a processing capacity of 50MIPS. We vary the disk processor speed from 10 MIPS to 100 MIPS to study the impact of disk processor power on the system performance.

Table 1 lists the costs of different operations that we will use as parameters in the simulations. We assume that the disk access latency is 15.0 ms. The cost for cache access(hit/miss)in a file manager and the network processing load are based on measurements done on IBM's OS/2 operating system [11]. We assume that the cache search time in the network-attached disk is half of that in the file manager cache because the file manager needs to do extra work(translating file name into disk block address, checking access permissions, etc.). Costs for disk access and network transfer are based on the size of the request. The costs per 4KB block and 64KB chunk reflect the efficiency of transferring data in larger size blocks (from the disk and over the network). We assume that the disk has a transfer rate of 8MB per second. Processor dependent costs are given in number of instructions such that the impact of changing the processor MIPS can be easily studied.

In our experiments, we use request response time as the performance measure. Previous studies [9] have used the load on the server as a measure of evaluating the network-attached disk organizations. The goal of our study is to investigate the impact of the new organizations on the response time of user's requests. The request response time is measured as the time interval to service all the blocks in a given request.

We use two different traces in our simulations. A

Table 1: Costs for different operations.

Operations	Per-block (4KB) cost	Per-chunk (64KB) cost
Getattr & similar	750 ins.	N/A
Cache hit in file manager	3,000 ins.	N/A
Cache miss in file manager	7,000 ins.	N/A
Cache hit in network-attached disk cache	1,500 ins.	N/A
Cache miss in network-attached disk cache	3,500 ins.	N/A
Disk access time	15 ms	22.5 ms
Private network transfer time	0.1 ms	1.6 ms
Private network latency (for control messages)	50 us	50 us
Public network(LAN) transfer time	10,000 ins.	108,000 ins.

Table 2: Description of the two trace files.

	NFS trace	Web trace
# of client machines	231	161,140
Total # of requests	6,302,418	2,955,038
Requested bytes (MB)	10,100	27,810
Trace Duration (hours)	40	236

trace based on NFS workload and a trace based on web accesses are used in this study. The NFS trace data is obtained from University of California at Berkeley [6]. This trace consists of network requests from 237 clients during one week period that are serviced by an Auspex file server. The trace was taken by snooping the network, so it only contains the post-client-cache request data. In other words, these requests are actually the local misses occurred at client caches. The original NFS trace includes a large amount of backup activity over weekends and at night. We only used the daytime activity (between 8 AM to 5 PM) on the server as input to our simulations.

The other trace we used in our simulations is the workload trace of the ClarkNet WWW server [12]. ClarkNet is a busy Internet service provider for the Metro Baltimore-Washington DC area. This trace contains the requests from 161,140 clients during a two week period. The original trace consists of successful accesses as well as unsuccessful accesses. We only consider the successful accesses since unsuccessful accesses do not incur any data transfer. Table 2 lists a brief description of these two trace files.

The NFS trace file consists of three major types of activities: getattr & setattr, block read & write, directory read & write. In all the organizations we study here, file manager has to deal with the accesses to file metadata and the translation of client requests into disk commands. Therefore the getattr & setattr and directory read & write operations are handled by the file manager in all the systems. In the net-disk

organizations, block read & write will occur between disk(or disk cache) and client without going through the file manager. The Internet trace file simply consists of file access operations, mostly file read operations.

4   Results

4.1   NFS trace

Fig. 3 shows the average request response time as a function of the disk processor MIPS. We used one file manager and 16 disk nodes in this experiment. The file manager has a processor capacity of 50 MIPS and a 128MB cache. The disk cache in the net-disk organizations is varied from 4MB to 32 MB. Since requests are processed entirely at the file manager in the server-disk organization, changes in disk processing capacity do not affect its performance. Higher disk processor capacity improves performance considerably in net-disk organizations since block data transfer and network processing are performed by the disk processor. However, we see that the response time is not always better than in the server-disk organization. With 4MB disk cache, net-disk organization has worse performance than the server-disk organization. Only with larger disk caches, net-disk organizations have better response times than server-disk organization. This shows that the benefit of distribution of data transfer brought by network-attached disks can be offset by the costs of extra disk accesses introduced due to insufficient caching. With 32 MB of disk cache and 25 disk MIPS, we see an improvement in overall performance-response time by up to 33% compared to server-disk organization. Even at a low disk processing speed of 10MIPS, the processing capacity at the disks(total of 160MIPS) outweighs the capacity at the file manager. This is part of the reason why a net-disk organization outperforms the server-disk organization. Net-disk organization also has extra amount of cache at the disk nodes. It is not clear if the higher MIPS in the system or the larger amount of cache space or the distribution of workload contributes to the improvement in response time in the net-disk organization. We will explore these issues further in later experiments.

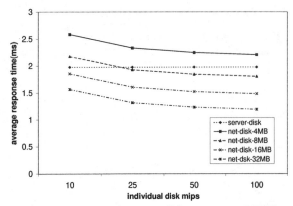

Figure 3: Response time vs. disk processor MIPS.

Fig. 4 shows the average request response time as a function of the number of disk nodes. We assumed that the system has a file manager with 50 MIPS and 128 MB of cache. With a larger number of disks, the disk accesses can be distributed over more disks to reduce the disk waiting times in all the organizations. Net-disk organizations see even more improvement because the data transfer load can be distributed to more disk nodes. However, we notice that with 4MB-8MB of disk cache, the net-disk organization has a higher response time than the server-disk organization. From figures 3 and 4, it seems that a disk cache of 16MB-32MB is needed for this NFS workload for net-disk organizations to outperform the server-disk organization.

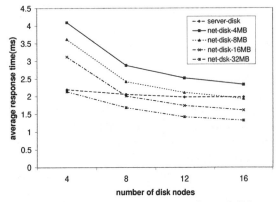

Figure 4: Response time vs. number of disks.

So far, we have considered varying the disk parameters (number, MIPS and cache sizes) while keeping the configuration of the file manager constant in all

the organizations. The server-disk cannot effectively utilize the enhancements at the disk (increased MIPS or increased caches). Given the same processing capacity and cache memory, the different organizations can utilize them more effectively in different locations in the system. How do the systems compare if we put the extra memory and the extra processing power at the file manager in the server-disk organization? To answer this question, we consider systems with equal processing capacity and equal amounts of cache memory.

Fig. 5 shows the average request response time as a function of total memory in the system. In server-disk organization, all the memory is located at the file manager. We assume that the file manager in the net-disk has 128 MB and the rest of the memory is distributed equally across the 16 disks in the system. For example, with a total memory of 192 MB, each disk has (192-128)/16 = 4MB in the net-disk organization. We assume that file managers have equal processing capacity of 50 MIPS in all the organizations. The disks are assumed to have a capacity of 25 MIPS. We notice that the response time of the server-disk organization is better than the net-disk organization in all the cases. However, as the amount of memory on each disk increases, the differences in response times reduce. Beyond 32MB per disk, the difference in response times doesn't reduce significantly further.

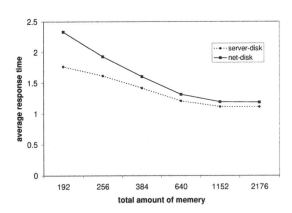

Figure 5: Response time vs. total amount of memory.

Next we considered file managers with different processing capacities. In net-disk organizations, the processing capacity and the load is distributed between the file managers and the disks. In server-disk organization, the processing capacity at the disks is unutilized and hence seems wasteful to locate any MIPS at the disk. For example, a net-disk organization with 50 MIPS at the file manager and 25 MIPS at each of the

16 disks in the system has a total processing capacity of 50+16*25 = 450 MIPS. How would such a system compare to a server-disk organization where all the 450 MIPS are located at the file manager? Fig. 6 shows the results from such experiments. We consider two processing capacities of 450 MIPS (as explained above) and 210 MIPS (with 10 MIPS at 16 disks and a 50 MIPS file manager in the net-disk organization). We also kept the total amount of the memory the same (640MB) in both the organizations. The server-disk organization has significantly better response times for both the processing capacities. With increased amount of memory, the performance differences are reduced. It is also noticed that the differences in response times have increased from the earlier results in figure 5. It could be possible to divide the total MIPS more optimally in the net-disk organization to reduce the differences in performance. But, Fig. 5 indicates that when the total memory in the two systems is the same, with NFS workload, the net-disk organization has worse performance even with extra processing capacity.

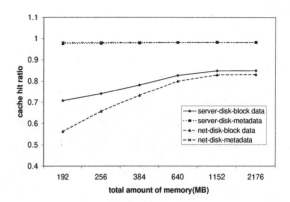

Figure 7: Hit ratios as a function of memory.

Fig. 8 shows the different components contributing to the response times in server-disk (on the left) and the net-disk (on the right) organizations. Fig. 8 shows that the disk access times are significantly higher in the net-disk organization. As shown earlier, this is mainly due to lower hit ratios for block data at the disks in the net-disk organizations. This lower hit ratio, which results in higher average disk service times, dominates the other possible advantages of the net-disk organization for the NFS workload.

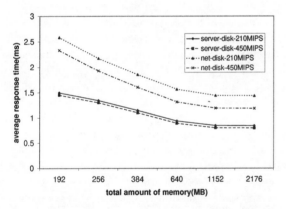

Figure 6: Response time with equal system MIPS.

Metadata requests constitute roughly 75% of the NFS workload requests and about 54% of the bytes accessed. These requests are processed at the file manager in both server-disk and net-disk organizations. With lower processor MIPS at the file manager in the net-disk organization, these requests will experience worse response times than in the server-disk organization. What about the response times for data requests? We observed that the data requests experience lower hit ratios in the net-disk organization as shown in figure 7. This reduced hit ratio offsets the gains due to distributing the network processing load. Hence, the overall response time is higher in the net-disk organization.

4.2 Web trace

We performed the same experiments using Clarknet trace file. In Web access, popular files are accessed frequently and other files are accessed rarely. It is shown in [12] that 10% of the distinct files were responsible for 85% of all the requests received by the server. Fig. 9 shows the performance of different organizations as a function of total memory in the system with a file manager of 50 MIPS and 128MB of cache memory and 16 disks (each with 25 MIPS). In all our experiments, cache hit ratio is already so high that increasing the total memory in the system does not show much performance improvement beyond 384MB. We observe that net-disk organization has 25% lower response time than the server-disk organization. This is in contrast to the earlier results observed in the NFS workload as shown in Fig. 5. This is mainly due to the high hit ratios (95-98%) observed even with small caches at the disks in the web workload.

Fig. 10 shows the contribution of different components to response times in both the organizations configured as explained above. Service times and waiting times at the file manager are the main contributers to the response time in the server-disk organization.

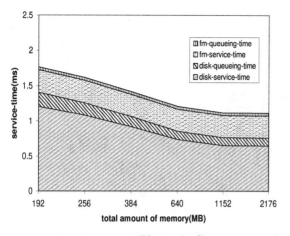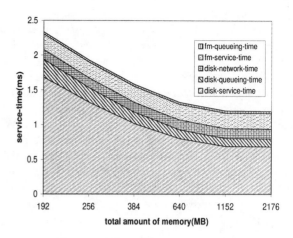

Figure 8: Components of request response time – NFS trace.

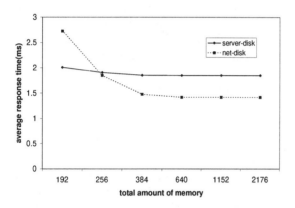

Figure 9: Response time vs. total amount of memory–Web trace.

The disk access time is not a major factor. It is observed that the distribution of network processing cost to the disks in the net-disk organization resulted in smaller service and waiting times at the file manager. This results in improved performance in the net-disk organization. At smaller amounts of disk cache, the disk access times become significant (because of lower hit ratios) in the net-disk organization.

5   Conclusions and future work

In this paper, we studied a number of issues in organizing a storage system based on network-attached disks. Through trace-driven simulations, we found that although using network-attached disks can reduce

workload at the file server, if sufficient caching is not employed at the disks, the overall system performance will be worse than the traditional system.

The two traces we have studied exhibited different behavior. Caching made a bigger impact on the NFS workload and distribution of network processing load made a bigger impact on the Clarknet Web workload. With the NFS workload, distributed caching at multiple disk caches performed worse than a single centralized pool at the file manager offsetting any possible gains due to distributing network processing load. However in the Clarknet Web workload, where a small cache is enough to make a big contribution to hit ratio, network processing played a bigger role in determining the performance. We conducted a number of other experiments to study the impact of varying the cost of a network reply, the cost of an average disk access, the fraction of metadata related requests in the workload and the amount of client caching. These results can be found in [13].

When systems with equal memory and equal processing capacity are compared, the traditional server-disk organization performed better than any net-disk organization in both the workloads. If we relax the constraint of equal processing capacity, the net-disk organizations could provide better performance than a server-disk organization in the web workload. If the server has to process the data, rather than just supplying it to the client, the server has to store this data in memory. In this case, caching at the disks in net-disk will not be useful for processing the data at the server. Database and transaction processing systems (which process retrieved data) may not be able

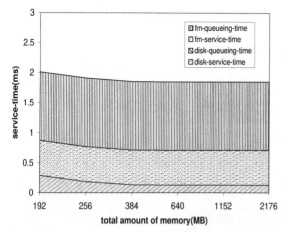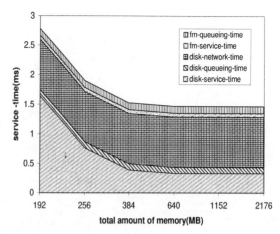

Figure 10: Components of request response time–Web trace.

to exploit the advantages of network-attached disks as well as a file system.

A number of issues require further study. Can a net-disk organization support higher loads due to the reduced load on the file manager? How does the workload impact the minimum required size of the disk cache in the net-disk organization? What workload characteristics determine if net-disk organization can provide better performance than a server-disk organization?

References

[1] J. H. Howard, M. L. Kazar, S. G. Menees, D.A. Nichols, M. Satyanarayanan, R. N. Sidebotham, and M. J. West. Scale and performance in a distributed file system. *ACM Transactions on Computer Systems*, 6(1):51–81, Feb 1988.

[2] P. Trautman, B. Nelson, and Auspex Engineering. An overview of NFS server using functional multiprocessing. Technical Report 10, Auspex Corporation, April 1997.

[3] J. H. Hartman and J. K. Ousterhout. The Zebra striped network file system. In *Proc. of the 14th SOSP*, pages 29–43, Dec. 1993.

[4] D. D. E. Long, B. R. Montague, and L. Cabrera. Swift/RAID: A distributed RAID system. *Computing Systems*, 7(3):333–359, 1994.

[5] E. D. Katz, M. Butler, and R. McGrath. A scalable HTTP server: The NCSA prototype. In *Proceedings of the First International WWW Conference*, May 1994.

[6] M. D. Dahlin, R. Y. Wang, Anderson T. E., and D. A. Patterson. Cooperative caching: Using remote client memory to improve file system performance. In *Proceedings of the First Symposium on Operating System Design and Implementation*, pages 267–280, November 1994.

[7] Seagate Corporation. Fibre channel: The digital highway made practical. Technical report, Seagate Corporation, 1994. http://www.seagate.com/support/disc/papers/fibp.shtml.

[8] Robert W. Horst. TNet: A reliable system area network. *IEEE Micro*, 15(1):37–45, Feb. 1995.

[9] Garth A. Gibson and et al. File server scaling with network-attached secure disks. In *Proceedings of the Sigmetrics Conference on Measurement and Modeling of Computer Systems*, Seattle, June 1997.

[10] D. A. Patterson, G. Gibson, and R. H. Katz. A case for redundant arrays of inexpensive disks(RAID). In *Proc. of SIGMOD*, pages 109–116, June 1988.

[11] B. Dimpsey. Private communication. *IBM Austin*, 1996.

[12] M. F. Arlitt and C. L. Williamson. Web server workload characterization: The search for invariants. In *Proceedings of the Sigmetrics Conference on Measurement and Modeling of Computer Systems*, pages 126–137, May 1996.

[13] Gang Ma. Evaluation of storage systems based on network-attached disks. *M.S. thesis, Texas A & M University*, May 1998.

Session 4C
Networking

Chair: Wei Zhao
Texas A&M University

Network Planning and Tuning in Switch-Based LANs

Wenjian Qiao and *Lionel M. Ni*

Department of Computer Science
Michigan State University
East Lansing, MI 48824-1027
{qiaow,ni}@cps.msu.edu

Abstract

Switch-based networks have received much attention in local area networks (LANs) due to their higher network bandwidth and greater interconnect scalability than shared-medium networks. While arbitrary topologies are allowed to provide the needed flexibility and scalability, the design of an appropriate network topology is a challenging issue. In this paper, we discuss design considerations and propose efficient methods for network planning and tuning in switch-based LANs. The idea of block design is applied to initial topology design. For network tuning, a systematic method is proposed to reduce message latency and increase network throughput. Simulations are conducted to demonstrate the performance improvement by applying our method.

1 Introduction

Switch-based networks have received much attention in local area networks (LANs) due to their higher network bandwidth and throughput, greater interconnect scalability and flexibility, and better fault handling capability than shared-medium networks. For example, switched Ethernet is emerging as a simple and cost-effective way to solve the problem due to traffic collision in a traditional CSMA/CD LAN. Many other switches, such as FDDI switches, FCS switches, and Myrinet switches have also been commercially available. In switch-based networks, each host computer has a network adapter connecting to a port of a network switch. When the scale of the network increases due to the increasing number of host computers and the increasing demand of aggregate network bandwidth, more switches can be added to the network. The interconnection of those switches defines various network topologies. For cost and performance reasons, switch-based networks should support arbitrary topologies.

Although arbitrary topologies do provide flexibility and incremental scalability, the design of an appropriate

network topology can be a complex undertaking. Network topology design has been an important issue for many years, and considerable research efforts have been spent on optimal topological design. Although these algorithms do have important contributions for topological design, they are usually very time consuming and have unrealistic assumptions. Moreover, they may not be applicable to switch-based networks due to the changes in network environment.

This paper studies the issues of network planning and tuning in switch-based networks. Our purpose is not to address an optimal solution for network design, which can be an NP-complete problem [1]. Instead, we propose a simple method based on block design for initial topology design and a systematic method for network tuning to deal with various situations in a network. To provide low message latency and high network throughput, our design criteria are minimizing routing path length, maximizing traffic locality, reducing inter-switch traffic, and balancing channel utilization.

The paper is organized as follows. Section 2 describes general considerations and Section 3 presents design variables and analytic models for network planning and tuning. A simple method based on block design is presented in Section 4 for initial topology design. Section 5 proposes solutions to handle network changes and network tuning. Section 6 uses simulation results to demonstrate the performance improvement after network tuning. Finally, Section 7 concludes the paper.

2 Design Considerations

A switch-based network consists of a number of switches. Each *switch* has a certain number of ports. Each *port* is associated with a pair of input/output channels (or a bidirectional channel). Each port may connect to a node which generates and consumes messages, connect to a port of another switch which defines the network topology, or open for a future connection. A *node* (or *end node*) can be a workstation, a multi-processor system, or a gateway to another network. In order to design an appropriate switch-based network, it is important to understand the basic considerations.

---
*This work was supported in part by NSF grants MIP-9204066 and MIP-9528903, DOE grant DE-FG02-93ER25167 and a grant from Hewlett-Packard Co..

2.1 Traffic Characteristics

To design an appropriate network, we should understand the traffic characteristics in LANs. LAN traffic analysis can be done by collecting LAN traffic and some common characteristics have been observed in previous work. These characteristics include client/server model, workgroup, and bursty traffic.

Network planners need to be responsive to these traffic characteristics. Since a server usually has much more amount of traffic than a client, dedicated bandwidth is needed to release server bottlenecks. Traffic within a workgroup is usually very high, nodes of each workgroup should be placed in a same switch if possible. To deal with burstiness, we have to compromise between the average rate and the peak rate. If a network is designed based on peak rate, it may cause an excessive cost. On the other hand, if network design considers only average rate, it may be under-engineered.

The knowledge of traffic distribution is very helpful for topology design and network tuning. Before a network is operational, the traffic distribution can only be estimated based on a good understanding of network applications in the future network. However, in general, traffic distribution is hard to be estimated accurately a priori. After the network is operational, traffic distribution can be measured by monitoring the total number of transmitted packets over the network, the size of each packet, and the source and destination information associated with each packet (e.g., SNMP management). Both average rate and bursty rate should be measured.

2.2 Routing Path Length

In general, a high-performance network will have as low an average path length as possible. Longer paths mean higher transmission latency and more channel bandwidth are consumed per packet sent, resulting in lower network throughput and higher message latency in most cases. Thus, when designing a network topology, a primary consideration should be minimizing the average path length and the maximum path length.

Given the number of switches, ports per switch, and the required number of nodes, it is a difficult problem to find a network with a minimal average path length. However, there are still some basic ideas that can make it easier. In general, each channel should run between a unique pair of switches; extra channels between a particular pair of switches does not decrease the path length. Connecting the long-distance switches with a new channel is usually a better idea than connecting two short-distance switches.

In addition to minimizing the average path length, we have to ensure that there is no obvious bottleneck. Such a bottleneck might be a small bisection[1] or a single switch connected with only one or two channels.

---

[1]Bisection is defined as the minimum number of channels to be removed in order to cut a network into two disjoint subnetworks with equal number of switches in each subnetwork.

2.3 Traffic Distribution and Channel Utilization

We define traffic within a switch as 'local traffic' and traffic between switches as 'remote traffic'. To efficiently utilize channel bandwidth, an important design principle is to maximize local traffic and minimize remote traffic as well. Exploiting traffic locality will benefit intra-workgroup communication. However, simply maximizing local traffic may cause unbalanced switch load and channel utilization.

Given channel bandwidth and message size, queuing theory has shown that message delay on a channel depends on the channel utilization. The higher the channel utilization is, the higher the message delay is. Since overloaded channels are usually traffic bottlenecks, we should balance channel utilization by designing appropriate network topology and routing algorithm.

2.4 Performance Metrics

From an application program's point of view, the most important performance metric of a network is *communication latency*, which is the time interval between the instant that a send command is issued until the instant that the message is completely received by the recipient.

From the network point of view, an important metric is *network throughput*, which is defined as the total amount of message data transmitted in the network per unit of time. To make comparisons, *normalized network throughput*, defined as the ratio of sustained network throughput over the maximum theoretic network throughput, is usually considered.

Fairness is also an important factor in network design although it is often ignored. Without some global fairness mechanism, switched networks can be naturally unfair, servicing some injection ports better than others, especially when the network workload is heavy. Let G_i be the amount of traffic generated from any node i. We define *fairness ratio* as $\frac{max(G_i)}{min(G_i)}$. The bigger fairness ratio is, the less the network is fair. In a fair network, fairness ratio should not be much higher than 2.

Other performance metrics like reliability and fault-tolerance will not be addressed due to the space limit.

3 Model Description

This section discusses the basic parameters and design variables for network planning and tuning. To design network topologies, fixed routing is generally assumed because it is easy to evaluate channel flows as a function of routing and traffic distribution [2]. The design of an appropriate network topology can be a complex undertaking, which concerns some basic parameters. In this paper, we define the following given parameters:

- N: the total number of nodes in the network.

- S (or s): the number of switches.

- c_i: the number of ports in switch i.

- β_k: the bandwidth of channel k (each unidirectional channel has a unique id k).

- X: a $N \times N$ matrix representing the traffic rate among nodes, where $x_{u,v}$ is the traffic rate from node u to node v.

- Y: a $S \times S$ matrix representing the traffic rate among switches, where $y_{i,j}$ is the aggregated traffic rate from switch i to switch j.

- W: *offered workload* of the network, which is defined as $W = \sum_{u=1}^{N}\sum_{v=1}^{N} x_{u,v} = \sum_{i=1}^{S}\sum_{j=1}^{S} y_{i,j}$.

To make efficient network design, we assume that traffic distributions are given. As mentioned in Section 2, before a network is operational, the traffic distribution can only be estimated based on the knowledge of expected network applications, which may not be accurate. After the network is operational, traffic distribution may be measured via monitoring network traffic.

For the purpose of analysis, the following design variables are defined:

- n_i: the number of nodes in switch i and $N = \sum_{i=1}^{S} n_i$.

- m_i: the number of channels in switch i and $n_i + m_i \leq c_i$.

- $p_{u,v}$: the length (i.e., the number of channels) of routing path from source node u to destination node v. For nodes u and v on the same switch, $p_{u,v}$ is defined as 0. Note that path length is related to the channel bandwidth, and a higher bandwidth channel contributes less path length.

- $\hat{p}$: the maximum path length, i.e. $max(p_{u,v})$.

- $\overline{p}$: the mathematical average of all $p_{u,v}$'s, i.e. $\frac{\sum_{u=1}^{N}\sum_{v=1}^{N} p_{u,v}}{\text{number of (u,v) pairs}}$.

- $\overline{P}$: the average path length with the consideration of the amount of traffic between each pair, which is defined as $\overline{P} = \frac{\sum_{u=1}^{N}\sum_{v=1}^{N}(p_{u,v} * x_{u,v})}{W}$. $\overline{P}$ should be more accurate than $\overline{p}$ to reflect both path length and traffic distribution.

- L: *local traffic*, defined as the total traffic transmitted within a switch. We have $L = \sum_{u=1}^{N}\sum_{v=1}^{N} x_{u,v}$, where u and v are in same switch.

- R: *remote traffic*, defined as the total traffic transmitted between switches. We have $R = \sum_{u=1}^{N}\sum_{v=1}^{N} x_{u,v}p_{u,v}$, where u and v are not in same switch.

- $\pi_{i,j}^{k}$, a decision variable, defined as 1 if the route from switch i to switch j passes channel k, or 0 otherwise.

- f_k: the average rate of traffic flow on channel k.

- μ_k: utilization of channel k, i.e., f_k/β_k.

Given a network topology and a routing algorithm, it is easy to compute the routes and path length for each source and destination pair. We can also calculate traffic flow f_k as shown in Equation 1. Our selection of fixed routing algorithm makes this calculation unambiguous.

$$f_k = \sum_{i=1}^{S}\sum_{j=1}^{S}(y_{i,j} * \pi_{i,j}^{k}) \qquad (1)$$

The calculations of f_k and μ_k help us identify traffic bottleneck under the current network configuration. The channel with $max(\mu_k)$ is usually the bottleneck channel. To improve network performance, we should minimize $max(\mu_k)$ by reducing remote traffic and balancing channel utilization.

4 Initial Topology Design

As we mentioned earlier, a primary consideration for topology design is minimizing both maximum and average path lengths. With shorter routing paths, less channel resources are consumed per packet send, resulting in lower message latency and higher network throughput. To efficiently design a topology, we adopt the idea of block design, which was previously suggested in multiprocessor networks [3] and switch-based LANs [4]. However, [3] and [4] only used the existing method called symmetric balanced incomplete block design in combinatorial theory, which provides solutions for very limited cases. In this section, we present our method to construct blocks and the initial topology for any given network parameters.

4.1 From Block Design to Network Design

Combinatorial design provides methodologies to distribute a set of objects into blocks to satisfy certain properties. One method is called *balanced incomplete block design* (BIBD), which distributes s objects to blocks of size d such that (1) each pair of the objects occurs in exactly λ blocks, (2) each object occurs in r blocks, and (3) there are b blocks. A BIBD with $s = b$ and $r = d$ is called symmetric, which can be denoted by (s, r, λ). For example, a symmetric BIBD (7,3,1) has seven objects $0, 1, \cdots, 6$ and seven blocks $B_0, B_1, \cdots, B_6$ as shown in Table 1, where each block has three objects.

To design a switch-based network from the block design, we have the following maps between blocks and the network:

1. Each object matches a switch and there are total s switches.

$B_0 = (0\ 1\ 3)$	$B_4 = (4\ 5\ 0)$
$B_1 = (1\ 2\ 4)$	$B_5 = (5\ 6\ 1)$
$B_2 = (2\ 3\ 5)$	$B_6 = (6\ 0\ 2)$
$B_3 = (3\ 4\ 6)$	

Table 1. Blocks of symmetric BIBD $(7,3,1)$

2. Each block defines a path for its objects (switches). For example, B_0 determines a bidirectional path $0 \leftrightarrow 1 \leftrightarrow 3$.

3. All paths within blocks are connected to construct a single bidirectional trail, which is considered as an Euler trail[2] of the network. The network topology is then decided by the Euler trail.

4. The average path length $\bar{p}$ and the maximum path length $\hat{p}$ depend on d.

5. The degree of each switch is $2r - 2$.

6. The number of routing paths between a switch pair is related to λ.

As shown in Fig. 1, the network topology corresponding to the block design in Table 1 is created from the Eulerian trail connecting all the blocks. When we place nodes to switches, we should follow the design considerations in Section 2. The network tuning algorithm in Section 5.3 may be applied if needed.

$$0 \leftrightarrow 1 \leftrightarrow 3 \leftrightarrow 4 \leftrightarrow 6 \leftrightarrow 0 \leftrightarrow 2 \leftrightarrow 3 \leftrightarrow 5 \leftrightarrow 6 \leftrightarrow 1 \leftrightarrow 2 \leftrightarrow 4 \leftrightarrow 5 \leftrightarrow 0$$

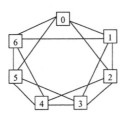

Figure 1. The network from BIBD $(7,3,1)$

Given the bidirectional Euler trail, it is easy to design a routing algorithm. One way is to route messages along one of the two unidirectional Euler trails. We can also adopt some existing routing algorithms like Euler trail-based routing in [5] or virtual ring routing in [4]. For wormhole switching, special considerations may be needed to avoid deadlock.

4.2 Construction of Blocks

Combinatorial theory has shown that an $(s, r, 1)$-symmetric block design exists when $(r - 1)$ is a power of a prime number and $s = r^2 - r + 1$. It means that we may not be able to find a symmetric BIBD for any s

and r. In [4], it is pointed out that the integers for which there is a constructive symmetric design with $\lambda = 1$ and $3 \le r \le 20$ are limited to 7, 13, 21, 31, 57, 73, 91, 133, 273, 307, and 381.

In a topology design, we are given the number of switches (s), number of ports per switch (c_i), and the required number of nodes (N). To simplify our description, we assume all $c_i's$ are equal to c. The average degree k of switches can be calculated by $2k + N \le cs$. Given k, we have $r = \lfloor k/2 \rfloor + 1$. To design a network for any reasonable size of s and r, we introduce the following definition as a variation of symmetric BIBD.

Definition 1 *Basic block design (BBD): in a basic block design $(s, r, \ge \lambda)$, there are s objects and s blocks, each block has r objects, each object occurs in r blocks, and each pair of objects occurs in at least λ blocks.*

Note that BIBD is a special case of BBD. As an example, an BBD $(14, 3, \ge 0)$ is shown in Table 2, where some pairs occur in one of blocks but other pairs (e.g., 5 and 10) occur in none of blocks.

$B_0 = (0\ 1\ 3)$	$B_7 = (7\ 8\ 10)$
$B_1 = (1\ 2\ 4)$	$B_8 = (8\ 9\ 11)$
$B_2 = (2\ 3\ 5)$	$B_9 = (9\ 10\ 12)$
$B_3 = (3\ 4\ 6)$	$B_{10} = (10\ 11\ 13)$
$B_4 = (4\ 5\ 7)$	$B_{11} = (11\ 12\ 0)$
$B_5 = (5\ 6\ 8)$	$B_{12} = (12\ 13\ 1)$
$B_6 = (6\ 7\ 9)$	$B_{13} = (13\ 0\ 2)$

Table 2. Blocks of BBD $(14, 3, \ge 0)$

Given s and r, we use the following method to construct a BBD. Switches are represented by numbers 0, 1, 2, ... $s - 1$. Suppose B_0 is $(b_0, b_1, \cdots b_{r-1})$, where each b_i represents a switch number. All the other blocks are constructed in such a way that block B_i is ($(b_0 + i)$ mod s, $(b_1 + i)$ mod s, $\cdots$, $(b_{r-1} + i)$ mod s) for $0 < i < s$. No matter if each pair occurs in one of blocks, messages can be routed along the Euler trail. However, a message may have to travel more than one block if its source and destination switch pair do not occur in any block. In this case, the maximum path length may be greater than the block size r.

In a real network, switches may not have the same number of ports. Even if they have the same number of ports, the switch degrees are not necessary to be same. If a switch has less degree, we may remove it from a certain block(s) depending on its degree requirement. If a switch has more degree, we can add it to a block which originally does not include the switch. In Table 2, if switch 10 has more degree(s), it could be added to B_0 as follows. We do not place the new switch in a boundary of a block because we will construct an Euler trail.

$$B_0 = (0\ 1\ 3) \Longrightarrow B_0 = (0\ 1\ 10\ 3)$$

---

[2] An Euler trail of a network is defined as a trail which passes each channel once and exactly once.

4.3 Construction of B_0

Because all the other blocks are determined by B_0, we only need to show the construction of B_0. To cover as many pairs as possible in a BBD, we use differences to construct B_0 based on s and r. A *difference* of two switches is defined as the difference of their numbers. For s switches, there are totally $s - 1$ distinct positive differences: $1, 2, \cdots, s - 1$. Every two switches i and j yield two s-complement differences: $(i - j) \bmod s$ and $(j - i) \bmod s$. For example, 0 and 1 yields differences 1 and $s - 1$. Due to the way a BBD is constructed, all $B_i's$ should yield a same set of differences. If B_0 yields a difference x, each switch pair, whose difference is x or $s - x$, will appear in one of the blocks in the BBD.

The more distinct differences B_0 yields, the more pairs a BBD covers. Our objective is to yield as many distinct differences as possible in B_0. We are especially interested in BBD $(s, r, \geq 1)$, where each pair occurs in at least one block so that the maximum path length is less than r. It is shown that each pair occurs in at least one block of the corresponding BBD if and only if B_0 yields all differences $1, 2, \cdots, s - 1$ [6].

Block B_0 of BBD $(s, r, \geq \lambda)$ yields at most $r(r - 1)$ distinct differences, if none of them are duplicated. Since there are totally $s - 1$ differences, r must be greater than $\sqrt{s}$ in order to yield all the $s - 1$ differences.

In general, a larger r yields more distinct differences in a block and more distinct pairs in a BBD. However, r is equal to $\lfloor k/2 \rfloor + 1$, where k is the average switch degree. Due to the limit on the switch degree, r may not be very big. Given s and r, a best solution of B_0, which covers as many distinct differences as possible, can always be found by exhausting search. But such an algorithm may take too much time for large s and r.

Therefore, we propose a heuristic algorithm to construct B_0. The algorithm considers local optima when selecting objects for B_0. It means that a new object, which yields the maximum number of new differences, will be added to B_0 until there are r objects in B_0. After all objects have been selected in B_0, the order of these objects may be reorganized to avoid double channels and reduce the maximum path length. Avoiding double channels saves one channel to connect two otherwise unconnected switches. The other blocks will be decided by the reordered B_0.

The detailed algorithm can be found in [6]. Although our algorithm considers only local optima, it shows that the results are close to the optimal results, especially when r is less than $\sqrt{s}$ [6].

5 Incremental Reconfiguration

Due to the lack of accurate knowledge of network traffic, the initial topology design may not be good enough to deliver demanded performance. Even if the initial network is good enough, network tuning and incremental reconfiguration are still needed to accommodate changes in the network. Some general ideas

have been proposed in [7] for network tuning in shared-medium LANs. However, as indicated in [1], the method proposed in [7] for high traffic locality and high load balance may contradict with each other. Moreover, those ideas are based on shared-medium LANs and may not be applicable to switch-based networks.

Based on queuing theory, message latency on channel k is proportional to $\frac{1}{1-\mu_k}$, where μ_k is the channel utilization. Therefore, to achieve lower latency, it is very important to reduce μ_k, i.e., reduce f_k. There are two necessary steps to reduce f_k's: minimizing remote traffic R and balancing channel utilization.

In the following, we present the sketch of our algorithms for some typical and frequent changes in the network: adding a new client, adding a new server, and network tuning. All the algorithms consider the following criteria: (1) maximize local traffic L and balance inter-switch traffic; (2) minimize remote traffic R; and (3) balance channel utilization. Each algorithm can be implemented in different heuristic methods.

5.1 Add A New Client

Client/server traffic is a common characteristic in LANs. It is often demanded to add a new client to a network. This is the easiest situation for network change and usually does not introduce much complexity. Where to connect a new client depends on its traffic distribution and the availability of spare ports. We also need consider the physical constraint of its location. If its server/workgroup is known, it should be placed as close to the server/workgroup as possible. The algorithm sketch is shown in Fig. 2.

Input: current topology, routing, and traffic
Output: the network after adding the new client
Algorithm:
    understand the server/workgroup of the new client;
    $positionS$ = {available ports for the new client};
    recalculate L and R for each port in $positionS$;
    recalculate $y_{i,j}$, f_k, and μ_k if changed;
    select the one based on minimizing $max(\mu_k)$, R,
        and $max(y_{i,j})$, and maximizing L;
    refer Section 5.3 if network tuning is needed;

Figure 2. Algorithm to add a new client to the network

5.2 Add A New Server

In general, adding a server is similar to adding a client. However, a server may easily cause traffic congestion and performance degradation, because it usually has much more traffic than a client and concentrates its traffic to a subset of clients. Therefore, a higher bandwidth port may be needed to connect a server. Multiple network interfaces on a server could also be a solution.

Input: current topology, routing, and traffic
Output: the network after adding the new server
Algorithm:
  find all clients of the new server;
  $positionS$ = {available ports for the new server};
  recalculate L and R for each port in $positionS$;
  recalculate $y_{i,j}$, f_k, and μ_k if changed;
  select the one based on minimizing $max(\mu_k)$, R,
      and $max(y_{i,j})$, and maximizing L;
  refer Section 5.3 if traffic balance is needed;

Figure 3. Algorithm to add a new server to the network

Input: current topology, routing, and traffic
Output: network after network tuning
Algorithm:
  /* Step 1: increase L and balance $y_{i,j}$ */
  increase local traffic by moving nodes;
  balance inter-switch traffic between switch pairs
     by changing node placement;

  /* Step 2: decrease R */
  minimize R by moving and/or adding channels;
  recalculate f_k and μ_k on influenced channels;

  /* Step 3: balance μ_k's by changing routing paths */
  calculate or measure f_k's, μ_k's;
  $BusySet$ = all channels whose utilization is over δ;
  sort $BusySet$ in a descending order;
  For each channel $BusyCh$ in $BusySet$ {
    $BusyUtil$ = $BusyCh$'s utilization;
    $PathSet$ = all paths which include $BusyCh$;
    find an alternate path for each path in $PathSet$, which
      reduces $BusyCh$'s utilization;
      does not increase $max(\mu_k)$;
      does not cause new μ_k over $BusyUtil$;
  }

  /* Step 4: balance μ_k's by changing node placement */
  recalculate f_k and μ_k;
  $BusySet$ = all channels whose utilization is over δ;
  sort $BusySet$ in a descending order;
  For each channel $BusyCh$ in $BusySet$ {
    $BusyUtil$ = $BusyCh$'s utilization;
    find all src and dst switches whose path include $BusyCh$;
    move nodes in these switches so that new node placement
      reduces $BusyCh$'s utilization;
      does not increase $max(\mu_k)$;
      does not make new μ_k over $BusyUtil$;
  }

Figure 4. Algorithm for network tuning

5.3 Network Tuning

Suppose we have sufficient network resources for the network workload. If an operational network does not provide demanded performance, network tuning is needed to improve performance. The reason to cause poor performance of the original network could be two-folded. First, network traffic may change so that the original network may not be able to deliver demanded performance under the new traffic. Second, the estimated workload may be different from the real workload so that the original network design is not suitable.

A systematic method is proposed in Fig 4 for network tuning. The major objective is to balance channel utilization and minimize $max(\mu_k)$. To identify the overloaded channels, we introduce δ as a threshold for channel utilization. If $\mu_k > \delta$, channel k is considered overloaded. For most design, δ should be about 40-50%. The method consists of four major steps: (1) increase local traffic L and balance inter-switch traffic $y_{i,j}$; (2) decrease remote traffic R; (3) balance traffic by changing routing paths; and (4) balance traffic by moving nodes. In any step, if none of μ_k is greater than δ, the algorithm can be stopped.

There is no straight-forward implementation for any of the above steps and physical constraints (if any) have to be considered. Moreover, we have to compromise between the criteria if we are not able to achieve all of them at the same time. The most important criterion should be minimizing $max(\mu_k)$.

6 Simulations

The algorithms of block design, Eulerian trail-based routing [5], and network tuning have been implemented in a simulator. The simulation results are measured to evaluate the network performance before and after network tuning under various topologies and workload.

6.1 Simulation Environment

Without loss of generality, the performance data shown in this section are measured from a switch-based network which has 10 switches and 200 nodes. The initial topology design is created from a BBD $(10, 4, \geq 1)$. The corresponding block design and initial topology is shown in Fig. 5, where the network has 30 bidirectional channels and the degree of each switch is 6.

In order to evaluate interconnection networks, a simulator should consider the following workloads: traffic patterns, message size distributions, and temporal distribution. Due to the space limit of this paper, we only show the results for one traffic pattern, where there are 5 servers and 5 client workgroups out of 200 nodes. The number of clients in each workgroup is listed in Table 3 and the traffic distribution is shown in Table 4. Each server or client also has 20% global uniform traffic as the background traffic.

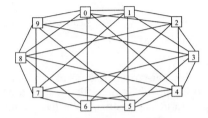

$B_0 = (3\,1\,0\,6)$	$B_5 = (8\,6\,5\,1)$
$B_1 = (4\,2\,1\,7)$	$B_6 = (9\,7\,6\,2)$
$B_2 = (5\,3\,2\,8)$	$B_7 = (0\,8\,7\,3)$
$B_3 = (6\,4\,3\,9)$	$B_8 = (1\,9\,8\,4)$
$B_4 = (7\,5\,4\,0)$	$B_9 = (2\,0\,9\,5)$

	srv 1	srv 2	srv 3	srv 4	srv 5	grp 1	grp 2	grp 3	grp 4	grp 5
srv 1		10%				40%			30%	
srv 2	20%					40%		20%		
srv 3							60%			20%
srv 4					10%				70%	
srv 5				10%						70%
grp 1	30%	30%	50%			20%				
grp 2		30%					30%			
grp 3		30%						50%		
grp 4	20%			40%					20%	
grp 5			10%	40%						30%

Table 4. Traffic distribution

Figure 5. Initial topology used for simulation

Two message size distributions are considered: (1) fixed size: all messages are 128 bytes long; and (2) bursty: 5% of the messages are 2048 bytes long and the rest of the messages are 64 bytes long.

Group 1	Group 2	Group 3	Group 4	Group 4
50	35	25	45	40

Table 3. Number of clients in each workgroup

We use finite input source to model the message generation. Message generation rate is decided by a random variable x, which is defined as the time duration between the time when the current message has completely left the source buffer and the time when the next message is generated in the node. In the simulations, x has exponential distribution based on a given mean.

A time unit is defined as the time needed to transmit a byte via a channel, which is decided by channel bandwidth. Unless otherwise specified, all ports connecting to switches or clients are assumed to have bandwidth of 1 byte per time unit, and all ports connecting to servers are assumed to have bandwidth 10 bytes per time unit. Higher bandwidth for server ports will efficiently reduce traffic congestion due to server bottleneck. We assume the header for each message is 6 bytes.

The switching technique is assumed to be cut-through switching and each port has an input FIFO buffer of 1000 bytes. Back-pressure flow control is used to avoid buffer overflow. Similar performance trend can be observed in store-and-forward switched networks.

Under each network workload, the simulator is run until at least 30000 messages are received. In each run, the first 2000 messages are passed to eliminate start-up transient effect. Average message latency and normalized network throughput are used to evaluate network performance.

6.2 Performance Improvement by Network Tuning

In the simulations, network tuning is applied in the following four levels:

- Tuning level 0: initial topology; random node placement; and no network tuning.
- Tuning level 1: implement step 1 in Fig. 4.
- Tuning level 2: implement steps 1 and 2 in Fig. 4.
- Tuning level 3: implement all 4 steps in Fig. 4.

In tuning levels 0-2, each switch has exactly 20 nodes and at most one of the 20 nodes is a server. In tuning level 3, a switch can have at most 22 nodes. Allowing at most one server in a switch is helpful to balance inter-switch traffic.

As shown in Fig. 6, each level of network tuning can achieve significant performance benefits for both fixed message size distribution and bursty message size distribution. The better performance after network tuning demonstrates the importance of network tuning and the efficiency of our algorithm. In tuning level 3, we use measured channel utilization because it is more accurate than calculations and can be measured after a network is operational. All the other network tuning levels are based on calculation.

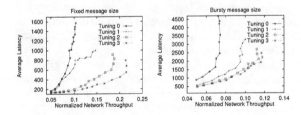

Figure 6. Performance improvement by network tuning

6.3 Server Bottleneck

To avoid server bottleneck, we assume that server ports have higher bandwidth. We have also measured network performance when all server ports have the same bandwidth (1 byte per time unit) as other ports.

293

As shown in Fig. 7, the network performance is dramatically decreased without higher bandwidth ports for servers. Further network tuning cannot improve performance very much due to server bottleneck. This result emphasizes the importance to release server bottleneck in a client/server environment.

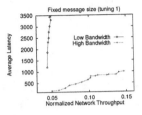

Figure 7. The importance of higher bandwidth to release server bottleneck

6.4 Fairness

In Section 2.4, we have defined fairness ratio. Note that the bigger the fairness ratio is, the less the network is fair. We have measured traffic generated by each node and calculated fairness ratio for each client workgroup. It is observed that fairness ratio is usually lower than 2 under light to medium workload, but the ratio could be as high as 7 under heavy workload. Network tuning can reduce fairness ratio for each workgroup and improve fairness for the whole network.

In the selected traffic pattern, the main reason causing high fairness ratio is the different locations of clients in a workgroup. Due to the limited number of ports in each switch, none of workgroups can be all placed in the same switch as its server. For a client which is located in the same switch as its server, its messages to the server do not compete channel bandwidth with other traffic. Therefore, its messages are transmitted to the server very quickly. However, for a client which is located in a different switch from its server, its messages have to compete at least one channel before they are transmitted to the server. Such a location difference can make big difference in terms of transmission latency and number of messages generated by a node.

To avoid such an unfair situation, we may consider using higher bandwidth channel to connect two switches if there is a significant portion of traffic transmitted between them. As an example, we use a higher bandwidth channel (10 bytes per time unit) to connect the two switches which host the clients of workgroup 2. Note that the corresponding server is located in one of the two switches. As shown in Fig. 8, under the new network configuration, fairness ratio of workgroup 2 is significantly reduced under heavy workload.

7   Conclusions

This paper studies issues of network planning and routing in switch-based LANs. Important design consid-

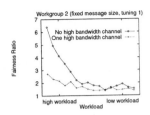

Figure 8. Comparison of fairness ratio for workgroup 2 with and without a higher bandwidth channel

erations have been discussed in terms of network characteristics, routing path length, traffic locality, traffic balance, and performance metrics. We have proposed a method for initial topology design based on block design. This method can efficiently minimize the maximum path length and the average path length. A systematic method has been presented for network tuning, which tries to maximize local traffic, balance interswitch traffic, reduce remote traffic, and balance channel utilization. Simulation results show that network tuning can significantly improve network performance.

To make our algorithms more practical, further research are needed to study efficient solutions for networks with highly dynamic traffic. The simulator is very helpful for us to evaluate network performance under various network situations. To make it more useful, we should consider real network traffic such as traffic traces from switch-based LANs. It is also important to study how to balance between peak rate and bursty rate.

References

[1] R. Elbaum and M. Sidi, "Topological design of local area networks using genetic algorithms," *INFOCOM'95*, pp. 64 – 71, Apr. 1995.

[2] M. Gerla and L. Kleinrock, "On the topological design of distributed computer networks," *IEEE Transaction on Communications*, vol. COM-25, pp. 48 – 60, Jan. 1977.

[3] J. Opatrny, N. Srinivasan, and V. S. Alagar, "Highly fault-tolerant communication network models," *IEEE Transactions on Circuits and Systems*, vol. 36, pp. 23 – 29, Jan. 1989.

[4] B. Yener, Y. Ofek, and M. Yung, "Topological design of loss-free switch-based LANs," *INFOCOM'95*, pp. 88 – 96, Apr. 1995.

[5] W. Qiao and L. M. Ni, "Adaptive routing in irregular networks using cut-throughput switches," *Proceedings of the 1996 International Conference on Parallel Processing*, vol. 1, pp. 52 – 60, Aug. 1996.

[6] W. Qiao, "Network routing and planning in switch-based networks," *Ph.D Dissertation, Michigan State University*, 1997.

[7] K. M. Khalil and P. A. Spencer, "A systematic approach for planning, tunning and upgrading local area networks," *GLOBECOM'91*, pp. 658 – 663, 1991.

A New Transparent Bridge Protocol for LAN Internetworking Using Topologies with Active Loops

Román García, José Duato and Juan José Serrano
Dept. DISCA, Polytechnical University of Valencia
46071 Valencia, SPAIN
roman@gap.upv.es, jduato@gap.upv.es, juanjo@aii.upv.es

Abstract

This paper proposes a new transparent bridge protocol for LAN interconnection that considerably improves the performance of current standard IEEE-802.1D bridges. The current standard is based on the Spanning Tree (ST) algorithm and the most important restriction is that it cannot work when the topology has active loops. The new protocol (named OSR for Optimal-Suboptimal Routing) allows them. Therefore, strongly connected regular topologies, like torus, hypercubes, meshes, etc., as well as irregular topologies, can be used without wasting bandwidth. As loops imply alternative paths, the OSR protocol uses optimal routing or, in the worst cases, suboptimal routing. The new protocol has been evaluated on highly connected regular topologies, like meshes. The results are compared with those of a network of the same size managed by the standard Spanning Tree protocol, showing the superior behavior of the OSR protocol.

1. Introduction

Routers and bridges are the basic devices for LAN interconnection. They have different properties and each one has its own scope. For example, routers work at network level (ISO level-3). They route packets using hierarchical addressing (i.e. IP) but they need that every station be configured to work with them (a level-3 address must be assigned). Bridges work at link level (ISO level-2). Bridges can be used to build a diameter-limited network, usually named "bridged LAN" or "extended LAN". The current standard bridge is a transparent bridge. Transparent means that the stations do not need to use special software to work with bridges. The most attractive feature of transparent bridges is their easy installation procedure and null maintenance. This feature has been very important in industrial environments where computers and networks have been progressively incorporated. Unfortunately, increased demand for computer communication (more stations, higher computer utilization, new multimedia applications, etc.), have

shown the limitations of current bridges. The most important limitation is their inability to work with loops. Therefore, the current standard bridge use the Spanning Tree (ST) algorithm to transform any topology to a tree.

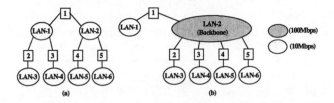

Figure 1. (a) Normal tree (b) Fat tree.

The ST is easy to understand and implement, but the generated tree does not provide a good interconnecting topology. The main concern is the excessive traffic around the root. Figure-1(a) shows a tree with 6 LANs and 5 bridges. LANs 1 and 2 must bear all the traffic between the rest of the LANs. The situation becomes worse when the network grows. This is the main reason why transparent bridges are only used for reduced diameter networks -bridged LANs.

In order to alleviate the problem, engineers have designed powerful bridges with multiple ports (10 and 12 ports per bridge are usual) and/or use -fat tree- topologies.

In a fat tree topology, the bridges and LANs are designed for a higher bandwidth as they become closer to root. Any bridged LAN based on a backbone LAN is a good example of a fat tree (Figure-1(b)). The problem in a fat tree is that the best performing technology has to be kept for the backbone LAN, and cannot be used in the rest of the LANs in order to balance traffic and bandwidth.

A detailed description of current standard bridge operations can be found in [1] and [2].

Many ideas have been proposed to enhance the current standard bridge behavior. Ideas like Distributed Load Sharing (DLS) [3] that enhance the use of point-to-point links between remote bridges, the Modular Solution [4],[5] involving a multilevel Spanning Tree or the Multi-tree proposal [6] that uses multiple spanning trees simultaneously in order to utilize all the original bandwidth. But none of them try to overcome the problem by using the existing loops in the original topology.

2. Optimal-Suboptimal Routing (OSR)

The OSR protocol is based on the idea that bridges can learn "which stations are in each LAN" or, in other words, where each station is. This is the main difference with respect to the ST based standard, in which the bridges only learn "from which direction" the station has been listened to. Thus, the ST is not strictly required, and the most favorable route can be used considering all the existing lines. The optimal route criteria can be based on different metrics: number of hops, bandwidth of each LAN, etc.

2.1. Preliminary Definitions

Definition 1: Line identification
According to the ST protocol, four states are defined for a bridge port: blocking, listening, learning and forwarding. A root port is also defined as the one used by the bridge to reach the root of the ST. These definitions are sufficient to know the location-connection of each port within the tree, but it is somehow cumbersome. The OSR protocol defines 3 types of lines according to their participation within the tree (see Figure-2).

Enabled-root (R) line: This is the line associated with the root port. The port must be in forwarding state. From the bridge point of view, it is the line used to communicate with the higher level of the tree.

Enabled (E) line: All lines associated with a port in forwarding status other than the line associated with the root port. From the bridge point of view, these are the lines used to communicate with the lower level of the tree.

Blocked (B) line: Associated with any port that is not in forwarding state. These are the lines used to communicate with the other branches of the tree.

Corollary 1: Every bridge has just one enabled-root line
Corollary 2: Every LAN has just one enabled line (the line to the designated bridge).

Definition 2: Proprietary bridge of a LAN
A bridge is "proprietary bridge of a LAN" if it is the bridge used by the LAN to reach the root across the tree. A bridge knows it is a proprietary based on Corollary-3.

Corollary 3: A bridge is a "proprietary bridge" of the LANs which are connected to its enabled lines.
Corollary 4: A LAN has just one proprietary bridge.
Corollary 5: The root bridge is proprietary of all LANs directly connected to it.

Definition 3: Proprietary bridge of a leaf-LAN
A bridge is a "proprietary bridge of a leaf-LAN" if
(1) It is proprietary bridge and
(2a) is the only one bridge for that LAN, or
(2b) it knows, by the ST configuration messages, that the remaining lines of that LAN are in blocked status.

This definition is important because the propietary bridges of leaf-LANs are the ones that will initiate the OSR learning process, as discussed in section 2.2 .

Definition 4: Proprietary bridge of a virtual leaf-LAN
A bridge is "proprietary bridge of a virtual leaf-LAN" if it has no enabled line.

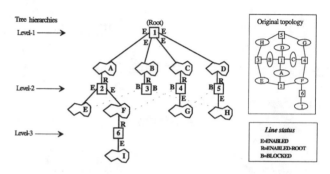

Figure 2. Bridge-1 is proprietary bridge of LANs A, B, C and D. Bridge-2 is proprietary bridge of LAN-F and proprietary bridge of leaf-LAN-E. Bridge-3 is proprietary bridge of virtual leaf-LAN, and so on.

2.2. OSR: Learning

OSR Learning Fundamentals
The OSR protocol learning process is based on the tree generated by the ST protocol, and evolves from the ST leaves towards the root. This is therefore a bottom-up process.

The OSR fundamentals are:

- Once the ST has been configured, a proprietary-bridge of a leaf-LAN knows that all the listened frames come from stations in that LAN.

- A proprietary-bridge, on a higher level of the tree hierarchy, decides that the listened frames are from stations in its LAN if they don't belong to LANs in the lower levels of the tree.

But the main goal of the learning process is to share the information among all the bridges of the bridged-LAN. Thus it is necessary to plan a spreading strategy to obtain an ordered full propagation. The plan is outlined in Table-1.

(7) Learning loop	(3) Phase-1	(1) Leaf-->root propagation	(bottom-up)
		(2) Lateral propagation	
	(6) Phase-2	(4) Root -->leaf propagation	(top-down)
		(5) Lateral propagation	

Table 1. Spreading strategy.

296

The learning process consists of the following steps:

(1) In this step only proprietary bridges are listening to frames to find stations in their LANs. Proprietary bridges store in a data base (db) the source MAC address of the frames received through their enabled lines. The proprietary bridge of leaf-LANs knows that all the frames that it receives through the line connecting to a leaf-LAN belong to stations in that LAN. Thus, it can associate a "cost to reach" equal to zero to the MAC address of the source station (hop count is the simplest metric, but other metrics are also possible).

The proprietary bridges of leaf-LANs transmit their knowledge to the proprietary bridges on the higher level of the hierarchy of the tree, and so on until that information reaches the root. In this process, each proprietary bridge learns which stations are in its LAN (cost = 0) and in lower levels (cost >0).

Bridge knowledge is transmitted to the neighboring bridges through OSR location messages. Basically it contains the transmitting bridge identification (bridge-id), a list of the new stations (MAC-addresses) and the cost to reach them.

(2) The location messages are transmitted through all the lines of each bridge, including blocked lines. Note that bottom-up learning process would only require each proprietary bridge to transmit information through its enabled-root line. Bridges accept the location messages transmitted through blocked lines. Usually, when a message is transmitted through a blocked line, a spread toward other branches of the tree is accomplished. This is the reason why we named it "lateral propagation".

(3) After phase-1 is completed, all bridges know their stations and the root bridge has a full knowledge of all the active stations in the bridged-LAN and their location (cost). The routes known by root are optimal since the ST is an optimal tree.

It is necessary a second learning/propagation top-down phase, in order to:

(4) Allow the root bridge to spread its knowledge to the rest of the bridges. Then all the bridges will know every new station and location (cost) across the tree, and

(5) To indicate to the remaining bridges to transmit their knowledge to their neighbors.

(6) With this phase-2 it is guaranteed that all the bridges know the location of every active station across the tree (by the bottom-up and top-down process) or across a shorter path (by lateral propagation).

It must be highlighted that it is not sufficient for a bridge to know the possibilities to reach a station. The bridge must also know the possibilities of all the others bridges connected to the same LAN. In other words, when a station of a LAN-x wants to transmit a frame to another station of LAN-y, the question is: which bridge connected to LAN-x will route the frame?. It is important to remember that just one of the bridges (the one that minimizes transmission cost) must transmit the frame and the other bridges should discard it.

It is also important to note that it is not possible to guarantee an optimal route to a destination until a number 'n' of learning loops have been performed, where 'n' is the diameter of the topology (worst case). Figure-3 shows the lateral propagation from LAN DESTination. Each shadowed area corresponds to a learning loop. With two learning loops, the optimal routing is ensured from any station in neighboring LANs. In the next loop the information is propagated to the neighboring LANs, and so on.

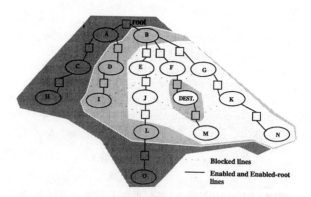

Figure 3. OSR knowledge propagation of stations in LAN-DEST. Four learning loops are enough to spread that knowledge to all OSR bridges.

As a result it may happen that, temporarily, OSR routing first evolves along the tree until arriving at a bridge that has an optimal route information available. This doesn't cause any problem: the route will just be only partially optimal. Note that if a bridge knows the optimal route to a destination, all bridges in the optimal route will also know it by the optimality principle.

Optimality principle:

If bridge-J is on the optimal path from LAN-I to LAN-K, then the optimal path from J to K is a subpath of the optimal path from LAN-I to LAN-K.

Learning Example

A small bridged-LAN (Figure-4), with 3 LANs and 4 bridges, has been chosen to show an example of learning evolution. Figure-4 (b) shows the same topology with root (bridge-1) on top.

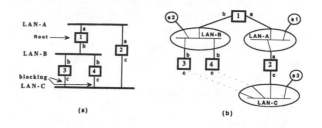

Figure 4. The example topology.

Table-2 shows the evolution of the learning process once the spanning tree has a stable configuration. For simplicity it is assumed that in each LAN only one station has transmitted. "s1" represents the LAN-A station, "s2" represents the LAN-B station, and "s3" the LAN-C station.

The table has four main blocks, one for each bridge. There is a column for each port on each bridge, where the received (Rx) or transmitted (Tx) frames are shown. Additionally there is a column named "db-0" (own data base) showing the knowledge evolution for each bridge.

Note that OSR bridges are not synchronizing but the example assumes, for simplicity, that some transmissions and receptions occur at the same time.

The information in the table is encoded as follows:

Location messages (port columns): "a.b.c.d" with

a= station-id, b= cost (hops), c= bridge-id, d= through this LAN? (1=yes –> same cost for you, 0=No –> add cost to reach me!)

Information in "db-0" columns: "a.b.c" with

a=station-id, b=cost, c=port to reach it

The lower part of the table summarizes the information collected by the bridges. Under each "port-x" column, "db-x" shows the data base associated with that port. This corresponds to the station reachability for the neighbors. Under "db-0" column the station reachability for this bridge is summarized. Therefore each bridge eventually knows the own cost to reach a station and the cost from the neighbors, so that it could decide whether the frame has to be routed by itself or not.

Table-2 Notes:

(a) At the beginning, it is assumed that bridges do not have any acknowledge about each other. Stations s1, s2 and s3 transmit a frame (that is routed through the spanning tree as usual) and the OSR learning process starts. Bridge-1 receives the frames from s1 and s2 but nothing can be derived from them because bridge-1 is not a proprietary of a leaf-LAN. Bridge-2 receives the frame from s3 and derives that s3 can be reached at cost = 0.

(b) First OSR message transmission. Bridges 2, 3 and 4 transmit configuration messages because they are proprietaries of (virtual) leaf-LANs. "0.0.x.0" message indicates that the bridge has no information to communicate. Transmission through ports "b" and "c" perform the bottom-up process and transmission through ports "c" (blocked lines) perform the lateral propagation.

(c) The OSR messages are received by the neighbors. Bridge-1 learns that it is proprietary of stations s1 and s2 because the neighbors do not report anything about them. Bridge-2 does not learn anything at this step. Bridges 3 and 4 learn that they can reach station s3 at the same cost (cost=0) that neighbor bridge-2.

(d) The top-down process is started. All information collected by root is now broadcast down the tree. Not all the information received by a bridge produces a new entry in the data base. For example, bridge-2 receives "s3.1.1.1" but it already has a better knowledge about s3 stored in its data

base (s3.0.c).

(e) Bridges proprietaries of a leaf-LAN start a new learning loop again. During this second learning loop all OSR bridges obtain a full knowledge of stations s1, s2 and s3. Note that this learning loop exchanges less useful information. This is because the example assumes that no more new stations start to transmit.

Learning fidelity criterion OSR bridges acquire their knowledge through transmission of location messages. We should consider the implications of lost location messages due to transmission errors.

In case of transmission errors, the cross information that each bridge has about the neighbors will not match the information recorded by these neighbors. So, there are two possibilities: (1) none of the LAN bridges will route a frame because none of them knows the optimal route, and (2) more than one bridge will route the same frame because they have information about the optimal route. Both possibilities are unacceptable, therefore it is mandatory to ensure reliable transmission for the location messages.

Reliability depends on LAN technology. On one hand, ring technology like FDDI ensures the reliable delivery for each MAC-LLC frame. There is a feedback that allows the transmitter to check if the transmission was successful. Therefore these types of LAN do not require any additional higher protocol to guarantee the coherence of the information in the OSR data bases.

In FDDI, the frame must be removed from the ring by the transmitter. Figure-5(a) shows the end of a FDDI frame. Bits "A" and "C" mean "Acknowledge" and "Copied" from receiver. Therefore FDDI has a mechanism that allows the transmitter to know if the receiver has received the frame.

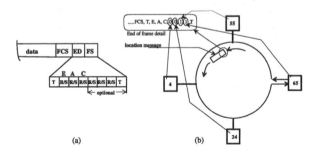

Figure 5. (a) The end of a FDDI frame. (b) OSR bridges set the corresponding bit to indicate a successful reception of the location message.

When there are multiple receivers, the latter procedure can be used if optional bits provided by FDDI are used. The idea is simple. Bridges know how many bridges are in a LAN and the bridge-ID of the others. Therefore each bridge can determine in which order they are located -based on their bridge-id. When an OSR bridge transmits a location message it must include as many optional R/S bits as OSR

	Bridge-1			Bridge-2			Bridge-3			Bridge-4		
	Port a	Port b	db-0	Port a	Port c	db-0	Port b	Port c	db-0	Port b	Port c	db-0
(a)	s1-frame	s2-frame	none		s3-frame	s3.0.c			none			none
	An ST configuration frame is received and a learning loop starts.											
(b) tx-1				s3.0.2.0	s3.0.2.1		0.0.3.0	0.0.3.0		0.0.4.0	0.0.4.0	
(c) rx-1	s3.0.2.0	0.0.3.0 0.0.4.0	s1.0.a s2.0.b s3.1.a		0.0.3.0 0.0.4.0		0.0.4.0	s3.0.2.1 0.0.4.0	s3.0.c	0.0.3.0	s3.0.2.1 0.0.3.0	s3.0.c
(d) tx-2	s1.0.1.1 s2.0.1.0 s3.1.1.1	s1.0.1.0 s2.0.1.1 s3.1.1.0										
rx-2				s1.0.1.1 s2.0.1.0 s3.1.1.1		s1.0.a s2.1.a	s1.0.1.0 s2.0.1.1 s3.1.1.0	s1.1.b s2.0.b		s1.0.1.0 s2.0.1.1 s3.1.1.0		s1.1.b s2.0.b
tx-3				s1.0.2.1 s2.1.2.1	s1.0.2.0 s2.1.2.0		s1.1.3.1 s2.0.3.1 s3.0.3.0	s1.1.3.0 s2.0.3.0 s3.0.3.1		s1.1.4.1 s2.0.4.1 s3.0.4.0	s1.1.4.0 s2.0.4.0 s3.0.4.1	
rx-3	s1.0.2.1 s2.1.2.1	s1.1.3.1 s2.0.3.1 s3.0.3.0 ------- s1.1.4.1 s2.0.4.1 s3.0.4.0	s3.1.b		s1.1.3.0 s2.0.3.0 s3.0.3.1 ------- s1.1.4.0 s2.0.4.0 s3.0.4.1	s2.1.c	s1.1.4.1 s2.0.4.1 s3.0.4.0	s1.0.2.0 s2.1.2.0 -------- s1.1.4.0 s2.0.4.0 s3.0.4.1	s1.1.c	s1.1.3.1 s2.0.3.1 s3.0.3.0	s1.0.2.0 s2.1.2.0 -------- s1.1.3.0 s2.0.3.0 s3.0.3.1	s1.1.c
	End of the learning loop. OSR bridges wait for a new ST configuration frame to start a new learning loop.											
(e) tx-4				s2.1.2.0	s2.1.2.1		s1.1.3.0	s1.1.3.1		s1.1.4.0	s1.1.4.1	
rx-4	s2.1.2.0 s1.1.3.0 s1.1.4.0		none		s1.1.3.1 s1.1.4.1	none	s1.1.4.0	s2.1.2.1 s1.1.4.1	none	s1.1.3.0	s2.1.2.1 s1.1.3.1	none
tx-5	s3.1.1.0	s3.1.1.1										
rx-5				s3.1.1.0		none	s3.1.1.1		none	s3.1.1.1		none
tx-6				0.0.2.0	0.0.2.0		0.0.3.0	0.0.3.0		0.0.4.0	0.0.4.0	
rx-6	0.0.2.0 0.0.4.0	0.0.3.0 0.0.4.0	none		0.0.3.0 0.0.4.0	none	0.0.4.0	0.0.2.0 0.0.4.0	none	0.0.3.0	0.0.2.0 0.0.3.0	none
	End of the learning loop. The row below shows the knoledge gathered by every bridge. Note that every bridge knows the own cost to reach a station and the cost from the neighbors.											
	db-a	db-b	db-0	db-a	db-c	db-0	db-b	db-c	db-0	db-b	db-c	db-0
TOTAL info. collected	s1.0.2 1 s2.1.2 1 s2.1.2 0 s3.0.2 0	s1.1.3 0 s1.1.3 1 s2.0.3 0 s3.0.3 0 ------- s1.1.4 0 s1.1.4 1 s2.0.4 1 s3.0.4 0	s1.0.a s2.0.b s3.1.a s3.1.b	s1.0.1 1 s2.0.1 0 s2.0.3 0 s3.1.1 0	s1.1.3 1 s1.1.3 0 s2.0.3 0 s3.0.3 1 ------- s1.1.4 1 s1.1.4 0 s2.0.4 0 s3.0.4 1	s1.0.a s2.1.a s2.1.c s3.0.c	s1.0.1 0 s2.0.1 1 s3.1.1 0 s3.1.1 1 ------- s1.1.4 0 s1.1.4 1 s2.0.4 1 s3.0.4 0	s1.0.2 0 s2.1.2 0 s2.1.2 1 s3.0.2 1 ------- s1.1.4 1 s1.1.4 0 s2.0.4 0 s3.0.4 1	s1.1.c s1.1.b s2.0.b s3.0.c	s1.0.1 0 s2.0.1 1 s3.1.1 0 s3.1.1 1 ------- s1.1.3 0 s1.1.3 1 s2.0.3 1 s3.0.3 0	s1.0.2 0 s2.1.2 0 s2.1.2 1 s3.0.2 1 ------- s1.1.3 1 s1.1.3 0 s2.0.3 0 s3.0.3 1	s1.1.c s1.1.b s2.0.b s3.0.c

Table 2. Evolution of learning process.

bridges are in a LAN. When the frame is received without problems by one of the OSR bridges it sets a R/S bit. Each OSR bridge has its own R/S bit: the first bridge sets the first R/S bit, the second bridge sets the second R/S bridge and so on. In this way, when the transmitter finally removes the frame, it knows whether all bridges in that LAN have correctly received the frame or not. Figure-5 (b) shows a LAN with four OSR bridges. Each bridge is labeled with its bridge-id. The location messages have four additional R/S bits. The write order is: 4, 24, 55 and 65. Bridges 65 (the transmitter) and 55 have set their bits and bridges 4 and 24 will set it if there is no transmission error.

On the other hand, for IEEE-802.3 LANs (Ethernet type) and IEEE-802.4 (Token-Bus) a higher level protocol, like for example a Stop & Wait protocol, must be used in order to guarantee the message delivery. This means that an additional acknowledgment frame must be sent by the receiving bridges. Therefore traffic will increase. This is an ac-

ceptable overhead because location messages are transmitted once per second (typically) and traffic generated by these messages and their acknowledgments only represents 0.7% of the total bandwidth of a LAN with 3 OSR bridges using 10Mbps technology. With four and five bridges, the OSR protocol uses 1.3% and 2% of the total bandwidth, respectively. It is unusual to install more than five bridges per LAN. Obviously, a smaller percentage is required when a faster technology is used.

Information Expiry Time

Like in the ST protocol, the information learnt by bridges has a expiry time. OSR uses the same expiry criterion as ST. There is a long cache time (5 to 15 min.) for the normal operation and a short cache time (3 to 15 sec.) when a topology change is produced.

The expiry time is only controlled by the owner bridge. When the station-related information is no longer valid, the proprietary bridge will set an infinite cost associated with that station in the next location message, (infinite = 255).

2.3. OSR: Routing

Tunneling

Before proposing OSR routing, it is important to remember that the OSR protocol must be compatible with the ST protocol. Compatibility imposes a restriction: OSR can not transmit a frame using its original format. Otherwise, it will interfere with the normal learning process of the ST. To solve the problem, a tunneling technique is used.

The standard learning process on a transparent bridge is based on the assumption that only one route exists toward each station. OSR eliminates this restriction. So, it is necessary to encapsulate frames in order to distinguish normal frames from OSR frames.

OSR encapsulates the original frame in a new special format frame that is only recognized by OSR bridges.

Destination address	Source address	Protocol Type	data
OSR group adr.	bridge adr.	OSR protocol	station original frame
6 bytes	6 bytes	2 bytes	máx. = 1514 bytes

Figure 6. OSR frame for Ethernet LAN.

Figure-6 shows a tunneling frame adapted to Ethernet format. The "destination address" field is a globally known multicast group address that identify all OSR bridges. The "source address" field is the MAC address of the OSR bridge that transmits the frame. The "protocol type" field identifies the OSR protocol and the "data" field contains the original frame. The maximum size of the new frame is 1528 bytes, slightly longer than the maximum standard size (1514 bytes). This does not cause any problem because only OSR bridges handle these frames.

The main issue about tunneling is: What bridge on the destination LAN has to decode the frame to recover the original frame (untunnel)?. There is a simple answer: the same bridge that would put the frame on the destination LAN when standard routing is used. This is required to avoid errors in the standard learning process of the ST protocol. If the frame reaches the destination LAN through a different bridge, then it is necessary to add a new step (hop) in the path in order to reach the bridge that has to decode the frame. This is the reason why OSR can not guarantee optimal routes, but only sub-optimal ones (optimal + 1 hop).

Example: Figure-7 shows an example of the untunnel restriction. Figure-7(a) shows a path from a station in LAN-3 to another station in LAN-4. In the standard route across the tree, bridge-3 delivers the frame to the destination LAN. However OSR routing uses bridge-5 to reach the destination LAN. If bridge-5 put the frame in the original format, an error in the standard learning process would occur in bridge-3. It would learn that the source station (in LAN-3) can be normally reached (across the tree) through the port connected to LAN-4. To avoid it, bridge-5 sends the encoded frame

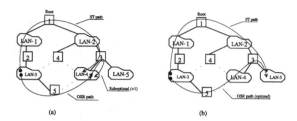

Figure 7. (a) Normal path and OSR suboptimal path (b) Normal path and OSR optimal path.

to bridge-3, which decodes it and sends it back to the destination LAN. Even in this case, OSR sub-optimal route (2 hops) is better than the normal route (3 hops). In some other cases, OSR supplies optimal routes. Figure-7(b) shows an example.

OSR Routing

OSR routing is performed in a distributed way. When a station in a LAN transmits a frame all the bridges connected to that LAN listen to the frame. Every bridge checks the OSR data base and decides if it must route the frame. Only the bridge with the minimal cost to reach the destination station will transmit the frame. If not all the bridges know the destination then the frame is routed through the tree.

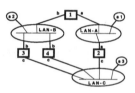

Figure 8. The example topology.

	Bridge-1			Bridge-2			Bridge-3			Bridge-4	
	a	b	data base	a	c	db	b	c	db	b	c
TOTAL info. collected	s1.0.2.1 s2.1.2.1 s3.0.2.0	s1.1.3.0 s1.1.3.1 s3.0.3.1 s3.0.3.0	s1.0.a s2.0.b s3.1.b	s1.1.1.1 s2.0.1.0 s2.1.1.1 s3.1.1.1	s1.1.3.1 s1.1.3.0 s2.0.3.0 s3.0.3.1	s1.0.a s2.1.a s2.1.c s3.0.c	s1.0.1.0 s2.0.1.1 s3.1.1.0	s1.0.3.0 s1.1.2.0 s2.1.2.1 s3.0.2.1	s1.1.c s1.1.b s2.0.b s3.0.c	s1.0.1.0 s2.0.1.1 s3.1.1.0	s1.0.2.0 s2.1.2.0 s3.1.1.0
		s1.1.4.0 s1.1.4.1 s2.0.4.1 s3.0.4.0			s1.1.4.1 s1.1.4.0 s2.0.4.1 s3.0.4.1		s1.1.4.1 s1.1.4.1 s2.0.4.1 s3.0.4.0	s1.1.4.1 s1.1.4.0 s2.0.4.0 s3.0.4.1		s1.1.3.0 s1.1.3.1 s2.0.3.1 s3.0.3.0	s1.1.3.0 s1.1.3.1 s2.0.3.0 s3.0.3.1

Table 3. Results from learning process (bottomline of Table-2).

Figure-8 shows the example topology used in the learning process. Let us assume that station "s1" in LAN-A transmits a frame towards station "s3" in LAN-C. All the bridges of the LAN-A listen to the frame and consult their data bases. Table-3 summarizes the knowledge of all the bridges on the bridged LAN. Bridge-1 checks its data base (columns labeled "Bridge-1") in the places pointed to by the arrows. From the data collected by port-a (the port where the frame was read from) bridge-1 knows that bridge-2 can reach station "s3" at cost=0 ("s3.0.2.0"). Furthermore, bridge-1 knows that it can reach "s3" with cost=1 ("s3.1.b"). Therefore bridge-1 will not re-transmit the frame. Bridge-2 also checks its data base. Bridge-2 has the same knowledge as bridge-1 and decides to route the frame through its port-c ("s3.0.c"). It is the best choice.

An interesting case arises when two or more bridges have the same minimal cost to reach a station. In this case a special procedure is used in order to distribute the traffic between them. For example (in Figure-8) if station "s2" transmits to station "s3" both bridges 3 and 4 are in the optimal route. The bridges must be able to take a coherent decision so that one bridge transmits and the other(s) not. The idea is to use information from a field of the frame to transmit. For example, bridges can use the operation module 2 (in general module N) over the CRC field. If result is "0" the first bridge (bridge-3 in this case) transmits and if result is "1" the second one transmits. A similar procedure can be used when more bridges are located in the optimal path.

3. OSR Protocol Performance Evaluation

In this section we evaluate the performance of the OSR protocol versus the ST using simulation. The simulation was carried out with both protocols, OSR and ST. The simulator was implemented in "C" language using the SMPL libraries [7]. SMPL is the base of other widely extended simulation programs like SIMPACK, CSIM, SIM++.

3.1. System Model

The standard and OSR bridges can work with any 802.2 compatible LAN technology but, in order to simplify the network models, we only used Ethernet (10 Mbps) and FDDI (100 Mbps) LANs.

Regarding the bridge technology, we assumed that both, ST and OSR bridges have the same performance. That is, both bridges are able to process 100% of the maximal theoretical throughput of the LANs they are connected to. Obviously, OSR bridges have to do more work than ST bridges but we assume both bridges are smart enough [8], [9]. Therefore, bridges never reach the saturation point and overflow will always be observed in LANs.

Load Characterization

Frame traffic in the bridged LAN is generated by:

(1) Stations:

We assume that one third of the frames are 64 bytes long and two third of them are 1500-byte long bulk frames. We take the Ethernet 1500-byte frame as the maximum size of the frame in any bridged LAN because it is the smallest maximum of all IEEE-802.2 compatible LANs.

Traffic is 50% local and 50% remote. The latter is uniformly distributed over the remaining LANs of the bridged LAN. Of course, this distribution is arbitrary. We tried to model the fact that usual resources (backup, file servers for diskless stations, etc.) are local, but new multimedia applications (like video conference, tele-presence, etc.) are remote by nature.

Frames are generated according to a Poisson process with mean l.

(2) Bridges:

Traffic is generated depending on which protocol is implemented. ST bridges transmit a control frame every 2 seconds (typical).

OSR bridges transmit a OSR control frame every second in addition to the control frames required for the ST protocol.

Hierarchical Model

In order to simplify the model of the bridged LAN, we have used a hierarchical model with two simulation levels. At the lower level, a closed model has been used to simulate Ethernet and FDDI LANs carefully. In this system a number of N clients ask for service and, once served, ask for service again and again with zero delay time. The value obtained for the throughput is used at the higher level.

At the higher level, a LAN is modeled as a M/M/1 queue with a variable service rate -the calculated throughput. Thus, the station that model the LAN is a Flow Equivalent Service Center (FESC) [10], [11].

The bridge model is a M/M/1 queue with a fixed service rate m. The inputs are all the frames transmitted in the LANs connected to it. The output can be null (the bridge does not route) or towards one of the LANs.

Finally, all simulations have been done with a confidence level of 95% (+/- 3.5%) using the replication method. The unit of time used in the simulations has been the time to transmit a 1Kbyte frame, that is, 0.8192 msec. with 10Mbps LANs, or 81.92 msec. with 100Mbps LANs.

3.2. Performance Evaluation

We present three studies: (1) To know what is the minimal loop topology for which it is worth to use OSR. (2) To know the OSR behavior over a medium size network, and (3) to compare a current backbone-based network with ST vs. a regular topology with OSR. From these studies, we analyzed the station-to-station average delay.

Study-1: Minimal topology adequate for OSR

An advantage for OSR is that it can use all the lines in a loop topology, but there are two drawbacks: (1) traffic increment due to OSR protocol -especially when no reliable MAC technology (i.e. Ethernet) is used-, and (2) the use of sub-optimal routes. Therefore, it may happen that OSR exhibits worse performance than ST over small loop topologies. To check it we use a 3-LAN ring (Figure-9) because it is the smallest loop topology.

Figure-10 shows the station to station mean delay using ST and OSR. On Y-axis, the delay is represented as a relative value with respect to the minimal delay to transmit a 1K frame between two local stations. So, the range 1 to 10 corresponds to a very good delay, the range from 10 to 100

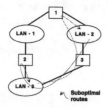

Figure 9. Original ring topology.

corresponds to an acceptable delay, and the range over 100 is unacceptable.

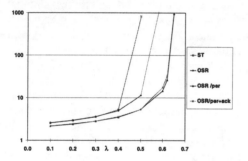

Figure 10. 3-ring. Station to station average delay.

The figure includes the performance curves of an hypothetical OSR perfect protocol (OSR/per) that always routes frames through optimal routes and OSR perfect protocol but including the cost of a reliable transfer protocol when location messages are transmitted (OSR/per+ack). The main conclusions are: (1) Differences between OSR/per and OSR/per+ack are minimal, therefore reliable transmission of location messages does not produce an important overhead -as we anticipated. (2) Sub-optimal routes are the main reason why OSR does not achieve better performance, but it is important to note that the overhead due to sub-optimal routes diminishes when routes are longer. (In the study, the normal routes only have one hop but sub-optimal routes have two hops). (3) OSR improves the performance obtained by ST even in this smallest ring, so OSR can be used successfully in any topology with loops.

Study-2: Performance in a medium size topology

In this section, we study the performance of a bridged LAN with 9 LANs using (1) a tree topology (ST) (2) a 2-D mesh (OSR) and (3) a 2-D torus (OSR).

Figure-11 shows the station to station mean delay. As a conclusion, peak throughput can be doubled using a torus with OSR bridges instead of the tree selected by ST protocol. Furthermore, as bridged LAN size increases, the unbalance produced by the tree is higher. So, the advantage of using OSR bridges becomes more evident as network size increases.

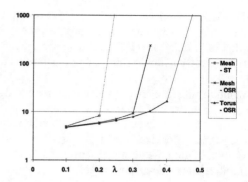

Figure 11. 9-LAN networks. Station to station mean delay.

Study-3: Bridged LAN based on backbone LAN using ST vs. a Cube using OSR

As mentioned, a backbone-based topology can be viewed as a fat tree (Figure-12 (a)). The implementation of a fat tree requires the use of at least two different performance levels for the LANs (for example, FDDI 100 Mbps in a backbone LAN and Ethernet 10 Mbps in the rest of LANs). However, a higher performance could be achieved by using the faster technology for all of the LANs. This study shows the advantage from using a regular topology (a cube in this case) with only one LAN technology and OSR bridges (Figure-12 (b)) instead of using a backbone-based topology with two LAN technologies and standard bridges.

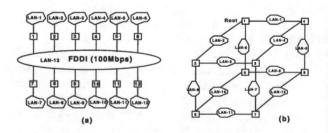

Figure 12. (a) Backbone-based bridged LAN (fat tree). (b) Cube-connected bridged LAN.

Figure-13 shows the station to station mean delay using (1) the cube topology with only 10Mbps LANs, (2) the backbone-based network using 100Mbps in the backbone LAN and 10Mbps in the rest of the LANs, (3) the backbone-based network using 100Mbps for all the LANs, and (4) the cube topology using 100Mbps for all the LANs. As can be seen, the ST cannot take full advantage of the additional bandwidth available in LANs 1 through 12. However, OSR does it, supporting a much higher throughput.

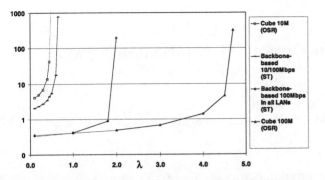

Figure 13. Backbone-based network with ST vs. cube with OSR. Station to station mean delay.

4. Conclusions

Transparent bridges have very interesting properties: they are easy to install and are maintenance free. Unfortunately, current bridges have a very important restriction: they only work on loop free topologies -trees. The standard IEEE-802.1D solution is to avoid the problem. Therefore, the Spanning Tree algorithm is used to transform any topology to a tree. But the tree is not an efficient topology for internetworking. The main problem is the traffic overhead near the root. To overcome it, bridges with multiple ports and fat trees (backbone LANs) are widely used.

A more logical solution is to design a bridge capable of working on topologies with active loops in order to use the same regular topologies used for multicomputer interconnection networks -meshes, hypercube, torus, etc.- or irregular topologies that offer several alternative paths. OSR protocol allows it. An OSR bridge learns "where a station is, in which LAN" instead of "from which direction the station has been listened to" performed by the standard bridge and finally, every bridge knows which line to use to reach each destination station at a minimum cost (optimal route). If there is more that one line with optimal route OSR distributes the traffic between them.

Simulations show the advantage of using regular topologies and OSR bridges vs. trees or even fat trees. With fat trees -like backbone-based networks- the best performing technology has to be kept for the backbone LAN. For example, typical current MAN are bridged LANs that use a FDDI LAN (100Mbps) as backbone and Ethernet (10Mbps) in the rest of LANs. New FAST Ethernet (100Mbps) is commercially available, but if it is used instead of normal Ethernet then FDDI backbone will not be fast enough to carry all the traffic between the rest of LANs. In that case, a backbone LAN with over 1 Gbps must be used. It could be too expensive. Therefore we think that OSR bridges offer a more elegant solution.

OSR also has some drawbacks. Bridges have to do more work; they must implement ST protocol and also OSR protocol. An advantage with OSR bridges is that many ports are not required. Therefore, all data processing capability is used to process frames received from two or three ports.

OSR is effective after the ST has converged and routing information has been propagated through the network. To take full advantage of the scheme, route information must propagate a number of times equal to the diameter of the network. So, if diameter is 7 (maximum diameter recommended by standard IEEE-802.1D) then 14 sec. are required. But this is not a important drawback. When a station is turned on (for example a diskless station), it normally communicates with a local file server and the initialization process usually takes more than 14 sec. When users start to work on it, all OSR bridges in the network know where the station is.

OSR needs that all location messages have a reliable transmission. With some LAN technologies -like Ethernet- this produces some overhead (around 2% in the worst case). So, we think that drawbacks are not very important compared with the advantages.

5. References

References

[1] Perlman R., "Interconnections: Bridges and Routers" Addison-Wesley, 1993.

[2] IEEE, "Mac bridges". ANSI/IEEE Std. 802.1D, 1993 Edition.

[3] Hart J., "Extending the IEEE802.1 MAC bridge standard to remote bridges". IEEE Network. Vol. 2, NO. 1, Jan. 1988.

[4] S. Casale, V. Catania, A. Puliafito and L. Vita, "A Multiple Spanning Tree protocol in bridged LANs".IFIP 1989, Elsevier Science Publishers. North-Holland.

[5] V.Catania, A.Puliafito, L.Vita, "A modular network architecture for performance enhancement in extended local area network". IEEE Transactions on Reliability, Vol.42, No.1, 1993 March.

[6] W.D.Sincoskie, C.J.Cotton, "Extended bridges algorithms for large networks". IEEE Network. Vol.2, No.1, Jan-1988.

[7] MacDougall, "Simulating computing systems, theory and tools". MIT Press, 1987.

[8] Scott O.Bradne, "Ethernet bridges and routers: Faster than fast enough" Data Comm Magazine. Lab Test. February 1992.

[9] M.Zitterbart, A.Tantawy and D.N.Serpanos, "A high performance transparent bridge" IEEE/ACM Trans. on Networking, Vol. 2, No. 4, August 1994.

[10] Chandy K.M., Herzog U., and Woo L., "Parametric Analysis of Queueing Networks". IBM Journal of Research and Development, 19(1), 36-42, 1975.

[11] Raj Jain, "The Art of Computer Systems Performance AnAlysis" Ed. Johm Wiley & Sons, Inc. 1991.

Media Access Protocols For A Scalable Optical Interconnection Network

by Thomas S. Jones and Ahmed Louri
Department of Electrical and Computer Engineering
The University of Arizona
Tucson, AZ 85721
email: louri@ece.arizona.edu

Abstract

Hierarchical optical interconnection networks have the potential of solving the communication bottleneck that has evolved in parallel processing systems due big increases in processor speeds. Hierarchical Optical Ring Interconnection Network (HORN) [12] is one network architecture that was proposed to provide scalability to a larger number of processing nodes (PNs) with low latency and high bandwidth. In HORN PNs are arranged in rings and those rings are grouped together hierarchically in higher level rings. While collisions of data from multiple sources in hierarchical networks like HORN are reduced by separating nodes spatially and by wavelength, they can't be prevented completely and a media access (MAC) protocols must be used to that end. An in depth analysis of five collision-free, single hop protocols is performed in terms of average delay and system throughput. The protocols analyzed are: time division multiple access (TDMA) [13, 14], TDMA with arbitration [12, 13, 14], FatMAC [6], DMON [15], and token hierarchical optical ring network (THORN). The first four protocols are documented in the literature but the fifth, THORN, was developed expressly for HORN. While all the protocols support the scalability objectives of HORN, THORN is shown to have the lowest delay and a throughput comparable to the other four protocols.

1. Introduction

The application of optical fibers to interconnection networks (INs) in parallel processing systems offers the potential to transmit on many wavelengths simultaneously thereby multiplying the number of available data paths. While current optical fiber technology permits simultaneous insertion onto a single fiber of about 20 wavelengths [1, 4], arranging networks hierarchically further increases the number of channels that can operate simultaneously by reusing these same 20 wavelengths over and over in por-

tions of a network that are separated spatially [3, 16]. This approach is also supported by conclusions by Bell [2], Dandamudi [5] and Goodman [7] that PNs engage in data transfers more frequently with nearby neighbors than with more distant ones.

HORN is a hierarchical optical IN we presented previously [12], that uses a ring of rings topology. Processing nodes (PNs) are connected by optical fibers in rings of up to 20 PNs and these first level rings are interconnected at routing nodes to form rings of local rings. This process is repeated recursively to form higher levels in the hierarchy as many times as necessary to meet the wavelength limitation for the desired number of PNs. A simple example of HORN is shown in Figure 1 in which 234 PNs are connected in a three layer hierarchy. The main objective is to obtain a network that is scalable with low delay and high throughput for data transmissions.

Wavelength division multiple access (WDMA) is also used in HORN to separate nodes or subrings on the same ring by wavelength. At the first level each node is assigned a unique wavelength for reception; a source selects a destination by transmitting on the wavelength assigned to the destination. At the higher levels a wavelength is uniquely assigned to each *ring* of PNs, or ring of rings of PNs, depending on the level at which communication occurs. At these higher levels special routing nodes are used to route messages optically.

Although WDMA provides multiple data paths, thereby reducing communication contentions, they can't be prevented completely in HORN without some method to regulate access to each channel. A MAC protocol is necessary to prevent two sources from attempting to transmit to the same destination simultaneously.

Two classes of MAC protocols were deemed unacceptable for HORN. Most MAC protocols in use today are multi-hop in nature since some processing of each packet must be performed at each intermediate node to determine where the packet should be routed next [9]. HORN, by its very nature, is a single hop architecture; messages are

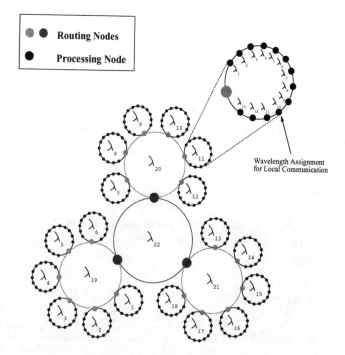

Wavelength Assignment
for Local Communication

Figure 1. Sample HORN interconnection network showing wavelength assignment.

mined by the length of each slot and by the number of slots needed, i.e. the number of nodes that need access to the channel, which varies under HORN according to the level in the hierarchy. If there are N_i nodes at level i in the hierarchy then cycle length is $N_i \times T_D$ where T_D is the data packet length in seconds of transmission time. The length of a time slot is a design issue and is primarily determined by the average message length. Figure 2 shows a typical channel and slot assignment for HORN using TDMA.

λ_1	P_1	P_4	P_3	P_2
λ_2	P_2	P_1	P_4	P_3
λ_3	P_3	P_2	P_1	P_4
λ_4	P_4	P_3	P_2	P_1
	Time Slot 1	Time Slot 2	Time Slot 3	Time Slot 4

Time Scale

Figure 2. Typical TDMA slot assignment for a structure with 4 nodes.

sent from source to destination without any intermediate electronic processing. Therefore multi-hop MAC protocols are unacceptable for HORN. Many protocols today also allow collisions to occur, requiring some collision detection mechanism and retransmission when collisions occur. Since we are attempting to maximize throughput, i. e. maximize the number of successful data transmissions, collision based MAC protocols are also unacceptable in HORN.

Four collision-free, single hop protocols presented in the literature [6, 12, 13, 14, 15] were selected for in depth analysis in terms of delay, throughput and node complexity. They are time division multiple access (TDMA), TDMA with arbitration, FatMAC and DMON. An additional protocol, called Token Hierarchical Optical Ring Network (THORN), is presented for the first time in this paper and is also analyzed against the same parameters.

2. Protocol Descriptions

2.1. TDMA

Under TDMA each cycle is divided into time slots and each node is assigned a slot, in turn, during which it has exclusive access to a channel for transmission. This process is repeated for every channel at all levels of the hierarchy in HORN. The length of a TDMA cycle is therefore deter-

2.2. TDMA with Arbitration

TDMA with arbitration is a variation on TDMA in which there are fewer time slots assigned to a level than there are nodes contending for access, requiring reservation or arbitration of the available slots. This has the potential advantage of greatly reducing the number of empty data slots when compared with pure TDMA.

2.3. FatMAC

FatMAC [6] is also a reservation or arbitration protocol but it is more sophisticated than TDMA/arbitration. Data slot reservation is broadcast optically in the first time slot, called the control slot, on each data channel. FatMAC uses a different approach than TDMA or TDMA/arbitration in assigning nodes and channels, channel assignment is *dynamic* with respect to destination nodes and sources reserve the first available slot on any channel in use at the level of transmission. This means that one slot is reserved on every channel before a second slot is reserved on any channel and that cycle lengths can vary by no more than one packet length between channels on the same ring.

2.4. DMON

DMON is a token based protocol presented by Pinkston [15] and is probably the most complicated protocol to be assessed here in terms of the hardware required at each node but it's a relatively simple protocol algorithmically. Any node may transmit on a data channel once it has reserved access on the control channel, but access to the control channel is controlled by a token on a dedicated channel. The same token also controls access to a dedicated broadcast channel, so a node may broadcast or transmit a reservation request each time it acquires the token, but not both. The procedure a node follows to transmit a data or broadcast packet is as follows: 1) node acquires token, 2) node transmits slot reservation on the control channel, 3) node releases token, and 4) node transmits data on the reserved channel (see Figure 3).

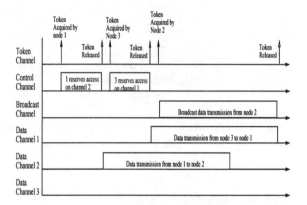

Figure 3. Timing diagram for DMON, only three data channels shown.

2.5. THORN

In this paper we propose a new protocol called Token Hierarchical Optical Ring Network (THORN) that is a variation of the token ring and DMON protocols. There is one dedicated token channel for each level of the hierarchy which is shared by all nodes at that level and the tokens for each of the data channels circulate on this channel as a packet. In order to allow a node to hold a channel (token) for multiple cycles, the token packet has a busy field and a request field. A token is acquired when a node discovers that the appropriate busy bit is clear and sets it. Once a node acquires a token it can hold the token and the corresponding channel until another node requests them by setting the appropriate request bit. The procedure a node follows to transmit a data packet is as follows: 1) node acquires the necessary token on the token channel, if the token can't be acquired immediately it is requested by setting the coresponding request bit, 2) Node transmits on the channel for which the token was acquired, and 3) node releases the token. Figure 4 shows a sample timing diagram for THORN.

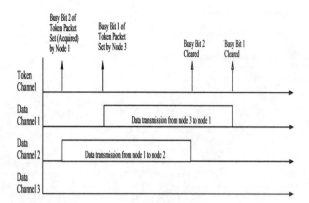

Figure 4. Sample timing diagram for THORN. Request bit usage is not shown.

3. Average Delay

3.1. TDMA

Average delay is defined as the expected delay in transmitting a message from any source node to any destination node, and includes data packet transmission time, time packet must wait in the output queue, and end-to-end transmission time of the network. For TDMA it will also include the time a node must wait for its dedicated slot to materialize on the channel. Spragins [17] gives an expression for average delay in a TDMA system:

$$D = \frac{X}{R} + \frac{NX}{2R} + \frac{NX}{2R}\frac{\rho}{1-\rho} + \tau \qquad (1)$$

Where X is the packet length in bits, R is the transmission rate in bits per second, τ is the end-to-end transmission time for the system, and ρ is the ratio of the average arrival rate, γ, to the average service rate, μ. The quantity $\frac{X}{R}$ is the length of time it takes to transmit a data packet of X bits at R bits per second. T_D is used for this quantity hereafter.

It can be shown for realistic numbers in HORN that τ is much less than T_D, so it's dropped from this Equation (1). In a network of 1000 contiguous nodes spaced 1 meter apart τ is on the order of $5\mu sec$ while even a small data packet of 100 kbits transmitted at 100 Mbits/sec has a transmission time (T_D) of 1 msec.

N is the number of slots in the cycle and for TDMA is the same as the number of nodes. In a hierarchical system the value to use for N will vary because communication is taking place simultaneously in many locations that require different numbers of slots, based on the level at which communication takes place, and we need to account for that in Equation (1). If we define communication locality, ℓ, as the number of data packets sent at level i versus the total number of data packets to be sent at higher levels in the hierarchy then the effective value for N for a system with r levels is:

$$N_{eff} \equiv \text{Effective (average) number of TDMA slots}$$

$$= \ell \sum_{i=1}^{r-1} n^i(1-\ell)^{i-1} + n^r(1-\ell)^{r-1} \quad (2)$$

With this we can calculate the average expected delay for TDMA in HORN:

$$D^{<TDMA>} = T_D \left(1 + \frac{N_{eff}}{2} + \frac{\rho N_{eff}}{2(1-\rho)} \right) \quad (3)$$

The first term in Equation (3) represents the length of time it takes to transmit to data packet, the second term is the average delay due to waiting for the assigned time slot to materialize, and the last term is the queuing delay.

3.2. TDMA With Arbitration

Average access delay for TDMA/arbitration will be the same as for TDMA except that the effective number of nodes will be much lower since there are fewer slots than nodes competing for them and there will be a term to account for the delay due to arbitration:

$$D^{<TDMA/arb>} = T_D + T_{queue} + \frac{1}{2}T_{channel} \quad (4)$$

The first two terms appear in the delay equation for pure TDMA. The last term, $\frac{1}{2}T_{channel}$, includes both the delay due to waiting for the assigned slot to materialize and the delay due to arbitration for the channel. $T_{channel}$ can then be expressed as:

$$T_{channel} = NT_D + Nt^* \quad (5)$$

As stated previously, the number of slots, N, will be much less than for pure TDMA. If there is one slot for every k_2 nodes then N becomes $\frac{N_{eff}}{k_2}$. The second term, Nt^*, is the arbitration time needed per node in a structure multiplied by the number of nodes to reflect the fact that as more nodes are added to a ring, more arbitration time will be needed; This will be a direct function of the number of nodes in the structure versus the number of slots available, but is also affected by other parameters such as processor speed. If we equate T_D to t^* by a constant, k_1, we obtain:

$$T_{channel} = NT_D(1 + k_1) \quad (6)$$

Combining Equations (4) and (5) and substituting $\frac{N_{eff}}{k_2}$ in for N as noted above yields:

$$D^{<TDMA/arb>} = T_D \left(1 + \frac{N_{eff}\rho}{2k_2(1-\rho)} \right)$$

$$+ T_D \left(\frac{N_{eff}(1-k_1)}{2k_2} \right) \quad (7)$$

Note that this reverts to Equation (3), the average delay in a pure TDMA system, when there is exactly one slot per cycle for every node in the structure ($k_2 = 1$) and no arbitration ($k_1 = 0$).

3.3. FatMAC

Average delay for FatMAC is the sum of data packet transmission time, queue wait time and average time until the next control slot, since a data packet may arrive at the output buffer at any time in the cycle:

$$D^{<FatMAC>} = T_D + \left(\frac{T_C + CT_D}{2} \right)$$

$$+ \left(\frac{T_C + CT_D}{2} \frac{\rho}{1-\rho} \right) \quad (8)$$

Where C is average cycle length in number of packets and is determined by the average arrival rate, the number of channels available and the number of nodes with messages to send. C can therefore be rather difficult to calculate since it changes dynamically under FatMAC. C is a ceiling function in that cycle length will increase by one for every Λ_i messages to be transmitted in a cycle, where Λ_i is the number of channels available to a structure at level i. If Λ_i is held constant at some value, Λ_0, for every layer and every structure at each layer then C is given by:

$$C = \left\lceil \frac{\gamma N_{eff}}{\Lambda_0} \right\rceil \quad (9)$$

The length of the control packet, T_C, is determined by the design and can be referenced to the data packet length:

$$T_D = LT_C \quad (10)$$

Substituting this into Equation (8) gives an expression for the average expected delay under FatMAC in terms of the data packet length:

$$D^{<FatMAC>} = T_D \left(1 + \frac{(1 + CL)}{2L(1-\rho)} \right) \quad (11)$$

3.4. DMON

An equation for average delay for a token based or polled protocol is given by Spragins [17]. The delay to acquire the token and transmit a control or broadcast packet is given by:

$$D_c = \frac{Y}{R} + \overline{\tau} + \frac{t'(1 - \frac{\rho}{M})}{2(1-\rho)} + \frac{\rho}{2(1-\rho)}\frac{Y}{R} \quad (12)$$

Where $\overline{\tau}$ is the average node to node transmission delay, M is the number of nodes and is equal to N_{eff} for HORN, Y is the length of the control packet in bits, and t' is the ring delay, that is the delay due to handling the token or polling all the nodes. The quantity $\frac{Y}{R}$ in this case is the length of the control packet in seconds, to which we previously assigned the variable T_C. We can again relate T_C and T_D by Equation (10). As assumed previously, $\overline{\tau}$ is usually much smaller than the other terms and can be ignored. The ring delay as given by Spragins is:

$$t' = \overline{\tau}N_{eff} + \frac{B}{R}N_{eff} \qquad (13)$$

Where B is the bit delay per node and R is the transmission rate in bits per second. The first term here $\overline{\tau}N_{eff}$ here is dropped and $\frac{B}{R}$ can be related to T_D by a constant since the bit delay in a network should be relatively constant and much less than T_D to keep overhead low:

$$t' = N_{eff}kT_D \qquad (14)$$

The constant k should be small, substantially less than one since it will be a design issue to keep the ring delay much lower than the data packet transmission time to minimize overhead. The effective number of system nodes, N_{eff}, is retained in this equation to reflect that fact that the ring delay will be a function of the number of system nodes and how those nodes are arranged.

However, Equation (12) only accounts for the delay to send the control packet or to broadcast a message. For point to point transmissions there will be additional term to account for the delay to send the data packet comprised of the queuing delay and the data packet transmission time. Note that the delay due to waiting for a time slot to materialize is absent since this is not time slotted protocol; once a node has captured the token it has exclusive access to the channel. The queuing delay in this case will be for a system with arbitrary or random arrival time and fixed service times [8, 10, 11]. This queuing delay and data transmission delay is given by:

$$
\begin{aligned}
D_d &= \frac{\rho^2}{2\gamma(1-\rho)} + T_D \\
&= \left[\frac{\rho}{2(1-\rho)} + 1\right]T_D \qquad (15)
\end{aligned}
$$

So for HORN, the average delay for DMON is given by:

$$
\begin{aligned}
D^{<DMON>} &= D_c + D_d \\
&= \frac{T_D(2-\rho)}{2(1-\rho)}\left(1 + \frac{1}{L}\right) \\
&\quad + \frac{T_Dk}{2(1-\rho)}(N_{eff} - \rho) \qquad (16)
\end{aligned}
$$

3.5. THORN

The expression given by Spragins (Equation (12) above) also applies here but the token is referenced to the data channel rather than the control channel:

$$
\begin{aligned}
D^{<THORN>} &= \frac{X}{R} + \overline{\tau} + \frac{t'(1-\frac{\rho}{M})}{2(1-\rho)} \\
&\quad + \frac{\rho}{2(1-\rho)}\frac{X}{R} \qquad (17)
\end{aligned}
$$

The variable X has replaced the Y in the previous form of this equation because it now represents the length of the *data* packet in bits. Consequently $\frac{X}{R}$ represents the data packet transmission time, which we previously defined as T_D. As with DMON, $\overline{\tau}$ is dropped because it is much smaller than the other terms and the ring delay is given by:

$$t' = N_{eff}kT_D \qquad (18)$$

Communication locality still determines the effective number of nodes participating at a given level so the effective number of nodes in the system with data to transmit is given by Equation (2). We can therefore substitute N_{eff} into Equation (17) for M. Making these substitutions and equating t' to T_D by Equation (14) yields:

$$
\begin{aligned}
D^{<THORN>} &= \frac{T_D(2-\rho)}{2(1-\rho)} \\
&\quad + \frac{T_Dk}{2(1-\rho)}(N_{eff} - \rho) \qquad (19)
\end{aligned}
$$

3.6. Summary of Average Delay Analysis

The average delay for the five protocols analyzed is graphed in Figure 5 as a function of the offered load and in Figure 6 as a function of the number of nodes for a system with data packet length of 1 millisecond. In Figure 5 the number of nodes is 1000; in Figure 6 the offered load is 0.5. Delays for THORN and DMON are nearly identical and are about ten times better than the nearest competitor, FatMAC. In contrast, the delay for TDMA is about 100 times longer than for THORN or DMON.

4. System Throughput

System throughput is generally accepted as a valuable metric for interconnection networks, yet few authors attempt to quantify it since it's affected by many factors that are difficult to fix except in very specific systems [3]. It is therefore with no small amount of trepidation that we attempt to assess these protocols in terms of system throughput. We are considering specific protocols on a specific type

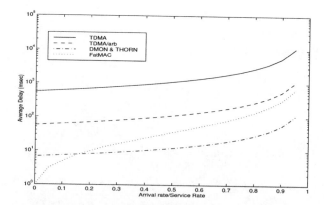

Figure 5. Delay as a function of the offered load for a hierarchy with three layers and a 1 msec data packet length (T_D).

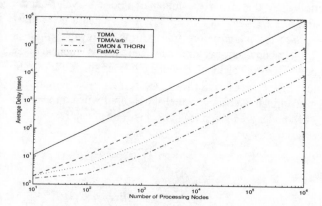

Figure 6. Delay as a function of the number of nodes for a hierarchy with three layers and a 1 msec data packet length (T_D).

of network and therefore can fix enough parameters to make the analysis valid and meaningful.

Using Equation (2) for the effective number of nodes in our system gives an expected throughput rate per channel:

$$S = \gamma N_{eff} \qquad (20)$$

For each of the protocols considered the average service rate is the inverse of the cycle length as only one message can be transmitted by each node in a cycle. Therefore we can quantify the system throughput in a way that is meaningful and will allow comparisons between the protocols by fixing the cycle lengths.

4.1. TDMA

The cycle length for TDMA is a simple term, each channel has n_i slots of length T_D in each cycle. We can again apply Equation (2) to give the effective number of slots across the entire system. Throughput for each channel under TDMA can therefore be expressed as:

$$
\begin{aligned}
S^{<TDMA>} &= \gamma N_{eff} \\
&= \rho \mu N_{eff} \\
&= \frac{\rho N_{eff}}{N_{eff} T_D} \\
&= \frac{\rho}{T_D} \qquad (21)
\end{aligned}
$$

This result says that the maximum channel throughput for TDMA is 1 packet for every period of time equal to the packet length in seconds, a result which should be apparent at least intuitively.

Maximum system throughput will be the maximum value possible for Equation (21) multiplied by the effective number of channels in the system. Channel throughput is maximum when ρ is its maximum value of one. Like N_{eff}, the effective number of channels in a system (Λ_{eff}) is determined by the communication locality of the system but is also determined by the number of channels available at each level. In HORN there is one channel assigned to each subring on a ring at any given level such that there are n channels at the highest level, n^2 channels at the next level down, n^3 at the third level down, and in general there are n^{r+1-i} channels at level i where $i = 1$ for the local level and $i = r$ for the highest level in a hierarchy of r levels. The channels at level i are used some percentage of the time based on ℓ, the communication locality. If communication were 100% local ($\ell = 1$) then Λ_{eff} would be equal to n^r because all communication would take place on the local rings. Conversely, if communication were 0% local, that is all communication occurring at the highest level of the hierarchy, then Λ_{eff} would be equal to n. Stated formally:

$$\Lambda_{eff} = \ell \sum_{i-2}^{r} n^i (1 - \ell)^{r=i} + n(1 - \ell)^{r-1} \qquad (22)$$

System throughput for HORN under TDMA is therefore given by:

$$S_T^{<TDMA>} = \frac{\rho}{T_D} \Lambda_{eff} \qquad (23)$$

4.2. TDMA with Arbitration

System throughput for TDMA/arbitration is also similar to pure TDMA with the added overhead due to arbitration but a reduced cycle length. Cycle length for TDMA/arbitration is $\frac{N_{eff}}{k_2}(1 + k_1)T_D$ which comes directly from the average delay equation. The constant k_2 is the ratio of the number of slots in pure TDMA to the number of slots in TDMA/arbitration and the constant k_1 is the ratio of the arbitration time per node requesting access to the data packet length in seconds. The throughput per channel under TDMA/arbitration is therefore given by:

$$S^{<TDMA/arb>} = \frac{N_{eff}}{k_2}\gamma$$

$$= \frac{\frac{N_{eff}}{k_2}\rho}{\frac{N_{eff}}{k_2}T_D(1+k_1)}$$

$$= \frac{\rho}{T_D(1+k_1)} \quad (24)$$

The number of channels and the communication locality are unchanged for TDMA/arbitration so the system throughput is given by Equation (24) multiplied by Λ_{eff}:

$$S_T^{<TDMA/arb>} = \frac{\rho\Lambda_{eff}}{T_D(1+k_1)} \quad (25)$$

4.3. FatMAC

Channel throughput for FatMAC will also be a function of C as derived in Equation (9). Cycle length under FatMAC is one control packet plus C data packets in length. Average channel throughput under FatMAC will therefore be:

$$S^{<FatMAC>} = \frac{\rho N_{eff}}{T_C + CT_D}$$

$$= \frac{\rho N_{eff}}{(\frac{1}{L} + C)T_D} \quad (26)$$

Although the effective number of channels under FatMAC is the same as under the other protocols considered so far, FatMAC doesn't use them the same way; channels at a given level aren't used independently of one another. The number of channels operating simultaneously in the system is reduced by Λ_0 over the other protocols as FatMAC fills the first slot in each channel before it lengthens the cycle. For this reason the throughput per channel is multiplied by Λ_{eff} and divided by Λ_0 to obtain the system throughput:

$$S_T^{<FatMAC>} = \frac{\Lambda_{eff}}{\Lambda_0}\frac{\rho N_{eff}}{(\frac{1}{L} + C)T_D} \quad (27)$$

4.4. DMON

Unlike the other protocols considered so far, DMON requires a control packet transmission for every data packet transmission which in turn requires acquiring the token for every data packet transmission. The cycle length therefore is $T_C + T_D + t'$, where t' is given by (14). When the average number of nodes transmitting is M then the channel throughput is given by:

$$S^{<DMON>} = \frac{M\rho}{M(T_C + T_D + t')}$$

$$= \frac{\rho}{(\frac{1}{L} + 1 + kN_{eff})T_D} \quad (28)$$

This yields a system throughput given by:

$$S_T^{<DMON>} = \frac{\rho\Lambda_{eff}}{(\frac{1}{L} + 1 + k)T_D} \quad (29)$$

4.5. THORN

As with the other protocols the channel throughput for THORN is equal to the average arrival rate per node multiplied by the effective number of nodes. Cycle lengths and service rates vary under THORN. When a node must acquire the token before transmitting the cycle length is $T_D + t'$; but when streaming can occur, that is when no other node needs the channel, then the cycle length goes down to just T_D. Under heavier loads the former cycle length will predominate and the channel throughput when an average of M nodes are using the channel will be given by:

$$S^{<THORN>} = \frac{M\rho}{M(T_D + t')}$$

$$= \frac{\rho}{(1 + kN_{eff})T_D} \quad (30)$$

This yields a system throughput given by:

$$S_T^{<THORN>} = \frac{\rho\Lambda_{eff}}{(1 + kN_{eff})T_D} \quad (31)$$

4.6. Summary of System Throughput

System throughput for the five protocols is graphed in Figure 7 as a function of the offered load and in Figure 8 as a function of the number of system nodes for a three level system with a data packet length of 1 millisecond. Locality (ℓ) for both figures is 0.5 for each level. Throughput for FatMAC is very nearly constant for all loads since the cycle length will vary with the offered load and there are very few empty slots. System throughput for DMON and THORN were expected to be much higher, but these results indicate that the ring delay has a significant impact on throughput and consequently must be held much lower than expected.

5. Conclusions

TDMA, TDMA/arbitration, FatMAC, DMON and THORN were analyzed in terms of delay and system

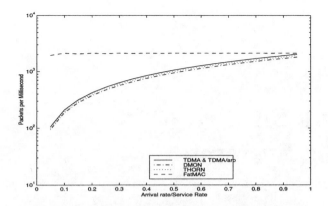

Figure 7. System throughput as a function of the offered load for a three level hierarchy.

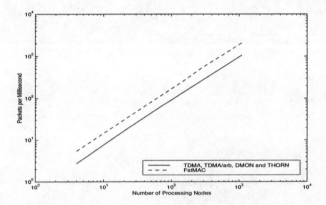

Figure 8. System throughput as a function of the number of nodes for a hierarchy with three layers.

throughput. Clearly THORN and DMON are the preferred protocols with respect to average delay, outperforming Fat-MAC by a factor of about ten at loads above about 0.5 and outperforming the TDMA based protocols by a factor of about 100 at all offered loads. In terms of throughput, most of the protocols performed about the same but FatMAC was shown to be the best at low offered loads due to the variable cycle length. For loads above about 0.5 this advantage was reduced to only about twice the system throughput of the other protocols.

HORN is scalable under any of the protocols analyzed as can be seen from Figures 6 and 8. Delay and throughput both increase linearly or very nearly linearly for all protocols as the number of PNs is increased. THORN was selected for use in HORN based on the above considerations.

References

[1] M. Adda. A Scalable Multibus Configuration for Connecting Transputer Links. *IEEE Transactions on Parallel and Distributed Systems*, 8:245 – 263, March 1997.

[2] G. Bell. Ultracomputers: A Teraflop Before Its Time. *Communication of the ACM*, 35:27 – 47, August 1992.

[3] C. Brackett. Dense Wavlength Division Multiplexing Networks: Principles and Applications. *IEEE Journal on Selected Areas in Communications*, 8:948 – 964, August 1990.

[4] L. A. Buckman. *Applications In Optical Communication: Optical Transmission of Millimeter Wave Signals; and, An All-Optical Wavelength Routed Switching Network*. PhD Dissertation, University of California, Berkeley, 1996.

[5] S. Dandamudi and D. Eager. Hierarchical Interconnection Networks for Multicomputer Systems. *IEEE Transactions on Computers*, 39:786 – 797, June 1990.

[6] P. Dowd, K. Bogineni, K. A. Aly, and J. A. Perreult. Hierarchical Scalable Photonic Architectures For High Performance Processor Interconnection. *IEEE Transactions on Computers*, 42:1105 – 1120, September 1993.

[7] J. W. Goodman, F. Leonberger, S.-Y. Kung, and R. A. Athale. Optical Interconnections for VLSI Systems. *Proceedings of the IEEE*, 72:850 – 866, July 1984.

[8] L. Gorney. *Queuing Theory: A Problem Solving Approach*. Petrocell Books, New York, 1982.

[9] K. Hwang. *Advanced Computer Architecture: Parallelism, Scalability, Programability*. McGraw-Hill Book Company, New York, 1993.

[10] L. Kleinrock. *Communication Nets: Stochastic Message Flow and Delay*. McGraw-Hill Book Company, New York, 1964.

[11] G. Louchard and G. Latouche. *Probability Theory and Computer Science*. Academic Press, New York, 1983.

[12] A. Louri and R. Gupta. Hierarchical Optical Interconnection Network (HORN): Scalable Interconnection Network for Multiprocessors and Multicomputers. *Applied Optics*, 36:430 – 442, January 1997.

[13] N. Maxenchuck. Twelve Random Access Strategies for Fiber Optic Networks. *IEEE Transactions on Computers*, 36:942 – 995, August 1988.

[14] B. Mukherjee. Architectures and Protocols for WDM-based Local Lightwave Networks, Part I: Single Hop Systems. *IEEE Network*, pages 12 – 27, May 1992.

[15] T. Pinkston and C. Kuznia. Smart Pixel-Based Network Interface Chip. *Applied Optics*, 36:4871 – 4880, 10 July 1997.

[16] K. Sivalingam and P. Dowd. A Multilevel WDM Access Protocol For An Optically Interconnected Multiprocessor System. *IEEE Journal of Lightwave Technology*, 13:2152 – 2167, November 1995.

[17] J. Spragins, J. Hammond, and D. Powlikowski. *Telecommunications: Protocols and Design*. Addison-Wesley Publishing Co., Reading, MA, 1991.

Session 5A
Multimedia Systems

Chair: Yoonho Park
IBM T.J. Watson Research

An Empirical Study of Admission Control Strategies in Video Servers

Tzi-cker Chiueh
Computer Science Department
State University of New York at Stony Brook
chiueh@cs.sunysb.edu

Michael Vernick
Bell Laboratories, Lucent Technology
vernick@dnrc.bell-labs.com

Abstract

A video server guarantees the I/O bandwidth required for the smooth playback of a video access request once it has been admitted into the system. To ensure that new video access requests will not jeopardize the bandwidth guarantees promised to existing streams, an admission control module that decides whether a new request should be granted based on the resource usage is essential in the design of video servers. This paper presents a general framework in which video server admission control algorithms can be described in terms of how I/O delays are estimated. Then five specific admission control algorithms are studied in detail. The performances of these algorithms are analyzed in the context of an operational disk-array-based video server called SBVS. Detailed measurements from actual implementations of these admission control algorithms are used to compare their performances in terms of the maximum numbers of streams that can be admitted without causing overloads. One surprising result from this work is that the performance gap between the statistical and deterministic algorithms is between 10% to 40%, which is much smaller than were reported in earlier work.

1. Introduction

A video server services requests to play back video sequences by guaranteeing the required bandwidth throughout the life time of the entire playback sessions. To ensure new video requests would not disturb the guarantees offered to previously granted requests, a video server relies on an *admission control* module to determine whether the addition of the new stream will affect the real-time guarantees of existing streams. If there is not enough bandwidth to service the new stream, the stream is not allowed to enter the system, and the user's request is denied. The design goal a video server's admission control module is to optimize the number of video streams being serviced simultaneously without breaking any disk I/O bandwidth guarantees previously promised. Although absolute bandwidth guarantees are useful from the applications' standpoints,

they are neither necessary nor desirable for designing video servers, because of other considerations such as buffering and perception tolerances.

Ferrari [4] has proposed three levels of *quality of service* (QOS) for multimedia network designs, which are equally applicable to video server design and are used in this study. In the *Deterministic* level, all deadlines are guaranteed to be met. For this level of service the server's admission control algorithm makes worst-case delay assumptions when admitting new clients. In the *Statistical* level, deadlines are not 100% guaranteed to be met but are usually reliable. To provide such guarantees, admission control algorithms must consider dynamic statistical behavior of the server while admitting new clients. By exploiting the statistical patterns, the *Statistical* approach tends to service more requests than the *Deterministic* approach without noticeable performance degradation. In the *Best Effort* level, no guarantees are given for meeting deadlines. The server just tries its best to service each access, and it continues to admit new requests until the system becomes overloaded.

The rest of this paper is organized as follows. In Section 2, previous works in this area are described to distinguish the unique contributions of this work. Section 3 and 4 present a general framework to estimate disk I/O service time, and the details of five specific algorithms we studied, respectively. In Section 5, we present a comprehensive comparison of the performance results of these admission control algorithms under various systems parameters. Section 6 concludes this paper with a summary of the main results.

2. Related Work

In [5], a deterministic algorithm is compared to a statistical algorithm. Simulations show that the statistical algorithm can service up to 70% more streams than the deterministic algorithm while reducing the overflow probability to the order of 10^{-7}. This work, however, did not describe the statistical algorithm in sufficient detail. [3, 2] compares the performance of two different deterministic algorithms when transporting variable-bit-

313

rate data streams using Constant Time Length (CTL) blocks. The admission control algorithm is more complex when using CTL blocks, than when using Constant Data Length (CDL) blocks. In the first algorithm, actual bit traces of each video stream are used to determine how much data is retrieved during each future cycle. In the second algorithm, statistics about the bit traces are used. Simulations show that the deterministic approach has better reliability. In the simulations, however, the disk seek and rotation times are fixed at worst-case values. The data transfer times are based on average disk transfer bandwidth and do not take into account the different transfer rates available in different portions of the disk surface. [9, 8] presented statistical admission control algorithms, in which new clients are admitted only if the extrapolation from the past measurements of the storage server performance characteristics indicate that the service requirements of all the clients can be met satisfactorily. The service requirement is the percentage of deadlines that can be missed. For example, a client can specify that it can tolerate up to 5% of missed deadlines. The experiments reported are based on simulation results, and do not take into account variables such as head switch and bus transfer overhead. The algorithm also assumes that a CTL media block size is used rather that a CDL media block. When using the statistical algorithm and allowing up to 3% of the cycles to overflow, three times the number of streams can be admitted compared to the deterministic approach. Compared to previous work, the results reported in this paper are new in that they are based on empirical measurements from actual implementations of the admission control algorithms in an operational disk-array video server. Moreover, because SBVS [?] implements a CDL data retrieval strategy, this work focuses on admission control algorithms for CDL-based rather than CTL-based video servers. Finally, this paper presents a general framework to describe and categorize admission control algorithms used in the design and implementation of video servers.

3. I/O Service Time Estimation

SBVS consists of two components: the storage subsystem called VSS and the network subsystem called NS. SBVS uses *cyclic scheduling* where time is divided into I/O cycles of length P_{io}. While the NS is sending data to the client machines over the network during the i-th cycle, the VSS is inserting data into memory with the data needed for the $(i+1)$-th cycle. Let SV_n be the actual service time for the VSS to read from disks into memory the data required to satisfy n streams. Note that SV_n depends on n as well as the videos that are actually accessed by the n streams. For all n streams to be serviced in an uninterrupted fashion, SV_n must

be less than P_{io}. This guarantees that the NS has valid data to send to the clients at the beginning of each cycle. The goal of the VSS admission control policy is to maximize n, while maintaining that $SV_n < P_{io}$ for every cycle.

When a request for a video stream arrives, the admission control algorithm attempts to predict the total service time when the new request is included for service, and bases the admission decision on the result of comparing the predicted service value and P_{io}. If the components of the I/O service time were all deterministic, admission control would be straightforward since it is relatively simple to compute PSV_n. The existence of several non-deterministic components, namely the rotational latency, head switches and track-to-track seeks, complicates the design of admission control algorithms since it is now difficult to calculate the exact values of PSV_n. The goal of this section is to set up a general framework to describe video server admission control algorithms in terms of the delay components of a disk-array-based I/O system.

Because the VSS uses a constant data length (CDL) data retrieval strategy, the data consumption rate in bytes/sec of the j-th stream, C_j, is fixed throughout the entire playback session. Therefore, in any given time duration in which no streams are added, deleted, or paused[1], the amount of data retrieved during any I/O cycle within the duration is constant. Thus, the admission control algorithm is greatly simplified since it only needs to make the prediction once for all future cycles until stream addition, deletion, or pause occurs. If a constant time length (CTL) strategy is used, C_j would vary from cycle to cycle. Consequently the VSS has to predict the service time in *every* cycle.

Assuming ns streams are currently running and the $(ns + 1)$-th stream requests admittance, The predicted total service time when the new stream is admitted is

$$PSV_{ns+1} = PSV_{ns} + Service_{ns+1}$$
$$= \left(\sum_{j=1}^{j=ns} Service_j \right) + Service_{ns+1} \quad (1)$$

The above prediction is based on the sum of the predictions for each active stream and the prediction for the new stream. Thus, the $(ns + 1)$-th stream can be admitted if an only if $PSV_{ns+1} < P_{io}$. In SBVS, if the stream is admitted, it is retrofitted into the current disk schedule to minimize the seek overhead.

The prediction for a single stream j, $Service_j$, has several terms; the time the disk takes to seek from stream $j - 1$ to stream j ($SEEK_{j-1,j}$); the disk rotational latency ($ROTLAT_j$) which is the time to rotate

---

[1] SBVS also supports other VCR-like functions such as fast/slow-forward/rewind.

the disk to the target sector; and the time to transfer the data from the disk medium to the disk cache[2] ($XFER_j$). In modern disks, while the data is being transferred from the disk medium to the disk cache, the data can also be transferred over the disk bus to main memory.

$$Service_j = SEEK_{j-1,j} + ROTLAT_j + XFER_j(X) \quad (2)$$

where X is the amount of data retrieved in each I/O cycle and is equal to $C_j * P_{io}$. The disk seek time is a function of the location of the data to be retrieved. A worst-case seek time or a measured average value can be used in the equation. The rotational latency depends on the location of the data to be retrieved and the speed of the disk. Since disks are always spinning, rotational latency cannot be accurately predicted on a request by request basis. The disk transfer time depends on the location the data, the speed of the disk and the amount of data to be retrieved. In modern disks $DISK_{raw}$ varies depending on the zone of the disk surface in which the retrieved block resides. Rracks on the outside zones of a disk have more sectors than the inside tracks. Measurements show that the bandwidth on the outside of the disk to be about *twice* the bandwidth of the inside of the disk. In addition, when retrieving consecutive sectors it is also possible that a disk read will cause a disk head switch between cylinders and/or a track to track seek if data crosses track boundaries. Let $Z_{sectors}(j)$ be the number of sectors on a track within the zone in which Stream j resides, $Size_{sector}$ the size of a sector, $O_{disk}(j)$ the overhead due to any head switches or track-to-track seeks for transferring Stream j, and ROT be the time for the disk to rotate once. A more accurate estimate of the time to transfer data from the disk medium to the disk cache is:

$$XFER_j(C_j * P_{io}) = \left(\frac{C_i * P_{io}}{Z_{sectors}(j) * Size_{sector}} * ROT \right) + O_{disk}(j) \quad (3)$$

The first term, $\frac{C_i * P_{io}}{Z_{sectors}(j) * Size_{sector}}$ determines the number of disk rotations required to retrieve the data. Multiplying it by ROT gives the total amount of disk transfer time. Although the times to perform a head switch or track-to-track seek are fixed, during retrieval of data for a stream, some cycles may incur this overhead, while others may not.

Equation 2 is the predicted time for servicing an individual stream on a single disk. This assumes that there is no contention when sending data from the disk cache to main memory. It also assumes that the data can be transferred over the disk bus while it is being transferred from the disk medium to the disk cache. However, if there are several disks on the disk bus, only one

---

[2]This is the cache inside the disk drive, not the one in main memory.

```
/* ns is the number of streams currently active
in the system*/
total = 0;
for(i = 0; i < ns + 1; i + +)
    total + = TransferTime(Stream[i] → sectorsToGet);
    +MAX_SEEK + MAX_ROTATION;
if(total < cycleTime)   admit the new stream
else   do not admit the new stream
```

Figure 1: *Deterministic/Worst-Case admission control algorithm. Worst-case values are used for all varying prediction terms.*

disk at a time can send its data to main memory over the bus. On the other hand, the disks work in parallel and can be transferring data from the disk medium into the disk cache while other disks transfer data over the disk bus. For example, in a N-disk system that supports disk striping and for an I/O request size of K bytes, each disk transfers $\frac{K}{N}$ bytes from the disk medium to the disk cache, and the disk bus takes $BUS(K)$ to transfer a total of K bytes serially. Because $C_j * P_{io}$ is the number of bytes to be retrieved by Stream j in one I/O cycle, Equation 2 is modified to be the following for a N-disk array.

$$Service_j = SEEK_{j-1,j} + ROTLAT_j + BUS(C_j * P_{io}) + XFER_j(\frac{C_j * P_{io}}{N}) \quad (4)$$

In summary, the service time for each stream in an I/O cycle is made up of components that can be accurately determined statically (called *tangible* terms) and those that can not (called *non-tangible* terms). The tangible terms are C_j, the consumption rate for Stream j, N, the number of disks, P_{io}, the I/O cycle time, $Size_{sector}$, the size of a disk sector, ROT, the time for a single revolution of the disk, and $BUS(KB)$ the time to transfer KB bytes over the disk bus. The non-tangible terms are $SEEK$, the time to do a disk seek, $ROTLAT$, the rotational latency, O_{disk}, the overhead due to disk head switches and/or track-to-track seeks, and $Z_{sector}()$. Because of the delays contributed by the non-tangible terms cannot be accurately modeled statically, it has to be dynamically estimated for admission control.

4. Admission Control Algorithms

Five different admission control algorithms are described in this section. Each of these algorithms differs in how it estimates values of the terms in Equation 4. Deterministic algorithms assume worst-case values for the non-tangible terms, whereas statistical algorithms estimate non-tangible terms according to run-time measurements from past history. The statistical

TransferTime(totalSectors)

/* Each request is striped across all of the disks in the array */
$sectorsPerDisk = totalSectors/numDisks$

/* Data transfer time is estimated based on the assumption
that video is located on the inner portion of the disk. */
$mediumXfer = \frac{sectorsPerDisk}{INNER\_SECTORS} * ROTATION\_TIME;$

/* A disk I/O may have to cross cylinder or track boundaries
when the retrieval size is larger than the sector size. */
$headSwitch = (\frac{secotrsPerDisk}{INNER\_SECTORS} + 1) * HEAD\_SWITCH;$
$mediumXfer+ = headSwitch;$

/* Calculate the time to transfer the data over the SCSI bus.
The SCSI overhead is measured and included. */
$busXfer = \frac{sectorsPerDisk*SECTOR\_SIZE}{SCSI\_BUS\_TRANSFER}$
$\qquad\qquad + SCSI\_OVERHEAD;$

/* The time for the first disk in a disk array to respond to
a request is the maximum between the time taken to transfer
data from the disk surface to the disk cache and the time
to transfer data from the disk cache to the main memory. */
$firstDisk = MAX(mediumXfer, busXfer);$

/* For the other disks, the transfer off of the medium is
done concurrently with the first disk. So, add in the time
to transfer over the disk bus which must be done serially. */
$otherDisks = (disksPerScsiBus - 1) * busXfer;$

$total = firstDisk + otherDisks;$

Figure 2: *Worst-case time to transfer sectorsToGet blocks from a disk array to main memory.*

algorithms themselves can be further classified according to whether the worst-case or average values of the run-time measurements are used in the estimation.

4.1. Deterministic Worst-Case

Worst-case values are used for each non-tangible term in the I/O service time prediction equation. To be realistic, the SCAN algorithm is assumed. Therefore, instead of the end-to-end seek time, the stream-to-stream seek delay is set to be 6 ms, which is based on the assumption that 20 videos are spaced uniformly across the disk surface. This scheme is not based on any dynamically measured values. The procedure *TransferTime*, shown in Figure 2, estimates the worst-case time for the *VSS* to service data for a video stream. This algorithm is absolutely conservative in that it makes worst-case assumptions about rotational delays, head switches and transfer times, but does not include any disk seek overhead.

/* CalculateStatistics returns the total service time
for *numCycles* cycles and *ns* streams.
It assumes that only one disk in the array takes a full
rotation, and others can start transferring while the
slow disk is rotating. */

$CalculateStatistics(ns, numCycles, totalTime)$
$average = totalTime/numCycles;$
$total = average + (ns * 0.5 * MAX\_ROTATION);$

/* Finally, add a worst case calculation for the new stream.*/
$total+ = TransferTime(Stream[ns] \rightarrow sectorsToGet);$

$if(total < cycleTime)$ admit the new stream
$else$ do not admit the new stream

Figure 3: *Deterministic/Average-Case admission control algorithm.*

4.2. Deterministic/Average-Case

In the previous deterministic algorithm, worst-case values are assigned to all of the terms in the I/O service time prediction, i.e., worst-case seek, rotational delay, and disk overhead for every stream in every cycle. Obviously this is over-conservative. During any period of time, there is an extremely low probability that every request actually takes the worst-case delays. For example, The Deterministic/Average algorithm, uses measured statistics of the running system but will still guarantee that all streams are serviced before their deadlines.

First, a prediction is made on the service time for each of the active streams. Service times over some past window of cycles, *numCycles*, are measured and the average service time is calculated. Note that *CalculateStatistics*() takes *ns*, the number of streams currently in the system, as an argument because *VSS* maintains a separate history of service time measurements for each distinct number of active streams. To be conservative, it is assumed that every disk request takes an additional rotational delay, which is half of the maximum rotation time. This results in a service time estimate that assumes a worst-case rotation delay with other terms derived from measurements. The estimate is done on a stream by stream basis. Finally a worst-case service time estimate of the new stream is added to the estimated service time for the active streams. If the total time is less than the cycle time, the stream is admitted.

4.3. Statistical/Worst-Case

Although the deterministic admission control approach offers 100% performance guarantees, we believe that the users of the *SBVS* are willing to tolerate some missed deadlines such as a few lost frames, or breaks in the audio. Therefore, $SBVS$ takes a statistical approach for admission control.

To estimate the time to service the active streams, PSV_{ns} in Equation 1, the actual service times for ns active streams is measured over some time interval. Depending on the type of statistical admission control, PSV_{ns} can be a worst case, average, or some other calculated value derived from the measured service times. Then the time to service the new stream, $Service_{ns+1}$, is estimated based on the amount of data to be retrieved and the location on the disk. This can be pre-calculated by running benchmark programs that retrieve varying amounts of data from different parts of the disk, or can be based on dynamic statistics or worst-case values. In addition, seek times can also be pre-calculated by measuring and saving the seek times between various zones of a disk. In the Statistical/Worst-Case algorithm shown in Figure 4, the actual service times are measured over some number of cycles. This measurement includes the average service time, the standard deviation, and the maximum service time. In this algorithm, PSV_{ns} is assigned to be the maximum service time measured over the interval. Next, the additional time to service the new stream is estimated using the worst-case time to service a single stream. This is simply the maximum service time divided by the number of active streams. To improve the accuracy of the service time prediction, we choose the final service time prediction to be the larger of the predicted value from running ns streams and the actual measured service times while running $ns + 1$ streams, if they are available.

4.4. Statistical/Average-Case

This algorithm is exactly the same as the previous Statistical/Worst-Case algorithm. Rather than using the maximum service time over some interval, it uses the average service time from the calculated statistics, i.e., *average*. In addition, when predicting the service time for the new stream, the algorithm also uses per-stream average service time, $\frac{average}{ns}$.

4.5. No Prediction

In this algorithm, no prediction is made. The algorithm will allow a new stream to enter if, the subsequent measured service times do not exceed the I/O cycle time.

5. Performance Analysis

5.1. Experiment Methodology

A generator program is run that randomly generates video numbers and starting times. The starting times

```
/* Estimate the service time for the current number of active
streams and its deviation based on past history. */
```
$CalculateStatistics(ns, numCycles, totalTime, stdev, max);$

```
/* Calculate average and standard deviation */
```
$maxServicePerStream = max/numCycles;$
$average = totalTime/numCycles;$

```
/* The SeekTime(f, t) function returns the measured seek time
from stream 'f' to stream 't'. Here we assume that the active
streams are sorted according to their disk locations from the
inside to the outside, and are numbered 0, 1, ..., ns-1.
Location(i) gives the start track number of Stream i.
The new stream is to be inserted between Streams 0 and ns-1 */
```
$if((Location(r) \leq Location(0))\ ||\ (Location(r) \geq Location(ns - 1)))$
    $additional = SeekTime(r, 0) - SeekTime(ns - 1, 0)+$
      $SeekTime(ns - 1, r);$
$else$ /* New stream goes between Streams k-1 and k */
    $additional = SeekTime(k - 1, r) + SeekTime(r, k)-$
      $SeekTime(k - 1, k);$
$endif$

```
/* Use the worst-case measured value for the new stream. */
```
$additional\ += maxServicePerStream;$

```
/* Add additional seek and stdev to the statistical maximum. */
```
$prediction = max + stdev + additional;$

$CalculateStatistics(ns + 1, numCycles, totalTime, stdev, max);$

```
/* Use the greater between the maximum measured time for
ns+1 streams plus the stdev, and the current prediction as
the final service time prediction.
```
$if\ (max + stdev > prediction)\ prediction = max + stdev;$

$if\ (prediction < cycleTime)\quad admit\ the\ new\ stream;$
$else\quad do\ not\ admit\ the\ new\ stream$

Figure 4: *Statistical/Worst-Case admission control algorithm based on the measured maximum service time over some interval.*

are exponentially distributed with a mean time of 10 cycles between each start. The output of the generator program is input to the admission control experiments such that each run of the five experiments uses the same input. The program that runs each experiment simply proceeds in cycles. At the end of each cycle, the service time of the cycle and the number of running streams is saved. The program then checks the generated input to decide if another stream needs to be added, and if so, uses the appropriate admission control algorithm to determine if the stream can be admitted. Each experiment is run so that it takes about one hour. Each algorithm is measured on three I/O subsystem configurations: two disks/one SCSI controller, four disks/two SCSI controllers, and six disks/three SCSI controllers.

Disks	Deterministic Worst-Case	Deterministic Average	Statistical Worst-Case	Statistical Average	No Prediction
2	16	21	24	25(3%)	26(32%)
4	26	29	32	33(4%)	35(66%)
6	31	33	38(.05%)	41(11%)	42(23%)

Table 1: *Admission control performance for an I/O cycle time of 1 second, using a uniformly distributed workload.*

Disks	Deterministic Worst-Case	Deterministic Average	Statistical Worst-Case	Statistical Average	No Prediction
2	21	29	31(2%)	31(8%)	33(99%)
4	35	42	45	46(7%)	46(11%)
6	46	53	58	61(3%)	62(16%)

Table 2: *Admission control performance for a cycle time of 2 second, using a uniformly distributed workload.*

In addition to measuring the maximum number of allowable streams, the percentage of I/O cycles that cannot service all of the streams when the maximum allowable number of streams are running is recorded. An I/O cycle can not service all of the streams if the total time to service the streams is greater than the cycle time. For example, as shown in Table 1 when running the *No Prediction* algorithm on six disks, a maximum of 42 streams were admitted into the system. But when running 42 streams, 23% of the cycles caused an overload. When running 41 streams, no cycles caused an overload.

5.2. Uniformly Distributed Workload

In this experiment there are six videos evenly striped across each disk such that each video takes up one sixth of every disk. Each video is accessed in uniformly distributed manner. When using 2 disks each video is about 30 minutes long. When using 4 disks, each video is an hour long and when using 6 disks, each video is an hour and a half long. With this setup, the physical disk array parameter such as stripe unit size and degree of striping per SCSI bus remain fixed across all three configurations. The bit rate of each stream is 1.5 Mbits/sec.

Tables 1 and 2 show the maximum allowable number of streams under each admission control algorithm for I/O cycle times of one and two seconds, respectively. The number in the parenthesis is the percentage of cycles where the service time exceeded the cycle time. The *No Prediction* algorithm determines the maximum number of streams that could have been allowed to enter with no overflows if the prediction algorithm were perfect. For example, with a one-second I/O cycle time and using two disks, 25 streams could be admitted with no overflows. When 26 streams were running, 32% of the cycles overflowed. The results show that both statistical algorithms perform very closely to what a perfect predic-

tion algorithm can achieve, and the difference between *Statistical/Worst-Case* and *Statistical/Average* is rather minor. On the other hand, the *Statistical/Worst-Case* is more reliable because it shows much smaller percentages of overloaded cycles. Therefore in *SBVS* we decided to use the *Statistical/Worst-Case* algorithm for admission control. Since the *Deterministic/Average* algorithm is better than the *Deterministic/Worst-Case* algorithm in all cases without causing overloaded I/O cycles, we will only focus on the former. Compared to the *Deterministic/Average* algorithms, the *Statistical/Worst-Case* is about 10% to 20% better, across different I/O cycle times and disk array configurations. This result is less optimistic than are reported in earlier papers [5] [9, 8]. We believe this is because the I/O service time model presented in Section 2 is more accurate and realistic. In addition, the measurements from real implementations include various overheads such as SCSI bus arbitration overheads that are simply overlooked in earlier studies.

The relative advantage of the *Statistical/Worst-Case* algorithm over the Deterministic/Worst-Case algorithm shrinks as more disks are added. Our conjecture is is that with more disks, the average service time decreases while the standard deviation of the measured service time remains the same. As a result, the prediction is relatively more conservative when there are more disks. For example, our measurements show that the standard deviations are 45%, 75%, and 105% of the average when there are 2, 4, and 6 disks in the I/O system.

In several cases, the service time exceeded the prediction when using the *Statistical/Worst-Case* algorithm. We conjecture this may be due to the short history used in the prediction. In each of the above experiments, the average time between requests for admission is only 10 cycles. This keeps the total time duration of each experiment run to about an hour. As a result, the admission control system only has a small time window from which to collect the measured service times used for prediction.

Window Size	10		20		30		40		50		60	
Cycle Time (sec)	1	2	1	2	1	2	1	2	1	2	1	2
2 Disks	26(36%)	31(9%)	25(8%)	30	24	30	24	30	24	29	24(.6%)	29
4 Disks	34(9%)	45	31	45	31	46	33(2%)	45	31	45	32	45
6 Disks	39	60	38	61	40	60	39	60	38	61	38	59

Table 3: *The effect of measurement window size on the accuracy of the service time prediction and thus the percentage of overloaded cycles for the Statistical/Worst-Case algorithm. Window size is in terms of number of I/O cycles.*

In a real production environment, it would be unlikely that users are asking to display a new video every 10 cycles (10 or 20 seconds). Table 3 shows the effect of the measurement window size on the accuracy of service time predictions for the *Statistical/Worst-Case* algorithm. As expected, the percentage of overloaded cycles decreases because the prediction tends to be more conservative when a larger amount of history is used in the prediction.

5.3. Non-Uniform Workload

In this experiment 10 movies are evenly distributed across the disk array. However, they are ordered such that the videos on the outside of the disk are considered 'favorite' videos and are accessed more frequently than the videos on the inside of the disk. The numbers of requests for the 0-th, 1-th, to 9-th video are as follows: 140, 86, 45, 31,, 26, 6, 7, 4, 2, 1. When streams are read more often from the outer portion of the disk surface, the effective disk transfer rate should be higher than a uniformly distributed workload that accesses data across all parts of the disk. In addition, seek times will be lower since the reads are closer together. The expectation is that the worst-case deterministic algorithms will perform more poorly while the performance of the statistical algorithms continue to be close to the optimum. As shown in Table 1 and 4, the performance gap between the *Statistical/Worst-Case* and *Deterministic/Worst-Case* algorithms indeed widens, although not as significantly as expected. This seems to indicate that non-disk-related overheads that exist independently of the access patterns of the workload play a non-trivial role in the overall resource consumption.

5.4. Lower Bit-Rate Workload

The objective of this experiment is to test the effects of lowering the playback rate of the videos. In this case, the non-tangible terms constitute a slightly larger proportion of the total service time. As in previous experiments six videos are evenly striped across each disk such that each video takes up one sixth of every disk. However, the playback rate of each video is lowered to 60KBps or one third of a normal MPEG video.

Since the playback rates of the videos are lowered, more streams can be admitted than in the previous experiments. Comparing Table 5 with Table 1 the deterministic algorithms do not allow as many (percentage of maximum) streams when using a lower bit rate. For example, when using six disks and a playback rate of 180KBps, the deterministic worst-case algorithm allows 31 streams or 76% of the maximum number of streams allowed by the no prediction algorithm. When lowering the playback rate to 60KBps, the algorithm allows 42 videos but only 64% of the maximum. The only change to the prediction equation when reducing the bit rates is the decrease of the estimated data transfer time from the disk medium to the disk cache. Other variables, i.e. seek and rotation overheads remain constant. As a result, the negative performance effects due to worst-case assumptions used in the deterministic algorithms are more pronounced when the bit rates are low when they are high.

6. Conclusion

This work takes an empirical approach to study the admission control algorithms used in video servers to guarantee smooth playback of existing streams when new streams are to be added. We devised a general framework to describe the admission control algorithms in terms of how non-tangible terms in the I/O service time prediction equation is estimated. Based on measurements of actual implementations on an operational video server, we compare the performance of these admission control algorithms under various workloads and architectural parameters. To our knowledge, this is the first paper that reports implementation-based rather than simulation-based performance comparison results of video server admission control algorithms. We found that the *Statistical/Worst-Case* algorithm achieves a performance level that is rather close to the optimum while maintaining the percentage of overloaded cycles to the minimum. Therefore, the *Statistical/Worst-Case* algorithm is the admission control algorithm used in *SBVS*. Also, contrary to the results reported by earlier work, the performance gap between the *Statistical*

Disks	Deterministic Worst-Case	Deterministic Average	Statistical Worst-Case	Statistical Average	No Prediction
2	17	23	26(.9%)	26(2%) | 27(29%)	27(37%)
4	26	30	35	35(2%) | 36(7%)	37(46%)
6	32	35	42(3%)	42(3%) | 43(13%)	43(12%)

Table 4: *Admission control performance for an I/O cycle time of 1 second, using a skewed workload in which movies at the outside tracks are accessed more frequently.*

Disks	Deterministic Worst-Case	Deterministic Average	Statistical Worst-Case	Statistical Average	No Prediction
2	32	40	46(1%) | 47(7%)	49(4%) | 50(54%)	49(41%)
4	39	45	55(.3%) | 56(.4%)	58(14%) | 59(24%)	58(17%)
6	42	48	61(.8%)	63(6%) | 64(27%)	66(54%)

Table 5: *Admission control performance for a cycle time of 1 second, using a uniformly distributed workload with low bit rate videos*

and *Deterministic* algorithms are between 10% to 40%, which is much smaller than were previously believed. We believe the discrepancy is due to the over-simplified assumptions by the simulators as well as other fixed software/hardware overheads that are completely overlooked. The experimental approach used in this study completely eliminates all these problems.

Acknowledgement

This research is supported by an NSF Career Award MIP-9502067, NSF MIP-9710622, NSF IRI-9711635, a contract 95F138600000 from Community Management Staff's Massive Digital Data System Program, as well as fundings from Sandia National Laboratory, Reuters Information Technology Inc., and Computer Associates/Cheyenne Inc.

References

[1] D. Anderson, Y. Osawa, and R. Govindan. A file system for continuous media. In *ACM Transactions on Computer Systems*, volume 10, page 331, Nov 1992.

[2] E. Chang and A. Zakhor. Cost analyses for vbr video servers. In *SPIE International Symposium on Electronic Imaging, Science and Technology; Multimedia Computing and Networks*, volume 2667, page 1, San Jose, CA, July 1996.

[3] E. Chang and A. Zakhor. Variable bit-rate mpeg video storage on parallel disk arrays. In *Proceedings IEEE First International Workshop on Community Networking*, page 127, San Francisco, CA, July 94.

[4] D. Ferrari and D. Verma. A scheme for real-time channel establishment in wide-area networks. In *IEEE Journal on Selected Areas in Communications*, page 386, Apr 1990.

[5] A. Mourad. I/o scheduling in a storage server for video-on-demand applications. In *Proceeding of the IASTED/ISMM International Conference. Distributed Multimedia Systems and Applications*, page 31, Honolulu, HI, Aug 1994.

[6] P. Rangan and H. Vin. Designing file systems for digital video and audio. In *Proceedings of the 13th Symposium on Operating Systems Principles, Operating Systems Review*, volume 25, page 81, October 1991.

[7] P. Rangan, H. Vin, and S. Ramanathan. Designing an on-demand multimedia service. *IEEE Communications Maganzine*, page 56, July 1992.

[8] M. Vernick, C. Venkatramani, and T. Chiueh. Adventures in building the stony brook video server. In *Proceedings ACM Multimedia*, Nov 1996.

[9] H. Vin, A. Goyal, and P. Goyal. An observation-based admission control algorithm for multimedia servers. In *Proceedings of the First IEEE International Conference on Multimedia Computing and Systems*, page 234, Boston, MA, 1994.

[10] H. Vin, P. Goyal, and A Goyal. A statistical admission control algorithm for multimedia servers. In *Proceedings ACM Multimedia*, page 33, San Francisco, CA, Oct 1994.

[11] H. Vin and P Rangan. Designing a multi-user hdtv storage server. *IEEE Journal on Selected Areas in Communications*, 11:153, Jan 1993.

Stream Scheduling Algorithms for Multimedia Storage Servers*

Xiaoye Jiang and Prasant Mohapatra
Department of Electrical and Computer Engineering
Iowa State University, Ames, Iowa 50011
E.mail: *prasant@iastate.edu*

Abstract

In this paper, we have proposed efficient stream scheduling algorithms for multimedia storage servers that are providers of variable bit rate media streams. We have developed three types of stream scheduling algorithms: In-Order Scheduling Algorithm (IOSA), Out-of-Order Scheduling Algorithm (OOSA), and Dynamic Merge Scheduling Algorithm (DMSA). In the IOSA scheme, media blocks must be transmitted according to their natural order. In the OOSA scheme, in-order transmission is not mandated and thus results in an out-of-order transmission. In the DMSA scheme, the requests that are possible to be merged are merged together at first. Then the OOSA scheduling scheme is used for the merged requests. The performance evaluations done through simulations show that the maximum bandwidth requirement, the fetch ahead distance, and the coefficient of variation for the bandwidth requirement are improved by using the IOSA, OOSA, and DMSA algorithms.

1 Introduction

Recent developments in computer systems and high speed networks have propelled the research on multimedia systems. A multimedia system requires the integration of communication, storage, retrieval, and presentation mechanisms for diverse data types including text, images, audio, and video to provide a single unified information system. The potential applications of multimedia systems span into domains such as computer-aided design, education, entertainment, information systems, and medical imaging. An efficient support mechanism for such a diverse class of application requires a suitable storage server connected to the clients through high speed networks. The architecture and organization of the storage server has a significant impact on the service of the multimedia clients. The design issues associated with the multimedia storage servers (MSS) differ from those associated with the services that support traditional textual and numeric data because of the difference in the characteristics of multimedia streams. A multimedia stream consists of a sequence of media quanta, such as audio samples and video frames, which convey meaning only when played continuously in time unlike the traditional textual streams [1].

An MSS should ensure that the retrieval of media streams occur at their real-time rate [2]. With a finite total bandwidth available from the storage devices attached to the server via network to the clients, an MSS can only support a limited number of clients simultaneously. Efficient scheduling of streams can decrease the overall bandwidth requirement of each media stream enabling an MSS to support more clients concurrently. Stream scheduling tries to smooth the bandwidth requirement curve and reduces the total number of disk requests.

Variable Bit Rate (VBR) streams exhibit significant rate variability. As a general real-time design principle, less bursty (i.e. smoother) workloads are easier to manage [3]. Therefore, smoothing has a significant impact on the performance of an MSS. Three basic techniques can be used to reduce the variability of VBR streams [3]: *temporal multiplexing, aggregation,* and *work ahead*. In temporal multiplexing, a stream oriented large buffer is implemented in the server-to-client path to smooth the peak rate. This technique introduces additional start-up latency to fill up the buffer and needs a large memory. In aggregation, when the server serves a large number of multiple independent streams simultaneously, although each of them has a high rate variability, the total bandwidth requirement converges to a Normal distribution. This is the result of Central Limit Theorem and this smoothing effect does not introduce delay. In the work ahead technique, when data is available to be sent and the corresponding buffer space at the client side is available, the server sends it. In this method, the server tries to push data to clients as early as pos-

---
*This research was supported in part by the EMC Corporation and the National Science Foundation through the grants CCR-9634547, MIP-9628801, and CDA-9617375.

sible to avoid the bursty effect. These three techniques are not mutually exclusive. They can be combined together at some point between the server and the clients [4, 5, 6, 7, 8].

There are several approaches to reduce the total disk requests through sharing. In the *batching* scheme, some of the incoming requests are grouped together by delaying some of them for a threshold time period [10]. After batching, the server serves the entire group as a single stream request. In *bridging* [11], if two successive requests are close enough, the server can hold the data read for the earlier one in a shared buffer space to serve the later one without issuing another disk request. An approach called *adaptive piggybacking* merges several requests in progress into one by adjusting their display rates [9].

Three different type of stream scheduling schemes, namely, In-Order Scheduling Algorithm (IOSA), Out-of-Order Scheduling Algorithm (OOSA), and Dynamic Merge Scheduling Algorithm (DMSA) are developed and evaluated in this work. In the IOSA scheme, media blocks must be transmitted on the basis of their natural ordering. In the OOSA scheme, in-order transmission is not mandated and it allows out-of-order transmission. In the DMSA scheme, the requests that are possible to be merged are merged together and then the OOSA scheduling scheme is used for the merged requests. The performance improvement obtained using the IOSA scheme is mainly because of buffering and is not significant. With the OOSA scheme, the improvement increases until a certain buffer size and remains constant thereafter. However, the performance improvement of the DMSA scheme is almost linear.

The rest of the paper is organized as follows. In Section 2, we review the requirements of stream scheduling algorithm. In Section 3, we present the IOSA, OOSA, and DMSA schemes and discuss the issues related to their implementation. In Section 4, we present the simulation results and discussions followed by the concluding remarks in Section 5.

2 Preliminaries
2.1 Stream Scheduling

While servicing multiple clients requesting different media streams, it might be necessary to arrange the order of transmission of the stream from the server to the clients. The ordering is dependent on the availability of buffer at both the server and the clients. This ordering mechanism of streams is regulated and is defined by the stream scheduling algorithm.

The main function of a stream scheduling algorithm is to determine the I/O access time point for each stream block during the playing time. The objective of the scheduling algorithm is to maximize the usage of the bandwidth that the server supports while guaranteeing the required QoS.

There are several ways to evaluate the performance of a stream scheduling algorithm. The worst case Bandwidth Requirement (BWR) of a fixed number of incoming streams, denoted as BWR_{max} is one of the widely used measures. The scheduling algorithm should smooth the BWR curve by reducing the BWR_{max} as much as possible. The standard deviation of BWR is also a measure of the performance of a stream scheduling algorithm. Lower values of the standard deviation reflects smooth BWR curves.

Another commonly used measurement for evaluating the stream scheduling algorithms is the total number of I/O accesses required, which can be reduced by using caches, merging streams, and other techniques. Stream cache uses server's main memory to trade number of I/O accesses. Stream merging tries to schedule the I/O accesses at the same time for the same data block for different stream requests that request for the same stream. Reduction of the total number of I/O accesses does not imply the reduction of the BWR. However, it does reduce the average BWR of the server. Thus, while possibly supporting more real-time streams, it can also support more non real-time applications, such as image or text retrieval.

We introduce the notion of *Fetch Ahead Distance* (FAD) that defines the ability of tolerating I/O access delay and communication delay. Assuming t_{D_i} is the deadline of block i's I/O access, and t_{F_i} is this block's scheduled I/O access time point, its FAD can be expressed as

$$FAD = \frac{\sum_{i=1}^{M}(t_{D_i} - t_{F_i})}{M},$$

where M is the total number of I/O accesses. When the server utilizes almost all of the available bandwidth, the I/O access will have a high possibility of being delayed. The network communication delay is also unpredictable. If the stream scheduling algorithm schedules the I/O access time point same as the corresponding deadline, FAD is equal to zero. Due to the unpredictable network delay, it may introduce a lot of jitters. When the FAD is increased by scheduling t_{F_i} well ahead of t_{D_i}, the server gets more ability to tolerate unpredictable delay so that a better QoS can be guaranteed.

A good stream scheduling algorithm should have a small value of BWR_{max} that is close to the average bandwidth requirement of the server. It should minimize the number of I/O accesses and maximize the FAD.

2.2 System Architecture

Multimedia streams are stored on servers and displayed on clients. In order to synchronize the retrieval at the servers, transmission in the network and display at the clients, buffers are introduced at both sides - the server and the clients. The simplest model of the buffer structure is double buffering. In this scheme, two data blocks are bounded together to be a buffer: one for the producer of data and the other for the consumer of data.

Because of the decreasing price of memory, not only the server, but also the clients can afford more memory. Thus, we suggest to allocate large buffers on client's machine for their stream requests, and change the stream associated buffer to the data block associated buffer pool at the server. In other words, we delegate the stream associated buffers from the server's side to the client's side.

In the proposed system architecture, buffers at the server side no longer take care of the stream smoothing. This task is moved to the corresponding client's side. Since, each client usually asks for one real-time stream, it is feasible to allocate a larger buffer for the requested stream to enable smoothing. The BWR can be reduced significantly by these larger buffers. At the server side, because there is no stream associated buffer, which means that for each stream the buffer size is not fixed, the server can allocate blocks to each stream dynamically from the shared buffer pool on the basis of their requirements. So the memory utilization of the server will be higher than the traditional DMS architecture.

3 Proposed Stream Scheduling Algorithms

In this paper, we consider VBR traffic of video streams used in video-on-demand (VOD) servers. We assume that the bandwidth requirement profiles of the videos are stored at the server ahead of time. So during the retrieval process, the scheduling algorithms selects the retrieval period such that the total bandwidth of the streams are minimized while meeting their respective deadlines.

3.1 Service Time Period

The unit of playback is a frame. The playback device will consume a frame for each time unit. Due to the VBR characteristic, each frame occupies different size space. However, for each block, the unit of storage has the same size. For the current operating systems, it is difficult to have a variable size space for different

blocks that can match different frames' size. For each block, the time length which it can support for playback is different. This time length is called playback time period (PTP).

The calculation of each block's PTP is related to the mapping from frames to blocks. The boundaries of block i's PTP are earliest playback time (EPT) and latest playback time (LPT). They are given as,

$$EPT_i = t, \ in \ which \ \sum_{j=0}^{t} S_j > (i-1) * block \ size,$$

$$\sum_{j=0}^{t-1} S_j \leq (i-1) * block \ size, \ and$$

$$LPT_i = t, \ in \ which \ \sum_{j=0}^{t} S_j \geq i * block \ size,$$

$$\sum_{j=0}^{t-1} S_j < i * block \ size,$$

where S_j is the size of frame j. $\sum_{j=0}^{t} S_j$ is the total frame size from frame 0 to frame t. $i * block \ size$ is the size of i blocks.

For the purpose of stream scheduling, it is necessary to distinguish between the time when a specific block can be fetched from storage devices and the deadline for fetching. The time period between the earliest fetching time and the deadline is the block's service time period (STP). Each block can be scheduled for fetching at any time point within its STP. The boundaries of STP, which is the time of the earliest fetching time and the deadline for fetching, are denoted as earliest service time (EST) and latest service time (LST), respectively.

If the system is using double buffering scheme, for any block, its STP is its previous block's PTP. When the buffering scheme is changed from double buffering to multiple buffering, the calculation of EST and LST will also be changed. When the size of buffer increases, the STP becomes larger and larger. It gives us more time to schedule the blocks. Thus the performance of the scheduling algorithm should improve with a large size buffer.

3.2 Scheduling Algorithms
3.2.1 In-Order Scheduling Algorithm

All the blocks in a VBR media stream are stored in a linear order. Each block can be scheduled to be fetched into the buffer within its STP. The exact fetching time point t_{f_i} of block i should meet the following condition to generate a smoothed BWR curve.

$$BWR(t_{f_i}) = \min(BWR(t)), \ where \ t \in [EST_i, LST_i].$$

If the server fetches blocks in an in-order fashion, which means, $t_{f_i} \leq t_{f_{i+1}}$, the earlier condition should be modified as

$$BWR(t_{f_i}) = \min(BWR(t)),$$

$$where, \quad t \in [\max(t_{f_{i-1}}, EST_i), LST_i].$$

The IOSA scheduling algorithm can thus be formalized as follows.

```
Input:   Blocks(i = 1...N)'s EST and LST;
         Beginning display time Tb;
         Already allocated BWR
            (j = Tb ... Tb + Block[N].LST).
Output: Fetching time points for each block,
            Tf(i = 1...N);
         Updated BWR
            (j = Tb ... Tb + Block[N].LST).

Tf[0] = Block[1].EST + Tb;
i = 1;
while (i <= N) {
    first = Tf[i - 1];
    if (first < Block[i].EST + Tb)
        first = Block[i].EST + Tb;
    last  = Block[i].LST + Tb;
    loc   = first;
    for (l = first + 1; l <= last; l++)
        if (BWR[loc] > BWR[l]) loc = l;
    Tf[i] = loc; BWR[loc] ++;
}
```

The IOSA is a simple algorithm. The total iterations will be no more than Block[N].LST, which is proportional to N. So the computational complexity is just O(N). Due to the linear access of blocks, this algorithm can be used in any instances including reading blocks from the tape drive. However, since each block tries to find its best place to be fetched without considering the later blocks, the later one may have a limited STP.

3.2.2 Out-of-Order Scheduling Algorithm

If the access to the storage device is not linear, the server can have random access to any blocks. In order to relax the in-order restriction, we proposed the Out-of-Order Scheduling Algorithm (OOSA). In this algorithm, the condition for the fetching time point should be the same as the original case, which is

$$BWR(t_{f_i}) = \min(BWR(t)), \ where \ t \in [EST_i, LST_i].$$

Since the media stream is VBR, its blocks' STPs are not of the same size. A block, which has a small STP, has higher priority during the scheduling. This enables us to do an out-of-order scheduling. In OOSA, the scheduling order is the block's priority order based on the value of their STP. Because of this order, the fetching time point may not follow the in-order sequence, which means $\forall i, t_{f_i} \leq t_{f_{i+1}}$ may not be held. This is the main attribute of the out-of-order scheduling. The pseudo code of the OOSA is given as,

```
Input:   Same as the IOSA
Output: Same as the OOSA

// Part 1: Sorting
Scan all the blocks once and find the
   maximum STP -- MAX_STP, and the minimum
   STP -- MIN_STP;
Scan all the blocks again, and distribute
   blocks into MAX_STP - MIN_STP + 1 lists
   according to their STP;
Concatenate lists from MIN_STP to MAX_STP
   into a new list led by variable head;
// Part 2: Scheduling
p = head->next;
while (p != NULL) {
    i = p->block_number;
    first = Block[i].EST + Tb;
    last  = Block[i].LST + Tb;
    loc   = first;
    for (l = first + 1; l <= last; l++)
        if (BWR[loc] > BWR[l]) loc = l;
    Tf[i] = loc; BWR[loc] ++; p = p->next;
}
```

This algorithm has two parts: Sorting and Scheduling. The computational complexity of the first part is O(N) and for the part two, the complexity is O(d*N), where d is the average STP. Adding these two, the total computation complexity is O(N + d*N) = O(d*N). In OOSA, the blocks are given priority on the basis of their STP. A block associated with a small value of STP will get higher priority. At first, the server sorts all blocks according to their priority. Then it scans through the whole sorted list and schedules blocks one by one. During the scheduling phase, it tries to find the best time point for each block based on the current BWR, irrespective of when other blocks will be fetched. This algorithm may yield higher FAD and a more smoothed BWR than IOSA, but requires random access ability for storage device and reordering scheme for buffer.

3.2.3 Dynamic Merge Scheduling Algorithm

In the run time, a lot of media stream requests are served simultaneously by the server. Based on the popularity, most of these requests constitute a small portion of the stored media streams. It means that two requests for the same "hot" media stream may not be far from each other on the time axis. When the clients have a large buffer, the STP becomes large for every block. So there is a high possibility that the corresponding block's STPs of those nearby requests on the same stream will overlap. If the server can merge these two or more block fetches into one, the total I/O requests will be reduced significantly. This defines the motivation of our Dynamic Merge Scheduling Algorithm (DMSA).

The DMSA algorithm consists of there parts. The first part involves merging as many block requests as possible. In the second and third parts, the two phases of the OOSA are applied to the merged block requests. The conditions for possible merging are given as

$$EST_i + t_{sa} < LST_i + t_{sb} \text{ and } EST_i + t_{sb} < LST_i + t_{sa},$$

where t_{sa} and t_{sb} are the beginning play time for stream requests a and b, and i is the corresponding block number. Once these conditions are TRUE, the server can merge those two block requests into one with its EST and LST as

$$EST_{new} = EST_i + \max(t_{sa}, t_{sb})$$

$$\text{and } LST_{new} = LST_i + \min(t_{sa}, t_{sb}).$$

After the server finishes merging the original two stream requests, it can go ahead and try to merge this merged block request with that of block i from stream request c. These conditions are given as

$$EST_{new} < LST_i + t_{sc} \text{ and } EST_i + t_{sc} < LST_{new},$$

where t_{sc} is the beginning play time for stream request c. If the merging can be done, the results are

$$EST'_{new} = \max(EST_{new}, EST_i + t_{sc})$$
$$= EST_i + \max(t_{sa}, t_{sb}, t_{sc})$$
$$LST'_{new} = \min(LST_{new}, LST_i + t_{sc})$$
$$= LST_i + \min(t_{sa}, t_{sb}, t_{sc})$$

After merging all the possible block requests, the server can sort the resulting block requests by their STP and then use the method in OOSA to schedule them. The pseudo code for the DMSA is as follows.

```
Input:   Blocks' EST and LST from stream
             requests a, b, ...;
         Beginning display time Ta, Tb, ...;
         Already allocated BWR.
Output:  Fetching time points for each block
             in stream requests a, b, ...
             as Tfa, Tfb, ...;
         Updated BWR.

// Part 1: Merging
Divide stream requests into different groups
    according to the stream they request;
In each group, apply the merging process and
    try to merge as many blocks as possible.
    In the mean time, record where the merged
    requests come from;
Concatenate all the merged blocks and the
    blocks that cannot be merged together into
    a linked list;
// Part 2: Same as Part 1 of OOSA
// Part 3: Scheduling
p = head->next;
while (p != NULL) {
    i = p->block_number;
    first = p->EST;
    last  = p->LST;
    loc   = first;
    for (l = first + 1; l <= last; l++)
        if (BWR[loc] > BWR[l]) loc = l;
    Use the information recorded in part 1 to
        find out where this block request comes
        from, e.g. stream request a, b, ...,
        then set {Tfa[i] = loc; Tfb[i] = loc}
        and so on;
    BWR[loc] ++; p = p->next;
}
```

The computational complexity for part 1 is $O(\sum_{i=1}^{M} N_i)$, where N_i is the total number of blocks in stream request i and M is the total number of stream requests. We can use the analysis of OOSA to get the computational complexity of parts 2 & 3, which is $O(d * N_M)$. N_M is the total number of block requests after merging. It is easy to see $N_M \leq \sum_{i=1}^{M} N_i$. After adding them up, the total computational complexity of DMSA can be $O(d * \sum_{i=1}^{M} N_i)$.

By using DMSA, the total number of I/O requests issued by the server is reduced, which in turn reduces the worst case BWR. As a consequence, the server can support more stream requests.

4 Performance Evaluation

The commonly used performance indicators of stream scheduling schemes are the maximum bandwidth required for a group of scheduled streams and the standard derivation for a period of bandwidth requirement. The standard derivation is dependent on the mean value of the measured data. Therefore, it is hard to compare the smoothness of the two sets of data with different bandwidth requirements and with different mean value. In this study, we choose the Coefficient of Variation (COV) to judge the smoothness. The COV can be expressed as

$$COV = \frac{standard\ deviation}{mean} = \frac{\sigma}{\mu}.$$

Besides these two measurements, we used two other parameters, namely, the Fetch Ahead Distance (FAD) and the Relative Number of I/O Requests. The FAD tells us how much "freedom" the stream scheduling schemes give to the I/O system. This could be a good measurement of the tolerance of the scheduling schemes. The relative number of I/O requests is used to measure the performance of merging in DMSA scheme. The lower this number is, the better is the performance obtained through merging.

4.1 Simulation Model

We have implemented a time driven simulator for the evaluation of the proposed algorithms. For the simulation, we used real frame size traces obtained from [12]. The simulator has the following components - a request generator, a media stream analyzer, and the stream scheduling units.

The request generator is responsible for generating media stream requests according to Poisson distribution. In this paper, we choose three different types of request traffic intensity to represent the heavy, moderate, and light traffic. The corresponding arrival intervals between two requests are 7.5 sec, 20 sec, and 200 sec. Furthermore, we assume that 80% of the requests are for 20% of the stored media streams. These 20% media streams are called hot-streams. We have fixed the number of stored streams to be 10.

The media stream analyzer is used to generate each block's EST and LST based on the block size, the buffer size, and the stream's frame size trace. The buffer size was varied from 16KB to 2048KB with steps of 16KB. The block size was varied from 16KB, 32KB, 64KB, 128KB, 256KB, and 512KB.

4.2 Results and Observations

We present a comparative evaluation of the performance of the IOSA, OOSA, and DMSA algorithms. The results are obtained with respect to the buffer size, the block size, the frame number, and for different types of traffic intensity.

Figure 1 shows the comparison of bandwidth requirements of the original stream, IOSA, OOSA, and DMSA with respect to the play back time. It can be observed that the original case has the largest variation of its bandwidth clip. The IOSA scheme may reduce the variation, but not as much as the OOSA scheme. The DMSA scheme not only reduced the variation, but also the mean. This figure is just a direct view of the performance of each scheduling schemes without any quantitative analysis.

In Figure 2, we show the maximum bandwidth requirement corresponding to the original case, IOSA, OOSA, and DMSA with respect to the buffer size. For the original case, it is a horizontal line as expected, which means it will not change with the change in buffer size. The maximum bandwidth requirement of the IOSA scheme also looks like a constant. It has a slight drop with the increase in buffer size, and then remains unchanged. However, compared to the original case, the bandwidth requirement is much less. The curve of the OOSA scheme starts from the same point as that of the IOSA's, but it decreases noticeably with a small increase in the buffer size. The rate of decrease diminishes with the increase in the buffer size. It may not be necessary or worth implementing larger buffer size for the OOSA scheme at the cost of added memory, because of the small reduction of the maximum bandwidth requirement. The curve for the DMSA scheme has an almost linear decrease with the increase in buffer size. This is due to the increase in STP which is caused by the increase in buffer size. With larger STP of each block, the chance of merging them together is also increased, which leads to the monotonous decrease of bandwidth requirement.

In order to tolerate the delaying or any unpredictable behavior of the I/O system, the stream scheduling scheme should schedule the fetching of blocks ahead of its deadline as much as possible. This can be measured by the FAD. The FADs of the IOSA, OOSA, and DMSA are illustrated in Figure 3. As expected, the FADs increase with the increase in buffer size. The rate of increase diminishes with the increase in buffer size in the IOSA, and OOSA schemes. It is observed that the FAD of the OOSA scheme does not vary significantly with the increase in the buffer size beyond a certain point. However, in the case of the DMSA scheme, there is almost a linear increase.

The COV of the IOSA, OOSA, and DMSA are shown in Figure 4. After a sharp decrease in the small buffer size, the IOSA and OOSA remain con-

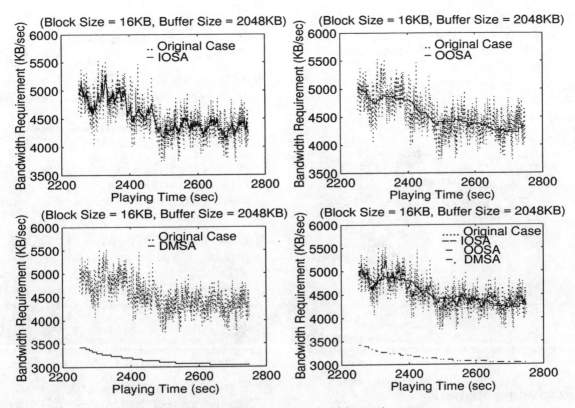

Figure 1: Comparison of bandwidth requirements.

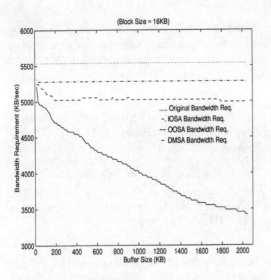

Figure 2: Comparison of maximum BWR.

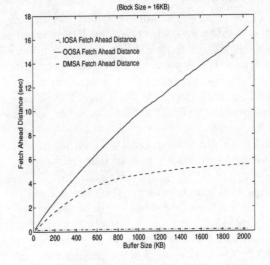

Figure 3: Comparison of the FADs.

stant. This confirms the results obtained from the two previous figures - the IOSA and OOSA schemes are good for relatively small buffer size. The trend of COV curve for the DMSA scheme is almost the same as its bandwidth requirement except for cases of a very large buffer size. The curve increases when it

goes beyond a certain buffer size. A possible reason for that is because after that point, aggressive merging results in a small STP when it tries to manipulate two blocks that had small overlap. This makes the second and third phases of the DMSA (smoothing) very hard. As the buffer size keeps increasing, the overlap for those blocks increases too, which leads to the second decrease of COV. This can be observed in the figure when the buffer size goes beyond 2000KB.

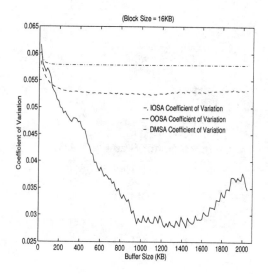

Figure 4: Comparison of the COVs.

5 Concluding Remarks

In this paper, we have proposed a new family of stream scheduling algorithms. These algorithms are media block oriented schemes instead of stream oriented. Three types of stream scheduling algorithms are proposed. The first scheme, called IOSA, schedules media blocks in their FIFO order and tries to find the lowest BWR point to fetch each block. In the second algorithm, called OOSA, blocks are scheduled based on the priority on the basis of their service time period (STP). The last algorithm, called DMSA, merges the requests for the same media block if their STPs overlap. Then OOSA algorithm is used for the merged requests. A new system architecture, which is suitable for the proposed algorithms, is also introduced. In this architecture, buffers become media block oriented in the server side and can be shared easily among different streams. Relatively large buffers can be introduced at the client side to increase each block's STP. The performance of the proposed stream scheduling algorithms is evaluated through simulation experiments using real traces. The results show the relative performance gain obtained through the use of the stream scheduling schemes.

References

[1] A. L. N. Reddy and J. C. Wyllie, "I/O Issues in a Multimedia System," *IEEE Computer*, pp. 69–74, March 1994.

[2] D. J. Gemmell, H. M. Vin, D. D. Kandlur, and P. V. Rangan, "Multimedia Storage Servers: A Tutorial," *IEEE Computer*, pp. 40–49, May 1995.

[3] J. D. Salehi, Z.-L. Zhang, J. F. Kurose, and D. Towsley, "Supporting Stored Video: Reducing Rate Variability and End-to-End Resource Requirements through Optimal Smoothing," in *Proceedings of ACM SIGMETRICS*, May 1996.

[4] W. Feng and S. Sechrest, "Smoothing and Buffering for Delivery of Prerecorded Compressed Video," *IS&T/SPIE Multimedia Computing and Networking*, pp. 234–232, February 1995.

[5] E. W. Knightly, D. E. Wrege, J. Liebeherr, and H. Zhang, "Fundamental Limits and Tradeoffs of Providing Deterministic Guarantees to VBR Video Traffic," in *Proceedings of ACM SIGMETRICS*, pp. 98–107, May 1995.

[6] S. S. Lam, S. Chow, and D. K. Y. Yau, "An Algorithm for Lossless Smoothing of MPEG Video," in *Proceedings of ACM SIGCOMM*, August 1994.

[7] T. Ott, T. V. Lakshman, and A. Tabatabai, "A Scheme for Smoothing Delay-Sensitive Traffic Offered to ATM Networks," in *Proceedinds of IEEE INFOCOM*, pp. 776–785, May 1992.

[8] N. Shroff and M. Schwartz, "Video Modeling within Networks using Deterministic Smoothing at the Source," in *Proceedings of IEEE INFO-COM*, pp. 342–349, 1994.

[9] L. Golubchik, J. C. S. Lui, and R. Muntz, "Reducing I/O Demand in Video-On-Demand Storage Servers," in *Proceedings of ACM SIGMETRICS*, May 1995.

[10] A. Dan, P. Shahabuddin, D. Sitaram, and D. Towsley, "Channel Allocation under Batching and VCR Control in Movie-On-Demand Servers," tech. rep., IBM, 1994.

[11] M. Kamath, D. Towsley, and K. Ramamritham, "Buffer Management for Continuous Media Sharing in Multimedia Database System," Tech. Rep. 94-11, University of Massachusetts, February 1994.

[12] O. Rose, "Statistical Properties of MPEG Video Traffic and Their Impact on Traffic Modeling in ATM Systems," Tech. Rep. 101, University of Wuerzburg, Institute of Computer Science, February 1995.

MPEG-4 Based Interactive Video using Parallel Processing

Yong He[1], Ishfaq Ahmad[2] and Ming L. Liou[1]

[1]Department of Electrical and Electronic Engineering
[2]Department of Computer Science
The Hong Kong University of Science and Technology, Clear Water Bay, Hong Kong

Abstract[†]

MPEG-4 which is currently being developed by MPEG (Moving Pictures Experts Group), is poised to become a standard for supporting current and emerging interactive multimedia applications. The objective of MPEG-4 is to support content-based compression, communication, access and manipulation of digital objects which can be natural or synthetic. Since MPEG-4 based video consists of objects and provides full interactivity between the client and the server, a software-based implementation seems to be the only viable approach for building an MPEG-4 encoder. Parallel processing solves the problem of large computational requirements for building a real-time encoder.

In this paper, we describe a parallel implementation of MPEG-4 video encoder using a cluster of workstations collectively working as a virtual machine. Parallelization of the MPEG-4 encoder poses an interesting problem since not only can objects be added or deleted from a video scene but their sizes and shapes may vary with time. Moreover, some of the computationally intensive parts of the encoder are non-uniform algorithms, which means their execution times are data dependent and cannot be predicted in advance. In order to guarantee the spatio-temporal relationship between various objects in a video, we propose a real-time scheduling algorithm for exploiting parallelism in the temporal domain. The algorithm divides the workstations into a number of groups and assigns one video object to one group of workstations for encoding. A dynamic shape-adaptive data partitioning strategy is proposed to exploit parallelism in the spatial domain. The partitioning strategy divides the data of an object among the workstations within a group. The scheduling scheme ensures the synchronization requirements among multiple objects while the dynamic data parallel approach adapts to the object shape variations to balance the load for all the workstations. The performance of the encoder can scale according to the number of workstations used. With 20 workstations, the encoder yields an encoding rate higher than real-time, allowing to encode multiple sequences simultaneously.

Keywords: MPEG-4, video compression, distributed and parallel processing, data partitioning, scheduling, MPI.

1 Introduction

With the development of workstations and networking technologies, the aggregated computing power of a cluster of workstations can match that of an expensive parallel computing system [6]. Because of the advantages such as scalable file storage, large memory, high performance-cost ratio, and efficient communication hardware/software support, many current parallel applications can use the cluster of workstations as the platform instead of parallel machines.

On the other hand, recently, there has been a technological revolution in the area of multimedia-based information technology. Progress in information technology is now recognized to be essential for the success of industrial and commercial businesses as well as for improving the quality of life for the masses in general. A majority of present and future multimedia-based applications require huge computing power. For instance, video is a fundamental component of multimedia systems, and the storage and transmission of large amount of required data inevitably calls for the compression and decompression of digital video. Video compression, if done through software, requires considerably extensive computing power than that offered by a single PC or workstation. Parallel processing then becomes a natural approach. The latest developments in cluster computing offer a higher degree of performance at an affordable cost (such as a network of workstations), provided the parallelism from the application at hand is effectively extracted and scheduling and load balancing schemes are properly designed.

MPEG-4, currently being developed by MPEG (Moving Picture Experts Group) [9], is expected to be finalized towards the end of this year. It will become a standard for compression, transmission, and presentation of current and emerging interactive multimedia applications. The objective of MPEG-4 is to support content-based communication, access and manipulation of digital objects which can be natural or synthetic [15]. With a flexible toolbox approach, MPEG-4 is capable of supporting diverse new functionalities and satisfy various application requirements on different aspects and hence will cover a broad range of present and future multimedia applications. In addition, due to its extensible system configuration architecture, MPEG-4 is aimed to be more compatible with advanced new technologies.

Because of its object-based features and flexible toolbox approach, MPEG-4 is considerably more complex and demands more computing power than previous video coding standards. Thus, a software-based implementation using parallel processing seems to be only viable approach for building MPEG-4 based systems.

Previous coding standards such has H.261, MPEG1/2, and H.263 have been implemented using either software (see [3], [4], [5] and [18]) or hardware-based (see [23], [2], [17] and [10]) approaches with each having its pros and cons. Interactive multimedia systems, such as digital television, that require real-time multimedia communication, both the encoder and decoder are desired to be highly efficient and must provide close to real-

---

†. This work was supported by the Hong kong Telecom Institute of Information Technology. The authors would also like to thank Dr. Robert Yung of Sun Microsystems and Dr. Ya-Qin Zhang of Sarnoff Corporation for technical support.

329

time operations. For example, mobile communication and database access require very low bitrate video coding and error resilience across various networks; virtual reality requires integration of natural and synthetic hybrid object coding; interactive video games require a high degree of object based interactivity. Instead of traditional frame based interaction such as fast-forward, fast-backward, etc., new ways of interactively are needed to efficiently realize such applications.

MPEG-4, due to its content-based representation nature and flexible configuration structure, is considerably more complex than previous standards. Any MPEG-4 hardware implementation is likely to be very much application specific. Therefore, software-based implementation is a natural and viable option. The main problem with such an approach is the requirement of a huge amount of computing power to support real-time encoding and decoding operations. As elaborated in the subsequent section, although MPEG-4 encoding is highly suitable for implementing using parallel and distributed systems, it is nevertheless a non-trivial task because of the unpredictable nature of MPEG-4 workload.

We are building an MPEG-4 based interactive multimedia environment for supporting applications in the areas of CAD, teaching, and animation. And as a part of this system, we have implemented an MPEG-4 encoder with a software-based approach using parallel processing. As illustrated in Figure 1, the system is conceptually based on a client-server model, with a number of clients making interactive requests to a server. The server encodes and delivers the requested information using MPEG-4 format. The problem addressed here is the implementation of MPEG-4 encoder which is done using a distributed cluster of workstations.

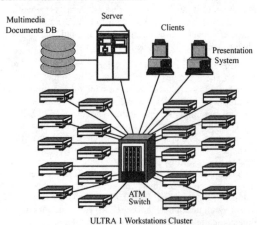

Figure 1: The MPEG-4 based interactive multimedia system.

The rest of this paper is arranged in the following manner: Section 2 gives a brief overview of MPEG-4 video verification model. Section 3 describes the proposed implementation approach in detail. A real-time scheduling algorithm is proposed to schedule various sub-tasks of the encoder. A dynamic shape-adaptive data partitioning scheme is also proposed to further divide the data of a sub-task. Section 4 provides the experimental results. The last section concludes the paper by providing an overview of our ongoing research in this area and future avenues of extending this work.

2 Overview of MPEG-4 Video

MPEG-4 is scheduled to become an international standard in November 1998. During the development, the so called "Verification Model" (VM) methodology is adopted to specify the candidate technologies which may be included in the final standard [14]. The VM is supposed to evolve through a core experimental process [19]. MPEG-4 video VM is one of the main parts of MPEG-4 with the objective to support three major functionalities: content-based interactivity, coding efficiency, and universal access [21]. Its bitrate can range from 10kbits/s up to several Mbits/s. The spatial resolutions include SQSIF/SQCIF, QSIF/QCIF, SIF/CIF, 4*SIF/CIF, and CCIR601. In contrast to the existing 'frame-based' or 'pixel-based' standards, such as MPEG-1/MPEG-2 and H.261/H.263, MPEG-4 video is object-based hybrid coding standard which specifies the technologies for representing and processing video object efficiently to support various content-based functionalities within the compression domain.

Figure 2 shows the conceptual architecture of MPEG-4 based multimedia systems. A user using a decoder can access arbitrarily shaped objects in the scene or send a request to the encoder which can manipulate the objects and deliver the requested objects. The encoder compresses the data and includes the additional necessary information such as the scene description and synchronization requirements.

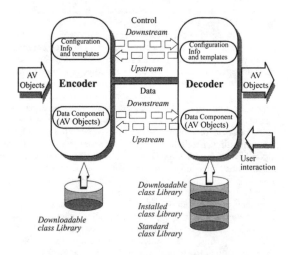

Figure 2: Overall MPEG-4 system architecture.

Figure 3 is the overall structure of the MPEG-4 video codec (encoder and decoder) which is based on the concept of video object planes (VOPs) defined as the instances of video objects at a given time. As illustrated in Figure 4, a video may have many sessions and each session may involve many objects or layers of objects which in turn may have multiple instances in time. A VOP lasts over a number of video frames.

The video encoder is composed of a number of identical VOP encoders. Each object is segmented from the input video signal and goes through the same encoding scheme separately. The bitstreams of different VOPs are then multiplexed and transmitted. At the decoder, the received bitstream are demultiplexed and decoded by each VOP decoder. The

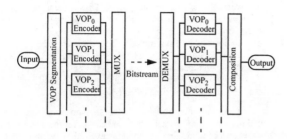

Figure 3: MPEG-4 video codec (encoder and decoder) structure.

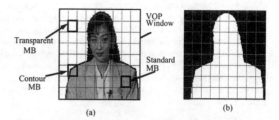

Figure 5: Representation of the VOP (person Akiyo). (a) Image of original 'Akiyo' VOP; (b) Binary alpha plane of the VOP

reconstructed video objects are then composited by the composition information (which is sent along with the bitstream) and presented to the user. The user interaction with the objects such as scaling, dragging, replacement and linking can be handled either in the encoder or in the decoder.

In order to encode the arbitrarily shaped VOPs, MPEG-4 defines the "VOP window" as the tightest rectangular of the VOP with the minimum number of macroblocks to represent the VOP. There are three kinds of macroblock (MB) within the VOP window, as depicted in Figure 5, the transparent MB, the contour MB and the standard MB. The contour and standard macroblocks include the pixels belonging to the VOP image, and transparent MB lies completely outside the object.

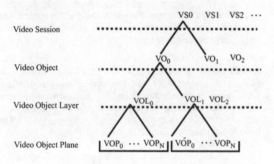

Figure 4: The concept of video object planes.

Each VOP encoder consists of three main functions: shape coding, motion estimation/compensation, and texture coding (see Figure 6). When the shape of a VOP is the standard rectangular size, MPEG-4 encoder structure is similar to that of MPEG1/2 encoder, shape coding can be skipped.

Shape coding is used to compress the alpha plane information which indicates the object region and contour within the scene. There are two types of alpha planes: binary alpha plane and grey scale plane, with both having the same format as the luminance file. The binary alpha plane is encoded by the algorithm called *content-based arithmetic encoding* (CAE). And the grey scale alpha plane is encoded by a block based DCT (Discrete Cosine Transform) with motion compensation which is similar to texture coding.

Motion estimation and compensation (ME/MC) are used to reduce temporal redundancies. Motion prediction is performed on the current block to find the best matched block within the

search window in the previous frame; the block size can be either 16×16 or 8×8. The motion vector which is the displacement between the current and the best matched block from the previous frame are then coded with respect to the neighboring three motion vectors already transmitted. In addition to the basic motion technique, unrestricted ME/MC, advanced prediction mode and bidirectional ME/MC (especially for B-frame) are supported by the MPEG-4 video VM to obtain a significant quality improvement. Unrestricted motion estimation extends the predicted VOP to a large enough size and performs ME/MC over the VOP boundaries. Thus, the motion vectors may be outside the predicted VOP area. Such a mode can achieve improved video quality when the object is moved by the camera or the object is located on the picture edge. In the advanced mode, each macroblock may have one, two, or four vectors. The advanced mode also uses *overlapped block motion compensation* for luminance, which can provide a significant quality improvement with a little increase in complexity.

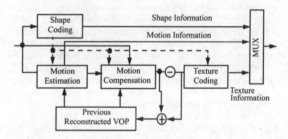

Figure 6: VOP encoder structure.

Since the shape of a VOP may be arbitrary and could vary over time, a padding technique is applied on the blocks on the previously reconstructed VOP borders to fill the values of the pixels outside the object. This allows polygon matching instead of block matching for rectangular image. SAD (Sum of Absolute Difference) is used as the error measure due to its lower computational complexity. SAD is calculated only on the pixels inside the object.

The texture coding which deals with the intra and residual data after motion compensation of VOPs includes algorithms that are similar or identical to the ones used in H.263. A 2D DCT is performed on each macroblock. The DC and AC coefficients are then quantized by either MPEG or H.263 quantization method. For I-VOP and P-VOP, the intra DC and

AC coefficients can be predicted from the corresponding coefficients in the previous neighboring blocks to get the differential DC/AC values. After using a scanning method (such as zigzag scan, alternate-horizontal scan and alternate-vertical scan), the quantized transform coefficients are further coded by variable length coding (VLC). The data of the blocks on the boundary of the object can be coded by low pass extrapolation (LPE) padding and shape adaptive DCT (SA-DCT).

MPEG-4 also supports scalable coding of video objects in both spatial and temporal domains, and provides error resilience across various media. In addition to the above basic technologies used in the encoder structure, the toolbox approach of MPEG-4 video makes it possible to achieve more improvement for some special cases by dedicated tools. Further details on the coding and syntax of MPEG-4 video can be found in [16].

3 Parallelizing the MPEG-4 Encoder

Since MPEG-4 supports many new functionalities that are not available in the existing standards, it will cover a broad range of multimedia applications, such as interactive video games, intra/internet multimedia mailing, and content-based database access. Most of these applications have real-time requirements which demand the codec to be highly efficient. In order to deal with arbitrarily shaped objects, more sophisticated techniques are needed to achieve an efficient compression. But this can introduce extra complexity in the encoder which in turn requires additional computational power. Since the encoder of MPEG-4 video is much more complex and time consuming in computing than the decoder, it is more challenging to speedup the computation in the encoder.

As mentioned earlier, no hardware-based MPEG-4 encoder can fully support the flexible and extensible features of MPEG-4 standard. The object-oriented nature of MPEG-4 requires a highly flexible and somewhat programmable encoder which is more feasible using a software-based approach. But the computational requirement of a software-based encoder is simply too enormous to be handled by a single processor PC or even a very fast workstation. It is, therefore, natural to exploit the high computational power offered by a high-performance parallel or distributed system. In our MPEG-4 based multimedia project, we have implemented an encoder on a cluster of dedicated workstations that collectively work as a virtual parallel machine. The architecture of MPEG-4 encoder as shown Figure 3 also happens to be very suitable for distributed computing. Each input VOP is encoded separately and efficient performance can be achieved by decomposing the whole encoder into separate tasks with individual VOP encoders and running them simultaneously. However, the task of parallelizing the MPEG-4 encoder VM on a cluster of workstations is a non-trivial as it requires a careful data distribution and scheduling of various parts of the encoder to ensure that spatio-temporal relationships between various VOPs are preserved.

In a simpler approach, one could use a single workstation to encode one VOP. But this scheme does not fully exploit the computational power of the system because it is not scalable and the degree of parallelism offered by this approach is rather limited. A more effective approach is to form groups of workstations, with each group working on a single VOP while parallelism is exploited by further partitioning the VOP among the workstations within the group. This scheme, however, requires a careful partitioning of both control and data. Furthermore, the sizes of VOPs change with time implying that distribution and partitioning of VOPs will need to be adjusted accordingly. Since this must be done in real-time, the cost of scheduling and distribution must be kept low to ensure that the benefits gained from an efficient parallelization are not outweighed by a long time taken by the scheduler.

In our scheme, the control parallelism is achieved by making groups of workstations, and assigning the task of one VOP encoding to one group. However, the distribution of VOPs to different groups of workstations must consider the relationships between the VOPs. This is done by using a scheduling algorithm that distributes VOPs to various groups of workstations in accordance with their priorities so that their encoding is complete before their presentation deadlines.

Data parallelism is exploited by dividing the data of a VOP among the workstations within a group, allowing further gain in computing speed. For distributing the data of a VOP various partitioning schemes are possible. The details of the scheduling algorithm and data partitioning schemes are described below.

3.1 Real-time Scheduling

In MPEG-4 video VM encoder, one of the most important issues to consider is the synchronization of various video objects. Each object may have certain presentation timing constrains which, in turn, may be dependent on the other objects. The playout time requirement and associated synchronization constrains among multiple video objects must be satisfied in real-time to guarantee a smooth flow of video sequence presented to the user.

The objective of real-time scheduling is to assign the tasks to the available processors and determine the execution order of each task so that tasks are completed before their deadlines [20]. A real-time scheduling can be characterized as being either static and dynamic. In static scheduling, the algorithm determines the schedule with the complete knowledge of all the tasks in advance. In contrast, a dynamic scheduling algorithm deals with task assignment at run-time because the information about the tasks is not available in advance. Static scheduling incurs little run-time cost but cannot adapt to the indeterministic behavior of the system. On the other hand, dynamic scheduling is more flexible as it can be adjusted to system changes but incurs a high run-time cost.

According to MPEG-4 video hierarchical syntax structure shown in Figure 4, we can employ a completely static scheduling at the VS level which requires the knowledge of all the objects within the session beforehand. Alternatively, we can perform dynamic scheduling on a frame by frame basis at the VOP level so as to adapt to the VOPs variations. Since in an MPEG-4 video session, the number of objects may change from time to time, their characteristics such as frame rate, playout deadlines, and spatial resolutions may also be different. Thus, while a static scheduling scheme at a VS level is feasible for some non-real-time applications, its is not suitable for most real-time applications because of the unpredictable characteristics of VOPs.

In our implementation, we have designed a hybrid static and dynamic scheduling scheme applied at the VO level. The knowledge of video objects can only be known after observing a time period. During that period, either the objects variation is arisen by the operations such as user interaction or content database retrieval, or the characteristics of these objects are relatively stable. The length of the period depends on the availability of objects. When a new object is added or dropped, we have to reschedule the tasks for the next period. The main advantage of such scheduling is its ability to adapt to the variation of both deterministic and indeterministic video objects on line with a little overhead. Figure 7 shows the playout time chart of a general MPEG-4 video example. The session has 4 video objects (VOs); VO_0, VO_1, VO_3 start at time 0, and VO_2 starts at time unit 4. VO_0 and VO_1 end at time unit 4, while VO_2 and VO_3 end at time unit 12. The frame rates of VOs are different. The duration of a frame for VO_1 is 1 time unit, while the duration of a frame is 2 for VO_1 and 4 for VO_2 and VO_3.

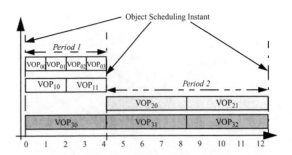

Figure 8: Scheduling time chart for video session.

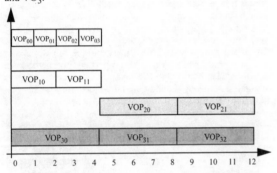

Figure 7: Playout time chart for video session.

Figure 8 indicates the scheduling period at VO level for the case of Figure 7. The scheduling period is bounded by the successive object scheduling instants (OSIs) and the complexity of the scheduling depends on the number of OSIs during the whole video session.

A number of scheduling algorithms have been developed for both distributed and parallel systems [8]. In our implementation, we use a variant of the *earliest-deadline-first* (EDF) algorithm which has been widely employed in many applications [22]. The principle of this algorithm is that the tasks with earlier deadlines are assigned higher priorities and run before tasks with lower priorities. In our implementation, VOPs with the earlier playout deadlines or synchronization points get to be encoded and delivered first. For the tasks with the same deadline, we assign a portion of available processors to each object, with the number of allocated processors depending upon the size ratio among these objects because a video object with a larger size generally requires more computing and vice versa.

3.2 Dynamic Shape-Adaptive Data Partition

Parallel programming paradigms can be classified into various models such as object-oriented model, control-parallel model, and data-parallel model. Data parallel paradigm emphasizes exploiting parallelism in a large data sets such as a video session which usually consists of a large amount of data. The main idea of data partitioning in video encoding is to decompose the whole frame data into a number of data blocks and map these blocks onto the corresponding processors. Because the processors of the parallel program perform the computation on their local memories and run the program on

the data blocks simultaneously, a high speedup can be achieved.

The exchange of the data and synchronization in a distributed system can only be done through message passing among processors. However, the communication overhead can penalize the gain achieved due to parallelism. Most tools specified by the MPEG-4 video standard, such as padding, DCT, quantization, and VLC, are block-based algorithms and perform the computing restricted within a macroblock. Therefore, we can employ macroblock-based data partition to map the integer number of macroblocks to each processor and enable the compression algorithm to be done locally. This is done by setting the workstations in a virtual two dimensional topology and then mapping the data onto the topology. As for motion estimation which finds the motion vector of current macroblock from the previous frame search window, both the current block data and search window data are involved in the computation.

To reduce the interprocessor communication overhead, we use an overlapped partition approach which minimizes the data exchange during the motion estimation procedure, but requires more memory in each processor to store the entire search window data from the previously processed frame (as shown in Figure 9). This approach allows to perform motion estimation on all the processors independently since the required data are available in the local memories.

The second problem to be addressed is the issue of load balancing. Due to the object-based nature of MPEG-4 video, the size and location of each object may vary with time, and such situations cannot be predicted beforehand. Therefore no matter how initial tasks are assigned, the workloads of the processors will become unbalanced later on, which will cause some processors to be highly loaded while others are idle or lightly loaded. Furthermore, some computationally intensive algorithms of the encoder are data dependent and their execution time are different to different data region. For example, some algorithms are performed on all macroblocks while others just acted on contour and standard MBs. Thus the problem of load balancing should be addressed carefully in the parallel processing in order to achieve real-time video encoding.

Figure 10 shows several commonly used partitioning methods. Strip-wise partition divides the whole VOP window horizontally or vertically into n subregions for n processors. It is easy to determine the area of subregions for corresponding processors. Block-wise partition divides the VOP window

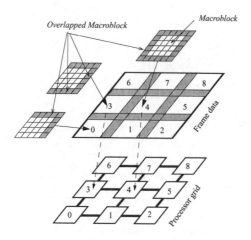

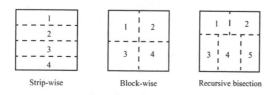

Figure 9: Overlapped data partitioning example.

Figure 10: Common partitioning methods.

Strip-wise   Block-wise   Recursive bisection

evenly along both the horizontal and vertical dimensions. The number of boundary pixels of the subregion is minimum, but the number of processors to be used is restricted and not suitable for heterogeneous systems. Recursive bisection method divides the whole VOP window recursively in binary fashion [7]. It is capable of optimally equally distributing the computational load, while it is relatively expensive to execute the recursive operations during the decomposition.

Due to the unpredictable variation of MPEG-4 objects, any simple and static partitioning scheme will cause workload imbalances which result in lower overall performance. A dynamic partition scheme can handle the indeterministic behavior of the system, but it depends on the trade-off between the balancing quality and overhead run-time cost [1]. In our implementation, since the partition must be done in real-time, the cost of partition and redistribution must be kept low to ensure that the benefits gained from an efficient parallelization are not negated by a long time taken by the partitioning method.

In order to adapt object variations and minimize partitioning cost, we developed a shape-adaptive data partition method to guarantee the workload balancing during the whole video session with low run-time overhead and fine granularity.

First, the entire MPEG-4 video session is defined as a a number of time intervals. The time interval boundary depends on the variation of the VOP window size. A new time interval begins whenever a VOP window changes above a certain

threshold. Since the knowledge of the video objects can be obtained at the beginning of the interval, we then perform the shape-adaptive partition within each time interval. During that interval, we can assume that the spatial computation distribution is relatively stable and no need to change partitions. Therefore, the proposed load balancing can handle the object variation with minimum overhead run-time. Since most of the algorithms are macroblock-based, we employ macroblock-based data partition to map an integer number of macroblocks to each processor and enable the compression algorithm to be done locally.

Most data partitioning methods restrict the subregion to be rectangular blocks to avoid a messy problem of the data structure. For MPEG-4, when the object is large enough and almost fill the VOP window, these methods may achieve good load balancing because the contour and standard MBs are likely to be distributed uniformly among multiprocessors. While in general cases, some subregions of the window may be full of transparent MBs while others may be full of contour and/or standard MBs. Therefore, no partitioning method can equally distribute the rectangular subregion in a straightforward way. In addition, the object size may become too tricky to do the strip-wise or block-wise partition.

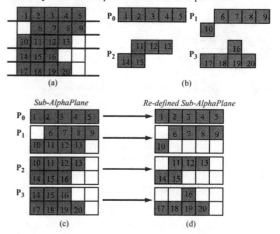

Figure 11: Arbitrary partitioning example.

Here, we present a shape-adaptive partitioning method whose subregions may have arbitrary shape, and the rectangular sub-alpha plane is further redefined to avoid the unnecessary computation for each processor. As depicted in Figure 11, the gray blocks represent the contour and standard MBs while the white blocks represent transparent MBs. By using the alpha plane information, we can get the statistical distribution of the contour and standard MBs. Then they are equally assigned to a given number of processors. As illustrated in Figure 11 (a), there are 20 contour and standard MBs within the window. Each processor is assigned 5 contour and standard MBs. Since each processor (P_0 to P_3) may get arbitrarily shaped subregions (see Figure 11 (b)), it may require complex data structures for processing. To overcome this problem, we extend these subregions to rectangular regions called sub-AlphaPlane (see Figure 11 (c)). Since some of the sub-alpha planes contain macroblocks which are redundant, we redefine the sub-Alpha planes by labelling those macroblocks as transparent MBs in order to avoid unnecessary computation (see Figure 11 (d)). For example, Processor 3 (P_3) encodes only the subregion that includes the contour and standard macroblock from 16 to 20 as shown in Figure 11 (b). In order to get a rectangular subregion which contains those blocks, we extend this subregion such that the whole sub-alpha plane contains the contour and standard MBs from 14 to 20. Then we define the 14th and 15th MB as the transparent MB to form a redefined sub-alpha plane (as shown in Figure 11 (d)). Therefore, processor 3 still processes 5 contour and standard MBs while keeps the subregion rectangular.

Because such a partition is based on macroblock decomposition, the granularity is small allowing a finer load balancing of the workload among the multiprocessors. In addition, by keeping the data block for each processor rectangular, the decoder can recover the entire object easily. Because the syntax definition of each bitstream contains the position and size information of the rectangular block, reconstruction of the object is just equal to the composition of the data blocks together and no bitstream combination required.

4 Experimental Results

The proposed parallel approach has been tested on a cluster of 20 UltraSparc-I workstations connected by a ForeSystems ATM switch (ASX-1000). The cluster is virtually configured as virtual 2D processor grid which is independent of the hardware topology.

For inter-processor communication and synchronization, we use *Message Passing Interface* (MPI) [24], ensuring the portability of our MPEG-4 video encoder across various machines. MPI is an industrial standard designed by MPI Forum for supporting a portable message-passing parallel program on massively parallel computers as well as networks of workstations. MPI includes the syntax and semantics of point-to-point and collective communication routines which are useful to most parallel programmers.

Several experiments have been performed on a sets of MPEG-4 video test sequences by using a number of workstations ranging from 1 to 20. A fast block-based motion estimation algorithm [12] is adopted to speedup the computation of motion estimation while maintaining the visual quality close to that of the full search.

Our experiments included video sequences of QCIF resolutions which are chosen from different classes of MPEG-4 library and represent various characteristic in terms of spatial detail and movement.

Figure 12 shows the encoding rates for different MPEG-4 video test sequences by using various numbers of workstations, and Figure 13 is the overall speedup ratio. Figure 14 shows the comparison between the static strip-wise/block-wise partition, object-based partition [11] and our proposed method for the test sequence 'Children21' with QCIF format. We can observe that a high real-time performance has been achieved by our method.

Figure 15 is one of the alpha planes of VOP 'Children21', we can observe that most transparent macroblocks located between two boys. Neither the block-wise or strip-wise partition can make the workload balancing when the number of processors increased. It is unavoidable that some processor might deal with the data block full of the transparent

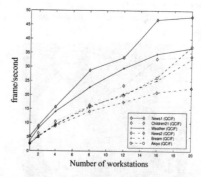

Figure 12: Encoding frame rate.

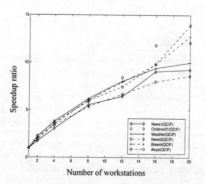

Figure 13: Overall speedup.

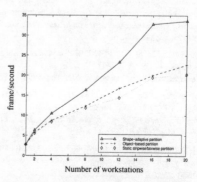

Figure 14: Partitioning performance comparison.

macroblocks that require little computation. Some processors need to process the entire data block that is full of the computationally intensive contour/standard macroblocks. The proposed object-based partitioning method [11] can determine the optimal rectangular grid from the available block-wise/strip-wise partitioning grid, and its performance is better than fixed grid partitioning, especially when the VOP shape changes significantly. One limitation of this method is that the number of possible grids is limited. When the number of processors increases, the same problem with fixed block-wise/strip-wise partition will occur. The shape-adaptive partition can guarantee the workload balancing in such a case since it can equally distribute the computationally intensive macroblocks to each processor without using an exhaustive search. Therefore, a higher encoding rate can be achieved compared to the other two methods.

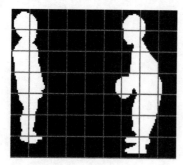

Figure 15: Alpha plane of VOP 'Children21' (QCIF).

5 Conclusions

In this paper a software-based parallel implementation of MPEG-4 video VM encoder using a cluster of workstations has been proposed. The experimental results on various test sequences have been provided and an encoding rate higher that real-time has been achieved on most sequences. The contribution of our work includes the use of a shape-adaptive data parallel scheme, and a real-time scheduling algorithm to implement MPEG-4 video encoder. In our present work, we are exploiting dynamic load balancing algorithms for heterogeneous computing environment for MPEG-4 applications.

References

[1] I. Ahmad, "Resource Management of Parallel and Distributed Systems with Static Scheduling: Challenges, Solutions and New Problems," *Concurrency: Practice and Experience*, vol. 7, no. 5, Aug. 1995, pp. 339-348.

[2] T. Akiyama, *et al.*, "MPEG-2 Video Codec using Image Compression DSP," *IEEE Transactions on Consumer Electronics*, vol. 40, no. 3, pp. 466-472, Aug. 1994.

[3] S. M. Akramullah, I. Ahmad, M. L. Liou, "A Portable and Scalable MPEG-2 Video Encoder on Parallel and Distributed Computing Systems," *Proc. of the SPIE*, vol. 2727, PT. 2, pp. 973-984, Mar. 1996.

[4] S. M. Akramullah, I. Ahmad, M. L. Liou, "A Software Based H.263 Video Encoder using Network of workstations," *Proceedings of SPIE*, vol. 3166, Aug. 1997.

[5] S. M. Akramullah, I. Ahmad, M. L. Liou, "Performance of a Software-Based MPEG-2 Video Encoder on Parallel and Distributed Systems," *IEEE Transactions on CSVT*, vol. 7, no. 4, pp. 687-695, Aug. 1997.

[6] T.E. Anderson, D.E. Culler, and D. Patterson, "A Case for NOW (Networks of Workstations)," *IEEE Micro*, vol.15, no.1, pp. 54-64, Feb. 1995.

[7] M. J. Berger and S. H. Bokhari, "A Partitioning Strategy for Nonuniform Problems on Multiprocessors," *IEEE Trans. on Computers, vol. C-36, no.5, pp.570-580*, May 1987.

[8] S. Cheng *et al.*, "Scheduling Algorithms for Hard-Real Time Systems - a Brief Survey," *Hard Real-time Systems*, IEEE Computer Society press, 1988.

[9] L. Chiariglione, "MPEG and Multimedia Communications," *IEEE Transactions on CSVT*, vol. 7, no. 1, pp. 5-18, Feb. 1997.

[10] H.A. Chow, H. Alnuweiri, "An FPGA-Based Transformable Coprocessor for MPEG Video Processing," *Proceedings of the SPIE - The International Society for Optical Engineering.* vol. 2914, pp. 308-320, 1996.

[11] Y. He, I. Ahmad and M. L. Liou, "An Implementation of MPEG-4 Video Verification Model Encoder using Parallel Processing," *Proceedings of the third Asia-Pacific Conference on Communications, pp.56-59*, Dec. 1997.

[12] Z. L. He and M. L. Liou, "A High Performance Fast Search Algorithm for Block Matching Motion Estimation," *IEEE Trans. on CSVT, vol.7, no.5, pp 826-828*, Oct. 1997.

[13] ITU-T Recommendation H.263 Draft, "Video Coding for Narrow Telecommunication Channel at <64 kbit/s," Apr. 1995.

[14] ISO/IEC, "Verification Model Development and Core Experiments," ISO/IEC JTC1/SC29/WG11 N1110, Nov. 1995.

[15] ISO/IEC, "MPEG-4 Proposal Package Description (PPD)," ISO/IEC JTC1/SC29/WG11 N0988, July 1995.

[16] ISO/IEC, "MPEG-4 Video Verification Model Version 8.0," ISO/IEC JTC1/SC29/WG11 N1796, July 1997.

[17] D. Kim, *et al.*, "A Real-Time MPEG Encoder using a Programmable Processor," *IEEE Transactions on Consumer Electronics* vol. 40, no. 2, pp. 161-170, May 1994.

[18] J. Nang and J. Kim, "An Effective Parallelizing Scheme of MPEG-1 Video Encoding on Ethernet-Connected Workstations," *Proceedings. Advances in Parallel and Distributed Computing (Cat.No.97TB100099)* pp. 4-11, March 1997.

[19] F. Pereira, and T. Alpert, "MPEG-4 Video Subjective Test Procedures and Results", *IEEE Transactions on CSVT*, vol. 7, no. 1, pp. 32-51, Feb. 1997.

[20] M. Pinedo, "Scheduling: Theory, Algorithms and System," Prentice Hall, 1995.

[21] T. Sikora, "The MPEG-4 Video Standard Verification Model," *IEEE Transactions on CSVT*, vol. 7, no. 1, pp. 19-31, Feb. 1997.

[22] J.M. Sohn, and G.Y. Kim, "Earliest-Deadline-First Scheduling on Nonpreemptive Real-Time Threads for a Continuous-Media Server," *Proceedings of High-Performance Computing and Networking. International Conference and Exhibition*, pp. 950-956, 1997.

[23] H.H. Taylor, D. Chin and A.W. Jessup, "An MPEG Encoder Implementation on the Princeton Engine Video Supercomputer," *Data Compression Conference 1993, pp. 420-429 1993*.

[24] D. W. Walker, and J.J. Dongarra, "MPI: a Standard Message Passing Interface," *Supercomputer* vol. 12, no. 1, pp. 56-68, Jan. 1996.

Session 5B
Compiler II: Implementation Strategies

Chair: Prith Banerjee
Northwestern University

Efficient Backtracking in And-Parallel Implementations of Non-deterministic Languages

Enrico Pontelli & Gopal Gupta*
Department of Computer Science
New Mexico State University
{epontell,gupta}@cs.nmsu.edu

Abstract

We consider the problem of efficiently supporting backtracking in independent and-parallel non-deterministic systems. We consider this problem in the context of logic programming, although the solution proposed is sufficiently general to be applicable to any non-deterministic language or system. Our model employs various optimizations, as well as a novel memory organization scheme in which processors are allowed to traverse each others' stacks to achieve this efficiency. The solution developed has been implemented in the ACE Prolog system. The performance of the system is analyzed on a variety of non-deterministic benchmarks.
Keywords: *Backtracking, and-parallelism*

1. Introduction

Non-determinism is the potential existence of multiple solutions to a problem. Search problems, generate-and-test problems, constrained optimization problems, etc., fall in this class. Non-determinism has also been incorporated in many programming languages: logic programming languages, concurrent constraint languages, rule based languages, and even in imperative languages [1].
Non-determinism present in a problem offers a rich source of parallelism. A problem is usually expressed as a *goal* to be achieved/proved/solved together with *rules* (or clauses) that specify how a given goal can be reduced to other subgoals. Given a (sub-)goal, there may be multiple ways of reducing it (non-determinism). On applying a rule, a (sub-)goal may reduce to a number of smaller (conjunctive) subgoals, each of which need to be solved to prove the original (sub-)goal. Two main forms of parallelism can be exploited in problems that admit non-determinism: *1 Or-parallelism:* the different potential solutions can be searched in parallel—i.e., given a subgoal, there may be

multiple rules that can be used to reduce it. *2 And-parallelism*: while looking for a specific solution, the different operations involved can be executed in parallel (i.e., reduce conjunctive subgoals in parallel). And-parallelism is distinguished in *Independent And-parallelism (IAP)*—only non-communicating subgoals are executed in parallel—and *Dependent And-parallelism (DAP)*.

A system that exploits parallelism from problems with non-determinism may look simple to implement at first, but experience shows that indeed it is quite a difficult task. A naive parallel implementation may incur a severe overhead compared to a corresponding state-of-the-art sequential system. This may cause a naive parallel system to run many times slower on one processor compared to a similar sequential system. Reduction of parallel overhead results in improved *sequential efficiency* (performance of the parallel system on one processor) and *absolute efficiency* (overall execution time). We can identify two major sources of inefficiency: scheduling (not dealt with in this paper) and non-determinism. Supporting non-determinism in and-parallel systems is extremely complex. Backtracking is an inherently sequential process which requires to produce a correct semantics, the traversal of the computation structure in a well-defined order. This paper overviews the issues involved in supporting non-determinism and backtracking in an *independent and-parallel* system and presents a simple and effective solution to the problem. Its simplicity guarantees the possibility of efficient implementation, and its generality allows its application to different and-parallel systems and frameworks. In the rest of the paper, we take logic programming systems as representatives of non-deterministic systems, and we illustrate the application of our model to the ACE [11] parallel Prolog system.

2. Independent And-Parallelism

Practical models and systems which exploit IAP from Prolog programs [6, 8, 12] have been generally designed for shared memory platforms and are based on the *marker*

---

*Ongoing work is supported by NSF Grants CCR 96-25358, HRD 96-28450, INT 95-15256, and CDA 97-29848.

model [6, 13]. This model has been shown to be practical and proved capable of obtaining significant speedups with respect to state-of-the-art sequential systems. Our design of the and-parallel component of ACE [11] is influenced by this model but adopts a different memory organization. As in the most of the proposed schemes for IAP [6, 8, 12], ACE exploits IAP using a recomputation based scheme [11]. We adopt the solution of *restricting* parallelism to a nested *parbegin-parend* structure. The different branches are assigned to different *and-agents* (i.e., processors working in and-parallel with each other). Since we are exploiting IAP, only independent subgoals are allowed to be executed concurrently by different and-agents. The ACE compiler [2, 10] performs automatic generation of *parallel annotations*.

The forward execution of a parallel conjunction can be divided into two phases. The first phase, called the *inside phase*, starts with the opening of the parallel call and the distribution of the subgoals between the different and-agents, and ends when each subgoal has reported a successful solution. Once the call is completed, then the *continuation*, i.e., the sequential code which follows the parallel call, is begun and the *outside phase* is entered. The execution of a subgoal in a parallel call uses a *segment* in each of the stacks belonging to an and-agent. In most models for IAP these segments are physically delimited using special data structures (*markers*).

3. Backtracking in IAP

In the presence of parallel calls, sequential backtracking must be modified in order to deal with computations which are spread across processors—more than one goal may be executing in parallel, one or more of which may encounter failure and backtrack at the same time. Thus, unlike in a sequential system, there is no *unique backtracking point*. Furthermore, the choice-point which offers a cure to a failure may lie within a segment belonging to an agent different from the one that encountered the failure, creating unsafe situations where different agents may be operating on the same stack segment. It must be ensured that the backtracking semantics is such that all solutions are reported, and in correct order. One such backtracking semantics has been originally described in [6]. Consider the goal: a, b, (c & d & e), g, h, where "&" denotes parallel conjunction and "," is used for sequential conjunction. Assuming that all subgoals can unify with more than one rule, there are several possible cases depending upon which subgoal fails: If subgoal a or b fails, sequential backtracking occurs, as usual. Since c, d, and e are mutually independent, if either one of them fails, backtracking must proceed to b, because c, d and e do not affect each other's search space—but see further below. If g fails, backtracking must proceed to the right-most choice point within the parallel subgoals c & d

& e, and re-compute all goals to the right of this choice point. If e were the rightmost choice point and e should subsequently fail, backtracking would proceed to d, and, if necessary, to c. Thus, backtracking within a set of and-parallel subgoals occurs only if initiated by a failure from outside these goals, i.e., "from the right" (also known as *outside backtracking*). If initiated from within, backtracking proceeds outside of all these goals, i.e., "to the left" (also known as *inside backtracking*). The latter behavior is a form of "intelligent" backtracking. When backtracking is initiated from outside, once a choice point is found in a subgoal g, an untried alternative is taken and all the subgoals to the right of g in the parallel conjunction are restarted.

In the presence of the stack segments, the backtracking activity has to "move" in the correct direction. This means that the different segments need to be properly *linked*, in order to allow backtracking to flow from one segment to the *logically* preceding one. In the marker model, the markers represent the entry and exit point of each subgoal. In ACE, as discussed later, segments are directly connected without the need of any additional data structure.

If failure occurs in the inside phase, inside backtracking is used—and the whole parallel call should fail, since all the goals in the parallel conjunction are independent. To realize this, the failing processor should send a *kill signal* to all processors that have stolen a goal from that parallel call, to undo any execution for the stolen goal. After all processors finish undoing the work, the goal before the parallel call will be backtracked over as in standard sequential execution.

3.1. Challenges

Designing and implementing proper mechanisms to *efficiently* support and-parallelism raise very difficult issues.
Logical vs. Physical: Sequential implementations take full advantage of the direct correspondence between logical structure of the execution and its physical layout in the abstract machine's data areas. This allows a considerably simpler execution of very complex operations—e.g., backtracking becomes very efficient, since a choice point on the stack is capable of completely identifying the execution state that exists at its creation time. This is not anymore true when dealing with unrestricted scheduling of goals[1]: the computation can be arbitrarily spread on the stacks of different agents, and the physical order of computations on each stack can be completely different from the logical one. Positioning on a choice point is not sufficient to get a view of a state of the execution (as in sequential computations). This correspondence has to be explicitly recreated, using additional data structures (pointers).
Backtracking Policy: the backtracking semantics described earlier specifies *what* (and *when*) has to be done,

---

[1] We use the term *unrestricted scheduling* to specify that no restrictions are imposed during scheduling on the selection of the next piece of work.

but does not state how backtracking on distributed computations can be implemented. Two approaches are feasible:
1. Private Backtracking: each agent is allowed to backtrack only over parts of the computation in its own stacks.
2. Public Backtracking: each agent is allowed to backtrack on other agents' stacks. Experiments performed in the ACE project have shown that public backtracking behaves considerably better—it only requires occasional locking of choice-points, while private backtracking requires exchanging large number of messages between agents, and most of these are served asynchronously.

Synchronization: any reasonable implementation of inside backtracking—i.e., an implementation which interrupts the execution of a goal as soon as it is determined to be a useless computation—requires communication between the different processors operating on a given parallel call. This is typically realized in the form of kill messages sent by the failing processor to all other subgoals in the parallel call. This imposes complex global synchronization requirements, and is considerably difficult to implement.

Trail Management: one of the main problems in managing backtracking in an and-parallel system is detecting the parts of the trail stack that need to be unwound (i.e., detecting bindings that have to be removed to restore the proper computation state). The current model used by ACE is based on a *segmented view* of the stack, where a segment is defined by a section of the stack between two consecutive choice-points (described next).

Garbage Collection: the use of public backtracking allows recovery of a considerable amount of garbage "on-the-fly" during local backtracking. Nevertheless, garbage collection remains more complicated, due to the lack of correspondence between logical order of backtracking and physical distribution of the computation. Parts of computation which are not on the top of the stack or are accessed remotely may leave behind *holes* in the stacks [11].

3.2. Existing Proposals

The issue of dealing with backtracking in and-parallel system has been tackled by various researchers (e.g., [6, 12, 4]). The execution model presented at the beginning for ACE originated from the scheme presented by Hermenegildo and Nasr [6]. In particular, Hermenegildo and Nasr emphasized the importance of taking advantage of the independence of the subgoals to produce an intelligent backtracking scheme. Nevertheless, many of the models presented did not take sufficiently into account the interaction between the backtracking algorithm and the execution model adopted to support IAP. [11, 12] presented complete schemes describing integration of a intelligent and-parallel backtracking policy into actual and-parallel implementations. The cost of the resulting implementations has been proved to be high, either making backward execution over

and-parallel calls inconvenient [11] or imposing additional overheads on the whole execution [12]. Hermenegildo has presented various static analysis schemes to improve and-parallel executions (e.g., [3]). Hermenegildo et al. [11] described an optimization, *backtracking families*, which allows to take advantage of special features of the computation to improve backtracking. Related optimizations have been presented by Gupta et al. [5]. In the context of dependent and-parallelism, Shen presented [12] an approach to improve backtracking by grouping parallel subgoals.

4. Backtracking in ACE

In typical (sequential) implementations of Prolog, backtracking is used to accomplish different objectives:
Alternatives: backtracking moves in the stack in search of a choice-point with unexplored alternatives.
Physical Memory: the installation of a new alternative implies that the computation between the choice point with unexplored alternatives and the point where backtracking was started is not needed any longer. Thus the scan of the stack can be used to immediately reclaim the memory used by the discarded computation;
Logical Memory: discarding a part of the computation implies not only garbage collecting the memory used, but also making sure that all the *logical* effects of such computation are removed. In particular, the effects of a computation are mainly represented by the collection of variable bindings generated during the computation. For this purpose, Prolog implementations maintain the *trail stack*, which is used to record each (conditional) binding performed.

Only two of these phases are *essential* for the computation, the selection of the alternative—fundamental to allow the computation to restart—and the logical removal of the discarded computation—needed to avoid the new computation from being affected by the discarded one. Most of the existing models do not make the above distinctions and try to accomplish all the three tasks concurrently. As a result these models are very complex—recovering and reusing memory which is "owned" by different processors requires expensive synchronization between the processors.

It is our opinion that in the context of an and-parallel implementation the three tasks above have to be kept separate and dealt with independently. In particular, the task of performing complete on-line garbage collection during backward execution appears to be in conflict with the requirement of being able to quickly switch to the new alternative. In the ACE system, garbage collection is performed on-line only for the part of the computation which is directly controlled by the backtracking processor.

Searching the Alternative: In and-parallel executions, the computation is spread across the stacks of different processors. Thus searching for a choice-point with unexplored alternatives requires additional effort. In particular, the search should be able to move from one stack to another whenever needed, it should be able to detect the *boundaries* of each subgoal, in order to decide when to switch do a different subgoal (which may lie in a different stack), and it should have knowledge of the ordering between the different fragments of the computation spread between the processors. In the marker model [6, 12] this is achieved by using additional data structures (the *markers*) which delimit each subgoal and connect the different subgoals in the correct order via pointers. The need of traversing all the different markers imposes considerable overhead. Furthermore, markers need to be properly created and linked during forward execution. In ACE this is avoided by immediately linearizing the parallel computation during forward execution and removing the need of allocating markers for each subgoal.

Managing the Trail: During sequential execution a single pointer (stored in the choice point) is sufficient to immediately detect the collection of bindings that need to cleared. In the case of and-parallel computations this is not the case. The trail itself is spread across different processors and, apparently, multiple accesses to different trails are needed to achieve the goal of clearing the bindings. For example, in the marker model the markers are used to denote sections of the local trail that are associated to the goal they represent. Thus, untrailing is achieved by traversing the various markers and removing bindings goal by goal. The possibility of having trapped subgoals implies that untrailing may leave behind "holes" in the trail. In ACE this problem has been solved in a different way. The trail is not anymore a stack but it's seen as a linked sequence of trail segments. A single pointer (and no traversals of the computation) is needed to detect the collection of bindings to remove. The process of untrailing is almost as efficient as in the sequential case. In addition to this, the technique illustrated below allows to considerably reduce the number of bindings that need to be untrailed in case of backtracking over a parallel call.

Synchronization during Backtracking: One of the main issues in killing computations (e.g., when the whole parallel call fails) is the removal of the bindings generated during the computation that is killed. In the presence of and-parallel computation, this operation needs to be carefully performed in order to avoid race conditions. If, for example, we are trying to kill the computation containing a, $(b$ $\&$ $c)$, where a, b have been executed by P_i and c by P_j, then a synchronization point needs to be introduced at the level of the parallel call. Without such point, it may happen that P_i returns to its original computation (the one interrupted by the kill message) before P_j completes unwinding b. This may lead to P_j overwriting memory space which has been just allocated on the heap by P_i. This essentially means that, in the presence of a parallel call, the killing of the part of the computation tree above the parallel call may be started only *after* all the subgoals of the parallel call have

been completely killed. The worker P that is in charge of continuing the killing above the parallel call will wait for all the subgoals to be completely removed.

4.1. Compile-time Support for Backtracking in IAP

In the ACE system we make use of a sophisticated compiler [2, 10] that statically annotates the program with both IAP and DAP. The compiler makes use of abstract interpretation to statically infer various properties regarding program's execution. In particular the abstract interpreter used in ACE [2, 10] is capable of providing various information like variable sharing, freeness, independence, granularity and predicate modes. All these information have been combined to support the process of variable protection during program execution, discussed in the next section.

Given a parallel call $(b_1 \& \ldots \& b_n)$ let us denote by *vars*(b_i) the variables present in the goal b_i. The result of the static analysis is used to improve the "independence" of the parallel call from the rest of the computation. In particular, we would like this independence to allow a processor to backtrack to the computation preceding the parallel call without having to worry about the computation performed by the other processors operating on the parallel call. In the previous implementation schemes this is not possible, since parallel subgoals may generate bindings for variables created before the parallel call—thus backtracking cannot proceed outside of the parallel call until all those bindings have been properly removed. This means that independence of subgoals applies for forward execution but does not hold for parallel backtracking. Let us call *external variables* w.r.t. a parallel call P all those variables which appear in the parallel call P but have been created before the parallel call itself. The intuition behind our approach is to try to improve the backward independence by allowing bindings to external variables to be posted only before or after, but not during, the parallel call. Thus, a failure of one subgoal will not prevent the processor from backtracking outside of P, since no bindings to external variables have been posted by other subgoals. Consider the goal:

$$\ldots \quad (\ldots \& b_i[X] \& \ldots) \quad \ldots$$

1. Parallel subgoals are guaranteed to be independent, thus for each variable in $\bigcup_{i=1}^{n}$ *vars*(b_i), there exist at most one goal b_i which will be able to affect the binding status for such variable; *2.* a variable X accessed by a goal b_i which is free after the parallel call can be safely ignored by the management of the parallel call (e.g., no trail/untrail, etc.); *3.* a variable X which has a ground binding before the parallel call is not going to need any special treatment. *4.* any variable which does fall in one of the previous cases is likely to receive a binding during the execution of the subgoal.

The two distinct cases *2.* and *3.* can be approximated using abstract interpretation (sharing, freeness, and groundness detection), and the ACE compiler detects them with good precision [2, 10]. There are two other cases that are not covered. The first one is characterized by the presence of an external variable which is free before the parallel call and bound after it. This case, again, is detectable with good precision via abstract interpretation, using in particular freeness information. In this case, the ACE compiler has been modified to generate a new class of instructions (init_protected, close_protected) which are used to initialize a new variable—which is going to be used by the parallel subgoal instead of the original external one, and to transfer the binding from the new variable to the external one at the end of the parallel call. A sequence of close_protected instructions is generated by the compiler at the end of the parallel call. The remaining case is the one in which an external variable has a partial binding before the parallel call and the binding can be affected by the parallel call. The abstract interpreter approximates this case as a complement of the other cases mentioned before. The compiler attempts to deal with this situation in two ways. A *depth-k* analysis [7] is applied with respect to the external variables in order to guess the structure of the existing bindings. All the variables that can be detected are treated as in the case previously discussed (generating init_protected/close_protected instructions). If depth-k analysis is insufficient to approximate the structure of the binding of an external variable, then a sequence of special instructions (protect_unknown) is generated to refer to the "unknown" parts of the binding. The behaviour of these instructions is illustrated in the next section.

4.2. Run-Time Support

Linearization is aimed at partially recreating the sequential structure of the execution that was lost during the parallel computation. This goal is achieved by *(i)* linearizing the sequence of choice points generated during the parallel computation (see Fig. 1); and *(ii)* connecting the different sections of trail into a linear structure; The advantage of linearization is that outside backtracking can be implemented essentially as sequential backtracking, without the need of traversing complex representations of the computation tree. Choice points are connected to form a linear list which is traversed by backtracking in search of unexplored alternatives. Computations which do not generate alternatives are immediately exposed and do not require any additional step during backtracking. This allows to keep outside backtracking comparable in efficiency to sequential backtracking, and allows to trigger many optimizations [5].

The implementation of choice-point linearization is relatively simple. Choice points are linked in a single-linked list, where each choice-point directly indicates its predecessor. This modification does not introduce overhead and is necessary to allow for IAP execution—to separate between physical and logical organization of the computation. Each

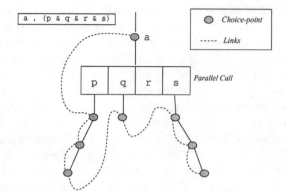

Figure 1. Choice-points linearization

goal descriptor in the parallel call is used to keep track of the beginning and the end points of a parallel computation (as pointers to the choice-point stack). Whenever a subgoal is completed, its first choice-point is linked to the last choice-point of the subgoal on its left, and its last choice-point is made the predecessor of the first choice-point of the goal on the right. If either of these links cannot be immediately established then information to complete the links are attached to the neighboring goals. The use of choice-point linearization allows to support IAP without the need of input and output markers. This implies considerable reduction in memory consumption [5], as well as some improvements in execution time during forward execution, thanks to the avoidance of the marker creation operations. The cost for updating the links between choice-points is negligible.

The second aspect of linearization deals with the management of the trail stack. One of the main reasons behind the speed of sequential backtracking is the ability of detecting the collection of bindings to be removed using a single pointer to the trail stack. In the case of IAP the trail is split into multiple segments associated to the different components of the parallel computation, as show in figure 2. Each choice-point B identifies a segment of the trail which contains the bindings generated between the time of creation of B and the time at which the successive choice-point is allocated. Since we adopt public backtracking, i.e., any processor can backtrack in the space of any other processor, the choice-points may belong to different stacks and refer to trail sections present in different processors areas. The situation, as show in figure 2, is further complicated by deterministic computations (see subgoal c in the figure): this opens the problem of finding a place to keep track of the bindings generated by the deterministic subgoals.

In ACE the trail is represented by a linked list of segments of variable size. A segment is associated to each subgoal at its creation time, and this solves the problem of both deterministic goals—all the bindings will be placed in the subgoal original segment—and the initial bindings (before creation of the first choice-point). Additionally, as in

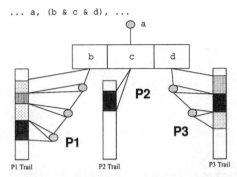

```
... a, (b & c & d), ...
```

Figure 2. Trailing in IAP Computations

the case of choice-points, segments are linked during the completion of a subgoal to create a single linear structure. During backtracking, this allows the determination of the sequence of bindings to untrail just by keeping a pointer to the linear structure of trail segments.

We have experimented with different implementations of this scheme. The first one was based on a simple linked list. This introduces a small penalty due to the need of identifying the links between the different segments. The second implementation reconstructs the linear organization of the trail by adding one level of indirection in the trail access and maintaining a segment table. The third scheme is similar to the first, with the difference that there are no explicit links between the segments. The switch from one segment to the other is obtained by pushing the trail pointer itself at the beginning of each trail segment. During untrailing the trail pointer is modified as any other variable. This last implementation behaves far better than the other two, reducing the overhead of backtracking to a negligible amount.

Variable Protection: the intuition behind variable protection is to extend the notion of independence to the level of variable bindings. Thus we want to make computations independent of each others at the level of public bindings created. The goal of this is to allow inside backtracking to leave the computation without having to suspend on the parallel call and without having to worry about undoing the public bindings created by other processors. Variable protection avoids making the external bindings public until all the subgoals have successfully completed. This is realized:

1. Creating local copies of variables that are known to be free (and to be bound by a parallel subgoal). Thus if X is known to be free before a parallel call and we know that one of the subgoal may produce a binding for it:

```
...  ⟨X free here⟩ ( ... & p(.. X ..) & ...)
          ⟨variable X bound here⟩ ...
```

then the variable protection will simply replace the variable X in the parallel with a brand new variable, introducing an explicit binding at the end of the parallel call:

```
...  ( ... & p(... X1 ...) & ...), X = X1 ...
```

Now, since X1 is a variable seen only by p, in case

of an inside failure no untrailing is immediately necessary. This means that backtracking can proceed outside of the parallel call without the need of synchronizing on it—i.e., without having to wait for all the processors to complete the untrailing of their local bindings. Furthermore, the binding X=X1 is very fast, since it just requires copying one pointer into the variable X. This protection is implemented by pairs of instructions `init_protected/close_protected`—the first one renames the variable while the second one posts the binding to the external variable. This pattern has been frequently observed in parallel benchmarks.

2. Variable protection becomes more complex if a variable accessed by an and-parallel subgoals is, before the parallel call, neither free nor ground. In this case the scheme adopted in the previous situation does not apply, since replacing X by X1 will disallow p from accessing the partial binding for X. We have explored two alternatives. The first one consists of creating a new copy of the term in X with all the variables properly renamed to new ones:

```
copy_term(X,X1), (..& p(..X1..) &..),X=X1,..
```

and performing the explicit binding of X and X1 at the end of the parallel computation. This approach may potentially introduce undesired overhead during forward execution, due to the time spent in creating a copy of the term and performing the final unification.

The second alternative we have considered consists of adapting the variable representation mechanism adopted to support execution of DAP in ACE [9]. This scheme allows to create a special class of variables, characterized by the fact that an attribute can be attached to the dereference link outgoing from the variable; the attribute is automatically checked during dereferencing and a mode flag is set depending on the value of the attribute. This scheme was used to implement the concept of shared variables for ACE: the mode flag was set whenever a dependent variable was dereferenced from one of its consumer goals. The attribute was linked to an information stored in the subgoal descriptor, which was sufficient to determine whether the goal was currently producer or consumer of the shared variable.

The same mechanism has been adapted to create a protected environment for the variables during execution of a parallel subgoal. The access to a annotated variable within a subgoal is unrestricted. The access from outside the subgoal can occur only in two cases: (1) the subgoal has been completed and we have entered the continuation of the parallel call; (2) the parallel call has failed and an alternative from a previous choice point is being explored. The two cases are easily identified by having the filter on the protected variables connected with the termination status of the subgoal. If the filter notifies that the subgoal is completed, i.e., with no parallel call failure, then the filter is immediately removed, thus making the bindings completely public.

If the filter notifies that the subgoal was not completed, then the binding is immediately removed. This second approach can be implemented very efficiently. We have modified the compiler to produce code to generate the initial annotations to the non-free, non-ground variables which are passed to the parallel subgoals. The binding process requires only one additional operation, performed only when an annotated variable is encountered for the first time. The publication of the binding is applied only the first time an annotated variable is encountered outside of the parallel call. The implementation of this mechanism is realized using the protect_unknown instruction. The variable protection mechanism allows to remove the need of suspending backtracking to wait for all the processors to complete.

5. Performance Results

The concrete implementation of these ideas has been realized in the context of the ACE parallel Prolog system. The performance of the forward execution phase of ACE has been described in various works [9, 11] and it has been shown to be highly competitive with the fastest existing IAP and DAP implementations of Prolog available.

With respect to outside backtracking, the performance offered by ACE is particularly good. We have run various benchmarks which involve creation of parallel calls and outside backtracking over them. Figure 3 presents the comparisons in execution time with respect to the corresponding sequential execution for some of them. Some of the benchmarks involved finding additional alternatives during outside backtracking, with relative reactivation of forward execution, while others simply used backtracking to produce a global failure of the execution. In almost all the case analyzed we have observed a global overhead (forward+backward execution) less than 7%, which is a remarkably good result. The only few cases where outside backtracking gave rise to higher overhead are those where subgoals have a very fine grain and failures tend to emerge late in the execution—which is a rather rare situation in most applications [14]. In these rare cases, the situation can be easily lifted using other optimization schemes [5].

The situation for inside backtracking is considerably more complex. In the preliminary implementation of ACE [11] we introduced a direct implementation of the scheme proposed in [6]. The implementation and some preliminary results are discussed in [11]. This system was the first reported implementation of this scheme in the context of IAP/DAP (successively Shen [12] presented performance results for a parallel implementation of DAP). The scheme for inside backtracking introduces excessive overhead and often results in slow down w.r.t. sequential execution—mainly due to the need of synchronizing over parallel calls.

The current version of ACE replaces the older scheme with the mechanisms presented in the previous sections,

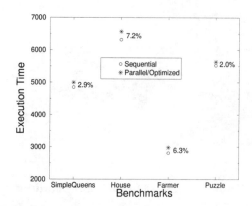

Figure 3. Outside/Sequential Backtracking

compile-time detection of variable status, linearization and variable protections. Once again, the only system we had available for the comparison purposes was the older version of ACE—DASWAM [12] did not report results on this matter, and &-Prolog unofficially reported similar problems. Furthermore, we believe that the implementation of the traditional scheme for inside backtracking realized in ACE system was highly optimized and stretched to achieve the best performance. Table 1 presents the performance results achieved on a representative pool of benchmarks which perform inside backtracking (times in sec.; *old* refers to unoptimized execution, *new* to the new system; times on Sun Sparc). The benchmarks are modifications of traditional benchmarks; these modifications attempt to create examples representative of the various possible backtracking situations. All the modifications are natural, i.e., they are not forced to create situations favorable to the implementation.

The *Hanoi* benchmark has been modified in order to produce a very deep failure, thus forcing inside backtracking to climb through a large number of nested parallel calls. The *Queens* is a representative of a goal which repeats the construction of the parallel call after inside backtracking. *Serialize* has been modified in two ways, one called *Serialize$_{deep}$* creates a deep failure with additional choice points in between, while *Serialize$_{flat}$* creates a failure in the higher levels of the nesting of parallel calls. In the case of *Mandelbrot*, the speed drops suddenly when at least 5 processors are used: this is caused by the presence of exactly four parallel calls before the one which is actually failing. With 5 processors the failure, which is present almost at the beginning of the call, is immediately detected.

The performance results are excellent. In all examples we have observed considerable improvement in execution speed. The removal of the need of synchronizing on a parallel call during inside backtracking allowed us to achieve super-linear speedups in various examples, e.g., *Compiler* and *Annotator* in table 1. This originates from the ability of detecting failures faster than sequential execution.

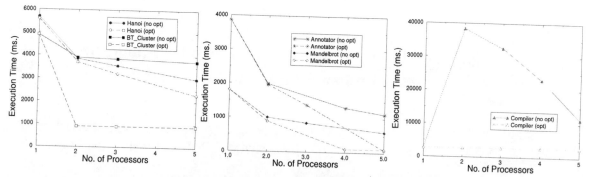

Figure 4. Comparison of Execution Times

Benchmark	ACE Processors						Max
	1		2		5		
	Old/New		Old/New		Old/New		
Hanoi	5.7/5.5		3.8/3.7		2.9/2.3		30%
Compiler	2.8/2.7		38.4/2.7		11.4/2.7		1405%
	2.8/2.7		5.1/2.7		5.1/2.7		87.3%
BT_Cluster	4.9/4.9		3.9/0.9		3.8/0.9		433%
Annotator	3.9/3.9		2.0/1.9		1.1/0.08		1411%
Queens	4.0/4.0		3.0/1.9		3.9/0.9		430%
Mandelbrot	1.8/1.8		1.0/0.8		0.6/0.1		600%
Serialize$_{deep}$	2.7/2.7		2.7/1.9		2.8/1.9		47.1%
Serialize$_{flat}$	1.6/1.6		2.1/1.2		2.4/1.2		97.4%

Table 1. Improvement with Fast Backtracking

The comparisons between execution times of selected benchmarks are presented also in figure 4. The results presented show the behaviour of the execution up to 5 processors. The speedups in most benchmarks consistently improve with higher number of processors.

6. Conclusions

In this paper we have analyzed the problem of efficiently performing backtracking in systems that exploit IAP. In particular, we have focused on the instance of this problem in the area of parallel logic programming—although our solution is general enough to be applied to other non-deterministic systems.

We have proposed an implementation model which allows to efficiently perform backtracking, respecting the correct semantics of the language and introducing a very limited amount of overhead. Furthermore, our scheme is capable of achieving super-linear speedups in situations where one parallel goal is unsuccessful—a possibility identified by other authors but difficult to realize in practice.

The execution model described has been implemented in the ACE parallel Prolog system, and we have described the performance of the system on various representative benchmarks involving backtracking over/during parallel calls. The performance results achieved are remarkable. We be-

lieve our approach is general enough to produce fast parallel implementations of other non-deterministic systems.

We believe the performance of the system can be further improved by making a more intense use of static analysis. In particular, we are currently exploring the possibility of using non-failure analysis and determinacy analysis [10, 3] to reorganize the parallel calls and drive the backtracking process in the best possible way (e.g., reusing deterministic goals).

References

[1] K. Apt and A. Schaerf. Search and Imperative Programming. *POPL*. ACM Press, 1997.
[2] F. Bueno et al. Effectiveness of Global Analysis in Strict Independence-based Automatic Program Parallelization. *Int. Logic Programming Symp.* MIT Press, 1994.
[3] S. Debray, P. Lopez-Garcia, and M. Hermenegildo. Non-failure Analysis for Logic Programs. *Int. Conf. on Logic Programming*. MIT Press, 1997.
[4] P. Dembinski and J. Maluszynski. AND-parallelism with Intelligent Backtracking for Annotated Logic Programs. *Int. Symp. on Logic Programming*, IEEE, 1985.
[5] G. Gupta and E. Pontelli. Optimization Schemas for Parallel Implementation of Nondeterministic Languages. *Int. Parallel Processing Symposium*. IEEE Computer Society, 1997.
[6] M. V. Hermenegildo and R. I. Nasr. Efficient Management of Backtracking in AND-parallelism. *Int. Conf. on Logic Programming*, Springer-Verlag, 1986.
[7] A. King and P. Soper. Depth-k Sharing and Freeness. *Int. Conf. on Logic Programming*. MIT Press, 1994.
[8] Y. J. Lin and V. Kumar. AND-Parallel Execution of Logic Programs on a Shared Memory Multiprocessor. *Int. Conf. and Symp. on Logic Programming*, MIT Press, 1988.
[9] E. Pontelli and G. Gupta. Parallel Symbolic Computation with ACE. *Annals of AI and Mathematics*, 1997.
[10] E. Pontelli et al. Automatic compile-time parallelization of prolog programs for dependent and-parallelism. *Int. Conf. on Logic Programming*. MIT Press, 1997.
[11] E. Pontelli et al. Efficient Implementation of Independent And Parallelism. *Computer Languages*, 22(2/3), 1996.
[12] K. Shen. Improving the Execution of the Dependent And-parallel Prolog DDAS. *Proc. of PARLE 94*, 1994.
[13] K. Shen and M. Hermenegildo. Divided We Stand: Parallel Distributed Stack Memory Management. *Implementations of Logic Programming Systems*, Kluwer Press, 1994.
[14] H. Touati et al. An Empirical Study of the WAM *Int. Symp. on Logic Programming*, IEEE, 1987.

High-Level Information – An Approach for Integrating Front-End and Back-End Compilers

Sangyeun Cho, Jenn-Yuan Tsai[†], Yonghong Song[‡], Bixia Zheng, Stephen J. Schwinn[*],
Xin Wang, Qing Zhao, Zhiyuan Li[‡], David J. Lilja[*], and Pen-Chung Yew

Dept. of Comp. Sci. and Eng.	[†]Dept. of Comp. Sci.	[‡]Dept. of Comp. Sci	[*]Dept. of Elec. and Comp. Eng.
Univ. of Minnesota	Univ. of Illinois	Purdue University	Univ. of Minnesota
Minneapolis, MN 55455	Urbana, IL 61801	West Lafayette, IN 47907	Minneapolis, MN 55455

http://www.cs.umn.edu/Research/Agassiz

Abstract

We propose a new universal High-Level Information (HLI) format to effectively integrate front-end and back-end compilers by passing front-end information to the back-end compiler. Importing this information into an existing back-end leverages the state-of-the-art analysis and transformation capabilities of existing front-end compilers to allow the back-end greater optimization potential than it has when relying on only locally-extracted information. A version of the HLI has been implemented in the SUIF parallelizing compiler and the GCC back-end compiler. Experimental results with the SPEC benchmarks show that HLI can provide GCC with substantially more accurate data dependence information than it can obtain on its own. Our results show that the number of dependence edges in GCC can be reduced by an average of 48% for the integer benchmark programs and an average of 54% for the floating-point benchmark programs studied, which provides greater flexibility to GCC's code scheduling pass. Even with the scheduling optimization limited to basic blocks, the use of HLI produces moderate speedups compared to using only GCC's dependence tests when the optimized programs are executed on MIPS R4600 and R10000 processors.

1 Introduction

Existing compilers for automatically parallelizing application programs are often divided into two relatively independent components. The *parallelizing front-end* of the compiler is often a source-to-source translator that typically is responsible for performing loop-level parallelization optimizations using either automatic program analysis techniques, or user-inserted compiler directives. This front-end then relies on an *optimizing back-end* compiler to perform the machine-specific instruction-level optimizations, such as instruction scheduling and register allocation.

This front-end/back-end separation is common due to the complexity of integrating the two, and because of the different types of data structures needed in both components. For example, the front-end performs high-level program analysis to identify dependences among relatively coarse-grained program units, such as subroutines and loop iterations, and performs transformations on these larger units. Because it operates at this coarse level of parallelism granularity, the front-end does not need detailed machine information. Not incorporating machine-specific details into the front-end eliminates the time and memory space overhead required to maintain this extensive information. The back-end, however, needs machine details to perform its finer-grained optimizations.

The penalty for this split, though, is that the back-end misses potential optimization opportunities due to its lack of high-level information. For example, optimizations involving loops, such as scalar promotion or array privatization [11], are difficult to perform in the back-end since complex loop structures can be difficult to identify with the limited information available in the back-end, especially for nested loops. Furthermore, the scope of the optimizations the back-end can perform, such as improving instruction issuing rates through architecture-aware code scheduling [7, 10, 12, 16], is limited to only short-range, local transformations. Another consequence of this split is that it is not uncommon for transformations performed in the front-end to be ignored, or even undone, in the back-end.

The types of high-level information that could be used by the back-end to enhance its optimization capabilities include the details of loop-carried data dependences, information about the aliasing of variable names, the results of interprocedural analysis, and knowledge about high-level, coarse-grained parallelization transformations. While this information could be easily passed from the front-end to the back-end in a completely integrated compiler, it is unfortunately very difficult to build an entire compiler from scratch. To be competitive, the new compiler must incorporate the state-of-the-art in both the front-end and the back-end, which is a massive undertaking.

Instead of building a completely new compiler, we note that the necessary information can be readily extracted from an existing parallelizing front-end compiler and passed in a condensed form to an existing optimizing back-end compiler. In this paper, we propose a new universal *High-Level Information* (HLI) format to pass front-end information to the back-end compiler. Importing this information into an existing back-end leverages the state-of-the-art analysis and transformation capabilities of existing front-end compilers to allow the back-end greater optimization potential than it has when relying on only locally-extracted information.

In the remainder of the paper, Section 2 presents the formal definition of the HLI format, showing what information is extracted from the front-end and how it is condensed to be passed to the back-end. Section 3 then describes our implementation of this HLI into the SUIF front-end parallelizing compiler [26] and the GCC back-end optimizing compiler [22]. Experiments with the SPEC benchmark programs [23] and a GNU utility are presented in Section 4. Related work is discussed in Section 5, with our results and conclusions summarized in Section 6.

2 High-Level Information Definition

A High-Level Information (HLI) file for a program includes information that is important for back-end optimizations, but is only available or computable in the front-end [24]. As shown in Figure 1, an HLI file contains a number of HLI entries. Each HLI entry corresponds to a program unit in the source file and contains two major tables — a *line table* and a *region table*, as described below.

2.1 Line table

The purpose of the line table is to build a connection between the front-end and the back-end representations. After generating the intermediate representation (IR), such as expression trees or instructions from the source program, a compiler usually annotates the IR with the corresponding source line numbers. If both the front-end and the back-end read the program from the same source file, the source line numbers can be used to match the expression trees in the front-end with the instructions in the back-end.

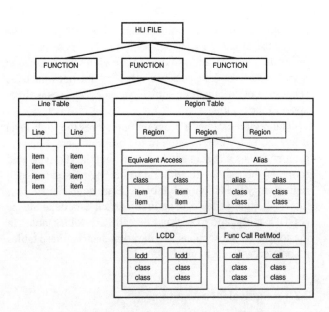

Figure 1. Top-level layout of an HLI file.

To reduce the amount of information that must be passed from the front-end to the back-end, the HLI focuses on only certain operations, such as memory accesses and function calls. These operations are called *items* in the HLI representation.[1] In the line table, each line entry corresponds to a source line of the program unit in the source file, and includes an item list for the line. The front-end also assigns each item a unique identification number (ID) that is used by the region table to address these items. In the item list, each item entry consists of an *ID* field and a *type* field. The ID field stores a unique number within the scope of the program unit that is used to reference the item. The type field stores the access type of the item, such as load, store, function call, etc.

Groups of items from the front-end are mapped to the back-end instructions by matching their source line numbers. However, this mapping information may not be precise enough to map items inside a group (*i.e.* a single source line) from the front-end to the back-end. To perform precise mapping, the front-end needs to know the instruction generation rules of the back-end and the order of items associated with each source line. Specifically, the order of items listed in the line table must match the order of the items appearing in the instruction list in the back-end.

2.2 Region table

To simplify the representation of the high-level information while maintaining precise data dependence information for each loop, we represent the high-level information of a program unit with scopes of *regions*. A region can be a

---

[1] An item may also represent an equivalent access class or a whole region, as discussed in Section 2.2.

program unit or a loop and can include sub-regions. The basic idea of using region scopes in the HLI is to partition all of the memory access items in a region into *equivalent access classes* and then describe data dependences and alias relationships among those equivalent access classes with respect to the region.

The region table of a program unit stores the high-level information for every region in the program unit. Each region entry has a region header describing the ID, type, and scope of the region. In addition to the region header, each region entry holds four sub-tables: (1) an equivalent access table, (2) an alias table, (3) a loop-carried data dependence (LCDD) table, and (4) a function call REF/MOD table. In the following subsections, we describe each of these tables associated with each region.

2.2.1 Equivalent access table

A region can contain a large number of memory access items. Recording all of the data dependences and alias relationships between every pair of memory access items would result in a huge amount of data. In fact, many memory access items in a region may refer to the same memory location since the same variable may be referenced multiple times in a region. Such memory access items can thus be grouped into a single equivalent access class.

The equivalent access table of a region partitions all memory access items inside the region, including those items enclosed by its sub-regions, into equivalent access classes. The region table includes a number of different equivalent access classes. Each equivalent access class has a unique item ID, which can be used to represent all of the memory access items belonging to the class. The members of an equivalent access class can be either memory access items immediately enclosed by the region that are not enclosed by any sub-region, or the equivalent access classes of its immediate sub-regions. Equivalent access classes of immediate sub-regions are used to represent the memory access items that are enclosed by the sub-regions. The equivalent access classes defined in a region must be mutually exclusive so that every memory access item inside the region, including those enclosed by its sub-regions, is represented by exactly one equivalent access class in the region.

Typically, the memory access items of an equivalent access class are considered to be definitely equivalent. However, the front-end compiler might want to group memory access items from different equivalent access classes in sub-regions that may access the same memory location into a single equivalent access class to reduce the amount of high-level information that must be passed to the back-end. In this case, the memory access items of an equivalent access class may not always access the same memory location. To distinguish this case, every equivalent access class has an

```
1:  int a[10];
2:  int b[10];
3:  int sum;
4:
5:  foo ()  /* region 1*/
6:  {
7:    int i, j;
8:
9:    for (i = 0; i < 10; i++) /* region 2 */
10:   {
11:     a[i] = 0;
            {1} /* item 1 */
12:     b[i] = i;
            {2}
13:   }
14:
15:   sum = 0;
          {3}
16:   for (i = 0; i <10; i++) /* region 3 */
17:   {
18:     a[i] = a[i] + b[0];
            {4}  {5}   {6}
19:     for (j = 1; j < 10; j++) /* region 4 */
20:     {
21:       b[i] = b[i] + b[j-1];
              {7}   {8}    {9}
21:       a[i] = a[i] + b[i];
              {10}  {11}  {12}
23:     }
24:     sum = sum + a[i];
            {13}  {14}   {15}
25:   }
26: }
```

Figure 2. The structure of the regions and equivalent access classes for an example program.

equivalent access type field, whose value can be *definitely equivalent* or *maybe equivalent*. The property of "maybe equivalence" will propagate along the corresponding equivalent access classes in enclosing regions.

If a region is a loop, its equivalent access table only describes the equivalent access relationships among memory access items or sub-region equivalent access classes WITHIN a single loop iteration. Also, when referred to by the alias table and by the LCDD table of the region, an equivalent class represents only the memory locations accessed in one loop iteration. However, when referred to by an outer region, the equivalent class represents all of the memory locations that will be accessed by the whole loop.

Figure 2 demonstrates the region structure of a procedure and its equivalent access tables. The outermost region of the procedure is Region 1, which represents the whole procedure. Region 1 has two immediate sub-regions (Regions

2 and 3) that represent the two *i* loops in the procedure. The second *i* loop (Region 3) has an inner *j* loop, which is represented by Region 4. In the equivalent access table of Region 1, all memory access items in the procedure are partitioned into three equivalent access classes: *sum*, *a[0..9]*, and *b[0..9]*. From the viewpoint of Region 1, every memory access item inside the procedure is represented by exactly one of those equivalent access classes. For example, in Region 1, item 11 (*a[i]*) inside the *j* loop is represented by the equivalent access class of *a[0..9]*. As mentioned above, equivalent access classes use the IDs of sub-regions' equivalent access classes to refer to the items residing in their sub-regions. For example, the equivalent access class of *sum* in Region 1 uses the equivalent access class of *sum* defined in Region 3 to refer to memory access items 13 and 14 enclosed by Region 3.

2.2.2 Alias table

The alias table describes the possible alias relationships among the equivalent access classes of a region. Two or more equivalent access classes are said to be *aliased* if they may access the same memory location at run time. If two equivalent access classes are aliased, all of the memory access items represented by the two equivalent access classes are also aliased. Each alias entry in the alias table consists of a set of equivalent access classes that the front-end has determined to be aliased. The equivalent access classes in the alias table must be equivalent access classes that are defined at the current region. Since the alias table only describes the alias relationships among the equivalent access classes within a loop iteration, data dependences caused by equivalent access classes in different loop iterations will be described in the LCDD table.

In Figure 2, equivalent access classes *b[0]* and *b[0..9]* in Region 3 may access the same memory location. Thus, the alias table of Region 3 will include an entry indicating that these two equivalent access classes are aliased.

2.2.3 Loop-carried data dependence (LCDD) table

If the region is identified as a loop, the LCDD table will list all of the LCDDs caused by the loop. Loop-carried data dependences are represented by pairs of equivalent access classes defined at the region. Each pair specifies a data dependence arc caused by the loop. The data dependence type can be *definite* or *maybe*. In addition, each dependence pair includes a distance field. To simplify the representation of the dependence distance, the direction of a dependence is always normalized to be '>' (forward), that is, from an earlier iteration to a later iteration.

For the example shown in Figure 2, the only LCDD is between equivalent access classes *b[j]* and *b[j-1]* in Region 4. The distance of the LCDD is one.

2.2.4 Function call REF/MOD table

The *function call REF/MOD table* of a region describes the side effects caused by function calls on the equivalent access classes of the region. If a function call is immediately enclosed by the region, the function call REF/MOD table will use the function call item ID defined in the line table to refer to the function call and will list the equivalent access classes that may be referenced or modified by the called function. For function calls inside a sub-region, the function call REF/MOD table will use the sub-region ID to represent all of the function calls and will list the equivalent access classes that may be referenced or modified by the function calls inside the sub-region. With this table, the front-end can pass interprocedural data-flow information to the back-end to enable the back-end to move instructions around a function call, for instance.

3 Implementation Issues

A version of the HLI described in the previous section has been implemented in the SUIF parallelizing compiler [26] and the GCC back-end compiler [22]. This section discusses some of the implementation details.[2] Note, however, that the HLI format is platform-independent, and many of the implemented functions are portable to other compilers [21]. Figure 3 shows an overview of our HLI implementation in the SUIF compiler and GCC.

3.1 Front-end implementation

The HLI generation in the front-end contains two major phases – *memory access item generation* (ITEMGEN) and *HLI table construction* (TBLCONST). The ITEMGEN phase generates memory access items and assigns a unique number (ID) to each item. The memory access items for a source line, ordered by the ID, can be one-to-one matched to the memory reference instructions in the GCC RTL chain[3] for the same line. These items are annotated in the SUIF expression nodes to be passed to the TBLCONST phase.

The TBLCONST phase first collects the memory access item information from the SUIF annotation to produce the line table for each program unit. It then generates information for the equivalent access table, alias table, and LCDD table for each region. Because it is both back-end compiler and machine dependent, separating the HLI generation into these two phases allows us to reuse the code for TBLCONST across different back-end compilers or target machines.

---

[2]Readers are referred to [4] for a more complete description.

[3]RTL (Register Transfer Language) is an intermediate representation used by GCC that resembles Lisp lists [22]. An RTL chain is the linked list of low-level instructions in the RTL format.

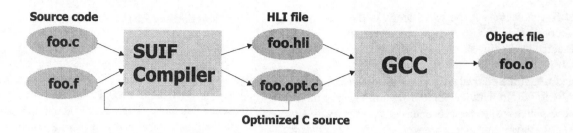

Figure 3. Overview of the HLI implementation using the SUIF front-end and GCC back-end compilers.

3.1.1 Memory access item generation (ITEMGEN)

The ITEMGEN phase traverses the SUIF internal representation (IR) to generate memory access items. It passes this memory access item information to the TBLCONST phase by annotating the SUIF IR. To guarantee that the mapping between the generated memory access items and the GCC RTL instructions is correct, the RTL generation rules in GCC must be considered in the HLI generation of SUIF.

Most of the memory access items correspond to variable accesses in the source program. However, when the optimization level is above -O0, GCC assigns a pseudo-register for a local scalar variable or a variable used for temporary computation results. An access to this type of variable does not generate a memory access item. Since GCC does not assign pseudo-registers to global variables and aggregate variables, they generate memory access items.

There are some memory access items produced in GCC that do not correspond to any actual variable accesses in the source program. These memory accesses are used for parameter and return value passing in subroutine calls. The actual number of parameter registers available is machine dependent. For each subroutine, GCC uses the parameter registers to pass as many parameters as possible, and then uses the stack to pass the remaining parameters. Hence, at a subroutine call site, if a memory value is passed to the subroutine via a parameter passing register, a memory read is used to load the value into the register. If a register value is passed to the subroutine via the stack, however, a memory write is generated to store the value to the stack. Similarly, at a subroutine entry point, if a memory value is passed into the subroutine via a register, a memory write is generated to store the value. If a register value is passed into the subroutine via the stack, though, a memory read is again used to load the value from the memory to the register.

A subroutine return value can also generate memory accesses that do not correspond to any variable accesses in the source program. One register is available to handle return values. When the returned value is a structure, the address of the structure is stored in that register at the subroutine call site. In this case, the return statement generates a mem-

ory write to store the return value to the memory location indicated by the value return register. If the return value is a scalar, the value return register directly carries the value, so no memory access is generated.

3.1.2 HLI table construction (TBLCONST)

The HLI table construction phase traverses the SUIF IR twice. The first traversal creates a line table for each routine by collecting the memory access item information from the SUIF annotations. It also creates a hierarchical region structure for each routine and groups all the memory access items in a region into equivalent access classes.

The second traversal of the IR visits the hierarchical region structure of each routine in a depth-first fashion. At each node, it gathers the LCDD information for each pair of equivalent access classes and calculates the alias relationship between each pair of equivalent access classes. All of the information propagates from the bottom up. If the SUIF data dependence test for a pair of array equivalent access classes in a region returns zero distance, the two equivalent access classes are merged. Otherwise, the test results are stored into the LCDD table. Then, all the pointer references that may refer to multiple locations are determined. An alias relationship is created between the equivalent access class for each pointer reference and the equivalent access class to which the pointer reference may refer. Next, the equivalent access class information and alias information is propagated to the immediate parent region. At the completion of these two phases, the HLI is ready to be exported to the back-end.

3.2 Back-end implementation

3.2.1 Importing and mapping HLI into GCC

The HLI file is read on demand as GCC compiles a program function by function. This approach eliminates the need to keep all of the HLI in memory at the same time, relieving the memory space requirements on the back-end. The imported information is stored in a separate, generic data structure to enhance portability. Mapping the items listed in the line table onto memory references in the GCC RTL chain is straightforward since the ITEMGEN phase in the front-end (Section 3.1.1) follows the GCC rules for memory reference generation. A hash table is constructed as the mapping procedure proceeds to allow GCC quick access to the HLI. A memory reference in GCC, or other back-end compilers, can be represented as a 2-tuple: (IRInsn, RefSpec), where IRInsn specifies an RTL instruction and RefSpec identifies a specific memory access among possibly several memory accesses in the instruction. The hash table forms a mapping between each item and the corresponding (IRInsn, RefSpec) pair.

```
/* remove from the hash table all the expressions with a mem. ref.
   clobbered by a function call (call, call_spec) */
static void invalidate_memory_clobbered (call, call_spec)
{
  for (i = 0; i < NBUCKETS; i++)
    for (p = table[i]; p; p = next) {
      next = p->next_same_hash;
      for each mem. ref. (mem, mem_spec) in p
        switch (HLI_GetCallAcc (mem, mem_spec, call, call_spec) {
          case HLI_CALL_MOD:
          case HLI_CALL_REFMOD:
            remove_from_table (mem, mem_spec);
        ... }
    ... }
}
```

Figure 4. Using call REF/MOD information to aid GCC's CSE optimization.

3.2.2 Using HLI

Information in the HLI can be utilized by a back-end compiler in various ways. Accurate data dependence information allows aggressive scheduling of a memory reference across other memory references, for example. Additionally, LCDD information is indispensable for a cyclic scheduling algorithm such as software pipelining [15]. In loop invariant code removal, a memory reference can be moved out of a loop only when there remains no other memory reference in the loop that can possibly alias the memory reference. High-level program structure information, such as the line type and the parent line, may provide hints to guide heuristics for efficient code scheduling.

To provide a common interface across different back-ends, the stored HLI can be retrieved only via a set of query functions. There are five basic query functions that can be used to construct more complex query functions [5]. There are another set of *utility functions* that simplify the implementation of the query and maintenance functions (Section 3.2.3) by hiding the low-level details of the target compiler. Two examples are given in this section to show how the query functions can be used in GCC.

In GCC's *Common Subexpression Elimination* (CSE)

pass, subexpressions are stored in a table as the program is compiled, and, when they appear again in the code, the already calculated value in the table can directly replace the subexpression. Without interprocedural information, however, all the subexpressions containing a memory reference will be purged from the table when a function call appears in the code since GCC pessimistically assumes that the function can change any memory location. In Figure 4, an HLI query function to obtain call REF/MOD information is used to remedy the situation by selectively purging the subexpressions on a function call.

The example in Figure 5 shows how the HLI provides memory dependence information to the instruction scheduler. It is used in Section 4.2 to measure the effectiveness of using HLI to improve the code scheduling pass.

```
/* given a mem. write A and a mem. read B, add a dependence
   edge if there is a true dependence from A to B */
{
  int gcc_value, hli_value, final_value;
  HLI_EquivAccType hli_qresult;

  gcc_value = true_dependence (A, B);  /* GCC query function */
  hli_qresult = HLI_GetEquivAcc (A, B);  /* HLI query function */
  hli_value = (hli_qresult != HLI_NONE);
  final_value = flag_use_hli ? gcc_value * hli_value : gcc_value;
  if (final_value)
    add_dependence (A, B, DEP_TRUE);
}
```

Figure 5. Using equivalent access and alias information for dependence analysis in GCC's instruction scheduling pass.

3.2.3 Maintaining HLI

As GCC performs various optimizations, some memory references can be deleted, moved, or generated. These changes break the links between HLI items and GCC memory references set up at the mapping stage, requiring appropriate actions to reestablish the mapping to respond to the change. Further, some of the HLI tables may need updating to maintain the integrity of the information. Typical examples of such optimizations include:

- The CSE pass, where an item may be deleted. The corresponding HLI must then be deleted.

- In the loop invariant removal optimization, an item may be moved to an outer region. The HLI item must be deleted and inserted in the outer region. All the HLI tables must be updated accordingly.

- In loop unrolling, the loop body is duplicated and preconditioning code is generated. The entire HLI components (tables) must be reconstructed using old information, and the old information must be discarded.

```
/* construct LCDD info. for the unrolled loop A', based on
    the info. about the original loop A */
for each LCDD [item i, item j, d, t] between item i and j with
                    distance d and type t in A {
  /* K is the unroll factor */
  /* item[a] b is the item b in the a'th unrolled loop */
  for all u (0 <= u < K) {
    if (floor ((u+d)/K) == 0)
      HLI_MergeEquivAcc (item[u] i, item[(u+d)%K] j);
    else
      HLI_AddLCDD (item[u] i, item[(u+d)%K] j, floor((u+d)/K), t);
  }
}
```

Figure 6. Updating the LCDD information for loop unrolling.

The HLI maintenance functions have been written to provide a means to update the HLI in response to these changes [5]. The functions allow a back-end compiler to generate or delete items, inherit the attributes of one item to another, insert an item into a region, and update the HLI tables. Changes such as the CSE or loop invariant code removal call for a relatively simple treatment – either deleting an item, or generating, inheriting, moving, and deleting an item. Loop unrolling, however, requires more complex steps to update the HLI. First, new items need be generated as the target loop body is duplicated multiple times. The generated items are inserted in different regions, based on whether they belong to the new (unrolled) loop body or the preconditioning code. Data dependence relationships between the new items are then computed using the information from the original loop. An example of updating the HLI tables for the loop unrolling pass is given in Figure 6.

4 Benchmark Results

4.1 Program characteristics

Table 1 lists all of the benchmark programs, both integer and floating-point, showing the number of lines of source code, the HLI size in KBytes, and the ratio of the HLI size to the code size. This ratio shows the average number of bytes needed for the HLI for each source code line. We have only a few integer programs due to current implementation limitations of the SUIF front-end tools.[4]

In general, this table shows that a floating-point program requires more space for the HLI than an integer program,

---

[4]Our implementation uses the SUIF parser twice (see Figure 3). After the program foo.c is compiled and optimized by SUIF, the optimized C file foo.opt.c is generated. This code is then used as the input to the HLI generation and GCC. When foo.opt.c is fed into the SUIF parser again for the HLI generation, it causes unrecoverable errors in some cases. We are currently developing a front-end compiler that will eliminate such difficulties.

Benchmark	Suite	Code size (# of lines)	HLI size (KB)	HLI per line (bytes)
wc	GNU	972	11	12
008.espresso	CINT92	37074	613	17
023.eqntott	CINT92	6269	99	16
129.compress	CINT95	2235	21	10
mean	–	–	–	13
015.doduc	CFP92	25228	1310	53
034.mdljdp2	CFP92	6905	121	18
048.ora	CFP92	1249	29	24
052.alvinn	CFP92	475	7	15
077.mdljsp2	CFP92	4865	109	23
101.tomcatv	CFP95	780	17	22
102.swim	CFP95	1124	76	69
103.su2cor	CFP95	6759	239	36
107.mgrid	CFP95	1725	35	21
141.apsi	CFP95	21921	442	21
mean	–	–	–	27

Table 1. Benchmark program characteristics.

implying that the former tends to have more memory references per line. The relatively large HLI size per source code line in *015.doduc* and *102.swim* is mainly due to a large number of items in nested loops, which cause the alias table and the LCDD table to grow substantially.

4.2 Aiding GCC dependence analysis

Instruction scheduling is an important code optimization in a back-end compiler. With this optimization, instructions in a code segment are reordered to minimize the overall execution time. A crucial step in instruction scheduling is to determine if there is a dependence between two memory references when at least one is a memory write. Accurately identifying such dependences can reduce the number of edges in the data dependence graph, thereby giving the scheduler more freedom to move instructions around to improve the quality of the scheduled code.

HLI can potentially enhance the GCC instruction scheduling optimization by providing more accurate memory dependence information when GCC would otherwise have to make a conservative assumption due to its simple dependence analysis algorithm. For the programs tested, Table 2 shows the total number of dependence queries (*i.e.* do A and B refer to the same memory location?) made in the first instruction scheduling pass of GCC, the average number of queries for each source code line, the number of times the GCC analyzer answers yes (meaning that it must assume there is dependence), the number of times HLI answers yes, and lastly, the number of times both GCC and HLI answer yes. Since the values in the table correspond to the number of dependence edges inserted into the DDG,

Benchmark	Total # of tests	# of tests per line	GCC result	HLI result	"Combined" result	Reduction	Speedups (on R4600)	(on R10000)
wc	113	0.12	40 (35%)	20 (18%)	20 (18%)	50%	1.00	1.00
008.espresso	4166	0.11	2615 (63%)	1316 (32%)	1006 (24%)	62%	1.00	1.00
023.eqntott	399	0.06	249 (62%)	191 (48%)	120 (30%)	52%	1.01	1.05
129.compress	274	0.12	56 (20%)	39 (14%)	37 (14%)	34%	1.06	1.07
mean	–	0.10	– (41%)	– (25%)	– (21%)	48%	1.00	1.03
015.doduc	10992	0.44	7712 (70%)	3293 (30%)	2855 (26%)	63%	1.00	1.03
034.mdljdp2	3013	0.44	1753 (58%)	393 (13%)	265 (9%)	85%	1.08	1.42
048.ora	363	0.29	52 (14%)	79 (22%)	34 (9%)	35%	1.00	1.00
052.alvinn	48	0.10	47 (98%)	20 (42%)	20 (42%)	57%	1.01	1.02
077.mdljsp2	2854	0.59	1765 (62%)	413 (14%)	271 (9%)	85%	1.19	1.59
101.tomcatv	286	0.37	191 (67%)	29 (10%)	14 (5%)	93%	1.00	1.01
102.swim	872	0.78	833 (96%)	83 (10%)	80 (9%)	90%	1.03	1.04
103.su2cor	4192	0.62	3549 (85%)	1602 (38%)	1453 (35%)	59%	1.02	1.08
107.mgrid	517	0.30	368 (71%)	330 (64%)	311 (60%)	15%	1.00	1.01
141.apsi	22347	1.02	8031 (36%)	6375 (29%)	5399 (24%)	33%	1.00	1.01
mean	–	0.42	– (59%)	– (26%)	– (19%)	54%	1.03	1.11

Table 2. Using the HLI in GCC's dependence checking routines can substantially reduce the number of dependence arcs that must be inserted into the DDG. The resulting speedups on MIPS R4600 and MIPS R10000 are also shown.

the smaller the number, the more accurate the corresponding analyzer. The "Reduction" column shows the reduction in the number of dependence edges for each program due to the use of the HLI.

The result shows that using HLI can reduce the number of dependence edges, by an average of 48% for the integer programs and 54% for the floating-point programs. Four floating-point programs – *034.mdljdp2, 077.mdljsp2, 101.tomcatv,* and *102.swim* – exhibited a reduction of over 80% in the number of dependence edges. These results confirm that the data dependence information extracted by the front-end analysis is very effective in disambiguating memory references in the back-end compiler.

Note that the numbers in the *HLI result* and *"Combined" result* columns in Table 2 are not the same in most of the cases. This difference means that there is room for additional improvement in the HLI. Current shortcomings in generating the HLI include – (1) the implemented front-end algorithms, such as the array data dependence analysis and the pointer analysis, are not as aggressive as possible, and (2) there are miscellaneous GCC code generation rules that the current HLI implementation has not considered. Ignoring these rules produces *unknown* dependence types between some memory references. The values of the *HLI result* are expected to become smaller as more aggressive front-end algorithms are developed and the current implementation limitations are overcome.

4.3 Impact on program execution times

To study the performance improvement attributable to using HLI in GCC's instruction scheduling optimization pass, execution times of the benchmark programs, compiled both with and without HLI, were measured on two real machines. One machine uses a pipelined MIPS R4600 processor with 64 MB of main memory. The other is a MIPS R10000 superscalar processor that contains a 32 KB on-chip data cache, a 32 KB on-chip instruction cache, a 2 MB unified off-chip second-level cache, and 512 MB of interleaved main memory. All the programs were compiled with GCC version 2.7.2.2 with the -O2 optimization flag. Each program execution used the "reference" input. The input to the program *wc* is 62 MB of C source codes. The last two columns in Table 2 summarize the results.

Three programs achieved a noticeable speedup of 5% or more on the R4600, with five programs (including the previous three) achieving similar results on the R10000. Two programs, *034.mdljdp2* and *077.mdljsp2*, obtained remarkable speedups of over 40% on the R10000. Note that a large reduction in dependence edges, as shown in Table 2, does not always result in a large execution time speedup, as can be seen in *101.tomcatv*, for instance. This is partly due to a limitation of the GCC instruction scheduler which schedules instructions only within basic blocks.

The integer programs achieved relatively small speedups compared to the floating-point programs. It is known that the basic blocks in integer programs are usually very small, containing only 5 − 6 instructions on average, and it is likely that each basic block contains few memory references. This is indirectly evidenced by comparing the number of dependence queries made per line (Table 2). Typically, an integer program requires fewer than half the number of dependence tests needed by a floating-point program.

Comparing the different processor types, the R10000 produces speedups equal to or higher than the corresponding speedup on the R4600 since the R10000, a four-issue superscalar processor, is more sensitive to the memory performance, and a load instruction in the load/store queue will not be issued to the memory system until all the preceding stores in the queue are known to be independent of the load. As a result, the impact of compile-time scheduling is more pronounced in the R10000 than the R4600.

5 Related Work

Traditionally, parallelizing compilers and optimizing compilers for uniprocessors have been largely two separate efforts. Parallelizing compilers perform extensive array data dependence analysis and array data flow analysis in order to identify parallel operations. Based on the results, a sequential program is transformed into a parallel program containing program constructs such as DOALL. Alternatively, the compiler may insert a directive before a sequential loop to indicate that the loop can be executed in parallel. Several research parallelizing Fortran compilers, including Parafrase [14], PFC [1], Parafrase-2 [18], Polaris [3], Panorama [11], and PTRAN [19], and commercial Fortran compilers, such as KAP [13] and VAST [25], have taken such a source-to-source approach.

Computer vendors generally provide their own compilers to take a source program, which has been parallelized by programmers or by a parallelizing compiler, and generate multithreaded machine code, *i.e.*, machine code embedded with thread library calls. These compilers usually spend their primary effort on enhancing the efficiency of the machine code for individual processors. Once the thread assignment to individual processors has been determined, parallelizing compilers have little control over the execution of the code by each processor.

Over the past years, both *machine independent* and *machine specific* compiler techniques have been developed to enhance the performance of uniprocessors [17, 6, 12, 7, 16]. These compiler techniques rely primarily on dataflow analysis for symbolic registers or simple scalars that are not aliased. Advanced data dependence analysis and data flow analysis regarding array references and pointer dereferences are generally not available to current uniprocessor compilers. The publically available GCC [22] and LCC [9] compilers exemplify the situation. They both maintain low-level IRs of the input programs, keeping no high-level program constructs for array data dependence and pointer-structure analysis.

With the increased demand for ILP, the importance of incorporating high-level analysis into uniprocessor compilers has been generally recognized. Recent work on pointer and structure analysis aims at accurate recognition of aliases due to pointer dereferences and pointer arguments [8, 27]. Experimental results in this area have been limited to reporting the accuracy of recognizing aliases. Compared with these studies, this paper presents new data showing how high-level array and pointer analysis can improve data dependence analysis in a common uniprocessor compiler.

There have been continued efforts to incorporate uniprocessor parameters and knowledge about low-level code generation strategies into the high-level decisions about program transformations. The ASTI optimizer for the IBM XL Fortran compilers [20] is a good example. Nonetheless, the register allocator and instruction scheduler of the uniprocessor compiler still lacks direct information about data dependences concerning complex memory references.

New efforts on integrating parallelizing compilers with uniprocessor compilers also have emerged recently. The SUIF tool [26], for instance, maintains a high-level intermediate representation that is close to the source program to support high-level analysis and transformations. It also maintains a low-level intermediate representation that is close to the machine code. As another example, the Polaris parallelizing compiler has recently incorporated a low-level representation to enable low-level compiler techniques [2]. Nonetheless, results showing how high-level analysis benefits the low-level analysis and optimizations are largely unavailable today. Our effort has taken a different approach by providing a mechanism to transport high-level analysis results to uniprocessor compilers using a format that is relatively independent of the particular parallelizing compiler and the particular uniprocessor compiler.

6 Conclusions and Future Work

Instead of integrating the front-end and back-end into a single compiler, this paper proposes an approach that provides a mechanism to export the results of high-level program analysis from the front-end to a standard back-end compiler. This high-level information is transferred using a well-defined format (HLI) that condenses the high-level information to reduce the total amount of data that must be transferred. Additionally, this format is relatively independent of the particular front-end and back-end compilers.

We have demonstrated the effectiveness of this approach by implementing it into the SUIF front-end and the GCC back-end compilers. Our experiments with the SPEC benchmarks show that using this information in the code scheduling pass of GCC substantially reduces the number of dependence arcs that must be inserted into the data dependence graph. The increased flexibility provided by this reduction allowed the code scheduler to improve execution time performance by up to 59% compared to using only the low-level information normally available to the back-end.

We believe that the HLI mechanism proposed in this paper makes it relatively easy to integrate any existing front-end parallelizing compiler with any existing back-end compiler. In fact, we are currently developing a new front-end parallelizing compiler[5] that will use the HLI mechanism to export high-level program information to the same GCC back-end implementation used in these experiments.

Acknowledgment

This work was supported in part by the National Science Foundation under grant nos. MIP-9610379 and CDA-9502979; by the U.S. Army Intelligence Center and Fort Huachuca under contract DABT63-95-C-0127 and ARPA order no. D346, and a gift from the Intel Corporation. The views and conclusions contained herein are those of the authors and should not be interpreted as necessarily representing the official policies or endorsements, either expressed or implied, of the U.S. Army Intelligence Center and Fort Huachuca, or the U.S. Government. Stephen Schwinn is currently with the IBM Corp., Rochester, MN.

References

[1] J. R. Allen and K. Kennedy. "Automatic Translation of FORTRAN Programs to Vector Form," *ACM Trans. on Prog. Lang. and Sys.*, 9(4): 491 – 542, Oct. 1987.

[2] E. Ayguade *et al.* "A Uniform Internal Representation for High-Level and Instruction-Level Transformations," *TR 1434*, CSRD, Univ. of Illinois at Urbana-Champaign, 1994.

[3] W. Blume *et al.* "Parallel Programming with Polaris," *IEEE Computer*, pp. 78 – 82, Dec. 1996.

[4] S. Cho, J.-Y. Tsai, Y. Song, B. Zheng, S. J. Schwinn, X. Wang, Q. Zhao, Z. Li, D. J. Lilja, and P.-C. Yew. "High-Level Information – An Approach for Integrating Front-End and Back-End Compilers," *TR #98-008*, Dept. of Computer Sci. and Eng., Univ. of Minnesota, Feb. 1998.

[5] S. Cho and Y. Song. "The HLI Implementor's Guide (v0.1)," *Agassiz Project Internal Document*, Sept. 1997.

[6] F. C. Chow. A Portable Machine-Independent Global Optimizer – Design and Measurements, *Ph.D. Thesis*, Stanford Univ., Dec. 1983.

[7] J. C. Dehnert and R. A. Towle. "Compiling for the Cydra 5," *J. of Supercomputing*, 7(1/2): 181 – 227, 1993.

[8] M. Emami, R. Ghiya and L. J. Hendren. "Context-Sensitive Interprocedural Points-to Analysis in the Presence of Function Pointers," *Proc. of the ACM SIGPLAN '94 Conf. on PLDI*, pp. 242 – 256, June 1994.

[9] C. Fraser and D. Hanson. *A Retargetable C Compiler: Design and Implementation*, Benjamin/Cummings Publishing Company, Inc., Redwood City, CA, 1995.

[10] J. R. Ellis. Bulldog: A Compiler for VLIW Architectures, MIT Press, Cambridge, Mass., 1986.

[11] J. Gu, Z. Li, and G. Lee. "Experience with Efficient Array Data Flow Analysis for Array Privatization," *Proc. of the 6th ACM SIGPLAN Symp. on PPOPP*, June 1997.

[12] W. W. Hwu *et al.* "The Superblock: An Effective Technique for VLIW and Superscalar Compilation," *J. of Supercomputing*, 7(1/2): 229 – 248, 1993.

[13] KAP User's Guide, *Tech. Report (Doc. No. 8811002)*, Kuck & Associates, Inc.

[14] D. J. Kuck *et al.* "The Structure of an Advanced Vectorizer for Pipelined Processors," *Proc. of the 4th Int'l Computer Software and Application Conf.*, pp. 709 – 715, Oct. 1980.

[15] M. Lam. "Software Pipelining: An Effective Scheduling Technique for VLIW Machines," *Proc. of the ACM SIGPLAN '88 Conf. on PLDI*, June 1988.

[16] P. G. Lowney *et al.* "The Multiflow Trace Scheduling Compiler," *J. of Supercomputing*, 7(1/2): 51 – 142, 1993.

[17] S. S. Muchnick. *Advanced Compiler Design and Implementation*, Morgan Kaufmann Publishers, 1997.

[18] C. D. Polychronopoulos *et al.* "Parafrase-2: An Environment for Parallelizing, Partitioning, Synchronizing and Scheduling Programs on Multiprocessors," *Proc. of the ICPP*, Aug. 1989.

[19] V. Sarkar. The PTRAN Parallel Programming System, *Parallel Functional Programming Languages and Compilers*, B. Szymanski, Ed., ACM Press, pp. 309 – 391, 1991.

[20] V. Sarkar. "Automatic Selection of High-Order Transformations in the IBM XL FORTRAN Compilers," *IBM J. of Research and Development*, 41(3): 233 – 264, May 1997.

[21] S. J. Schwinn. "The HLI Interface Specification for Back-End Compilers (v0.1)," *Agassiz Project Internal Document*, Sept. 1997.

[22] R. M. Stallman. Using and Porting GNU CC (version 2.7), Free Software Foundation, Cambridge, MA, June 1995.

[23] The Standard Performance Evaluation Corporation, http://www.specbench.org.

[24] J.-Y. Tsai. "High-Level Information Format for Integrating Front-End and Back-End Compilers (v0.2)," *Agassiz Project Internal Document*, March 1997.

[25] VAST-2 for XL FORTRAN, User's Guide, Edition 1.2, *Tech. Report (Doc. No. VA061)*, Pacific-Sierra Research Co., 1994.

[26] R. P. Wilson *et al.* "SUIF: An Infrastructure for Research on Parallelizing and Optimizing Compilers," *ACM SIGPLAN Notices*, 29 (12): 31 – 37, Dec. 1994.

[27] R. P. Wilson and M. S. Lam. "Efficient Context-Sensitive Pointer Analysis for C Programs," *Proc. of the ACM SIGPLAN '95 Conf. on PLDI*, pp. 1 – 12, June 1995.

---

[5]See http://www.cs.umn.edu/Research/Agassiz/.

Concurrent SSA Form in the Presence of Mutual Exclusion

Diego Novillo   Ron Unrau   Jonathan Schaeffer

Department of Computing Science, University of Alberta
Edmonton, Alberta, Canada

E-mail: {diego,unrau,jonathan}@cs.ualberta.ca

Abstract

Most current compiler analysis techniques are unable to cope with the semantics introduced by explicit parallel and synchronization constructs in parallel programs. In this paper we propose new analysis and optimization techniques for compiling explicitly parallel programs that use mutual exclusion synchronization. We introduce the CSSAME form, an extension of the Concurrent Static Single Assignment (CSSA) form that incorporates mutual exclusion into a data flow framework for explicitly parallel programs. We show how this analysis can improve the effectiveness of constant propagation in a parallel program. We also modify a dead-code elimination algorithm to work on explicitly parallel programs. Finally, we introduce lock independent code motion, a new optimization technique that attempts to minimize the size of critical sections in the program.

1. Introduction

Although recent advances in parallelizing compilers and data-parallel languages have been impressive [4, 8], there are important problem domains for which parallelizing the best sequential algorithm or data layout yields sub-optimal performance relative to an implementation that is explicitly parallel from the outset. Furthermore, popular systems like Java incorporate parallel constructs at the language level and commodity multiprocessors are becoming increasingly popular. For these reasons, we believe that there is a need for compilers that accept explicitly parallel programs, and that the demand for such compilers will increase.

To correctly compile and optimize explicitly parallel programs the compiler must have an innate knowledge of the parallelism in the program and the semantics of synchronization primitives. In addition to the standard optimization techniques used by sequential compilers, an optimizing parallel compiler should exploit the parallel structure of the program to achieve better performance. Unfortunately, standard optimization techniques used in sequential programs cannot be directly applied to explicitly parallel programs because they may generate incorrect transformations [11]. This has motivated recent developments that have started to uncover the potential benefits of analysis and optimization techniques for explicitly parallel programs [3, 7, 13]. Like any incipient technology, these techniques are still in their primitive stages, especially when compared to their sequential counterparts.

Initial work by Shasha and Snir proposed re-ordering memory references in a program to increase concurrency while maintaining the sequential consistency dictated by the code [13]. Midkiff and Padua demonstrated that a direct application of optimization techniques designed for sequential languages fail on explicitly parallel programs [11]. Grunwald and Srinivasan developed data-flow equations to compute reaching definition information on explicitly parallel programs with `cobegin/coend` parallel sections [3]. However, their work only deals with a weak memory consistency model dictated by the PCF Fortran standard. Parallel sections are required to be data independent; memory updates are done at specific points in the program using the `copy-in/copy-out` model. Synchronization is limited to event-based synchronization using `Set` and `Wait` operations. Knoop, Steffen and Vollmer developed a bitvector analysis framework for parallel programs with shared memory and interleaving semantics [6]. They show how to adapt standard optimization algorithms to their framework. However, they do not incorporate synchronization operations in their analysis. Lee, Midkiff and Padua propose a Concurrent SSA framework (CSSA) for explicitly parallel programs and interleaving memory semantics [7]. They only consider event-based synchronization and impose some restrictions on the input program.

A major limitation of existing techniques for optimizing explicitly parallel programs is the restricted knowledge about synchronization in the program. To the best of our knowledge, the only synchronization construct recognized is a subset of event-based synchronization (i.e., `Set` and `Wait` usually with no `Clear`). We see this as a severe limitation because event synchronization can only be used to describe a small class of parallel algorithms. One of the

356

```
cobegin /* Begin concurrent execution */
  T 0: begin              /* Launch thread T0 */
    Lock(L);
    a = a + b;
    Unlock(L);
  end

  T 1: begin              /* Launch thread T1 */
    f(a);
    Lock(L);
    a = 3;                /* This kills the assignment to a in T0 */
    b = b + g(a);        /* Variable a is always 3 */
    Unlock(L);
  end
coend
```

Figure 1. Mutual exclusion can reduce data dependencies across threads in a parallel program.

goals of our work is to incorporate knowledge about common synchronization structures into the compiler so it can perform more aggressive optimizations. As a first step to that goal, we have extended the Concurrent Static Single Assignment (CSSA) form [7] to handle mutual exclusion synchronization. Specifically, we

• extend the concurrent control flow graph used by Lee et al. (Section 3.1) and show how to detect mutual exclusion synchronization in a parallel program (Section 3.3),

• introduce the CSSAME[1] form, an extension to the CSSA form to account for the semantics introduced by mutual exclusion synchronization (Section 4),

• show how CSSAME can improve the effectiveness of the Concurrent Sparse Conditional Constant (CSCC) propagation algorithm [7] (Section 5.1),

• adapt a sequential dead-code elimination algorithm to work on explicitly parallel programs (Section 5.2), and

• introduce *lock independent code motion*, a new optimization technique for explicitly parallel programs which attempts to reduce the size of mutual exclusion sections in the program (Section 5.3).

2. Our approach

In an explicitly parallel program with interleaving memory semantics, the use of a shared variable v can be reached by any definition of v in another concurrent thread. However, mutual exclusion may prevent some variable definitions from being visible in other threads. For example, consider the code fragment in Figure 1. If we ignore the mutual exclusion regions created by the locks we will conclude that the definition for variable a in thread T_0 can reach both uses of a in thread T_1. However, the synchronization used in the program serializes the references to a so that the assignment to a in T_0 cannot reach the second use of a in T_1. Therefore, the call to function $g()$ in T_1 will always be executed with $a = 3$.

----
[1] Pronounced *sesame*.

Understanding mutual exclusion has important implications from an optimization point of view because it allows the compiler to reduce the number of data dependencies that need to be considered. It also allows the compiler to conservatively validate the synchronization structures expressed inside the code. This paper focuses on the former; future work will also investigate correctness and user interface issues.

To determine the effects of mutual exclusion on the dataflow of the program the compiler must recognize which sections of the program execute under the protection of a lock. We base our analysis on the concept of *mutex structures* first introduced by Masticola and Ryder in their work on nonconcurrency analysis [10]. Basically, a mutex structure is associated with each lock variable used in the program and it contains the sets of flow graph nodes that are guaranteed to execute under the protection of the associated lock variable. Once mutual exclusion information is gathered into mutex structures, we modify the Concurrent SSA (CSSA) form proposed by Lee *et al.* [7] to account for it.

Explicitly parallel programs start as a single thread of computation. New threads are logically created when execution reaches a parallel section. Although the creation, placement and scheduling of threads is not significant for our research, the compiler must be able to recognize parallel sections in the code. We assume that threads run in a shared address space with interleaving semantics (i.e., updates to shared memory made by one thread are immediately visible to other threads). There are a variety of mechanisms for expressing parallel activity. Some examples include `cobegin/coend` constructs, explicit `fork` statements, parallel loops, etc. In this paper parallel sections are specified using `cobegin/coend` constructs (Figure 1).

Mutual exclusion is used to serialize references to shared variables in the program. We will assume, without loss of generality, that programmers use standard `Lock` and `Unlock` instructions to serialize access to shared variables.

3. Mutual exclusion analysis

3.1. Parallel Flow Graphs

We introduce the Parallel Flow Graph (PFG), an extension to the Concurrent Control Flow Graph (CCFG) [7] that also represents mutual exclusion synchronization. In addition to the directed synchronization edges in the original CCFG, we incorporate undirected mutex synchronization edges which represent mutual exclusion constraints and do not enforce a specific execution order. Each `Lock` and `Unlock` operation is represented by a separate node in the PFG. Mutex synchronization edges join `Lock` and `Unlock` nodes that operate on the same variable in concurrent threads.

Definition 1 A *Parallel Flow Graph (PFG)* is a directed

```
a = 0;
b = 0;
cobegin
  T 0: begin
    Lock(L);
    a = 5;
    b = a + 3;
    if (b > 4) {
      a = a + b;
    }
    x = a;
    Unlock(L);
  end

  T 1: begin
    Lock(L);
    a = b + 6;
    y = a;
    Unlock(L);
  end
coend
print(x);
print(y);
```

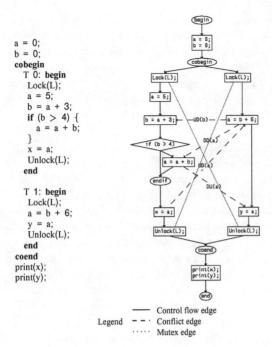

Legend
— Control flow edge
− − − Conflict edge
····· Mutex edge

Figure 2. A program and its PFG.

graph $G = \langle N, E, Entry_G, Exit_G \rangle$ such that:

1. N is the set of parallel basic blocks in the program.

2. $Entry_G$ and $Exit_G$ are the unique entry and exit points of the program.

3. Lock and Unlock operations are represented by their own nodes.

4. $E = E_{ct} \bigcup E_{sy} \bigcup E_{cf}$ is the set of edges in the graph such that E_{ct} is the set of control flow edges. These edges have the same meaning as in a sequential control flow graph (CFG). $E_{sy} = E_{mutex} \bigcup E_{dsync}$ is the set of synchronization edges. Two different kinds of synchronization are recognized: E_{mutex} and E_{dsync}. E_{mutex} is the set of mutex synchronization edges representing mutual exclusion constraints. Mutex synchronization edges are undirected edges between related Lock and Unlock operations. E_{dsync} is the set of directed synchronization edges representing ordering constraints. These edges join related Set and Wait statements in different threads. Finally, E_{cf} is the set of conflict edges. Conflict edges are directed edges that join any two parallel basic blocks that conflict. Two letter labels on the edge represent the memory operations done at each end of the edge: def (D) or use (U). □

An example of a PFG is shown in Figure 2. Memory access conflicts are represented by dashed edges between the conflicting nodes in each thread (most conflict edges have been removed to improve readability). Mutual exclusion synchronization is represented by dotted edges between Lock and Unlock nodes in concurrent threads.

Definition 2 A path from x to y is a *control path* if it only contains edges in E_{ct}. □

In subsequent sections we will use the standard concepts of dominance and post-dominance [1] applied exclusively to control paths.

3.2. Mutex structures

The concepts and algorithms described in this section are based on the non-concurrency analysis techniques developed by Masticola and Ryder [10]. Our work differs from theirs in the following aspects:

1. Our analysis targets locks instead of binary semaphores.

2. The analysis is intended to gather data flow information for the purposes of program optimization instead of deadlock detection.

3. Even though the notation is similar, there are differences in the definitions and the algorithms used. In particular, we use a simpler notion of mutex body that is not based on the concept of *strict interval* defined by Masticola [9]. Strict intervals require other structural conditions that are not needed in our case. For instance, strict intervals do not include ambiguous or illegal mutex bodies. If at the end of the mutex analysis there is at least one unmatched Lock operation for a lock variable L, the whole set of mutex bodies for L will be discarded. In our case, we allow mutex structures with ill-formed mutex bodies. Our data-flow analysis will still be conservative because illegal mutex bodies in a mutex structure will not be considered when reducing data dependencies.

Definition 3 Given a PFG G, a synchronization variable L and two nodes $n, x \in G$, the set $B_L(n, x) = SDOM^{-1}(n) \bigcap PDOM^{-1}(x)$ is a *mutex body* for L if the following conditions are met:

1. $n = $ Lock(L) and $x = $ Unlock(L),

2. n DOM x and x PDOM n, and

3. $\forall a \in B_L(n, x)$ such that $a \neq n \wedge a \neq x \Rightarrow a$ is not a Lock(L) or an Unlock(L) node. □

A mutex body defines a single-entry, single-exit region of the graph delimited by nodes n and x. The mutex body includes all the nodes strictly dominated by n and post-dominated by x (i.e., node n is not included in $B_L(n, x)$).

Definition 4 A *mutex structure* for a synchronization object L, denoted M_L, is the set of all mutex bodies $B_L(n, x)$ in the program. □

3.3. Identifying mutex structures in the code

Algorithm A.1 returns the set of all the mutex structures in an explicitly parallel program. The algorithm starts by pairing up Lock and Unlock nodes that comply with conditions 1 and 2 of Definition 3. The final phase of the algorithm (lines 19–26) examines all the mutex bodies found to eliminate those mutex bodies that do not comply with condition 3 of Definition 3. That is, it removes any body found by the previous step that contains Lock or Unlock nodes for the same variable (other than the entry and exit nodes for the body).

4. CSSA with Mutual Exclusion support

The main goal of mutual exclusion analysis is to reduce the number of incoming conflict edges to nodes in the PFG that use shared variables. In the CSSA framework concurrent modifications to the same memory location by different threads are modeled using π terms which are placed in the *parallel join nodes* of the graph. A parallel join node is one that contains a conflicting use for a shared variable v. Each π term has $n + 1$ arguments; one for the unique incoming control flow edge and n for the n incoming conflict edges. The goal of the extensions described in this section is to remove superfluous arguments from π terms inside mutex bodies.

Theorems 1 and 2 give sufficient conditions to reduce the number of reachable definitions for uses inside mutex bodies. Both theorems rely on the concepts of upward-exposed uses [15] and reaching definitions [1].

Theorem 1 Let M_L be a mutex structure for lock variable L. Let D_v^B be a definition for a shared variable v inside a mutex body $B_L(n, x) \in M_L$. If D_v^B does not reach node x then D_v^B cannot reach uses of v in any other mutex body $B_L'(n', x') \in M_L$. □

PROOF Let $U_v^{B'}$ be a use of v in $B_L'(n', x')$. Let d be the node containing D_v^B. Let u be the node containing $U_v^{B'}$. Since d and u are inside mutex bodies in the same mutex structure they cannot execute concurrently. Therefore, the definition in d cannot reach the use in u via the conflict edge that joins d and u. Since $B_L(n, x)$ and $B_L'(n', x')$ cannot execute concurrently, for every execution of the program that includes both mutex bodies there can only be two possible partial orderings between them:

1. $B_L(n, x)$ executes to completion before $B_L'(n', x')$. Even though node d executes before node u, the definition D_v^B cannot reach $U_v^{B'}$ because it is always killed by some other definition before it reaches the exit node of $B_L(n, x)$.

2. $B_L'(n', x')$ executes to completion before $B_L(n, x)$. Node u executes before node d, therefore D_v^B cannot reach $U_v^{B'}$. ∎

Theorem 2 Let M_L be a mutex structure for lock variable L. Let U_v^B be a use for a shared variable v inside a mutex body $B_L(n, x) \in M_L$. If U_v^B is not upward-exposed from $B_L(n, x)$ then U_v^B cannot be reached by definitions from any other mutex body $B_L'(n', x') \in M_L$. □

PROOF Let $D_v^{B'}$ be a definition for variable v in mutex body $B_L'(n', x')$. Let d be the node in $B_L'(n', x')$ that contains the definition $D_v^{B'}$. Let u be the node in mutex body $B_L(n, x)$ that contains the use U_v^B. Since d and u are inside mutex bodies in the same mutex structure, they cannot execute concurrently. Therefore, the definition in d cannot

reach the use in u via the conflict edge that joins d and u. We need to consider two possibilities:

1. $D_v^{B'}$ does not reach node x'. In this case it is clear that $D_v^{B'}$ cannot reach U_v^B (Theorem 1).

2. $D_v^{B'}$ reaches node x'. Now we need to consider the partial execution ordering between $B_L(n, x)$ and $B_L'(n', x')$:

(a) $B_L(n, x)$ executes to completion before $B_L'(n', x')$. Node u executes before node d, therefore $D_v^{B'}$ cannot reach U_v^B.

(b) $B_L'(n', x')$ executes before $B_L(n, x)$. Since U_v^B is not upward-exposed from $B_L(n, x)$, any definitions of v made before $B_L(n, x)$ starts executing are guaranteed to be killed by some other definition inside $B_L(n, x)$. Therefore, $D_v^{B'}$ cannot reach U_v^B. ∎

We now introduce the CSSAME form, an extension to the CSSA form to handle mutual exclusion synchronization. Algorithm A.2 transforms an explicitly parallel program P to CSSAME form. The algorithm starts by building the PFG for P. Once the PFG has been built, the algorithm creates the mutex structures for the mutual exclusion synchronization used in the program. The next step builds the CSSA form using the algorithms proposed in [7]. The only difference in our approach is that the underlying sequential SSA form is computed using factored use-def (FUD) chains [15] with appropriate modifications to avoid placing superfluous ϕ terms at coend nodes. The computation of partial orderings and the placement of π functions use the same algorithms described in [7]. Notice that since analyzing mutual exclusion synchronization does not require execution ordering information, we do not impose restrictions on the input program.

Once the CSSA form has been computed, π terms are modified using Algorithm A.3. This algorithm examines every mutex body of the program trying to remove arguments from each π term using theorems 1 and 2. A π term will be removed from the graph if and only if at the end of the algorithm it contains only one argument. If the π term only contains one argument, it must be the argument for the incoming control edge to the node because this is the only argument that is never removed by Algorithm A.3.

5. Optimizing explicitly parallel programs

5.1. Constant propagation

Lee *et al.* [7] adapted the sequential Sparse Conditional Constant propagation (SCC) algorithm [14] to work with explicitly parallel programs. We will use the program in Figure 2 to show how our extensions to the original CSSA framework can be used to improve the constant propagation algorithm when mutual exclusion is taken into account. There are two different CSSA forms for the program in Fig-

```
a0 = 0;                          a0 = 0;
b0 = 0;                          b0 = 0;
cobegin                         cobegin
   T 0: begin                      T 0: begin
      Lock(L0);                       Lock(L0);
      a1 = 5;                         a1 = 5;
      ta1 = π(a1, a4);                b1 = a1 + 3;
      b1 = ta1 + 3;                   if (b1 > 4) {
      if (b1 > 4) {                      a2 = a1 + b1;
         ta11 = π(a1, a4);            }
         a2 = ta11 + b1;             a3 = φ(a1, a2);
      }                              x0 = a3;
      a3 = φ(a1, a2);                Unlock(L0);
      ta12 = π(a3, a4);            end
      x0 = ta12;
      Unlock(L0);                  T 1: begin
   end                                Lock(L0);
                                      tb0 = π(b0, b1);
   T 1: begin                         a4 = tb0 + 6;
      Lock(L0);                       y0 = a4;
      tb0 = π(b0, b1);                Unlock(L0);
      a4 = tb0 + 6;                end
      ta4 = π(a4, a1, a2);       coend
      y0 = ta4;                  a5 = φ(a3, a4);
      Unlock(L0);               print(x0);
   end                          print(y0);
coend
a5 = φ(a3, a4);
print(x0);
print(y0);

 a. CSSA form                    b. CSSAME form
```

Figure 3. CSSA forms for the program in Figure 2.

```
a0 = 0;                          a0 = 0;
b0 = 0;                          b0 = 0;
cobegin                         cobegin
   T 0: begin                      T 0:
      Lock(L0);                       begin
      a1 = 5;                            Lock(L0);
      ta1 = π(a1, a4);                   a1 = 5;
      b1 = ta1 + 3;                      b1 = 8;
      if (b1 > 4) {                      a2 = 13;
         ta11 = π(a1, a4);               a3 = 13;
         a2 = ta11 + b1;                 x0 = 13;
      }                                  Unlock(L0);
      a3 = φ(a1, a2);                 end
      ta12 = π(a3, a4);
      x0 = ta12;                      T 1:
      Unlock(L0);                        begin
   end                                   Lock(L0);
                                         tb0 = π(b0, b1);
   T 1: begin                            a4 = tb0 + 6;
      Lock(L0);                          y0 = a4;
      tb0 = π(b0, b1);                   Unlock(L0);
      a4 = tb0 + 6;                   end
      ta4 = π(a4, a1, a2);        coend
      y0 = ta4;                   a5 = φ(a3, a4);
      Unlock(L0);                 print(x0);
   end                            print(y0);
coend
a5 = φ(a3, a4);
print(x0);
print(y0);

 a. Using CSSA                   b. Using CSSAME
```

Figure 4. Constant propagation for Figure 2.

ure 2. The one in Figure 3a is the original CSSA form without mutual exclusion extensions. Figure 3b shows the CSSAME form built using the algorithms in Section 4 (notice the reduction of π terms in Figure 3b).

Figure 4a shows the result of applying the constant propagation algorithm to the program using CSSA. Notice that the constant propagation is conservatively correct but since the original CSSA framework does not recognize the mutual exclusion semantics of the program, no constants can be propagated. On the other hand, translating the program to CSSAME form allows the compiler to remove all the π terms for variable a in thread T_0. The key to this is the assignment to variable a in thread T_0 right after the lock operation. Since all the statements in thread T_0 execute indivisibly as one atomic operation, uses of variable a after the first assignment cannot possibly be affected by definitions of a made by thread T_1. This allows the compiler to propagate constants inside thread T_0 as if it were a sequential program (Figure 4b).

5.2. Parallel Dead Code Elimination

Dead code refers to program statements that have no effect on any program output [2]. Although it is not common for the programmer to introduce dead code intentionally, dead code may be generated by optimizing transformations [1]. We introduce the Parallel Dead Code Elimination algorithm (PDCE), an extension of the dead code elimination algorithm proposed by Cytron et al. [2] to work on explicitly

parallel programs. The algorithm starts by marking dead all the statements of the program except those that are assumed to affect the program output such as I/O statements or assignments to variables outside the current scope. This initial set of live statements is used to seed the work list maintained by the algorithm. The list is updated with every new statement that is marked live. When the list empties, all the statements still marked dead are removed from the program. A statement will be marked live if it satisfies one of the following conditions [2]: (1) The statement is assumed to affect the program output. Examples include I/O statements, assignment to global variables, calls to procedures that may have side effects, etc. (2) The statement contains a definition that reaches uses in statements already marked live. (3) The statement is a conditional branch and there are live statements that are control dependent on this conditional branch.

The sequential algorithm needs two important modifications to work on explicitly parallel programs:

1. Condition 2 of Cytron et al.'s algorithm calls for the computation of reaching definition information for each live statement of the program. The rationale is that if statement s is live then any other statement that defines variables used by s must also be marked live. We compute reaching definition information using both ϕ and π terms when following use-def chains in the program. Algorithm A.4 computes the set of reaching definitions for every use of a variable in an explicitly parallel program. The algorithm is a modified version of an algorithm for finding reaching definitions in a se-

```
b0 = 0;                      b0 = 0;
cobegin                      cobegin
  T 0: begin                   T 0: begin
    Lock(L0);                    Lock(L0);
    b1 = 8;                      b1 = 8;
    x0 = 13;                     Unlock(L0);
    Unlock(L0);                  x0 = 13;
  end                          end

  T 1: begin                   T 1: begin
    Lock(L0);                    Lock(L0);
    tb0 = π(b0, b1);             tb0 = π(b0, b1);
    a4 = tb0 + 6;               a4 = tb0 + 6;
    y0 = a4;                     Unlock(L0);
    Unlock(L0);                  y0 = a4;
  end                          end
coend                        coend
print(x0);                   print(x0);
print(y0);                   print(y0);

a. After PDCE               b. After LICM
```

Figure 5. PDCE and LICM for Figure 4b.

quential SSA framework [15]. The main modification done to the original algorithm is the additional test for π terms when traversing use-def chains in the PFG. We have also extended the algorithm to compute def-use links (needed by the constant propagation algorithm).

2. A `cobegin` statement will be marked live if there is at least one statement in one of its children threads marked live. If at the end of the algorithm there is only one thread with live statements in it, the `cobegin/coend` construct will be replaced by the sequential code corresponding to the live thread.

These modifications to the sequential DCE algorithm are necessary to account for the concurrent activity in the program. Since reaching definition information will be computed using both π and ϕ terms, if a use u is live in one thread, any definition made by other concurrent threads that reach u will also be marked live. Furthermore, the reduction of dependencies made possible by CSSAME directly benefits the elimination of dead code in the program.

To show the effects of dead code elimination consider the program in Figure 2 after constant propagation has been performed (Figure 4b). As can be seen in the example program, all the assignments to variable a in T_0 are dead because they do not affect the output of the program (i.e., they do not reach any other use of a in the program). On the other hand, the assignment to b in T_0 cannot be considered dead because it is used by T_1. Note that a sequential dead code elimination algorithm would have erroneously marked the assignment to b dead because it lacks the appropriate reaching definition information. Figure 5a shows the result of a dead code pass on the code in Figure 4b.

5.3. Lock independent code motion

Because of the restrictions imposed by mutual synchronization operations, it is often desirable to minimize the time spent inside mutex bodies in the program. To achieve

this goal we can optimize the code inside mutex bodies as much as possible. Alternatively, we can minimize the amount of code executed inside a mutex body by moving code that does not need to be locked outside the mutex body. In this section we introduce *lock independent code motion* (LICM), a new technique that performs safe code motion on mutex bodies.

To determine what code can be safely moved outside a mutex body we must find those interior statements that are not affected by the presence of the lock. We call these *lock independent* statements. Although it is unlikely for the programmer to write lock independent statements inside a mutex body, other compiler optimizations might produce lock independent code (e.g., the statement $x0 = 13$ in Figure 5a is lock independent due to constant propagation and PDCE). This is similar to the concept of loop-invariant code for standard loop optimization techniques [1]. However, the conditions that make a statement lock independent are different than those that make it loop invariant. Loop invariant computations are basically statements with all their operands constant or with reaching definitions outside the loop. Lock independent code computes the same result whether it is inside a mutex body or not. For instance, a statement that references variables private to the thread will compute the same value whether it is executed inside a mutex body or not. This is also true if the statement references variables not used by any other concurrent thread in the program.

Definition 5 A statement inside a mutex body is *lock independent* if the variables that it defines and/or uses cannot be modified concurrently. □

Although lock independence is a necessary condition to do code motion, it is not sufficient because the motion should also preserve all the control and data dependencies for the statement. For instance, if the statement is inside a loop it cannot be moved out unless the whole loop is lock independent.

To perform code motion we need to modify the flow graph to add two special nodes that will act as landing pads for statements moved out of each mutex body $B_L(n, x)$. We call these two nodes the *pre-mutex* and *post-mutex* node. The *pre-mutex* node is placed as an immediate strict dominator of n, while the *post-mutex* node is placed as an immediate strict post-dominator of x.

Theorem 3 Let s be a lock independent statement inside a mutex body $B_L(n, x)$. Let a be the node containing s:

1. If a dominates all the nodes in B and s does not have any reaching definitions within a then s can be moved to the pre-mutex node of B.

2. If x immediately post-dominates a and s does not have any reached uses within a then s can be moved to the post-mutex node of B. □

PROOF   1. If a dominates all the nodes in B then its immediate dominator must be node n. If s does not have any reaching definitions within a then s can be moved to a node dominating a without affecting its internal data dependencies. Furthermore, definitions reaching s cannot reach through conflict edges because s is lock independent. Neither can they reach from node n because there are no definitions in that node. Therefore, moving s to the pre-mutex node will not alter any data dependencies in the program. Notice that when moving s to the pre-mutex node, it should be placed as the last statement of the node. This will preserve any data dependencies from statements already present in the node.

2. If x immediately post-dominates a then a is the last node to be executed before leaving the mutex body. If definitions made by s do not reach any use within a then moving s to the post-mutex node will not alter any data dependencies inside a. Furthermore, definitions make by s cannot reach other threads through conflict edges because s is lock independent. Therefore, moving s to the post-mutex node will not alter any data dependencies in the program. Notice that when moving s to the post-mutex node, it should be placed as the first statement of the node. This will preserve any data dependencies to statements already present in the node. ∎

These conditions guarantee that the statement being moved will not break any data dependencies with other nodes in the body and will not introduce any conflict edges with any concurrent node. Applying Theorem 3 to the program in Figure 5a allows the compiler to move some statements out of the mutex bodies to obtain the equivalent program in Figure 5b. Notice that both assignments to variables x and y can be safely moved out of each mutex body because there are no conflicting definitions in their sibling threads. Algorithm A.5 implements the concepts described previously. After code motion is complete, any empty mutex bodies will be removed from the program.

6. Implementation

The algorithms discussed in previous sections have been implemented in a prototype compiler for the C language using the SUIF compiler system [4]. To avoid modifying SUIF's front-end we added support for `cobegin/coend` and `doall` parallel structures via language macros. These macros re-define control structures of the language so that the compiler can recognize them as parallel at the intermediate language level.

Once the program has been parsed by the SUIF front-end, the compiler creates the corresponding PFG and its CSSAME form. The PFG implementation is an extension of the sequential Control Flow Graph library provided by Machine SUIF [5]. The PFG can be displayed using a variety of graph visualization systems. The flow graphs in this

paper were generated with the VCG tool (Visualization of Compiler Graphs) [12]. The CSSA form for the program can also be displayed as an option. Mutual exclusion analysis can also issue warning messages like unmatched `Lock` and `Unlock` operations or improperly nested locks. A limited form of data race detection capability is also built-in for inconsistent use of locks to protect shared variables. For instance, if modifications to a variable are not always protected by the same lock, the compiler will warn the user about a potential data race.

A simple extension to algorithm A.1 allows the compiler to perform some semantic checking on the synchronization structure of the program. At the end of the algorithm, every `Lock` or `Unlock` node in $p_i^{lock} \bigcup p_i^{unlock}$ that is not part of a mutex body can be reported as a warning to the user. The compiler will recognize several potentially unsafe situations and report a warning.

7. Future work

We have found that the CSSAME form facilitates the translation of scalar optimizations to the parallel case, especially if the sequential strategy is SSA based. We are presently investigating the representation of parallel loops in the CSSA framework. Different semantics for parallel loops (i.e., `doaccross`, `doall`, etc.) will have different data-flow properties. Another extension the CSSAME framework involves other commonly used synchronization primitives such as barriers and semaphores.

With the lock independent code motion strategy we have entered the field of new optimization techniques that are specifically targeted at explicitly parallel programs. We are presently designing new optimization techniques that take advantage of the parallel and synchronization structure of these programs.

A. Algorithms

A.1. Identification of mutex structures

Input: A PFG G and a set $L = \{L_1, L_2, \ldots, L_m\}$ containing all the lock variables used in the program.
Output: A set of mutex structures $M = \bigcup_i M_i$ where M_i is the set of mutex bodies for lock variable L_i.

```
1:  /* Find nodes in G that lock and unlock each Li */
2:  foreach lock variable Li do
3:      pi^lock ← {n ∈ N : n = Lock(Li)}
4:      pi^unlock ← {x ∈ N : x = Unlock(Li)}
5:  end for

6:  /* Build the dominator and post-dominator trees for G */
7:  call buildDomTree(G)
8:  call buildPDomTree(G)

9:  /* Find candidate mutex bodies */
10: foreach lock variable Li do
11:     foreach n ∈ pi^lock do
12:         foreach x ∈ pi^unlock do
```

13:       **if** $n \in DOM(x)$ and $x \in PDOM(n)$ **then**
14:         add (n, x) to the set of candidates M_i
15:       **end if**
16:     **end for**
17:   **end for**
18: **end for**

19: /* Remove illegal mutex bodies from each M_i */
20: **foreach** $(n, x) \in M_i$ **do**
21:   **foreach** $m \in p_i^{lock} \bigcup p_i^{unlock}$ **do**
22:     **if** $m \neq n$ and $m \neq x$ and $n \in DOM(m)$ and $x \in PDOM(m)$ **then**
23:       remove (n, x) from M_i
24:     **end if**
25:   **end for**
26: **end for**

27: $M \leftarrow \bigcup_i M_i$
28: **return** M

A.2. CSSAME algorithm

Input: An explicitly parallel program P

Output: The program P in CSSAME form
1: Build the PFG for P using an extended version of the CFG algorithm in [5]
2: Identify mutex structures using Algorithm A.1.
3: Compute the CSSA form for the graph using the algorithms in [7].
4: Rewrite π terms using Algorithm A.3.

A.3. Rewrite π terms

Input: A PFG G in CSSA form

Output: The graph G in CSSA form with π terms modified to account for mutual exclusion synchronization
1: /* Traverse mutex bodies looking for π terms to rewrite */
2: **foreach** lock variable L_i **do**
3:   **foreach** mutex body $b \in MutexStruct(L_i)$ **do**
4:     **call** $rewrite(b)$
5:   **end for**
6: **end for**

7: /* Examine all the π terms in b */
8: **procedure** $rewrite(b)$
9: **foreach** node $n \in b$ **do**
10:   **foreach** π term $p \in n$ **do**
11:     v is the variable referenced by p
12:     /* If an argument complies with theorems 1 or 2, */
13:     /* then we may safely remove the argument from the π term */
14:     **foreach** p argument d coming from a conflict edge **do**
15:       **if** d comes from another mutex body $b' \in MutexStruct(b)$ **then**
16:         **if** (the use of v is not upward exposed from b) or (d does not reach the exit node of b') **then**
17:           Remove d from p
18:         **end if**
19:       **end if**
20:     **end for**
21:     /* If π term p has no conflict arguments then remove it */
22:     **if** p has only one argument **then**
23:       $chain(u) \leftarrow$ first argument of p
24:       Remove p from n
25:     **end if**
26:   **end for**
27: **end for**

A.4. Parallel reaching definitions

Input: A PFG G in CSSAME form
Output: The set of reaching definitions for each variable used in the program and the set of reached uses for each variable defined in the program
1: **foreach** variable definition d in the program **do**
2:   $marked(d) \leftarrow \perp$
3:   $uses(d) \leftarrow \emptyset$
4: **end for**
5: **foreach** variable use u in the program **do**
6:   $defs(u) \leftarrow \emptyset$
7:   **call** followChain(chain(u), u)
8: **end for**

9: **procedure** $followChain(d, u)$
10: **if** $marked(d) = u$ **then**
11:   **return**
12: **end if**
13: $marked(d) \leftarrow u$
14: **if** d is a definition for u **then**
15:   Add d to $defs(u)$
16:   Add u to $uses(d)$
17: **end if**
18: **if** (d is a ϕ term) or (d is a π term) **then**
19:   **foreach** term argument j **do**
20:     **call** followChain(j, u)
21:   **end for**
22: **end if**

A.5. Lock independent code motion

Input: A PFG G in CSSAME form
Output: The graph with lock independent code moved to the corresponding pre-mutex and post-mutex nodes
1: **foreach** lock variable L_i **do**
2:   **foreach** mutex body $B_{L_i}(n, x) \in MutexStruct(L_i)$ **do**
3:     insert pre-mutex node immediately dominating n
4:     insert post-mutex node immediately post-dominating x
5:   **end for**
6: **end for**

7: **foreach** lock variable L_i **do**
8:   **foreach** mutex body $B_{L_i}(n, x) \in MutexStruct(L_i)$ **do**
9:     $PRE \leftarrow$ the pre-mutex node of B
10:     $POST \leftarrow$ the post-mutex node of B

11:     done $\leftarrow$ FALSE
12:     **while not** done **do**
13:       $a \leftarrow$ node immediately dominated by n
14:       **foreach** statement $s \in a$ **do**
15:         **if** s is lock independent **then**
16:           **if** $Definers(s)$ does not contain a statement from a **then**
17:             move s to the end of node PRE
18:           **end if**
19:         **end if**
20:       **end for**
21:       **if** $a = \emptyset$ **then**
22:         remove a from the graph
23:       **else**
24:         $done \leftarrow$ TRUE
25:       **end if**
26:     **end while**

27:     done $\leftarrow$ FALSE
28:     **while not** done **do**
29:       $b \leftarrow$ node immediately post-dominated by x
30:       **foreach** statement $s \in b$ **do**
31:         **if** s is lock independent **then**

```
32:              if Users(s) does not contain a statement from b then
33:                  move s to the beginning of node POST
34:              end if
35:          end if
36:      end for
37:      if b = ∅ then
38:          remove b from the graph
39:      else
40:          done ← TRUE
41:      end if
42:  end while

43:  if DOM⁻¹(n) ∩ PDOM⁻¹(x) = ∅ then
44:      remove n and x from the graph
45:  end if
46:  end for
47: end for
```

References

[1] A. V. Aho, R. Sethi, and J. Ullman. *Compilers: Principles, Techniques, and Tools*. Reading, Mass.: Addison-Wesley, Reading, MA, second edition, 1986.

[2] R. Cytron, J. Ferrante, B. Rosen, M. Wegman, and K. Zadeck. Efficiently computing static single assignment form and the control dependence graph. *TOPLAS*, 13(4):451–490, Oct. 1991.

[3] D. Grunwald and H. Srinivasan. Data flow equations for explicitly parallel programs. *ACM SIGPLAN Notices*, 28(7):159–168, July 1993.

[4] M. Hall, J. Anderson, S. Amarasinghe, B. Murphy, S. Liao, E. Bugnion, and M. Lam. Maximizing multiprocessor performance with the SUIF compiler. *IEEE Computer*, 29(12):84–89, Dec. 1996.

[5] G. Holloway and C. Young. The flow analysis and transformation libraries of Machine SUIF. In *Proc. 2nd SUIF Compiler Workshop*, Stanford University, Aug. 1997.

[6] J. Knoop, B. Steffen, and J. Vollmer. Parallelism for free: Efficient and optimal bitvector analyses for parallel programs. *TOPLAS*, 18(3):268–299, May 1996.

[7] J. Lee, S. Midkiff, and D. A. Padua. Concurrent static single assignment form and constant propagation for explicitly parallel programs. In *Proc 10th Workshop on Languages and Compilers for Parallel Computing*, Aug. 1997.

[8] D. Loveman. High Performance Fortran. *IEEE Parallel and Distributed Technology*, 1(1):25–43, 1993.

[9] S. Masticola. *Static Detection of Deadlocks in Polynomial Time*. PhD thesis, Department of Computer Science, Rutgers University, 1993.

[10] S. Masticola and B. Ryder. Non-concurrency analysis. In *Proc 4th ACM SIGPLAN Symposium on Principles and Practice of Parallel Programming*, San Diego, CA, May 1993.

[11] S. P. Midkiff and D. A. Padua. Issues in the optimization of parallel programs. In *Int'l Conference on Parallel Processing*, volume II, pages 105–113, Aug. 1990.

[12] G. Sander. Graph layout through the VCG tool. In R. Tamassia and I. G. Tollis, editors, *Proc. Graph Drawing, DIMACS International Workshop GD'94, Lecture Notes in Computer Science 894*, pages 194–205. Berlin: Springer Verlag, 1995.

[13] D. Shasha and M. Snir. Efficient and correct execution of parallel programs that share memory. *TOPLAS*, 10(2):282–312, Apr. 1988.

[14] M. Wegman and K. Zadeck. Constant propagation with conditional branches. *TOPLAS*, 13(2):181–210, Apr. 1991.

[15] M. J. Wolfe. *High Performance Compilers for Parallel Computing*. Reading, Mass.: Addison-Wesley, 1996.

Session 5C
Multicasting

Chair: Kyungsook Lee
Denver University

An Euler-Path-Based Multicasting Model for Wormhole-Routed Networks with Multi-Destination Capability[*]

Yu-Chee Tseng, and Ming-Hour Yang,
Dept. of Computer Science and Information Engineering
National Central University
Chung-Li, 32054, Taiwan

Tong-Ying Juang
Dept. of Computer Science
Chung-Hua University
Hsin-Chu, 30067, Taiwan

Abstract

Recently, wormhole routers with multi-destination capability have been proposed to support fast multicast in a multi-computer network. In this paper, we develop a new multicasting model for such networks based on the concept of Euler path/circuit in graph theory. The model can support multiple concurrent multicasts freely from deadlock and can be applied to any network which is Eulerian or is Eulerian after some links being removed. No virtual channels are needed. In particular, we demonstrate the potential of this model by showing its fault-tolerant capability in supporting multicasting in the currently popular torus/mesh topology of any dimension with regular fault patterns (such as single node, block, L-shape, +-shape, U-shape, and H-shape) and even irregular fault patterns. The result has improved over existing fault-tolerant routing algorithms for meshes/tori in at least one of the following aspects: the number of faults tolerable, the shape of fault patterns, the number of deactivated healthy nodes, the requirement of support of virtual channels, and the range of network topology acceptable.

1. Introduction

In a multicomputer network, processors often need to communicate with each other for various reasons, such as data exchange and event synchronization. The more recent parallel computers (such as Intel Touchstone DELTA, Intel Paragon, MIT J-machine, IBM SP2, and Cray T3D) have adopted wormhole routing [14], which is known to be quite insensitive to routing distance and can offer fast interprocessor communication. This paper studies the *multiple multicast* problem in a wormhole-routed network, where any node in the network may issue a multicast to any set of destination nodes at any time.

One major advance in solving this problem is the recently proposed path-based solutions, by enhancing routers with *multi-destination* capability [6, 13]. Examples include

[6, 13] for meshes, [12, 7, 11, 15] for *k*-ary *n*-cubes, and [12, 16, 18] for arbitrary networks. Simple hardware is added to the router to enable it to copy the content of a worm while forwarding the worm to the next router. The header of such a worm can carry a number of destination addresses for the worm to visit. So such worms are also termed as *multidestination worms* [7, 15]. When seeing its address in the header, a router retrieves its address and forwards the worm (according to the routing function) to the next router. As the worm passes by, the router also makes a copy of the worm body for itself. As a worm can deliver a message to multiple destinations with only one startup cost, the defficiency of high startup cost associated with the unicast-based approach is elliminated.

In [13], to avoid the deadlock problem, a *Hamiltonian path* is constructed first from the network to restrict the order of destinations to be visited by the multidestination worms. A similar approach is proposed in [16], but instead an Euler path/cycle needs to be constructed to restrict the routing order. Observing that both [13, 16] are too restrictive in requiring the network being Hamiltonian or Eulerian, a more relaxed solution is proposed by [12], which only requires the existence of a pseudo-Hamiltonian in the network (a *pseudo-Hamiltonian* path in an undirected graph is a path which visits each vertex at least once and each edge at most once). In [18], it is suggested to use a *trip* instead of a Hamiltonian path to enforce such ordering. As a trip always exists in any netwok, this extends the applicability of the path-based model to arbitrary network topologies. To save hardware cost, [11, 15] propose not to modify the routing function in the routers, but only route a worm *conforming to* the routing function originally provided for *point-to-point* communication. Several levels of worms may be used to complete a multicast. This scheme is tested on the *k*-ary *n*-cube architecture to demonstrate its efficiency. Following the similar line of thinking, [7] derives a multi-destination multicasting on meshes based on the *turn model* [8].

Each of the above results has its strength and weakness. While most commonly used networks are Hamiltonian/Eulerian, the approaches in [13, 16] have little fault-tolerant capability as any faulty node in the network may de-

[*]This research is supported by the National Science Council of the Republic of China under Grant # NSC86-2213-E-008-029 and Grant # NSC86-2213-E-216-021.

stroy its Hamiltonian/Eulerian property*. The same problem also exists in [7, 11, 15] as the given base routing function may not be fault-tolerant. The pseudo-Hamiltonian model by [12] is more fault-tolerant. Through somewhat complicated methods, [12] shows how to constructed a pseudo-Hamiltonian path in a mesh network with some faulty blocks such that the no two faulty blocks are of a distance of 3. But we conjecture that finding a pseudo-Hamiltonian path in an arbitrary graph is just as difficult as determining whether the graph is Hamiltonian, The solution by [18] can be used in any network topology, and thus most fault-tolerant. However, this requires two virtual channels per physical channel.

In this paper we propose a new multicast model called *Euler-path-based model* which can be applied to any network that (i) is Eulerian, or (ii) is Eulerian after some links being removed. This is more flexible than requiring the network being Eulerian (as in [16]), but easier to be satisfied than requiring the network being Hamiltonian or pseudo-Hamiltonian (as in [13, 12]). The model does not rely on the existence of virtual channels and thus is more hardware-efficient than [18].

One major emphasis of this paper is to extend the previous version of this paper [10] by demonstrating the potential of our model when applied to the torus/mesh topology of any dimension with faults. Many schemes have been proposed for fault-tolerant routing on mehs/torus-like networks [1, 2, 4, 5, 9]. However, most results can only tolerate a limited number of faults, usually proportional to the dimension of the mesh/torus [5, 9]. To tolerate more faults, a typical approach is to "deactivate" some healthy nodes (i.e., regard them as faulty) so that faults are in rectangular shapes [1, 2, 4, 12]. Deactivating healthy nodes is certainly undesirable. The only scheme known to us that can handle non-rectangular fault patterns (such as T and L fault patterns) is [3]. However, this is achieved by using four virtual channels per physical channel. Furthermore, all these results are only for point-to-point communication and thus can not enjoy the benefits of multi-destination routing capability. In this paper, we show that many regular fault patterns (such as single node, block, L-shape, +-shape, U-shape, and H-shape) and even irregular fault patterns are tolerable by our model. In most cases there is no need of deactivating healthy nodes. Simulations have also been conducted to study the performance behavior of our model when applied to 2D tori.

2 The Euler-Path-Based Multicasting Model

A multicomputer network is represented by an undirected *system graph* $G = (V, E)$ with vertex set V corresponding to

---

*We exemplify such a situation by a 5×5 mesh. The mesh is a *bipartite graph* and we can partition its nodes into two groups, one with 12 and the other with 13 nodes. If any node in the former group is damaged, then the mesh becomes non-Hamiltonian. The reason is that a Hamiltonian path must visit nodes of these two groups *alternatively*. It is easy to extend such arguments to meshes of other sizes and even tori.

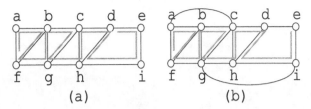

Figure 1. (a) A system graph containing an Euler path $\alpha = [f, a, b, f, g, b, c, g, h, c, d, h, i, e, d]$, **and (b) a system graph which is not Eulerian.**

processors (nodes) and edge set E to communication links. Each *undirected* edge (u, v) consists of two *directed* links $\langle u, v \rangle$ and $\langle v, u \rangle$, which can transmit data independently. An *Euler path* in G (if any) is an undirected path that traverses each edge of G exactly once (and thus each node once or more).

Lemma 1 *[17] A graph is Eulerian iff one of the following conditions holds true:*

(a) all nodes have even degrees, or

(b) all nodes, except exactly two nodes, have even degrees.

Fig. 1(a) shows a system graph with an Euler path from f to d. The graph in Fig. 1(b) is not Eulerian as there are more than two odd-degree nodes. As a convention, we denote an Euler path α by a sequence of nodes $[\alpha_1, \alpha_2, \ldots, \alpha_n]$, where each $\alpha_i, i = 1..n$, is a node. Finding an Euler path is a simple job in graph theory, while finding a Hamiltonian path is NP-complete [17].

Our model can be applied to any system graph $G = (V, E)$ which contains an Eulerian subgraph $G' = (V, E_1)$. We will use any Euler path α in G' as a basis to avoid communication deadlock, and use links in $E_2 = E - E_1$ as shortcuts to accelerate the multicasting.

Definition 1 Let $\alpha = [\alpha_1, \alpha_2, \ldots, \alpha_n]$ be an Euler path in G'. Associated with each α_i, $1 \leq i \leq n$, define $\hat{\alpha}_i$ to be the 2-tuple (α_i, i). Also, let $\hat{\alpha}$ be the sequence $[\hat{\alpha}_1, \hat{\alpha}_2, \ldots, \hat{\alpha}_n]$.

Note that each $\hat{\alpha}_i$ is associated with α_i's location, i, in the Euler path. So $\hat{\alpha}_i \neq \hat{\alpha}_j$ iff $i \neq j$ (but not necessarily $\alpha_i \neq \alpha_j$).

Definition 2 The *f-graph* (read as forward graph) with respect to α, denoted as $G_f(\alpha) = (V_f, E_f)$, is a directed graph such that

$$V_f = \{\hat{\alpha}_1, \hat{\alpha}_2, \ldots, \hat{\alpha}_n\}$$

$$E_f = \{\langle \hat{\alpha}_i, \hat{\alpha}_{i+1} \rangle | i = 1..n - 1\} \cup$$

$$\{\langle \hat{\alpha}_i, \hat{\alpha}_j \rangle | (i < j) \wedge (\alpha_i, \alpha_j) \in E_2\} .$$

Using the system graph in Fig. 1(b) as an example, we can let $E_2 = \{(a, c), (g, i), (d, e)\}$ and draw the corresponding f-graph $G_f(\alpha)$ as shown in Fig. 2. Intuitively, we regard α (i.e., the first set in the equation of E_f) as the "backbone" of $G_f(\alpha)$. All links $(\alpha_i, \alpha_j) \in E_2$ are added between all occurrences of $\hat{\alpha}_i$ and $\hat{\alpha}_j$ from left to right (i.e., the second set in

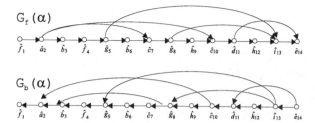

$G_f(\alpha)$

$\hat{f}_1 \quad \hat{a}_2 \quad \hat{b}_3 \quad \hat{f}_4 \quad \hat{g}_5 \quad \hat{b}_6 \quad \hat{c}_7 \quad \hat{g}_8 \quad \hat{h}_9 \quad \hat{c}_{10} \quad \hat{d}_{11} \quad \hat{h}_{12} \quad \hat{i}_{13} \quad \hat{e}_{14}$

$G_b(\alpha)$

$\hat{f}_1 \quad \hat{a}_2 \quad \hat{b}_3 \quad \hat{f}_4 \quad \hat{g}_5 \quad \hat{b}_6 \quad \hat{c}_7 \quad \hat{g}_8 \quad \hat{h}_9 \quad \hat{c}_{10} \quad \hat{d}_{11} \quad \hat{h}_{12} \quad \hat{i}_{13} \quad \hat{e}_{14}$

Figure 2. The f-graph and b-graph corresponding to the example in Fig. 1(b).

the equation of E_f) as shortcuts. In a similar way, we define the backward-graph as follows.

Definition 3 The *b-graph* (read as backward graph) with respect to α, denoted as $G_b(\alpha) = (V_b, E_b)$, is a directed graph such that

$$V_b = \{\hat{\alpha}_1, \hat{\alpha}_2, \ldots, \hat{\alpha}_n\}$$

$$E_b = \{\langle \hat{\alpha}_i, \hat{\alpha}_{i-1}\rangle | i = 2..n\} \cup \{\langle \hat{\alpha}_i, \hat{\alpha}_j \rangle | (i > j) \wedge (\alpha_i, \alpha_j) \in E_2\}.$$

Suppose a source node s wants to multicast a message M to a set D of destinations. We will develop our multicast algorithm based on the two tool graphs $G_f(\alpha)$ and $G_b(\alpha)$. A multicast request will generate one worm (called *f-worm*) on $G_f(\alpha)$ and another (called *b-worm*) on $G_b(\alpha)$. A worm, once initiated, will remain in the same graph until it is retrieved from the network. The algorithm is presented below.

Step 1: From D, we construct two sequences D_f and D_b, which are the nodes to be visited by the f-worm and b-worm injected into $G_f(\alpha)$ and $G_b(\alpha)$, respectively. The f-worm will be injected from node $\hat{\alpha}_f = (\alpha_f, f)$ such that $\alpha_f = s$ and f is *minimal* (i.e., the first occurrence of s in α). However, the b-worm will be injected from node $\hat{\alpha}_b = (\alpha_b, b)$ such that $\alpha_b = s$ and b is *maximal* (i.e., the last occurrence of s in α). To calculate D_f and D_b, for each $x \in D$, we randomly select an $\hat{\alpha}_i$ such that $\alpha_i = x$. The following rules are used to add $\hat{\alpha}_i$ to one of D_f and D_b.

(a) If $i < f$, add $\hat{\alpha}_i$ to D_b (since $\hat{\alpha}_i$ is not reachable from $\hat{\alpha}_f$ in $G_f(\alpha)$).

(b) If $b < i$, add $\hat{\alpha}_i$ to D_f (since $\hat{\alpha}_i$ is not reachable from $\hat{\alpha}_b$ in $G_b(\alpha)$).

(c) Otherwise, $\hat{\alpha}_i$ is reachable from both $\hat{\alpha}_f$ in $G_f(\alpha)$ and $\hat{\alpha}_b$ in $G_b(\alpha)$; we randomly add $\hat{\alpha}_i$ to either of D_b and D_f.

The above is repeated for all x in D.

Step 2: Sort D_f in the ascending order (based on the node indices) and then inject a f-worm carrying D_f and M into $G_f(\alpha)$ starting from $\hat{\alpha}_f$. Also, sort D_b in the descending order and inject a b-worm carrying D_b and M into $G_b(\alpha)$ starting from $\hat{\alpha}_b$.

Step 3: On a node $\hat{\alpha}_i$ receiving a f-worm or b-worm carrying a sequence, say D', and a message M, it examines

$head(D')$, where $head()$ is a function which will return the first element in D'. If $head(D') = \hat{\alpha}_l$ such that $\alpha_i = \alpha_l$, then $\hat{\alpha}_i$ makes a copy of M and removes $\hat{\alpha}_l$ from D'. If the new D' becomes an empty sequence, retrieve the worm from the network and stop; otherwise, go to step 4.

Step 4: For a node $\hat{\alpha}_i$ owning a f-worm (resp., b-worm) carrying a sequence D' and a message M, it needs to select a channel $\langle \hat{\alpha}_j, \hat{\alpha}_k \rangle \in E_f$ (resp., $\in E_b$) to forward the worm. If this is a f-worm, then channel $\langle \hat{\alpha}_j, \hat{\alpha}_k \rangle$ must satisfy the following conditions: (i) $\alpha_i = \alpha_j$, and (ii) $i \leq j < k \leq l$, where l is the index of $head(D)$ (i.e., $\hat{\alpha}_l = head(D)$). The first condition states that the channel is an outgoing channel from α_i. The second condition guarantees that the f-worm always moves in the forward direction of the Euler path. It also ensures that the f-worm *never* arrives at a node $\hat{\alpha}_k$ that can not reach the next destination $\hat{\alpha}_l$.

If this is a b-worm, the same condition (i) should also hold, but condition (ii) should be changed to: $i \geq j > k \geq l$. Similarly, it is guaranteed that the b-worm will progress in the backward direction of the Euler path and sequentially visit nodes in D_b.

It is to be noted that although the algorithm is presented based on the tool graphs $G_f(\alpha)$ and $G_b(\alpha)$, a message routed on $\langle \hat{\alpha}_j, \hat{\alpha}_k \rangle$ is actually delivered on the link $\langle \alpha_j, \alpha_k \rangle$. The router needs to do such a mapping. The mapping is 1-to-1 if $\langle \alpha_j, \alpha_k \rangle \in E_1$, but could be many-to-1 if $\langle \alpha_j, \alpha_k \rangle \in E_2$ since nodes α_j and α_k may appear more than once in α. If there are more than one candidate channel. We will use the following *channel selection policy*:

(a) The selection prefers a channel that is free.

(b) The selection prefers a channel that leads to a shortest path to $head(D')$.

(c) If all candidate channels are busy, we never wait on a channel in the link set E_2.

3 Applying to 2-D Tori with Faults

A fault-free 2D torus is already Eulerian as each node has a degree of 4. However, when there are some faulty nodes in the network, the Eulerian property may be destroyed. One possible solution, as suggested by our model, is to find a link set E_2 whose removal from the network will make the network Eulerian again.

Two nodes are regarded as *neighbors* if their x-indices differ by at most 1 and their y-indices differ by at most 1 (thus a node has 8 neighbors). A *faulty cluster* is a maximum set of faulty nodes that forms a connected component, in the sense of neighborhood relationship defined above, in the torus. A *simple cycle* is one that does not have any subcycles. A faulty cluster is *simple* if there is a simple cycle that is fault-free and directly wrapping around the cluster and only the cluster. We call the simple cycle the *perimeter* of the faulty cluster. For instances, the faulty clusters in

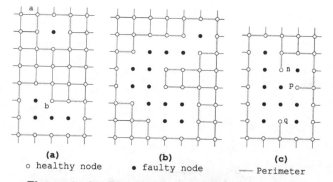

(a)   **(b)**   **(c)**

o healthy node   • faulty node   — Perimeter

Figure 3. Simple and non-simple faulty clusters. Perimeters are shown in gray lines.

Fig. 3(a) and (b) are simple, while that in Fig. 3(c) is non-simple.

In the following discussion, we only consider faulty clusters that are simple (the reason will be discussed later). We deal with single faulty cluster first, and then multiple faulty clusters.

3.1 Single Faulty Cluster

Lemma 2 *[19] The length of the perimeter of any simple faulty cluster is even.*

A node on a perimeter is called a *corner* node if it falls on a position of the perimeter where a 90-degree turn is made; otherwise it is a *non-corner* node. For instances, nodes a and b in Fig. 3(a) are corner nodes.

Lemma 3 *On the perimeter of a simple faulty cluster, every corner node has an even degree, while every non-corner node has an odd degree.*

Lemma 4 *[19] On the perimeter of a simple faulty cluster, there must be an even number of corner nodes and an even number of non-corner nodes.*

In the following, suppose there is only one simple faulty cluster C in the network. We discuss how to construct the link set E_2 in two stages.

3.1.1 Stage 1: Making All Nodes' Degrees Even

We run the procedure $CF()$ in Fig. 4 using C as the input. Mainly, $CF()$ traverses the perimeter of C and moves some links to E_2 to keep all perimeter nodes' degrees even. Lemma 3 suggests two guidelines to do so:

(i) when a non-corner node x is traversed, move one of the perimeter links incident to x to E_2, and

(ii) when a corner node x is traversed, either move both perimeter links incident to x to E_2, or move none of them.

Procedure $CF(C)$; /∗ input C = a simple faulty cluster ∗/
begin

    $f := 1;$ $E_2 = \emptyset;$
    Let the sequence of links $[e_1, e_2, \ldots, e_p]$ be C's perimeter;
    for $i := 2$ **to** p **do**

        if (the node incident by e_{i-1} and e_i is a non-corner node) **then** $f := \bar{f};$

        if ($f = 0$) **then** $E_2 := E_2 \cup \{e_i\};$

    end for;

end.

Figure 4. Procedure $CF()$

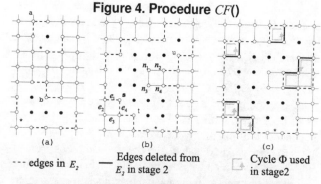

(a)   **(b)**   **(c)**

- - - edges in E_2 — Edges deleted from E_2 in stage 2   ▢ Cycle Φ used in stage2

Figure 5. Parts (a) and (b) show the results after executing $CF()$ **on the examples in Fig. 3(a) and (b), respectively; part (c) shows the result after executing the** *Connection-Scheme* **on (b).**

In the procedure, this is reflected by the binary flag f; whenever $f = 0$, the corresponding link is moved to E_2. It can be proved the $CF()$ does observe rules (i) and (ii) [19], so we have the following lemma.

Lemma 5 *Given a simple faulty cluster, procedure $CF()$ can construct a link set E_2 whose removal from the torus induces a network in which all nodes have even degrees.*

For instances, if we execute procedure $CF()$ on the faulty clusters in Fig. 3(a) and (b), the possible results are shown in Fig. 5(a) and (b), respectively. The removed links are shown in dotted lines. In these examples, the perimeters are traversed counter-clockwise and the first links traversed (i.e. e_1) are marked by ∗ (however, any perimeter link can serve as e_1).

3.1.2 Stage 2: Making the Network Connected

Although procedure $CF()$ generates a network with only even-degree nodes, the removal of E_2 may disconnect the network. This is due to at least two reasons: (i) a corner node originally having a degree of 2 is isolated because both links incident to it are removed (e.g., node b in Fig. 5(a) and nodes s,t and u in Fig. 5(b)), or (ii) two segments of the perimeter are adjacent and parallel to each other (e.g., the block containing nodes $n_1 \ldots n_4$ in Fig. 5(b)). In the following, we propose a general solution to the isolation problem. Suppose G' (obtained from G by removing E_2) is disconnected and H_1 and H_2 are two connected components in G'. The scheme works in two steps:

Algorithm: *Connection-Scheme*

1. Find a simple cycle Φ in G which contains at least one node in H_1 and at least one node in H_2.

2. For each edge e in Φ, if $e \in E_2$, then delete e from E_2; otherwise, add e into E_2.

Intuitively, we try to use the cycle Φ to join the two components H_1 and H_2 together by reversing its links in E_2. After the adjustment, every perimeter node still has an even degree [19]. For instances, in Fig. 5(b), to connect the isolated node s, we can let Φ be the cycle consisting of edges $\{e_1, e_2, e_3, e_4\}$. This will result in e_1 and e_4 being deleted from E_2, and e_2 and e_3 added into E_2. The isolated node t can be treated similarly. The scheme can even be used to connect multiple components together. For instance, in Fig. 5(b), the isolated node u and the isolated block formed by $n_1 \ldots n_4$ are joined with the rest of the network with only one cycle. The cycles Φ used and the final result is shown in Fig. 5(c).

One can easily observe that the application of these rules may introduce new isolated components due to the edges newly added into E_2. While this is true, our experiments and experiences have revealed that this approach is general enough to solve most of the isolation problems.

3.2 Extension to Multiple Faulty Clusters

In procedure $CF()$, to deal with one faulty cluster, we *only* move some links on the perimeter to E_2. Thus, if no two perimeters are overlapping, $CF()$ can directly be used to handle multiple faulty clusters to make all nodes' degrees even. Below we discuss some problems that may need to be taken care of. First, the isolation problem similar to what discussed earlier may occur if two faulty cluster are too close. For instance, Fig. 6(a) shows two faulty clusters in a network. After executing $CF()$ on each of them, a 2×2 block between them is disconnected from the rest of the network. One remedy is to use the *Connection-Scheme* in Section 3.1.2 to modify link set E_2; such possibility is shown in Fig. 6(b) using the cycle drawn in gray.

When the perimeters of two faulty clusters overlap with each other, directly applying $CF()$ will not work as inconsistency may take place during making decisions of moving which links to set E_2. Fig. 7(a) demonstrates such a dilemma. Below we propose a general approach to solve this problem, given two simple faulty clusters C_1 and C_2 whose perimeters are overlapping.

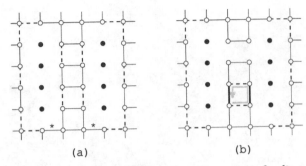

Figure 6. (a) execution of $CF()$ on two faulty clusters, and **(b)** adjustment after using the *Connection-Scheme*.

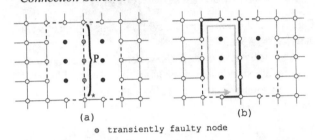

∘ transiently faulty node

Figure 7. (a) execution of $CF()$ by combining transiently and permanently faulty nodes into one large cluster, and **(b)** execution of *Connection-Scheme* to join the transiently faulty nodes with the rest of the network.

1. Consider the path, say P, that is in common to the perimeters of both C_1 and C_2. Let's call the healthy nodes in P, excluding the two endpoints, as *transiently faulty nodes*.

2. Join the transiently faulty nodes and the faulty clusters C_1 and C_2 together into a larger faulty cluster (which must be simple) and run procedure $CF()$ on it.

3. Construct a simple cycle Φ which contains P and run the *Connection-Scheme* in Section 3.1.2 to make the network connected.

For instance, Fig. 7(a) shows the result after executing $CF()$ by combining all transiently and permanently faults into one large faulty cluster. Fig. 7(b) shows how to join the transiently faulty nodes with the rest of the network using a cycle Φ.

3.3 What Our Model Can and Can't Do?

Our formulation has required that the perimeters of faulty clusters be simple cycles. To see why our approach can not handle perimeters which are non-simple cycles, observe the example in Fig. 3(c); it is impossible to construct an Eulerian subnetwork because there are at least three nodes, n, p, and q, having degrees of 1, thus violating Lemma 1.

Even with such a limitation, simple faulty clusters are still powerful enough to represent a large group of common fault patterns. For instance, the most frequently seen failure is probably the single-node fault, which is obviously simple. Another commonly seen faulty pattern which is also simple is the *block fault*, where the faulty nodes form a rectangle.

Many faulty clusters with regular shapes are also simple. Examples include the L-shape, T-shape, and +-shape clusters The other regular patterns, such as U-shape and H-shape faulty clusters, are not guaranteed to be simple if they have one or more "dead-ends" (such as nodes n, p, and q in Fig. 3(c)). Excluding these cases, a U- or H-shape faulty cluster is highly possible to be simple.

Many irregular faulty patterns are also solvable under our approach (e.g., Fig. 3(b)). So our model can deal with very broad coverage of fault patterns, thus significantly improving over the approaches in [1, 2, 4] by restricting fault patterns to be rectangular.

If unfortunately a faulty cluster is non-simple, one remedy to this problem is to sacrifice (deactivate) some healthy nodes neighboring to the cluster (by regarding them as faulty) to make the perimeter a simple cycle. For example, by regarding nodes n, p, and q in Fig. 3(c) as faulty, the faulty cluster will become simple. Although this is somewhat undesirable, the result is still better than restricting faulty cluster to be rectangular.

4 Extensions to Tori of Higher Dimensions with Faults

The following lemma is a generalization of what the earlier procedure $CF()$ has done.

Lemma 6 *[19] Given a sequence of nodes $S = (x_0, x_1, \ldots, x_{p-1})$ in a network such that*

(a) p is even, and

(b) there are an even number of even-degree nodes (and thus an even number of odd-degree nodes) in S,

it is possible to add and/or delete some links $(x_i, x_{i+1 \bmod p})$, $0 \le i \le p - 1$, to and from the network to make all nodes in S of even degrees.

We comment that the condition (a) in Lemma 6 is always true in an n-D torus.

4.1 3-D Torus with Faulty Blocks

We denote a fault block B in a 3-D torus by identifying its two anti-podal nodes, (x, y, z) and (x', y', z'). That is, all nodes (i, j, k) such that $x \le i \le x'$, $y \le j \le y'$, and $z \le k \le z'$ are inside the block (for simplicity, we omit saying "mod" that is necessary whenever wrapping-around occurs).

We will remove some links from the *surface* of B, which is defined to be the block B' excluding the block B, where block B' is identified by the anti-podal nodes $(x - 1, y - 1, z - 1)$ and $(x' + 1, y' + 1, z' + 1)$. Intuitively, the surface contains

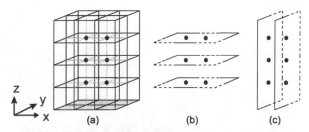

Figure 8. (a) A 3-D torus with a $2 \times 1 \times 3$ faulty block, (b) after step 1, and (c) after step 2.

the healthy nodes and links directly wrapping around B. We propose the following link removal procedure:

Step 1: For each $i = z..z'$, consider the rectangle formed by the four corners $(x - 1, y - 1, i)$, $(x' + 1, y - 1, i)$, $(x' + 1, y' + 1, i)$, and $(x - 1, y' + 1, i)$. The rectangle forms a simple cycle on the surface of B. The cycle must satisfy the pre-conditions in Lemma 6 (the proof is trivial). So it's possible to use Lemma 6 to remove some links from the cycle to make all nodes' degrees even. See the example in Fig. 8. After this step, all surface nodes, except those on the top and bottom, have even degrees.

Step 2: For each $i = x..x'$, consider the rectangle formed by the four nodes $(i, y - 1, z - 1)$, $(i, y' + 1, z - 1)$, $(i, y' + 1, z' + 1)$, and $(i, y - 1, z' + 1)$. Again, the rectangle forms a simple cycle, which satisfies the pre-conditions in Lemma 6 (we leave the proof to the reader). Apply Lemma 6 on each of these cycles. See the example in Fig. 8.

4.2 3-D Torus with Faulty Clusters

It will be helpful to summarize what has been done above: we remove some links from the surface of a faulty block first along xy-planes, and then along yz-planes. Similarly, for a faulty cluster of any shape, we define its *surface* to be the healthy nodes and links direct wrapping around the cluster.

Definition 4 In a 3-D torus, a faulty cluster is said to be *simple* if its surface satisfies: for each xy-plane and yz-plane, the intersection (if any) between the plane and the surface consists of only simple cycle(s).

For instance, the faulty cluster in Fig. 9(a) is simple. Now suppose there is a simple faulty cluster C in a 3-D torus. We remove links from C's surface as follows:

Step 1: For each xy-plane, consider the simple cycles (if any) obtained from the intersection between the plane and the surface of C. For each node in each simple cycle, we consider *only* its degree summing over the x and y axes. Apply Lemma 6 on the cycle to make all its nodes' degrees, summing over *only* x and y axes, even. An example is shown in Fig. 9(b).

Lemma 7 *[19] After step 1, on each simple cycle (if any) obtained from the intersection between a yz-plane and the*

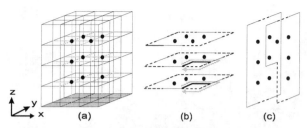

Figure 9. (a) A 3-D torus with a faulty cluster, (b) after step 1, and (c) after step 2.

surface of C, there are an even number of odd-degree nodes and thus an even number of even-degree nodes.

Step 2: For each *yz*-plane, consider the simple cycles (if any) obtained from the intersection between the plane and the surface of *C*. For each node in a simple cycle, consider its total degree summing over *all* axes. Guaranteed by Lemma 7, we can apply Lemma 6 on each cycle to fix nodes' degrees. (See the example in Fig. 9(c).)

4.3 *n*-D Torus with Faulty Clusters

First, we need the concept of planes. In an *n*-D torus, an (i, j)-plane, $1 \leq i, j \leq n$, is a hyperplane consisting of nodes which have *common* indices along each dimension k such that $k \neq i$ and $k \neq j$. Still, we define the *surface* of a faulty cluster in an *n*-D torus to be the nodes and links directly wrapping around the cluster. We only consider faulty clusters that are *simple* in the sense that for each $(i, i+1)$-plane, $i = 1..n - 1$, the intersection (if any) between the plane and the surface of the faulty cluster consists of only simple cycles.

Suppose there is a simple faulty cluster C in an *n*-D torus. The link removal procedure consists of $n - 1$ steps as follows $(i = 1..n - 1)$:

Step *i*: For each $(i, i + 1)$-plane, consider the simple cycles (if any) obtained from the intersection between the plane and *C*'s surface. For each node on each simple cycle, we consider its degree summing over *only* dimensions $1, 2, \ldots, i + 1$. Apply Lemma 6 on the cycle to fix nodes' degrees.

Two important properties hold true after step *i*. First, all surface nodes will have even degrees summing over dimensions $1, 2, \ldots, i + 1$. Second, on each $(i + 1, i + 2)$-plane, for each simple cycle (if any) obtained from the intersection between the plane and *C*'s surface, there are an even number of odd-degree nodes, and the same for even-degree nodes, where degrees are summed over dimensions $1, 2, \ldots, i + 2$. The proof is similar to that of Lemma 7. This inductively guarantees the applicability of Lemma 6 in step $i + 1$. At the end, all surface nodes will have even degrees. Fig. 10 shows an example in a 4-D torus containing a $1 \times 1 \times 2 \times 1$ faulty block; after three steps, each removing links on (1,2)-, (2,3)-, and (3,4)-planes, all surface nodes will have even degrees.

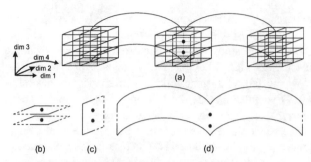

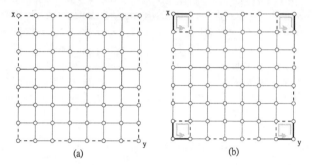

Figure 10. (a) a 4-D Torus containing a $1 \times 1 \times 2 \times 1$ faulty block, and (b)–(d) the link removal after steps 1 to 3, respectively.

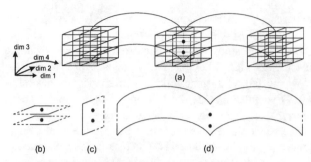

Figure 11. Applying to an 8×8 mesh: (a) after executing *CF*() on the boundary, and (b) after applying the *Connection-Scheme*.

5 Applying to Meshes with Faults

Although meshes are in general considered close families to tori, they are not node-symmetric. To us, the main problem limiting the applicability of the Euler-based model is that some boundary nodes may have odd degrees. Below, we show how to remove some links on, or close to, the boundary of a mesh. The new network will become Eulerian. One nice, direct implication of doing so is that all techniques presented earlier for tori can be easily applied to meshes.

Given a 2-D mesh, we let Φ be the cycle on its boundary. One easily observes that only the four corner nodes will have even degrees. Thus, we can run procedure *CF*() on Φ to remove some links (see the example in Fig. 11(a)). Note that the isolation problem may occur (e.g., see the four corner nodes). We can apply the *Connection-Scheme* to solve this problem (the result is in Fig. 11(b)).

For an *n*-D mesh, consider the surface of the mesh. Clearly, the surface is *simple* (recall the definition in Section 4). It is easy to extend the link removal scheme for *n*-D tori to this case: (1) apply Lemma 6 on the cycle obtained from the intersection of each (1,2)-plane and the surface, by considering nodes' degrees summing over *only* dimensions 1 and 2, (2) apply Lemma 6 on the cycle obtained from the intersection of each (2,3)-plane and the surface, by considering nodes' degrees summing over *only* dimensions from 1

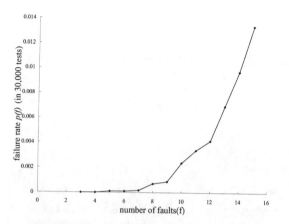

Figure 12. Failure rate of our scheme in a 16×16 **torus.**

to 3, ..., and so on until $(n-1, n)$-plane.

6 Simulation Results

We simulated a 16×16 torus. Recall our algorithm for constructing link set E_2. Our model always works as long as the removal of E_2 does not partition the network. It is interesting to see how resilient our model is *without* the necessity of deactivating healthy nodes. In this simulation, given an integer f, we randomly generate f faulty nodes in the network and observe the probability, $p(f)$, that an Eulerian subnetwork can *not* be found using the proposed technique. Fig. 12 shows the probability at different values of f. Each experiment is from 30,000 tests. Surprisingly, when $f \leq 4$, the failure rate is 0%. When $f \leq 14$, the rate is still below 1%. Suppose the probability that the system has f faulty nodes is $q(f)$. Then the probability that our model is unavailable (unable to find a good link set E_2) is $p(f) * q(f)$, which should be pretty small. As in reality the value of f tends to be small, our model should be resilient enough for use in most practical situations.

7 Conclusions

We have presented a new multicasting model that can be applied to any network that is Eulerian or is Eulerian after some links being removed. We have shown the strength of this model by applying it to damaged tori/meshes of any dimension with faults. A lot of regular and irregular faulty patterns are shown to be tolerable by our model.

Given a multicast request, we have only limited our attention to injecting two worms (f-worm and b-worm) to the network. It should be interesting to study the possibility of injecting more worms as in [13] or even multiple levels of worms as in [7, 11, 15].

References

[1] R. V. Boppana and S. Chalsani. Fault-tolerant wormhole routing algorithms for mesh networks. *IEEE Trans. on Comput.*, 44(7):848–864, July 1995.

[2] Y. M. Boura and C. R. Das. Fault-tolerant routing in mesh networks. In *Int'l Conf. on Parallel Processing*, pages I–106–109, 1995.

[3] S. Chalasani and R. V. Boppana. Communication in multicomputers with nonconvex faults. In *EURO-PAR Conf.*, pages 673–684, 1995. (also in *IEEE Trans. on Comput.*, 46(5), May 1997, pp. 616-622).

[4] K.-H. Chen and G.-M. Chiu. Fault-tolerant routing algorithm for meshes without using virtual channels. Technical report, Nat'l Taiwan Inst. of Tech., 1997. Tech. Rpt., Dept. Elec. Engr. and Tech.

[5] J. Duato. A theory of fault-tolerant routing in wormhole networks. In *Int'l Conf. on Paral. and Distrib. Sys.*, pages 600–607, 1994.

[6] J. Duato. A theory of deadlock-free adaptive multicast routing in wormhole networks. *IEEE Trans. on Paral. and Distrib. Sys.*, 6(9):976–987, Sep. 1995.

[7] K.-P. Fan and C.-T. King. Turn grouping for efficient multicast in wormhole mesh networks. In *Symp. of Frontiers of Massively Parallel Computation*, pages 50–57, 1996.

[8] C. J. Glass and L. M. Ni. Maximally fully adaptive routing in 2D meshes. In *Int'l Conf. on Parallel Processing*, pages 101–104, 1992.

[9] C. J. Glass and L. M. Ni. Fault-tolerant wormhole routing in meshes without virtual channels. *IEEE Trans. on Paral. and Distrib. Sys.*, 7(6):620–636, June 1996.

[10] T.-Y. Juang, Y.-C. Tseng, and M.-H. Yang. An euler-path-based multicasting model for wormhole-routed networks: Its applications to damaged 2d tori and meshes. In *Int'l Performance, Computing, and Communications Conf.*, pages 444–450, 1997.

[11] R. Kesavan and D. K. Panda. Minimizing node contention in multiple multicast on wormhole k-ary n-cube networks. In *Int'l Conf. on Parallel Processing*, 1996.

[12] R. Libeskind-Hadas, K. Watkins, and T. Hehre. Fault-tolerant multicast routing in the mesh with no virtual channels. In *High-Performance Computer Arch. Conf.*, pages 180–190, 1996.

[13] X. Lin, P. K. McKinley, and L. M. Ni. Deadlock-free multicast wormhole routing in 2D mesh multicomputers. *IEEE Trans. on Paral. and Distrib. Sys.*, 5(8):793–804, Aug. 1994.

[14] L. M. Ni and P. K. McKinley. A survey of wormhole routing techniques in directed networks. *IEEE Computer*, 26:62–76, Feb. 1993.

[15] D. K. Panda, S. Singal, and P. Prabhakaran. Multidestination message passing mechanism conforming to base wormhole routing scheme. In *Parallel Computer Routing and Communication Workshop*, pages 131–145, 1994. LNCS, No. 853.

[16] W. Qiao and L. M. Ni. Adaptive routing in irregular networks using cut-through switches. In *Int'l Conf. on Parallel Processing*, pages I–52–60, 1996.

[17] K. H. Rosen. *Discrete Mathematics and its Applications*. McGraw-Hill, New York, 1995.

[18] Y.-C. Tseng, D. K. Panda, and T.-H. Lai. A trip-based multicasting model in wormhole-routed networks with virtual channels. *IEEE Trans. on Paral. and Distrib. Sys.*, 7(2):138–150, Feb. 1996.

[19] Y.-C. Tseng, M.-H. Yang, and T.-Y. Juang. An Euler-path-based multicasting model for wormhole-routed networks with multi-destination capability. Technical report, Dept. of Comp. Sci. and Info. Engr., Nat'l Central Univ., 1997.

Two-phase Multicast in Wormhole-Switched Bidirectional Multistage Banyan Networks[†]

W. Kwon
CSD KAIST
373-1 Kusong-Dong,
Yusong-Gu,Taejon
305-701,Korea
wnkwon@camars.
kaist.ac.kr

B. Kwon
CEED
Andong National Univ.
388 Songchun-Dong,
Andong, Kyung-Book
760-380, Korea
bskwon@camars.
kaist.ac.kr

J. Park
CSD Purdue Univ.
West Lafayette,
IN, 47907, USA
hyeoung@cs.
purdue.edu

H. Yoon
CSD KAIST
373-1 Kusong-Dong,
Yusong-Gu,Taejon
305-701,Korea
hyoon@camars.
kaist.ac.kr

Abstract

A multistage interconnection network is a suitable class of interconnection architecture for constructing large-scale multicomputers. Broadcast and multicast communication are fundamental in supporting collective communication operations such as reduction and barrier synchronization. In this paper, we propose a new multicast technique in wormhole-switched bidirectional multistage banyan networks for constructing large-scale multicomputers. To efficiently support broadcast and multicast with simple additional hardware without deadlock, we propose a two-phase multicast algorithm which takes only two transmissions to perform a broadcast and a multicast to an arbitrary number of desired destinations. We encode a header as a cube and adopt the most upper input link first scheme with periodic priority rotation as arbitration mechanism on contented output links. We coalesce the desired destination addresses into multiple number of cubes. And then, we evaluate the performance of the proposed algorithm by simulation. The proposed two-phase multicast algorithm makes a significant improvement in terms of latency. It is noticeable that the two-phase algorithm keeps broadcast latency as efficient as the multicast latency of fanout 2^m where m is the minimum integer satisfying $2^m \geq \sqrt{N}$ (N is a network size).

1. Introduction

Multistage interconnection networks(MINs) are a popular class of interconnection architecture for constructing scalable multicomputers, such as TMC CM-5[5], IBM SP-1[1], and Meiko CS-2[7]. Efficient data communication among processing nodes is critical to the performance of message-based multicomputers [10]. In most existing MIN-based multicomputers, wormhole-switching[6] which is designed for low latency and high performance has been adopted. However, the wormhole-switching is susceptible to deadlock due to the resource competition among multiple worms. Once deadlock occurs, the performance degrades quickly and remarkably. Hence, deadlock avoidance is an important issue for improving performance in these switching networks[6].

Multicast techniques that deliver a packet from a source to multiple destinations in wormhole-switched bidirectional-MINs have been studied. U-min algorithm [10] and C-min algorithm [3] are software techniques and don't cause deadlock. But, it takes at least $\lceil \log d \rceil$ (d is the number of destinations) number of setups and transmissions for these algorithms to perform a multicast. [2] proposes a multicast technique on central-buffer-based and input-queue-based switch architectures. This technique adopts buffered wormhole-switching which stores blocked flits in buffers in switching elements, and asynchronous replication which allows flits of a multicast packet to be transmitted to the successfully reserved subset of requested output links. Moreover, this technique requires only one setup and transmission for a multicast and does not cause deadlock. Therefore, this technique can support multicast efficiently. However, the hardware complexity of the switch architectures is very high because the architectures must contain input queues or a central buffer of large space to avoid deadlock and to get desired performance gain. Therefore, this technique has difficulties in constructing large-scale multicomputer systems [9].

In this paper we propose a new multicast algorithm in

[†]This work is supported by network technology project of Ministry of Information and Commmunication Republic of Korea in 1998

pure wormhole-switched bidirectional multistage banyan networks without central buffers nor queues. The proposed multicast algorithm is a software technique, which is supported by one-flit output buffers and simple replication hardware. The multicast algorithm consists of two phases : phase I and II. In phase I, a multicast packet is copied from a source through a network to computed destinations. In phase II, the destinations generated in phase I send the received multicast packets to the desired destinations of the multicast. The multicast algorithm employs cube-encoding as header encoding and adopts *the most upper input link first scheme* with periodic priority rotation as arbitration mechanism among multiple multicast packets to avoid deadlock. The proposed algorithm requires only 2 transmissions to achieve a multicast. Hence, we call this multicast technique two-phase (multicast) algorithm. The architecture is so simple to be suitable for constructing large-scale multicomputer systems, and two-phase algorithm can support efficient multicast and broadcast in large-scale multicomputer systems.

The remainder of this paper is organized as follows. The next section describes the system architecture and section 3 describes our two-phase multicast algorithm. We evaluate the performance of the proposed algorithm in section 4 and conclude this paper in section 5.

2. System Architecture

We assume $N \times N$ bidirectional banyan networks constructed by $2k \times 2k$ switching elements. Figure 1 shows a

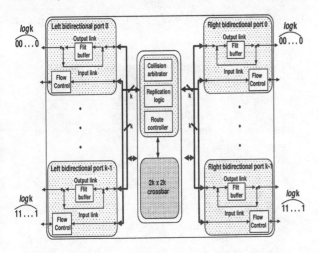

Figure 1. A $2k \times 2k$ **bidirectional switching element**

$2k \times 2k$ switching element which consists of a $2k \times 2k$ crossbar and $2k$ bidirectional ports. Unidirectional arrows and bidirectional arrows denote unidirectional links and bidirectional links, respectively. Each port can be implemented

by two unidirectional ports with an input link and an output link. Notice that a switching element has an one-flit output buffer per bidirectional port. The addresses of bidirectional ports are represented as binary numbers between $\overbrace{0 \cdots 0}^{\log k}$ and $\overbrace{1 \cdots 1}^{\log k}$. A bidirectional port can send and receive flits simultaneously.

The network employs a pure wormhole-switching technique without input queues nor central buffers. And it adopts synchronous replication because it is difficult for asynchronous replication to get up desired performance without large buffer. The replicated flits of a multicast are transmitted only when none of replicated flits of the multicast packet is blocked. Otherwise, all of them is blocked in place. Synchronous replication is controlled by flow control logic. Flow control logics communicates feedback control information one another to synchronize transmission of a multicast packet.

In this network, after the flits of a multicast packet are transmitted adaptively up to the *least common ancestor*(LCA) stage[4] of the source and its destinations, they synchronously replicate downwards on the way back from the LCA stage to reach the destinations. Assume that all processing elements are in the left side of the network connecting them, like figure 3. A switching element replicates and routes incoming flits to output links by using the crossbar and the hardware replication logic therein. When a header flit arrives at a input link, the switching element routes it to the ouput buffer(s) of detined output port(s). If a header flit is forwarding up to its LCA stage, the switch element routes it to the output buffer of an available most upper right bidirectional port. If a header flit is at its LCA stage or is backwarding down to its destination processing node, the switching element routes or replicates and routes it to the output buffer(s) of the left bidirectinal port(s) determined by destination tag routing.

3. Two-Phase Multicast Algorithm

3.1 Multicast Packet Format

The formats of multicast packets are shown in Figure 2. Each multicast packet of phase I and II consists of a header flit and following data flits. The header flits of phase I and II contain the destination tags for their own destinations. The destinations of phase I and II are called intermediate destinations and desired destinations, respectively. Notice that in the multicast packet of phase I the information of desired destinations is placed in front of the series of data to transmit. At the end of the information of desired destinations, EOD(End-Of-Destination) flit is put because the number of desired destinations is variable. In the ends of both multicast

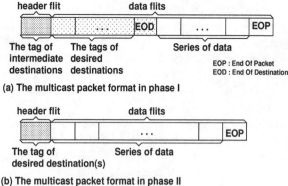

(a) The multicast packet format in phase I

(b) The multicast packet format in phase II

Figure 2. The packet formats of phase I and II in two-phase multicast

packets, EOP(End-Of-Packet) flits are appended to mark the end of multicast packets.

3.2 Header Encoding

We encode headers as k-ary cubes defined in below definition. A k-ary cube is represented as the corresponding binary cubes. The binary representations of k-ary cubes are

Definition k-ary cube :
k-**ary digit** is d, y, or X where
d is a number satisfying $0 \leq d \leq k-1$,

y is a binary cube $b_{\log k-1} \cdots b_m \overbrace{x \cdots x}^{m}$
where for m and j satisfying $0 \leq m \leq j \leq \log k - 1$, $b_j \in \{0, 1\}$ and x is a don't care, and
X is $\overbrace{x \cdots x}^{\log k}$.
k-**ary cube** of size $2^m k^c$ is defined as

$$d_{n-1} \cdots d_{c+1}(y) \overbrace{X \cdots X}^{c} (0 \leq c \leq n),$$
where $d_i(c + 1 \leq i \leq n - 1)$ is a number
satisfying $0 \leq d_i \leq k - 1$.

used for replicating and routing flits in switching elements. For example, when $n = 3$, all 4-ary digits from 220 to 233 constitue a 4-ary cube $2(1x)X$. The cube size is 2^3 and the binary representation is $101xxx$.

3.3 Multicast Algorithm

We propose a multicast algorithm, called two-phase multicast algorithm, which consists of phase I and phase II. Before both phases, every multicast packet is re-constructed into a header flit and following data flits. In order to perform a multicast to multiple desired destinations, in phase I a multicast packet is copied from a source through a network to

computed intermediate destinations, and then, in phase II all or some of intermediate destinations transmit the received multicast packets to the corresponding desired destinations.

Algorithm Phase I : a multicast at a source s
Input :
  $D = \{D_0, \ldots, D_{d-1}\}$: a sorted list of desired destination addresses
  p : data to send
Procedure :
  $C(= \{C_0, \ldots, C_{c-1}\}) \leftarrow Encode(D)$;
  Calculate the minimum integer c such that $2^c \geq |C|$;
  Select a k-ary cube H of size 2^c;
  Construct a multicast packet $P(= H|C|EOD|p|EOP)$;
  Send P to the intermediate destinations H;
End

The setup algorithms of phase I and II are shown in algorithm **Phase I** and **Phase II**, respectively. Before a multicast, in phase I, a source computes the set of the tags of its desired destinations(C) with *Encode* algorithm to be explained in the next section, and then encodes the header of phase I as a k-ary cube(H) with the smallest size that is power of two and greater than the number of elements in C. After this, the source constructs its multicast packet by writing H on a header flit, and C and data p on data flits, like Figure 2.(a). The setup of phase I terminates by starting to push the multicast packet P into the network.

Algorithm Phase II : a multicast at a intermediate destination i
Input : $P(= H|C|EOD|p|EOP)$: the multicast packet of phase I
Procedure :
  if i gets, P, a multicast packet of phase I **then**
    Calculate $d(0 \leq d \leq c - 1)$ that i is the d-th one within H;
    if $d > c - 1$ **then** Discard P;
    else if $C_d = i$ **then** Absorb P; /* self destination */
    else
      /* i re-transmits P to the corresponding desired destination */
      Extract C_d and p from P;
      Construct the multicast packet $P'(= C_d|p|EOP)$;
      Send P' to the desired destination C_d;
    endif
  endif
End

Phase II begins after an intermediate destination receives the packet P of phase I. In the setup of phase II, the d-th intermediate destination extracts the d-th desired destination tag C_d and data p from the received packet P. It re-constructs its multicast packet by writing C_d on a header flit and p on data flits, like Figure 2-(b). After that, it terminates and the source starts to transmit P'.

3.4 *Encode* **Algorithm**

Encode algorithm may be simply designed to do no operation or just sort the desired destinations. As the number of desired destinations becomes more, the fanout of phase I becomes larger, the blocking probability gets higher, and consequently latency becomes longer. At this, we propose **Coalesce** algorithm as *Encode* algorithm to decrease the fanout of phase I. **Coalesce** algorithm coalesces the desired destination addresses into multiple k-ary cubes, as shown in below algorithm. In the algorithm, a maximal k-ary cube means the cube has the greatest size among k-ary cubes that the subset of D can construct. This al-

> **Algorithm Coalesce :** Coalesce into k-ary cubes
> **Input :** $D = \{D_0, \ldots, D_d\}$: a set of k-ary numbers
> **Procedure :**
> $C \leftarrow \emptyset$;
> **do**
>   **do**
>   Construct a k-ary cube $C_i (= d_{n-1} \cdots (y) \overbrace{X \cdots X}^{c})$ in D;
>   **until** C_i is maximal;
> $C \leftarrow C \cup \{C_i\}$; $D \leftarrow D - \{C_i\}$;
> **until** C is not changed;
> Report C;
> **End**

gorithm keeps multicast fanout values under the half of network size. For example, *Encode* coalesces a set of 4-ary numbers, $\{00, 02, 03, 12, 22, 23, 30, 31, 32, 33\}$, into $\{00, 0(1x), 12, 2(1x), 3X\}$ with **Coalesce** algorithm.

3.5 Broadcast

The proposed two-phase algorithm with **Coalesce** algorithm has trouble to perform a broadcast, because the fanout of phase II is same with the size of the network wherein the broadcast takes place. To keep the fanout of broadcast in both phase I and II as small as possible, *Encode* partitions N desired destinations into k-ary cubes with below **Partition** algorithm. **Partition** algorithm partitions the destination addresses so that the sum of cube sizes of phase I and II is minimum. For example, if $N = 256$, *Encode* partitions 256 desired destination addresses into 16 k-ary cubes of size 16 with **Paritition** algorithm.

3.6 Deadlock Avoidance

Two-phase multicast algorithm suffers from potential deadlock due to multiple multicast packets in a network. In

> **Algorithm Partition :** Partition into 2^m k-ary cubes of size 2^l
> **Input :** $N(= 2^n)$
> **Procedure :**
> Compute the maximum integer l such that $l \leq n/2$;
> Compute the minimum integer m such that $m \geq n/2$;
> Construct 2^m k-ary cubes of size 2^l from N;
> Report the constructed cubes;
> **End**

multistage banyan networks using distributed control, one replicated flit of a multicast packet does not know whether other flits of the multicast packet are blocked or not. As a result, contention on output links can cause deadlock. Therefore, to avoid deadlock by eliminating circular waiting, we present *the most upper input link first scheme* as arbitration mechanism on contended output links. This scheme gives priority to the flit from the most upper input link, to reserve the desired output links, when contention occurs on same output links. *The most upper input link first scheme* guarantees a deadlock-free transmission through multistage banyan networks. In order to prevent starvation, priority rotates periodically. This arbitration mechanism is called *the most upper input link first scheme* with periodic priority rotation.

3.7 An Example of Two-Phase Multicast Algorithm

In a 16×16 bidirectional cube network where 8×8 switching elements are connected with butterfly permutation, a source 10 begins to transmit a multicast packet to its desired destinations, $00, 02, 03, 12, 22, 23, 30, 31, 32,$ and 33 with two-phase multicast algorithm, as shown in figure 3. In phase I, the source coalesces the desired destinations into $00, 0(1x), 12, 2(1x), 3X$ and computes a 4-ary cube of size 8, $(1x)X$, at random. And then, the source constructs the corresponding multicast packet and transmits it to $(1x)X$. All intermediate destinations receive the multicast packet of phase I and phase II begins. In phase II, after re-constructing the multicast packet of phase II, intermediate destinations $20, 21, 22, 23,$ and 31 transmit their multicast packets to desired destinations $00, 0(1x), 12, 2(1x),$ and $3X$, respectively. Other intermediate destinations discard their received packets.

4. Performance Evaluation

To assess the performance of two-phase multicast algorithm, we implemented and compared our algorithm and the binomial tree-based u-min[10] with several set of parameters. We did not compare two-phase algorithm with

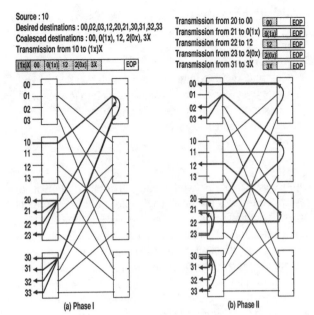

Figure 3. An example of two-phase multicast algorithm with Coalesce algorithm

[2] because of their architectural differences such as pure wormhole-switching vs. buffered wormhole-switching, and an one-flit output buffer per bidirectional port vs. one or more buffers of large space per switching element.

4.1 Simulation Issues and Parameters

Multicast traffic evaluation raises several additional issues beyond unicast traffic. First, multicast latency can be defined as the latency of the last received packet of a multicast, or as the average of the latency of each received packet of a multicast. The former definition is more important term in assessing packet-passing collective communication performance[8] and in assessing the performance of multicast used for cache line invalidations in shared-memory systems. Therefore, we chose the former one as latency.

Second, the load of a network injected by multicast packets can be defined as injected load or effective load. Because the effective load of our multicast algorithm cannot be estimated intuitively, we chose injected load as network load and defined the load as the viewpoint of the interarrival time of packets.

Finally, while a unicast has negligible startup overhead, the startup overhead of a multicast cannot be ignored due to multicast packet construction latency. We assume that startup latency is $2 \log N$ like in [10].

We assume 2-byte flit and count latency by the cycle in which a flit goes through a switching element. We simulated random traffic of 32-byte data packets. For simulating

multicast of fanout F in an N-node system, we randomly chose F uniformly distributed destinations for each multicast packet. Packet arrival time, I, for each node were exponentially distributed. Measured latency includes queuing time at source nodes. To get stable environments for statistics collection, we ran the simulations with $50,000$ wormup cycles before collecting statistics data. We simulated for bidirectional cube networks whose $2K \times 2K$ switching elements are connected by butterfly permutations, We collected statistics when $N = 256$, $K = 4$ and 16, and $F = 16, 64, 128, 192, 240$, and 256, and when $N = 64$, $K = 4$, and $F = 16, 32, 48$, and 64.

4.2 Simulation Results

The simulation results of two-phase multicast algorithm are shown in figure 4. Figure 4.(a) and (b) compare two-phase algorithm with u-min algorithm. Figure 4.(a) shows that the latency of two-phase algorithm is much less than that of u-min and increases less dramatically. And figure 4.(b) compares the impacts of fanout on the latency of two-phase and u-min algorithm. As F/N grows greater, the latency ratio of two algorithms increases. As a result, two-phase algorithm improves the performance at least about 200 percent than u-min algorithm from the viewpoint of latency.

Figure 4.(c) shows the impact of fanout on latency of two-phase algorithm with and without **Coalesce**. The doted lines show that without **Coalesce**, the latency of multicast to more than $N/2$ desired destinations increases seriously and abruptly. This is because the blocking probability becomes greater due to the large fanout of phase I. However, as the solid lines show, with **Coalesce** the latency of multicast is bounded even when fanout becomes greater than $N/2$. This is because **Coalesce** keeps the fanout values of multicasts same with or less than $N/2$. In other words, if F/N is over some value, the coalesceing effect increases and the latency decreases.

Figure 4.(d) shows multicast packet overhead defined as the total number of header flits, flits of desired destination tags, EOD flits, and EOP flits which have traversed through a network during a multicast. The multicast packet overheads of two-phase algorithm is less than that of u-min. And, as fanout value becomes greater, the overheads of u-min grows greater, but that of two-phase algorithm is bounded. This is because fanout decreases due to coalescing effects when the number of desired destinations grows above some value.

Figure 4.(e) shows that the size of switching elements, 8×8 and 32×32, impacts little on the latency of varing fanout. Figure 4.(f) shows the impact of network size on latency. The graphs of different network size are similar in shape but the latency in smaller networks is less than that in larger ones due to the smaller number of stages of networks.

It is noticeable that the broadcast latency of two-phase

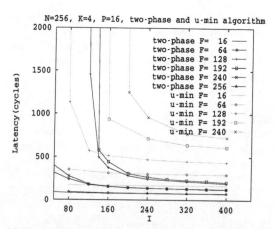

(a) Impact of interarrival time : latency vs. interarrival time for two-phase and u-min multicast algorithm

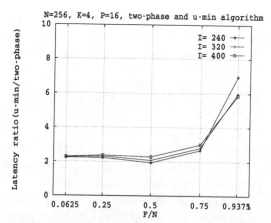

(b) Impact of fanout : the latency ratio of (two-phase)/(u-min) vs. (fanout)/(network size) for two-phase and u-min multicast algorithm

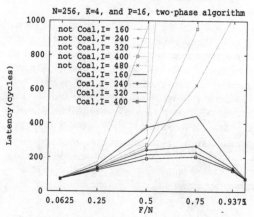

(c) Impacts of **Coalesce** : latency vs. (fanout)/(network size) for two-phase multicast algorithm

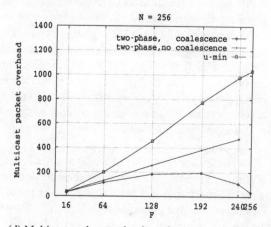

(d) Multicast packet overhead vs. fanout for two-phase and u-min multicast algorithm

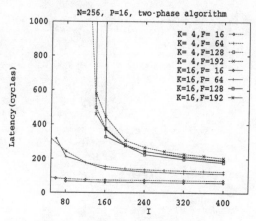

(e) Impacts of a switching element size : latency vs. fanout for two-phase multicast algorithm

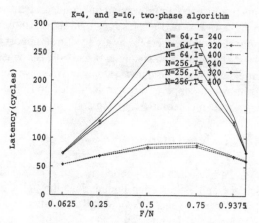

(f) Impacts of network size : latency vs. (fanout)/(network size) for two-phase multicast algorithm

Figure 4. The simulation results

algorithm is much less than that of u-min, and that is bounded approximately under the latency of multicast of fanout 2^m where m is the minimum integer satisfying $2^m \geq \sqrt{N}$. Figure 4.(f) shows that when $N = 256(64)$, the broadcast latency is similar to the multicast latency of fanout $16(8)$ in the network, as expected by **Partition** algorithm.

5. Conclusions

This paper proposed two-phase multicast algorithm in pure wormhole-switched bidirectional banyan networks where a $2k \times 2k$ switching element has synchronous replication logic and a bidirectional port has an one-flit output buffer. We compared the proposed algorithm with other by simulation in terms of multicast latency and multicast packet overhead.

To get high performance without deadlock, two-phase multicast algorithm solved multicast issues with the viewpoint of multicast latency. The algorithm requires only two transmissions to send a multicast packet to an arbitrary number of desired destinations. The headers of phase I and II are encoded as k-ary cubes and desired destination addresses are coalesced into multiple k-ary cubes. Contention on output links is arbitrated by the *most upper input link first scheme* with periodic priority rotation.

As the number of desired destinations increases, the multicast latency and the multicast packet overhead of two-phase algorithm increase. However, they are bounded due to coalescing effects and also decreases when the number of desired destinations reaches above some value. The broadcast latency of two-phase algorithm is much less than that of u-min, and is similar to the latency of multicast of fanout 2^m where m is the minimum integer satisfying $2^m \geq \sqrt{N}$. This is noticeable improvement on broadcast performance.

As a result, two-phase algorithm significantly outperforms than other scheme. The architectural support for two-phase algorithm is so simple to be suitable for constructing large-scale multicomputer systems. Thus, two-phase algorithm can supports efficient multicast and broadcast in large-scale multicomputer systems.

Acknowledgement

J. Park's work is supported in part by KOSEF(Korea Science and Engineering Foundation) through *Center for Artificial Intelligence Research* at Korea Advanced Institute of Science and Technology.

References

[1] C.B.Stunkel and et al. Architecture and implementation of Vulcan. In *Proc. of the Int'l Parallel Processing Symposium*, pages 268–274, Jun. 1995.

[2] R. C.B.Stunkel and D.K.Panda. Implementing Multidestination Worms in Switch-Based Parallel Systems: Architectural Alternatives and their Impact. In *Proc. of the 24th ACM Annual Symposium on Computer Architecture*, pages 50–61, June. 1997.

[3] C.-M. Chiang. *Multicasting in Multistage Interconnection Networks*. PhD thesis, Dept. of Comp. Sci., Michigan State Univ., East Lansing, MI, 1995.

[4] I.D.Scherson and D.-H.Chien. Least Common Ancestor Networks. In *Proc. of the 7th Int. Parallel Processing Symposium.*, pages 507–513, 1993.

[5] C. E. Leiserson and et al. The Network Architecture of the Connection Machine CM-5 . In *Proc. of the ACM Symposium on Parallel Algorithms and Architectures*, pages 272–285, 1992.

[6] L.M.Ni and P.K.McKinley. A survey of wormhole routing techniques in direct networks. *IEEE Computer*, 26:62–76, Feb. 1993.

[7] M. Meiko Limited, Waltham. Computing Surface: CS-2. In *Communications Networks*, Jun. 1993.

[8] N.Nupairoj and L.M.Ni. Issues in Designing Efficient and Practical Algorithms for Collective Communication in Wormhole-Routed Systems. In *1st International Workshop on Communication and Architectural Support for Network-Based Parallel Computing*, pages 212–226, Feb 1997.

[9] D. K. Panda and R. Sivaram. Fast Broadcast and Multicast in Wormhole Multistage Networks with Multidestination Worms. Technical Report OSU-CISRC-4/95-TR21, Dept. of Comp. and Info. Sci., Ohio State Univ., 1995.

[10] H. Xu, Y.-D. Gui, and L. M. Ni. Optimal Software Multicast in Wormhole-Routed Multistage Networks. In *Proc. of Supercomputing*, pages 1252–1265, Dec. 1994.

Efficient Multicast on Myrinet Using
Link-Level Flow Control*

Raoul A.F. Bhoedjang   Tim Rühl   Henri E. Bal
Vrije Universiteit, Amsterdam, The Netherlands
{raoul, tim, bal}@cs.vu.nl

Abstract

This paper studies the implementation of efficient multicast protocols for Myrinet, a switched, wormhole-routed, Gigabit-per-second network technology. Since Myrinet does not support multicasting in hardware, multicast services must be implemented in software. We present a new, efficient, and reliable software multicast protocol that uses the network interface to efficiently forward multicast traffic. The new protocol is constructed on top of reliable, flow-controlled channels between pairs of network interfaces. We describe the design of the protocol and make a detailed comparison with a previous multicast protocol. We show that our protocol is simpler and scales better than the previous protocol. This claim is supported by extensive performance measurements on a 64-node Myrinet cluster.

1. Introduction

The importance of efficient multicast implementations is well understood. Multicasting occurs in many communication patterns, ranging from a straightforward broadcast to the more complicated all-to-all exchange. Message-passing systems like MPI [7] directly support such patterns by means of collective communication services and thus rely on an efficient multicast implementation.

We study the implementation of efficient multicast protocols for Myrinet, a switched, wormhole-routed, Gigabit-per-second network technology [3]. Today's wormhole-routed networks, including Myrinet, do not support reliable multicasting in hardware; multidestination wormhole routing is a hard problem and the subject of ongoing research [10, 16]. Meanwhile, multicast services must be implemented in software.

In this paper, we present an efficient and reliable multicast protocol for Myrinet. Like most software multicast schemes, our protocol forwards multicast packets along spanning trees, which allows packets to travel to different destinations in parallel. In most spanning-tree protocols packet forwarding is performed by *processors*: a processor receives a packet, delivers it to the application, and sends it to its children in the tree. Our protocol, in contrast, uses the *network interface* (NI) to forward multicast packets, thus avoiding expensive host-NI interactions. While several researchers have proposed NI-level multicast schemes [10, 11, 13, 17], few implementations exist. Moreover, several proposals ignore flow control, which is one of the key issues in implementing a reliable multicast. Even if the network hardware is reliable (as for Myrinet), flow control is needed to avoid receiver buffer overruns.

Our protocol has been implemented as part of a communication substrate called LFC (for Link-level Flow Control). LFC is targeted at developers of communication software for parallel systems and provides reliable, packet-based, point-to-point and multicast communication. Using LFC, we have ported MPI [7], Orca [2], and other systems to Myrinet.

LFC implements flow control at the *network interface* level. By implementing reliable, flow-controlled, communication channels between pairs of network interfaces the multicast protocol is greatly simplified. To avoid buffer deadlocks, LFC's basic multicast protocol restricts the shapes of multicast trees. By default, LFC uses binomial spanning trees, which give good overall performance.

This paper makes the following contributions. First, we show that NI-level flow control allows a simple and efficient multicast implementation. LFC avoids using centralized components, needs no special mechanism to deal with buffer overflow on NIs, and uses a single flow control scheme for unicast and multicast traffic. To illustrate these issues, we make a detailed comparison with a previous multicast implementation for Myrinet. This implementation, FM/MC [17], is one of the few NI-level multicast implementations that we are aware of and clearly demonstrated the performance advantage of implementing multicast at the NI level.

---
*This research is supported in part by a PIONIER grant from the Netherlands Organization for Scientific Research (N.W.O.).

Second, we show how LFC's basic multicast protocol can be extended with a deadlock recovery mechanism, such that arbitrary multicast trees can be used. Most store-and-forward multicast protocols restrict the topology of multicast trees to avoid buffer deadlocks. This is unfortunate, because it is well known that the optimal shape of a multicast tree depends on the communication behavior at the application level [4, 12, 13]. LFC assumes that deadlocks are infrequent and uses deadlock recovery instead of avoidance. When an NI suspects deadlock, it uses a slower, but deadlock-free protocol, which uses extra NI buffers to build escape paths [8].

Third, we evaluate the performance of LFC's multicast protocol on a Myrinet cluster. We show that LFC achieves both low latency (59 μs on 61 processors) and high throughput (13.3 MB/s on 61 processors). We study the performance impact of different multicast tree topologies and the deadlock recovery algorithm. Finally, we compare the performance of LFC and FM/MC.

The remainder of the paper is organized as follows. Section 2 describes the Myrinet architecture and summarizes FM/MC's multicast protocol. In Section 3, we describe LFC and its basic multicast protocol. This protocol is compared (qualitatively) to FM/MC's multicast protocol. Section 4 extends the basic protocol with a deadlock recovery scheme that removes restrictions on the multicast trees that are present in the basic protocol. In Section 5, we demonstrate that LFC's multicast protocol achieves good performance and in most cases outperforms FM/MC. Section 6 discusses related work and Section 7 concludes the paper.

2. Multicasting on Myrinet

Before describing LFC's multicast protocol, we summarize the Myrinet architecture and the FM/MC multicast protocol. FM/MC was implemented as an extension of Illinois Fast Messages 1.1 [15]. Both FM/MC and LFC implement multicast at the NI level, but their multicast protocols are very different, so it is interesting to compare these protocols and their performance.

2.1. Myrinet

Myrinet is a high-speed, wormhole-routed, switched LAN technology [3]. Myrinet network interfaces are attached to the host system's I/O bus and connect to each other via crossbar switches and high-speed links. Packets are wormhole-routed from one NI to another through a series of crossbar switches. Due to hardware flow control, Myrinet does not drop packets unless receiving NIs fail to drain the network.

Myrinet network interfaces have a programmable RISC processor (LANai), three DMA engines, and fast SRAM memory. The DMA engines are used to send to the network, receive from the network, and transfer data to and from host memory. All data transfers between the host and the network are staged through the NI's memory, which also holds the code and data for the program that controls the NI.

To avoid operating system overheads, the network interface's memory is mapped into the virtual address space of processes that use Myrinet. This allows the processor to move both data and commands to the NI's memory using programmed I/O (PIO). The NI, on the other hand, can access host memory only via DMA. Neither FM/MC nor LFC implements protection or device sharing between processes. These issues have been addressed in various other projects [5, 9].

2.2. The FM/MC multicast protocol

A detailed description of the FM/MC protocol is given in [17]. Below, we describe how FM/MC addresses the issues that arise in the design of a reliable multicast protocol.

Reliability and flow control. Reliability and flow control are closely related. In general, packet loss can have two different causes: unreliable hardware or receiver-side buffer overruns. The Myrinet hardware does not drop packets, but packets may be lost or corrupted when a receiving NI processes incoming packets more slowly than they arrive. Given a flow control scheme that stalls senders before receiver buffer overruns can occur, reliability can be obtained without retransmitting packets. Multicast flow control, however, is difficult, because buffer space is needed at multiple receivers, not just one.

FM/MC uses the following protocol. Each receiver allocates two types of buffers in host memory: one set of buffers is used for unicast messages, the other for multicast messages. An equal part of a host's unicast receive buffers is allocated to each sender. These unicast buffers are managed by a standard sliding window protocol that runs on the host. Multicast buffers, in contrast, are not partitioned statically among senders. Instead, a central credit manager, running on one of the NIs, keeps track of the number of free multicast buffers on each host. Before a process can multicast a message, it must obtain credits from the credit manager. To avoid the overhead of a credit request-reply pair for every multicast message, hosts can request multiple credits and cache them. Once consumed, credits are returned to the credit manager by means of a rotating token.

At the network interface level, no software flow control is present. Each NI contains a single receive queue for all inbound packets. When this queue fills up, FM/MC moves part of the receive queue to host memory to make space for inbound packets. Eventually, senders will run out of credits and the pressure on receiving NIs will drop; packets can then be copied back to NI memory and processed further. The idea is that this type of swapping to host memory will only occur under exceptional conditions, and it is assumed that swapping will not take too much time.

Deadlock. A multicast packet requires buffer space at all its destinations. This buffer space can be obtained before sending the packet or it can be obtained more dynamically, as the packet travels from one node in the spanning tree to another. The first approach, used by FM/MC, is conceptually simple, but requires a global protocol to reserve buffers at all destination nodes. The latter approach introduces the danger of buffer deadlocks. A sender may know that its multicast packet can reach the next node in the spanning tree, but does not know if the packet can travel further once it has reached that node.

In FM/MC, the credit and swapping mechanism avoid buffer deadlocks at the NI level: when NI buffers fill up, they are copied to host memory. The centralized credit mechanism guarantees that buffer space is available on the host. Also, since packets are not forwarded from host memory, there is no risk of buffer deadlock at the host level.

Multicast tree topology. Many different tree topologies have been described in the literature [4, 12, 13]. Depending on the type of multicast traffic generated by an application, one topology gives better performance than another. Shallow trees, for example, are best for low latency, because the path to each leaf in the multicast tree is short. Deep trees, on the other hand, give better throughput, because internal nodes need to forward packets fewer times, so they use less time per multicast. Our goal in this paper is not to invent or analyze a particular topology that is optimal in some sense. We simply note that since no single tree shape is optimal under all circumstances, it is desirable that a multicast protocol does not prohibit topologies that are appropriate for the application at hand.

FM/MC uses a binary tree (per sender) to forward multicast packets; it was established empirically that binary trees give good overall performance [17]. FM/MC's protocol, however, allows the use of arbitrary trees.

Division of labor between host and network interface. Programmable network interface processors typically are an order of magnitude slower than the host they connect to. Common sense therefore dictates that complicated protocol tasks be left to the host processor. Nevertheless, the programmability of an NI allows a number of simple, but effective optimizations.

FM/MC uses the NI for packet forwarding and credit management. NI-level packet forwarding is the key to its good performance. Both latency and throughput are improved because multicast packets need not travel to the host before they can be forwarded. Unicast flow control is performed entirely on the host. The multicast flow control protocol, however, uses one NI to manage credits and all NIs to forward the credit garbage collection token.

FM/MC's protocol has several disadvantages, some of which were identified in [10]. An important problem is that all credit traffic flows to and from the credit manager. This may increase multicast latencies and introduces a potential bottleneck. FM/MC is pessimistic in that it reserves buffers on all hosts before starting a multicast (but optimistic in that it never reserves NI buffers). Since only host buffers are subject to flow control, the NI may need to swap its receive buffers to host memory under heavy load. Finally, FM/MC uses two different flow control mechanisms: one for unicast and another for multicast. The two protocols cannot share each other's buffers.

3. LFC flow control and multicast

3.1. Link-level flow control

In contrast with other high-performance communication substrates (e.g., [15]), which minimize the amount of protocol code executed on the network interface, LFC carefully exploits Myrinet's programmable NI to implement flow control, to forward multicast traffic, and to reduce the overhead of network interrupts.

Unlike FM/MC, LFC implements peer-to-peer flow control at the network interface level. The flow control protocol guarantees that no NI will send or forward a packet to another NI before it knows that the receiving NI can store the packet.

LFC runs a straightforward sliding window protocol between each pair of network interfaces. Each NI dedicates part of its memory to receive buffers and assigns an equal number of buffers to each NI in the system. An NI that needs to transmit a packet to another NI may only do so when it has at least one *send credit* for the receiving NI. Each send credit for a particular NI corresponds to a receive buffer on that NI. Credits can be returned to their senders in two ways: by means of an explicit credit update message (when a low-water mark is reached); or by means of piggybacking (when a packet happens to travel back to the sender).

Figure 1 illustrates LFC's send path. The host copies message data into a free packet from the send buffer pool and enqueues a send descriptor in the send queue. The send descriptor contains the packet's destination and a reference to the packet. The NI, which polls the send queue, inspects the send descriptor. When credits are available for the specified destination, the descriptor is moved to the transmit queue; the packet will be transmitted when the descriptor reaches the head of this queue. When no send credits are available, the descriptor is added to a *blocked-sends queue* associated with the packet's destination. When credits flow back from some destination, descriptors are moved from that destination's blocked-sends queue to the transmit queue. Since the blocked-sends queue is always checked before other packets

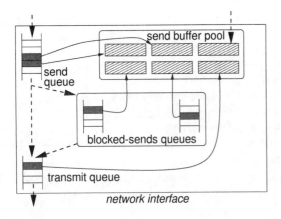

Figure 1. Send path and data structures.

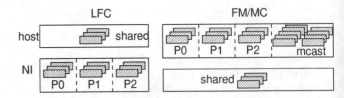

Figure 2. Buffering in LFC and FM/MC.

can consume credits, packets are transmitted and received in FIFO order.

Receiving hosts are responsible for posting (via a shared queue) free host receive buffers to the NI. When no buffers are available, the NI simply does not copy packets to the host and does not release the packet's buffer space. Eventually, senders will be stalled and remain stalled until the host posts new buffers.

The sliding window protocol is essentially identical to the *host*-level protocol that Fast Messages (and FM/MC) uses for point-to-point messages. It is simple and efficient; LFC achieves similar point-to-point latencies as Fast Messages (10 μs, on the same hardware), which uses the host-level variant. Since the protocol preserves the reliability of the underlying hardware by avoiding receiver buffer overruns, senders need not buffer packets for retransmission, nor need they manage any timers. The main disadvantage of the protocol is that it statically partitions the available receive buffer space among all senders, so it needs more NI memory as the number of processors is increased.

3.2. Basic multicast protocol

LFC's multicast protocol is implemented on top of the reliable, NI-level protocol described above; it uses the same flow control mechanism and the same buffers. The protocol operates as follows. Each NI contains a table that specifies for each sender how packets from that sender must be forwarded along the multicast tree. Each sender has its own multicast tree. The NI uses the table to find the forwarding destinations of each multicast packet that it needs to send for its host or that arrives from the network. When the NI has to forward a packet, it creates a send descriptor for each forwarding destination. From then on, exactly the same procedure is followed as for a unicast packet. The packet will only be transmitted to a forwarding destination if credits are

available for that destination; otherwise, the send descriptor is moved to the destination's blocked-sends queue.

3.3. Protocol comparison

LFC and FM/MC offer similar multicast functionality: both provide a reliable, flow-controlled multicast primitive that preserves the (FIFO) ordering among multicast packets that originate from the same sender. Internally, however, LFC and FM/MC differ significantly in the ways they perform buffer management, flow control, and the tree topology they use. Below, we discuss these issues in more detail.

Figure 2 shows how LFC and FM/MC allocate receive buffers. At the network interface level, FM/MC uses a single queue of NI buffers for all inbound network packets, while LFC logically partitions its NI buffers among all senders. FM/MC's shared-buffer approach at the NI level is attractive when the amount of NI memory is small, because the number of buffers need not grow with the number of nodes in the system. Given a reasonable amount of memory on the NI and a modest number of nodes, however, partitioning buffers at this level poses no problems, and obviates the need for FM/MC's buffer swapping mechanism. On our 64-node system, LFC allocates 8 NI receive buffers (each 1 KB) per sender, which amounts to 0.5 MB per NI. With 8 credits, senders rarely run out of credits.

At the host level, the situation has almost been reversed. FM/MC allocates a fixed number of unicast buffers per sender and has another, separate class of multicast buffers. Senders are not given a fixed number of multicast buffers; instead, multicast buffer space must be requested from the credit manager. LFC, in contrast, does not partition its host buffers.

LFC and FM/MC also differ markedly in the way flow control is implemented. A multicast credit in FM/MC represents a buffer on *every* receiving host and is obtained by sending a request to the centralized credit manager. So, FM/MC always waits until every receiver has space before sending the next multicast packet(s). LFC, in contrast, does not distinguish between unicast and multicast credits and does not employ a centralized credit manager. The sender of a multicast packet does not need to wait for space on all receiving hosts or NIs, but only needs credits for its children in the multicast tree. No request messages are needed to obtain these credits: receivers know when senders are low on credits and send credit update messages without receiving explicit requests. In FM/MC, credits are not returned to senders, but to the credit manager.

The reason that multicast flow control in LFC is so much simpler, is that LFC decouples host buffers and NI buffers. In FM/MC, host buffers must act as a backing store for NI buffers. Reliability is only guaranteed when there are enough host buffers. To make sure enough host buffers are available, FM/MC uses the centralized credit manager. Multicast flow control cannot be integrated easily with unicast flow control, because the decision to forward a packet is taken on the NI, where the flow control information is not available. One solution is to let the host forward multicast packets, but this is expensive; the other solution is to move the flow control protocol to the NI, which is what LFC does.

Finally, we consider the types of multicast trees employed by both protocols. FM/MC uses binary trees, but its protocol is in no way tied to this topology. In contrast, LFC's multicast protocol (as described so far), is susceptible to deadlock when an arbitrary topology is used. When each sender's multicast tree is a linear chain, for example, deadlock can easily occur.

By default, LFC uses binomial spanning trees to forward multicast packets. Such trees restrict the routes that packets take to the routes prescribed by e-cube routing, which is deadlock-free [6]. In the next section, we show how LFC's multicast protocol can be extended with a deadlock recovery mechanism, thus allowing arbitrary multicast trees.

Summarizing, LFC's multicast protocol has important advantages over FM/MC. The most important advantage is its simplicity. A single flow control scheme is used for unicast and multicast traffic; there are no centralized components in the protocol; and there is no need to swap buffers back and forth between host and NI. The price to pay for this simplicity is the restriction on the tree topologies that can be used, but this restriction can be removed (see Section 4). With respect to performance, we note that LFC never sends credit requests and that credits are returned directly to their senders without waiting for a token to come by. Also, multicast packets can be forwarded as soon as credits are available for the next hop.

4. Deadlock recovery

To allow LFC to use arbitrary multicast trees, we have extended LFC's multicast protocol with a deadlock recovery mechanism. When an NI suspects deadlock, it switches to a slower, but deadlock-free protocol. This protocol requires $P - 1$ extra buffers on each NI, where P is the number of NIs used by the application. Each NI owns one extra buffer on every other NI. The buffers owned by an NI form a dedicated *deadlock channel* on which only the owner may initiate communication. Deadlock channels are used to ensure forward progress when deadlock is suspected.

4.1. Deadlock detection

Deadlock recovery is triggered when a network interface suspects deadlock. LFC uses only local information to detect potential deadlocks, so no communication is needed to detect deadlocks. Multiple NIs can detect (and recover from) a deadlock simultaneously. While simultaneous recoveries do not interfere, they can be inefficient [14].

The detection algorithm is simple: each NI assumes deadlock as soon as it finds that it has run out of send credits for some destination that it needs to send a packet to. That is, nonempty blocked-sends queues signal deadlock immediately. Since a deadlock need not involve all NIs, we must monitor each individual queue; progress on some, but not all queues does not guarantee freedom of deadlock. Checking for a nonempty blocked-sends queue is efficient, but may signal deadlock sooner than a timeout-based mechanism. In Section 5 we evaluate the overhead of our detection mechanism.

When an NI has signaled a potential deadlock, it initiates a recovery action. No new recoveries are started while a previous recovery is still in progress. When a recovery terminates, the NI that initiated it will search for other nonempty blocked-sends queues and start a new recovery if it finds one. To avoid livelock, the blocked-sends queues are served in a round-robin fashion.

4.2. Deadlock recovery

The deadlock recovery algorithm must satisfy two requirements. Obviously, it must ensure forward progress. This is done using the extra deadlock buffers. Second, it must preserve the order among packets that are multicast on the same spanning tree.

The recovery protocol is illustrated in Figure 3. In this figure, vertices represent NIs and edges represent communication channels. Dashed edges represent channels where the parent has no credits for the child. When network interface R suspects deadlock, it selects a blocked packet p at the head of one of its blocked-sends queues and determines the multicast tree T that this packet is being forwarded on. The destination D of packet p forms the root of a *deadlocked subtree*, indicated with black vertices in Figure 3. The deadlocked subtree is a subtree of T in which parents do not have credits for their children and thus cannot forward packets of T. During a recovery, every node in the deadlocked subtree will be allowed to forward one packet to all its children in T.

We will now explain the protocol in more detail. First, R marks the selected packet p with a deadlock flag and trans-

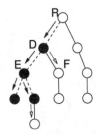

Figure 3. Deadlocked subtree.

mits it to D, where it will occupy one of the extra buffers. When an NI (e.g., D) receives a packet with this flag set, it belongs to the deadlocked subtree. Such an NI clears the flag and adds the packet to the blocked-sends queues for all its children in T. It then forwards, to each child, the first blocked packet (for that child) that belongs to T. This could be the packet just enqueued, but it could also be another packet sent earlier on T. Selecting the first packet in the blocked-sends queue preserves FIFOness between packets on the same tree. The NI transmits the packets to its children, setting the deadlock flag again only when no credits are available for some child. This way, the deadlocked subtree is extended. In Figure 3, D sets the deadlock flag in the packet sent to E, but not in the packet sent to F.

Using this algorithm, an NI that receives a packet with the deadlock flag set, will always forward, to each of its children in T, a packet of T (not necessarily the same packet that it received and not necessarily the same packet to all children). The key observation is that this will free at least one packet of T. The NI will tell its parent in T, by means of an acknowledgement packet, that it has freed a buffer. It will only do so, however, when it has received acknowledgements from all children that it added to the deadlocked subtree. That is, acknowledgements are propagated and merged in reverse direction along the deadlocked subtree. In Figure 3 one acknowledgement is sent for each black arrow, but in the opposite direction. When NI R receives an acknowledgement, it knows that its deadlock buffers on all NIs in the deadlocked subtree are free and it may initiate another recovery.

5. Performance evaluation

Below, we evaluate the performance of the basic protocol (without deadlock recovery) and the impact of deadlock recovery under conditions of light and heavy loads. In addition, we compare the performance of LFC and FM/MC. The fairly large number of nodes (64) in our cluster allows us to compare the scalability of LFC and FM/MC.

All experiments described below were performed on a cluster of 64 200 MHz Pentium Pros running BSD/OS 3.0.

Each processor has 64 MB of DRAM, on-chip L1 caches (8 KB data and 8 KB instruction), and a unified L2 cache (256 KB). Each network interface has a 37.5 MHz LANai 4.1 processor and 1 MB of SRAM. The NIs are interconnected in a hypercube topology using sixteen 8-port switches and 2 × 1.28 Gbit/s cables. Each NI connects to its host's PCI bus (33 MHz, 32 bits wide).

At the sending side, both LFC and FM/MC move data from the host to the NI using programmed I/O. Receiving NIs use cache-coherent DMA transfers to move packets to host memory. Packets are received through polling and copied once after they have been DMAed. While LFC allows packets to be processed without being copied, most client systems make at least one copy, so we feel this extra copy makes the benchmarks more representative.

5.1. Performance of the basic multicast protocol

We first examine the performance of LFC's basic multicast protocol. For the following measurements, deadlock recovery has been disabled. We use 1 KB packets and allocate 8 send credits per sender per destination.

Figure 4 shows the latency (top) and throughput (bottom) for various message sizes and various numbers of processors. In both cases, we use binomial spanning trees. We report the latency observed by the last receiver of each (empty) multicast message. With 4 nodes, we obtain a latency of 22 μs; with 61 nodes[1], the latency is 59 μs.

Throughput is measured using a straightforward blast test. We report the throughput observed by the sender. With 4 nodes, the peak throughput is 42.9 MB/s; with 61 nodes, the peak throughput is 13.3 MB/s. Note that the 4-processor throughput curve declines when the message size reaches the size of the L2 cache (256 KB). At this point, the receiving processors, which copy data into a receive buffer, start to suffer from L2 capacity misses. The resulting memory traffic interferes with the NI's DMA transfers to host buffers. This does not occur for larger numbers of processors, because the incoming packets do not arrive at a sufficiently high rate to interfere with the host's memory copy.

5.2. Impact of deadlock recovery and tree shape

An interesting question is how much overhead the deadlock recovery scheme adds to the basic multicast protocol. We first examine the case in which no deadlock recovery is needed. In Figure 5, we show throughput results for the basic multicast protocol (BP) and the protocol with deadlock recovery (DR) for three packet sizes (512 bytes, 1 KB, and 2 KB). Receiver buffer space is kept constant at 0.5 MB. We use 61 processors and the same deadlock-free binomial spanning tree as before, so no true deadlocks can occur.

---

[1]At the time of writing, only 61 out of 64 processors were available.

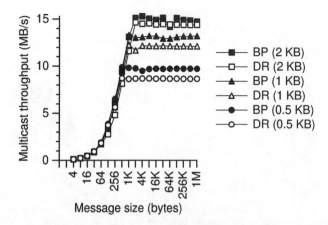

Figure 5. Multicast throughput with (DR) and without (BP) deadlock recovery.

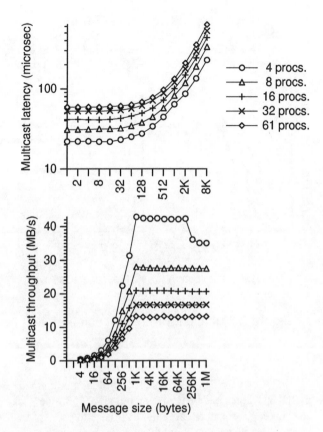

Figure 4. Multicast latency and throughput.

Since our deadlock recovery scheme makes a local, conservative decision, however, it may still signal deadlock. In this experiment, processors that are near the root frequently initiate deadlock recovery. In the case of 1024-byte packets, for example, almost 25% of all multicasts results in a deadlock recovery action initiated by the root or a processor near the root. As the figure shows, however, this has only a modest impact on single-sender throughput. This is due to the small size of the deadlocked subtrees; in this example, an average of 1.3 (out of 60) packets per multicast is transmitted via a deadlock recovery channel.

Figure 6 (left) shows the impact of tree shape on single-sender multicast throughput. We compare binomial spanning trees, binary trees, and linear chains. We use a large number of processors (61), because that is when we expect the performance characteristics of different tree shapes to be most visible. In all cases, deadlock recovery was enabled, because with binary trees and chains, deadlocks can occur when multiple senders multicast concurrently.

First, we consider the impact of tree shape on single-sender throughput. In this case, no deadlocks can occur and we expect deep trees to perform well. This expectation is confirmed in Figure 6 (left). The linear chain outperforms

both the binary and binomial spanning trees by a large margin; the difference between the binary tree and the binomial spanning tree is small. With 61 nodes, the binary tree is almost full; it has 6 levels and 30 nodes at the last level. The binomial spanning tree is broader and shallower: it has only 4 nodes at the last (6th) level and a maximum fanout of 6.

To test the behavior of the deadlock recovery scheme in the case that deadlocks *can* occur, we performed an all-to-all benchmark in which all senders broadcast simultaneously. We use the same multicast trees (binomial, binary, and chain) as in the single-sender case. The all-to-all benchmark is a worst-case scenario for our deadlock recovery scheme. First, true deadlocks are likely to occur for the trees that are not deadlock-free, especially for the chain. Second, since all processors multicast at the same time, the occupancy of the NIs increases because they need to forward many multicast packets. As a result, senders need to wait longer before their send credits are returned to them and deadlock will be triggered sooner.

Figure 6 (right) shows the per-sender throughput for all three multicast topologies (on 61 processors). First note that the per-sender throughput is much lower than in the single-sender case, due to contention for network resources (links, buffers, and NI processor cycles). As expected, the chain topology performs badly. The binomial spanning tree performs better than the binary tree.

Table 1 reports the frequency of deadlock recovery (as a fraction of the number of multicasts) and the average number of deadlock recovery packets per multicast. These statistics are for an all-to-all exchange of 64 KB messages on 61 processors. From these statistics it is clear why the chain performs badly: every multicast triggers a deadlock recovery action and all children in the multicast tree are without credits, so we are forced to always use the slow deadlock

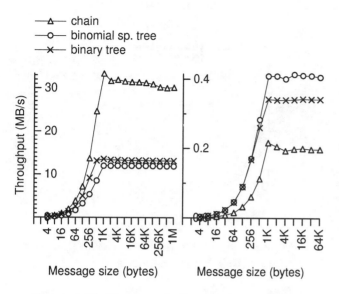

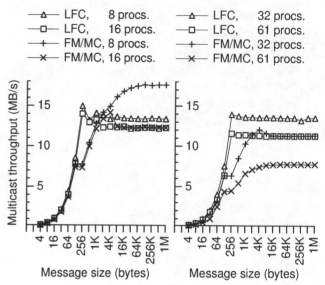

Figure 6. Multicast and all-to-all throughputs.

Figure 7. Multicast throughput comparison.

Tree shape	Recoveries per multicast	Avg. #deadlock recovery packets
binary tree	0.362	2.7
binomial sp. tree	0.853	3.5
chain	1.000	59.9

Table 1. Deadlock recovery statistics.

channels. With binary and binomial spanning trees deadlock recoveries also occur frequently, but here the size of the deadlocked subtrees is much smaller. Finally, note that binary trees trigger fewer and smaller recoveries than binomial spanning trees, but yet perform worse. Apparently, the performance difference is not caused by the deadlock recovery protocol.

Summarizing, we find that deadlock recovery is triggered frequently, but that its effect on performance is modest when the communication load is moderate and true deadlocks do not occur. To reduce the number of false alarms, we are considering a more refined, timeout-based, mechanism as in [14].

5.3. Comparison with FM/MC

Below, we compare LFC and FM/MC using the single-sender and all-to-all throughput benchmarks. We focus on throughput, because throughput benchmarks stress the flow control protocol. The difference in unicast and multicast latency obtained by LFC and FM/MC is small; usually, LFC's latencies are slightly lower. Before turning to the measurements, we discuss two factors that affect the performance of both systems: packet size and tree shape.

LFC uses variable-length packets with a maximum size of 1 KB, whereas FM/MC uses fixed-size, 256-byte packets. Fixed-size packets are slightly easier to process than variable-length packets, but have the disadvantage that they have to be relatively small to avoid a large increase in latency. Using small packets, however, often limits throughput. Due to its variable-length packets, LFC achieves both low latency and high throughput. On 61 processors, for example, LFC obtains a peak multicast throughput of 13.3 MB/s, versus 7.7 MB/s for FM/MC. To allow a fair comparison, we configured LFC to use 256-byte packets. This is a disadvantage for LFC, because LFC has slightly higher per-packet overheads which it can normally hide behind its larger packets.

To avoid differences in performance that result from differences in tree shape, we configured LFC to use binary trees, just like FM/MC. Since binary trees are not deadlock-free for LFC, we also enabled LFC's deadlock recovery mechanism. In a single-sender throughput benchmark, no deadlocks can occur, so we expect little overhead from the deadlock recovery mechanism. In the all-to-all benchmark, however, true deadlocks can occur, so we expect performance to suffer more noticeably.

Figure 7 shows single-sender throughputs on 8, 16, 32, and 61 processors. For 8 processors and large messages, FM/MC outperforms LFC, due to LFC's larger per-packet overheads. At 256 bytes, FM/MC begins to fragment messages, because FM/MC does not allow the user to completely fill the first packet of a message.[2] This explains the

---

[2]One word is used to store an active message handler.

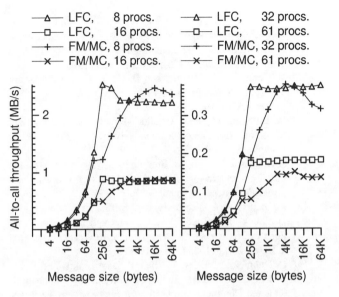

Figure 8. All-to-all throughput comparison.

step in FM/MC's throughput curves. Unlike LFC, FM/MC manages to increase its throughput while fragmenting messages; LFC always reaches its peak throughput exactly where fragmentation starts.

With 16 processors, FM/MC's peak throughput is better than LFC's, but for larger messages, FM/MC's throughput is the same as LFC's throughput. With more than 16 processors, LFC achieves much higher throughputs, which indicates that LFC's multicast protocol scales better than FM/MC's protocol.

Figure 8 shows the performance results for the all-to-all throughput benchmark on 8, 16, 32, and 61 processors. Again, for 8 processors and large messages, FM/MC outperforms LFC and at 16 processors performance is about equal. At 32 processors, however, LFC outperforms FM/MC and this continues to be the case for larger numbers of processors. In this benchmark, FM/MC suffers not only from its centralized credit manager, but also from its lack of NI-level flow control, which triggers the swapping mechanism described in Section 2.2 and degrades performance.

6. Related work

Using the network interface instead of the host to forward multicast traffic is not a new idea. Our NI-level protocol is original, however, in that it integrates unicast and multicast flow control and uses a deadlock recovery scheme to avoid routing restrictions.

In [11], the authors propose to exploit ATM network interfaces to implement collective communication operations, including multicast. In their symmetric broadcast protocol, NIs use an ATM multicast channel to forward messages

to their children; multicast acknowledgements are also collected via the NIs. The sending host maintains a sliding window; it appears that a single window is used per broadcast group. LFC, in contrast, uses sliding windows between each pair of NIs. This allows LFC to integrate unicast and multicast flow control. The authors of [11] do not discuss unicast flow control and present simulation results only.

Gerla et al. [10] also discuss using NIs for multicast packet forwarding. Their scheme avoids deadlock by dividing receive buffers in two classes. The first class is used when messages travel to higher-numbered NIs, the second when going to lower-numbered NIs. This scheme requires buffer resources per multicast tree, which is problematic in a system with many small multicast groups.

Kesavan and Panda studied optimal multicast tree shapes for systems with programmable network interfaces [13]. They describe two packet-forwarding schemes, first-child-first-served and first-packet-first-served (FPFS), and show that the latter performs best. The paper does not discuss flow control. LFC integrates FPFS with its flow control scheme. As in FPFS, LFC forwards packets to all children as they arrive, but queues packets when no buffer space is available at the forwarding destination.

Several Myrinet-based systems employ different forms of link-level flow control. VMMC-2 [9], for example, treats the hardware as unreliable and saves transmitted packets in NI memory until they have been acknowledged by the receiving NI. In a multicast setting, the network interfaces would not only have to buffer packets that originate from their host, but also the packets that they must forward along the spanning tree.

AM-II [5], a protected cluster communication system, implements part of its flow control mechanism on the network interface. At that level AM-II uses multiple logical channels and runs an alternating bit protocol on each channel. Since AM-II does not statically partition NI buffers among senders, this scheme is augmented with a host-level sliding window protocol and NI-level retransmission.

LFC's multicast protocol can be implemented using any protocol that provides reliability at the NI level. Both VMMC-2 and AM-II provide this. Unlike VMMC-2 and AM-II, however, LFC assumes that the hardware is reliable and trades NI buffer space for a simpler flow control scheme between NIs.

Deadlock in spanning tree multicast protocols is often avoided by means of a deadlock-free routing algorithm. Most research in this area, however, applies to routing at the hardware level. Also, most protocols *avoid* deadlock by imposing routing restrictions [6] and this is the approach taken by LFC's basic multicast protocol. To allow different types of multicast trees that fit the communication pattern of an application, we have added a deadlock recovery scheme. This scheme was inspired by the DISHA protocol [1]. DISHA, however, is a deadlock recovery scheme for unicast worms, whereas our scheme recovers from buffer deadlock in a store-and-forward protocol for multicasting.

7. Conclusions

We have presented a simple, efficient multicast protocol for Myrinet. The protocol uses Myrinet's programmable network interfaces to efficiently forward multicast packets along a spanning tree. The key characteristic of the protocol is its use of hop-by-hop flow control at the network interface level. This is quite different from the flow control scheme employed by FM/MC, which uses end-to-end flow control and a centralized credit manager for buffer reservations. LFC's protocol is simpler and has two important advantages: multicast flow control is easily integrated with unicast flow control (e.g., buffers can be shared) and no centralized buffer management is needed for multicast buffers.

The main disadvantage of LFC's hop-by-hop flow control is the potential for buffer deadlocks. LFC's basic multicast protocol avoids such deadlocks by restricting the shape of multicast trees. We have shown that this restriction can be removed by means of a deadlock recovery scheme that requires extra buffer space on each NI. When no deadlocks occur, the overhead of this scheme is small.

LFC's basic multicast protocol performs well. Due to its use of variable-length instead of fixed-length packets, LFC achieves much higher throughputs than FM/MC. Even when we use equal packet sizes and the same multicast trees for both protocols, LFC almost always outperforms FM/MC for more than 16 processors. This performance gain is the result of LFC's NI-level flow control which does not use any centralized components and which avoids excessive pressure on network interface buffers.

Acknowledgements We thank Rutger Hofman, Thilo Kielmann, Koen Langendoen, Aske Plaat, Kees Verstoep, and the anonymous referees for their feedback on this work. We thank Andrew Chien and Scott Pakin for making FM available to us.

References

[1] K. Anjan and T. Pinkston. An Efficient, Fully Adaptive Deadlock Recovery Scheme: DISHA. In *Proc. of the 22nd Int. Symp. on Computer Architecture*, pages 201–210, Santa Margherita Ligure, Italy, June 1995.

[2] H. Bal, R. Bhoedjang, R. Hofman, C. Jacobs, K. Langendoen, T. Rühl, and M. Kaashoek. Performance Evaluation of the Orca Shared Object System. *ACM Trans. on Computer Systems*, 16(1):1–40, Feb. 1998.

[3] N. Boden, D. Cohen, R. Felderman, A. Kulawik, C. Seitz, J. Seizovic, and W. Su. Myrinet: A Gigabit-per-second Local Area Network. *IEEE Micro*, 15(1):29–36, 1995.

[4] J. Bruck, L. De Coster, N. Dewulf, C.-T. Ho, and R. Lauwereins. On the Design and Implementation of Broadcast and Global Combine Operations Using the Postal Model. *IEEE Trans. on Computers*, 7(3):256–265, Mar. 1996.

[5] B. Chun, A. Mainwaring, and D. Culler. Virtual Network Transport Protocols for Myrinet. In *Hot Interconnects '97*, Stanford, CA, Apr. 1997.

[6] W. Dally and C. Seitz. Deadlock-Free Message Routing in Multiprocessor Interconnection Networks. *IEEE Trans. on Computers*, 36(5):547–553, May 1987.

[7] J. Dongarra, S. Otto, M. Snir, and D. Walker. A Message Passing Standard for MPP and Workstations. *Communications of the ACM*, 39(7):84–90, July 1996.

[8] J. Duato. A Necessary and Sufficient Condition for Deadlock-Free Routing in Cut-Through and Store-and-Forward Networks. *IEEE Trans. on Parallel and Distributed Systems*, 7(8):841–854, Aug. 1996.

[9] C. Dubnicki, A. Bilas, Y. Chen, S. Damianakis, and K. Li. VMMC-2: Efficient Support for Reliable, Connection-Oriented Communication. In *Hot Interconnects '97*, Stanford, CA, Apr. 1997.

[10] M. Gerla, P. Palnati, and S. Walton. Multicasting Protocols for High-Speed, Wormhole-Routing Local Area Networks. In *Proc. of the SIGCOMM '96 Symposium*, pages 184–193, Stanford University, CA, Aug. 1996.

[11] Y. Huang and P. McKinley. Efficient Collective Operations with ATM Network Interface Support. In *Proc. of the 1996 Int. Conf. on Parallel Processing*, volume I, pages 34–43, Bloomingdale, IL, Aug. 1996.

[12] R. Karp, A. Sahay, E. Santos, and K. Schauser. Optimal Broadcast and Summation in the LogP Model. In *Proc. of the 1993 Symp. on Parallel Algorithms and Architectures*, pages 142–153, Velen, Germany, June 30–July 2 1993.

[13] R. Kesavan and D. Panda. Optimal Multicast with Packetization and Network Interface Support. In *Proc. of the 1997 Int. Conf. on Parallel Processing*, pages 370–377, Bloomingdale, IL, Aug. 1997.

[14] P. López, J. Martínez, and J. Duato. A Very Efficient Distributed Deadlock Detection Mechanism for Wormhole Networks. In *Proc. of the 4th Int. Symp. on High-Performance Computer Architecture*, pages 57–66, Las Vegas, NV, Feb. 1998.

[15] S. Pakin, M. Lauria, and A. Chien. High Performance Messaging on Workstations: Illinois Fast Messages (FM) for Myrinet. In *Supercomputing '95*, San Diego, CA, Dec. 1995.

[16] C. Stunkel, R. Sivaram, and D. Panda. Implementing Multidestination Worms in Switch-based Parallel Systems: Architectural Alternatives and their Impact. In *Proc. of the 24th Int. Symp. on Computer Architecture*, pages 50–61, Denver, CO, June 1997.

[17] K. Verstoep, K. Langendoen, and H. Bal. Efficient Reliable Multicast on Myrinet. In *Proc. of the 1996 Int. Conf. on Parallel Processing*, volume III, pages 156–165, Bloomingdale, IL, Aug. 1996.

Panel Session
Convergence Points on
Commercial Parallel Systems:
Do We Have the Node Architecture?
Do We Have the Network?
Do We Have the Programming Paradigm?

Organizer and Moderator: H.J. Siegel
Purdue University

Convergence Points on Commercial Parallel Systems:
Do We Have the Node Architecture?
Do We Have the Network?
Do We Have the Programming Paradigm?

Howard Jay Siegel
Parallel Processing Laboratory
School of Electrical and Computer Engineering
Purdue University
West Lafayette, IN 47907-1285 USA
E-mail: hj@purdue.edu

This is a brief introduction to the panel:
Convergence Points on Commercial Parallel Systems:
Do we have the node architecture?
Do we have the network?
Do we have the programming paradigm?
The title of the panel is also the main set of questions the panelists will be asked to address, where the panelists can consider a cluster as a commercial parallel system. The purpose of the panel is to assess, from the variety of viewpoints represented by the panel, the current state of commercial parallel systems. The panel will also discuss what components of the system seem to have reached a convergence point in the designs that are commercially available, if any.

The panel organizer and moderator is H. J. Siegel, Purdue University. The panelists are scheduled to be:
Hank Dietz, Purdue University
Jose Duato, Universidad Politecnica de Valencia
Steve Scott, Cray Research/Silicon Graphics
Thomas Sterling, JPL/Caltech
Craig Stunkel, IBM Research
Stephen Wheat, Intel

A brief biography for each of the panelists is below.

Henry (Hank) Dietz, who served as Program Chairman for ICPP 97, is an Associate Professor of Electrical and Computer Engineering at Purdue University. The over 130 technical papers he has authored or coauthored center on optimizing, parallelizing, compilers and parallel computer architecture; his group also has produced several well-known software and hardware systems, including PCCTS (the Purdue Compiler Construction Tool Set) and PAPERS (Purdue's Adapter for Parallel Execution and Rapid Synchronization). Dietz has worked with a wide range of parallel supercomputers and is the author of the Linux Documentation Project's "Parallel Processing HOWTO."

Jose Duato is a Professor at the Department of Informa-tion Systems and Computer Architecture, Technical University of Valencia, Spain, and Vice-President for R&D at this University. Prof. Duato developed a theory of deadlock-free routing that has been used in the design of the MIT Reliable Router and the Cray T3E router. He also co-authored the book titled "Interconnection Networks: An Engineering Approach," recently published by IEEE Computer Society Press.

Steve Scott received his Ph.D. in computer science in 1992 from the University of Wisconsin at Madison, where he was a Wisconsin Alumni Research Foundation and Hertz Foundation Fellow. He was a principal architect of the Cray T3E, and is currently a Chief Scientist at Cray Research/Silicon Graphics working on future scalable multiprocessors.

H. J. Siegel is a Professor in the School of Electrical and Computer Engineering at Purdue University. He received two B.S. degrees from MIT, and the M.A., M.S.E., and Ph.D. degrees from Princeton University. He is a Fellow of the IEEE and a Fellow of the ACM. He has coauthored over 250 technical papers, has coedited seven volumes, and wrote the book *Interconnection Networks for Large-Scale Parallel Processing*. Prof. Siegel was a Coeditor-in-Chief of the *Journal of Parallel and Distributed Computing*, and served on the Editorial Boards of both the *IEEE Transactions on Parallel and Distributed Systems* and the *IEEE Transactions on Computers*. He published his first paper on parallel processing over 20 years ago, in the *Proceedings of the 1975 International Conference on Parallel Processing*.

Thomas Sterling has been engaged in research related to parallel computer architecture, system software, and evaluation for more than a decade. He was a key contributor to the design, implementation, and testing of several experimental parallel architectures. The focus of Dr. Sterling's research has been on the modeling and evaluation of performance factors determining scalability of high performance computing systems. Upon completion of his Ph.D. as a Hertz Fellow from MIT in 1984, Dr. Sterling served as a research scientist at Harris Corporation's Advanced Technology Department, and later with the systems group of the IDA Supercomputing Research Center. In 1992, Dr. Sterling joined the USRA Center for Excellence in Space Data and Information Sciences to support the NASA HPCC earth and space sciences project at the Goddard Space Flight Center. Dr. Sterling was Adjunct Associate Professor at the University of Maryland College Park, where he lectured on computer architecture. He holds six patents, is the co-author of two books and has published dozens of papers in the field of parallel computing. Dr. Thomas Sterling is currently Senior Staff Scientist, High Performance Computing Systems Group, Jet Propulsion Laboratory; and Visiting Associate, Center for Advanced Computing Research, California Institute of Technology.

Craig Stunkel is a research staff member at IBM's T. J. Watson Research Center in Yorktown Heights, NY. He received the Ph.D. degree in electrical engineering from the University of Illinois, Urbana in 1990. At IBM Research, Dr. Stunkel was a co-designer of the original IBM SP1/SP2 switching networks (called Vulcan). He also made architectural contributions to the new SP Switch which became available in 1996, and consults on future switching networks for IBM. He holds nine U.S. patents related to switching networks. Dr. Stunkel is an associate editor of the IEEE Transactions on Parallel and Distributed Systems. His current research interests include parallel architectures and performance analysis.

Stephen Wheat is the software engineering manager for Intel's Workstations Products Division. His organization is responsible for the software components (including BIOS, drivers, and system performance enhancements) for WPDs IA32 and IA64 multi-processor board and system products. Stephen came to WPD from Intel's Supercomputer Systems Division, where he started his Intel career three years ago. In SSD, Stephen designed and managed the development effort for the operating system that runs on the compute nodes in Intel's TFLOPS machine. Prior to Intel, Stephen was at the US Dept. of Energy's Sandia National Laboratories and at AT&T Bell Laboratories. Stephen has a Ph.D. in Computer Science and has 15 years of systems software experience in the area of technical, multi-processor computing.

Acknowledgments – I thank the following for very useful discussions that led to the panel title: Hank Dietz, Rudi Eigenmann, Jose Fortes, Dave Meyer, and Tom Downar.

Keynote Address
Where is the Internet Heading to?
From Workplace to Livingspace

Speaker: Iwao Toda
Fujitsu Labs

Session 6A
Scientific Computing

Chair: Yousef Saad
University of Minnesota

Scalable Parallel Implementations of the GMRES Algorithm via Householder Reflections

Maria Sosonkina
Department of Computer Science
University of Minnesota
320 Heller Hall, 10 University Drive,
Duluth, MN 55812
masha@d.umn.edu

Donald C. S. Allison and Layne T. Watson
Department of Computer Science
Virginia Polytechnic Institute and
State University
Blacksburg, VA 24061
{allison, ltw}@cs.vt.edu

Abstract

Applications involving large sparse nonsymmetric linear systems encourage parallel implementations of robust iterative solution methods, such as GMRES(k). One variation of GMRES(k) is to adapt the restart value k for any given problem and use Householder reflections in the orthogonalization phase to achieve high accuracy. The Householder transformations can be performed without global communications and modified to use an arbitrary row distribution of the coefficient matrix. The effect of this modification on the GMRES(k) performance is discussed here. This paper compares the abilities of various parallel GMRES(k) implementations to maintain fixed efficiency with increase in problem size and number of processors.

1. Introduction

For large scale problems, the task of writing efficient parallel linear system solvers is particularly important. These problems usually involve sparse linear systems and require general purpose iterative methods. These methods preserve the sparsity of matrices and do not involve complete matrix factorization. A variation of the popular linear system solution tool GMRES [9] is considered in this paper. This variation [13] uses an adaptive strategy to deal with varying difficulties of linear systems which are to be solved by a nonlinear algorithm. Several parallel GMRES implementations are proposed and analyzed using the isoefficiency metric [5]. This metric is closely related to parallel efficiency.

Section 2 gives a brief description of the adaptive GMRES(k) algorithm and its parallel implementations using Householder reflections. A derivation of the isoefficiency function for restarted GMRES is presented in §3 followed by numerical experiments in §4. Section 5 contains conclusions.

2. Adaptive GMRES algorithm

The GMRES algorithm is used to solve a linear system $Ax = b$ with an $n \times n$ nonsymmetric invertible coefficient matrix A. Similar to the classical conjugate gradient method, GMRES produces approximate solutions x_j which are characterized by a minimization property over the Krylov subspaces $K(j, A, r_0) \equiv \text{span}\{r_0, Ar_0, A^2r_0, \cdots, A^{(j-1)}r_0\}$, where $r_0 = b - Ax_0$ and j is the iteration number. However, unlike the conjugate gradient algorithm, the work and memory required by GMRES grow proportionately to the iteration number since GMRES needs all j vectors to construct an orthonormal basis for $K(j, A, r_0)$. In practice, a restarted version GMRES(k) is used, where the algorithm is restarted every k iterations. GMRES(k) takes x_k as the initial guess for the next cycle of k iterations, and continues until the residual norm is small enough.

The disadvantage of the restarted version is that it may stagnate and never reach the solution. The essence of the adaptive GMRES strategy is to adapt the parameter k to the problem, in the same way a variable order ODE algorithm tunes the order k. With modern programming languages, which provide pointers and dynamic memory management, dealing with the variable storage requirements implied by varying k is not difficult. A test of stagnation developed in [3] detects an insufficient residual norm reduction in the restart number k of steps by estimating the GMRES behavior on a particular linear system. Slow progress of GMRES(k), indicating that an increase in the restart value k may be beneficial [14], can be detected with a similar test.

The convergence of GMRES may also be seriously affected by roundoff error, which is especially noticeable when a high accuracy solution is required. When the orthogonalization phase of GMRES is performed by the modified Gram-Schmidt process, GMRES is susceptible to numerical instability. As shown in [1], the orthogonalization with Householder reflections is more robust. In theory, the implementation of GMRES using Householder reflections is about twice as expensive as when modified Gram-Schmidt is used [15]. However, the Householder reflection method produces a more accurate orthogonalization of the Krylov subspace basis when the basis vectors are nearly linearly dependent and the modified Gram-Schmidt method fails to orthogonalize the basis vectors; this can result in fewer GMRES iterations compensating for the higher cost per iteration using Householder reflections. GMRES(k) may exceed an iteration limit when it is affected by roundoff errors in the case of a (nearly) singular GMRES least-squares problem. The condition number of the GMRES least-squares problem is monitored by the incremental condition estimate [2] as in [3]. GMRES(k) aborts when the estimated condition number is greater than some large number, e.g., $1/(50\mathbf{u})$. Pseudocode for an adaptive version of GMRES(k) with orthogonalization via Householder reflections (as in [15]) is given in [13].

In parallel environments, the choice of the orthogonalization process for the Krylov subspace basis vectors depends not only on the accuracy of the process but also on the amount and type of global communication it incurs. For some orthogonalization procedures, only one of the two requirements is satisfied. For example, in serial implementations of the GMRES method, the modified version of the Gram-Schmidt process is often used as being sufficiently accurate for a number of problems. In parallel GMRES implementations, however, the modified Gram-Schmidt process exhibits a large communication overhead Here an implementation of the Householder reflection orthogonalization in GMRES(k) proposed in [15] is adapted to work in parallel. The parallel version employs an algorithm developed in [10] for generating and applying Householder reflections. This algorithm avoids dot-products and all-to-all communications. Pseudocode for the algorithm generating Householder reflections (called HG) at the jth GMRES(k) iteration on the processor $proc$ (in a ring of p processors) is given in Figure 1 (top). It is followed by the pseudocode of the application of Householder reflections in Figure 1 (bottom).

In Figure 1, H and G denote the Householder transformation matrix and the Givens rotation matrix (as given in [4]), respectively; v_{loc} denotes a portion of the Krylov subspace vector $A^j r_0$ located on a processor; p, $left$, $right$ are the processors with the highest rank, with the $proc - 1$ rank, and the $proc + 1$ rank, respectively. It is also assumed that the first processor has the jth row of the input matrix. However, the design

presented in Figure 1 admits only a special case of the matrix row distribution: assignment of a block of contiguous rows to each processor (called block-striped distribution), which is rarely advantageous for an arbitrary unstructured matrix. For unstructured matrices a graph partitioning is used to minimize the communication to computation ratio. In the current implementation, a graph partitioning algorithm from the MeTiS package [7] is used and the parallel version of the matrix-vector multiply is performed as in [8]. The matrix-vector product requires that the components of all vectors are distributed in accordance with the corresponding matrix rows and allows overlapping of computation and communication.

if ($proc = 1$) **then** $s := j$ **else** $s := 0$ **end if**
determine H_{s+1} such that $H_{s+1}v_{loc} \equiv w_{loc}$ has zeros
    after the $(s + 1)$st component;
if ($proc = 1$) **then**
    send $w_{loc}(s + 1)$ to $right$;
else
    receive w from $left$;
    determine G_1 such that $w_{loc}(1) = 0$; update w;
    if ($proc \neq p$) send w to $right$;
end if

---

    for $i := j$ **downto** 1 **step** -1
        if ($proc = 1$) **then**
            send $w_{loc}(i)$ to p;
            receive $w_{loc}(i)$ from $right$;
            $sc := i$;
        else
            receive w from $right$;
            apply G_1 to $(w, w_{loc}(1))$;
            send w to $left$;
            $sc := 1$;
        end if
        apply H_{sc} to $w_{loc}(sc :)$;
    end for

Figure 1.   Parallel Householder reflection generation (top) and application (bottom).

To use the algorithms in Figure 1, the redistribution of a vector requires $\mathcal{O}(p^2)$ communications at each GMRES(k) iteration, which is highly impractical and reduces the efficiency gained by the distributed matrix-vector product. Thus, it is beneficial to develop an extension (called MHG) of the algorithms in Figure 1 which accepts an arbitrary row distribution among processors. Figure 2 (top) shows the pseudocode for MHG, where the row indexing refers to the original matrix before graph partitioning. Usually, the subspace dimension is much smaller than the matrix dimension and the graph partitioning algorithm produces a balanced workload by assigning an almost equal number of rows to each processor.

```
if (j = 1) then
    s := 1;
else
        if (proc has (j − 1)st row) then s := s + 1;
end if
determine H_s such that H_s v_loc ≡ w_loc has zeros
    after the sth component;
if (proc has jth row) then
    ring_end := left;
    send w_loc(s + 1) and ring_end to right;
else
        receive w and ring_end from left;
        determine G_s such that w_loc(s) = 0; update w;
        if (proc ≠ ring_end) then send w to right;
end if
```

```
    sc := s;
    for i := j downto 1 step -1
        if (proc has ith row) then
                if (sc ≠ 1) then sc := sc − 1;
                send w_loc(sc) to left;
                receive w_loc(sc) from right;
        else
                receive w from right;
                if (G_sc exists) then
                    apply G_sc to (w, w_loc(sc));
                end if
                send w to left;
        end if
        apply H_sc to w_loc(sc :);
    end for
```

**Figure 2. Modified Householder reflection
generation (top) and application (bottom).**

Thus, the case when the index s within v_{loc} becomes
equal to the size of a local partition (size of v_{loc}) occurs rarely for large matrices, unless the number of
processors is very large.

3. Comparative scalability analysis

An algorithm-architecture scalability analysis estimates, in a single expression, characteristics of the
algorithm as well as parameters of the architecture
on which the algorithm is implemented. Thus, testing an algorithm on a few processors allows one to
predict its performance on a larger number of processors. The following terminology is needed to support
the proposed scalability analysis. A *parallel system* is
a parallel algorithm and machine combination. The
useful work W is the total number of basic floating
point operations required to solve the problem. W
depends on the *problem size* $\bar{N}$, which is a vector of
problem-specific parameters such as problem dimensions and the number of nonzero entries in a matrix.
For numerical linear algebra problems solved by iterative methods, $\bar{N}$ may also include an indication of
problem difficulty, such as the Krylov subspace dimension k used in GMRES(k) or the condition number. In
general, choosing $\bar{N}$ requires a detailed investigation
of a given problem and of the way scaling of problem
dimensions affects the increase in W [11]. The *sequential execution time* T_1 characterizes the time interval
needed to solve a given problem on a uniprocessor. If
the time of executing an integer operation is negligible compared with the time t_c of performing a floating
point operation and if T_1 is spent in useful work only,
then $T_1 = t_c W$. The *parallel execution time* T_p is the
time taken by p processors to solve the problem. The
total parallel overhead V is the sum of all overheads
incurred by all the processors during parallel execution of the algorithm. For a given parallel system, V
is a function of the useful work W and number of processors p: $V = pT_p(W, p) - T_1(W)$. The *efficiency* E is
the ratio of the speedup $S(p)$ to p, where the speedup
$S(p) = T_1/T_p$. Hence, $E = \frac{T_1}{pT_p} = \frac{1}{(1+V/T_1)}$. A parallel
system is called *scalable* if $V = \mathcal{O}(W)$ and unscalable
otherwise. For scalable systems, it is possible to keep
the efficiency fixed and to monitor the rate of increase
in W and p with the *isoefficiency function* $f_E(p)$, as
proposed in [5]. The isoefficiency function is defined
implicitly by the following relation between W and the
parallel overhead V:

$$W(\bar{N}) = eV(W(\bar{N}), p, \bar{h}), \qquad (1)$$

where $e = \frac{E}{t_c(1-E)}$ is a constant and $\bar{h}$ is a vector of
machine-dependent parameters affecting the amount
of the parallel overhead. Usually, the communication
cost of the total parallel overhead incorporates these
parameters, which are defined in accordance with a
communication model supported by a given architecture.

3.1. Operation count for the useful work

Let N be the scaled matrix dimension and N_z be
the number of nonzeros in the scaled matrix. To
obtain an operation count for the useful work in
GMRES(k) at the jth iteration the following parts of
the pseudocode for GMRES(k) can be distinguished:
(a) matrix-vector product, which takes N_z operations;
(b) Householder reflection generation, which takes
$2(N - j + 1)$ operations; (c) Householder reflection
application, which requires $4(N - i + 1)$ operations,
$i = 1, \ldots, j$. The remaining work is accomplished in
$\mathcal{O}(k)$ operations. For a single restart cycle, the useful
work

$$W \approx (k + 1)N_z + N(2k^2 + 5k + 3) + C_k, \qquad (2)$$

where C_k is a term depending only on k.

3.2. Description of the test problem

The scalability analysis is performed on a real-world problem representing a commercial circuit design at AT&T Bell Laboratories. The dimension of this problem is $n = 125$ and the number of nonzeros $n_z = 782$. Here scaling the problem K times means assembling K replicas of the $n \times n$ matrix of coefficients in an $N \times N$ matrix, where $N = K \times n$ and the number of nonzeros $N_z = K \times n_z$, as shown in Figure 3 for $K = 5$. Both the initial solution vector and right-hand side are $e_N^t = (0, \dots, 0, 1)^t$.

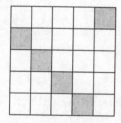

Figure 3. Scaling of problem size.

3.3. Derivation of the isoefficiency function

When GMRES(k) is used for solving the test problem, Equation (1) takes the following form:

$$W(Kn, k) = eV(W(Kn, k), p, \bar{h}), \qquad (3)$$

where $\bar{h} = (t_s, t_w)^t$. Parallel GMRES(k) with Householder reflection orthogonalization incurs an overhead in matrix-vector product, Householder reflection generation and application, and in the residual norm update, which is performed on a single processor.

The isoefficiency function is derived under the following assumptions for the serial time calculation, graph partitioning of a matrix, and communication handling: (a) all the work in the sequential algorithm is considered useful; (b) graph partitioning algorithm produces balanced partitions; (c) for large scale problems, partitions produced by graph partitioning keep the computation to communication ratio no smaller than block-striped partitioning; (d) each processor holds Kn/p rows of the matrix (Figure 3), where $p \leq K$; (e) if $p \leq K$, then each $n \times n$ matrix block is partitioned between no more than two processors; (f) in matrix-vector product, communication is performed by asynchronous sends and synchronous receives; (g) the time complexity of the MPI broadcast operation implemented on the Intel Paragon, IBM SP2, and Cray T3E does not grow substantially as the number of processors increases. Note that, since for the majority of realistic applications the amount

of computation grows superlinearly in the number of processors, assumption (d) is not very constraining.

The parallel overhead due to a matrix-vector product can be predicted by considering the nonzero structure of a given coefficient matrix. For the type of matrices shown in Figure 3, a processor receives at most n vector components from no more than $\lceil p/K \rceil$ processors and sends its Kn/p vector components to at most $\lceil p/K \rceil$ processors. Let $V_{r_j}^{MV}$ and $V_{s_j}^{MV}$ be the total overheads incurred by the processors at data receiving and sending stages of a matrix-vector product, respectively. Then the total parallel overhead of the matrix-vector product at the jth iteration is $V_j^{MV} = V_{r_j}^{MV} + V_{s_j}^{MV}$ with

$$V_{r_j}^{MV} \approx \left(\left\lceil \frac{p}{K} \right\rceil t_s + n t_w + C_0 \right) \times p \quad \text{and}$$

$$V_{s_j}^{MV} \approx \left(\left\lceil \frac{p}{K} \right\rceil t_s + \frac{Kn}{p} t_w - C_1 \right) \times p,$$

where the constants C_0 and C_1 describe the waiting and communication-computation overlapping times for asynchronous communications, respectively. For the problem sizes considered here, $Kn/p \geq n$, and thus $\lceil p/K \rceil t_s \leq t_s$. Combining $V_{r_j}^{MV}$ and $V_{s_j}^{MV}$ yields

$$V_j^{MV} \approx \left(2t_s + \left(n + \frac{Kn}{p} \right) t_w + C_0 - C_1 \right) \times p. \quad (4)$$

Observe that $C_0 - C_1 \approx 0$ since the waiting time of each processor during asynchronous matrix vector product is compensated by the time gain in communication-computation overlapping while sending the information. Thus, $C_0 - C_1$ will be dropped from the expression for V_j^{MV}.

Householder reflection generation and application cause a noticeable communication and nonessential work overhead. At the jth GMRES(k) iteration, the overhead V_j^H due to Householder reflection generation and application comprises the overheads $V_{a_j}^H$ and $V_{c_j}^H$ caused by applying and generating Householder reflections, respectively, such that $V_j^H = 2V_{a_j}^H + V_{c_j}^H$ with

$$V_{a_j}^H \approx \left[jp \big(2(t_s + t_w) + g_a \big) \right] \times p \quad \text{and}$$

$$V_{c_j}^H \approx \left[p \big(2(t_s + t_w) + g_c \big) \right] \times p, \quad (5)$$

where g_c is the number of operations needed to create a Givens rotation and g_a is the number of operations needed to perform a Givens rotation to zero out one vector component. Since Householder reflections are applied twice per GMRES iteration, $V_{a_j}^H$ has a coefficient of two.

Another source of the parallel overhead appears in estimating the condition number of the GMRES least squares problem, which is done on a single processor.

For a typical case, when the Krylov subspace dimension is $j, j = 1, \ldots, k$, gathering $\mathcal{O}(j)$ vector components on a processor, estimating the condition number incrementally, and updating the residual norm are relatively inexpensive, since the subspace dimension is much smaller than the matrix dimension N for large scale problems. Global all-to-all communication would be required to perform the condition number estimation in parallel. At the jth GMRES(k) iteration, the parallel overhead V_j^{IC} is caused by the time spent to exchange $\mathcal{O}(j)$ values, to update the residual norm by application of j previous Givens rotations and by generation of a new Givens rotation, and to perform approximately $(j - 1)$ operations of the incremental condition number estimation. Thus,

$$V_j^{IC} \approx \left[2j(t_s + t_w) + jg_a + g_c + (j - 1) \right] \times p. \quad (6)$$

The total parallel overhead V_j ($V_j = V_j^{MV} + V_j^H + V_j^{IC}$) incurred at the jth iteration of the GMRES(k) algorithm with Householder reflections in its orthogonalization stage is

$$V_j \approx \left[2t_s + \left(n + \frac{Kn}{p} \right) t_w \right] p$$

$$+ \left[2jp \Big(2(t_s + t_w) + g_a \Big) + p \Big(2(t_s + t_w) + g_c \Big) \right] p$$

$$+ \left[2j(t_s + t_w) + jg_a + g_c + (j - 1) \right] p.$$

When a restart cycle is finished, i.e., $j = k$, the GMRES(k) algorithm has performed k matrix-vector products, $k + 1$ Householder reflection generations, k residual norm updates along with k incremental condition number estimates, and $2k$ Householder reflection applications. At the end of a restart, GMRES(k) calculates the true residual norm using one more matrix-vector product and one more Householder reflection application to correct the current solution. Combining all the overhead terms incurred during k iterations, the expression for the total overhead is

$$V = \sum_{j=1}^{k+1} \left(V_j^{MV} + V_{c_j}^H \right) + \sum_{j=1}^{k} \left(2V_{a_j}^H + V_j^{IC} \right) + V_{a_k}^H.$$

Substituting equations (4), (5), and (6) into this equation results in

$$V \approx C_g p^2 + (\bar{h}^t \bar{c} + C_k') p + Kn(k + 1) t_w, \quad \text{where}$$

$$C_g = k(k+2) \Big(2(t_s + t_w) + g_a \Big) + (k+1) \Big(2(t_s + t_w) + g_c \Big),$$

$$C_k' = k \left(\frac{(k + 1)}{2} g_a + \frac{(k - 1)}{2} + g_c \right),$$

and $\bar{h} = (t_s, t_w)^t$, $\bar{c} = (c_1, c_2)^t$ with $c_1 = k^2 + 3k + 2$ and $c_2 = k^2 + (n + 1)k + n$. The expression for V is

a quadratic polynomial in p. Thus for a fixed k, the fastest growing term is the leading term. The leading term in V comes from creating and applying Givens rotations on processors logically connected in a ring. In the test problem considered here, $N_z \approx 6Kn$. Thus $W \approx Kn(2k^2 + 11k + 9) + C_k$. By substituting the expressions for V and W into equation (3), the relation can be derived for K:

$$K \approx e \times \left[\frac{C_g}{n\left(2k^2 + 11k + 9 - e(k+1)t_w\right)} p^2 \right.$$

$$\left. + \frac{\bar{h}^t \bar{c} + C_k'}{n\left(2k^2 + 11k + 9 - e(k+1)t_w\right)} p \right]. \quad (7)$$

Note that since the term containing C_k is small and has no dependence on either K or p, it does not appear in equation (7).

If one considers the GMRES(k) solution process as consisting of l restart cycles and including the computation of the initial residual r_0 (which requires one matrix-vector product and one subtraction), then equation (7) takes the following form

$$l \times Kn \left[2k^2 + 11k + 9 - e(k+1)t_w \right]$$

$$+ Kn(7 - et_w) \approx l \times e \times \left[C_g p^2 + (\bar{h}^t \bar{c} + C_k') p \right].$$

4. Numerical Experiments

The behavior of six different parallel systems has been studied. An algorithm component of each parallel system is either GMRES(k) with HG orthogonalization or GMRES(k) with MHG orthogonalization, denoted by HG_ and MHG_, respectively. An architecture component is one of three parallel computers: IBM SP2, Cray T3E, or Intel Paragon, denoted by the characters S, T, or P, respectively, appended to HG_ and MHG_. To examine the isoefficiency scalability of these parallel systems, the (processor number, problem size) pairs with the same efficiency were selected. For the efficiency computation, the parallel time needed to perform two GMRES(k) restart cycles and the initial residual r_0 computation by a parallel system was recorded as well as the time for executing the same algorithm on a uniprocessor.

4.1. Machine-dependent constants

To calibrate the expression of the isoefficiency function, the constants t_c, t_s, and t_w are determined for the target parallel computers. Their numerical values are obtained using simple appropriate models, for which a sufficient amount of empirical data can be collected to estimate accurately these values. The time t_c needed to perform a floating point operation is obtained as the parameter of a linear regression model $T_1 = t_c W'$, where W' includes an operation count for W and additional terms capturing the effects of memory hierarchy operations when solving large scale problems by a sequential algorithm. Clearly, the value of W' differs from one parallel architecture to another depending on such factors as the memory size and the interface mechanism among memory layers and processor. The amount of time that accounts for the memory hierarchy operations can often be modeled only by studying particular cases of a problem solved on a given architecture. On supercomputers with small cache size and a centralized I/O mechanism, such as the Intel Paragon (16KB of level-one on-board data cache), slow memory (paging) operations affect the overall computation time considerably. In a given sequential algorithm, this effect is noticeable already for medium-size ($N \approx 5000$) problems. Thus the cost of memory accesses (the cost of load/store operations) to compute a floating point value is added to the overall number of operations performed by the sequential algorithm. To perform a floating point operation, two loads from slow memory and one store operation are needed in the worst case.

Observation of the performance of the sequential algorithm on the IBM SP2 also suggests that a portion of its execution time is spent on fetching data from a slower memory. An IBM SP2 processor has a significant amount of data cache (64KB and 256KB for Models 390 and 590, respectively), but this cache is not placed on chip. Thus, its hit time is rather large. Solution of large scientific problems usually incurs high cache miss rate causing miss penalty affect significantly the execution time. Such an affect is especially pronounces in the architectures, such as IBM SP2 Model 390 and 590, without a two-level cache. Similarly to the Intel Paragon, the useful work W on the IBM SP2 was augmented by the cost of the load and store operations. The total work of a sequential algorithm W' is approximately equal to $3\left[(k+1)N_z + N(2k^2 + 5k + 3) + C_k\right]$ on the Intel Paragon and IBM SP2.

On the other hand, each processor of the Cray T3E is coupled with 8KB of data cache and a 96KB of the level-two data cache. In addition, there are another 4MB of on-board data cache. This is enough cache capacity to hold all the floating point data of the problem sizes considered here with a high cache hit rate. Thus, $W' \approx W$ is acceptable in this case.

The communication start-up time and the transmission time of a double precision number are determined from a communication cost model $T_{comm} = t_s + t_w L$, where T_{comm} is the response variable and L is the predictor variable. This model estimates the communication time T_{comm} between two processors under the assumption that the time required to send a message from one processor to another is independent of processor location and the number of other processors that might be communicating at the same time. The experimental data were gathered from measuring the time T'_{comm} needed to exchange a message between two processors ($T'_{comm} = 2T_{comm}$).

For the IBM SP2, the linear regression $T_1 = 0.024W'$ models the uniprocessor CPU time with the standard deviation of errors equal to 1.84. The regression explains 81% of the variation in T_1, because the coefficient of determination of this model is 0.81. For the linear regression $T_{comm} = 69 + 0.45L$, the standard deviation of errors is 9.6 and the coefficient of determination is 0.97.

For the Intel Paragon, the linear model is $T_1 = 0.33W'$ with the standard deviation of errors equal to 2.25. The regression explains 99% of the variation in T_1. The standard deviation of values T_{comm} observed in each repetition of the experiment was very large, which is characteristic to the Intel Paragon design. Nevertheless, if the message length is known or lies within a certain range, some constant value of T_{comm} can be estimated by the linear regression within that specific range. In particular, if a small array of double precision constants is transmitted, the communication latency can be approximated by the start-up time, i.e., $T_{comm} = 605\mu s$.

For the Cray T3E, the linear model is $T_1 = 0.019W'$ with the standard deviation of errors equal to 0.07. The regression explains 99% of the variation in T_1. To estimate the communication time T_{comm}, the linear regression $T_{comm} = 50 + 0.16L$ is obtained. For this regression, the standard deviation of errors is 6.3 and the coefficient of determination is 0.91.

As a result, the times spent for computing a million floating point operations are 0.024s, 0.33s, and 0.019s for the IBM SP2, Intel Paragon, and Cray T3E, respectively. The reciprocal of t_c defines uniprocessor computing rates of 41.6 Mflop/s, 3.0 Mflop/s, and 53 Mflop/s, correspondingly. Start-up–transmission time pairs (in microseconds) are (69, 0.45) and (50, 0.16) for the IBM SP2 and Cray T3E, respectively.

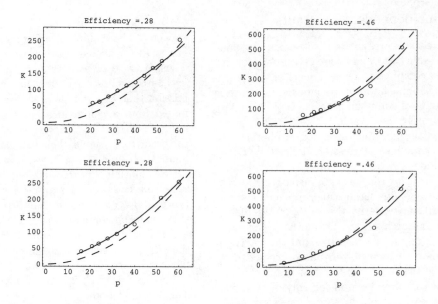

Figure 4. Isoefficiency curves for HG_P (k = 15, top) and MHG_P (k = 15, bottom). Dashed line — theoretical; solid line — fit to data.

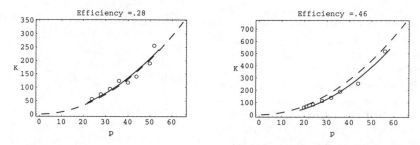

Figure 5. Isoefficiency curves for HG_P (k = 35). Dashed line — theoretical; solid line — fit to data.

4.2. Isoefficiency on the Intel Paragon

Least squares fits to HG_P data in Figure 4 (top) for efficiencies .28, and .46 with $k = 15$, respectively, are $0.03p^2 + 1.98p$ and $0.13p^2 + 0.05p$. Least squares fits to MHG_P data in Figure 4 (bottom) for efficiencies .28, and .46 with $k = 15$, respectively, are $0.05p^2 + 1.58p$ and $0.13p^2 + 0.54p$. Predicted isoefficiency functions for the same efficiences and value of k, respectively, are $0.07p^2 + 0.04p$ and $0.15p^2 + 0.08p$.

Least squares fits to HG_P data in Figure 5 for efficiencies .28, and .46 with $k = 35$, respectively, are $0.08p^2 + 0.28p$ and $0.18p^2 - 1.14p$. Predicted isoefficiency functions for the same efficiences and $k = 35$, respectively, are $0.08p^2 + 0.04p$ and $0.18p^2 + 0.09p$. For the Intel Paragon parallel systems, each least squares approximation grows similarly to the corresponding predicted isoefficiency. Thus, the same function can be used to estimate the isoefficiency scalabilities of MHG_P and HG_P. As reflected in the form of the

isoefficiency function, the larger the efficiency to be maintained, the larger the increase in the problem size required with scaling of an architecture component.

When the restart parameter k increases, the leading term coefficient also increases. This variation in the isoefficiency function value is in agreement with consideration of the whole restart cycle in the isoefficiency analysis of GMRES(k), which differs in this sense from the analysis of the preconditioned conjugate gradient method conducted in [6] for a single iteration of the method.

In the case of problem size scaling considered here, changing matrix dimensions (K times) can lead to a variation in test problem difficulty as well as in its size. This often happens in practical applications, such as postbuckling analysis of structures, with increase in problem size. By definition, adaptive GMRES(k) proceeds qualitatively differently on different problems. Therefore, for adaptive GMRES(k), the operation count of the full convergence history (or of the convergence history until the maximum subspace dimension

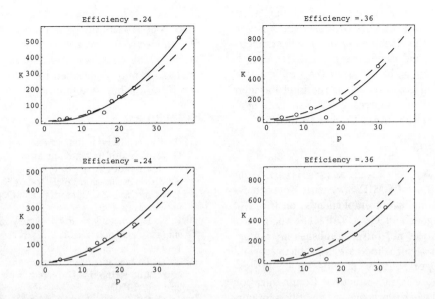

Figure 6. Isoefficiency curves for HG_T (k = 15, top) and MHG_T (k = 15, bottom). Dashed line — theoretical; solid line — fit to data.

is reached) represents the useful work to be considered in the isoefficiency analysis. Otherwise, since it is not known in advance when increases in k occur during the solution process, the isoefficiency characteristics of adaptive GMRES(k) are unpredictable [12]. Variation in the Krylov subspace dimension makes the scalability analysis of the adaptive GMRES(k) algorithm more complicated than the analysis of the conjugate gradient method [6], where an operation count and parallel overhead per iteration is sufficient to derive an isoefficiency function. Likewise, the definition of both useful work and parallel overhead differ from their expressions in the analysis of GMRES(k), which can be performed for a particular subspace dimension k and a particular operation count of a GMRES iteration.

4.3. Isoefficiency on the IBM SP2

Least squares fits f_E of a quadratic polynomial to HG_S data for efficiencies .14, .22, .34, and .42 with $k = 15$, respectively, are $0.17p^2 - 1.11p$, $0.31p^2 - 4.15p$, $0.48p^2 - 6.06p$, and $0.74p^2 - 7.42p$. Least squares fits to MHG_S data for efficiencies .14, .22, .34, and .42 with $k = 15$, respectively, are $0.10p^2 + 5.15p$, $0.17p^2 + 3.14p$, $0.40p^2 - 1.17p$, and $0.56p^2 - 4.31p$. The shapes of the isoefficiency curves for the IBM SP2 are similar to those displayed in Figures 4 and 5. Predicted isoefficiency functions for the same efficiences and the same value of k, respectively, are $0.13p^2 + 0.07p$, $0.23p^2 + 0.13p$, $0.42p^2 + 0.23p$, $0.58p^2 + 0.33p$. Least squares fits to MHG_S data for efficiencies .22 and

.42 and $k = 25$, respectively, are $0.24p^2 + 2.03p$ and $0.75p^2 - 5.06p$. Predicted isoefficiency functions, respectively, are $0.26p^2 + 0.14p$ and $0.66p^2 + 0.36p$. Each least squares approximation grows according to the corresponding predicted isoefficiency.

4.4. Isoefficiency on the Cray T3E

Least squares fits to HG_T data in Figure 6 (top) for efficiencies .24 and .36, respectively, are $0.45p^2 - 1.87p$ and $0.70p^2 - 5.36p$. Least squares fits to MHG_T data in Figure 6 (bottom) for efficiencies .24 and .36, respectively, are $0.32p^2 + 1.87p$ and $0.58p^2 - 2.71p$. Predicted isoefficiency functions for the same efficiences, respectively, are $0.33p^2 + 0.18p$ and $0.59p^2 + 0.32p$. For the Cray T3E parallel systems, each least squares fit grows similarly to the corresponding predicted isoefficiency. Since the architectures considered here have different values of machine-dependent constants, the corresponding isoefficiency functions have different coefficients, even though they include terms of the same order. For example, the isoefficiency function f_{E_T} on the Cray T3E differs significantly from the isoefficiency function f_{E_S} on the IBM SP2. In particular, for $E = 0.42$, $f_{E_T} = 0.76p^2 + 0.48p$ and $f_{E_S} = 0.58p^2 + 0.33p$. The coefficient of the leading term of f_{E_T} is larger than that of f_{E_S} since the computing rate $1/t_c$ on the Cray T3E is faster than on the IBM SP2, while the improvement in t_s and t_w is not sufficient to hide the communication latency. Hence, the idling time on the Cray T3E is larger than on the IBM SP2. The isoefficiency function of the Paragon architecture presents the case when moderate values for *all* the machine-dependent constants involved result in good isoefficiency scalability characteristics. However, with scaling of the problem size, less powerful architectures, such as the Intel Paragon, tend to exhaust their resources faster than more powerful ones, such as the Cray T3E and IBM SP2.

5. Conclusions

In this paper, the isoefficiency analysis is carried out for parallel versions of GMRES(k) with Householder reflection orthogonalization implemented on the IBM SP2, Intel Paragon, and Cray T3E. The theoretical part of this analysis not only establishes an asymptotic relation between the increase in problem size and number of processors, but also provides an analytic expression for the isoefficiency function. Communication and nonessential work overheads are identified for parallel GMRES(k) applied to solve a real-world circuit simulation problem distributed among processors in a block-striped fashion. For vertex-based partitioning of the problem, the theoretical overhead is claimed to be the same under certain assumptions on load balancing by a partitioning algorithm. Thus, the same isoefficiency function is derived for the parallel GMRES(k) implementations used with each of these two partitioning schemes. On target parallel architectures, experimental results support the claim and match closely predicted isoefficiency functions. Both theoretical and experimental results show that the isoefficiency function is a quadratic polynomial with a small leading term coefficient, which implies that the given parallel GMRES(k) implementations are reasonably scalable on the given parallel architectures. In general, a parallel algorithm is considered scalable if the isoefficiency function (in any form) exists; that is, given a parallel architecture and a fixed efficiency value, the amount of useful work in a given algorithm can be determined such that a given parallel system achieves the desired efficiency. For adaptive GMRES(k), the results indicate a strong dependency of the efficiency of a parallel version of the method on the variability in problem difficulty when problems are scaled. Thus a measure of the problem difficulty has to be a parameter of a scaling procedure, or scalable preconditioning has to be applied to normalize the problem difficulty with increasing problem size, or isoefficiency is not a meaningful concept for adaptive algorithms.

Because of resource saturation when useful work scales up, there is an upper bound on the problem size beyond which the sequential execution time is affected by memory hierarchy operations. In this case, the time measurement of solving large problems on a uniprocessor may impede the isoefficiency analysis. The efficiency becomes greater than one and the relation (1) between the useful work and the parallel overhead cannot be applied to study scalability of an algorithm-machine combination.

References

[1] Å. Björck. Solving linear least squares problems by Gram-Schmidt orthogonalization. *BIT*, 7:1–21, 1967.

[2] C. H. Bischof and P. T. P. Tang. Robust incremental condition estimation. *Tech. Rep. CS-91-133, LAPACK Working Note 33*, Computer Sci. Dept., Univ. of Tennessee, May, 1991.

[3] P. N. Brown and H. F. Walker. GMRES on (nearly) singular systems. *SIAM J. Matrix Anal. Appl.*, 18(1):37–51, January 1997.

[4] G. H. Golub and C. F. Van Loan. *Matrix Computations*. Johns Hopkins University Press, Baltimore MD, 2nd ed., 1989.

[5] A. Y. Grama, A. Gupta, and V. Kumar. Isoefficiency: Measuring the scalability of parallel algorithms and architectures. *IEEE Parallel and Distrib. Technol.*, 1:12–21, 1993.

[6] A. Gupta, and V. Kumar. Performance and scalability of preconditioned conjugate methods on parallel computers. *IEEE Trans. Parallel and Distrib. Systems*, 6:455–469, 1995.

[7] G. Karypis and V. Kumar. MeTiS: Unstructured graph partitioning and sparse matrix ordering system. *User's Guide—Version 2.0*, Dept. of Computer Sci., Univ. of Minnesota, Minneapolis MN 55455, 1995.

[8] G.-C. Lo and Y. Saad. Iterative solution of general sparse linear systems on clusters of workstations. *Tech. Report, UMSI 96/117*, Supercomputer Institute, Univ. of Minnesota, 1200 S. Washington Ave., Minneapolis MN 55415, August 1996.

[9] Y. Saad and M. H. Schultz. GMRES: a generalized minimal residual algorithm for solving nonsymmetric linear systems. *SIAM J. Sci. Stat. Comput.*, 7:856–869, 1986.

[10] R. B. Sidje. Alternatives for parallel Krylov subspace basis computation. *Numer. Linear Algebra Appl.*, 4:305–331, 1997.

[11] J. P. Singh, J. L. Hennessy, and A. Gupta. Scaling parallel programs for multiprocessors: methodology and examples. *Computer*, 7:42–50, 1993.

[12] M. Sosonkina. Parallel sparse linear algebra for homotopy methods. *Ph.D. Thesis*, Computer Sci. Dept., Virginia Tech, Blacksburg VA 24061, September 1997.

[13] M. Sosonkina, L. T. Watson, R. K. Kapania, and H. F. Walker. A new adaptive GMRES algorithm for achieving high accuracy. *Numer. Linear Algebra Appl.*, accepted.

[14] H. A. van der Vorst and C. Vuik. The superlinear convergence behaviour of GMRES. *J. Comp. Appl. Math.*, 48:327–341, 1993.

[15] H. F. Walker. Implementation of the GMRES method using Householder Transformations. *SIAM J. Sci. Stat. Comput.*, 9:152–163, 1988.

Reducing the Synchronization Overhead in Parallel Nonsymmetric Krylov Algorithms on MIMD Machines

Muthucumaru Maheswaran, Kevin J. Webb, and Howard Jay Siegel
Parallel Processing Laboratory
School of Electrical and Computer Engineering
Purdue University
West Lafayette, IN 47907-1285 USA
E-mail: {maheswar, webb, hj}@ecn.purdue.edu

Abstract

By considering electromagnetic scattering problems as examples, a study of the performance and scalability of the conjugate gradient squared (CGS) algorithm on two MIMD machines is presented. A modified CGS (MCGS) algorithm, where the synchronization overhead is effectively reduced by a factor of two, is proposed in this paper. This is achieved by changing the computation sequence in the CGS algorithm. Both experimental and theoretical analyses were performed to investigate the impact of this modification on the overall execution time.

1. Introduction

This is an application-driven study of solutions to linear systems of equations ($\mathbf{Ax} = \mathbf{b}$) on MIMD parallel machines. The application being considered is the finite element method (FEM) modeling of open-region electromagnetic problems in the frequency domain [5, 6]. The matrices obtained in this problem are very large, very sparse, nonsymmetric, and have complex-valued elements. The challenge is to be able to solve very large order problems effectively.

The conjugate gradient squared (CGS) algorithm [13] is used for the solution of the linear system. This study focuses on the performance and scalability of this algorithm on MIMD machines by examining the synchronization and communication overheads, and is summarized from [7]. The communication overhead is dependent on the sparsity structure of $\mathbf{A}$. Therefore, matrix reordering techniques can be used to reduce this overhead. The synchronization overhead depends on the number of vector-vector inner products performed per iteration of the algorithm. For MIMD machines, the synchronization cost rises significantly with increasing machine size. Hence, for scalable MIMD implementations, the amount of synchronization has to be minimized.

This paper proposes a modified CGS (MCGS) algorithm where the synchronization overhead is effectively reduced by a factor of two. This is achieved by changing the computation sequence in the CGS algorithm. An approximate complexity analyses using a mesh-connected model indicates that for larger machine sizes the performance of the MCGS algorithm may be up to 34% better than that of the CGS algorithm, depending on the machine architecture. For smaller machine sizes, CGS performs better than MCGS. The experimental studies on a 128-processor Intel Paragon reveals that MCGS is about 20% better than the CGS for larger number of processors. The experiments are also performed on a 16-processor IBM SP2.

Because neither algorithm is better than the other for all values of input data sizes and system parameters, a set of algorithms approach is presented (e.g., [12, 15]). This provides a scalable solution scheme for $\mathbf{Ax} = \mathbf{b}$. Conditions for choosing a particular algorithm depending on input data size and system parameters are also provided. Conditions such as the ones developed here to choose between CGS or MCGS are also useful in the area of heterogeneous computing (HC) mapping systems [8]. In HC mapping, the input data size (e.g., matrix size) and the system parameters are varied, i.e., the mapping system estimates the performance on different machines and executes the application on the machine that is expected to yield the best performance. To obtain the best mapping, it is necessary for the HC mapping systems to use input data size and system information to select either MCGS or CGS.

Dazevedo et al. [3] developed two reformulations for the conjugate gradient (CG) algorithm that reduce the synchronization overhead associated with the parallel implementations. Meurant [9] and Saad [10] also discuss the reduction of the synchronization overhead in the parallel implementations of the CG algorithm. The work presented in the fol-

This work was supported in part by the DARPA/ITO Quorum Program under the NPS subcontract numbers N62271-97-M-0900 and N62271-98-M-0217.

lowing sections extends these ideas to reduce the synchronization overhead in the CGS algorithm, which is applicable to nonsymmetric **A** matrices.

Section 2 presents the machine model and notation used to parameterize the algorithms and examines the issues involved in parallelizing some of the basic linear algebra subroutines needed for implementing a Krylov algorithm. A modified CGS algorithm is provided in Section 3 and this algorithm is compared with the CGS algorithm in Section 4.

2. Model and Krylov Algorithms

The analysis of algorithms presented in this paper is based on the distributed memory MIMD machine model. The machine has $\underline{P}$ processors and each processor is paired with a memory module to form a processing element (PE).

The algorithm complexity analysis performed in the next section is for a mesh-based distributed memory MIMD machine model. A simplified model of the wormhole routing in the Intel Paragon [2] was used in the analytical portion of this work. This will cause some differences in communication time predictions from the analytical evaluation in comparison to the experimental results. A detailed model of the Paragon mesh wormhole routing, including the number of intermediate switches used by each data item and the impact of any conflicts at the switches, is outside the scope of this study. The computation is modeled by counting the floating point operations (FLOPs) at the source code level (the C language is used). The following notation is used in this paper: (1) P: number of PEs, (2) N: dimension of the **A** matrix (here **A** is a 2-D $N \times N$ matrix), (3) $\underline{k}$: number of non-zero elements per row of the **A** matrix (for the 2-D problems considered in this paper the maximum value of k is 8), (4) t_{fp}: time for a floating-point operation (at the source code level), (5) $\underline{t_s}$: setup time for message passing, and (6) t_w: time to transfer a single word between two PEs.

The CGS algorithm for the solution of the linear system $\mathbf{Ax} = \mathbf{b}$ is shown in Figure 1 [13]. An initial guess for the solution vector $\mathbf{x}_0$ and an arbitrarily chosen vector $\tilde{\mathbf{r}}_0$ such that $\tilde{\mathbf{r}}_0^H \mathbf{r}_0 \neq 0$ are input to the algorithm, in addition to the vector **b** and the sparse matrix **A**. The convergence criterion is based on the error measure, $\mathbf{e}_n$.

All Krylov algorithms require a basic linear algebra subroutine kernel that implements vector-vector operations, vector inner products, and matrix-vector multiplication. The vector inner product and matrix-vector multiplication operations need inter-PE communications on a distributed memory parallel machine. The **A** matrix is represented using a parallel version of the modified sparse row format [11]. In this format, each row of the matrix is represented as a variable length array. Each element of this array is a record containing an element of **A** and the corresponding

(1) $\mathbf{r}_0 = \mathbf{b} - \mathbf{Ax}_0;\ \mathbf{q}_0 = \mathbf{p}_{-1} = \mathbf{0};$
(2) $\rho_{-1} = 1;\ n = 0;\ \rho_0 = \tilde{\mathbf{r}}_0^H \mathbf{r}_0;$
(3)   **while** (not converged) **do**
(4) $\beta = \rho_n / \rho_{n-1};$
(5) $\mathbf{u}_n = \mathbf{r}_n + \beta \mathbf{q}_n;$
(6) $\mathbf{p}_n = \mathbf{u}_n + \beta(\mathbf{q}_n + \beta \mathbf{p}_{n-1});$
(7) $\mathbf{v}_n = \mathbf{Ap}_n;$
(8) $\sigma = \tilde{\mathbf{r}}_0^H \mathbf{v}_n;\ \alpha = \rho_n / \sigma;$
(9) $\mathbf{q}_{n+1} = \mathbf{u}_n - \alpha \mathbf{v}_n;$
(10) $\mathbf{f}_{n+1} = \mathbf{u}_n + \mathbf{q}_{n+1};$
(11) $\mathbf{r}_{n+1} = \mathbf{r}_n - \alpha \mathbf{Af}_{n+1};$
(12) $\mathbf{x}_{n+1} = \mathbf{x}_n + \alpha \mathbf{f}_{n+1};$
(13) $n = n + 1;$
(14) $\rho_n = \tilde{\mathbf{r}}_0^H \mathbf{r}_n;\ e_n = \mathbf{r}_n^H \mathbf{r}_n;$
(15)   **endwhile**

Figure 1. CGS algorithm.

column index.

For simplicity, assume that the matrix dimension N is a multiple of P. Let the **A** matrix and the vectors be distributed over the PEs in row striped format, where each PE gets $\frac{N}{P}$ contiguous rows, as shown in Figure 2; in particular, PE i gets rows $(\frac{N}{P})i$ to $(\frac{N}{P})(i+1) - 1$. With the data distribution given in Figure 2, any element-wise vector-vector operation can be performed concurrently by all PEs without inter-PE communication. Call the time for an element-wise vector-vector operation $\underline{t_{vop}}$. For the row striped format,

$$t_{vop} = (\frac{N}{P}) t_{fp}. \tag{1}$$

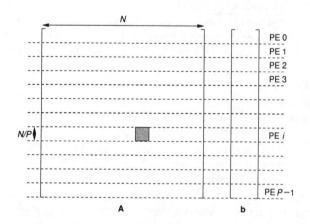

Figure 2. Row striped format.

For the inner-products, the evaluation is done in two phases. In the first phase, each PE computes a local inner product on its $\frac{N}{P}$ elements. Because each PE has $\frac{N}{P}$ elements and for each element a multiplication and addition operation are performed, for π local inner products the computation time is $2(\frac{\pi N}{P})t_{fp}$. In the next phase, the local inner products are combined to form a global sum. The time taken for this phase is dependent on the interconnection network used by the parallel system. In the Intel Paragon, the processors are organized in a $\sqrt{P} \times \sqrt{P}$ mesh. Figure 3, shows one way to perform the combining sequence for a sum-to-one-PE operation in a 4×4 mesh (without the wormhole routing). The labels on the arrows are step numbers (e.g., 0 indicates the transfers performed in the initial step). The global summing operation needs the result on all PEs, hence four more steps are required to distribute the sum back to all PEs.

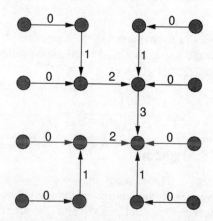

Figure 3. Summing for a 4×4 mesh.

In general, for a $\sqrt{P} \times \sqrt{P}$ mesh, the global summing and distribution can be performed in $2\sqrt{P}$ steps, where each step takes $(t_s + \pi t_w)$. Therefore, on the Paragon the combining phase to form the global sum takes $2(t_s + \pi t_w)\sqrt{P}$. Let the time for π vector inner-products be $\underline{t_{inner}(\pi)}$, which becomes

$$t_{inner}(\pi) = 2(\frac{\pi N}{P})t_{fp} + 2(t_s + \pi t_w)\sqrt{P}. \quad (2)$$

The time taken for a matrix-vector multiplication operation depends on the sparsity pattern of the $\mathbf{A}$ matrix. Consider the situation when $\mathbf{A}$ has an unstructured sparsity pattern and is distributed among the PEs using the row striped format of Figure 2. The shaded square in Figure 2 represents those elements of $\mathbf{A}$ in rows $(\frac{N}{P})i$ to $(\frac{N}{P})(i+1) - 1$ and columns $(\frac{N}{P})i$ to $(\frac{N}{P})(i+1) - 1$. To perform the matrix-vector multiplication operation $\mathbf{Ax}$, PE i needs the values of row r of $\mathbf{x}$ if column r of any of rows $(\frac{N}{P})i$ to $\frac{N}{P}(i+1) - 1$ of $\mathbf{A}$ contains a non-zero element. Thus, given PE i contains rows $(\frac{N}{P})i$ to $(\frac{N}{P})(i+1) - 1$ of $\mathbf{x}$, PE i needs to perform an inter-PE communication for each column j of $\mathbf{A}$ that has at least one non-zero element and $(\frac{N}{P})(i+1) \le j$ or $j < (\frac{N}{P})i$ (i.e., for all non-zero elements of $\mathbf{A}$ that are in PE i and lie outside the shaded area in Figure 2). Because $\mathbf{A}$ is unstructured, PE i could potentially need elements of $\mathbf{x}$ from all other PEs to perform the matrix-vector multiplication.

For the complexity analysis, the worst-case situation of PE i needing $\mathbf{x}$ vector elements from all other PEs is considered. Therefore, an all-to-all broadcast of the $\mathbf{x}$ vector elements is required before each matrix-vector multiplication operation. In a 2-D mesh network of PEs, the all-to-all broadcast can be performed in two phases. In the first phase, each PE broadcasts its $\frac{N}{P}$ elements of the $\mathbf{x}$ vector along the columns of PEs of the 2-D mesh. This operation requires $\sqrt{P} - 1$ steps and each step takes $t_s + \frac{N}{P}t_w$ time. At the end of this phase, each PE will hold $\frac{N}{P}\sqrt{P} = \frac{N}{\sqrt{P}}$ elements of the $\mathbf{x}$ vector. The next phase is similar, but the broadcast is performed along the rows of PEs of the 2-D mesh and each PE sends $\frac{N}{\sqrt{P}}$ elements it now has instead of the $\frac{N}{P}$ elements sent by each PE in the first phase. The time taken for the second phase is $(t_s + \frac{N}{\sqrt{P}}t_w)(\sqrt{P} - 1)$. Therefore, the total communication time is $t_{mcomm} = (t_s + (N/P)t_s)(\sqrt{P} - 1) + (t_s + (N/\sqrt{P})t_s)(\sqrt{P} - 1)$. The computation time per row of the $\mathbf{A}$ matrix is k multiplications and $k-1$ additions, thus, for the whole matrix the computation time $t_{mcomp} = (2k-1)(N/P)t_{fp}$. From the above results, the time for matrix-vector multiplication for an unstructured $\mathbf{A}$ matrix is t_{umult} (<u>u</u>nstructered <u>mult</u>iplication):

$$\begin{aligned} t_{umult} &= t_{mcomp} + t_{mcomm} \\ &= (2k-1)(\frac{N}{P})t_{fp} + 2t_s(\sqrt{P} - 1) \\ &\quad + \frac{N(P - \sqrt{P})t_w}{P}. \end{aligned} \quad (3)$$

For large P,

$$t_{umult} = (2k-1)(\frac{N}{P})t_{fp} + 2t_s\sqrt{P} + Nt_w. \quad (4)$$

The analysis of the algorithms provided in this paper assumes the large P case.

The unstructured $\mathbf{A}$ matrix can be reordered to obtain a reordered $\mathbf{A}$ matrix with a banded sparsity pattern. Let the reordered $\mathbf{A}$ matrix have an odd bandwidth of β (i.e., $a_{ij} = 0$ for $|i - j| > \lfloor \frac{\beta}{2} \rfloor$), then PE i needs to communicate with PEs that are within the range $[i - \lceil \lfloor \frac{\beta}{2} \rfloor / \frac{N}{P} \rceil .. i + \lceil \lfloor \frac{\beta}{2} \rfloor / \frac{N}{P} \rceil]$ to perform the matrix-vector multiplication. Instead of performing a broadcast operation before every matrix-vector multiplication, in the banded case `send` and `receive` type communication is used. Hence, the banded structure of the reordered $\mathbf{A}$ matrix reduces the communication cost, but the time spent on computation remains the same as the unstructured case.

For very large and very sparse reordered matrices such as those encountered in the application that is considered here, β is such that $\frac{\beta P}{N} \le c$ for a small constant c. For the reordered matrices and the number of processors considered here, c is equal to two (i.e., PE i needs to perform inter-PE transfers with PEs $i-1$ and $i+1$). If β does not satisfy this condition, then reordered $\mathbf{A}$ is considered to have an unstructured sparsity pattern and broadcasts are used instead of the `send` and `receive` calls.

The total multiplication time for this case is called t_{bmult} (banded multiplication), which is given by

$$t_{bmult} = (2k-1)\left(\frac{N}{P}\right)t_{fp} + 2t_s + \beta t_w. \tag{5}$$

The parameters derived above are used to obtain expressions for the parallel run time per iteration.

The amount of work done per iteration of the algorithm is approximated by the body of the "while" loop (in Figure 1 for example), i.e., the initialization overhead prior to loop entry is considered negligible. In the CGS algorithm of Figure 1, it can be observed that for each iteration of the "while" loop three inner products and two matrix-vector multiplications are required. Two of the inner products can be performed with a single global summing operation, i.e., the local inner products corresponding to the two inner products in Line (14) of Figure 1 can be reduced in a single global operation (with two operands). Vector-vector additions, vector-vector subtractions, and vector-scalar multiplications are also needed to implement the algorithm. However, these operations are completely parallelizable, i.e., no inter-processor communication is involved in a distributed memory machine.

Let the time taken for the ith iteration of the CGS algorithm be t_{CGS}^i. An expression for the value of t_{CGS}^i can be obtained by counting the different types of operations performed per iteration of the CGS algorithm. Therefore,

$$t_{CGS}^i = \left(3 + \frac{13N}{P}\right)t_{fp} + t_{inner}(1) + t_{inner}(2) + 2t_{mult}, \tag{6}$$

where the $(6 + 13N/P)t_{fp}$ term comes from Lines (4), (5), (6), (8), (9), (10), (11), (12), and (13), the $t_{inner}(1)$ term comes from Line (8), the $t_{inner}(2)$ term comes from Line (14), and the $2t_{mult}$ term comes from Lines (7) and (11) of Figure 1. The number of PEs that result in the minimum parallel execution time, P_{CGS}, can be derived by solving for P in $\frac{\partial t_{CGS}^i}{\partial P} = 0$.

If $\mathbf{A}$ has an unstructured sparsity pattern, then Equation (6) can be simplified by substituting the value of t_{inner} from Equation (2) and the value of t_{umult} for t_{mult} from Equation (4). For an unstructured $\mathbf{A}$ matrix, let the time per iteration of the CGS algorithm be $t_{CGS\_u}^i$.

$$t_{CGS\_u}^i = (8t_s + 6t_w)\sqrt{P} + \frac{(17+4k)Nt_{fp}}{P} + 3t_{fp} + 2Nt_w \tag{7}$$

The number of PEs that result in the minimum parallel execution time, P_{CGS_u}, can be derived as the following by

solving for P in $\frac{\partial t_{CGS\_u}^i}{\partial P} = 0$.

$$P_{CGS\_u} = \left(\frac{(17+4k)Nt_{fp}}{4t_s + 3t_w}\right)^{2/3} \tag{8}$$

Similarly, for a reordered $\mathbf{A}$ (obtained by reordering the unstructured $\mathbf{A}$) with a bandwidth of β, let the time per iteration of the CGS algorithm be $t_{CGS\_b}^i$ and the number of PEs for minimum parallel execution time be P_{CGS_b}. From Equations (2), (5), and (6):

$$\begin{aligned} t_{CGS\_b}^i &= (4t_s + 6t_w)\sqrt{P} + \frac{(17+4k)Nt_{fp}}{P} \\ &\quad + 3t_{fp} + 4t_s + 2\beta t_w \end{aligned} \tag{9}$$

The number of PEs that result in the minimum parallel execution time, P_{CGS_b}, can be derived as the following by solving for P in $\frac{\partial t_{CGS\_b}^i}{\partial P} = 0$.

$$P_{CGS\_b} = \left(\frac{(17+4k)Nt_{fp}}{2t_s + 3t_w}\right)^{2/3} \tag{10}$$

3. MCGS Algorithm

In Figure 1, The element-wise vector-vector, vector-scalar, scalar-scalar, and matrix-vector operations that follow the inner products in Lines (8) and (14) depend on the values generated by the inner product operations. Therefore, the operation in Lines (8) and (14) form two distinct synchronization operations per iteration of the "while" loop. Depending on the values of N and P, the synchronization overhead can cause a significant impact on the actual execution time. The synchronization overhead can be reduced by merging the inner products together so that a single global summing is sufficient for an iteration of the "while" loop.

The basic idea in formulating the MCGS algorithm is to merge the inner products present in the CGS algorithm so that they can be evaluated using a single global summing operation per iteration of the "while" loop. One way of merging the inner products is to reformulate the algorithm so that the inner product in Line (8) of Figure 1 can be combined with that in Line (14) of Figure 1. Let $\mathbf{s}_i = \mathbf{A}\mathbf{r}_i$, $\mathbf{w}_i = \mathbf{A}\mathbf{q}_i$, and $\mathbf{y}_i = \mathbf{A}\mathbf{p}_i$. From Figure 1, consider Lines (5), (6), (7), and (8)

$$\begin{aligned} \sigma &= \tilde{\mathbf{r}}_0^H \mathbf{v}_n \\ &= \tilde{\mathbf{r}}_0^H \mathbf{A}\mathbf{p}_n \\ &= \tilde{\mathbf{r}}_0^H \mathbf{A}(\mathbf{r}_n + 2\beta\mathbf{q}_n + \beta^2\mathbf{p}_{n-1}) \\ &= \tilde{\mathbf{r}}_0^H \mathbf{s}_n + 2\beta\tilde{\mathbf{r}}_0^H \mathbf{w}_n + \beta^2\tilde{\mathbf{r}}_0^H \mathbf{y}_{n-1} \end{aligned} \tag{11}$$

Consider Line (6) of Figure 1,

$$\begin{aligned} \mathbf{p}_n &= \mathbf{u}_n + \beta(\mathbf{q}_n + \beta\mathbf{p}_{n-1}) \\ \mathbf{A}\mathbf{p}_n &= \mathbf{A}\mathbf{r}_n + 2\beta\mathbf{A}\mathbf{q}_n + \beta^2\mathbf{A}\mathbf{p}_{n-1} \\ \mathbf{y}_n &= \mathbf{s}_n + 2\beta\mathbf{w}_n + \beta^2\mathbf{y}_{n-1} \end{aligned} \tag{12}$$

From Line (9) of Figure 1,

$$
\begin{aligned}
\mathbf{q}_{n+1} &= \mathbf{u}_n - \alpha \mathbf{v}_n \\
&= \mathbf{u}_n - \alpha \mathbf{A}\mathbf{p}_n \\
&= \mathbf{u}_n - \alpha \mathbf{y}_n \qquad (13)
\end{aligned}
$$

From Lines (5), (10), and (11) of Figure 1,

$$
\begin{aligned}
\mathbf{r}_{n+1} &= \mathbf{r}_n - \alpha \mathbf{A}(\mathbf{u}_n + \mathbf{q}_{n+1}) \\
&= \mathbf{r}_n - \alpha(\mathbf{A}\mathbf{r}_n + \beta \mathbf{A}\mathbf{q}_n + \mathbf{A}\mathbf{q}_{n+1}) \\
&= \mathbf{r}_n - \alpha(\mathbf{s}_n + \beta \mathbf{w}_n + \mathbf{w}_{n+1}) \qquad (14)
\end{aligned}
$$

Using the derivations given in the Equations (11), (12), (13), and (14), the CGS algorithm of Figure 1 can be reformulated as the MCGS algorithm of Figure 4.

(1) $\gamma_{-1} = 1; \mathbf{p}_0 = \mathbf{0}; \mathbf{q}_0 = \mathbf{0}; \mathbf{w}_0 = \mathbf{0};$
(2) $\mathbf{w}_{-1} = \mathbf{0}; \mathbf{y}_{-1} = \mathbf{0}; \mathbf{r}_0 = \mathbf{b} - \mathbf{A}\mathbf{x}_0; \mathbf{s}_0 = \mathbf{A}\mathbf{r}_0;$
(3) $\gamma_0 = \tilde{\mathbf{r}}_0^H \mathbf{r}_0; \eta = \tilde{\mathbf{r}}_0^H \mathbf{s}_0;$
(4) $\mu = \tilde{\mathbf{r}}_0^H \mathbf{w}_0; \lambda = \tilde{\mathbf{r}}_0^H \mathbf{y}_{-1}; \rho_{-1} = 1; n = 0;$
(5) **while** (not converged) **do**
(6) $\beta = \gamma_n/\gamma_{n-1}; \sigma = \eta + \beta(2\mu + \lambda\beta);$
(7) $\alpha = \gamma_n/\sigma;$
(8) $\mathbf{u}_n = \mathbf{r}_n + \beta \mathbf{q}_n;$
(9) $\mathbf{y}_n = \mathbf{s}_n + 2\beta \mathbf{w}_n + \beta^2 \mathbf{y}_{n-1};$
(10) $\mathbf{q}_{n+1} = \mathbf{u}_n - \alpha \mathbf{y}_n;$
(11) $\mathbf{w}_{n+1} = \mathbf{A}\mathbf{q}_{n+1};$
(12) $\mathbf{r}_{n+1} = \mathbf{r}_n - \alpha(\mathbf{s}_n + \beta \mathbf{w}_n + \mathbf{w}_{n+1});$
(13) $\mathbf{s}_{n+1} = \mathbf{A}\mathbf{r}_{n+1};$
(14) $\mathbf{x}_{n+1} = \mathbf{x}_n + \alpha(\mathbf{u}_n + \mathbf{q}_{n+1});$
(15) $n = n + 1;$
(16) $\gamma_n = \tilde{\mathbf{r}}_0^H \mathbf{r}_n; \eta = \tilde{\mathbf{r}}_0^H \mathbf{s}_n; \mu = \tilde{\mathbf{r}}_0^H \mathbf{w}_n;$
       $\lambda = \tilde{\mathbf{r}}_0^H \mathbf{y}_{n-1}; e_n = \mathbf{r}_n^H \mathbf{r}_n;$
(17) **endwhile**

Figure 4. MCGS algorithm

In the MCGS algorithm of Figure 4, the inner products are all grouped together so that a single global summing operation (with five operands) is sufficient to evaluate them. The number of matrix-vector multiplications in the MCGS algorithm remain the same as the number of matrix-vector multiplications in the CGS algorithm. Due to the modifications, additional scalar-scalar, scalar-vector, and element-wise vector-vector operations are performed in the MCGS algorithm compared to the operations performed by the CGS algorithm. However, these additional operations scale linearly with the inverse of the number of PEs.

The parallel run time for the i-th iteration of the MCGS algorithm is

$$
t_{MCGS}^i = \left(10 + \frac{16N}{P}\right) t_{fp} + t_{inner}(5) + 2t_{mult}, \qquad (15)
$$

where the $(10 + 16N/P)t_{fp}$ term comes from Lines (6), (7), (8), (9), (10), (12), (14), and (15), the $t_{inner}(5)$ term comes from Lines (16), and the $2t_{mult}$ term comes from Lines (11) and (13) of Figure 4. The number of PEs that result in the minimum parallel execution time, P_{MCGS}, can be derived by solving for P in $\frac{\partial t_{MCGS}^i}{\partial P} = 0$.

If $\mathbf{A}$ has an unstructured sparsity pattern, then Equation (15) can be simplified by substituting the value of t_{inner} from Equation (2) and the value of t_{umult} for t_{mult} from Equation (4), giving

$$
\begin{aligned}
t_{MCGS\_u}^i &= (6t_s + 10t_w)\sqrt{P} + \frac{(24 + 4k)Nt_{fp}}{P} \\
&\quad + 10t_{fp} + 2Nt_w \qquad (16)
\end{aligned}
$$

$$
P_{MCGS\_u} = \left(\frac{(24 + 4k)Nt_{fp}}{3t_s + 5t_w} \right)^{2/3} \qquad (17)
$$

Similarly, for a banded $\mathbf{A}$ (obtained by reordering the unstructured $\mathbf{A}$) with a bandwidth of β, from Equations (2) and (5),

$$
\begin{aligned}
t_{MCGS\_b}^i &= (2t_s + 10t_w)\sqrt{P} + \frac{(24 + 4k)Nt_{fp}}{P} \\
&\quad + 10t_{fp} + 4t_s + 2\beta t_w \qquad (18)
\end{aligned}
$$

$$
P_{MCGS\_b} = \left(\frac{(24 + 4k)Nt_{fp}}{t_s + 5t_w} \right)^{2/3} \qquad (19)
$$

4. Comparison of the Algorithms

From the derivation of the MCGS algorithm in Section 3, it can be observed that MCGS and CGS are basically the same algorithms, but with a different computing sequence. Because both algorithms are doing exactly the same calculations, they are numerically equivalent, unless rounding-off errors create a difference. The experimental results presented later in this section further support this claim.

Reordering the matrix $\mathbf{A}$ for bandwidth reduction reduces the time taken for the matrix-vector multiplication operation, but the time for the other operations remains almost the same. Therefore, reordering the $\mathbf{A}$ matrix reduces the total execution time. Because the total execution time for the banded $\mathbf{A}$ matrix is lower than the execution time for the unstructured $\mathbf{A}$ matrix case, the inner product operation contributes a bigger percentage towards the overall execution time. Hence, the optimizations to reduce the global synchronization overhead is likely to have a more significant impact with the banded $\mathbf{A}$ matrix.

Because MCGS and CGS take the same number of iterations to converge, the parallel run time of the algorithms can be compared using the time taken per iteration of the algorithm, i.e., for MCGS to perform better than CGS, t_{MCGS}^i should be less than t_{CGS}^i. Consider the case where $\mathbf{A}$ is banded with a bandwidth β and $t_s \gg t_w$, so the t_w term can be ignored. Using the expressions derived in Equations (9) and (18) for $t^i_{CGS\_b}$ and $t^i_{MCGS\_b}$, respectively, for MCGS to perform better than CGS

$$P > \left(\frac{7Nt_{fp}}{2t_s}\right)^{2/3} \quad \text{for } t_s \gg t_w. \tag{20}$$

While for fixed t_{fp} and t_s, P grows with $N^{2/3}$, for practical problem sizes, as will be seen, P can be as small as 32. Let $t^{min}_{MCGS\_b}$ and $t^{min}_{CGS\_b}$ be the minimum parallel execution times for the MCGS and CGS algorithms, respectively. The value of P_{CGS_b} can be substituted from Equation (10) into Equation (9) to obtain the following expression for $t^{min}_{CGS\_b}$:

$$
\begin{aligned}
t^{min}_{CGS\_b} &= (4t_s + 6t_w)\left[\sqrt{P_{CGS\_b}} + \right. \\
&\quad \frac{1}{2}\left(\frac{(17+4k)Nt_{fp}}{2t_s + 3t_w}\right)\frac{1}{P_{CGS\_b}}\Bigg] \\
&\quad + 3t_{fp} + 4t_s + 2\beta t_w \\
&= (6t_s + 9t_w)\sqrt{P_{CGS\_b}} + 3t_{fp} + 4t_s + 2\beta t_w \tag{21}
\end{aligned}
$$

Similarly, Equations (18) and (19) can be used to derive the expression for $t^{min}_{MCGS\_b}$:

$$
\begin{aligned}
t^{min}_{MCGS\_b} &= (2t_s + 10t_w)\left[\sqrt{P_{MCGS\_b}} + \right. \\
&\quad \frac{1}{2}\left(\frac{(24+4k)Nt_{fp}}{t_s + 5t_w}\right)\frac{1}{P_{MCGS\_b}}\Bigg] \\
&\quad + 10t_{fp} + 4t_s + 2\beta t_w \\
&= (3t_s + 15t_w)\sqrt{P_{MCGS\_b}} + \\
&\quad 10t_{fp} + 4t_s + 2\beta t_w \tag{22}
\end{aligned}
$$

For distributed memory MIMD machines, where $t_s \gg t_w$, from Equations (21) and (22), $t^{min}_{CGS\_b}$ and $t^{min}_{MCGS\_b}$ can be approximated as follows:

$$t^{min}_{CGS\_b} = 6t_s\sqrt{P_{CGS\_b}} \tag{23}$$

$$t^{min}_{MCGS\_b} = 3t_s\sqrt{P_{MCGS\_b}} \tag{24}$$

$$
\begin{aligned}
\frac{t^{min}_{MCGS\_b}}{t^{min}_{CGS\_b}} &= \frac{3}{6}\sqrt{\frac{P_{MCGS\_b}}{P_{CGS\_b}}} \\
&= \frac{1}{2}\left[\frac{(24+4k)Nt_{fp}(2t_s+3t_w)}{(t_s+5t_w)(17+4k)Nt_{fp}}\right]^{1/3} \\
&\approx \left(\frac{(24+4k)}{4(17+4k)}\right)^{1/3} \\
&= 0.66 \text{ for } k = 8 \tag{25}
\end{aligned}
$$

Hence, the best MCGS timing is approximately up to 34% better than the best CGS timing.

This approach will allow heterogeneous computing management systems [8] to adaptively select the best algorithm to use from a set of algorithms. The best algorithm depends on the input data size, N, and system parameters P, t_s, and t_{fp}. For the heterogeneous computing management systems to make the best decision, it is necessary to provide information such as that in Equation (20) to the management systems.

Experiments were conducted on up to 128-nodes of the Purdue mesh-connected Intel Paragon XP/S [2] and up to 16 thin nodes of the Purdue multistage network connected IBM SP2 [1, 2, 14]. The algorithms were implemented on the Paragon using C and NX message passing library routines. The algorithms were implemented on the IBM SP2 using C and message passing interface (MPI) library routines. The global summing operations are performed using the recursive doubling routines provided by the NX and MPI libraries.

Two electromagnetic scattering matrices were used in the experiments reported in this section. The bigger matrix that is referred to as A_1 is 36818-by-36818 and the smaller one that is referred to as A_2 is 2075-by-2075. A_1 is for a 5λ radius circular computation domain, a rectangular $6 \times 0.1\lambda$ perfect conductor scatterer, and TM polarization with an incidence angle of $45°$ with respect to the plate normal. A_2 is for an incident angle of $270°$. Each matrix was reordered to form a banded matrix by a reverse Cuthill-McKee algorithm [4], obtaining two more matrices A_{1b} and A_{2b}, where A_{1b} is from A_1 and A_{2b} is from A_2.

The execution time of the CGS algorithm is dependent on the time taken for the basic operations: matrix-vector multiplication (referred as `matvec`), inner-products (referred as `innerprod`), element-wise vector-vector operations, scalar-vector operations, and scalar-scalar operations. The last three do not involve inter-PE communication (i.e., each PE executes them independently) and will be collectively referred to as `indops`. Figure 5 shows the three timing curves corresponding to `innerprod` time, `matvec` time, and `indops` time for the Paragon.

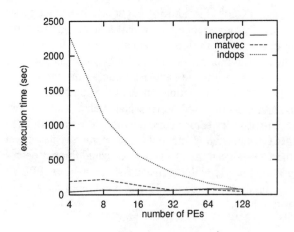

Figure 5. CGS on Paragon for A_1.

410

The `innerprod` time includes the time needed to compute the local product terms and the time needed to sum the local products. The computation time for the local products decreases with increasing P, whereas the global summing time increases with increasing P. Likewise, the `matvec` time includes the time to do the multiplications and additions and the inter-PE communication time needed to retrieve remote vector values. From Figure 5 it can be noted that the timing for `matvec` decreases with increasing P. This is due to the decrease in the computation time associated with the `matvec` operation. Similarly, the time for the `indops` decreases with increasing number of PEs.

For the larger matrix ($\mathbf{A}_1$) and $4 \leq P \leq 16$, the `indops` time is the dominant component of the total execution time. Therefore, any optimizations done for the `innerprod` and `matvec` times will not have a significant impact on the overall execution time. However, as the number of PEs are increased the `indops` time decreases and at 128 PEs the `innerprod` and `matvec` times are nearly as same as the `indops` time. Reordering the matrix $\mathbf{A}_1$ has a reducing effect on the `matvec` time, as shown in Figure 6 for the Paragon. The `indops` and `innerprod` times are independent of the reordering. The overall execution time of the CGS algorithm is reduced, due to the reordering of $\mathbf{A}$ for bandwidth reduction. For the bandwidth-reduced $\mathbf{A}$, `innerprod` time forms a higher percentage of the overall execution time compared to the situation where matrix $\mathbf{A}$ is unstructured. Therefore, the optimizations towards reducing the `innerprod` are likely to have a relatively high impact on the overall execution time when the matrix $\mathbf{A}$ is reordered for bandwidth reduction.

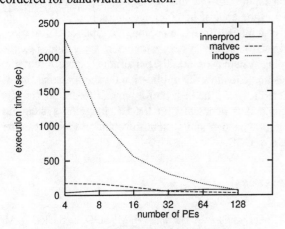

Figure 6. CGS on Paragon for $\mathbf{A}_{1b}$

From the discussion of MCGS in Section 3, it is evident that the modifications performed in merging one inner product with the other one in the CGS algorithm to formulate the MCGS algorithm has introduced additional element-wise vector operations, vector-scalar, scalar-scalar operations (i.e., `indops` forms a higher percentage of the

total number of operations performed by the MCGS algorithm compared to the `indops` performed by the CGS algorithm). For smaller P and larger N values, the `indops` time dominates the other two components, `innerprod` and `matvec`. Therefore, for smaller P and larger N values, MCGS takes more time than the CGS algorithm, as shown in Figure 7 with $\mathbf{A}_{1b}$ for the Paragon. As P is increased MCGS starts to perform better. The same comparison is shown for $\mathbf{A}_{2b}$ in Figure 8. The experimentally derived difference of 20% confirms a significant improvement using MCGS for this set of parameters.

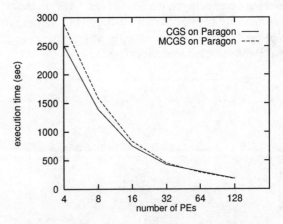

Figure 7. Paragon CGS vs MCGS for $\mathbf{A}_{1b}$.

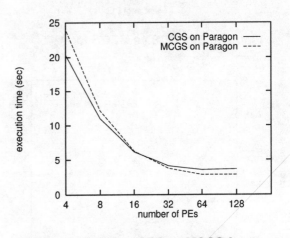

Figure 8. Paragon CGS vs MCGS for $\mathbf{A}_{2b}$.

Equation (20) is used to predict the value of $\underline{P^*}$, where P^* is the number of PEs beyond which the MCGS algorithm should outperform the CGS algorithm. The values of N, t_s, and t_{fp} are needed to predict P^*. The values of t_{fp} and t_s are experimentally determined as 1.078 μs and 112 μs respectively. For Paragon, using the above values of t_s and t_{fp}, P^* is estimated by Equation (20) to be 115 for $\mathbf{A}_{1b}$ and 17 for $\mathbf{A}_{2b}$.

In Figure 9, the MCGS algorithm is compared with the

CGS algorithm on the IBM SP2 for $\mathbf{A}_{2b}$. The PEs in the SP2 are faster and have larger cache memory than the PEs in the Paragon, and the SP2 has a relatively smaller t_{fp}/t_s ratio than the Paragon. Therefore, in the SP2, the MCGS algorithm is the better algorithm for even smaller number of PEs, as compared to the Intel Paragon. A complexity analysis of the algorithms was not performed for the SP2 machine, because only empirically derived communication models are available for the SP2 [16]. From Figure 10, it can be observed that for matrix $\mathbf{A}_{1b}$ that CGS outperforms MCGS, however, as the number of PEs are increased the performance gap between the MCGS and CGS decreases. At a sufficiently large P, the MCGS algorithm should perform better than the CGS algorithm for larger matrices (e.g., $\mathbf{A}_{1b}$) as it did for smaller matrices (e.g., $\mathbf{A}_{2b}$).

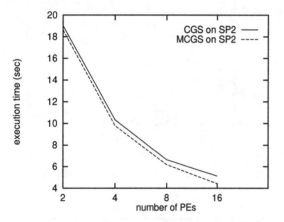

Figure 9. SP2 CGS vs MCGS for $\mathbf{A}_{2b}$**.**

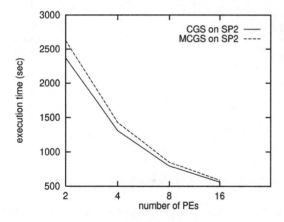

Figure 10. SP2 CGS vs MCGS for $\mathbf{A}_{1b}$**.**

5. Conclusions

A reformulation of the CGS algorithm called the MCGS was presented in this paper. The system of linear equations obtained from finite element modeling of open-region electromagnetic problems was solved using the CGS and MCGS algorithms. This work examined ways of reducing the communication and synchronization overhead associated with implementing the CGS algorithm on MIMD parallel machines.

An experimental and theoretical complexity analysis was performed to evaluate the performance benefits. The approximate complexity analysis of the CGS and MCGS algorithms on a mesh-based multiprocessor model estimates that the performance of the MCGS algorithm may be up to 34% better than the performance of the CGS algorithm, depending on the machine architecture. The experimental results obtained from a 128-processor Intel Paragon show that the performance of the MCGS algorithm is about 20% better than the performance of the CGS algorithm for a 2075×2075 sparse matrix. The experimental results on the IBM SP2 indicate that the MCGS is the better algorithm for the 2075×2075 sparse matrix and the CGS algorithm is the better algorithm for the 36818×36818 sparse matrix. The MCGS can be expected to be the better algorithm for the larger matrix as the number of PEs increases. Any optimization or preconditioning that is used on CGS to reduce the overall computation time can be used on MCGS as well.

Because MCGS is not the best method for all situations, the use of a set of algorithms approach is proposed. In the set of algorithms approach, either CGS or MCGS is selected depending on the values of N and P. The set approach provides an algorithm that is more scalable than either the CGS or MCGS algorithms alone. Conditions such as the one developed here to choose between CGS or MCGS depending on input data size and the system parameters are also useful in the area of heterogeneous computing (HC) mapping systems [8]. In HC mapping, the input data size (e.g., matrix size) and the system parameters are varied, i.e., the mapping system estimates the performance on different machines and executes the application on the machine that is expected to yield the best performance. To obtain the best mapping, it is necessary for the HC mapping systems to use input data size and system information to select either MCGS or CGS.

References

[1] T. Agerwala, J. L. Martin, J. H. Mirza, D. C. Sadler, D. M. Dias, and M. Snir, "SP2 system architecture," *IBM Systems Journal,* Vol. 34, No. 2, 1995, pp. 152-184.

[2] G. S. Almasi and A. Gottlieb, *Highly Parallel Computing, Second Edition,* Benjamin Cummings, Redwood City, CA, 1994.

[3] E. Dazevedo, V. Eijkhout, and C. Romaine, *Reducing Communication Costs in the Conjugate Gradient Algorithm on Distributed Memory Multiprocessors,* LaPack Working Note 56, 1992.

[4] A. George and J. W. Lu, *Computer Solution of Large Sparse Positive Definite Systems,* Prentice-Hall, NJ, 1981.

[5] B. Lichtenberg, *Finite Element Modeling of Wavelength-scale Diffractive Element,* PhD Thesis, Purdue University, School of Electrical and Computer Engineering, 1994.

[6] B. Lichtenberg, K. J. Webb, D. B. Meade, and A. F. Peterson, "Comparison of two-dimensional conformal local radiation boundary conditions," *Electromagnetics,* Vol. 16, No. 4, July-Aug. 1996, pp. 359-384.

[7] M. Maheswaran, *Software Issues on Mapping Applications onto Heterogeneous Machines and the Performance of Krylov Algorithms on Parallel Machines,* PhD Thesis, Purdue University, School of Electrical and Computer Engineering, 1998, under preparation.

[8] M. Maheswaran, T. D. Braun, and H. J. Siegel, "High-performance mixed-machine heterogeneous computing," *6th Euromicro Workshop on Parallel and Distributed Processing,* Jan. 1998, pp. 3-6.

[9] G. Meurant, "Multitasking the conjugate gradient on the Cray X-MP/48," *Parallel Computing,* Vol. 5, No. 3, Nov. 1987, pp. 267-280.

[10] Y. Saad, "Krylov subspace methods on supercomputers," *SIAM Journal on Scientific and Statistical Computing,* Vol. 10, No. 6, Nov. 1989, pp. 1200-1232.

[11] Y. Saad, *SPARSKIT: A Basic Tool Kit for Sparse Matrix Computations,* LaPack Working Note 50, 1994.

[12] H. J. Siegel, L. Wang, J. E. So, and M. Maheswaran, "Data Parallel Algorithms," in *Parallel and Distributed Computing Handbook,* A. Y. Zomaya, ed., McGraw Hill, New York, NY, 1996, pp. 466-499.

[13] P. Sonnevald, "CGS: A fast Lanczos-type solver for non-symmetric linear systems," *SIAM Journal on Scientific and Statistical Computing,* Vol. 10, No. 1, Jan. 1989, pp. 36-52.

[14] C. B. Stunkel, D. G. Shea, B. Abali, M. G. Atkins, C. A. Bender, D. G. Grice, P. H. Hochschild, D. J. Joseph, B. J. Nathanson, R. A. Swetz, R. F. Stucke, M. Tsao, and P. R. Varker, "The SP2 high-performance switch," *IBM Systems Journal,* Vol. 34, No. 2, 1995, pp. 185-204.

[15] M-C. Wang, W. G. Nation, J. B. Armstrong, H. J. Siegel, S. D. Kim, M. A. Nichols, and M. Gherrity, "Multiple quadratic forms: A case study in the design of data-parallel algorithms," *Journal of Parallel and Distributed Computing,* Vol. 21, No. 1, Apr. 1994, pp. 124-139.

[16] Z. Xu and K. Hwang, "Modeling communication overhead: MPI and MPL performance on the IBM SP2," *IEEE Parallel and Distributed Technology,* Vol. 4, No. 1, Spring 1996, pp. 9-23.

413

PLAPACK: High Performance Through High-Level Abstraction

Greg Baker*   John Gunnels   Greg Morrow   Beatrice Riviere
Robert van de Geijn
The University of Texas at Austin
Austin, TX 78712
USA
{gunnels,morrow,rvdg}@cs.utexas.edu
riviere@ticam.utexas.edu

Abstract

Coding parallel algorithms is generally regarded as a formidable task. To make this task manageable in the arena of linear algebra algorithms, we have developed the Parallel Linear Algebra Package (PLAPACK), an infrastructure for coding such algorithms at a high level of abstraction. It is often believed that by raising the level of abstraction in this fashion, performance is sacrificed. Throughout, we have maintained that indeed there is a performance penalty, but that by coding at a higher level of abstraction, more sophisticated algorithms can be implemented, which allows high levels of performance to be regained. In this paper, we show this to be the case for the parallel solver package implemented using PLAPACK, which includes Cholesky, LU, and QR factorization based solvers for symmetric positive definite, general, and overdetermined systems of equations, respectively. Contributions of this paper include new parallel algorithms for these factorizations and performance results on a Cray T3E-600.

1. Introduction

In this paper, we show that by creating an infrastructure for high-level specification of parallel dense linear algebra algorithms, not only is the code greatly simplified, but higher performance can be achieved. Due to the simplicity of the specification of the code, more sophisticated implementations can be attempted, which in turn yield higher performance. We demonstrate the validity of this observation through the use of the Parallel Linear Algebra Package (PLAPACK) infrastructure to code high performance parallel implementations of matrix decomposition algorithms for the Cholesky, LU, and QR factorizations. What is somewhat surprising is that despite the fact that the literature on implementation of these algorithms is vast (indeed too large to properly cite in this paper), we derive new algorithms for these factorizations, which are shown to yield superior performance.

High performance libraries for matrix operations like the various factorizations first became available with the arrival of the LAPACK [2] library in the early 90's. This library recognized the necessity to code in terms of Basic Linear Algebra Subprograms (BLAS) [5] for modularity and portable performance. In particular, it explores the benefits of recoding such algorithms in terms of matrix-matrix kernels like matrix-matrix multiplication in order to improve utilization of the cache of a microprocessor.

Extensions of LAPACK to distributed memory architectures like the Cray T3E, IBM SP-2, and Intel Paragon are explored by the ScaLAPACK project [3]. While this package does manage to provide a subset of the functionality of LAPACK, it

---

*Currently with Lockheed Martin Federal Systems, Inc., 700 N. Frederick Avenue, Gaithersburg, MD 20879-3328

414

is our belief that it has also clearly demonstrated that mimicking the coding styles that were effective on sequential and shared memory computers does not create maintainable and flexible code for distributed memory architectures. The PLAPACK infrastructure attempts to show that by adopting an object-based coding style, already popularized by the Message Passing Interface (MPI) [9], the coding of *parallel* linear algebra algorithms is *simplified* compared to the more traditional *sequential* coding approaches. We contrast the coding styles in [1].

It is generally believed that by coding at a higher level of abstraction, one pays a price of higher overhead and thus reduced performance. While it is certainly true that the PLAPACK infrastructure does impose such an overhead, we demonstrate that one can overcome this overhead by implementing more sophisticated algorithms. While one can argue that these algorithms can also be implemented using more traditional methods, it is the higher level of abstraction that makes the task manageable, especially when a large number of algorithms are to be implemented.

This paper is structured as follows: In Section 2, we explain matrix-vector and matrix-matrix operation based versions of an algorithm for computing the Cholesky factorization of a symmetric positive definite matrix. We show how this algorithm is parallelized and coded using PLAPACK, progressively incorporating more sophistication into the implementation. The final improvement yields a previously unpublished algorithm, which is shown to outperform previously published implementations. In Sections 3–4, we present a similar discussion of parallel implementation of the LU and QR factorizations. In Section 5, we present initial performance results on the Cray T3E, including a comparison with ScaLAPACK. Concluding remarks are given in the final section.

2. Cholesky Factorization

The Cholesky factorization of an $n \times n$ symmetric positive definite matrix A is given by $A = LL^T$, where L is an $n \times n$ lower triangular matrix.

2.1. Basic algorithm

The right-looking algorithm for implementing this operation can be described by partitioning the matrices

$$A = \left(\begin{array}{c|c} \alpha_{11} & \star \\ \hline a_{21} & A_{22} \end{array} \right) \quad \text{and} \quad L = \left(\begin{array}{c|c} \lambda_{11} & 0 \\ \hline l_{21} & L_{22} \end{array} \right)$$

where α_{11} and λ_{11} are scalars. As a result, a_{21} and l_{21} are vectors of length $n - 1$, and A_{22} and L_{22} are matrices of size $(n-1) \times (n-1)$. The $\star$ indicates the symmetric part of A, which will not be updated. Now,

$$
\begin{aligned}
A &= \left(\begin{array}{c|c} a_{11} & \star \\ \hline a_{21} & A_{22} \end{array} \right) \\
&= \left(\begin{array}{c|c} \lambda_{11}^2 & \star \\ \hline \lambda_{11} l_{21} & l_{21} l_{21}^T + L_{22} L_{22}^T \end{array} \right)
\end{aligned}
$$

From this we derive the equations

$$\lambda_{11} = \sqrt{\alpha_{11}} \qquad (1)$$
$$l_{21} = a_{21}/\lambda_{11} \qquad (2)$$
$$A_{22} - l_{21} l_{21}^T = L_{22} L_{22}^T \qquad (3)$$

An algorithm for computing the Cholesky factorization is now given by

- Partition $A = \left(\begin{array}{c|c} \alpha_{11} & \star \\ \hline a_{21} & A_{22} \end{array} \right)$

- $\alpha_{11} \leftarrow \lambda_{11} = \sqrt{\alpha_{11}}$

- $a_{21} \leftarrow l_{21} = a_{21}/\lambda_{11}$

- $A_{22} \leftarrow A_{22} - l_{21} l_{21}^T$

- continue recursively with A_{22}

Note that only the upper or lower triangular part of a symmetric matrix needs to be stored, and the above algorithm only updates the lower portion of the matrix with the result L. As a result, in the step $A_{22} \leftarrow A_{22} - l_{21} l_{21}^T$ only the lower portion of A_{22} is updated, which is typically referred to as a *symmetric rank-1 update*.

One question that may be asked about the above algorithm is what is stored in the matrix after k steps. We answer this by partitioning

$$A = \left(\begin{array}{c|c} A_{TL} & \star \\ \hline A_{BL} & A_{BR} \end{array} \right) = \left(\begin{array}{c|c} L_{TL} & 0 \\ \hline L_{BL} & L_{BR} \end{array} \right)$$

where A_{TL} and L_{TL} are $k \times k$. Here "TL", "BL", and "BR" stand for "Top-Left", "Bottom-Left", and "Bottom-Right", respectively. Similar to the derivation of (1)–(3),

$$A = \left(\begin{array}{c|c} A_{TL} & \star \\ \hline A_{BL} & A_{BR} \end{array} \right)$$

$$= \left(\begin{array}{c|c} L_{TL}L_{TL}^T & \star \\ \hline L_{BL}L_{TL}^T & L_{BL}L_{BL}^T + L_{BR}L_{BR}^T \end{array} \right)$$

so that

$$
\begin{aligned}
A_{TL} &= L_{TL}L_{TL}^T \\
A_{BL} &= L_{BL}L_{TL}^T \\
A_{BR} - L_{BR}L_{BR}^T &= L_{BL}L_{BL}^T
\end{aligned}
$$

It can be easily verified that the above algorithm has the effect that after k steps (1) A_{TL} has been overwritten by L_{TL}, (2) A_{BL} has been overwritten by L_{BL}, and (3) A_{BR} has been overwritten by $A_{BR} - L_{BL}L_{BL}^T$. Thus, the matrix with which the algorithm is continued at each step is the submatrix A_{BR} and to complete the Cholesky factorization, it suffices to compute the factorization of the updated A_{BR}.

2.2. Blocked algorithm

The bulk of the computation in the above algorithm is in the symmetric rank-1 update, which performs $O(n^2)$ operations on $O(n^2)$ data. It is this ratio of computation to data volume (requiring memory accesses) that stands in the way of high performance. To overcome this, one can reformulate the algorithm in terms of matrix-matrix multiplication (or rank-k updates) which have a more favorable computation to data volume ratio, allowing for more effective use of a microprocessor's cache memory. A blocked (matrix-matrix operation based) algorithm is given in Fig. 1(a).

2.3. Parallel implementation using PLAPACK

In PLAPACK, information (e.g. size and distribution) regarding a linear algebra object (e.g. matrix or vector) is encoded in a data structure (opaque object) much like MPI encodes communicators. Thus, the calling sequence for a Cholesky factorization need only have one parameter, the object that describes the matrix. One advantage of this approach is that references into the same data can be created as new objects, called *views*. PLAPACK provides routines that query information associated with an object and other routines that create views. Finally, parallelizing the above blocked algorithm in essense comes down to parallelizing the different major operations:

- Factor $A_{11} \leftarrow L_{11} = $ Chol. fact(A_{11}).

- Update $A_{21} \leftarrow L_{21} = A_{21}L_{11}^{-T}$.

- Symmetric rank-k update $A_{22} \leftarrow A_{22} - L_{21}L_{21}^T$.

PLAPACK provides parallel kernels that perform these operations.

Basic parallel implementation: Fig. 1 (a)–(b) illustrate how the developed algorithm is translated into a PLAPACK code. It suffices to know that object A refers to the original matrix to be factored. Object ABR is a view into the current part of the matrix that still needs to be factored (A_{BR} in the preceding discussion). The remainder of the code is self explanatory when compared to the algorithm in (a) of that figure. Note that the call to Chol_level2 is a call to a basic (nonblocked) implementation of the Cholesky factorization. That routine itself closely resembles the presented code in (b).

Basic optimizations: While the code presented in Fig. 1 (b) is a straightforward translation of the developed algorithm, it does not provide high performance. The primary reason for this is that the factorization of A_{11} is being performed as a call to a parallel matrix-vector based routine, which requires an extremely large number of communications. These communications can be avoided by choosing the size of A_{11} so that it exists entirely on one node.

In Fig. 1 (c) we show how minor modifications to the PLAPACK implementation in (b) allows us to force A_{11} to exist on one node. To understand the optimizations, one must have a rudimentary understanding of how matrices are distributed by PLAPACK. A given matrix A is partitioned like

$$A = \left(\begin{array}{c|c|c} A_{0,0} & \cdots & A_{0,(N-1)} \\ \hline \vdots & & \vdots \\ \hline A_{(M-1),0} & \cdots & A_{(M-1),(N-1)} \end{array} \right)$$

partition $A = \left(\begin{array}{c|c} A_{TL} & \star \\ \hline A_{BL} & A_{BR} \end{array} \right)$

where A_{TL} is 0×0

do until A_{BR} is 0×0

    determine block size b

    repartition

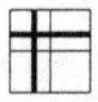

$$\left(\begin{array}{c||c} A_{TL} & \star \\ \hline A_{BL} & A_{BR} \end{array} \right) = \left(\begin{array}{c||c|c} A_{00} & \star & \star \\ \hline A_{10} & A_{11} & \star \\ \hline A_{20} & A_{21} & A_{22} \end{array} \right)$$

where A_{11} is $b \times b$

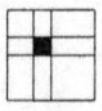

$A_{11} \leftarrow L_{11} = \text{Chol. fact.}(A_{11})$

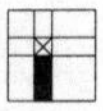

$A_{21} \leftarrow L_{21} = A_{21} L_{11}^{-T}$

$A_{22} \leftarrow A_{22} - L_{21} L_{21}^{T}$

continue with

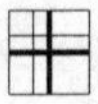

$$\left(\begin{array}{c||c} A_{TL} & \star \\ \hline A_{BL} & A_{BR} \end{array} \right) = \left(\begin{array}{c|c||c} A_{00} & \star & \star \\ \hline A_{10} & A_{11} & \star \\ \hline A_{20} & A_{21} & A_{22} \end{array} \right)$$

enddo

(a) Blocked algorithm

```
PLA_Obj_view_all( A, &ABR );
while ( TRUE ) {
  PLA_Obj_global_length( ABR , &b );
  b = min( b, nb );
  if ( 0 == b ) break;

  PLA_Obj_split_4( ABR, b, b, &A11, PLA_DUMMY,
                               &A21, &ABR );

  Chol_level2( A11 );

  PLA_Trsm( PLA_SIDE_RIGHT, PLA_LOW_TRIAN,
            PLA_TRANS, PLA_NONUNIT_DIAG,
            one, A11, A21 );
  PLA_Syrk( PLA_LOW_TRIAN, PLA_NO_TRANS,
            minus_one, A21, one, ABR );
}
```

(b) Basic PLAPACK implementation

```
PLA_Obj_view_all( A, &ABR );
while ( TRUE ) {
  PLA_Obj_split_size( ABR, PLA_SIDE_LEFT,
                      &b_l, &owner_l );
  PLA_Obj_split_size( ABR, PLA_SIDE_TOP,
                      &b_t, &owner_t );
  b = min( min( b_t, b_l ), nb );
  if ( 0 == b ) break;

  PLA_Obj_split_4( ABR, b, b, &A11, PLA_DUMMY,
                              &A21, &ABR );
  PLA_Obj_objtype_cast( A11, PLA_MSCALAR );

  PLA_Local_chol( A11 );

  PLA_Mscalar_create_conf_to( A11,
       PLA_ALL_ROWS, PLA_INHERIT, &A11_dup );
  PLA_Copy( A11, A11_dup );

  PLA_Local_trsm( PLA_SIDE_RIGHT, PLA_LOW_TRIAN,
                  PLA_TRANS, PLA_NONUNIT_DIAG,
                  one, A11_dup, A21 );
  PLA_Syrk( PLA_LOW_TRIAN, PLA_NO_TRANS,
            minus_one, A21, one, ABR );
}
```

(c) Basic optimizations

```
PLA_Obj_split_4( A, 0, 0, &ATL, PLA_DUMMY,
                          &ABL, &ABR );
PLA_Mvector_create_conf_to( ABL, nb, &A1_mv );

while ( TRUE ) {
  PLA_Obj_global_length( ABR, &b );
  b = min( b, nb );
  if ( 0 == b ) break;

  PLA_Obj_vert_split_2( ABR,    b, &A1,    &A2 );
  PLA_Obj_vert_split_2( A1_mv, b, &A1_mv1, PLA_DUMMY );

  PLA_Copy( A1, A1_mv1 );
  PLA_Chol_mv( A1_mv1 );
  PLA_Copy( A1_mv1, A1 );

  PLA_Obj_split_4( ABR, b, b, &A11, PLA_DUMMY,
                              &A21, &ABR );
  PLA_Syrk( PLA_LOW_TRIAN, PLA_NO_TRANS,
            minus_one, A21, one, ABR );

  PLA_Obj_horz_split_2( A1_mv, b, PLA_DUMMY,
                                  &A1_mv );
}
```

(d) New parallel algorithm

Figure 1. Various versions of level-3 BLAS based Cholesky factorization using PLAPACK.

For understanding the code, the sizes of the blocks are not important. What *is* important is that these blocks are assigned to an $r \times c$ logical mesh of nodes using a two-dimensional cartesian distribution: All blocks in the same row of blocks, $A_{i,*}$, are assigned to the same row of nodes, and all blocks in the same column of blocks, $A_{*,j}$, are assigned to the same column of nodes.

Given that the currently active submatrix, A_{BR}, is distributed to a given logical mesh of nodes, determining a block size so that A_{11} resides on one node requires us to take the minimum of the number of columns that can be split off from the left of A_{BR} while remaining in the same block of columns of A_{BR}, and the number of rows that can be split off from the top of A_{BR} while remaining in the same block of rows of A_{BR}. Once it is guaranteed that A_{11} resides within one node, the call to `Chol_level2` can be replaced by a sequential factorization provided by `PLA_Local_chol`.

Notice that if A_{11} exists within one node, then A_{21} exists within one column of nodes. Recognizing that $A_{21} \leftarrow L_{21} = A_{21} L_{11}^{-T}$ is a row-wise operation and thus parallelizes trivially if L_{11} is duplicated within the column that owns L_{11} (and thus A_{21}), a further optimization is attained by duplicating L_{11} within the appropriate column of nodes, and performing the update of A_{21} locally on those nodes. The resulting PLAPACK code is given in Fig. 1 (c).

A new parallel algorithm: To understand further optimizations, one once again needs to know more about some of the principles underlying PLA-PACK. PLAPACK's approach to distributing vectors is distinct from that of ScaLAPACK. For scalability reasons, parallel dense linear algebra algorithms must be implemented using a logical two-dimensional mesh of nodes [4, 8]. However, for the distribution of vectors, that two-dimensional mesh is linearized by ordering the nodes in column-major order. Assignment of a vector to the nodes is then accomplished by partitioning the vector in blocks and wrapping these blocks onto the linear array of nodes in round-robin fashion. Assignment of matrices is then dictated by the following principle: the *i*th *row* of the matrix is assigned to the same *row* of nodes as the *i*th element of the vector, and the *j*th *column* of the matrix is assigned to the same *column*

of nodes as the *j*th element of the vector. In [6, 11] we call this approach to generating a matrix distribution from a vector distribution *physically based matrix distribution*. A consequence of this assignment strategy is that a column of a matrix can be redistributed like a vector by *scattering* the elements appropriately within rows of nodes. Similarly, a row of a matrix can be redistributed like a vector by *scattering* the elements appropriately within columns of nodes. Naturally, redistributing a vector like a column or row of a matrix can be accomplished by reversing these communications.

Note that as a consequence of the last optimization, all computation required to factor A_{11} and update A_{21} is performed within one column of nodes. This is an operation that is in the critical path, and thus contributes considerably to the overall time required for the Cholesky factorization. If one views

$$\left(\frac{A_{11}}{A_{21}} \right)$$

as a collection (*panel*) of columns, then by simultaneously scattering the elements of these columns of matrices within rows of nodes one can redistribute the panel as a collection of vectors (*multivector*). Subsequently, A_{11} can be factored as a multivector and, more importantly, considerably more parallelism can be attained during the update of A_{21}, since the multivector is distributed to nodes using a one-dimensional data distribution.

It should be noted that the volume of data communicated when redistributing (scattering or gathering) a panel of length n and width b is $O(\frac{n}{r} b)$, where r equals the number of rows in the mesh of nodes. The cost of (parallel) computation subsequently performed on the panel is $O(\frac{n}{r} b^2)$. Thus, if the block size b is relatively large, there is an advantage to redistributing the panel.

Often, the algorithmic block size used in the sequential blocked algorithm is tied to the distribution block size used to assign blocks of matrices to processors. These two block sizes can be conveniently divorced by choosing the dimension of A_{11} to be the algorithmic block size, and performing the factorization of A_{11} and update of A_{21} using the distribution block size.

A further optimization: The multivector distribution is a natural intermediate distribution for the data movement that subsequently must be performed to duplicate the data as part of the parallel symmetric rank-k update [11]. A final optimization takes advantage of this observation. However, due to space limitations we do *not* present code in Fig. 1. We do, however, present performance results for this in Section 5.

3. LU Factorization (with Pivoting)

Next, we discuss the computation of the LU factorization $PA = LU$, where A is an $m \times n$ matrix, L is an $m \times n$ lower trapezoidal matrix with unit diagonal, and U is an $n \times n$ upper triangular matrix. P is an $m \times m$ permutation matrix which has the property that $P = P_{n-1} \cdots P_1$, where P_j is the permutation matrix that swaps the jth row with the pivot row during the jth iteration of the outer loop of the algorithm. Due to space limitations, we will discuss only the blocked algorithm.

3.1. Blocked Algorithm

Given $m \times n$ matrix A, a blocked outer-product based (right-looking) algorithm for the LU factorization is given by
- Partition $A = (\ A_1 \ | \ A_2 \ )$, with A_1 of width b.
- Compute the LU factorization of A_1:

$$P_b \cdots P_1 A_1 = \left(\frac{L_{11}}{L_{21}} \right) U_{11}$$

- Partition $P_b \cdots P_1 A = \left(\begin{array}{c|c} A_{11} & A_{12} \\ \hline A_{21} & A_{22} \end{array} \right)$
- Overwrite A_{11} with L_{11} and U_{11}.
- Overwrite A_{21} with L_{21}.
- Update A_{12} with $U_{12} = L_{11}^{-1} A_{12}$.
- Update A_{22} with $A_{22} - L_{21}U_{12}$.
- Continue recursively with updated A_{22}.

Notice that the computation of the LU factorization of A_1 can be accomplished by a similar algorithm with $b = 1$.

3.2. Parallel Implementation

The parallel implementation of the PLAPACK LU factorization is similar to the new parallel algorithm for the Cholesky factorization. It recognizes that there is an advantage to redistributing A_1 like a multivector before factorization of that panel.

A further observation is that A_{12} could be redistributed like a multivector before being updated. In the implementation that we report in Section 5 we did *not* implement this final optimization.

4. Householder QR Factorization

In this section, we discuss the computation of the QR factorization $A = QR$ where A is $m \times n$, Q is $m \times n$ and R is $n \times n$. Here $m \geq n$, Q has orthonormal columns ($Q^T Q = I$) and R is upper triangular.

The Householder QR factorization does not compute Q explicitly. Rather, it computes a sequence of Householder transforms $\{H_1, \ldots, H_n\}$ where $H_n \cdots H_1 A = R$ and $Q = H_1 \cdots H_n$. Householder transforms have the form $H_i = I - 2u_i u_i^T$, so that the compution of u_i totally determines H_i, which is never formed explicitly. We will outline a blocked algorithm for the Householder QR algorithm, leaving out details, which can be found in standard texts like [7].

4.1. Blocked Algorithm

A blocked algorithm for computing the QR factorization is given by
- Partition

$$A = (\ A_1 \ | \ A_2 \ ) \text{ and } R = \left(\begin{array}{c|c} R_{11} & R_{12} \\ \hline 0 & R_{22} \end{array} \right)$$

where A_1 has width b and R_{11} is $b \times b$.
- Compute $\{H_1, \ldots, H_b\}$ where $H_b \cdots H_1 A_1 = R_{11}$.
- Form WY transform $I + WY^T = H_b \cdots H_1$.
- Update $A_2 \leftarrow A_2 + W(Y^T A_2) = (I + WY^T)A_2$.
- Partition $A_2 = \left(\dfrac{A_{12}}{A_{22}} \right)$ where A_{12} has b rows.
- Continue recursively with A_{22}.

The factorization of A_1 can be implemented similarly by setting $b = 1$ and noticing that the WY transform becomes the Householder transform.

4.2. Parallel Implementation

The PLAPACK implementation of the QR factorization performs all computations on A_1 and forms W and Y while this information is distributed like a multivector.

5. Performance

In this section, we present performance data measures on a Cray T3E-600 (300 MHz).

In our performance graphs, we report millions of floating point operations per second (MFLOPS) *per node* attained by the algorithms. For the Cholesky, LU, and QR factorizations, we use the accepted operation counts for square matrices of $\frac{1}{3}n^3$, $\frac{2}{3}n^3$, and $\frac{4}{3}n^3$, respectively. All computation was performed in 64-bit arithmetic. Version information is given as follows:

UNICOS/mk	2.0.3.10
C compiler	6.0.0.0
F90 compiler	3.0.2.0
Assembler	2.3.0.0
Cray Libs	3.0.0.0
CrayTools	3.0.0.0
Options	-O3
Streams	on

The PLAPACK version used will be released shortly as Version R.1.2. We compare against ScaLAPACK as provided as part of the Cray scientific library. In particular, this means that the ScaLAPACK version against which we compare uses an optimized version of the BLACS (the communication library used by ScaLAPACK) rather than MPI.

Performance of Cholesky factorization: In Fig. 2 (left), we report performance of the various Cholesky factorization implementations. Notice that as predicted, the new parallel algorithm outperforms the other PLAPACK implementations. Careful observation will show that there is a crossover point for very small problems. When comparing against ScaLAPACK, one notices that for

large problems the best PLAPACK implementation outperforms ScaLAPACK. This is in part due to (1) PLAPACK uses a larger algorithmic blocking size (for ScaLAPACK, algorithmic block size is bounded by distribution block size, and thus large algorithmic block size can cause load imbalance) and (2) the specifics of the implementation of the local computation. For small problems, ScaLAPACK outperforms PLAPACK since (1) the BLACS are highly optimized using the shmem library while PLAPACK uses MPI and (2) while the new parallel algorithm reduces communication volume, it initiates more messages, thus increasing cost due to message latency. In Fig. 2 (right), we show performance as a function of the number of processors used, where local memory use is held constant (equivalent to storing locally a $B \times B$ matrix, where $B \in \{1000, 2000, 3000\}$). Note that as more processors are used, performance is maintained.

In Fig. 3 we present only the "new parallel algorithm" versions of LU factorization and QR factorization. Performance behavior is quite similar to that observed by the Cholesky factorization. Asymptotic performance differences between ScaLAPACK and PLAPACK can again be attributed to the difference in algorithmic block size. Differences in performance for smaller matrices are due to the number of messages generated and the fact that the communication library used by ScaLAPACK was optimized by Cray. Figures reporting scalability results for these algorithms were qualitatively and quantitatively similar to the corresponding figure for the Cholesky factorization in Fig. 2 and are thus not included in this paper.

It should be noted that the ScaLAPACK QR factorization performs notably better than the PLAPACK implementation for small and even medium sized problems. This can be attributed to the fact that rather than forming a WY transform to achieve a blocked algorithm, ScaLAPACK uses a variant that forms a transform of the form $(I - UTU^T)$ where T is a $b \times b$ triangular matrix. This variant reduces the communication overhead while applying the transform to A_2. Naturally, we will optimize PLAPACK to use this variant as well.

Performance of LU and QR factorizations: The performance data presented in this section

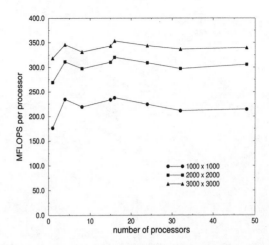

Curve	Algorithm	nb_alg	nb_distr
Global level 3 BLAS	Fig. 1 (b)	96	48
Local Cholesky and Trsm	Fig. 1 (c)	48	48
Redist. panel as multivector	Fig. 1 (d)	96	48
All optimizations	Further optimizations	96	48
ScaLAPACK		≤48	48

Figure 2. Performance of the various Cholesky factorization algorithms.

is intended to show that high-level abstraction does not preclude high performance. As new releases of ScaLAPACK and PLAPACK become available, relative performance of the two packages is likely to leapfrog.

6. Conclusion

In this paper, we have presented algorithms for the Cholesky, LU, and QR factorizations and shown how they can be implemented for distributed memory parallel architectures at a high level of abstraction. Although at this moment there is a considerable overhead for this high level abstraction, for large enough problems this is not as noticeable. Indeed, by implementing more ambitious algorithms, considerable performance gains can be made, when compared to more traditional approaches.

We would like to point the reader to a paper by Peter Strazdins [10], which further investigates algorithms similar to the "new" parallel implementations presented in this paper.

For additional information on PLAPACK, visit the PLAPACK web site:

http://www.cs.utexas.edu/users/plapack

7. Acknowledgments

We are indebted Dr. P. Alpatov, Dr. H.C. Edwards, J. Overfelt, and Dr. Y.-J. J. Wu for helping provide the infrastructure that made this research possible.

Primary support for this project came from the Parallel Research on Invariant Subspace Methods (PRISM) project (ARPA grant P-95006) and a grant from the Intel Research Council. Additional support for PLAPACK came from the NASA High Performance Computing and Communications Pro-

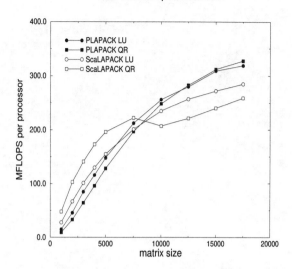

LU and QR performance

Figure 3. Performance of the LU and QR factorizations.

gram's ESS Project (NRA Grants NAG5-2497 and NAG5-2511), and the Environmental Molecular Sciences construction project at PNNL[1].

Access to equipment was provided by the National Partnership for Advanced Computational Infrastructure (NPACI), The University of Texas Advanced Computing Center (TACC), and the Texas Institute for Computational and Applied Mathematics (TICAM).

References

[1] P. Alpatov, G. Baker, C. Edwards, J. Gunnels, G. Morrow, J. Overfelt, R. van de Geijn, and Y.-J. J. Wu. Plapack: Parallel linear algebra package – design overview. In *Proceedings of SC97*, 1997.

[2] E. Anderson, Z. Bai, J. Demmel, J. E. Dongarra, J. DuCroz, A. Greenbaum, S. Hammarling, A. E. McKenney, S. Ostrouchov, and D. Sorensen. *LAPACK Users' Guide.* SIAM, Philadelphia, 1992.

[3] L. S. Blackford, J. Choi, A. Cleary, E. D'Azevedo, J. Demmel, I. Dhillon, J. Dongarra, S. Hammarling, G. Henry, A. Petitet, K. Stanley, D. Walker, and R. C. Whaley. *ScaLAPACK Users' Guide.* SIAM, 1997.

[4] J. Dongarra, R. van de Geijn, and D. Walker. Scalability issues affecting the design of a dense linear algebra library. *J. Parallel Distrib. Comput.*, 22(3), Sept. 1994.

[5] J. J. Dongarra, J. Du Croz, S. Hammarling, and I. Duff. A set of level 3 basic linear algebra subprograms. *ACM Trans. Math. Soft.*, 16(1):1–17, March 1990.

[6] C. Edwards, P. Geng, A. Patra, and R. van de Geijn. Parallel matrix distributions: have we been doing it all wrong? Technical Report TR-95-40, Department of Computer Sciences, The University of Texas at Austin, 1995.

[7] G. H. Golub and C. F. Van Loan. *Matrix Computations.* The Johns Hopkins University Press, Baltimore, second edition, 1989.

[8] B. A. Hendrickson and D. E. Womble. The torus-wrap mapping for dense matrix calculations on massively parallel computers. *SIAM J. Sci. Stat. Comput.*, 15(5):1201–1226, 1994.

[9] M. Snir, S. Otto, S. Huss-Lederman, D. Walker, and J. Dongarra. *MPI: The Complete Reference.* The MIT Press, 1996.

[10] P. E. Strazdins. Optimal load balancing techniques for block-cyclic decompositions for matrix factorization. Submitted to PDCN'98.

[11] R. van de Geijn. *Using PLAPACK: Parallel Linear Algebra Package.* The MIT Press, 1997.

[1]PNNL is a multiprogram national laboratory operated by Battelle Memorial Institute for the U.S. Department of Energy under Contract DE-AC06-76RLO 1830.

Session 6B
Scheduling

Chair: Sajal K. Das
University of North Texas

Optimal and Near-Optimal Allocation of Precedence-Constrained Tasks to Parallel Processors: Defying the High Complexity Using Effective Search Techniques

ISHFAQ AHMAD[1] AND YU-KWONG KWOK[2]

[1]Department of Computer Science
The Hong Kong University of Science and Technology, Clear Water Bay, Hong Kong
[2]Parallel Processing Laboratory, School of Electrical and Computer Engineering
Purdue University, West Lafayette, IN 47907-1285, USA

Abstract[†]

Obtaining an optimal schedule for a set of precedence-constrained tasks with arbitrary costs is a well-known NP-complete problem. However, optimal solutions are desired in many situations. In this paper we propose search-based algorithms for determining optimal schedules for moderately large problem sizes. The first algorithm which is based on the A* search technique uses a computationally efficient cost function for guiding the search with reduced complexity. We propose a number of state-pruning techniques to reduce the size of the search space. For further lowering the complexity, we parallelize the search. The parallel version is based on reduced interprocessor communication and is guided by static and dynamic load-balancing schemes to evenly distribute the search states to the processors. We also propose an approximate algorithm that guarantees a bounded deviation from the optimal solution but takes considerably shorter time. Based on an extensive experimental evaluation of the algorithms, we conclude that the parallel algorithm with pruning techniques is an efficient scheme for generating optimal solutions for medium to moderately large problems while the approximate algorithm is a useful alternative if slightly degraded solutions are acceptable.

Keywords: Optimal Scheduling, Task Graphs, Parallel Processing, Parallel A*, State-Space Search Techniques, Multiprocessors.

1 Introduction

Scheduling a parallel program to the processors is crucial for effectively harnessing the computing power of a multiprocessor system. A scheduling algorithm aims to minimize the overall execution time of the program by properly allocating and arranging the execution order of the tasks on the processors such that the precedence constraints among the tasks are preserved. If the characteristics of a parallel program, including task processing times, data dependency and synchronizations, are known *a priori*, the program can be modeled by a node- and edge-weighted *directed acyclic graph* (DAG). The problem of static scheduling of a DAG is in general NP-complete. Hitherto, the problem can be solved in a polynomial-time for only a few highly simplified cases [1], [5], [7]. If the simplifying assumptions of these cases are relaxed, the problem becomes NP-hard in the strong sense. Thus, it is unlikely that the problem in its general form can be solved in a polynomial-time, unless $P = NP$.

In view of the intractability of the scheduling problem, many polynomial-time heuristics are reported to tackle the problem under more pragmatic situations [12], [18]. While these heuristics are shown to be effective in experimental studies, they usually cannot generate optimal solutions, and there is no guarantee in their performance in general. In addition, in the absence of optimal solutions as a reference, the average performance deviation of these heuristics is unknown.

On the other hand, there are many advantages of having optimal schedules: Optimal schedules may be required for critical applications in which performance is the primary objective. Also, optimal solutions for a set of benchmarks problems can serve as a reference to assess the performance of various scheduling heuristics. Moreover, once an optimal schedule for a given problem is determined, it can be re-used for efficient execution of the problem. For obtaining optimal schedules, techniques such as integer programming, state-space search, and branch-and-bound methods can be used [6], [8], [10], [11], [15], [17]. However, the solution space of the problem can be very large (for example, to schedule a DAG with v nodes to p processors, more than p^v possible solutions exist). Furthermore, the solution space in general does not maintain a regular structure to allow state pruning. Thus, a need exists to explore search-based algorithms with efficient state pruning techniques to produce optimal solutions in a short turnaround time.

Kasahara and Narita [9] pioneered the research in using branch-and-bound algorithms for multiprocessor scheduling. However, inter-task communication delays were not considered in the design of their algorithm and such assumption renders the algorithm not useful in more realistic models. Recently, a few other branch-and-bound algorithms for solving the scheduling problem have been reported in the literature [2], [3], [4]. These algorithms also possess one drawback or the other, making them impracticable except for very special cases. For example, some algorithms can handle only restricted DAGs, such as those with unit computation cost and no communication [2], [4]. Some algorithms use more complicated cost functions but their evaluation of a search state computationally is expensive [3]. A huge memory requirement to store the search states is also another common problem.

Our objective in this paper is to propose optimal scheduling schemes that are fast and can be used for problems with practical sizes and without simplifying assumptions. We propose an algorithm based on the A* search technique with an effective yet computationally efficient cost function. The proposed A* algorithm is also equipped with several highly effective state-space pruning techniques, which can dramatically reduce the required scheduling time. The effectiveness of these pruning techniques are analyzed experimentally. We also propose an efficient parallelization methodology for our proposed algorithm. Since a parallel program is executed on multiple processors, it is natural to utilize the same processors to speedup the scheduling of the program. Indeed, using multiple processors to search for an optimal solution not only shortens the computation time but also reduces the memory requirement and allows for a larger problem size. Surprisingly, very little amount of work has been done in parallelizing scheduling algorithms [13]. We also propose a variation of our algorithm which does not provide an optimal solution but guarantees a bounded degradation of the

† This research was supported by the Hong Kong Research Grants Council under contract number HKUST 734/96E.

solution quality and is much faster. This algorithm can be useful if efficiency, but not an optimal solution, is the primary goal.

The remainder of the paper is organized as follows. Section 2 provides the problem statement. Section 2 contains some of the previous work on generating optimal solutions for scheduling. Section 3 presents the proposed serial, parallel, and approximate algorithms. Section 4 contains the details of our experimental study as well as the experimental results. The last section concludes the paper by providing final remarks.

2 Problem Statement

In static scheduling, a parallel program is modeled by DAG $G = (V, E)$, where V is a set of v nodes and E is a set of e directed edges. A node in the DAG represents a task which in turn is a set of instructions that must be executed sequentially without preemption in the same processor. The weight associated with a node, which represents the amount of time needed for a processor to execute the task, is called the *computation cost* of a node n_i and is denoted by $w(n_i)$. An edge in the DAG, denoted by (n_i, n_j), corresponds to the communication messages and precedence constraints among the nodes. The weight associated with an edge, which represents the amount of time needed to communicate the data, is called the *communication cost* of the edge and is denoted by $c(n_i, n_j)$. The *communication-to-computation-ratio (CCR)* of a DAG is defined as its average communication cost divided by its average computation cost on a given system.

The source node of an edge directed to a node is called a *parent* of that node. Likewise, the destination node directed from a node is called a *child* of that node. A node with no parent is called an *entry* node and a node with no child is called an *exit* node. The precedence constraints of a DAG dictate that a node cannot start execution before it gathers all of the messages from its parent nodes. The communication cost among two nodes assigned to the same processor is assumed to be zero. If node n_i is scheduled, $ST(n_i)$ and $FT(n_i)$ denote the start time and finish time of n_i, respectively. After all nodes have been scheduled, the *schedule length* is defined as $max_i\{FT(n_i)\}$ across all nodes. The objective of scheduling is to assign the nodes to the processors and arrange the execution order of the nodes such that the schedule length is minimized and the precedence constraints are preserved.

An example DAG, shown in Figure 1(a), will be used in our discussion. We assume that the processors or *processing elements* (PEs) in the target system do not share memory so that communication solely relies on message-passing. The processors may be heterogeneous or homogeneous. Heterogeneity of processors means the processors have different speeds or processing capabilities. However, we assume every module of a parallel program can be executed on any processor though the computation time needed on different processors may be different. The processors are connected by an interconnection network based on a certain topology. The topology may be fully-connected or of a particular structure such as a hypercube or mesh. Although processors may be heterogeneous, we assume the communication links are homogeneous. That is, a message is transmitted with the same speed on all links. An example processor graph is shown in Figure 1(b).

The arbitrary DAG scheduling problem is an NP-complete problem [7]. However, a few attempts for optimal scheduling of DAGs under more relaxed assumptions have been reported. Chou and Chung [4] proposed an algorithm for optimal unit-computation DAG scheduling on multiprocessors. However, communication among tasks is ignored. Chang and Jiang [2]

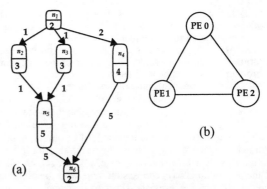

Figure 1: (a) An example DAG; (b) A 3-processor ring target system.

proposed several state-space search approaches for scheduling DAGs with arbitrary precedence relations. Although the algorithm assumes arbitrary computation costs, communication among tasks is also ignored. Chen and Yu [3] proposed a branch-and-bound algorithm for optimal scheduling of arbitrary structured DAG with arbitrary node- and edge-weights. Their algorithm uses a complicated underestimate cost function to prune the solution space. For generating a new state, the function is computed by first determining all of the complete execution paths extended from the node to be scheduled. To take into consideration inter-processor communication, an exhaustive matching of the execution paths and the processor graph is then performed to determine the minimum communication required. Finally, the finish time of the last exit node is taken as the value of the underestimate cost function. Since the problem considered in that study is the closest to our problem, we will compare our approach with Chen and Yu's algorithm.

3 The Proposed Algorithms

In this section, we first formulate the scheduling problem in terms of a state-space search, and then define a cost function used for guiding the search. We also describe a number of effective search space pruning techniques to enhance the efficiency of our algorithm. Subsequently, we present the proposed parallel optimal scheduling algorithm. Finally an approximate algorithm for obtaining solutions with a bounded solution quality is presented.

3.1 State-Space Search Formulation

Formulation of a problem in a state-space search framework requires four basic components: *state representation, initial state, expansion operator,* and *goal state.*

In the context of the scheduling problem, we define these components as follows:

- *State Representation.* State representation describes how a search state represents a partial solution. A state in the search space for the scheduling problem is a partial schedule in which a sub-graph of the DAG is assigned to a certain number of processors.
- *Initial State.* The initial state is the starting state. In the case of scheduling, it is an empty partial schedule.
- *Expansion Operator.* An expansion operator dictates a scheme for constructing larger partial solutions from an existing partial solution. For expanding a search-state, the first node from the list of *ready nodes (*the nodes whose predecessors have been scheduled) is selected. The selected node is considered for assignment to each of the available processors. Each possible assignment generates one new state. The next node from the list is then selected,

and state expansion continues in a similar fashion. The state expansion stops when all of the ready nodes have been considered for assignment.

- *Goal State.* A goal state is a solution state and hence the terminating point of a search. In the case of the scheduling problem, it is a complete schedule.

The above components only outline the search scheme for obtaining a solution. To obtain an optimal solution we need an "intelligent" algorithm to navigate the search space using effective exploration techniques. We use the A* algorithm from the area of artificial intelligence [16] to find an optimal solution for the scheduling problem. In the A* algorithm, a cost function $f(s)$ is attached to each state, s, in the search-space, and the algorithm always chooses the state with the minimum value of $f(s)$ for expansion. The cost function $f(s)$ is a lower-bound estimate of the exact minimum cost of the search path from the initial state through state s to the goal state, denoted by $f^*(s)$. The function $f(s)$ is usually defined by using problem-dependent heuristic information, and is considered to be *admissible* (or *consistent*) if it satisfies $f(s) \leq f^*(s)$ for any state s. With an admissible function, the A* algorithm guarantees to find an optimal solution.

The function $f(s)$ can be decomposed into two components $g(s)$ and $h(s)$ such that $f(s) = g(s) + h(s)$, where $g(s)$ is the cost from the initial state to state s, and $h(s)$ (which is also called the *heuristic function*) is the estimated cost from state s to a goal state. Since $g(s)$ represents the actual cost of reaching a state, it is $h(s)$ where the problem-dependent heuristic information is captured. Indeed, $h(s)$ is only an estimate of the actual cost from state s to a goal state, denoted by $h^*(s)$. An $h(s)$ is called admissible if it satisfies $h(s) \leq h^*(s)$ which in turn implies $f(s) \leq f^*(s)$. A properly defined and tightly bounded $h(s)$ (hence $f(s)$) is, therefore, crucial to enhance the search efficiency. One trivial definition of $h(s)$ is to make it zero for any s; the search, however, then degenerates to an exhaustive enumeration of states, incurring an exponential time.

For the DAG scheduling problem, our definition of $f(s)$ is aimed at making the computation of the function efficient, since the time required to expand can be very costly. We first define $g(s)$ to be the maximum finish time of all the scheduled nodes. That is, $g(s) = max_i\{FT(n_i)\}$. Obviously $g(s)$ is well-defined in that it essentially represents the length of the partial schedule.

The function $h(s)$ is defined as: $h(s) = max_{n_j \in succ(n_{max})}\{sl(n_j)\}$, where n_{max} is the node corresponding to the value of $g(s)$. Thus, $h(s)$, which can also be easily computed, represents an estimate of the "remaining" schedule length.

Theorem 1: $h(s)$ is admissible.
Proof: Observe that the function $h(s)$ is less than or equal to the time period between the finish time of the exit node, which is lying on the same path as n_{max}, and $FT(n_i)$. Thus, we have $h(s) \leq h^*(s)$ for any state s, and hence $h(s)$ is admissible. (Q.E.D.)

It should be noted that the simple definition of the heuristic function $h(s)$ permits very efficient implementation of the states expansion process which is critical to enhance the efficiency of the A* algorithm. This issue will be illustrated again later when we describe our experimental results. Furthermore, notice that both $g(s)$ and $f(s)$ are monotone functions.

The algorithm, conforming to the convention, uses two lists: a list called OPEN for keeping the un-expanded states, and a list called CLOSED for keeping the expanded states.

THE SERIAL A* SCHEDULING ALGORITHM:

(1) Put the initial state Φ in the OPEN list and set $f(\Phi) = 0$.
(2) Remove from OPEN the search state s with the smallest f, and put it on the list CLOSED.
(3) If s is the goal state, a complete and optimal schedule is found and the algorithm stops; otherwise, go to the next step.
(4) Expand the state s by exhaustively matching all the ready nodes to the processors. Each matching produces a new state s'. Compute $f(s') = g(s') + h(s')$ for each new state s'. Put all the new states in OPEN. Go to step (2).

In the worst case, the A* algorithm can require an exponential time and a large memory space to determine the optimal solution. However, with a properly defined admissible under-estimate function $f(s)$, the algorithm is reasonably efficient on average.

3.2 State-Space Pruning

To enhance the search efficiency we propose to augment the A* algorithm by incorporating a number of state-space pruning techniques outlined below:

Processor Isomorphism: If the target system is composed of homogeneous processors connected by a regular network, generation of equivalent state can be avoided (for a ready node with different processors). To identify isomorphic processors, we need the following definitions.

Definition 1: The ready time of PE i, denoted by RT_i, is defined as the finish time of the last node scheduled to PE i.
Definition 2: Two processors PE i and PE j are isomorphic if:
(i) $neighbors_i = neighbors_j$, and
(ii) $RT_i = RT_j = 0$.

The first condition in Definition 2 requires that the two PEs have the same node-degree in the processor-graph and have the same set of neighboring PEs. According to the second condition, two isomorphic PEs have to be empty. This is a strong requirement. A weaker condition could be: $RT_i = RT_j$ *and* the node currently under consideration for scheduling does not have any predecessor and successor scheduled to either PE i and PE j. However, verifying this weaker condition increases the time-complexity of scheduling because every nodes scheduled to both processors have to be checked. Thus, we assume the stronger condition for the sake of reducing the time-complexity in state-space pruning.

For example, consider the task graph and processor network shown in Figure 1. Suppose we want to generate new search states by scheduling n_1 to the processors. It is obvious that we need to generate only one search state by assigning n_1 to PE 0. Exhaustively matching n_1 to all three processors is not needed since PE 1 and PE 2 are equivalent to PE 0 at this search step.

Priority Assignment: When more than one nodes are ready for scheduling for generating a new state, not all them need to be considered. Instead, only the node with a higher priority will be examined for scheduling before a node with a lower priority. The rationale is that less important nodes (those with less impact on the final schedule length) should be considered later in the search process so as to avoid regenerating some of the already explored states. If more than one node has the same priority, ties are broken randomly.

Node priorities can be assigned using various attributes. Two common attributes for assigning priority are the *t-level* (top level) and *b-level* (bottom level). The *t-level* of a node n_i is the length of the longest path from an entry node to n_i (excluding n_i). Here, the length of a path is the sum of all the node and edge weights along the path. The *t-level* of n_i highly correlates with n_i's *start time* which is determined after n_i is scheduled to a processor. The *b-level* of a node n_i is the length of the longest path from node n_i to an exit node. The *b-level* of a node is bounded by the length of the *critical path*. A critical path (CP) of a DAG is a path with the longest length; clearly, a DAG can have more than one CP. Both the *t-level* and *b-level* can be computed in $O(e)$ time using standard graph traversal procedures like depth-first search. The *b-level* of a node without the edge costs is called the *static b-level* or simply *static level* (*sl*). The *t-levels*, *b-levels*, and *sl*'s of the DAG depicted in Figure 1(a) are shown in Figure 2.

	sl	b-level	t-level
n_1	12	19	0
n_2	10	16	3
n_3	10	16	3
n_4	6	10	4
n_5	7	12	7
n_6	2	2	17

Figure 2: The *sl*'s (static levels), *b-levels*, and *t-levels* of the DAG shown in Figure 1(a).

In the proposed scheduling algorithms, the ready nodes for scheduling while generating a new state are considered in a decreasing order of *b-level* + *t-level*. That is, the node with the largest value of *b-level* + *t-level* will be chosen for generating a new state.

Node Equivalence: By considering the equivalence relation among the nodes, states leading to the same schedule length can be avoided. By equivalence we mean the two states will lead to schedules with the same schedule length. By using *b-level* and *t-level*, we can define the equivalence relation between two nodes in the DAG.

Definition 3: Two nodes n_i and n_j are **equivalent** *if:*
(i) $pred(n_i) = pred(n_j)$,
(ii) $w(n_i) = w(n_j)$, and
(iii) $succ(n_i) = succ(n_j)$.

Notice that conditions (i) and (iii) together imply that $t\text{-}level(n_i) = t\text{-}level(n_j)$, and $b\text{-}level(n_i) = b\text{-}level(n_j)$. With this definition, if two nodes are equivalent, they have the same relationships with the predecessors and successors in that they incur the same amount of communication with the predecessors and successors. Furthermore, they will be *ready* simultaneously and the schedule length will be the same no matter which node is selected first. Thus, only one of the two corresponding new states needs to be stored while the other can be safely discarded. For example, in the task graph shown in Figure 1(a), n_2 and n_3 are equivalent. This is obvious with reference to the values of *b-levels* and *t-levels* shown in Figure 2.

Upper-Bound Solution Cost: In this method, we use an upper bound cost U to eliminate a newly generated state. That is, if the state s has its $g(s)$ greater than U, we can safely discard such a state because it can never lead to an optimal schedule since $g(s)$ is a monotonic increasing function. We use a fast heuristic to determine U. The heuristic runs in a linear time and consists of two steps [14]:

(1)   Construct a list of tasks ordered in decreasing priorities for the DAG.
(2)   Schedule the nodes on the list one by one to the processor that allows the earliest start time.

As both steps take $O(e)$ time, the upper bound cost can be determined in a linear time.

To illustrate how the proposed A* algorithm and the state-space pruning techniques work, we apply the algorithm to schedule the example task graph shown in Figure 1(a) to the 3-processor ring shown in Figure 1(b). The search tree depicting the scheduling steps is shown in Figure 3. Each state in the

search tree contains the node chosen for scheduling and the processor to which the node is scheduled. The cost of the state, decomposed into two $g(s)$ and $h(s)$, is also shown. The numbers shown next to some of the states in the search tree indicate the order of state expansion. For this example 26 states are generated and 9 states are expanded. The effectiveness of the proposed A* algorithm is clear when we compare this search tree size with the size of an exhaustive search tree, which contains more than $3^6 = 729$ states.

At the beginning of the search, only n_1 is ready for scheduling and is therefore expanded. Only one state is generated as a result of this expansion. This is because we used the processor isomorphism criterion to avoid generating two equivalent states as initially there is no difference between PE 0, PE 1, and PE 2. This pruning is important since it eliminates a large part of the search space by avoiding the expansion of states situated at a higher level of the search tree. In the next step, this newly generated state is then expanded because it is the only state in the OPEN list. Now four states are generated by scheduling n_2 and n_4 to PE 0 and PE 1. Only two processors are considered because PE 1 and PE 2 satisfy the processor isomorphism criterion at this stage. Note that we could have generated two more states by scheduling n_3 to PE 0 and PE 1. However, since n_2 and n_3 are equivalent nodes by Definition 3, only one of them is chosen for scheduling. Again a large part of the search space is disregarded. In the next step, the state representing the scheduling of n_4 to PE 0 is chosen for expansion because of its least cost. Two states are generated by scheduling n_2 to PE 0 and PE 1. Again we used the equivalence relation between n_2 and n_3 to avoid generating two more states. Since the costs of the two newly generated states are higher than that of a previously generated state, namely the state representing the scheduling of n_4 to PE 1, the latter is chosen for expansion. Next three states are generated because the empty processor PE 2 is different from PE 1, to which n_4 is scheduled, so that processor isomorphism cannot be used. Once again the equivalence relation is used to avoid generating three redundant states. One of the newly generated states, which represents the scheduling of n_2 to PE 0, has the minimum cost, and therefore, is chosen for expansion. As a result of this expansion, only two new states are generated since n_3 is the only ready node and processor PE 2 is not considered due to processor isomorphism. As higher costs states are generated, the search reverts to expanding the left-most state on the second level of the search tree (note that we do not count the initial state as one level).

The state representing the scheduling of n_4 to PE 1 is not generated because it has been visited before on the right-most branch of the search tree. The search then proceeds in a similar fashion and eventually reaching a goal state with a final cost of 14 time units. The path of the search tree representing the optimal scheduling is shown in thick edges in the tree of Figure 3. The final optimal schedule is shown in Figure 4.

3.3 The Parallel A* Algorithm for Scheduling

An efficient parallelization of the above algorithm is non-trivial and requires several design considerations, which will be elaborated below. First, to avoid ambiguity, we will hereafter call the processors executing the parallel A* algorithm as *physical processing elements* (PPEs). The PPEs should be distinguished from the *target processing elements* (TPEs), to which the DAG is to be scheduled. The PPEs are connected by a certain network topology; for instance, the PPEs in the Intel Paragon are connected by a mesh topology.

The initial load distribution phase of the parallel algorithm involves all the PPEs in the system. Every PPE initializes the OPEN list by expanding the initial empty state. Suppose there

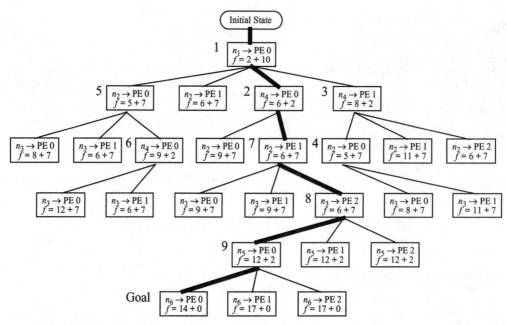

Figure 3: The search tree for scheduling the example task graph shown in Figure 1(a) to the 3-processor ring shown in Figure 1(b).

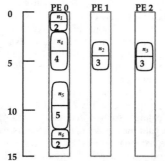

Figure 4: The optimal schedule generated by the A* algorithm (schedule length = 14 time units).

are q PPEs in the parallel machine and each PPE has d neighbor PPEs; for instance, in the case of the Intel Paragon, the value of d is 4. Moreover let there be k states in OPEN. For distributing k states to q PPEs, there are three cases to consider:

Case 1 ($k > q$): Each PPE expands only the initial empty state which results in k new states. Every PPE then gets one state while the extra states are distributed in a round-robin (RR) manner.

Case 2 ($k = q$): Each PPE expands the initial empty state and then gets exactly one state.

Case 3 ($k < q$): Each PPE keeps on expanding states in OPEN starting from the initial empty state until the number of states in OPEN is greater than or equal to q. The list OPEN is then sorted in an increasing order of cost values. Each PPE then gets one state from OPEN in an interleaved manner. That is, the first state in OPEN will go to PE 0, the second state to PE $q - 1$, the third state to PE 1, the fourth state to PE $q - 2$, and so on. The extra states, if any, will be distributed in a RR fashion. Although there is no guarantee that a best state at the initial level of the search tree will lead to a promising state after some expansions, the algorithm tries to distribute the good states as evenly as possible among all PPEs.

Following the distribution, the PPEs start searching by expanding the states. In the absence of communication among the PPEs, some of the PPEs may work on more promising parts of the search space while others may expand unnecessary states, which are the ones the serial algorithm would not expand. This will inevitably result in a poor speedup since the parallel algorithm would be quite inefficient. To avoid this, the PPEs must periodically communicate with each other to exchange information about the costs of the nodes in the OPEN list. In our scheme, each PPE only communicates with its neighboring PPEs to execute the following local load-balancing algorithm:

ROUND-ROBIN LOAD SHARING:

(1) Determine the average number of un-expanded states N_{avg} in all the OPEN lists.
(2) Every PPE which has the number of local un-expanded states is more than N_{avg}, distribute the surplus states to the deficit PPEs in a round-robin fashion.

The duration of the communication period is set to be T number of expansions, where T is initially $v/2$, then $v/4$, $v/8$, and so on, until it reaches 2 which is the minimum we used. The periods are exponentially decreasing because at the beginning of the search, the costs of the search states differ by a small margin. At such early stages, exploration is more important than exploitation and, therefore, the PPEs should work independently for a longer period of time. When the search reaches the later stages of the search tree, the best cost state tends to have a much smaller cost than the locally best ones.

To avoid excessive overhead, communication is performed only among the neighboring PPEs instead of globally involving all the PPEs. During communication, the neighboring PPEs vote and elect the best cost state, which is then expanded by all the participating PPEs. The resulting new states then go to each neighboring PPE in a RR fashion. Once a goal state is found by any one PPE, it is sent to all the PPEs in the system so that the search can terminate.

Using the above mentioned partitioning, communication, and load balancing schemes, we outline the algorithm as follows.

PARALLEL A* SCHEDULING ALGORITHM:

(1) Expand the initial (empty) state and generate a number of new states;
(2) Eliminate redundant equivalent states;
(3) Every PPE participates in the initial RR load sharing phase;
(4) Set $i = 2$;
(5) repeat
(6)   Set $T = \left\lceil \dfrac{v}{i} \right\rceil$;
(7)   **repeat** /* search */
(8)   Run A* to expand the local states;
(9)   **until** the number of expanded states is equal to T;
(10)   Globally exchange cost information and import the best cost state;
(11)   Expand the imported best cost state and perform RR load sharing of the generated states;
(12)   Set $i = i \times 2$;
(13) **until** a complete schedule is found;

It should be mentioned that in our implementation, each PPE only checks for redundant states in its own CLOSED list before adding newly generated states. Although a globally maintained CLOSED list can guarantee no states will be ever re-visited, the communication and synchronization overhead of maintaining the list in a distributed manner can severely limit the scalability of the algorithm. Furthermore, we believe that the states pruning techniques incorporated in the algorithm can effectively discard any redundant states.

When the parallel A* algorithm is applied to schedule the example task graph shown in Figure 1(a) to the 3-processor ring shown in Figure 1(b) using 2 PPEs, the search tree generated, shown in Figure 5, is slightly different. Three more states are generated on the left-most branch of the root in the search tree. This phenomenon can be explained as follows. According to the parallel A* algorithm, both PPEs generate the first two levels of the search tree (note that we do not count the empty initial state as one level) at the beginning as there are not enough states for distribution. One PPE (call it PPE 0) then gets the first and the fourth states, while the other gets the second and the third ones. Initially the period of communication is set to be $6/2 = 3$. Thus, both PPEs work independently until they have expanded 3 states (see Figure 5 for the order of state expansions).

At the time of communication, PPE 0 has fully expanded the right-most branch of the root as shown in Figure 5 (after expansions 1 and 2). For the left-most branch, the states at level 3 (corresponding to assigning n_3 and n_4) are generated. Thus, the best local cost of PPE 0 is 11, corresponding to the state of assigning n_4 to PE 0. On the other hand, PPE 1 has expanded the branch, which contains the goal state, up to the 4th level (corresponding to the states of assigning n_3 to PE 0, 1 and 2). Thus, the best local cost of PPE 1 is 13 (corresponding to assigning n_3 to PE 2).

During the communication, therefore, PPE 0 transfers its best cost state to PPE 1, which is the state of assigning n_4 to PE 0. After the communication, both PPEs expand the best state. However, as a result of the expansion, two states with costs higher than 13 are generated. Therefore, PPE 0 continues to expand the descendant of the best state. On the other hand, PPE 1 reverts to expand its locally best state, the one corresponding to assigning n_3 to PE 2. This expansion leads to generating the parent state of the goal state. Consequently, the goal state is found and PPE 1 broadcasts the result to PPE 0 and the algorithm terminates.

We tested this example on the Intel Paragon using two processors and obtained a speedup of 1.7. Linear speedup is not possible because of the communication overhead and the computation load incurred due to the extra processing in generating more states.

3.4 The Approximate A* Algorithm

According to Pearl *et al.* [16], if a solution with cost bounded by $(1+\varepsilon)$ of the optimal cost is good enough, the A* algorithm can be modified to generate such a solution efficiently. We adopt their notations and call the modified A* algorithm, which is in fact an approximate algorithm, as the A_ε^* algorithm. One more list called FOCAL is needed for A_ε^*. This list contains a subset of states currently on the OPEN list. Specifically, we put only the states s' with $f(s') \le (1+\varepsilon)min_{s \in OPEN}\{f(s)\}$. That is, the costs of the states in FOCAL are no greater than the minimum cost in OPEN by a factor $(1+\varepsilon)$. Thus A_ε^* only expands states from FOCAL. Furthermore, A_ε^* always finds a solution with cost not exceeding the optimal cost by more than a factor of $(1+\varepsilon)$. This is formalized by the following theorem.

Theorem 2: [16] A_ε^* is ε-admissible.
Proof: By definition of FOCAL, the cost of the goal state f_{goal} is within a factor of $(1+\varepsilon)$ from the minimum cost f_{min} in FOCAL. Since f is admissible by Theorem 1, we also have $f_{min} \le f_{opt}$. Thus: $f_{goal} \le (1+\varepsilon)f_{min} \le (1+\varepsilon)f_{opt}$ [16]. (Q.E.D.)

4 Performance Results

In this section we present the performance results of the proposed serial and parallel A* algorithms. We first compare the results generated by the serial A* algorithm with that of the branch-and-bound algorithm proposed by Chen and Yu [3]. We then describe the speedup achieved with the parallel A* algorithm implemented on the Intel Paragon, over the proposed serial algorithm. Finally, we also compare the results generated by using the parallel A_ε^* algorithm with those of the exact algorithm.

4.1 Workload

As no widely accepted benchmark graphs exist for the DAG scheduling problem, we believe using random graphs with diverse parameters is appropriate for testing the performance of the algorithms. In our experiments we used three sets of random task graphs, each with a different value of CCR (0.1, 1.0, and 10.0). Each set consists of graphs in which the number of nodes vary from 10 to 32 (with an increment of 2); thus, each set contains 12 graphs. The graphs were randomly generated as follow. First the computation cost of each node in the graph was randomly selected from a uniform distribution with mean equal to 40. Beginning from the first node, a random number indicating the number of children was chosen from a uniform distribution with mean equal to $v/10$. Thus, the connectivity of the graph increases with the size of the graph. The communication cost of an edge was also randomly selected from a uniform distribution with mean equal to 40 times the specified value of CCR. Notice that as we were also interested in the minimum TPEs required for each optimal schedule, we let the algorithms use $O(v)$ TPEs. However, in practice, the algorithms used far less than v TPEs during the search process because redundant states were generated when the algorithms tried to use a new TPE.

4.2 Results of the Serial A* Algorithm

In our first experiment, we ran the serial A* algorithm using a single processor on the Intel Paragon. We also implemented the branch-and-bound algorithm proposed by Chen *et al.* on the same platform. We measured the running times (in seconds) of both algorithms. The results are shown in Table 1. To assess the effectiveness of the pruning techniques,

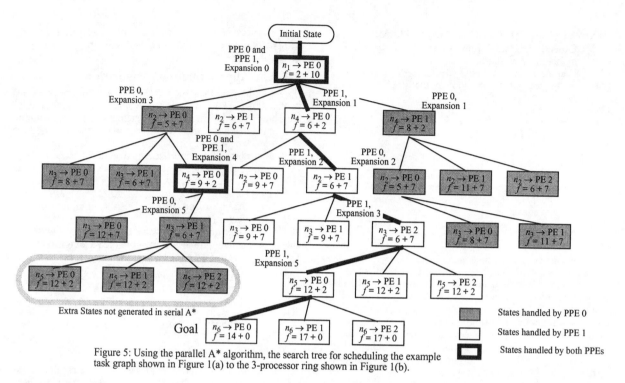

Figure 5: Using the parallel A* algorithm, the search tree for scheduling the example task graph shown in Figure 1(a) to the 3-processor ring shown in Figure 1(b).

Legend:
- (shaded) States handled by PPE 0
- (white) States handled by PPE 1
- (bold outline) States handled by both PPEs

Table 1: The running times (in seconds) of the Chen *et al.'s* branch-and-bound algorithm and the proposed A* algorithm, with and without pruning, using a single processor on the Intel Paragon for task graphs with CCR equal to 0.1, 1.0, and 10.0.

Size	CCR = 0.1			CCR = 1.0			CCR = 10.0		
	Chen	A*$_{full}$	A*	Chen	A*$_{full}$	A*	Chen	A*$_{full}$	A*
10	202	150	120	289	260	191	367	256	204
12	458	295	245	558	410	312	703	537	428
14	1043	675	567	1349	867	682	1873	903	735
16	2781	1523	1209	3218	2098	1543	3965	2014	1689
18	5231	3109	2465	6345	3568	2863	7624	3731	3025
20	13492	7128	5667	16112	9546	6751	17872	9043	7365
22	29484	15680	12098	32367	15785	13257	34650	19754	15324
24	60129	32045	25688	68492	35689	28462	70326	35789	30257
26	139852	74570	59809	142725	80234	63125	153247	89964	68532
28	289092	153473	125687	309356	179835	142568	324687	180053	152371
30	593412	305673	256892	620605	357923	276581	687001	347900	302674
32	—	652489	525788	—	687924	563284	—	701235	598352

the running times of the A* algorithm without state-space pruning are also shown in the middle column of the table.

As can be observed from the values in the first two columns of the table in Table 1 (results for CCR equal to 0.1) the proposed A* algorithm consistently used much less time than the branch-and-bound algorithm, even without the state-space pruning strategies. This is primarily due to the our algorithm's lower time-complexity for computing the cost of each state. This observation reveals that reducing the complexity of the cost function evaluation method itself can reduce the algorithm's running time. The result for a graph size with 32 nodes was not available for the algorithm by Chen *et al.* because the running time exceeded the limit.

Similar observations can be made about the results with CCR equal to 1.0 and 10.0. There is one major difference, though. The running times spent by both algorithms increased with the value of CCR. This is because with a larger value of CCR, the costs of the intermediate states vary more vigorously and, thus, the search has to explore a wider scope in the search-space.

Comparing the data on the second and third column of Table 1, we can see that the pruning techniques reduce the running times consistently by about 20%. One plausible explanation is that for general graph structures, the proposed A* algorithm behaves more conservatively in that it does not prune many search-states by the solution cost bounding strategy. This is because the f costs of some search-states (where some nodes are sub-optimally scheduled) are less than the upper bound solution cost.

4.3 Results of the Parallel A* Algorithm

In the second experiment, we ran the parallel A* algorithm on the Intel Paragon using 2, 4, 8, and 16 PPEs. The running times used were compared with the serial A* algorithm. The results are presented as speedup plots shown in Figure 6. As can be noticed from the three plots, the speedup of the parallel A* algorithm is moderately less than linear, which is very encouraging. An explanation for the good speedups is that during the communication phases, only neighboring PPEs exchange information on the locally best states. Furthermore, the Intel Paragon has a very fast communication network which permits the PPEs exchange small messages (i.e., the partial nodes assignment and cost) in a short time compared with the processing time for states expansion.

We also observe that the speedup dropped slightly with increasing graph sizes. This is because the parallel A* algorithm tends to generate slightly more search states, which are not generated by the serial algorithm. Another reason is that the communication overhead becomes more significant for larger graph sizes. Comparing the three plots, we find that the speedup curves become more irregular when the value of CCR is higher. This is because as CCR gets higher, the parallel algorithm uses more diverged search directions which are then regulated by the inter-PPE communication.

4.4 Results of the Parallel A_ε* Algorithm

In the last experiment, we ran the parallel A_ε* algorithm using 16 PPEs on the Intel Paragon with approximation factor ε equal to 0.2 and 0.5. The percentage deviations from optimal

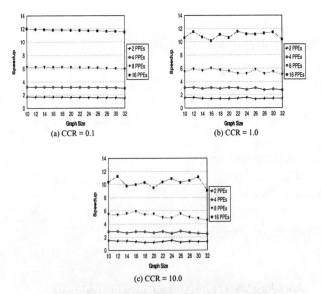

(a) CCR = 0.1

(b) CCR = 1.0

(c) CCR = 10.0

Figure 6: Speedups of the parallel A* algorithm using 2, 4, 8, and 16 PPEs on the Intel Paragon for task graphs with CCR equal to (a) 0.1; (b) 1.0; and (c) 10.0.

schedule lengths were measured and the scheduling time ratios of the parallel A_ε^* algorithm to the parallel A* algorithm were noted. The results are plotted in Figure 7, indicating that the actual percentage deviations from optimal are not as great as the approximation factor in both cases. This is particularly true for smaller graphs, and is due to the fact that the FOCAL list does not exclude the states leading to an optimal goal for a reasonably effective cost function. Regarding the scheduling time ratios, we find that the computation time saved for each case is of considerable margin—ranges from 10 to 40% for ε equal to 0.2 and from 50 to 70% for ε equal to 0.5. Thus, the parallel A_ε^* algorithm is an attractive choice if slightly inferior to optimal solutions are acceptable.

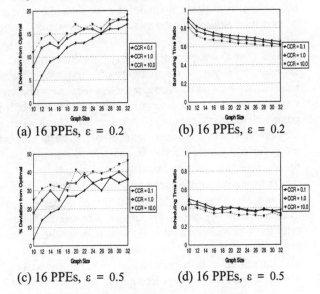

(a) 16 PPEs, $\varepsilon = 0.2$

(b) 16 PPEs, $\varepsilon = 0.2$

(c) 16 PPEs, $\varepsilon = 0.5$

(d) 16 PPEs, $\varepsilon = 0.5$

Figure 7: The deviation from optimal schedule length (plots (a) and (c)) of the schedules generated by the parallel A_ε^* algorithm using 16 PPEs on the Intel Paragon and the scheduling time ratio (plots (b) and (d)) of the A_ε^* algorithm to the A* algorithm with $\varepsilon = 0.2$ and 0.5.

5 Conclusions

In this paper, we have presented algorithms for optimal static scheduling of an arbitrary DAG to an arbitrary number of processors. The proposed algorithms are based on the A* search technique with a computationally efficient cost function as well as a number of effective state-space pruning techniques. The serial A* algorithm is found to outperform a previously proposed branch-and-bound algorithm by using considerably less time to generate a solution. The parallel A* algorithm, using a dynamic load balancing strategy, yields a close-to-linear speedup. Based on experimental evaluation, the parallel A_ε^* algorithm has shown high capability to prune the search-space; thereby reducing the running time dramatically. The A_ε^* algorithm is scalable and an attractive choice if slightly inferior to optimal solutions are acceptable.

References

[1] H.H. Ali and H. El-Rewini, "The Time Complexity of Scheduling Interval Orders with Communication is Polynomial," *Parallel Processing Letters*, vol. 3, no. 1, 1993, pp. 53-58.

[2] P.C. Chang and Y.S. Jiang, "A State-Space Search Approach for Parallel Processor Scheduling Problems with Arbitrary Precedence Relations," *European Journal of Operational Research*, 77, 1994, pp. 208-223.

[3] G.-H. Chen and J.-S. Yu, "A Branch-And-Bound-With-Underestimates Algorithm for the Task Assignment Problem with Precedence Constraint," Proc. *Int'l Conf. Distributed Computing Systems*, 1990, pp. 494-501.

[4] H.-C. Chou and C.-P. Chung, "Optimal Multiprocessor Task Scheduling Using Dominance and Equivalence Relations," *Computers Operations Research*, 21 (4), 1994, pp. 463-475.

[5] E.G. Coffman, *Computer and Job-Shop Scheduling Theory*, Wiley, New York, 1976.

[6] R. Correa and A. Ferreira, "On the Effectiveness of Synchronous Parallel Branch-and-bound Algorithms," *Parallel Processing Letters*, vol. 5, no. 3, 1995, pp. 375-386.

[7] M.R. Garey and D.S. Johnson, *Computers and Intractability: A Guide to the Theory of NP-Completeness*, W.H. Freeman and Company, 1979.

[8] R.M. Karp and Y. Zhang, "Randomized Parallel Algorithms for Backtrack Search and Branch-and-Bound Computation," *Journal of the ACM*, vol. 40, no. 3, July 1993, pp. 765-789.

[9] H. Kasahara and S. Narita, "Practical Multiprocessor Scheduling Algorithms for Efficient Parallel Processing," *IEEE Trans. Computers*, vol. C-33, Nov. 1984, pp. 1023-1029.

[10] W.H. Kohler and K. Steiglitz, "Characterization and Theoretical Comparison of Branch-and-Bound Algorithms for Permutation Problems," *J. ACM*, vol. 21, Jan. 1974, pp. 140-156.

[11] V. Kumar, K. Ramesh, and V.N. Rao, "Parallel Best-First Search of State-Space Graphs: A Summary of Results," Proc. *7th Int'l Conf. Art. Intell. (AAAI'88)*, Aug. 1988, vol. 1, pp. 122-127.

[12] Y.-K. Kwok and I. Ahmad, "Dynamic Critical-Path Scheduling: An Effective Technique for Allocating Task Graphs onto Multiprocessors," *IEEE Transactions on Parallel and Distributed Systems*, vol. 7, no. 5, May 1996, pp. 506-521.

[13] —, "Efficient Scheduling of Arbitrary Task Graphs Using A Parallel Genetic Algorithm," *Journal of Parallel and Distributed Computing*, vol. 47, no. 1, Nov. 1997, pp. 58-77.

[14] Y.-K. Kwok, I. Ahmad, and J. Gu, "FAST: A Low-Complexity Algorithm for Efficient Scheduling of DAGs on Parallel Processors," Proc. *25th Int'l Conf. on Parallel Processing*, Aug. 1996, vol. II, pp. 150-157.

[15] N.R. Mahapatra and S. Dutt, "Scalable Global and Local Hashing Strategies for Duplicate Pruning in Parallel A* Graph Search," *IEEE Trans. Parallel and Distributed Systems*, vol. 8, no. 7, July 1997, pp. 738-756.

[16] J. Pearl and J.H. Kim, "Studies in Semi-Admissible Heuristics," *IEEE Trans. on Pattern Analysis and Machine Intelligence*, vol. PAMI-4, no. 4, July 1982, pp. 392-399.

[17] D.R. Smith, "Random Trees and the Analysis of Branch-and-Bound Procedures," *Journal of the ACM*, vol. 31, no. 1, Jan. 1984, pp. 163-188.

[18] T. Yang and A. Gerasoulis, "DSC: Scheduling Parallel Tasks on an Unbounded Number of Processors," *IEEE Trans. on Parallel and Distributed Systems*, vol. 5, no. 9, Sep. 1994, pp. 951-967.

Response Time Analysis for Distributed Real-Time Systems with Bursty Job Arrivals

Chengzhi Li   Riccardo Bettati   Wei Zhao

Department of Computer Science
Texas A & M University
College Station, TX 77843-3112
Phone 409 - 845 - 5098
Email: {chengzhi,bettati,zhao}@cs.tamu.edu

Abstract

This paper presents a new schedulability analysis methodology for distributed hard real-time systems with bursty job arrivals. The schedulability is analyzed by comparing worst-case response times of jobs with their timing constraints. We compute response times with a new method, which uses the amount of received service time to determine the response time of instances of a job. We illustrate how this method can be applied to exactly determine worst-case response times for processors with preemptive static-priority schedulers, and how it gives a good approximation on the response times for processors with non-preemptive static-priority scheduling or first-come-first-served scheduling. Our schedulability analysis method is the first to support systems with arbitrary job arrival patterns. Nevertheless, it performs better than other known approaches used for systems with periodic job arrivals.

1. Introduction

In a distributed real-time system, jobs have stringent timing constraints and often require to be executed on a sequence of processors. Timing constraints are typically given in form of end-to-end deadlines. A job in such a system meets its timing constraint if it completes before its end-to-end deadline. If one or more jobs miss their deadlines, a timing failure occurs. The possibility of such timing failures makes the system difficult to validate, since their occurrence can have unexpected effects. Furthermore, timing failures can cause the system to behave in an unpredictable or unstable way, with potentially serious consequences. It is a design goal to guarantee a priori that timing requirements are met during the system's operation. If the job set in the system is static, design-time analysis validates that no timing constraints are violated in the system. If the job set is dynamic, additional run-time analysis, typically as part of an admission control system, may be required.

The system workload is typically modeled as a set of job with end-to-end timing requirements. If all jobs in the system can meet their timing requirements, we call the system *schedulable*. The validation step required to test whether a system is schedulable is called *schedulability analysis*. The schedulability analysis can be performed during design time or as part of the admission control. In addition to being efficient, a method for schedulability analysis must satisfy a number of requirements. First, a schedulability analysis methodology must be correct and robust: it must never wrongly determine that a system is schedulable if it is not, and the error should be bounded if the schedulability decision is based on incorrect data. Second, a good schedulability analysis methodology should make good use of existing resources in the system, and allow for high resource utilization.

The central component of every schedulability analysis methodology is the computation of worst-case response times of the jobs under consideration. Once the worst-case response time has been determined for a particular job, it is compared against the timing requirements to check whether they are met [1]. In this paper, we present a general methodology for computing worst-case end-to-end response times for aperiodic jobs in distributed systems.

Traditionally, work on schedulability analysis focuses on periodic jobs, where the inter-arrival time of requests is fixed to be the period of the job. Non-periodic workload is typically transformed into a periodic workload by either one of three ways: (i) treating the non-periodic jobs as periodic jobs with the minimum inter-arrival time being the period, or (ii) having servers, which look like periodic jobs to the rest of

---

[1] Some approaches for schedulability analysis do not require the explicit computation of response times, but determine the schedulability indirectly, for example by relying on resource utilization [23].

the system, execute the non-periodic jobs (e.g. [16]), or (iii) splitting the non-periodic jobs each into collections of periodic jobs of different sizes and periods. In all three cases, well-known schedulability analysis methodologies for periodic workloads can be used.

Applying the same methods for distributed real-time systems, where jobs execute on more than one processor, shows poor results, even for periodic workloads. While the arrival of instances of a periodic job may indeed be periodic at the first processor, the completion of these instances almost certainly is not. If no special action is taken, and the completion of an instance on the first processor indicates that the second processor can go ahead, the "arrival" of instances of the job at the second processor is not periodic.

By appropriately synchronizing the execution of the job on the first processor and the start of the job on the second processor, the execution of the job on the second processor may be made to look like a periodic job. In [1], a number of such synchronization schemes are described and their relative performance is compared. The advantage of these synchronization schemes is that they allow the use of traditional schedulability analysis methods for periodic workloads.

As was pointed out in [1], appropriate synchronization reduces the worst-case end-to-end response times as compared to systems with no such synchronization (in [1] this is called Direct Synchronization). However, it adds overhead to the system, and increases the average end-to-end response times for jobs. In addition, it is of limited applicability in systems with jobs that are inherently aperiodic. The theory presented in this paper is designed to analyze aperiodic workloads. As such, it can handle periodic and aperiodic jobs, and combinations thereof, and more accurately determines the schedulability of periodic jobs in distributed systems with no synchronization than other approaches, for example [1].

2. Previous Work

The first result on schedulability analysis was presented in [23]. This schedulability test was performed by giving a utilization bound if the total utilization of the single processor is less than 69%, the rate monotonic scheduling will guarantee that all jobs meet their deadlines.

Since then, the results of [23] have greatly been generalized. For example, Lehoczky, Sha, and Ding [12] provide a sufficient and necessary schedulability test to determine the worst case response time. Leung and Whitehead [22] formulate an alternative priority assignment policy, where the job deadline can be less than the period of a job, and provide simple algorithm to determine the schedulability of such jobs. Sha, Rajkumar, and Lehoczky [14] discover a concurrency control protocol to permit jobs to share critical sections of codes. Audsley, Burns, Richardson, and

Welling [8] permit the addition of guaranteed sporadic tasks (where there is a minimum time between the re-arrivals of such jobs). Tindell, Burns, Richardson, Tindell, and Welling [9] extended the approach further to characterize the re-arrival pattern, covering 'bursty' sporadic and periodic jobs, and introduced the concept of release jitter (where a task is not released into the system immediately upon arrival, but may suffer a bounded deferral time). Bettati [4] provides a method for end-to-end schedulability analysis for distributed system. This approach relies on a synchronization scheme between processors called *Phase Modification*. Once an instance of a job completes on a processor, the release of the corresponding instance on the next processor is delayed so that the arrivals of that job on the second processor are periodic.

In [1, 2] Sun and Liu compare various synchronization mechanisms and describe an iterative algorithm to bound the end-to-end response times of jobs in distributed systems with *Direct Synchronization*. Direct synchronization between two processors means that the completion of an instance of a job on the first processor signals that the correspondent instance can be immediately released on the second processor. Sun and Liu correct a weakness in the holistic schedulability analysis proposed in [6]. However the upper bounds obtained by using their algorithm are still rather loose.

Most of the above work relies on one key technique, *busy period analysis*, which was first proposed in [13] and later extended in [6, 7, 9, 10]. A k-level busy period of a processor is a continuous time interval during which only these instances of jobs with priorities higher than or equal to k are executed. The crucial step of the busy period analysis can be roughly drafted as following: given a set of periodic jobs at the processor, for a particular job T_i with priority k, the maximum number of instances of job T_i, which arrive during k-level busy period D_k, can be bounded by $\lceil \frac{D_k}{\rho_i} \rceil$, where ρ_i is the period of job T_i, then the upper bound of the response time of each instance of job T_i can be obtained by only considering the first $\lceil \frac{D_k}{\rho_i} \rceil$ instances of job T_i.

Unfortunately, busy period analysis in this form relies on jobs being periodic, and these schedulability analysis algorithms based on it are not applicable for job sets with bursty job arrivals.

3. System Model

In this section we describe the model for distributed real-time systems used in the following sections.

3.1. Jobs

We consider a distributed real-time system that consists of m processors $P_1, P_2, \cdots, P_m$ and n independent jobs $T_1, T_2, \cdots, T_n$. Each job T_k consists of a chain of n_k subjobs, $T_{k,1}, \cdots, T_{k,n_k}$. Subjobs of a job are executed on different processors sequentially. In particular, subjob $T_{k,j}$ is executed for $\tau_{k,j}$ time units on processor $P(k,j) \in \{P_1, P_2, \cdots, P_m\}$. We call $\tau_{k,j}$ the *execution time* of subjob $T_{k,j}$.

Each job consists of a (possible infinite) sequence of job instances. The *release time* of an instance of a (sub-)job is the time when the instance of the (sub-)job is ready to be executed. Hence, by the definitions of job and subjob, the release time of an instance of job T_k is equal to the release time of the corresponding instance of subjob $T_{k,1}$. We say that the i-th instance of subjob $T_{k,j}$ is released at time $t_{k,j,i}$. Naturally, we have $0 \leq t_{k,j,1} < t_{k,j,2} < \cdots < t_{k,j,i} < \cdots$.

Most previous studies assume that jobs are *periodic*. That is, the release time of the i-th instance of T_k follows the following relations: $t_{k,1,i} = t_{k,1,1} + (i-1) * \rho_k$, where ρ_k is the period of job T_k. In this study, we remove this assumption. We allow that instances of jobs are released at any point in time, not necessarily periodically. Examples for both periodic and aperiodic job arrivals are given in Figure 1. Each job T_k is associated with a deadline D_k.

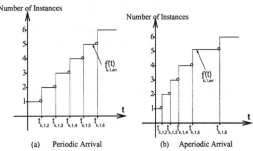

(a) Periodic Arrival (b) Aperiodic Arrival

Figure 1. Arrival functions of the first subjob.

For each instance of job T_k, the end-to-end response time (the time between the release time of the first subjob and completion time of the last subjob) must be no more than the deadline.

3.2. Scheduling algorithms

A processor typically executes more than one subjob. Hence, a scheduler is needed in order to coordinate the executions of subjobs on the processor. Priority scheduling is widely used. With priority scheduling, subjobs waiting for execution on a processor are assigned priorities. Among all the ready subjobs, the scheduler picks the one with the highest priority. A priority scheduling algorithm is *static* if all instances of a subjob have the same priority. Static priority scheduling is easy to manage and implement. A priority scheduling algorithm is *preemptive* if it preempts the current subjob in order to run an instance of a higher-priority subjob which just arrives. In this paper, we will consider both *static priority preemptive* (SPP) and *static priority non preemptive* (SPNP) scheduling algorithms. Given that SPP or SPNP scheduling is used, the response time of jobs is sensitive to how priorities are assigned to subjobs. Priority assignment algorithms have been widely studied in [9, 22, 23], and are not further discussed in this paper, since our results apply to

arbitrary priority assignments. In the following we assume that subjob is assigned priority $\phi_{k,j}$ on processor $P(k,j)$. The smaller the value of $\phi_{k,j}$, the higher the priority of $T_{k,j}$.

In addition to static priority scheduling, we analyze first-come-first-served (FCFS) scheduling, where instances of subjobs are served in accordance to the order of their arrivals.

As described earlier, we do not enforce a particular synchronization scheme except that dependency constrains between subsequent subjobs must be maintained. We therefore assume that the completion of an subjob on one processor signals that the corresponding instance of the next subjob is released on the subsequent processor. This assumption can be enforced with the help of the Direct Synchronization Protocol [1] to signal the completion of a subjob. When an instance of a subjob completes processing, a synchronization signal is sent to the processor where its immediate successor executes. Consequently, an instance of its successor is released immediately. This protocol is easy to use and implement. We also assume that the scheduler overhead has been taken into account in the execution time of the subjob. The inter-processor communication overhead is assumed to be constant and, hence, is ignored.

4. Response Time Analysis

To determine the worst case end-to-end response times of jobs, we need to describe job arrivals and departures to and from processors, the time requested by subjobs from a particular processor, and the time offered by processors to a particular job. We define the following notations for this purpose.

Definition 1 *The* arrival function, $f_{k,j},arr(t)$, *of subjob* $T_{k,j}$ *is defined as the number of instances of subjob* $T_{k,j}$ *that are released during the time interval* $[0, t]$.

Obviously, the value of the *arrival function* increases at every release time of a subjob instance. In particular, we have $f_{k,j},\mathrm{arr}(t) = i$ for $t_{k,j,i} \leq t < t_{k,j,i+1}$.

Definition 2 *The* departure function, $f_{k,j,dep}(t)$, *of subjob* $T_{k,j}$ *is defined as the number of instances of subjob* $T_{k,j}$ *that are* completed *during time interval* $[0, t]$.

Since jobs become ready on a succeeding processor as soon as they complete on the current processor, we always have $f_{k,j},\mathrm{dep}(t) = f_{k,j+1},\mathrm{arr}(t)$. In particular, we have $f_{k,j},\mathrm{dep}(t) = i$ for $t_{k,j+1,i} \leq t < t_{k,j+1,i+1}$.

Definition 3 *The* workload function *of subjob* $T_{k,j}$ *is defined as*

$$c_{k,j}(t) = f_{k,j},arr(t) * \tau_{k,j}, \qquad (1)$$

where $\tau_{k,j}$ *is execution time of subjob* $T_{k,j}$.

Definition 4 *The* service function, $S_{k,j}(t)$, *of processor* $P(k,j)$ *for subjob* $T_{k,j}$ *is defined as the time of processor* $P(k,j)$ *taken to execute ready instances (if any) of subjob* $T_{k,j}$ *during the time interval* $[0,t]$.

These arrival, departure, workload, and service functions play a key role when deriving the end-to-end response times of jobs. Before we formally derive our main results, we need to introduce a few more mathematical notations.

Definition 5 *For a nondecreasing function* $g(t)$, *the* inverse function *of* $g(t)$ *is defined as*

$$g^{-1}(t) = \min\{s|g(s) \geq t\}. \qquad (2)$$

For example, the *inverse function* of the *arrival function* $f_{k,j},\mathrm{arr}(t)$ can be written as follows: for $m = 1, 2, \cdots$

$$f_{k,j}^{-1},\mathrm{arr}(m) = t_{k,j,m}. \qquad (3)$$

That is, while $f_{k,j},\mathrm{arr}(t)$ denotes the numbers of instances of subjob $T_{k,j}$ released during time interval $[0,t]$, $f_{k,j}^{-1},\mathrm{arr}(m)$ is the time when the m-th instance of subjob $T_{k,j}$ is released.

Definition 6 *A function* $\underline{g}(t)$ *(or* $\overline{g}(t)$*) is called a* lower bound function *(or an* upper bound function*) of function* $g(t)$ *if for* $t \geq 0$,

$$g(t) \geq \underline{g}(t) \quad (or\ g(t) \leq \overline{g}(t)). \qquad (4)$$

For example, t is an upper bound of $S_{k,j}(t)$ and 0 is a lower bound of $S_{k,j}(t)$. Hence, we have

$$\overline{S}_{k,j}(t) = t, \qquad (5)$$

and

$$\underline{S}_{k,j}(t) = 0. \qquad (6)$$

Of course, these bounds are very loose. As we will see below, the quantity of the response time bounds directly depends on whether tight upper and lower bounds on *service functions* can be found.

4.1. Exact analysis

4.1.1 Main results
The following theorem provides a fundamental formula for computing the exact value of worst case end-to-end response times.

Theorem 1 *The worst case end-to-end response time* d_k *of job* T_k *is given as follows:*

$$d_k = \max_{m \geq 0}(f_{k,n_k}^{-1},dep(m) - f_{k,1}^{-1},arr(m)). \qquad (7)$$

Proof: Due to space limitation, all proofs in this paper are omitted. An interested reader is referred to [18].   Q.E.D

Typically for real-time systems we may assume that the *arrival functions* of the first subjobs are known. Hence, we need to determine the *departure function* on the last processor in order to use Formula (7). The following theorem establishes a relationship between *service function* and *departure function* on a single processor.

Theorem 2 *Let* $S_{k,j}(t)$ *be the service function for subjob* $T_{k,j}$ *at processor* $P(k,j)$. *Then, its departure function* $f_{k,j},dep(t)$, *is given by*

$$f_{k,j},dep(t) = \lfloor \frac{S_{k,j}(t)}{\tau_{k,j}} \rfloor. \qquad (8)$$

4.1.2 Service Functions for SPP Scheduling
As described above, we need to derive the *service function* in order to use Formula (7) to compute the end-to-end response time of a job. *Service functions* depend on the scheduling algorithm used by processors. In general, the derivation of exact *service function* is difficult. For a number of scheduling algorithms it can be derived rather easily, however. The following theorem illustrates this for the case of static priority preemptive (SPP) scheduling.

Theorem 3 *The service function* $S_{k,j}(t)$ *for subjob* $T_{k,j}$ *on processor* $P(k,j)$ *that uses SPP scheduling is given by*

$$S_{k,j}(t) = \min_{0 \leq s \leq t}\{A_{k,j}(t) - A_{k,j}(s) + c_{k,j}(s)\}, \qquad (9)$$

where

$$A_{k,j}(t) = \begin{cases} t, & \phi_{k,j} = 1 \\ t - \sum_{P(h,i)=P(k,j),\phi_{h,i}<\phi_{k,j}} & \\ S_{h,i}(t), & \phi_{k,j} > 1 \end{cases} \qquad (10)$$

Equations (9) (10) illustrates that the *service function* of $T_{k,j}$ depends on two items: (i) *service functions* of higher-priority subjobs that are also executed on processor P(k,j) and (ii) the *workload function* of $T_{k,j}$, which in turn depends on the *arrival function* of $T_{k,j}$. Thus, the *service function* of $T_{k,j}$ can be obtained by first computing all the *service functions* of higher priority subjobs and the *service function* at predecessor processor. Once the *service function* is computed, we can obtain the *departure function* with the help of Formula (8). The *departure function* in turn is the *arrival function* on the subsequent processor. Substituting the *departure function* on the last processor $P(k,n_k)$ into Formula (7), we have the worst case end-to-end response time of T_k.

4.2. Approximate Analysis
In order to use Formula (7) directly, one must be able to accurately compute *departure functions* at every processor. For many scheduling algorithms, this is either too difficult or computationally very intensive. In this situation, we have to use approximation techniques. We address this problem in this subsection.

4.2.1 Main results
According to the following theorem, we see that if the *departure functions* can be lower bounded and the *arrival functions* can be upper bounded, then the worst case end-to-end response time can be upper bounded.

Theorem 4 *If* $\overline{f}_{k,j},arr(t)$ *and* $\underline{f}_{k,j},dep(t)$ *are known for all the subjobs of job* T_k, *its worst case end-to-end response time* d_k *can be approximated by*

$$d_k \leq \sum_{j=1}^{n_k} d_{k,j}, \qquad (11)$$

where $d_{k,j}$ *is given by*

$$d_{k,j} = \max_{m \geq 0}(\underline{f}_{k,j}^{-1},dep(m) - \overline{f}_{k,j}^{-1},arr(m)). \qquad (12)$$

Given the above theorem, in order to compute an upper bound of the worst case response time, we need to estimate the lower bound of the *departure function* and the upper bound of the *arrival function*. The following lemmas relate these bounds to those of *service functions*.

Lemma 1 *A lower bound function on the departure function* $\underline{f}_{k,j,dep}(t)$ *of subjob* $T_{k,j}$ *on processor* $P(k,j)$ *is given by*

$$\underline{f}_{k,j,dep}(t) = \lfloor \frac{\underline{S}_{k,j}(t)}{\tau_{k,j}} \rfloor. \qquad (13)$$

Lemma 2 *An upper bound on the arrival function* $\overline{f}_{k,j+1,arr}(t)$ *of subjob* $T_{k,j+1}$ *on processor* $P(k,j+1)$ *is given by*

$$\overline{f}_{k,j+1,arr}(t) = \lfloor \frac{\overline{S}_{k,j}(t)}{\tau_{k,j}} \rfloor. \qquad (14)$$

The question is how to obtain the upper and lower bounds of the service function. We address this problem in the next section for the special cases of static priority non-preemptive scheduling (SPNP), and the first-come-first-served scheduling (FCFS).

4.2.2 Bounds on Service Functions for SPNP Scheduling

Recall that in a processor that uses non-preemptive static priority scheduling once a subjob begins to execute, it cannot be interrupted, even if higher priority subjobs subsequently arrive. Lower priority jobs thus can temporarily prevent higher priority jobs from executing. In such a situation, the higher priority subjob is said to be *blocked* by the lower priority subjobs. This blocking complicates the response time computation.

The maximum blocking time $b_{k,j}$ of subjob $T_{k,j}$ is the maximum execution time of subjobs that are assigned lower priority than subjob $T_{k,j}$ on processor $P(k,j)$. Formally,

$$b_{k,j} = \max_{P(l,m)=P(k,j),\phi_{l,m}>\phi_{k,j}} \{\tau_{l,m}\}. \qquad (15)$$

Once the blocking time is known, we can estimate the bounds on *service functions* as described in the following theorems.

Theorem 5 *A lower bound function on the service function* $\underline{S}_{k,j}(t)$ *of subjob* $T_{k,j}$ *on processor* $P(k,j)$, *which uses static priority non-preemptive scheduling, is given by*

$$\underline{S}_{k,j}(t) = \begin{cases} 0, & t \le b_{k,j} \\ \min_{0\le s\le t-b_{k,j}}\{B_{k,j}(t) \\ \quad -B_{k,j}(s)+c_{k,j}(s)\}, & t > b_{k,j} \end{cases} \qquad (16)$$

where

$$B_{k,j}(t) = \begin{cases} 0, & t \le b_{k,j} \\ t-b_{k,j}, & t > b_{k,j}, \ \phi_{k,j} = 1 \\ t-b_{k,j}-\sum_{P(h,i)=P(k,j),\phi_{h,i}<\phi_{k,j}} \\ \quad \underline{S}_{h,i}(t), & t > b_{k,j}, \ \phi_{k,j} > 1 \end{cases} \qquad (17)$$

Theorem 6 *An upper bound function service function on the service function* $\overline{S}_{k,j}(t)$ *on processor* $P(k,j)$, *which uses static priority non-preemptive scheduling, is given by*

$$\overline{S}_{k,j}(t) = \min_{0\le s\le t}\{B_{k,j}(t) - B_{k,j}(s) + c_{k,j}(s)\}, \qquad (18)$$

where $\underline{S}_{h,i}(t)$ *is defined in Theorem 5 and*

$$B_{k,j}(t) = \begin{cases} t, & \phi_{k,j} = 1 \\ t-\sum_{P(h,i)=P(k,j),\phi_{h,i}<\phi_{k,j}} \\ \quad \underline{S}_{h,i}(t), & \phi_{k,j} > 1 \end{cases} \qquad (19)$$

Thus, with the above theorems, the lower and upper bounds of service functions can be obtained. These bounds can be substituted into Equations (13) and (14) to derive lower and upper bounds on *departure* and *arrival functions*, respectively. These are then substituted into Equation (12) to determine a bound on the local response time for a single subjob. The bound on the end-to-end response time is then determined as the sum of local response times for all the subjobs.

4.2.3 Bounds on service functions for FCFS scheduling

In order to estimate *service functions*, we need to know how much time offered to execute subjobs in time interval $[0,t]$ by the processor. We derive this with the notation of the *utilization function* defined as follows:

Definition 7 *The utilization function* $U_j(t)$ *of processor* P_j *is defined as the time processor* P_j *is busy executing subjobs during the time interval* $[0,t]$.

Obviously, $U_j(t)$ can not exceed t. If $U_j(t) = t$, $t \in [0,T]$, processor P_j is busy during the entire time interval $[0,T]$. If $U_j(t) < t$, processor P_j must be idle for some time before time t. So $U_j(t)$ can be seen as an indicator of how busy processor P_j is.

Theorem 7 *The utilization function* $U_j(t)$ *of processor* P_j, *for the case of FCFS scheduling, is given by*

$$U_j(t) = \min_{0\le s\le t}\{t - s + G_j(s)\}, \qquad (20)$$

where,

$$G_j(t) = \sum_{P(k,l)=P_j} c_{k,l}(t). \qquad (21)$$

While the FCFS algorithm seems to be a simple one, analyzing it in order to obtain the service function is not trivial. This is because, with FCFS scheduling, a processor arbitrarily picks up a subjob to execute from more than one subjobs if they arrive at the same time. Thus, it is difficult, if not impossible, to obtain the exact *service function* for a subjob executed on a processor using FCFS scheduling. Nevertheless, the following theorems provide upper and lower bounds on the service functions when using FCFS scheduling. In the following, we will have $U_{k,j}(t)$ denote the utilization function of processor $P(k,j)$. Similarly, $G_{k,j}(t)$ denotes the total workload of all subjobs on processor $P(k,j)$.

Theorem 8 *If $P(k, j)$ uses the FCFS scheduling algorithm, the service function $S_{k,j}(t)$ for subjob $T_{k,j}$ is lower bounded by*

$$\underline{S}_{k,j}(t) = c_{k,j}(G_{k,j}^{-1}(U_{k,j}(t))), \qquad (22)$$

where $G_{k,j}(t)$ and $U_{k,j}(t)$ are defined in Theorem 7.

Theorem 9 *If $P(k, j)$ uses the FCFS scheduling algorithm, the service function $S_{k,j}(t)$ of subjob $T_{k,j}$ is upper bounded by*

$$\overline{S}_{k,j}(t) = c_{k,j}(G_{k,j}^{-1}(U_{k,j}(t))) + \tau_{k,j}. \qquad (23)$$

where $G_{k,j}(t)$ and $U_{k,j}(t)$ are given in (21) and (20), respectively.

As in the case of the static priority non-preemptive scheduling (Section 4.2.2), once the lower and upper bounds on service functions are obtained, an upper bound on the worst case end-to-end response time can be computed by using (13), (14), (12), and (11).

5. Evaluation

We conducted a series of simulations to study the performance of the proposed methods for analysis of response time in the distributed real-time systems with various scheduling algorithms. We are going to demonstrate that our new method generates tighter bounds on response time than approaches proposed by others [1, 2], for both the case of periodic and aperiodic job arrivals.

5.1. Simulation model and assumptions

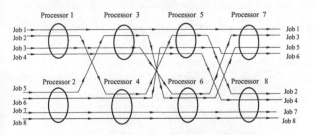

Figure 2. A System with Four Stages

In our experiments, we simulate the execution of jobs in a job shop. The shop consists of a sequence of stages, each of which contains a number of processors. All jobs traverse the stages of the shop in the same order, and each job is assigned to execute on one processor in each stage. Figure 2 shows a shop configuration, which consists of four stages with two processor in each stage. For example, job T_1 is assigned to execute on P_1 in the first stage, and on P_3, P_5 and P_7 in the second, third and fourth stage, respectively. Job T_2 executes on P_1 in the first stage, and on P_4, P_5, and P_8 on the subsequent stages.

In the case of static priority scheduling, the priority assignment must be determined. We use a relative deadline monotonic priority assignment algorithm [1], which assigns priorities to subjobs as follows: First, a sub-deadline of subjob $T_{i,j}$ is defined as follows

$$D_{i,j} = \frac{\tau_{i,j}}{\sum_{k=1}^{n_i} \tau_{i,k}} D_i. \qquad (24)$$

Then, subjobs on a particular processor are assigned priorities in accordance to their sub-deadlines. The smaller the sub-deadline of a subjob, the higher its priority.

We simulate four different methods for obtaining worst case end-to-end response times:

- SPP/Exact: The exact analysis method for static priority preemptive scheduling as proposed in Section 4.1.

- SPNP/App: The approximate method for static priority non preemptive scheduling (SPNP) as proposed in Section 4.2.2.

- FCFS/App: The approximate method for FCFS scheduling as proposed in Section 4.2.3

- SPP/S&L: The method proposed in [1, 2]. This method is associated with static priority preemptive scheduling.

We measure the performance of each scheme in terms of admission probability. The *admission probability* is defined as the probability that a randomly generated job set can meet its deadline requirements. We are interested in measuring how the different analysis methods perform with different scheduling algorithms. In each run of the simulation, $1,000$ sets of jobs are randomly generated. We apply each analysis method separately to determine how many sets of jobs can be admitted (i.e., meet their deadline requirements). The admission probability is estimated by the percentage of job sets that are admitted. Separate simulation runs are made to measure the admission probability when job arrivals are periodic and aperiodic.

5.2. Numerical results

The results of our experiments with periodic and aperiodic jobs arrivals are presented in Figure 3 and Figure 4, respectively.

In Figure 3 we compare the admission probability of the four analysis methods for the case of periodic job arrival. For each job T_k, we use following formula to generate release times of the first subjob $T_{k,1}$: for $m = 1, 2, \cdots$,

$$t_{k,1,m} = \frac{m-1}{x_k}, \qquad (25)$$

where x_k is a random variable with uniform distribution in $(0, 1)$. The end-to-end deadline of job T_k is a multiple of the period $\frac{1}{x_k}$. Furthermore, we generate a random variable $w_{k,j}$ with uniform distribution in $(0, 1)$ for each subjob $T_{k,j}$ and the execution time $\tau_{k,j}$ of subjob $T_{k,j}$ is defined as:

$$\tau_{k,j} = \frac{w_{k,j} * \frac{1}{x_k}}{\sum_{P(l,i)=P(k,j)} w_{l,i} * \frac{1}{x_l}} * Utilization. \qquad (26)$$

Figure 3 shows the effects of increasing the number of stages in the shop (from top to bottom) and of increasing

437

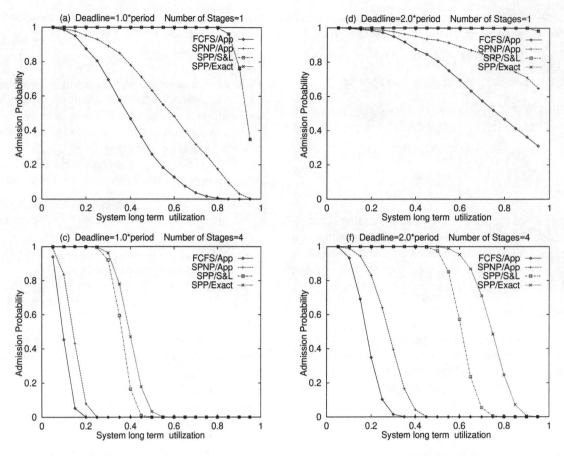

Figure 3. Admission Probability vs. System Utilization for Periodic Arrival Pattern.

the end-to-end deadlines of jobs (from left to right). We note that both FCFS/App and SPNP/App perform consistently poorer than the other two approaches. This is only partly due to the approximate analysis. Preemptive static priority scheduling is inherently superior to non-preemptive static priority scheduling or to FCFS, independently of the analysis methodology. More interesting are the results for SPP/Exact and SPP/S&L, which compare two different analysis methodologies for identical systems, with identical scheduling algorithm. When the number of stages of jobs is one (i.e., Figure 3 (a) and (d)), both systems using SPP/Exact and SPP/S&L result in the identical performance. This means that for a single processor system, both methods predict the same response time. However, when the number of stages is more than one (i.e., Figure 3 (c) and (f)), SPP/Exact performs better. This is because our SPP/Exact is an exact analysis method, which accurately compute the end-to-end response time, while SPP/S&L implicitly over-estimates the subjob arrivals and result in a loose bound on end-to-end response time. As to be expected the performance of all four methods improves significantly as the end-to-end deadline is doubled.

Figure 4 compares the performance of SPP/Exact,

SPNP/App, and FCFS/App for aperiodic job arrivals. In these experiments, we do not compare with SPP/S&L, because their analysis method works for periodic job arrivals only. For each job T_k, we use following formula to generate release times of the first subjob $T_{k,1}$: for $m = 1, 2, \cdots$,

$$t_{k,1,m} = \frac{1}{x_k}\sqrt{x_k^2 + (m-1)^2} - 1, \qquad (27)$$

where x_k is a random variable with uniform distribution in $(0, 1)$. The end-to-end deadline of job T_k is a random variable with exponential distribution. Furthermore, we generate a random variable $w_{k,j}$ with uniform distribution in $(0, 1)$ for each subjob $T_{k,j}$ and the execution time $\tau_{k,j}$ of subjob $T_{k,j}$ is defined as:

$$\tau_{k,j} = \frac{w_{k,j} * \frac{1}{x_k}}{\sum_{P(l,i)=P(k,j)} w_{l,i} * \frac{1}{x_l}} * Utilization. \qquad (28)$$

Figure 4 shows how the performance of the three methods compare with varying deadline distributions, from top to bottom the variance of the distribution increases, while the average value increases from left to right. As expected, performance improves as the deadlines are larger, as there are more slack in the systems. The figure shows, however,

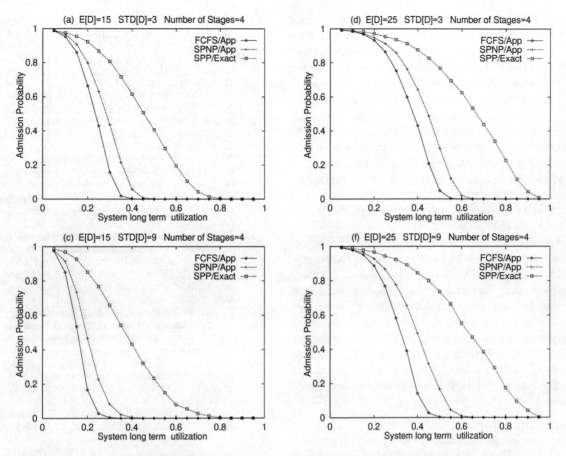

Figure 4. Admission Probability vs. System Utilization for Aperiodic Arrival Pattern.

that changing the variance of deadlines has a little effect on the admission probability.

The results show here are obtained for a limited number of parameters. However, we also found that other parameter values led to similar observations and are not represented here due to the lack of space.

6. Conclusion

In this paper, we have presented a novel approach to schedulability analysis of distributed real-time systems that have arbitrary job arrival patterns, and that consist of processors that run preemptive and non-preemptive static priority schedulers and FCFS schedulers. The basis of our new theory is the development of formulae that use the service received by the job from the processor and the service required by the job from the processor to bound the worst case response time of the job on that processor.

This paper makes a number of contributions. First, it allows the schedulability analysis for very general aperiodic workloads. Second, we have shown how this methodology can be used for systems that have a variety of different schedulers, be they static-priority (preemptive or non-preemptive) or FCFS. Of course the proposed methodology can handle

heterogeneous systems, where different processors run different schedulers. Third, we have shown that our approach gives good results for systems with periodic job arrivals as well, in particular in comparison with recently developed methods, such as [1, 2].

A number of questions remain open. We are investigating more general methodology to deal with the "physical loop" caused by jobs 0Φvisiting the same processor more than once and the "logical loop" caused by certain jobs disturbing each other on different processors. In these situations, the arrival functions of some subjobs, which play the key in computing the worst case response time, depend on each other and form a closed relationship chain. For example, the arrival function of subjob $T_{k,j}$ depends on the arrival function of subjob $T_{n,i}$, because subjob $T_{k,j-1}$ and subjob $T_{n,i}$ are served by the same processor and the priority of subjob $T_{n,i}$ is higher than that of subjob $T_{k,j-1}$. Furthermore, the arrival function of subjob $T_{n,i-1}$ depends on the arrival function of subjob $T_{k,j}$, because subjob $T_{n,i-1}$ and subjob $T_{k,j}$ are served by the same processor and the priority of subjob $T_{k,j}$ is higher than that of subjob $T_{n,i-1}$. In order to evaluate the worst case response time, we need to virtually break the closed chain. Observing that an upper bound of arrival function of each subjob can be obtained from the arrival function of its precursory subjob and the worst case response time experienced by the its precursory subjob. Let the worse case response time of each subjob be an unknown variable. According to above observation, we can obtain the upper bounds of arrival functions for each subjob even though they may contain some unknown parameters. From the mathematical point of view, after setting the worse case response time as unknown variable, we can construct a nonlinear vector function, $\vec{X} = F(\vec{X})$, where $\vec{X}$ is the unknown vector consisting of all unknown worst case response time experienced by each subjob. Therefore, we can find the numerical solution $\vec{X}$ by using the iteration scheme: $\vec{X}^{n+1} = F(\vec{X}^n)$, $\vec{X}^1 = \vec{0}$, $n = 1, 2, \cdots$.

In this paper we restricted ourselves to distributed systems with no contention for resources, except for the processors. Large-scale distributed systems cannot be modeled without taking into account remote resource access and contention for such resources. We are currently investigating how to model the access to shared resources (with and without resource access protocols) with the help of service functions. This will open the way for a fully integrated methodology for the schedulability analysis of distributed real-time systems with both shared processors and shared resources.

Acknowledgment

This work was partially sponsored by the Air Force Office of Scientific Research, Air Force Material Command, USAF, under grant number F49620-96-1-1076, by the Defense Advanced Research Projects Agency (DARPA) through the Honeywell Technology Center under contract number B09333438, and by Texas Higher Education Coordinating Board under its Advanced Technology Program with grant number 999903-204. The U.S. Government is authorized to reproduce and distribute reprints for governmental purposes notwithstanding any copyright notation thereon. The views and conclusions contained herein are those of the authors and should not be interpreted as necessarily representing the official policies or endorsements, either expressed or implied, of the Air Force Office of Scientific Research, Honeywell, DARPA, the U.S. Government, Texas State Government, Texas Higher Education Coordinating Board, or Texas A&M University.

References

[1] J. Sun and J. W. S. Liu. Synchronization protocols in distributed real-time systems. In *Proc. of IEEE ICDCS*, 1996.

[2] J. Sun and J. W. S. Liu. Bounding the end-to-end response times of tasks in a distributed real-time system using the direct synchronization protocol. Technical report UIUCDCS-R-96-1949, University of Illinois at Urbana-Champaign, Dept. of Computer Science, March 1996.

[3] J. Sun. *Fixed-Priority Scheduling Of Periodic Tasks With End-To-End Deadlines*. PhD thesis, University of Illinois at Urbana-Champaign, 1996.

[4] R. Bettati. *End-to-End Scheduling to Meet Deadlines in Distributed System*. PhD thesis, University of Illinois at Urbana-Champaign, 1994.

[5] R. Bettati and J. W. S. Liu. End-to-End Scheduling to Meet Deadlines in Distributed Systems. In *Proc. of IEEE ICDCS*, 1992.

[6] K. Tindell and J. Clark. Holistic schedulability analysis for distributed hard real-time system. In *Microprocessing and Microprogramming*, 50(2), April 1994.

[7] K. Tindell, A. Burns and A. J. Wellings. An extensible approach for analyzing fixed priority hard real-time tasks. In *J. of Real-Time Systems*, 6(2), March 1994.

[8] N. C. Audsley, A. Burns, M. F. Richardson, and A. J. Wellings. Hard real-time scheduling: the deadline-monotonic approach. In *Proc. of IEEE Workshop on Real-Time Operating Systems and Software*, 1991.

[9] N. C. Audsley, A. Burns, M. F. Richardson, K. Tindell and A. J. Wellings. Applying new scheduling theory to static priority preemptive scheduling. In *J. of Software Eng.*, vol 8, no. 5, Sept. 1993

[10] A. Burns, K. Tindell and A. J. Wellings. Fixed priority scheduling with deadlines prior to completion. In *Proc. of Euromicro Workshop on Real-Time Systems*, 1994.

[11] R. I. Davis, K. Tindell and A. Burns. Scheduling slack time in fixed priority pre-emptive systems. In *Proc. of IEEE RTSS*, 1993.

[12] J. Lehoczky, L. Sha, and Y. Ding. The rate monotonic scheduling algorithm: Exact characterization and average case behavior. In *Proc. of IEEE RTSS*, 1989.

[13] J. Lehoczky. Fixed priority scheduling of periodic task sets with arbitrary deadlines. In *Proc. of IEEE RTSS*, Dec. 1990.

[14] L. Sha, R. Rajkumar and J. Lehoczky. Priority inheritance protocols: an approach to real-time synchronization. In *IEEE Transactions on Computers*, vol. 39, no. 9, Sept. 1990.

[15] J. Lehoczky and S. Ramos-Thuel. An optimal algorithm for scheduling soft-aperiodic tasks in fixed-priority preemptive systems. In *Proc. of IEEE RTSS*, 1992.

[16] S. Ramos-Thuel and J. Lehoczky. On-line scheduling of hard deadline aperiodic tasks in fixed-priority systems. In *Proc. of IEEE RTSS*, 1993.

[17] C. Li, R. Bettati and W. Zhao. Static priority scheduling for ATM networks. In *Proc. of IEEE RTSS*, 1997.

[18] C. Li, R. Bettati and W. Zhao. Response time analysis for distributed real-time systems with bursty job arrivals. Technical report, Department of Computer Science, Texas A&M University, 1998.

[19] M. Joseph and P. Pandya. Finding response times in a real-time system. In *Journal of Computerl*, vol. 29, no. 5, 1986.

[20] R. L. Cruz. A calculus for network delay, part I,II: Network analysis. In *IEEE Trans. on Inform. Theory*, 37(1), Jan. 1991.

[21] R. L. Cruz. Quality of service guarantees in virtual circuit switched networks. In *IEEE Journal on Selected Areas in Commu.*, vol. 13, no. 6, 1995.

[22] J. Y.-T. Leung and J. Whitehead. On the complexity of fixed-priority scheduling of periodic, real-time tasks. In *Performance Evaluation*, 2, December 1982.

[23] C. L. Liu and J. W. Layland. Scheduling algorithms for multiprogramming in a hard-real-time environment. In *J. of the Association for Computing Machinery*, 20(1), Jan. 1973.

[24] J. A. Stankovic. Misconceptions about real-time computing: A serious problem for next generation systems. In *J. of IEEE Computer*, 21(10), Oct. 1988.

[25] J. A. Stankovic and K. Ramamritham, editors. *Hard Real-Time Systems*. IEEE Computer Society Press, 1988.

[26] Chang-Gun Lee, J. Hahn, Y. M. Seo, S. L. Min and R. Ha. Analysis of Cache-related Preemption Delay in Fixed-priority Preemptive Scheduling. In *Proc. of IEEE RTSS*, 1996.

GAST: A Flexible and Extensible Tool for Evaluating Multiprocessor Assignment and Scheduling Techniques

Jan Jonsson

Department of Computer Engineering
Chalmers University of Technology
S–412 96 Göteborg, Sweden
janjo@ce.chalmers.se

Abstract

Automatic tool support for scheduling applications on multiprocessor platforms is of paramount importance both to guarantee critical application demands and to keep development costs down. In this paper, we present GAST, an object-oriented evaluation environment for multiprocessor assignment and scheduling techniques. GAST is based on a decomposition approach where existing assignment and scheduling techniques have been broken down into a set of common operations. By combining these operations into a complete scheduling process, GAST offers a powerful toolbox of existing assignment and scheduling techniques. GAST has been implemented on several popular operating systems and is accompanied by a graphic visualization tool that allows for flexible interaction with the application scheduling process.

1 Introduction

For economical reasons, single-processor computers have traditionally been the only viable option for many computer system designers. This has, in turn, limited the sphere of feasible applications. However, the recent dramatic improvement of the price–performance ratio for high-performance multiprocessor platforms has provided for entirely new possibilities for applications with requirements for high performance and strict real-time or quality-of-service (QoS) constraints. This have motivated system designers to extend their attention to multiprocessor platforms.

As the complexity of modern applications rapidly increases, it becomes difficult to perform task scheduling and resource allocation by hand. Therefore, system designers often resort to automated approaches. However, in confronting the plethora of scheduling methods proposed in the literature, it is not easy to choose the best method for a particular design problem because (i) reported evaluations of a method often are made with respect to theoretically optimal results, and usually under ideal, simplified conditions, and (ii) reported evaluations of different methods cannot be used for drawing objective conclusions as the methods often are proposed and described under different assumptions about architecture, application and run-time environment properties. Thus, in order to extend the application field and to make good design decisions, powerful methodologies for evaluating application scheduling on multiprocessor architectures must be used.

This paper presents *GAST* (*Generic Allocation and Scheduling Tool*), a flexible and extensible software package for evaluating assignment and scheduling techniques for multiprocessor architectures. GAST is an object-oriented software, based on the C++ programming language, that achieves a high degree of flexibility and extensibility by separating its major components into different classes, representing system parameters such as application workload, processor and network architecture, and assignment/scheduling policies for tasks and messages. By carefully defining the boundaries between these components, GAST facilitates adding or modifying implementations of a class without altering the internal representation of the other classes. As long as an implementation of a class adheres to the specified class interface, it can have an arbitrary functionality and its complexity can vary from a simple, high-level model to a realistic, low-level model with intricate details. This capability of the object-oriented programming paradigm has been fully exploited to make GAST a powerful and flexible evaluation environment for system designers.

In comparison with similar tools reported in research literature (see Section 2), GAST stands out as a unique tool in that it provides support for (i) aperiodic as well as periodic applications, (ii) applications with and without explicit timing constraints, (iii) preprocessing operations for improving application performance, and (iv) support for the generation of synthetic application workloads. In its basic form, GAST is available as a command-line-based tool that runs on the UNIX and the Windows 95/NT operating systems. In addition, GAST can be controlled via a graphic visualization environment that allows for flexible user interaction during rapid prototyping or powerful support for batch processing during extensive simulation studies.

The rest of the paper is organized as follows: Section 2 describes work related to ours. Section 3 introduces multiprocessor scheduling terminology. Section 4 summarizes the decomposition approach taken in the design of GAST. Section 5 describes the software structure of GAST. In Section 6, the facilities of GAST are demonstrated by means of decomposition examples, an application case study, and sample simulation experiments. Section 7 discusses our experience with GAST and possible future work, and Section 8 summarizes the contents of this paper.

2 Related Work

The main purpose of GAST is to provide a powerful framework for the evaluation of different assignment and scheduling policies. Other frameworks and tools with similar goals have been proposed in the open research literature.

The *schedalyzer* (*sched*ulability ana*lyzer*) by Stoyenko [50] was one of the first tools for schedulability analysis. A special real-time language, Real-Time Euclid [34], was developed with provisions for schedulability analysis built into it. The main limitation with the schedalyzer is that it is targeted for a specific high-level language, a specific run-time system, and a specific platform architecture.

Scheduler 1-2-3 [53] is a schedulability analyzer for the ARTS kernel [54] that can also generate synthetic workloads for use in extensive experimental studies. Interaction with the tool is supported through a graphical interface. The Scheduler 1-2-3 tool supports distributed systems but is only aimed at a specific operating system environment.

The SRT tool [7] allows a model of a real-time system to be constructed and then evaluated, by simulation, using a static or dynamic-priority scheduling policy. A model is constructed using a graphical user interface that allows the designer to build a system with entities for sensors, actuators, processes and a scheduler. The task assignment problem is not addressed in the SRT tool.

STRESS [6] is a real-time system evaluation environment that encompasses a number of separate tools based on a single simulation language. The language is specifically designed to enable the description of application software, dispatcher software, and platform architecture hardware. Simulation results are presented using a graphical interface. STRESS provides support for static- and dynamic-priority scheduling strategies and resource-access protocols. In addition, it provides support for heterogeneous systems, but focuses exclusively on hard real-time systems with static task assignment.

PERTS [42] is an analytical model-based toolset developed for real-time systems analysis. Using a library of scheduling algorithms and resource-access protocols, PERTS supports the evaluation of new and competing designs. Schedulability analysis is provided through a graphical interface, and support is provided for heterogeneous systems. Recently, PERTS was complemented by DRTSS [49], a powerful simulation framework that provides a suite of task assignment, task scheduling, and resource access protocols, for hard and soft real-time systems with capabilities for static and dynamic task assignment.

CAISARTS [22] is a rule-based system that can be used for obtaining advice on different aspects of real-time system design: assignment of tasks, choice of scheduling paradigm, and analysis of overhead associated with dispatcher implementations. CAISARTS contains a rich task model, including resource requirements, precedence constraints and end-to-end requirements, and provides support for multiprocessor and distributed systems. The focus in CAISARTS is on providing advice at a variety of abstraction levels. The knowledge is extendible by the user via a rule interface [19]. The main limitation with the CAISARTS tool is its weak support of simulation capabilities.

The Parallax tool [40] is a graphical evaluation environ-ment for the list-scheduling technique. Parallax supports several list-scheduling algorithms that differ mainly in the assumed interprocessor communication model. Parallax focuses on techniques for minimizing the completion time of the application and does not account for explicit timing constraints such as application deadlines.

CASCH [4] is a powerful graphical evaluation tool that offers a smorgasbord of assignment and scheduling techniques for multiprocessor systems. Among other things, CASCH provides support for list-scheduling, clustering and replication techniques. The tool also has facilities for performing sequential–to–parallel transformations of the application program. Similar to the Parallax tool, CASCH lacks support for real-time applications.

The most distinguishing feature of GAST is its decomposition approach (see Section 4) that allows a wide variety of assignment and scheduling policies — with radically different scheduling objectives — to be easily integrated in the tool. This is in sharp contrast to the tools listed above where typically only one type of scheduling objective (*e.g.*, minimize completion time or fulfill real-time constraints) is supported. The main drawback with GAST is that it currently offers no advice on how to increase performance or schedulability should a scheduling attempt fail or otherwise be unacceptable.

3 Multiprocessor Scheduling

A *schedule* is a mapping from the application domain to the hardware resource and time domain. The solution to the *multiprocessor scheduling problem* is a schedule for which sufficient amounts of hardware resources, such as processors, memory, and communication links, have been assigned for sufficient amounts of time to each task in the application in such a way that the constraints imposed on the system will be fulfilled. Scheduling is performed using a *scheduling algorithm*. The process of finding hardware resources for the tasks is referred to as *task assignment*. The process of finding time resources for the tasks given a set of hardware resources is called *task scheduling*. The combined process of task assignment and scheduling is referred to as *task allocation*.

The search for a solution to the multiprocessor scheduling problem can be performed with the aid of a *search tree* that represents the solution space of the problem, that is, all possible permutations of task–to–processor assignments and schedule orderings. Each vertex in the search tree represents one specific task–to–processor assignment and schedule ordering, and one or many vertices represent the optimal solution whenever one exists. The *root vertex* of the search tree represents an empty schedule, and each of its descendant vertices (children) represents the scheduling of one specific task on one specific processors. The children of each of these child vertices represent the scheduling of yet another task on one processor. A *goal vertex* is a vertex in the search tree that represents a complete solution where all tasks have been scheduled onto the processors. An *intermediate vertex* is a vertex that represents a not-yet-complete schedule. The *level* of a vertex is the number of tasks in the application that have been scheduled so far. The *cost* of a vertex is the quality of the partial or complete schedule represented by the vertex.

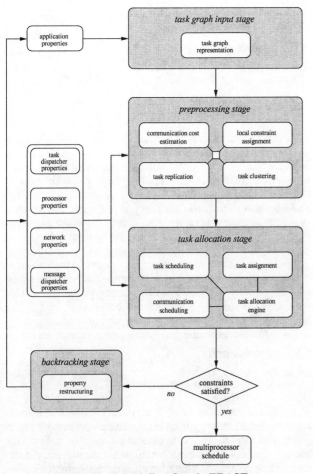

Figure 1: Scheduling flow in FEAST.

4 Decomposition Approach

GAST is an implementation of FEAST [24, 25], a framework based on a *decomposition* strategy in which existing assignment and scheduling policies — proposed in different contexts — are broken down into a set of independent parameters. From a system viewpoint, FEAST consists of a set of basic scheduling stages which takes as input the application and architecture properties. These scheduling stages collectively attempt to schedule the application onto the architecture under given application constraints.

The decomposed structure of FEAST is shown in Figure 1. Scheduling starts at the top with a *task graph input stage*, where the application properties are converted into a suitable task graph representation. To attain a high scheduling quality, a flexible and expressive task graph representation must be chosen since the task graph is typically constructed once and never modified during scheduling. It is often the system designer's responsibility to construct this task graph by defining tasks and identifying their computational and communication requirements and their precedence relations. Since this is clearly a tedious and error-prone approach for complex applications, a tool should be used for automating the construction of task graphs.

The scheduling flow then proceeds downwards to a *pre-*

processing stage, where a set of operations are performed on the task graph, primarily to get it into a format suitable for scheduling, but also to increase the likelihood that the scheduling will succeed [24]. FEAST defines four such operations: Preliminary *communication-cost estimation* is often needed during static-level calculation [15], task clustering decisions [43] or deadline assignment [27, 25]. When complete knowledge about task–to–processor assignments is not available beforehand, as-accurate-as-possible predictions on the interprocessor communication cost must be made. In *local-constraint assignment*, the application's end-to-end timing constraints (*e.g.*, deadlines and periods) must be distributed over the component tasks so as to allow for a feasible scheduling of the tasks. Examples of local-constraint assignment problems are the distribution of end-to-end deadlines [32, 13, 44, 27] and the derivation of task periods [18, 26, 46]. By means of *task replication*, the performance of the application can be greatly improved. Much work in recent years has shown that replication may be needed for fault-tolerance [21, 43] or schedulability [9, 18] reasons, or for minimizing schedule length [36, 11, 3, 37]. The purpose of *task clustering* is to provide directions to the subsequent task allocation stage as regards the task–to–processor assignments. Task clustering has, primarily, been used for guaranteeing that certain tasks that exchange large amounts of data are assigned to the same processor in order to minimize communication overhead [33, 17, 48, 43].

After preprocessing, the scheduling flow proceeds to a *task allocation stage*, where each task in the task graph is assigned to and scheduled on a processor, and messages transmitted between tasks are scheduled on the network. This stage is powered by an *allocation engine* that performs the actual assignment and scheduling based on a technique such as list scheduling [39, 47], branch-and-bound [21, 28], or non-guided search [52, 14]. In the task allocation stage, three operations are performed: (i) each application task is assigned to a processor in the architecture, (ii) each task is scheduled on its assigned processor, and (iii) interprocessor communication is scheduled on the network.

If all tasks in the task graph can be successfully scheduled, the scheduling flow terminates with a valid multiprocessor schedule. In case the scheduling fails or is otherwise unacceptable, an optional *backtracking stage* is invoked that can be used for restructuring the application and/or architecture properties in an attempt to increase the likelihood of succeeding in a new scheduling attempt. Backtracking may involve changing application properties — for instance, by splitting or combining tasks, or selecting a different sampling rate. It can also entail changing the architecture properties — for instance, by changing the number of processors. An example of a method that exploits backtracking is the scheduler presented in [51]. Here, simulated annealing [52] is used for assigning tasks to processors. When the scheduler fails, given a certain task assignment, the simulated annealing algorithm is invoked to generate a new task assignment. Other techniques that utilize backtracking are presented in [21] (increase degree of task replication for fault-tolerance reasons), [26] (increase task periods for schedulability reasons), and [55] (increase application parallelism for schedulability reasons).

5 Software Structure

The software structure of GAST reflects the decomposition structure outlined in the previous section. This guarantees that clean and powerful interfaces are maintained between the main components, without restricting the flexibility of the tool. Below, we describe the primary object classes used in GAST and also present some of the techniques that have been implemented in the current version of GAST.

5.1 Software components and interfaces

The main software components of GAST are a set of C++ classes that correspond to the different scheduling stages in FEAST. Each class provides a set of generic variables, functions, and procedures that serve as the interface to the class. Below follows a description of the primary classes used in GAST and their associated C++ class interfaces. During initialization, GAST creates one object from each primary class. These objects are then accessible from all other object functions and procedures.

5.1.1 TaskSet

```
class TaskSet {
    virtual void  Load(void);

    Set<Task>     EntireSet;
    Set<Task>     RootSet;
    Set<Task>     LeafSet;
    Set<Conn>     ConnSet;
    Set<Cluster>  ClusterSet;
};
```

This class encapsulates the task graph input strategy and holds the internal representation of the application workload and its constraints. This is done with objects of the **Task** and **Conn** classes, representing the nodes and arcs in the task graph, respectively. After creation of the **TaskSet** object, the application is loaded with a call to the Load() procedure. This call should create one **Task** class object for each task in the application, and insert it into the EntireSet element. Input and output tasks should be identified and inserted in the LeafSet and RootSet, respectively. Similarly, one **Conn** class object should be created for each intertask communication channel (precedence constraint) in the application. These objects should then be inserted in the ConnSet element. In addition, the call to Load() should initialize the ClusterSet element with the task clusters that exist in the architecture. This will enable the task allocator to determine whether a task is allowed to execute on a certain processor or whether it must execute together with certain tasks.

5.1.2 ProcSet

```
class ProcSet {
    virtual void  Init(void);

    Set<Proc>     EntireSet;
    Set<PClass>   ClassSet;
};
```

This class encapsulates the set of processors in the system and works as a container for objects representing the individual processors in the architecture. After creation of the **ProcSet** object, the set of processors is generated with a call to the Init() procedure. This call should create one **Proc** class object for each processor in the architecture, and insert it into the EntireSet element. In addition, the call to Init() should initialize the ClassSet element with the different processor classes that exist in the architecture. This will enable the task

allocator to calculate a correct execution time for each task–processor pair during scheduling.

5.1.3 Topology

```
class Topology {
    virtual void  Init(void);

    Set<Link>       Links;
    Matrix<Bool>    Adjacent;
    Matrix<Link *>  LinkTable;
};
```

This class encapsulates the interconnection network topology used in the system and works as a container for objects representing the communication links in the architecture. After creation of the **Topology** object, the set of links is generated with a call to the Init() procedure. This call should create one **Link** class object for each communication link in the architecture, and insert it into the Links element. In addition, the call to Init() should initialize an adjacency matrix describing the topology of the architecture. The Adjacent element is a matrix — indexed by a source–destination processor pair — indicating whether the processors are directly connected with a communication link. That is, if Adjacent[q][r] is true, then processors P_q and P_r are adjacent. The LinkTable element is a matrix holding references to the corresponding communication link objects.

5.1.4 Approximate

```
class Approximate {
    virtual void  Do_Approximate(void);
};
```

This class encapsulates the interprocessor communication-cost estimation strategy used during the preprocessing stage. After creation of the **Approximate** object, a call to the Do_Approximate() procedure will make preliminary communication cost estimations for all intertask communication channels in the application (found in the ConnSet element in the **TaskSet** object).

5.1.5 Deadline

```
class Deadline {
    virtual void  Do_Distribute(void);
};
```

This class encapsulates the deadline-distribution strategy used during the preprocessing stage. After creation of the **Deadline** object, a call to the Do_Distribute() procedure will assign local arrival times and deadlines to all tasks in the application (found in the EntireSet element in the **TaskSet** object). In order to allow for deadline distribution techniques that also assign arrival times and deadlines to intertask communication channels, the Do_Approximate() procedure is called prior to Do_Distribute().

5.1.6 Cluster

```
class Cluster {
    virtual void  Do_Cluster(void);
};
```

This class encapsulates the task clustering strategy used during the preprocessing stage. After creation of the **Cluster** object, a call to the Do_Cluster() procedure will cluster tasks in the application according to the selected implementation of the class. In order to allow for clustering techniques that utilize information regarding intertask communication costs, the Do_Approximate() procedure is called prior to Do_Cluster().

5.1.7 Replicate

```
class Replication {
  void          Do_Replication_Time(void);
  virtual void  Do_Replication_Space(void);
};
```

This class encapsulates the task replication strategy used during the preprocessing stage. After creation of the **Replicate** object, a call to the Do_Replicate_Space() procedure will perform a spatial replication of tasks in the application according to the selected implementation of the class. After spatial replication has been performed, a call to the Do_Replicate_Time() procedure is made to perform a temporal replication of the tasks, should that option have been selected by the user. Note that temporal replication only works for periodic tasks. This operation uses the concept of a meta-period (that is, the least-common-multiple of all task periods) and hence requires that a period is defined for each task. In order to allow for the application of preprocessing operations on the replicated tasks, the replication procedures are called prior to all other preprocessing operations.

5.1.8 Allocate

```
class Allocate {
  virtual void  Do_Allocate(void);
};
```

This class encapsulates the functionality of the task assignment and scheduling strategy. After creation of the **Allocate** object, a call to the Do_Allocate() procedure will initiate the task assignment and scheduling process, evaluating task–processor pairs drawn from the EntireSet elements in the **TaskSet** and **ProcSet** objects.

5.1.9 Schedule

```
class Schedule {
  virtual void  Schedule_Mode(SchedMode, Proc&);
  virtual void  Do_Schedule(Task&, Proc&);
};
```

This class encapsulates the functionality of the task dispatching policy assumed in the architecture. The task allocator calls the Do_Schedule() procedure with the task–processor pair of the currently explored search tree vertex in an attempt to schedule the task on the processor, taking into account any precedence constraints and communication-cost overhead. The Do_Schedule() procedure should then perform the necessary schedulability tests (*i.e.*, checking that the task deadline is met) for the selected implementation of the class. The Schedule_Mode() procedure call selects the type of scheduling attempt — permanent or tentative — for a subsequent call to Do_Schedule().

5.1.10 CModel

```
class CModel {
  virtual void  CModel_Mode(CModelMode);
  virtual void  Do_Estimate(Conn&);
  virtual void  Do_Communicate(Link&, Conn&);
};
```

This class encapsulates the functionality of the message dispatching strategy assumed in the scheduled system. The task allocator calls the Do_Communicate() procedure for each link used by an intertask communication channel (as defined by the **Route** class). The communication channels from each immediate predecessor of the currently explored task are scheduled by the task allocator, and communication cost overhead is calculated for each channel. The Do_Communicate() procedure should perform the necessary schedulability tests for the selected implementation of the class. The CModel_Mode() procedure call selects the type of scheduling attempt (permanent or tentative) for a subsequent call to Do_Communicate(). For the Do_Approximate() procedure, a corresponding Do_Estimate() procedure is available for preliminary communication-cost estimation during the preprocessing stage.

5.1.11 Route

```
class Route {
  virtual void  Do_Route(Conn&);
  virtual void  Route_Mode(RouteMode);

  Matrix<List<Proc *>>  RouteTable;
};
```

This class encapsulates the strategy by which messages are routed in the interconnection network. Before the task allocator calls the Do_Communicate() procedure to establish an intertask communication channel, the Do_Route() procedure is called to define what links will be used to transport messages from the source task to the destination task. The communication channels from each immediate predecessor of the currently explored task are scanned by the task allocator. The Route_Mode() procedure call selects the type of routing attempt (permanent or tentative) for a subsequent call to Do_Route(). The RouteTable element is a matrix — indexed by a source–destination processor pair — holding lists of references to processors between which link routes can be established for the given processor pair.

5.1.12 ObjFunc

```
class ObjFunc {
  virtual void  Calculate_Lower_Bound(Vertex&);
  virtual Bool  Dominates(Vertex&, Vertex&);
};
```

This class encapsulates the functionality of the objective function used by the task allocator. During task allocation (initiated by a call to the Do_Allocate() procedure) task–processor pairs are drawn from the EntireSet elements in the **TaskSet** and **ProcSet** objects. Each new task–processor pair constitutes a new vertex in the search tree of the scheduling problem. To calculate the cost for a vertex during task allocation, the Calculate_Lower_Bound() procedure is called with the currently explored search tree vertex as the parameter. To evaluate and compare two competing vertices during task allocation, the Dominates() function is called with the candidate vertices as parameters. The function should return an affirmative result if the first parameter vertex is better than the second with respect to the performance measure used for the selected implementation of the class.

5.1.13 Backtrack

```
class Backtrack {
  virtual void  Do_Backtrack(void);
};
```

This class encapsulates the global backtracking strategy. Whenever the task allocator fails to schedule the application on the given architecture, the Do_Backtrack() procedure is called to allow for modification or restructuring of the application or architecture properties.

Object class	Technique	Description
TaskSet	File	Input specification file
	Random	Parametrized random task graph generator
ProcSet	Identical	WCET independent of processor
	Uniform	WCET related with a scaling factor
	Unrelated	WCET not necessarily related
Topology	Shared bus	Common communication medium
	2D mesh	Point-to-point links in 2-dim. mesh
	n-cube	Point-to-point links in k-ary n-cube
Approximate	None	No cost assumed
	All	Full cost always assumed
	Random	Full/no cost assumed in 50% of the cases
Deadline	Period	Deadline equal to period [41]
	MinMax	Overlapping execution windows [16, 10]
	Slicing	Non-overlapping execution windows [13, 27]
Cluster	Explicit	Clustering as provided by TaskSet class
	Pairwise	Pairwise clustering [43]
	Period	Period-based clustering [1]
Replicate	Explicit	Replication as provided by TaskSet class
Allocate	Exhaustive	Branch-and-bound strategy [35, 28]
	Greedy	Greedy strategy (subset of *Exhaustive*)
ObjFunc	HSL	Highest-static-level [2]
	HDL	Highest-dynamic-level [47]
	EST	Earliest-start-time [39]
	EFT	Earliest-finish-time [30]
	EDF	Earliest-deadline-first [41]
	LST	Latest-start-time [43]
	Makespan*	Minimize max. task completion time [45, 47]
	Lateness*	Minimize max. task lateness [8, 56]
	Failure*	Minimize probability of dynamic failure [21]
Schedule	Time	Time-driven dispatching [56]
	Fixed	Fixed-priority dispatching [5]
	Dynamic	Dynamic-priority dispatching [23]
CModel	Ideal	Zero communication cost
	Constant	Constant communication cost
	TDC	Fixed message priorities [29]
	KSF	Dynamic message priorities [31]
Route	xy-routing	Torus chip xy-routing [12]
Backtrack	IncPeriod	Increase application period [26]
	IncReplicate	Increase task replication degree [21]

Table 1: Techniques currently implemented in GAST.

5.2 Implemented classes

Many scheduling and scheduling-related techniques have been implemented in the current version of GAST. Table 1 shows examples of some of these techniques. Below follows some clarifying remarks as regards the implemented classes.

There are two main techniques for loading the application in GAST. The first technique uses a text file written in a simple specification language (described in Section 6.2.2), and is typically used when GAST should be used to schedule an existing application. The second technique implements a parametrized random task-graph generator suitable for extensive simulation experiments. The random task-graph generator can generate many types of task graph structures with the aid of user-changeable value ranges for parameters such as task execution time, intertask message size, task successor/predecessor count, and task graph depth.

GAST supports the notion of processor classes as proposed by Graham *et al.* [20]. In that classification, processors can be classified as being either *identical*, *uniform*, or *unrelated*. For identical processors, the hardware configuration is the same for all processors and the worst-case execution time (WCET) of a task is the same on any processor. For uniform processors, a task's WCET is the product of a basic execution time and a scaling factor associated with each processor. For unrelated processors, a task's WCET on one processor is not necessarily related to its WCET on some other processor.

Two types of objective functions are implemented in

GAST: those that only optimize a local performance measure (*e.g.*, EST or EDF) and those that optimize a global performance measure (*e.g.*, makespan). Objective functions of the latter type are indicated by a star ('*') in the table.

GAST currently provides support for two task allocation strategies: The *Exhaustive* option is based on the *branch-and-bound* (*B&B*) strategy [38]. The *Greedy* option selects an implementation of a greedy search strategy. A large set of parameters from the B&B model of Kohler and Steiglitz [35] is available for the *Exhaustive* option, which allows for the emulation of both the B&B and the greedy search strategy. A more in-depth description of the implementation of the B&B strategy in GAST can be found in [28, 25].

6 Demonstrating the Features of GAST

In this section, we demonstrate the most salient features of GAST. First, we illustrate how a set of scheduling techniques with different objectives and assumptions can be modeled in GAST. We then present an application case study to highlight the user interaction aspect of GAST. Finally, we summarize some sample simulation experiments to show the practicality of GAST in a research context.

6.1 Decomposition examples

Below we describe how one can perform the decomposition on four existing scheduling techniques for subsequent integration into GAST. These examples clearly demonstrate how the decomposition approach can be useful for a broad spectrum of multiprocessor scheduling techniques.

The real-time data flow (RTDF) scheduling technique proposed by Jonsson *et al.* [26] is designed for pipelined scheduling of applications for which the task periods are typically shorter than the makespan. The main objective of RTDF is to find the shortest possible global task period that makes the application schedulable. Starting with a given global task period, RTDF selects in each scheduling step the task that can be scheduled to complete its execution as early as possible while still meeting the periodicity constraint. In case of a scheduling failure, RTDF uses *IncPeriod*, a global backtracking strategy that increases the length of the task periods by a certain amount before attempting to schedule the application again. Before scheduling commences, RTDF generates a list of the application tasks sorted according to a depth-first traversal of the task graph. The tasks are then scheduled in the order of that list, input tasks first.

The dynamic-level scheduling (DLS) technique proposed by Sih and Lee [47] is a refined version of the traditional list-scheduling algorithm that is able to overlap task execution and intertask communication as a means for finding the shortest possible makespan for an application. DLS uses a scheduling heuristic that selects in each scheduling step the task that has the highest dynamic level. DLS uses a breadth-first, data flow approach for traversing the application tasks. Starting with a ready task set consisting of all input tasks, each scheduling step inserts the immediate successors of the scheduled task in the set of ready tasks.

Hou and Shin [21] present an optimal scheduling algorithm for applications with reliability constraints. Starting with a given degree of task replication, the algorithm minimizes the probability of dynamic failure — that is, the proba-

Object class	RTDF [26]	DLS [47]	Hou/Shin [21]	Ramamritham [43]
TaskSet	*	*	*	*
ProcSet	Identical	*	Identical	Identical
Topology	*	*	*	*
Approximate	—	—	—	All
Deadline	Period	—	MinMax	Period
Cluster	—	—	—	Pairwise
Replicate	—	—	—	—
Allocate	Greedy	Greedy	Exhaustive	Greedy
ObjFunc	EFT	HDL	Failure	LST
Schedule	Time	Time	Time	Time
CModel	*	*	*	*
Route	*	*	*	*
Backtrack	IncPeriod	—	IncReplicate	—

Table 2: Examples of parameter combinations.

bility that at least one application timing constraint will be violated due to failing processors or communication links. For this purpose, a lower-bound function (*Failure*) is utilized for predicting the probability of dynamic failure during the exhaustive search. If the probability of dynamic failure for the complete schedule is higher than a given limit, the algorithm uses *IncReplicate*, a global backtracking strategy that increases the degree of replication before attempting to schedule the application again. The algorithm generates a list of the application tasks sorted in order of decreasing static levels. Tasks are then scheduled in the order of that list, highest static levels first. Before scheduling, task arrival times and deadlines are assigned according to the *MinMax* strategy.

Ramamritham [43] presents a scheduling algorithm for applications with given replication constraints. His algorithm utilizes a latest-start-time (LST) scheduling heuristic that selects in each scheduling step the task that has the least difference between its deadline and static level. In addition to task execution times, the static levels include approximate costs for intertask communication. Whether communication costs will exist between tasks or not is governed by the *Pairwise* clustering strategy that attempts to assign tasks that communicate heavily to the same processor. The scheduling algorithm uses the breadth-first, data flow approach for traversing the application tasks.

Table 2 summarizes the choice of parameters for the techniques analyzed. A long dash ('—') in the column of a particular technique indicates that the parameter either is of no interest for the technique or can be ignored because similar operations have been performed in advance. A wild-card ('*') in a column indicates that any parameter setting is acceptable.

6.2 Application case study

We now demonstrate the user-interaction aspect of GAST by means of an accompanying graphic visualization tool. The object of our case study is a simple control application, originally described in [13]. Figure 2 illustrates the task graph of the application. In the graph each node is labeled with the corresponding task identifier T_i and execution time c_i, and each arc representing an interprocessor message between tasks T_i and T_j is labeled with the message size $m_{i,j}$. Arcs representing local communication are treated as pure precedence constraints. For output tasks, the absolute deadline D_i is given in conjunction with the corresponding node. All input tasks have an arrival time equal to zero. In [13], interprocessor communication is modeled as separate tasks. We have chosen a different representation where interprocessor com-

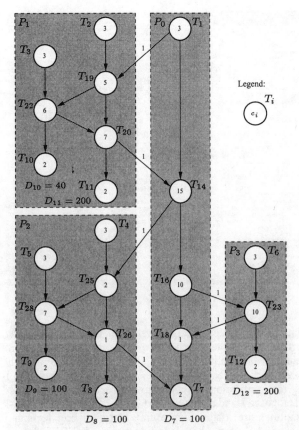

Figure 2: Example task graph.

munication channels are not treated as tasks, but as precedence constraints with message communication that must be scheduled separately on the network. All remaining tasks, however, are identified by the numbers used in [13].

6.2.1 Graphical interface

The body of GAST is a command-line-based program that takes as input a set of command-line parameters and an optional task graph input file, and leaves as output a set of files that contain complete scheduling information. Because the number of options to GAST can be quite large and the input and output file formats are somewhat cryptic to the human eye, a graphic visualization tool, called XGAST, has been developed. XGAST is written in the Tcl/Tk language and administrates a set of widgets encompassing buttons, menus, and text fields that correspond to the object classes in GAST.

Figure 3 shows the XGAST main window. The figure clearly illustrates how, for each main object class (described in Section 5.1) in GAST, a corresponding menu widget exists in XGAST. There are also widgets that correspond to other functions in GAST, such as selecting whether to use replication in the time domain or whether task deadlines should be hard or soft. After selecting the parameter options, the application is scheduled on the chosen platform architecture with the Schedule button. This will cause XGAST to invoke the GAST program to perform the actual scheduling.

The large text window in XGAST displays various statistics from the scheduling attempt — for example, the applica-

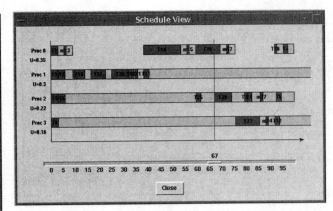

Figure 3: The main window in XGAST.

tion's workload and average parallelism, number of explored vertices during the search, and average/maximum/minimum values of task laxity, lateness and processor utilization. The statistics displayed in the figure are the results from scheduling the application in Figure 2 on a four-processor, shared bus topology, and a time-driven task dispatching policy. Task deadlines are assigned according to the slicing technique [13] and tasks are scheduled using the greedy EDF heuristic. Among other information, the statistical window in XGAST shows that the minimum task laxity of the application is 2.57, which corresponds to the results reported in [13].

If GAST reports a valid schedule, a timing diagram can be called up from XGAST with the View Schedule button. Figure 4 illustrates the appearance of the XGAST schedule window, again assuming the scheduled application in Figure 2. The schedule window shows the respective start and finish times of each task (recall that we assume a time-driven dispatching policy) in the application on its designated processor. The total processor utilization is also shown for each processor in the left part of the window. A slider widget can be used for examining in greater detail the start and finish times of each task. In our example, the slider has been positioned at 67 time units, which is the scheduled start time for task T_{28}.

For larger experimental studies, typically using randomly-generated task graphs, the actions of XGAST can be controlled by a Tcl/Tk script file. All variables internal to XGAST are available for direct modification by the script file, which allows for exhaustive evaluation of the effect of various parameter settings on the performance of a chosen scheduling technique. The commands in the script file are executed at the activation of the Batch button.

6.2.2 Input specification

For specific applications, the task graph input to GAST is done via a file using a simple row format as shown in Figure 5. The specification in the figure is again for our example application in Figure 2. Lines 3–6 in the specification define

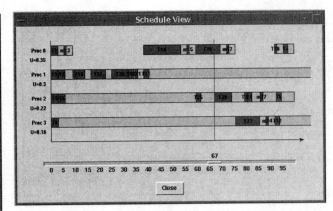

Figure 4: The schedule window in XGAST.

application-specific task clusters and the mapping between task clusters and a corresponding processor. Lines 10–37 in the specification define the application tasks with respect to their symbolic name, WCET, associated cluster, arrival time, deadline, period, and degree of replication. Similarly, lines 41–72 define communication channels with respect to source and destination task, identified by their descriptor names, and the amount of data to be transmitted between the tasks. Question marks ('?') in the specification of a task denote unspecified values that need to be defined by the operations in the preprocessing stage. In our example, task arrival times and deadlines denoted '?' are derived using the slicing technique [13]. Task periods not specified are set by GAST to the maximum application makespan (in this case, 97.4 time units).

6.3 Simulation experiments

During its development, GAST has been successfully used in a broad range of studies for evaluating assignment and scheduling policies under varying architecture configurations and application workloads. Below we summarize the results from some sample experiments demonstrating the flexibility of GAST as a simulation tool.

In [27], we proposed an adaptive deadline-assignment technique for precedence-constrained task sets that accounts for potential contention over processors during deadline assignment. In an extensive simulation study, we demonstrated that the adaptive technique outperforms the original, non-adaptive, technique [13] with respect to both success ratio and maximum task lateness, and also exhibits very robust behavior for variations in system size, deadline tightness, and execution time distribution. Using the adaptive technique, we also evaluated strategies for communication-cost estimation in a system with relaxed locality constraints. The simulation studies revealed that the highest success ratio is attained when using a strategy that always assumes (during deadline assignment) that there is no communication cost in the system.

In [30], we studied the choice of objective function in a list-scheduling algorithm. We performed a simulation study involving four objective functions (see Table 1 for an explanation): two global heuristics, HSL and HDL, that prioritize task static levels during scheduling, and two local heuristics, EST and EFT, that make their decisions based on the earliest start/finish time of a task. The performance measure of interest in the study was the application makespan. The ex-

```
 1 Nclusters 4                                    38
 2 # Cluster Desc Proc                            39 Nconns 32
 3 Cluster  C1   0                                40 # Conn Src  Dst  Data
 4 Cluster  C2   1                                41 Conn   T1   m13  1
 5 Cluster  C3   2                                42 Conn   m13  T14  1
 6 Cluster  C4   3                                43 Conn   m13  T19  1
 7                                                44 Conn   T2   T19  1
 8 Ntasks 28                                      45 Conn   T3   T22  1
 9 # Task Desc WCET Clust Arrv Dead Peri Repl     46 Conn   T4   T25  1
10 Task   T1   3    C1    0    ?    ?    ?        47 Conn   T5   T28  1
11 Task   T2   3    C2    0    ?    ?    ?        48 Conn   T6   T23  1
12 Task   T3   3    C2    0    ?    ?    ?        49 Conn   T18  T7   1
13 Task   T4   3    C3    0    ?    ?    ?        50 Conn   T26  m27  1
14 Task   T5   3    C3    0    ?    ?    ?        51 Conn   m27  T7   1
15 Task   T6   3    C4    0    ?    ?    ?        52 Conn   m27  T8   1
16 Task   T7   2    C1    ?    100  ?    ?        53 Conn   T28  T9   1
17 Task   T8   2    C3    ?    100  ?    ?        54 Conn   T22  T10  1
18 Task   T9   2    C3    ?    100  ?    ?        55 Conn   T20  m21  1
19 Task   T10  2    C2    ?    40   ?    ?        56 Conn   m21  T11  1
20 Task   T11  2    C2    ?    200  ?    ?        57 Conn   m21  T14  1
21 Task   T12  2    C4    ?    200  ?    ?        58 Conn   T23  m24  1
22 Task   m13  1    C1    ?    ?    ?    ?        59 Conn   m24  T12  1
23 Task   T14  15   C1    ?    ?    ?    ?        60 Conn   m24  T18  1
24 Task   m15  1    C1    ?    ?    ?    ?        61 Conn   T19  T22  1
25 Task   T16  10   C1    ?    ?    ?    ?        62 Conn   T19  T20  1
26 Task   m17  1    C1    ?    ?    ?    ?        63 Conn   T22  T20  1
27 Task   T18  1    C1    ?    ?    ?    ?        64 Conn   T14  m15  1
28 Task   T19  5    C2    ?    ?    ?    ?        65 Conn   m15  T16  1
29 Task   T20  7    C2    ?    ?    ?    ?        66 Conn   m15  T25  1
30 Task   m21  1    C2    ?    ?    ?    ?        67 Conn   T16  m17  1
31 Task   T22  6    C2    ?    ?    ?    ?        68 Conn   m17  T18  1
32 Task   T23  10   C4    ?    ?    ?    ?        69 Conn   m17  T23  1
33 Task   m24  1    C4    ?    ?    ?    ?        70 Conn   T25  T26  1
34 Task   T25  2    C3    ?    ?    ?    ?        71 Conn   T25  T28  1
35 Task   T26  1    C3    ?    ?    ?    ?        72 Conn   T28  T26  1
36 Task   m27  1    C3    ?    ?    ?    ?        73
37 Task   T28  7    C3    ?    ?    ?    ?        74
```

Figure 5: Example task graph specification.

periments revealed that the local strategies are very suitable choices for scheduling fine-grain applications on architectures with significant communication cost. For architectures with negligible communication cost, the simulations indicate that global techniques are the preferred choice.

In [28], we evaluated a parametrized branch-and-bound (B&B) strategy for multiprocessor scheduling. The performance measure of interest in the study was the number of explored vertices during the search for an optimal solution. Simulation experiments indicated that a last-in, first-out (LIFO) vertex selection strategy is by far the best choice for real-time multiprocessor scheduling. We also proposed a new lower-bound cost function that outperforms existing ones when resource contention is non-negligible.

7 Discussion

The decomposition approach used in GAST represents a first attempt to fit a number of different types of scheduling strategies into a common framework. While our experience so far is that the approach works extremely well, we do not exclude the possibility that there are better ways to do the decomposition. This is something we intend to investigate further by attempting to include more methods in the tool.

Recall that GAST has been designed primarily for the purpose of evaluation and comparison. Therefore, it will probably not be suitable for generating scheduling data and machine code. Instead, GAST can aid in the design of more specialized tools for specific applications, or be used as a prototyping tool in a design process.

One limitation of the current version of GAST is that it only supports pre-run-time assignment and scheduling policies for multiprocessor architectures. Therefore, work has begun to also include support for simulation of the run-time mechanisms of a real-time system, including dynamic load balancing and QoS negotiation. Preliminary efforts indicate that the object-oriented approach used so far in the design of GAST will be very beneficial in upgrading the functionality.

Finally, it should be noted that the current version of

GAST (v.0.5.0.3) runs on the UNIX (Linux, Solaris) and the Microsoft Windows 95/NT operating systems.

8 Conclusions

This paper has presented GAST, an object-oriented tool for the objective evaluation of task assignment and scheduling techniques in multiprocessor systems. GAST is based on a decomposition approach where existing scheduling techniques have been broken down into a set of common parameters. These parameters can then be chosen from a toolbox of existing techniques. This paper has clearly demonstrated the powerful software facilities of GAST and its capabilities for use as a simulation tool.

Acknowledgments

The author is grateful to Jonas Vasell, Jim Nilsson, Ola Lundqvist, Björn Johansson and Monika Andersson for their valuable contributions to the GAST development project.

References

[1] T. F. Abdelzaher and K. G. Shin. Period-based load partitioning and assignment for large real-time applications. Technical report, Dept. of Electrical Engineering and Computer Science, University of Michigan, Ann Arbor, Michigan 48109-2122, May 1996.

[2] T. L. Adam, K. M. Chandy, and J. R. Dickson. A comparison of list schedules for parallel processing systems. Communications of the Association for Computing Machinery, 17(12):685–690, December 1974.

[3] I. Ahmad and Y.-K. Kwok. A new approach to scheduling parallel programs using task duplication. In Proc. of the Int'l Conf. on Parallel Processing, volume 2, pp. 47–51, August 15–19, 1994.

[4] I. Ahmad, Y.-K. Kwok, M.-Y. Wu, and W. Shu. Automatic parallelization and scheduling of programs on multiprocessors using CASCH. In Proc. of the Int'l Conf. on Parallel Processing, pp. 288–291, Bloomingdale, Illinois, August 11–15, 1997.

[5] N. Audsley, A. Burns, M. Richardson, K. Tindell, and A. J. Wellings. Applying new scheduling theory to static priority pre-emptive scheduling. Software Engineering Journal, 8(5):284–292, September 1993.

[6] N. C. Audsley, A. Burns, M. F. Richardson, and A. J. Wellings. STRESS: A simulator for hard real-time systems. Software – Practice and Experience, 24(6):543–564, June 1994.

[7] S. Berryman and I. Sommerville. Modeling and evaluating the feasibility of timing constraints under different real-time scheduling algorithms. Real-Time Systems, 4(4):287–306, December 1992.

[8] P. Brucker, M. R. Garey, and D. S. Johnson. Scheduling equal-length tasks under treelike precedence constraints to minimize maximum lateness. Mathematics of Operations Research, 2(3):275–284, August 1977.

[9] S.-T. Cheng, S.-I. Hwang, and A. K. Agrawala. Schedulability-oriented replication of periodic tasks in distributed real-time systems. In Proc. of the IEEE Int'l Conf. on Distributed Computing Systems, pp. 196–203, Vancouver, Canada, May 30 –June 2, 1995.

[10] H. Chetto, M. Silly, and T. Bouchentouf. Dynamic scheduling of real-time tasks under precedence constraints. Real-Time Systems, 2(3):181–194, September 1990.

[11] Y.-C. Chung and S. Ranka. Applications and performance analysis of a compile-time optimization approach for list scheduling algorithms on distributed memory multiprocessors. In Proc. of Supercomputing '92, pp. 512–521, Minneapolis, Minnesota, November 16–20, 1992.

[12] W. J. Dally and C. L. Seitz. The Torus Routing Chip. Distributed Computing, 1(4):187–196, 1986.

[13] M. Di Natale and J. A. Stankovic. Dynamic end-to-end guarantees in distributed real-time systems. In Proc. of the IEEE Real-Time Systems Symposium, pp. 216–227, San Juan, Puerto Rico, December 7–9, 1994.

[14] M. Di Natale and J. A. Stankovic. Applicability of simulated annealing methods to real-time scheduling and jitter control. In Proc. of the IEEE Real-Time Systems Symposium, pp. 190–199, Pisa, Italy, December 5–7, 1995.

[15] H. El-Rewini and T. G. Lewis. Scheduling parallel program tasks onto arbitrary target machines. *Journal of Parallel and Distributed Computing*, 9(2):138–153, June 1990.

[16] M. R. Garey, D. S. Johnson, B. B. Simons, and R. E. Tarjan. Scheduling unit-time tasks with arbitrary release times and deadlines. *SIAM Journal on Computing*, 10(2):256–269, May 1981.

[17] A. Gerasoulis and T. Yang. A comparison of clustering heuristics for scheduling directed acyclic graphs on multiprocessors. *Journal of Parallel and Distributed Computing*, 16(4):276–291, December 1992.

[18] R. Gerber, S. Hong, and M. Saksena. Guaranteeing real-time requirements with resource-based calibration of periodic processes. *IEEE Trans. on Software Engineering*, 21(7):579–592, July 1995.

[19] R. T. Goettge, E. Brehm, C. Palczak, J. A. Stankovic, and M. Humphrey. Knowledge-based assistance for real-time systems. In *Proc. of the IEEE Int'l Conf. on Engineering of Complex Computer Systems*, pp. 223–226, Ft. Lauderdale, Florida, November 6–10, 1995.

[20] R. L. Graham, E. L. Lawler, J. K. Lenstra, and A. H. G. Rinnooy Kan. Optimization and approximation in deterministic sequencing and scheduling: A survey. In P. L. Hammer, E. L. Johnson, and B. H. Korte, editors, *Annals of Discrete Mathematics*, volume 5: Discrete Optimization II, pp. 287–326. North-Holland, Amsterdam, 1979.

[21] C.-J. Hou and K. G. Shin. Replication and allocation of task modules in distributed real-time systems. In *Proc. of the IEEE Int'l Symposium on Fault-Tolerant Computing*, pp. 26–35, Austin, Texas, June 15–17, 1994.

[22] M. Humphrey and J. A. Stankovic. CAISARTS: A tool for real-time scheduling assistance. In *Proc. of the IEEE Real-Time Technology and Applications Symposium*, pp. 150–159, Brookline, Massachusetts, June 10–12, 1996.

[23] K. Jeffay, D. F. Stanat, and C. U. Martel. On non-preemptive scheduling of periodic and sporadic tasks. In *Proc. of the IEEE Real-Time Systems Symposium*, pp. 129–139, San Antonio, Texas, December 4–6, 1991.

[24] J. Jonsson. Exploring the importance of preprocessing operations in real-time multiprocessor scheduling. In *Proc. of the IEEE Real-Time Systems Symposium – Work-in-Progress Session*, pp. 31–34, San Francisco, California, December 3–4, 1997.

[25] J. Jonsson. *The Impact of Application and Architecture Properties on Real-Time Multiprocessor Scheduling*. Ph.D. thesis, School of Electrical and Computer Engineering, Chalmers University of Technology, Göteborg, Sweden, September 1997.

[26] J. Jonsson, A. Olsson, and J. Vasell. Predicting real-time behaviour for data flow computations. In *Proc. of the EuroMicro Workshop on Real-Time Systems*, pp. 270–275, Odense, Denmark, June 14–16, 1995.

[27] J. Jonsson and K. G. Shin. Deadline assignment in distributed hard real-time systems with relaxed locality constraints. In *Proc. of the IEEE Int'l Conf. on Distributed Computing Systems*, pp. 432–440, Baltimore, Maryland, May 27–30, 1997.

[28] J. Jonsson and K. G. Shin. A parametrized branch-and-bound strategy for scheduling precedence-constrained tasks on a multiprocessor system. In *Proc. of the Int'l Conf. on Parallel Processing*, pp. 158–165, Bloomingdale, Illinois, August 11–15, 1997.

[29] J. Jonsson and J. Vasell. A comparative study of methods for time-deterministic message delivery in a multiprocessor architecture. In *Proc. of the IEEE Int'l Parallel Processing Symposium*, pp. 392–398, Honolulu, Hawaii, April 15–19, 1996.

[30] J. Jonsson and J. Vasell. On objective function selection in list scheduling algorithms for digital signal processing applications. In *Proc. of the IEEE Int'l Conf. on Acoustics, Speech and Signal Processing*, pp. 667–670, Munich, Germany, April 21–24, 1997.

[31] D. D. Kandlur, K. G. Shin, and D. Ferrari. Real-time communication in multihop networks. *IEEE Trans. on Parallel and Distributed Systems*, 5(10):1044–1055, October 1994.

[32] B. Kao and H. Garcia-Molina. Deadline assignment in a distributed soft real-time system. In *Proc. of the IEEE Int'l Conf. on Distributed Computing Systems*, pp. 428–437, Pittsburgh, Pennsylvania, May 25–28, 1993.

[33] S. J. Kim and J. C. Browne. A general approach to mapping of parallel computations upon multiprocessor architectures. In *Proc. of the Int'l Conf. on Parallel Processing*, volume 3, pp. 1–8, 1988.

[34] E. Kligerman and A. D. Stoyenko. Real-Time Euclid: A language for reliable real-time systems. *IEEE Trans. on Software Engineering*, 12(9):941–949, September 1986.

[35] W. H. Kohler and K. Steiglitz. Enumerative and iterative computational approaches. In E. G. Coffman, Jr., editor, *Computer and Job-Shop Scheduling Theory*, chapter 6, pp. 229–287. Wiley, New York, 1976.

[36] B. Kruatrachue and T. Lewis. Grain size determination for parallel processing. *IEEE Software*, 5(1):23–32, January 1988.

[37] Y.-K. Kwok and I. Ahmad. Exploiting duplication to minimize the execution times of parallel programs on message-passing systems. In *Proc. of the IEEE Symposium on Parallel and Distributed Processing*, pp. 426–433, Dallas, Texas, October 26–29, 1994.

[38] E. L. Lawler and D. E. Wood. Branch-and-bound methods: A survey. *Operations Research*, 14(4):699–719, July/August 1966.

[39] C.-Y. Lee, J.-J. Hwang, Y.-C. Chow, and F. D. Anger. Multiprocessor scheduling with interprocessor communication delays. *Operations Research Letters*, 7(3):141–147, June 1988.

[40] T. Lewis and H. El-Rewini. Parallax: A tool for parallel program scheduling. *IEEE Parallel and Distributed Technology*, 1(2):62–72, May 1993.

[41] C. L. Liu and J. W. Layland. Scheduling algorithms for multiprogramming in a hard-real-time environment. *Journal of the Association for Computing Machinery*, 20(1):46–61, January 1973.

[42] J. W.-S. Liu, J. L. Redondo, Z. Deng, T. S. Tia, R. Bettati, A. Silberman, M. Storch, R. Ha, and W. K. Shih. PERTS: A prototyping environment for real-time systems. In *Proc. of the IEEE Real-Time Systems Symposium*, pp. 184–188, Raleigh-Durham, North Carolina, December 1–3, 1993.

[43] K. Ramamritham. Allocation and scheduling of precedence-related periodic tasks. *IEEE Trans. on Parallel and Distributed Systems*, 6(4):412–420, April 1995.

[44] M. Saksena and S. Hong. Resource conscious design of distributed real-time systems: An end-to-end approach. In *Proc. of the IEEE Int'l Conf. on Engineering of Complex Computer Systems*, pp. 306–313, Montreal, Canada, October 21–25, 1996.

[45] R. Sethi. Algorithms for minimal-length schedules. In E. G. Coffman, Jr., editor, *Computer and Job-Shop Scheduling Theory*, chapter 2, pp. 51–99. Wiley, New York, 1976.

[46] D. Seto, J. P. Lehoczky, L. Sha, and K. G. Shin. On task schedulability in real-time control systems. In *Proc. of the IEEE Real-Time Systems Symposium*, pp. 13–21, Washington, D.C., December 4–6, 1996.

[47] G. C. Sih and E. A. Lee. A compile-time scheduling heuristic for interconnection-constrained heterogeneous processor architectures. *IEEE Trans. on Parallel and Distributed Systems*, 4(2):175–187, February 1993.

[48] G. C. Sih and E. A. Lee. Declustering: A new multiprocessor scheduling technique. *IEEE Trans. on Parallel and Distributed Systems*, 4(6):625–637, June 1993.

[49] M. F. Storch and J. W.-S. Liu. DRTSS: A simulation framework for complex real-time systems. In *Proc. of the IEEE Real-Time Technology and Applications Symposium*, pp. 160–169, Brookline, Massachusetts, June 10–12, 1996.

[50] A. D. Stoyenko. A schedulability analyzer for Real-Time Euclid. In *Proc. of the IEEE Real-Time Systems Symposium*, pp. 218–227, San Jose, California, December 1–3, 1987.

[51] K. Tindell and J. Clark. Holistic schedulability analysis for distributed hard real-time systems. *Microprocessing and Microprogramming*, 40(2/3):117–134, April 1994.

[52] K. W. Tindell, A. Burns, and A. J. Wellings. Allocating hard real-time tasks: An NP-hard problem made easy. *Real-Time Systems*, 4(2):145–165, June 1992.

[53] H. Tokuda and M. Kotera. A real-time tool set for the ARTS kernel. In *Proc. of the IEEE Real-Time Systems Symposium*, pp. 289–299, Huntsville, Alabama, December 6–8, 1988.

[54] H. Tokuda and C. W. Mercer. ARTS: A distributed real-time kernel. *ACM Operating Systems Review*, 23(3):29–53, July 1989.

[55] J. P. C. Verhoosel, D. K. Hammer, E. Y. Luit, L. R. Welch, and A. D. Stoyenko. A model for scheduling of object-based, distributed real-time systems. *Real-Time Systems*, 8(1):5–34, January 1995.

[56] J. Xu and D. L. Parnas. Scheduling processes with release times, deadlines, precedence, and exclusion relations. *IEEE Trans. on Software Engineering*, 16(3):360–369, March 1990.

Session 6C
Collective Communication

Chair: Jose Duato
Universidad Politecnica de Valencia

Where to Provide Support for Efficient Multicasting in Irregular Networks: Network Interface or Switch?*

Rajeev Sivaram[†]   Ram Kesavan[†]   Dhabaleswar K. Panda[†]   Craig B. Stunkel[‡]

[†]Dept. of Computer and Information Science
The Ohio State University
Columbus, OH 43210
Email: {sivaram,kesavan,panda}@cis.ohio-state.edu

[‡]IBM T. J. Watson Research Center
P. O. Box 218
Yorktown Heights, NY 10598
Email: stunkel@watson.ibm.com

Abstract

Recent research has proposed methods for enhancing the performance of multicast in networks with irregular topologies. These methods fall into two broad categories: (a) network interface (NI) based schemes that make use of enhanced functionality of the software/firmware running at the NI processor, and (b) switch-based methods that use enhancements to the switch architecture to support hardware multicast. However, it is not clear how these methods compare to each other and when it makes sense to use one over the other. In order to answer such questions, we perform a number of simulation experiments to compare the performance of three efficient multicasting schemes: an NI-based multicasting scheme that uses a k-binomial tree [5], a switch-based multicasting scheme that uses path-based multidestination worms [4], and a switch-based multicasting scheme that uses a single tree-based multidestination worm [14]. We first study the performance of the three schemes for single multicast traffic while changing a number of system parameters one at a time to isolate their impact. We then study the performance of these schemes under increasing multicast load. Our results show that the switch-based multicasting scheme using a single tree-based multidestination worm performs the best among the three schemes. However, the NI-based multicasting scheme is capable of delivering high performance compared to the switch-based multicast using path-based worms especially when the software overhead at the network interface is less than half of the overhead at the host. We therefore conclude that support for multicast at the NI is an important first step to improving multicast performance. However, there is still considerable gain that can be achieved by supporting hardware multicast in switches. Finally, while supporting such hardware multicast, it is better to support schemes that can achieve multicast in one phase.

1   Introduction

In a world where computing needs are increasing by the day, there is a constant search for cost-effective high-performance computing solutions. Using a network of commodity workstations as a parallel computing environment has the potential to provide such a cost-effective high-performance computing environment. Much recent research has therefore focussed on extending parallel processing solutions to such networks of commodity workstations (NOWs).

However, networks of workstations environments have typically evolved from computing environments where communication requirements are less stringent (both in terms of latency and bandwidth). In such an environment, the workstations that form the processing nodes are typically interconnected in arbitrary, irregular topologies. Using such topologies allows easy addition and deletion of nodes to the computing environment making the overall environment more amenable to network reconfigurations and resistant to faults. However, these topologies do not possess many of the attractive mathematical properties of the regular topologies. A lot of the problems relating to inter-processor/inter-node communication that have been solved for regular topologies are therefore being revisited for such irregular topologies. One such problem is that of collective communication.

Collective communication plays an important role in parallel systems, and involves communication among groups of (2 or more) processes [9]. Examples of collective operations include multicast [8], barrier synchronization, reduction, etc. The importance of such operations is underlined by the inclusion of several primitives for collective communication in the Message Passing Interface (MPI) standard [7]. Such collective operations are also used for system level operations in distributed shared memory systems, such as for cache invalidations, acknowledgment collection, and synchronization [2].

Of these collective operations, multicast is most fundamental and important and is used for implementing several of the other collective operations. Traditionally, multicast has been implemented using the underlying support for point-to-point (unicast) communication. The best of these schemes reduces the impact of the high overhead associated with sending/receiving point-to-point messages by allowing multiple nodes to simultaneously transmit/receive messages in a given phase. Such multicasting schemes require at least $log_2(n+1)$ communication steps, and are the best achievable using unicast communication primitives.

A number of schemes have been recently proposed to further improve multicast performance. These schemes can be classified into two main categories. The first category of schemes is referred to as *switch-based multicasting schemes*. These schemes use enhancements at the routers/switches of the network to allow an incoming packet to be forwarded to multiple output ports of the router/switch [15]. Such a method allows messages (christened *multidestination messages*) to be communicated to multiple destinations incurring a single software overhead for sending the message. There are two subclasses of switch-based multicasting schemes: tree-based [14] and path-based [4]. In the best tree-based multicasting scheme, multicast can be performed in a single phase using one multidestination worm from the source node to all the destinations [14, 15]. The path-based multicasting schemes typically require multiple multidestination worms to perform multicast

*This research is supported in part by NSF Career Award MIP-9502294, NSF Grant CCR-9704512, an IBM Cooperative Fellowship, and an Ohio State University Presidential Fellowship.

to arbitrary destination sets. These worms are transmitted in multiple phases with the destinations in a phase acting as secondary sources in succeeding phases of the multicast [4].

The second category of multicasting schemes is referred to as *network interface-based* or *NI-based multicasting schemes*. Typically, communication between two nodes incurs software overhead at both the host and at the network interface for both sending and receiving a message. The NI-based schemes use enhancements at the network interface so that multicast messages are forwarded to the next destination as soon as they are received at the network interface of an intermediate destination (and the message has begun to be transferred to the memory of the local host) [16]. This hides the significant software overhead for receiving a message at an intermediate destination host, and eliminates the overhead at the host for sending the message to other destinations in the succeeding phases of the multicast.

It is obvious that a multicasting scheme with enhanced support at the network interface *and* the switches will perform better than a scheme that makes use of support at *either* the network interface or at the switches. However, it is necessary to first compare the effect of improved support for multicast at the switches to support for multicast at the network interface to decide which of these schemes results in better performance and when. While making such a comparison, we must therefore assume no network interface support for the switch-based multicasting schemes, i.e., every communication phase under the tree-based and path-based schemes should incur software overhead at the host and network interface of the source and (intermediate) destinations. Such a comparison is needed for an architect to evaluate the relative merits of these two categories of multicasting schemes and to decide which scheme to support and when. In order to make such a decision, a number of questions need to be answered: how quickly can multicast be performed with support at the network interfaces and low overhead messaging layer support? How does multicast with switch/router support (alone) compare with multicast implemented with network interface support? For what range of system parameters does it make sense to use one over the other?

The goal of this paper is to provide answers to these questions by comparing the performance of the single phase tree-based multicasting scheme to the best path-based multicasting scheme and to an optimal NI-based multicasting scheme. We perform extensive simulations to evaluate the impact of various system parameters on the performance of the three schemes by considering the performance of single multicasts and by varying each of the parameters one at a time. These parameters include message length, number of switches, and the ratio of the overhead at the host to the overhead at the network interface. Finally, we study the latency of these schemes under increasing multicast load with a variation of a few selected parameters.

Our analysis and simulations show that the single phase tree-based multicasting scheme studied in this paper is the most powerful multicasting scheme. However, the NI-based scheme can deliver extremely high performance, especially when the software overhead for absorbing and retransmitting messages at the interface is considerably lower than the corresponding overheads at the host. The path-based multicasting scheme's performance varies with variation in a number of network parameters and it can perform worse than the NI-based scheme in a number of cases. We therefore conclude that support for multicast at the NI is an important first step to improving multicast performance. However, there is still considerable gain that can be achieved by supporting hardware multicast in switches. Finally, while supporting such hardware multicast, it is better to support schemes that can achieve multicast in one phase.

The remaining part of the paper is organized as follows. In Sec. 2 we present our network model and the underlying routing algorithm assumed in this paper. We then present in Sec. 3 an overview of the multicasting schemes used for our comparison in this paper. An exhaustive simulation based comparison of the three schemes is then presented in Sec. 4. Finally, we present our conclusions in Sec. 5.

2 System Model

In this section, we present the network model assumed in this paper. The related deadlock-free routing issues for such a network are also discussed.

2.1 Network Model

Figure 1(a) shows a typical parallel system using a switch-based interconnect with irregular topology. Such a network consists of a set of switches where each switch has a set of ports. The system in the figure consists of eight switches with eight ports per switch. Some of the ports in each switch are connected to processors, some ports are connected to ports of other switches to provide connectivity between the processors, and some ports are left open for further connections. Such connectivity is typically irregular and the only thing that is guaranteed is that the network is connected. Thus, the interconnection topology of the network can be denoted by a graph $G = (V,E)$ where V is the set of switches, and E is the set of bidirectional links between the switches [1, 12]. Figure 1(b) shows the interconnection graph for the irregular network in Fig. 1(a). It is to be noted that all links are bidirectional and multiple links between two switches are possible.

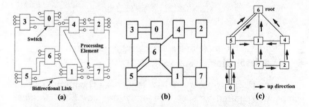

Figure 1. (a) An example system with switch-based interconnect and irregular topology; (b) corresponding interconnection graph G; (c) corresponding BFS spanning tree rooted at node 6.

2.2 Routing Issues

Several deadlock-free routing schemes have been proposed in the literature for irregular networks [1, 12]. Without loss of generality, in this paper we assume the routing scheme for our irregular network to be similar to that used in Autonet [12] due to its simplicity and its commercial implementation. Such routing allows adaptivity, and is deadlock-free.

In this routing scheme, a breadth-first spanning tree (BFS) is first computed on the graph G using a distributed algorithm. The algorithm has the property that all nodes will eventually agree on a unique spanning tree. Deadlock-free routing is based on a loop-free assignment of direction to the operational links. In particular, the "up" end of each link is defined as: 1) the end whose switch is closer to the root in the spanning tree; or 2) the end whose switch has the lower ID, if both ends are at switches at the same tree level. The result of this assignment is that the directed links do not form loops. Figure 1(c) shows the BFS spanning tree corresponding to the interconnection graph shown in Fig. 1(b), and the assignment of the "up" direction to the links. To eliminate deadlocks while still allowing all links to be used, this routing uses the following up/down rule: a legal route must traverse zero or more links in the "up" direction followed by zero or more links in the "down" direction. Putting it in the negative, a packet may never traverse a link along the "up" direction after having traversed one in the "down" direction. Details of this routing scheme can be found in [12].

3 Multicasting Approaches

We now present an overview of the three multicasting schemes that we compare in this paper. We first describe the traditional approach to multicasting using multiple phases of unicast messages. We then present the two categories of techniques for providing enhanced support for efficient multicast and present the three schemes studied in this paper.

3.1 Multi-phase Software Approaches to Multicast

Efficient multicast algorithms are typically hierarchical in nature. This means that some destinations serve as intermediate sources, i.e., when they receive a message, they forward copies of it to other destinations. Many such hierarchical algorithms have been proposed in the literature [3] to implement multicast. Figure 2 shows an example of a multicast from a source node to seven other destinations. In the figure, the numbers in brackets indicate the step numbers.

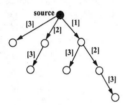

Figure 2. Example of a hierarchical multicast algorithm on a destination set size of 7.

It can be easily observed that $\lceil log_2(n+1) \rceil$ communication steps are required for such a binomial tree based hierarchical multicast to be completed [3]. A communication step is the time required for a message to be sent from one host node to another. Even with lightweight messaging layers, the latency of such a multicast operation is still dominated by the communication software overhead. Recent research to reduce the effect of this overhead on multicast performance has been in two main directions.

3.2 Enhanced Multicasting Schemes

The two major directions in which enhancements have been proposed for reducing the effect of the communication overhead are: (a) increasing the functionality of the software/firmware running at the NI processor, and (b) supporting hardware multicast at the switch. We describe these concepts in greater detail in the following subsections.

3.2.1 Multicasting using Network Interface Support

Let us consider the multicast of a message that spans multiple packets. Figure 3(a) shows the forwarding of a 2-packet multicast message at an intermediate node of a multicast tree. Each of the packets of the message is received at the network interface and copied to host memory using DMA. The host

processor at the intermediate node receives the complete message and then initiates send operations to each of its children in the multicast tree. For each of the send operations, a copy of the message is sent to the network interface, from where it is sent into the network. Therefore, an intermediate node incurs the message send overhead for every copy of the message that it forwards to other destinations. This overhead includes the software start-up overhead and the overhead at the NI for each packet transmission.

Smart NI support can reduce this overhead for multicast, especially for multi-packet messages. Current lean messaging layers allow modification of part of the software running on the NI processor. This part of the software can be modified to allow it to identify a multicast packet [5, 16]. If the next outgoing packet in the send queue of the source node is a multicast packet, the NI processor forwards replicas of the packet to the nodes adjacent to the root of the multicast tree. When a multicast packet is received at the NI of an intermediate node, the NI processor starts copying (using DMA) the packet to host memory. Simultaneously, it forwards replicas of the packet to its children in the multicast tree. Thus, the overhead at the intermediate node's host to receive a packet is hidden, and the overhead at the host to send the packet to its children in the multicast tree is eliminated. Figure 3(b) shows such forwarding with smart network interface support. An implementation of such a smart network interface has been described in [16].

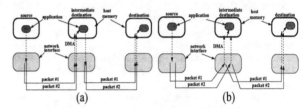

Figure 3. Forwarding of a 2-packet long multicast message by intermediate node using (a) conventional NI support, and (b) smart NI support.

In this paper, we use the FPFS (First-Packet-First-Served) implementation of the smart network interface support [5]. In this implementation, the NI forwards the message on a per-packet basis. The NI at the source node sends the first packet to all the children of the source, then sends the second packet to all the children of the source, and so on. When the first packet of the multicast message arrives at the NI of an intermediate node, it forwards the packet to each of the children of the intermediate node. Subsequently, when the second packet of the multicast message arrives at the NI, it forwards the packet to each of the children, and so on till the last packet is forwarded.

A k-binomial tree has been shown to be optimal for multipacket multicast on systems with such smart NI support [5]. A k-binomial tree is defined as a recursively doubling tree where each vertex has at most k children. The value of k is a function of the size of the multicast set and the number of packets in the multicast message. A method for constructing k-binomial trees with minimized contention on irregular switch-based networks has been proposed in the literature [5]. In this paper we therefore use the k-binomial tree for our multicasting scheme using network interface support.

3.2.2 Multicasting using Switch Support

Another method for improving multicast performance is to provide switches with support for replicating incoming messages to multiple output ports. The basic idea behind such a scheme is to communicate a single message (called a *multi-destination message*) from a source to multiple destinations in almost the same time it takes to send a unicast message to one node [6]. The number of destinations covered depends on the type of encoding/decoding used for the message header.

Given support for replication at the switches, there are two schemes that have been proposed for carrying out multicast in switch based irregular networks: tree-based [14] and path-based [4]. The two schemes differ in the restrictions placed on worm replication, the number of worms required to perform multicast to an arbitrary destination set, the complexity of multicast header formation, and the complexity of the header decoding logic required at the switches. However, we assume the multidestination worms under either scheme conform to the base up*/down* routing algorithm, i.e., the path followed by a multicast packet does not violate any of the rules for routing unicast packets in the system [11]. These schemes are discussed in greater detail in the following two subsections.

3.2.3 Tree-based Multicasting using Multidestination Worms

Tree-based multicasting places no restriction on the replication of a worm at a given switch. The basic idea of tree based replication is to have multiple copies of a packet propagate down a tree which has switches as internal vertices and destinations nodes as leaf vertices.

Two methods have been proposed for tree-based multicast in irregular networks [14]. In this paper, we use the method that uses a single multidestination worm with a bit-string encoded header to perform multicast [14, 15] as a representative of the tree-based multicasting method. The basic idea is to encode the multidestination worm header using an N-bit string where N is the number of nodes in the system. The destinations of the multicast are identified by setting the ith bit of the the bit string to '1' if node i is a destination of the multicast (all other bits are set to '0'). Every switch has a similar N-bit string (called the *reachability string*) associated with every one of its output ports that lead to links in the "down" direction. The reachability string specifies the set of destination nodes that are reachable through the given ("down") output port (subject to the restrictions of the base routing algorithm). After traveling adaptively to a *least common ancestor* switch using links in the "up" direction, a multicast packet is forwarded to those "down"-ward output ports whose reachability string has one or more '1' bits in the same position(s) as in the packet header [14].

Figure 4 illustrates the tree-based multidestination scheme using bit-string encoding for a sample multicast. Figure 4(a) shows the BFS graph of a sample irregular network. Let us assume that there is at least one destination node connected to each of the switches that are highlighted, and that the source node is connected to switch 10. Figure 4(b) shows the tree-based multidestination worm that covers all the destinations of the multicast. Finally, Fig. 4(c) shows an example of a bit-string encoded header and the reachability strings in a 4-port switch of an 8-node system. The worm with the header shown in Fig. 4(c) must be replicated to all the output ports of the switch.

3.2.4 Path-based Multicasting using Multidestination Worms

Under the path-based multicasting scheme [4], multidestination worms use almost exactly the same path followed by a unicast worm from a source to one of its destinations (as allowed under the base routing algorithm). However, at every

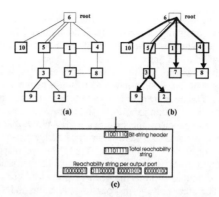

Figure 4. Illustrating the single-phase tree-based multicasting scheme: (a) sample BFS graph of an irregular network with participating switches in the multicast highlighted, (b) the tree-based multidestination worm, and (c) an example of a bit-string encoded header and the various reachability strings in a 4-port switch.

switch along its path, the multidestination worm is allowed to replicate and cover all the destinations of the multicast that are directly connected to that switch. At every switch, the worm is allowed to replicate to multiple output ports that are connected to destination nodes and (if needed) to exactly one other output port that is connected to a switch. Such multidestination worms are called *multi-drop path-based* worms. Figure 5(a) shows an example of a multi-drop path-based multidestination worm. Since there may be no single path from the source which covers all of the destinations, path-based multicasting requires multiple multidestination worms to cover an arbitrary multicast destination set. Furthermore, to arrive at a relatively small number of multidestination worms that cover a given destination set, an algorithm is needed that chooses appropriate paths so that as many destinations as possible are covered by each of the worms. Multiple algorithms have been proposed for this [4]. In addition, a multi-phase algorithm is required to cover the destination set using the multidestination worms so that contention is reduced and multicast can be performed efficiently. In this paper, we use the Multi-Drop Path-based Less Greedy (MDP-LG) algorithm that finds a small number of multidestination worms to cover the destination set and decides how to send these worms in multiple-phases so as to reduce contention and enhance performance. Details of this algorithm can be found in [4], where this algorithm was shown to perform best among the proposed algorithms.

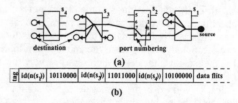

Figure 5. The Multi-drop mechanism: (a) example of a multidestination worm and (b) the header encoding.

The encoding used for the header of each of the multidestination worms under the path-based scheme is as follows. The header of a path-based multidestination worm consists of $2r$ fields, where r is the number of switches on the worm's path in which replication occurs. The header consists of alternating fields consisting of a node ID field followed by a p-bit string field (where p is the number of input ports/output ports in each switch). Figure 5(b) shows the header encoding of the worm shown in Fig. 5(a). The expression $id(n(s_i))$ is the ID of any arbitrary destination node which is connected to the switch s_i. The node ID field is used to index into the tables for unicast message routing and to route the message towards the switch that connects to the specified node. When that switch is reached, the node ID field is stripped and the p-bit string field is examined. The p-bit string has '1' bits corresponding to the output ports to which the worm must be forwarded. As mentioned above, at most one of these ports leads to another switch. The other ports correspond to destination nodes where the message is absorbed. The p-bit string field is stripped before the worm is forwarded to the next switch (if any) where the procedure is repeated. When the message reaches the last switch on its path, the node ID field is stripped away and the message is forwarded to the output ports that correspond to the '1' bits in the last (p-bit string) field of the header.

3.3 Comparison of Architectural Requirements

We now qualitatively compare the three enhanced multicasting schemes described above. The NI-based multicasting scheme requires the computation of the entire k-binomial multicast tree. It may also require additional memory at the network interfaces to buffer multicast packets. This is because each packet is forwarded to multiple destinations, and has to be buffered till the NI-processor has injected all required copies into the network. However, the NI-based multicasting scheme requires no additional support at the switches than what is required for traditional point-to-point message communication.

The tree-based multicasting scheme only requires a single multidestination worm to perform multicast. Furthermore, encoding the multidestination worm header is fairly simple: start with an N bit string and set the bits in the positions corresponding to the destinations to '1'. However, decoding the multidestination header is more complex. First, the switches need to be equipped with reachability strings, which means space is required at the switches for this. Second, there is a one time cost of setting up the values in the strings (which can be done at the time of network startup or reconfiguration). Third, the N bit string has to be compared with the reachability strings of each of the N output ports and the copy of the worm forwarded through a given output port should carry a modified header. Depending on the size of the bit string (which in turn depends on the system size), the cost of such logic may be significant. Finally, support for deadlock-free replication is required at the switches.

The path-based multicasting scheme also requires support for replication at the switches. Furthermore, encoding the worm header is relatively harder. The source needs to know the network topology and needs to run an algorithm to decide on paths that can cover the destination set using very few multidestination worms. Once the paths have been formed, the header must be formed in the format described above. However, decoding the multidestination header may be relatively easy. First, there is no necessity for maintaining reachability strings at each of the switches. Second, the decoding operation at the switches is relatively simple: it is the same table lookup operation required for unicast messages or it is the simple processing of a k-bit string. Finally, the cost of decoding logic does not increase with increase in system size.

We have provided the various trade-offs relating to the cost and complexity of each of three multicasting schemes above. In the next section we compare the performance of the three schemes using simulation experiments.

4 Simulation-based Evaluation

The relative performance of the three multicasting schemes described in the previous sections may depend on a number of parameters. To study the factors that may affect multicast performance in the presence of network contention, we performed simulation experiments varying a number of system parameters one at a time. In the following subsection we present the experiments we performed and the parameters that we varied. The results of our experiments with single multicast are presented next, followed by the results for our experiments to measure the impact of increasing applied load on multicast latency.

4.1 Experiments and Performance Measures

We used a C++/CSIM based simulation testbed [10] for our experiments. The simulation testbed models a large number of topologies, and uses cut-through routing as the flow control technique with an input buffer size of 640 flits.

For each of our experiments, we assume the following default parameters. We assume that the I/O Bus at every host has a bandwidth of 266 MB/s. The current PCI Bus standard calls for a bandwidth of 133 MB/s: our assumptions reflect the belief that I/O bus bandwidths will increase in the future. Let the communication software overhead per message at the sending and receiving host processors be t_{hs} and t_{hr}, respectively, and let the corresponding overhead at the sending and receiving NI processors be t_{ns} and t_{nr}, respectively. For all our experiments, we assume $t_{hr} = t_{hs}$ and $t_{nr} = t_{ns}$. We use the term R to denote the ratio of t_{hs} to t_{ns}, and we assume a default value of $R = 1$. This reflects our belief that messaging layers will become thin and efficient, and that while most work relating to initiating a message may still be done on the host processor, the relatively low speed of the NI processor makes the value of t_{ns} comparable to t_{hs}. We assume a default cycle time of 5 ns, and a default value of 1000 cycles for t_{hs}. This value corresponds to the software overhead incurred at the host using many of the current-day lightweight messaging layers.

In the network, we assume that links are 1 byte wide and that this is equal to the flit size. The link propagation time for a flit across a physical link is assumed to be 1 cycle, as is the time to propagate through a switch crossbar from the input to the output buffer of the switch. We assume a uniform routing overhead of 1 cycle for all three schemes. This reflects our assumption that while the *cost* of the logic involved for decoding and routing a header under the different schemes may vary, the approximate *latency* for doing these operations is likely to be kept within a cycle in most switch implementations. We assume a default packet size of 128 flits, and a default message size of 1 packet. Finally, we assume a default system of 32 nodes that are interconnected by eight 8-port switches in an irregular topology. Our method for generating different irregular topologies is described in [13]. Using this method we generated 10 different topologies, and our results are averaged over all these topologies.

We use two types of experiments to measure the performance of the three multicasting schemes. In the first type of experiments, we measure the latency of single multicasts for each of the three schemes and study the effect of different parameters on the relative latencies of the three schemes. We assume that exactly one multicast occurs in the system at any given time and that there is no other network traffic. This

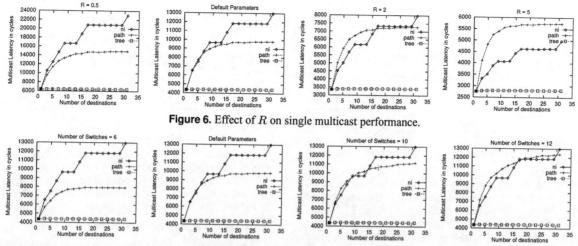

Figure 6. Effect of R on single multicast performance.

Figure 7. Effect of Number of Switches

gives us an estimate of the best possible performance of each of the three schemes in isolation. We use traffic consisting of multiple concurrent multicasts for our second type of experiments. We apply an increasing load consisting of multicast traffic alone and examine the load at which the network saturates with each of the three multicasting schemes under the influence of the various parameters. As in [15], we use effective applied load as a measure of our stimulus. For a multicast of degree m and a load of B, the effective applied load is mB.

4.2 Single Multicast Performance

We now present our results for the effect of single multicasts on the three different multicasting schemes. One by one, we examine the effect of each parameter on the performance of the schemes. As mentioned in Sec. 1, it must be kept in mind that the multi-phase path-based multicasting scheme can also make use of support at the NI to further enhance multicast performance. However, since we are evaluating the effect of support at the NI versus support at the switches, we assume that under the path-based scheme, every intermediate destination receives the incoming message completely at the host and then retransmits the message to the NI and then onto the network.

4.2.1 Effect of R

We first examine the effect of variation in the ratio R (t_{hs}/t_{ns}) on the performance of the three multicasting schemes. Given our default value of $t_{hs} = 1000$ cycles we vary the value of t_{ns} to take on the values 2000, 1000 (default), 500, and 200 cycles (to generate the following values of R: 0.5, 1, 2, and 5, respectively). Figure 6 presents the results of our experiments. We find here (as well as in the other single multicast experiments to follow) that the tree-based multicasting scheme performs extremely well, since it requires only one message and therefore only one communication phase. The interplay between the NI-based and path-based schemes is more interesting. As the ratio increases (i.e. t_{ns} shrinks relative to t_{hs}), the NI-based multicasting scheme begins to outperform the path-based scheme. This is because although the NI-based scheme involves more communication phases, every communication phase incurs a receive overhead of t_{nr} and a send overhead of t_{ns}. On the other hand, the fewer phases of the path-based scheme each incur a receive overhead of $t_{nr} + t_{hr}$ and a sending overhead of $t_{hs} + t_{ns}$.

4.2.2 Effect of Number of Switches

To see the effect of increase in number of switches on multicast performance we increased the number of switches used while keeping the system size (i.e., the number of nodes) constant. However, all switches had 8 ports.

As the number of switches for a given system size increase, the average number of nodes per switch decreases as does the average number of multicast destinations per switch. The results of Fig. 7 show that the number of multidestination worms, the number of phases for multicast, and the multicast latency for the path-based scheme increase with decrease in the average number of destinations per switch. The other two multicasting schemes remain largely unaffected by this increase in the number of switches.

It is to be noted that for the NI-based scheme, the average path length increases with larger number of switches. However, this affects only the propagation time of the worms. Furthermore, since we are using cut-through routing (which is almost "distance independent") this increase in propagation time is negligible.

4.2.3 Effect of Message Length

Figure 8 shows the effect of increasing message length on multicast performance. Here too the path-based scheme begins to perform worse than the NI-based multicast beyond a message length of 512 flits. However, the reason for this decrease in the relative performance of the path-based scheme can be attributed to the increase in the latency of each of its phases: the number of phases remains unchanged. We assume a packet size of 128 flits. Messages larger than this size are split into multiple packets. Under the path-based scheme, a phase finishes only when all the packets of the message arrive at an intermediate destination: only then can the node initiate the path-based multidestination worm of the next phase. On the other hand, under the NI-based scheme (and following the FPFS discipline outlined earlier), a packet can be forwarded to the each of the recipients of the next phase as soon as it arrives at the network interface of an intermediate destination node. The NI-based scheme therefore begins to gain in performance as the number of packets in a message increases.

We also performed a number of experiments to study the effect of startup overhead at the host, system size, and packet length. However, due to lack of space, these results are not presented. Interested readers may refer to [13] for details.

457

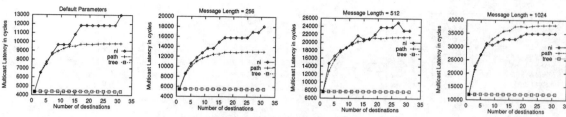

Figure 8. Effect of Message Length

4.3 Latency versus Applied Load for Multicast

We now present our results for multicast latency under an increasing multicast load for each of the three schemes. We used two different multicast degrees in our experiments: 3-way and 15-way multicasts (i.e., multicasts with 3 and 15 destinations, respectively). For each of our experiments, our simulations were run for at least one million cycles, with measurements beginning after a cold-start time of 500,000 cycles. It is worth keeping in mind that for each of the networks, the maximum unicast throughput (assuming no software overheads and no contention for the I/O bus) was observed to be less than 0.18 using up*/down* routing. Also, each of the plots in this section show multicast latency against *effective applied load* as discussed in Sec. 4.1.

4.3.1 Effect of R

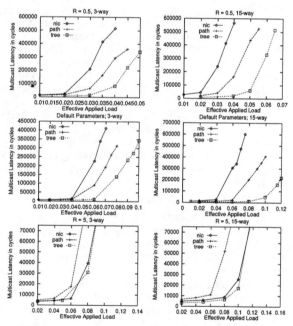

Figure 9. The effect of parameter R on the latency of multicasts under increasing multicast load for 3-way and 15-way multicasts.

Figure 9 shows the results of our experiments under variation of R. In general, for a value of R less than or equal to 1.0, the NI-based scheme performs worst followed by the path-based scheme. The tree-based scheme performs best for such values of R. However, when R becomes greater than 1.0, we note an interesting trend. Now the NI-based scheme performs comparably to the tree-based scheme and much better than the path-based scheme. A possible reason for this is that

the tree-based scheme causes an almost simultaneous reception in all its recipients leading to an increase in the contention for resources at the recipient nodes. On the other hand, the NI-based scheme "spreads" the receive times among the recipients of the multicasts, causing the performance improvement.

4.3.2 Effect of Number of Switches

Our experiments with single multicasts in systems with increasing number of switches has shown that the path-based scheme begins to perform worse as the number of switches in the system increases. We observe a similar trend for our results with multiple multicast traffic (shown in Fig. 10). As the number of switches increases, the saturation load for the path-based scheme approaches that of the NI-based scheme. However, the NI-based scheme results in a greater amount of traffic and higher contention in the network. The tree-based multicast performs almost uniformly well with increase in the number of switches and saturates much later than the other two schemes.

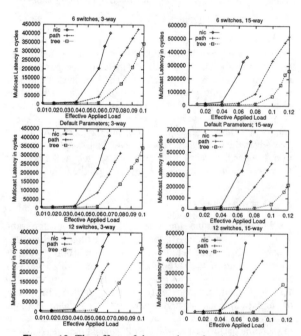

Figure 10. The effect of the number of switches on the latency of multicasts under increasing multicast load for 3-way and 15-way multicasts.

4.3.3 Effect of Message Length

Our results for multicast performance under increasing message length are shown in Fig. 11. The results show that the tree-based multicasting scheme performs best for all message lengths. Furthermore, as was noted for single multicasts, the

458

performance of the NI-based and path-based schemes become comparable as the message lengths increase. Recall that for a single multicast with a message length of 1024 flits (Sec. 4.2.3) we observed that the NI-based scheme performs better than the path-based scheme. Under multiple multicast traffic, the NI-based scheme performs worse (has a lower saturation point and higher latencies) than the path-based scheme for this value of message length, especially for large multicast degrees. This is because the NI-based scheme involves more communication phases and results in more traffic than the path-based scheme, thereby increasing the contention in the network.

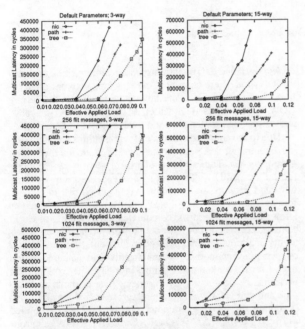

Figure 11. The effect of the message length on the latency of multicasts under increasing multicast load for 3-way and 15-way multicasts.

5 Conclusion

In this paper, we have compared three schemes for efficient multicast in switch-based irregular networks. We find that the tree-based multicasting scheme performs better than the path-based and NI-based schemes. The relative performance of the path and NI-based schemes is sensitive to a number of parameters. The most important of these parameters is the ratio R of overhead at the host to the overhead at the NI. We find that the path-based scheme performs better than the NI-based scheme for values of R less than 1, smaller system sizes, larger switch sizes, fewer switches for a given system size, and for multicasts with fewer packets. In all other cases, the NI-based scheme outperforms the path-based scheme.

Since a wealth of research has focussed on more efficient network interfaces, the value of R is likely to rise in the future. It is also important that the performance of multicast scale with increasing system size and with increase in the number of switches. We therefore conclude that support for multicast at the NI is an important first step to improving multicast performance. However, there is still considerable gain that can be achieved by supporting hardware multicast in switches. In particular, unlike with the NI-based schemes, the performance of the switch-based multicasting schemes is able to scale with

the trend of increasing switch size. Finally, while supporting such hardware multicast, it is better to support schemes that can achieve multicast in one phase even at a (perhaps) additional cost.

Additional Information: A number of related papers and technical reports can be obtained from http://www.cis.ohio-state.edu/~panda/pac.html.

References

[1] N. J. Boden, D. Cohen, et al. Myrinet: A Gigabit-per-Second Local Area Network. *IEEE Micro*, pages 29–35, Feb 1995.

[2] D. Dai and D. K. Panda. Reducing Cache Invalidation Overheads in Wormhole DSMs Using Multidestination Message Passing. In *ICPP*, pages I:138–145, Chicago, IL, Aug 1996.

[3] R. Kesavan, K. Bondalapati, and D. K. Panda. Multicast on Irregular Switch-based Networks with Wormhole Routing. In *HPCA-3*, pages 48–57, February 1997.

[4] R. Kesavan and D. K. Panda. Multicasting on Switch-based Irregular Networks using Multi-drop Path-based Multidestination Worms. In *PCRCW '97*, pages 179–192, June 1997.

[5] R. Kesavan and D. K. Panda. Optimal Multicast with Packetization and Network Interface Support. In *ICPP*, pages 370–377, Aug 1997.

[6] X. Lin and L. M. Ni. Deadlock-free Multicast Wormhole Routing in Multicomputer Networks. In *ISCA*, pages 116–124, 1991.

[7] Message Passing Interface Forum. *MPI: A Message-Passing Interface Standard*, Mar 1994.

[8] L. Ni. Should Scalable Parallel Computers Support Efficient Hardware Multicasting? In *ICPP Workshop on Challenges for Parallel Processing*, pages 2–7, 1995.

[9] D. K. Panda. Issues in Designing Efficient and Practical Algorithms for Collective Communication in Wormhole-Routed Systems. In *ICPP Workshop on Challenges for Parallel Processing*, pages 8–15, 1995.

[10] D. K. Panda, D. Basak, D. Dai, R. Kesavan, R. Sivaram, M. Banikazemi, and V. Moorthy. Simulation of Modern Parallel Systems: A CSIM-based approach. In *WSC '97*, pages 1013–1020, December 1997.

[11] D. K. Panda, S. Singal, and R. Kesavan. Multidestination Message Passing in Wormhole k-ary n-cube Networks with Base Routing Conformed Paths. *IEEE TPDS*, to appear.

[12] M. D. Schroeder et al. Autonet: A High-speed, Self-configuring Local Area Network Using Point-to-point Links. Technical Report SRC research report 59, DEC, Apr 1990.

[13] R. Sivaram, R. Kesavan, D. K. Panda, and C. B. Stunkel. Where to Provide Support for Efficient Multicasting in Irregular Networks: Network Interface or Switch? Technical Report OSU-CISRC-02/98-TR05, The Ohio State University, February 1998.

[14] R. Sivaram, D. K. Panda, and C. B. Stunkel. Multicasting in Irregular Networks with Cut-Through Switches using Tree-Based Multidestination Worms. In *PCRCW '97*, pages 35–48, June 1997.

[15] C. B. Stunkel, R. Sivaram, and D. K. Panda. Implementing Multidestination Worms in Switch-Based Parallel Systems: Architectural Alternatives and their Impact. In *ISCA-24*, pages 50–61, June 1997.

[16] K. Verstoep, K. Langendoen, and H. Bal. Efficient Reliable Multicast on Myrinet. In *ICPP*, pages III:156–165, Aug 1996.

Efficient Collective Communication on Heterogeneous Networks of Workstations *

Mohammad Banikazemi   Vijay Moorthy   Dhabaleswar K. Panda

Department of Computer and Information Science
The Ohio State University
Columbus, OH 43210
Email: {banikaze,moorthy,panda}@cis.ohio-state.edu

Abstract

Networks of Workstations (NOW) have become an attractive alternative platform for high performance computing. Due to the commodity nature of workstations and interconnects and due to the multiplicity of vendors and platforms, the NOW environments are being gradually redefined as Heterogeneous Networks of Workstations *(HNOW) environments. This paper presents a new framework for implementing collective communication operations (as defined by the Message Passing Interface (MPI) standard) efficiently for the emerging HNOW environments. We first classify different types of heterogeneity in HNOW and then focus on one important characteristic: communication capabilities of workstations. Taking this characteristic into account, we propose two new approaches (*Speed-Partitioned Ordered Chain *(SPOC) and* Fastest-Node First *(FNF)) to implement collective communication operations with reduced latency. We also investigate methods for deriving optimal trees for broadcast and multicast operations. Generating such trees is shown to be computationally intensive. It is shown that the FNF approach, in spite of its simplicity, can deliver performance within 1% of the performance of the optimal trees. Finally, these new approaches are compared with the approach used in the MPICH implementation on experimental as well as on simulated testbeds. On a 24-node existing HNOW environment with SGI workstations and ATM interconnection, our approaches reduce the latency of broadcast and multicast operations by a factor of up to 3.5 compared to the approach used in the existing MPICH implementation. On a 64-node simulated testbed, our approaches can reduce the latency of broadcast and multicast operations by a factor of up to 4.5. Thus, these results demonstrate that there is significant potential for our approaches to be applied towards designing scalable collective communication libraries for current and future generation HNOW environments.*

1 Introduction

Networks of Workstations (NOW) are becoming increasingly popular for providing cost-effective and affordable parallel computing for day-to-day computational needs [1]. Such environments consist of clusters of workstations connected by *Local Area Networks* (LANs). Hardware and software LAN technology was not initially developed for parallel processing, and thus the communication overhead between workstations can be quite high. In order to achieve performance comparable to Massively Parallel Processor (MPP) systems, many research projects are currently being undertaken in academia and industry to provide fast communication and synchronization in NOW systems. However, most of these research projects focus

on *homogeneous* NOW systems where similar kinds of workstations (nodes) are connected over a single network architecture. Some popular network architectures used in the current NOW environments are Ethernet, ATM, FDDI, Fiber-Channel, and cut-through routed networks such as SP-2 and Myrinet.

Due to the commodity nature of workstations and networking equipment, LAN environments are gradually becoming *heterogeneous*. The capability of a LAN environment to incrementally expand by incorporating new generations of workstations and network architectures over a period of time is also forcing this trend. Such heterogeneity may get reflected in terms of varying speed and communication capability of workstations, coexistence of multiple network architectures, availability of alternative communication protocols, and availability of specialized support for communication and synchronization over a set of workstations. Thus, in today's networked high performance computing environment, heterogeneity is common and its extent will continue to grow over the years. This is forcing the NOW environments to be gradually redefined as *Heterogeneous Networks of Workstations* (HNOW) environments.

A portable parallel programming environment is key to the success of the NOW/HNOW paradigm. Over the last few years, researchers have developed software packages like PVM [14] and *Message Passing Interface* standards like MPI [3, 10] to provide such portability. Even though these softwares and standards do not force an application developer to understand the intricate details of the hardware, software, and network characteristics, the performance of an application in a NOW/HNOW environment heavily depends on these characteristics.

The need for *collective communication* operations such as *broadcast, multicast, global reduction, scatter, gather, complete exchange,* and *barrier synchronization* arises frequently in parallel applications [9]. Thus, it is critical that the collective communication operations be implemented in the best possible manner (scalable as well as high performance) in a HNOW system. Recently, some projects have emphasized issues related to collective communication in NOW systems. These projects have been centered around the following interconnects: ATM, Ethernet, and Myrinet. Performance of collective communication operations in NOW environments have been evaluated in [7, 11]. However, all these studies focus on only one type of interconnect in a NOW system. They also do not consider heterogeneity in workstation speeds, communication protocols, etc. Thus, the solutions derived in these research projects cannot be directly applied to HNOW systems to obtain maximum performance.

*This research is supported in part by NSF Career Award MIP-9502294, NSF Grants CCR-9704512 and CDA-9514898, and an OCARNet grant from the Ohio Board of Regents.

To the best of our knowledge, the ECO [8] package has been the only effort made to consider the heterogeneity of workstations in NOW environments. ECO is built on top of PVM. It proposes heuristics to partition the participating workstations of a collective communication operation into subnetworks based on pair-wise round-trip latencies. Next, it divides the required communication steps into two major phases: inter-subnetwork and intra-subnetwork. Different trees are used for performing collective communication operations in each of these phases. However, the proposed partitioning approach based on pair-wise round-trip latencies may result in incorrect partitioning in the presence of many factors such as background traffic and workstations with different communication capabilities. This may cause inefficient implementation of collective communication operations. This framework also does not consider other types of heterogeneity. This leads to the following challenges: 1) how to characterize the heterogeneity of a HNOW environment and 2) how to implement efficient collective communication on HNOW environments by exploiting one or more of the heterogeneous characteristics.

In this paper we take on these challenges. We first classify different types of heterogeneity that can exist in HNOW environments and characterize them. Then, we focus on one major characteristic, *communication capabilities of workstations*. We study the impact of this characteristic on the communication overhead of MPI point-to-point communication in a typical LAN environment consisting of heterogeneous workstations. The experimental results indicate that the communication overhead among workstations in a HNOW environment may vary as much as 5:1. Using this observation, we propose a generalized framework to implement efficient collective communications on HNOW systems. We first introduce a new *Speed-Partitioned Ordered Chain* (SPOC) approach to order the participating nodes of a collective communication based on their communication capabilities. Using this framework, broadcast and multicast collective communication operations are implemented with reduced latency using binomial trees. Then, we argue that using binomial trees might not be the best approach for implementing these collective operations. We propose a method for finding optimal trees for broadcast and multicast operations. We show that deriving an optimal tree for a set of nodes with arbitrary communication capabilities is however a computationally intensive operation. Next, we introduce a more efficient approach called *Fastest-Node First* (FNF) for implementing these operations. A performance comparison of the FNF scheme with that of optimal trees suggests that the FNF scheme (with its low complexity) can deliver performance within 1% of the performance of optimal trees.

Finally, the SPOC and FNF approaches are evaluated on an experimental testbed consisting of a cluster of 24 SGI workstations and compared with the existing approach used in the MPICH implementation of the MPI standard. Furthermore, these approaches are evaluated on a 64-node simulated HNOW environment with different architectural characteristics. It is shown that latency of these collective communication operations can be reduced by a factor of up to 4.9 using the proposed algorithms. These results show that considerable benefits can be obtained by using the proposed approaches for implementing collective communication operations in HNOW environments.

The remaining part of the paper is organized as follows. Different types of heterogeneity are characterized in section 2. Experimental results on message initiation cost on a set of workstations are also presented. The basic idea behind the development of the proposed algorithms is presented in section 3. The new SPOC framework for collective communication and its corresponding algorithms are proposed in section 4, and the method for finding optimal trees is introduced in section 5. The FNF approach, its application for implementing efficient broadcasts and multicasts, and its comparison with the SPOC and optimal tree approaches are presented in section 6. Experimental and simulation results are presented in section 7. Finally, we conclude the paper with conclusions and future research directions.

2 Characterizing Heterogeneous Networks of Workstations

In this section we characterize factors leading to heterogeneity in HNOW systems. We show how overhead for MPI point-to-point communication can vary significantly in a HNOW system by considering only one factor - communication capabilities of the nodes.

2.1 Major Characteristics

A typical HNOW system can be characterized by the following four factors: 1) Communication Capabilities of Workstations (Nodes), 2) Network Architectures, 3) Communication Protocols, and 4) Dedicated Support for Communication and Synchronization [2]. These factors are orthogonal to each other. A typical HNOW environment can have one or more of these characteristics.

All of the above factors have significant impact on the implementation of collective communication operations on HNOW systems. To illustrate this significance, in this paper, we limit our scope to the first characteristic only. Similar approach can also be used for other characteristics and we are currently working along these directions.

2.2 Overhead of Point-to-Point Communication under Heterogeneity

We present experimental results to show the effect of communication capabilities of workstations on the latency of MPI point-to-point communication. We measured round trip latency between four different pairs of workstations in a heterogeneous environment. The workstations were connected via Ethernet and used MPICH communication library [4] to communicate. Table 1 shows these results. Since the results are symmetric, values are shown for only the upper triangle entries. These values indicate how processor speed affects the time taken to transmit a message from one workstation to another. The fastest workstation we used was an HP 735 and the slowest one was a Sun 4. It can be observed that the communication startup time for a Sun 4 is around 5 times that of an HP 735.

Table 1. Roundtrip times in microseconds between different types of workstations in a heterogeneous network. (Entries with * indicate that the sender and receiver were in different clusters.)

	HP735	HP715/100	HP715/64	Sun4
HP735	871	973	2491 *	5806 *
HP715/100		1020	2538 *	5871 *
HP715/64			1869	6050 *
Sun4				4196

These experimental results demonstrate that workstation speeds can have direct impact on the communication latency.

Since collective communication operations involve more than one workstations the question arises whether we can use the heterogeneity to our advantage to implement the operations faster. We propose such a framework in the following section.

3 A New Framework for Collective Communication

In this section we propose a framework to take advantage of heterogeneity in communication capabilities to implement a collective communication operation faster. First, we provide the basic idea behind such a framework and then formalize the problem. In the following sections, we provide alternative approaches to solve the problem.

As we observed earlier, various factors such as processor speed, memory speed, and network interface support affect the communication capability of a node. The above parameters can be combined together to a single parameter known as message initiation cost, t_{ini}. Let us consider a broadcast operation on an example HNOW environment consisting of eight workstations $(1, 2, \cdots, 8)$. Let node 1 be the source node. Let six of these workstations $(2, 3, 4, 5, 7,$ and $8)$ be slow ones having a message initiation cost, t_{ini}^s. Similarly, let the other two $(1$ and $6)$ be fast ones and have lower message initiation cost, t_{ini}^f. Based on our experimental data (shown in Table 1) , it can be observed that the t_{ini}^s/t_{ini}^f can be as large as 5. For an example quantitative evaluation, let us consider t_{ini}^f = 100.0 microsec and t_{ini}^s = 300.0 microsec, leading to $t_{ini}^s/t_{ini}^f = 3$. Because of the high value of t_{ini} (which is typical of NOW systems) let us ignore the time required for transmitting the messages in our example.

Consider a naive and simple binomial-tree-based scheme, based on node numbering. This leads to the broadcast tree as shown in Fig. 1(a). Using this scheme the broadcast can be completed in 700.0 microsec in this HNOW environment. However, a more efficient scheme, as shown in Fig. 1(b), can be designed by considering the differences in the communication capabilities of the workstations. Here although we are still using a binomial tree, the fast workstations are used as intermediate nodes to broadcast the message faster. This scheme takes only 500.0 microsec to implement the broadcast and demonstrates a 29% improvement in broadcast latency. However, this is not the best way of implementing broadcast in this system. Fig. 1(c) illustrates the optimal implementation with a latency of 400.0 microsec (43% improvement over the naive implementation). This example shows that binomial trees which are optimal trees for implementing broadcast on homogeneous systems might not be optimal in heterogeneous environments.

It can be observed from this example that several alternatives exist to implement a broadcast communication faster by considering the communication capabilities of the participating nodes and the tree used for implementing the collective operations. In this example we assumed that there are only two types of workstations. The problem becomes more complex if we have multiple levels of communication capabilities. In general, the communication capabilities of the nodes in an N-node HNOW environment can be totally different. This leads to the following problem:

Problem Statement: *How to design efficient algorithms for collective communication operations on an N-node HNOW environment with each node having arbitrary communication capability: t_{ini}^i, $0 \le i \le N - 1$.*

In the following sections, we provide alternative solutions

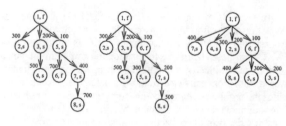

Figure 1. Different ways to implement broadcast in an eight workstation HNOW environment: (a) simple binomial tree-based scheme using node numbering, (b) a better implementation by considering communication capabilities of the workstations, and (b) the optimal implementation.

to solve this problem. We first present a generalized approach to design efficient binomial broadcast trees by considering multiple levels of communication capabilities across nodes, and develop algorithms for broadcast and multicast collective communication operations. Then, we propose a method to derive optimal trees for performing broadcast and multicast operations. Since deriving such trees is computationally expensive, we finally propose a simple approach which can deliver performance close to those of the optimal trees.

4 Speed-Partitioned Ordered Chain (SPOC) Approach

This approach uses information about the message initiation cost (t_{ini}) of nodes which are participating in a collective communication operation. Using this information, an efficient ordering of participating nodes is derived to implement the operation faster.

Consider a collective communication operation, say broadcast, which can be implemented by using a binomial-tree. The binomial-tree algorithm is well suited for homogeneous networks. However, nodes that are higher up in the binomial tree send more messages and therefore incur more message startup overhead. Thus, if faster nodes appear higher up in the binomial tree, then the overall startup overhead incurred during the collective communication operation can be reduced. For example, in Fig. 1(a) node 5 is a slow node and has 3 descendents while node 6 is a fast node and has no descendent. In Fig. 1(b) node 6 has 3 descendent and node 5 has none. Other faster nodes have also been moved to tree nodes having more children. As a result, the latency of the broadcast in Fig. 1(b) is 200 microsec lower than the latency of the tree in Fig. 1(a).

The above observation leads to the following: The problem of finding the fastest way to implement a binomial tree-based algorithm for broadcast is just finding a way to assign faster workstations to nodes in the binomial tree which have to send more messages. Let us assume that the number of participating workstations in this operation is N. We can always construct a binomial-tree consisting of N tree nodes and having a depth of $\lceil \log_2 N \rceil$. The source node of the broadcast operation remains fixed as the root of the tree, but we have the flexibility of assigning the rest of the participating nodes to any of the other tree nodes as we please.

In order to find an efficient assignment we construct the binomial tree for the given number of participating nodes and find the total number of descendents at each tree node. The number of descendents of a tree node simply specifies the number of nodes that should receive the message from that node, directly or indirectly. We sort the tree nodes from the node with the highest number of descendents to the node with the lowest number of descendents. Obviously, the root of the tree will have the highest number of descendents $(N - 1)$, but the source node is already assigned to it. Thus, we have flexibility of assigning other participating nodes to tree nodes. We can sort participating nodes in ascending order of message initiation cost and then assign faster participating nodes to tree nodes with greater number of descendents from these two sorted lists. We call this ordered chain of participating nodes a *Speed-Partitioned Ordered Chain* (SPOC). The outline of this algorithm is illustrated in Fig. 2.

The completion time of broadcast, where W_0 is the source and $\{W_1, W_2, \cdots, W_{N-1}\}$ is the list of other participating nodes in a nondecreasing order with respect to their message initiation cost, can be expressed as:

$$T_{broadcast}^{SPOC} = \sum_{i=0}^{\lceil \log N \rceil - 1} \max(t_{ini}^0, t_{ini}^{2^i - 1}) \quad (1)$$

The same algorithm can be easily used for implementing the multicast [12] operation. An algorithm similar to the algorithm used for multicast can also be used to implement the multiple multicast with the only difference being the fact that different trees are used for each multicast.

SPOC-based tree construction for broadcast

Input:

> *root*: the source node of broadcast;
> L_n: The list of participating nodes with their respective initiation costs (t_{ini}).

Tree construction steps:

1. $N \leftarrow number\_of\_nodes(L_n)$
2. $T_b \leftarrow construct\_binomial\_tree(N)$
3. $SL_t \leftarrow sort(list(T_b), Desc, Num\_Desc)$
   // $SL_t = \{T_i \mid 0 \leq i < N, num\_decs(T_i) \leq num\_decs(T_j)\ for\ i < j\}$
4. $SL_n \leftarrow sort(L_n, Ascending, T\_ini)$
   // $SL_n = \{W_i \mid 0 \leq i < N, t\_ini(W_i) \leq t\_ini(W_j)\ for\ i < j\}$
5. $SL_n \leftarrow remove(SL_n, root)$
6. $assign\_node\_tree(item(SL_t, 0), root)$
7. for $i = 1$ to N do
   $assign\_node\_tree(item(SL_t, i), item(SL_n, i - 1))$

Figure 2. Outline of the SPOC-based tree construction for broadcast.

---

5 Optimal Trees

In Section 3 we showed that binomial trees might not be the best tree for implementing broadcast (or multicast) operations on a HNOW. Consider the construction of an optimal tree for performing broadcast (or multicast) among N nodes, $\{W_0, W_1, \cdots, W_{N-1}\}$, where W_0 is the source node. In the first step W_0 sends the message to W_i. Then, W_0 and W_i will be responsible for sending the message to the rest of the participating nodes through two subtrees. First, the Node W_i must be chosen such that the overall tree is *optimal*. Second, the two subtrees must themselves be *optimal*. The same procedure can be applied recursively to each of the multicast subtrees. Therefore, this optimization problem which exhibits optimal substructure and overlapping subproblems properties can be

solved by using the dynamic programming technique. This technique can be used for the current problem as follows.

Let $L_{i,A}$ be the minimum latency required to multicast the message from node W_i to all nodes in the set A. If A is an empty set, the latency will be equal to zero. Otherwise, in the first step, message is sent to a node in A (say W_j), and the latency would be the maximum of latencies associated with the two obtained subtrees (where W_i and W_j are the roots of these subtrees and descendents of these two nodes will be all nodes in $A - \{j\}$). Therefore, the overall latency can be obtained through the following recurrence:

$$L_{i,A} = \begin{cases} 0 & \text{if } |A| = 0 \\ min\{t_{ini}^i + max(L_{i,B}, L_{j,C})\}, & \text{otherwise} \\ \text{where } j \epsilon A, \text{ and } B + C = A - \{j\} \end{cases}$$

It is to be noted that the total running time for finding the optimal tree for broadcasting a message among N nodes will be $O(N^2 2^{2N})$. However, this method for finding the optimal tree is too computationally intensive to be useful in any practical system. In the following section, we propose a near-optimal algorithm which runs in polynomial time. Before describing this near-optimal algorithm, let us look at two important properties of optimal trees presented as the following two lemmas (the proofs can be found in [2]).

Lemma 1 *Let W_0 be the source node of a broadcast (or multicast) operation and $\{W_1, W_2, \cdots, W_{N-1}\}$ be the set of other participating nodes in the order of the time they have received the message. There exists an optimal tree for performing the broadcast (or multicast) operation such that W_k $(1 \leq K \leq N - 1)$ receives the message from one of the nodes in the set $\{W_0, W_1, \cdots, W_{k-1}\}$ and the time at which it receives the message is the earliest possible time.*

Lemma 2 *Let W_0 be the source node of a broadcast (or multicast) operation and $\{W_1, W_2, \cdots, W_{N-1}\}$ be the set of other participating nodes. Let t_{ini}^i be the message initiation cost of node W_i. There exists an optimal tree for performing the broadcast (or multicast) operation in which the message initiation cost of any node other than the source node is less than or equal to that of its children.*

In the next section we use these two properties to propose a near-optimal algorithm which runs in polynomial time with respect to the number of participating nodes.

6 Fastest-Node First (FNF) Approach

Using the above properties of an optimal tree, we propose a greedy algorithm called Fastest-Node First (FNF). In each iteration of this algorithm, one node which has not received the message is added to the tree. Obviously at each instance, we need to make two decisions. First, we need to decide which node is going to send the message to the new node. From Lemma 1 we can easily find the node which should deliver the message to the new node. The second decision to be made is selecting the new node among the nodes which have not been added to the tree yet. To make sure that the property presented in Lemma 2 is preserved, we select the fastest node among the nodes not in the tree. This way, we can generate trees through which multicast and broadcast operations can be implemented. Now, we describe how FNF can be specifically applied for implementing broadcast and multicast operations.

FNF-based tree construction for broadcast

Input:

$Tini$: the initiation costs of all nodes(t_{ini});
root: the source node of broadcast;
L_n: The list of other participating nodes.

Tree construction steps:

1. $N \leftarrow number\_of\_nodes(L_n) + 1$
2. $R_0 \leftarrow 0$
3. for $i = 1$ to $N - 1$ do
   $\quad R_i \leftarrow \infty$
4. $Senders \leftarrow \{root\}$
5. $Receivers \leftarrow L_n$
6. $Solution \leftarrow \{\}$
7. for $i = 1$ to $N - 1$ do
   $sender \leftarrow k$,where $k \in Senders$ and
   $\quad \forall l \in Senders\ (R_k + Tini_k) \leq (R_l + Tini_l)$
   $receiver \leftarrow k$,where $k \in Receivers$ and
   $\quad \forall l \in Receivers\ Tini_k \leq Tini_l$
   $Solution \leftarrow concat(Solution, (sender, receiver))$
   $R_{sender} \leftarrow R_{sender} + Tini_{sender}$
   $R_{receiver} \leftarrow R_{sender}$
   $Receivers \leftarrow remove(Receivers, receiver)$
   $Senders \leftarrow concat(Senders, receiver)$
   endfor

Figure 3. Outline of the FNF algorithm.

6.1 Broadcast

Consider a HNOW system in which N workstations are participating in a broadcast. Let the workstations be partitioned into C workstation classes ($C_0, C_1, \cdots, C_{C-1}$), where $1 \leq C \leq N$ (note that when $C = 1$ we actually have a homogeneous NOW with respect to the message initiation cost). The number of workstations in each class can also vary. Let t_{ini}^i be the message initiation cost for the workstations in class C_i. The FNF algorithm whose outline is presented in Figure 3, starts by creating a list of the nodes which have a copy of the message ($Senders$), and a list of the nodes which are participating in broadcast but have not received the message yet ($Receivers$). Obviously, at the beginning the first list contains only the source node and the second list contains all other nodes. A variable (R_i) is associated with each node indicating the earliest time when the node can send out a message to another node. Since at the beginning of the operations none of the nodes except the source node has the message, infinity is assigned to this variable of all nodes except that of the source which is set to zero. The FNF tree which is presented as a set of (parent, child) two-tuples ($Solution$) is also initialized. Then, in $N - 1$ successive iterations, the node from which the message is supposed to be received at one of the participating nodes (except the root) is found. In each iteration, the best candidate for sending the message to one of the nodes which have not received the message is found by minimizing the time by which this message can be delivered. On the other hand, the fastest node among those which have not received the message yet is chosen as the receiver. After both sender and receiver are selected, the times at which these nodes can send out a new message are each adjusted. During this step, the receiver is taken out of the $Receivers$ list and is added to the $Senders$ list.

It should be noted that the order of the tuples in $Solution$ is important. For any two-tuples whose first items (or sender nodes) are the same, the sender node will send the message to the receiver mentioned in the first two-tuples before sending

the message to the other receiver. In other words, the obtained tree is an ordered tree. It should also be noted that for an efficient implementation of the algorithm, nodes can be sorted based on their message initiation costs. This algorithm can be easily implemented with $O(N^2)$ complexity where N is the number of participating nodes.

6.2 Multicast (Single and Multiple)

Similar to the broadcast operation, multicast can be implemented in a more efficient manner under this approach. The FNF algorithm can be directly applied for implementing multicast operation by limiting the list of the participating nodes to the nodes participating in the multicast operation. Similarly, FNF can also be used for implementing multiple multicast by constructing one tree for each multicast operation.

6.3 Comparison With Optimal Trees

To compare the performance of the FNF-based algorithms with that of the optimal algorithms in a qualitative fashion, we evaluated the latency of broadcast and multicast operations obtained from these algorithms. We considered a system with 9 nodes. (We could not go further because of the complexity of the optimal algorithm which is exponential with respect to the number of participating nodes.) The message initiation cost of each node was randomly chosen from the $\{100, 200, 300, \cdots, 800\}$ set. For each operation, the source node and other participating nodes were chosen randomly. We recorded the latency of the FNF-based algorithm (L_{FNF}) and that of the optimal algorithm (L_{opt}) for 10000 cases for each particular number of participating nodes. We then calculated the average latency of the FNF-based and the optimal algorithms. Table 2 shows these latencies. It can be observed that the latency of FNF-based algorithms is equal to that of the optimal algorithms up to 5 participating nodes. Beyond that, the FNF algorithm produces latencies which are within 1% of the latency produced by the optimal algorithm. Furthermore, trees generated by the FNF-based algorithm were found to be identical to those generated by the optimal algorithm for 90-100% of the cases. Considering the very minor difference between the latency of the FNF-based and the optimal algorithms, and the very low complexity of the FNF-based algorithms, we conclude that FNF-based algorithms will be more practical to be incorporated in future HNOW environments. Thus, for the remaining part of the paper, we does not consider the optimal algorithm any further. We only consider the FNF-based algorithms.

Table 2. Comparison between FNF-based and optimal algorithms for implementing broadcast and multicast on a system with 9 nodes.

# Participating Nodes	L_{FNF}	L_{opt}	$\frac{(L_{FNF} - L_{opt})}{L_{opt}}$
2	453.37	453.37	0.00%
3	705.60	705.60	0.00%
4	805.70	805.70	0.00%
5	871.01	871.01	0.00%
6	914.90	913.15	0.19%
7	947.56	942.26	0.56%
8	976.90	967.27	0.99%
9	984.29	977.12	0.73%

6.4 Comparisons between FNF-based and SPOC-based Trees

Let us compare the trees produced by the FNF-based and SPOC-based trees. In general, they will be different because SPOC-based trees are always binomial in nature. It is to be noted that when all nodes participating in broadcast or multicast have the same message initiation startup (i.e. the participating nodes are homogeneous), the tree obtained from the FNF algorithm will be the same as that obtained from the SPOC algorithm and the tree produced by the naive binomial tree algorithm (such as the one used in the existing MPI implementations). It is also to be noted that where 50% of the participating nodes (including the source node) belong to the fastest group of participating nodes, the trees obtained from the SPOC and FNF algorithms will be identical.

7 Performance Evaluation

In this section, the performance of the algorithms developed in the previous sections are compared. First, we present experimental results obtained from a cluster of SGI workstations connected by an ATM network. Due to the limitations of our experimental testbed (limited number of nodes and only two levels of speed), we also carried out simulation results for larger number of nodes with greater variation in speed. We present these simulation results next.

7.1 Experimental Results

We used an ATM network of 24 SGI workstations to implement and evaluate the proposed algorithms. We compared the performance of our algorithms with those of MPICH v1.1. In the following subsections, the setup used in the experiments is explained and then the results are presented.

7.1.1 Experimental Setup

The testbed used in our experiments consisted of 24 SGI workstations with two different speeds. There were 16 slow and 8 fast nodes. This allowed us to take measurements on three different 16-node configurations with 12.5% (2), 25% (4), and 50% (8) fast nodes, respectively. Using the MPICH point-to-point communication, the roundtrip latency for a short message (4-byte long) was measured to be 1380 microsec between two fast nodes and 2960 microsec between two slow nodes. The ratio of the communication capabilities of slow and fast nodes is therefore 2.15.

7.1.2 Broadcast

For measuring the broadcast latency we followed a method similar to the one used in [6]. A broadcast operation starts when the source node initiates it. It is said to be complete when all the other nodes have received the broadcast message. The broadcast latency is defined as the time elapsed between the source node initiating it and the last recipient receiving it. Measurement of broadcast latency was done in the following way. For an N node system, $N-1$ broadcasts were performed. Each time, after the broadcast, one of the $N-1$ recipients sent back an acknowledgment (instead of issuing another broadcast as in [6]). At the source node the time between initiation of the broadcast and receipt of the acknowledgment was measured. The maximum of these $N-1$ time readings corresponds to the last broadcast recipient sending back the acknowledgment. Therefore, this maximum is the sum of the broadcast latency and half of the round trip latency between the source node and the last recipient. Since the roundtrip time can be easily measured, the broadcast latency is obtained by subtracting half of the roundtrip time from the maximum reading. Furthermore,

each experiment was repeated 100 times for a given source node and the minimum broadcast latency was taken into account.

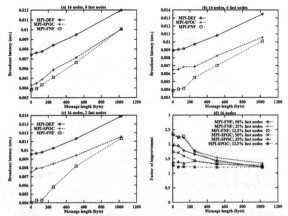

Figure 4. Broadcast latency and factor of improvement on a HNOW system with 16 nodes and different number of fast nodes.

Figure 4 shows the results. In the graphs, latencies of the MPICH implementation are referred to as MPI-DEF (MPI with default implementation) latencies. The modified version of MPICH routines in which SPOC-based algorithms are used, is called MPI-SPOC. We refer to the modified version of MPICH in which FNF-based algorithms are employed to perform MPI-Bcast as MPI-FNF. It can be observed that the proposed algorithms always perform better than the naive ordering scheme used in MPICH. Factors of improvement over MPI-DEF are shown in Figure 4(d). As the fraction of fast nodes in the system increases, so does the factor of improvement. A factor of improvement of 1.7 is achieved in a system with 50% faster nodes by using the SPOC-based algorithm. Factors of improvement up to 2.3 are achievable when FNF-based algorithms are used. As predicted in section 6.4, when 50% of the nodes (including the source node) are fast nodes, SPOC-based algorithms perform as good as FNF-based algorithms. It can also be observed that for different fractions of faster nodes, the factor of improvement curves almost coincide beyond a certain message length due to the fact that with increasing message length, the message transmission time begins to dominate the latency. For shorter messages, where the startup overhead dominates, we get higher factors of improvement.

7.1.3 Multicast

In a multicast, the set of recipients is a subset of the set of nodes. The same procedure was therefore used to measure multicast latencies, that is, each experiment for multicast was repeated $100 \times (r-1)$ times, where r is the number of recipients.

Figures 5 and 6 show results for multicast. Characteristics similar to broadcast results are observed. The factor of improvement increases with increasing system size. Again, as the message length increases, transmission time dominates and the factor of improvement decreases. For an 8 node multicast with 50% fast participating nodes, factors of improvement of up to 2.5 are observed.

7.2 Simulation Results

Several experiments were performed to measure the impact of different workstation speeds, number of workstations

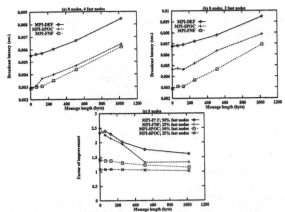

Figure 5. Multicast latency and factor of improvement on a HNOW system with 8 nodes and different number of fast nodes.

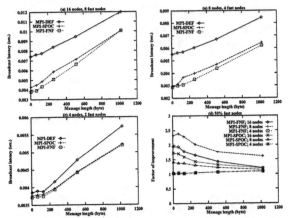

Figure 6. Multicast latency and factor of improvement on configurations with half of the nodes being fast nodes.

and fraction of faster nodes on the performance of our algorithms. In the following subsections, first the simulation setup is described in detail. Next, the results for broadcast, single multicast, and multiple multicast are presented.

7.2.1 Simulation Setup

We modeled a representative HNOW system where workstations are interconnected with Myrinet switches. A detailed flit-level simulator (built using CSIM [13]) was used to model irregular topologies and the wormhole switching technique. A 64-node HNOW system was considered. Based on the experimental results, presented in Section 2.2, we considered the following communication startup times. Two classes of workstations were considered. The communication startup time for faster class was kept constant at t_{ini}^f = 400.0 microsec. The time for slower class (t_{ini}^s) was varied (800, 1600 and 2400 microsec). These values lead to *speed factors* (ratio of communication cost between the slow class to the fast class) of 2, 4, and 6, respectively. Such a variation helps to study a wide range of HNOW systems.

With respect to the interconnection network, the following parameters, representing current generation systems, were used: t_{phy} (link propagation time per byte) = 12.5 nanoseconds, t_{route} (routing delay at switch) = 500 nanoseconds, t_{sw} (switching time across the router crossbar for a flit) = 12.5 nanoseconds, t_{inj} (time to inject a flit into network) = 12.5

nanoseconds and t_{cons} (time to consume a flit from network) = 12.5 nanoseconds. For all experiments we assumed the following default system configuration: a 64 workstation system interconnected by 16 eight-port switches and a network having 50% connectivity[1].

We performed several experiments to study the impact of message length, speed factor and fraction of faster nodes. We evaluated our new algorithms (indicated as SPOC and FNF in the graphs) with the default ordering algorithm (indicated as DEF) which is used by the current MPI implementations. Participating nodes for a given collective communication and the network configurations were generated randomly. Latency value for each data point in the graphs was averaged over 100 experiments (10 different sets of participating nodes for each of 10 different network configurations). Due to the space limitations, and since broadcast is a special case of multicast, we only present the multicast results. The simulation results for broadcast can be found in [2].

7.2.2 Multicast

Figures 7, 8, and 9 show the impact of speed factor, percentage of faster nodes, and message length on the latency of single multicast with varying sizes of destination sets. The factor of improvement of the SPOC and FNF approaches over the DEF increases with increasing number of destinations, increasing speed factor, and decrease in message length. For a multicast involving 1 KBytes message on a system with 25% faster nodes and a speed factor of 4, SPOC and FNF algorithms give factors of improvement of 2.3 and 3.3, respectively.

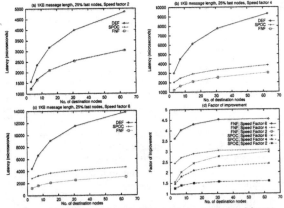

Figure 7. Impact of speed factor on single multicast latency with 25% fast nodes: (a) speed factor 2, (b) speed factor 4, (c) speed factor 6, and (d) factor of improvement for (a) - (c).

Results for multiple multicasts with varying number of sources and destinations are presented in Figure 10. It can be observed that the factor of improvement increases as more and more sources are involved in the multiple multicast. It can be observed that for a system with 50% faster nodes and a speed factor of 4, multiple multicast latency can be reduced by a factor of 2.4 using our new algorithms.

8 Conclusions and Future Research

In this paper, we have presented three new approaches to implement fast collective communication in the emerging HNOW systems. Major factors in HNOW systems have been

---

[1]Connectivity is defined as the fraction of ports in a switch which are used for interconnection with other switches [5].

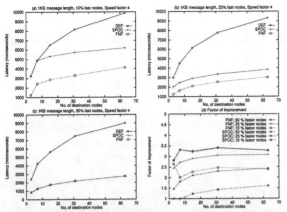

Figure 8. Impact of percentage of faster nodes on single multicast latency with speed factor 4: (a) 10% fast nodes, (b) 25% fast nodes, (c) 50% fast nodes, and (d) factor of improvement for (a) - (c).

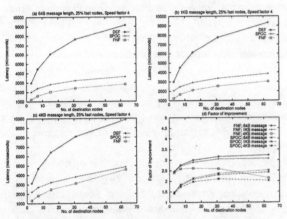

Figure 9. Impact of message length on single multicast latency with 25% fast nodes and speed factor 4: (a) 64 Bytes, (b) 1 KBytes, (c) 4 KBytes, and d) factor of improvement for (a) - (c).

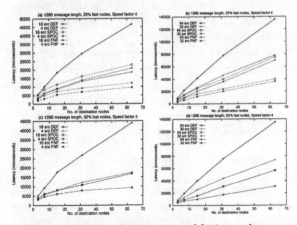

Figure 10. Impact of percentage of faster nodes on latency for multiple multicast: (a) 25% fast nodes with 4 and 16 sources, (b) 25% fast nodes with 32 and 64 sources, (c) 50% fast nodes with 4 and 16 sources, and (d) 50% fast nodes with 32 and 64 sources.

characterized. A new SPOC-based framework has been introduced to order the participating nodes of a collective communication based on their communication capabilities. Using this framework, algorithms for frequently used collective communication operations (broadcast, single multicast, and multiple multicast) have been developed. An algorithm for generating optimal trees for these problems have been proposed. Furthermore, a new approach (FNF) with a low complexity has been introduced in which near-optimal trees are used for implementing collective communications efficiently. Performance evaluation of these new algorithms on a 24-node experimental testbed and a 64-node simulated testbed indicates that latency of collective communication operations can be reduced by a factor up to 4.5 compared to the naive algorithms used in current MPI implementations.

In this paper, we have used only the heterogeneous communication capabilities of nodes to implement collective communication efficiently. We are also developing schemes to take advantage of heterogeneity in network architectures, communication protocols, and dedicated communication/synchronization units to obtain further improvements. Finally, we plan to propose a combined framework which can take advantage of all these factors and build a scalable collective communication library for HNOW systems.

Acknowledgment and Additional Information: We would like to thank Ohio Supercomputing Center for access to their workstation cluster. A number of related papers and technical reports can be obtained from http://www.cis.ohio-state.edu/~panda/pac.html.

References

[1] T. Anderson, D. Culler, and D. Patterson. A Case for Networks of Workstations (NOW). *IEEE Micro*, pages 54–64, Feb 1995.

[2] M. Banikazemi, V. Moorthy, and D. K. Panda. Efficient Collective Communication on Heterogeneous Networks of Workstations. Technical report OSU-CISRC-03/98-TR07, Dept. of Computer and Information Science, The Ohio State University, March 1998.

[3] J. Bruck et al. Efficient Message Passing Interface (MPI) for Parallel Computing on Clusters of Workstations. *JPDC*, pages 19–34, Jan 1997.

[4] W. Gropp, E. Lusk, N. Doss, and A. Skjellum. A High-Performance, Portable Implementation of the MPI, Message Passing Interface Standard. Technical report, Argonne National Laboratory and Mississippi State University.

[5] R. Kesavan, K. Bondalapati, and D. K. Panda. Multicast on Irregular Switch-based Networks with Wormhole Routing. In *HPCA-3*, pages 48–57, February 1997.

[6] M. Lauria. High Performance MPI Implementation on a Network of Workstations. Master's thesis, Department of Computer Science, University of Illinois at Urbana-Champaign , Oct 1996.

[7] M. Lin, J. Hsieh, D. H. C. Du, J. P. Thomas, and J. A. MacDonald. Distributed Network Computing over Local ATM Networks. *IEEE JSAC*, 13(4), May 1995.

[8] B. Lowekamp and A. Beguelin. ECO: Efficient Collective Operations for Communication on Heterogeneous Networks. In *IPPS*, pages 399–405, 1996.

[9] P. K. McKinley and D. F. Robinson. Collective Communication in Wormhole-Routed Massively Parallel Computers. *IEEE Computer*, pages 39–50, Dec 1995.

[10] Message Passing Interface Forum. *MPI: A Message-Passing Interface Standard*, Mar 1994.

[11] N. Nupairoj and L. M. Ni. Performance Evaluation of Some MPI Implementations on Workstation Clusters. In *Proceedings of the SPLC Conference*, 1994.

[12] D. K. Panda. Issues in Designing Efficient and Practical Algorithms for Collective Communication in Wormhole-Routed Systems. In *ICPP Workshop on Challenges for Parallel Processing*, pages 8–15, 1995.

[13] D. K. Panda, D. Basak, D. Dai, R. Kesavan, R. Sivaram, M. Banikazemi, and V. Moorthy. Simulation of Modern Parallel Systems: A CSIM-based approach. In *Proceedings of the 1997 Winter Simulation Conference (WSC'97)*, pages 1013–1020, December 1997.

[14] V. S. Sunderam. PVM: A Framework for Parallel and Distributed Computing. *Concurrency: Practice and Experience*, 2(4):315–339, December 1990.

Efficient All-to-All Personalized Exchange in Multidimensional Torus Networks

Young-Joo Suh

Dept. of Computer Science and Engineering
Pohang University of Science and Technology
San 31, Hyoja-Dong
Pohang 790-784, Korea
yjsuh@postech.ac.kr

Kang G. Shin

Real-Time Computing Laboratory
Dept. of Electrical Engineering and Computer Science
The University of Michigan
Ann Arbor, MI 48109-2122
kgshin@eecs.umich.edu

Abstract

This paper presents new algorithms for all-to-all personalized exchange in multidimensional torus-connected multiprocessors. Unlike existing message-combining algorithms in which the number of nodes in each dimension should be power-of-two and square, the proposed algorithms accommodate non-power-of-two tori where the number of nodes in each dimension need not be power-of-two. In addition, destinations remain fixed over a larger number of steps in the proposed algorithms, thus making them amenable to optimizations. Finally, the data structures used are simple, hence making substantial saving of message-rearrangement time.

1. Introduction

Interprocessor communication may become a main bottleneck to scalable parallel implementations of computation-intensive applications. This has motivated the development of efficient and innovative algorithms for demanding interprocessor communication patterns such as *collective communication* [4,6]. Among several collective communication patterns, *all-to-all personalized exchange* or *complete exchange* is generally the most demanding communication pattern, where every node communicates a distinct message to every other node in the system. In an N-node system, each node P_i, $1 \le i \le N$, has N blocks of data $B[i, 1], B[i, 2], ..., B[i, N]$, one distinct block for each other node. After the all-to-all personalized exchange operation, each node P_i has N blocks of data, $B[1, i], B[2, i], ..., B[N, i]$, one from each other node. Many scientific parallel applications require this all-to-all personalized exchange communication.

Bokhari and Berryman [1], Sunder et al. [10], and Tseng et al. [13] proposed all-to-all personalized exchange algorithms using message combining in $2^d \times 2^d$ meshes or tori. These algorithms incur an execution time of $O(2^d)$ due to message startups and $O(2^{3d})$ due to message transmissions. In [8,9], Suh and Yalamanchili proposed algo-

rithms using message combining in $2^d \times 2^d$ and $2^d \times 2^d \times 2^d$ tori or meshes with $O(d)$ time complexities due to message startups and $O(2^{3d})$ (in 2D) or $O(2^{4d})$ (in 3D) due to message transmissions. These algorithms differ from each other primarily in the way that pairwise exchange operations are scheduled. However, they have all been defined for meshes or tori where the number of processors in each dimension is an integer power-of-two and square.

In this paper, we present new algorithms for all-to-all personalized exchange for multidimensional tori. The algorithms utilize message combining to reduce the time associated with message startups. They are suitable for a wide range of torus topologies. The salient features of the proposed algorithms are (i) unlike existing message-combining algorithms in which the number of nodes in each dimension should be power-of-two and square, they accommodate non-power-of-two and non-square tori, (ii) they are simple in that destinations remain fixed over a larger number of steps, and are thus amenable to optimizations, e.g., caching of message buffers, locality optimizations, etc., (iii) they are the first message-combining algorithms for such 3D or higher dimensional tori, (iv) the data structures are simple and save substantial message-rearrangement time, and (v) they can be extended to higher-dimensional networks.

The following section presents the performance model and parameters used in this paper. We propose the algorithm for 2D tori in Section 3. The algorithm is extended to multidimensional networks in Section 4. Section 5 evaluates the performance of the proposed algorithms. Our results are summarized in Section 6.

2. Performance Model and Parameters

The target architecture is torus-connected, wormhole-switched [5] multiprocessors. The proposed algorithms apply equally well to networks using virtual cut-through or packet switching. Each packet is partitioned into a number of *flits*. We assume that each processor has N distinct m-

byte message blocks. We also assume that the channel width is one flit, the flit size is one byte, and each processor has one pair of injection/consumption buffers for the internal processor-router channel (i.e., one-port architecture). All links are full duplex channels. In this paper, a *step* is the basic unit of a contention-free communication and a *phase* is a sequence of steps.

A common metric used to evaluate the performance of inter-processor communication is *completion time* or *communication time*. In general, the completion time includes startup time, message-transmission time, propagation delay, and data-rearrangement time between communication steps/phases. Performance parameters include the startup time per message (t_s), message-transmission time per flit (t_c), per-hop propagation delay (t_l), and data-rearrangement time per byte (ρ). Thus, completion time (T) for one communication step can be expressed as $T = t_s + mt_c + ht_l$, if one message block is transmitted to the destination over h hops in a contention-free manner using wormhole switching. It does not include the data-rearrangement time between steps.

In this paper, the logical data structure in each node is a 2D (in Section 3) or nD array (in Section 4). We also assume that if physically non-contiguous blocks are transmitted from this array, a message-rearrangement step must be taken place prior to transmission.

3. Algorithm for 2D Tori

For an $R \times C$ torus, where R and C are multiples of four and $R \leq C$, each node is identified by a label $P(r, c)$, where $0 \leq r \leq R-1$ and $0 \leq c \leq C-1$. Each node is included in one of 16 node groups according to the following rule:

IF r mod $4 = i$ and c mod $4 = j$, P(r,c) is included in group ij.

For example, in a 12×12 torus shown in Figure 1(b), nine nodes of identical marking are included in the same group. The nodes in a group form an $\frac{R}{4} \times \frac{C}{4}$ subtorus. Figure 1(a) illustrates the 3×3 subtorus formed by group 00 to which nine nodes, P(0,0), P(0,4), P(0,8), P(4,0), P(4,4), P(4,8), P(8,0), P(8,4), and P(8,8) belong. In addition, if we divide an $R \times C$ torus into 4×4 contiguous submeshes (SMs), each node in a SM is included in one of 16 distinct groups.

3.1 An Overview

The proposed 2D algorithm consists of four phases. In phases 1 and 2, messages are exchanged, performing all-to-all personalized exchange, among nodes in the same group. For an illustrative purpose, we consider all-to-all personalized exchange in a 12×12 torus. Figure 1(c) is a simplified representation of Figure 1(a), where only SMs and nodes in group 00 are shown. Each node has 144

blocks to scatter, and the blocks are divided into nine 4×4 block groups (BGs) considering nine SMs (SM00, SM01, SM02, SM10, SM11, SM12, SM20, SM21, and SM22) and 16 nodes in each SM. In Figure 1(d), each node in group 00 has 9 BGs to scatter with distinct markings, where each BG is destined for the SM which has the same marking as the BG in Figure 1(c). Thus, BGs of identical marking will be gathered in one node in the SM which has the same marking as the BGs, when all-to-all personalized exchange operation is completed successfully. Before starting transmission, the BGs are stored in a 2D array and they are arranged by considering the following steps (to be described in Section 3.3). In step 1 of phase 1, each node transmits the BGs in the second and third columns while receiving the same number of blocks along a row as illustrated in Figure 1(d). The data arrays after step 1 are illustrated in Figure 1(e). In step 2 of phase 1, each node transmits the BGs in the third column while receiving the same number of BGs (see Figure 1(e)). After step 2, BGs in each node are those destined for nodes in its SM and SMs in the same column as shown in Figure 1(f). Now, phase 2 starts and each node changes dimensions and transmits BGs along a column. In step 1 of phase 2 (step 2 of phase 2), each node transmits the BGs in the second and third rows (third row) while receiving the same number of BGs along a column as shown in Figure 1(f) (Figure 1 (g)). After step 2 of phase 2, all BGs gathered in each node have the same marking (see Figure 1(h)), which indicates that all-to-all personalized exchange among nodes in group 00 is achieved successfully.

In phases 1 and 2, nodes in the same group performs all-to-all personalized exchange operation among them, just as described above. However, since nodes in 16 distinct groups perform the operations in parallel, we should schedule links to avoid channel contention. If we consider a row (or column), each node in the row (or column) is included in one of four node groups. Since nodes in four groups cannot transmit message blocks along two directions in the row (or column) in parallel without channel contention, two node groups should be assigned to two directions in the other dimension for contention-free transmissions. Since there are four directions, positive row (+r), negative row (-r), positive column (+c), and negative column (-c), four node groups share distinct directions according to the result of *(r+c) mod 4* operation (see Figure 1(b)). In phase 2, each node changes dimensions then performs transmission along the new dimension.

After phase 2, each node in a SM has blocks originated from nodes in the same node group and destined for the 16 nodes in the same SM to which the node belongs. In the next two phases (phases 3 and 4), message transmissions are performed among nodes in distinct groups and in the same SM. Each SM can be divided into four 2×2 sub-

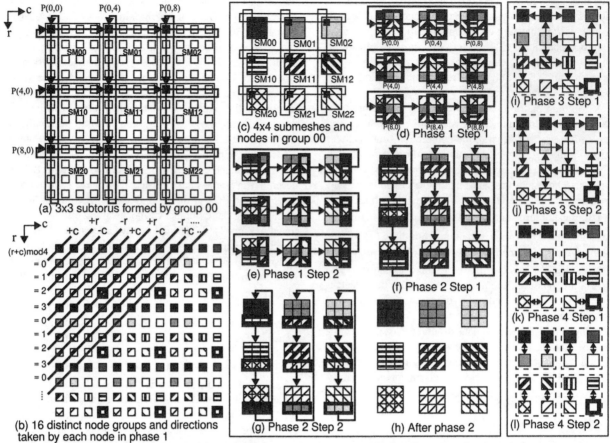

(a) 3x3 subtorus formed by group 00

(b) 16 distinct node groups and directions taken by each node in phase 1

(c) 4x4 submeshes and nodes in group 00

(d) Phase 1 Step 1

(e) Phase 1 Step 2

(f) Phase 2 Step 1

(g) Phase 2 Step 2

(h) After phase 2

(i) Phase 3 Step 1

(j) Phase 3 Step 2

(k) Phase 4 Step 1

(l) Phase 4 Step 2

Figure 1. Node groups, a 3x3 subtorus formed by a node group, and all-to-all personalized exchange operation among nodes in a subtorus.

meshes. In each 2×2 submesh, there are four nodes in upper left, upper right, lower left, and lower right. In the two steps of phase 3, four nodes in the same position in 2×2 submeshes exchange blocks (see Figures 1(i) and (j), where only one SM is shown). In each step, each node transmits blocks destined for the destination node itself as well as blocks destined for the other three nodes in the 2×2 submesh to which the destination node belongs. After phase 3, each node in a 2×2 submesh has blocks originated from nodes in distinct four groups and destined for nodes in the same 2×2 submesh to which the node belongs. In the two steps of phase 4, four nodes in each 2×2 submesh exchange blocks to complete all-to-all personalized exchange (see Figures 1(k) and (l)). The following subsections describe the algorithm in detail.

3.2 Communication Pattern

In phase 1, the following operations are performed:

Phase 1:
IF *(r+c) mod 4 =0*, P(r,c) → P(r, (c+4) *mod C*).　　(1)
IF *(r+c) mod 4 =1*, P(r,c) → P((r+4) *mod R*, c).　　(2)

IF *(r+c) mod 4 =2*, P(r,c) → P(r, (c-4) *mod C*).　　(3)
IF *(r+c) mod 4 =3*, P(r,c) → P((r-4) *mod R*, c).　　(4)

Phase 1 requires $\frac{C}{4}-1$ steps. Throughout these $\frac{C}{4}-1$ steps of phase 1, each node transmits message blocks to a fixed destination node along the direction selected by the node. Since the size of a subtorus is $\frac{R}{4} \times \frac{C}{4}$, there are at most $\frac{C}{4}$ nodes in a row or column (note that $R \leq C$). Consider blocks of a node (e.g., node A) to be scattered to all nodes. In step 1, node A transmits all of its blocks except those to be transmitted by itself in phases 2, 3, and 4, to the next node (e.g., node B) along the direction selected by the nodes. In step 2, node B extracts blocks to be transmitted by itself in phases 2, 3, and 4, then transmits the remaining blocks to the next node (e.g., node C) along the direction selected by the nodes. This procedure repeats and in the last step in phase 1, the last node (e.g., node L) along the direction receives only the blocks to be transmitted by the node in phases 2, 3, and 4. In the same manner, the other nodes also scatter their blocks to all nodes in the same node group and in the same column or row. If $R \neq C$, then

470

each node that satisfies the above conditions (2) and (4) finish the operations in phase 1 in $\frac{R}{4}-1$ steps, and idle or send empty messages during the remaining $\frac{C-R}{4}$ steps.

In phase 2, all nodes change dimensions then transmit message blocks along the new dimension. In phase 2, the following operations are performed:

Phase 2:
IF *(r+c) mod 4 =0*, P(r,c) → P((r+4) *mod R*, c).   (5)
IF *(r+c) mod 4 =1*, P(r,c) → P(r, (c+4) *mod C*).   (6)
IF *(r+c) mod 4 =2*, P(r,c) → P((r-4) *mod R*, c).   (7)
IF *(r+c) mod 4 =3*, P(r,c) → P(r, (c-4) *mod C*).   (8)

Phase 2 also requires $\frac{C}{4}-1$ steps and the communication pattern is the same as that in phase 1. Each node in a row or column of phase 1 (e.g., each node A, B, C,..., L) transmits blocks along a column or row in its new dimension in parallel. In each step, each node extracts blocks for itself and blocks to be transmitted by itself in phases 3 and 4, then transmits the remaining blocks to the next destination node. Thus, after $\frac{C}{4}-1$ steps of phase 2, each node has blocks originated from nodes in the same group, destined for itself and to be transmitted by the node in phases 3 and 4. As in phase 1, if $R \neq C$ then each node that satisfies the above conditions (2) and (4) finish the operations in phase 1 in $\frac{R}{4}-1$ steps and idle or send empty messages during the remaining $\frac{C-R}{4}$ steps.

Now, the network can be divided into $\frac{RC}{16}$ 4×4 submeshes. All nodes in a 4×4 submesh are included in distinct node groups and have blocks originated from nodes in their respective groups. In the next two phases all-to-all personalized exchange operation is performed among nodes within each submesh. In phase 3, the following operations are performed:

Step 1 of Phase 3:
IF *(r+c) mod 4 =even* AND *c mod4=0 or 1*, P(r,c) → P(r, c+2).
IF *(r+c) mod 4 =even* AND *c mod4=2 or 3*, P(r,c) → P(r, c-2).
IF *(r+c) mod 4 =odd* AND *r mod4=0 or 1*, P(r,c) → P(r+2, c).
IF *(r+c) mod 4 =odd* AND *r mod4=2 or 3*, P(r,c) → P(r-2, c).
Step 2 of Phase 3:
IF *(r+c) mod 4 =even* AND *r mod4=0 or 1*, P(r,c) → P(r+2, c).
IF *(r+c) mod 4 =even* AND *r mod4=2 or 3*, P(r,c) → P(r-2, c).
IF *(r+c) mod 4 =odd* AND *c mod4=0 or 1*, P(r,c) → P(r, c+2).
IF *(r+c) mod 4 =odd* AND *c mod4=2 or 3*, P(r,c) → P(r, c-2).

In phase 4, the network is further divided into 2×2 submeshes and two steps are required as follows:

Step 1 of Phase 4:
IF *c mod 2=0*, P(r,c) → P(r, c+1).
IF *c mod 2=1*, P(r,c) → P(r, c-1).
Step 2 of Phase 4:
IF *r mod 2=0*, P(r,c) → P(r+1, c).
IF *r mod 2=1*, P(r,c) → P(r-1, c).

3.3 Data Array

In this subsection, the contents of transmitted blocks and the array structure in each communication step are described in detail.

Initially, $P(r,c)$ has RC distinct blocks to distribute to other nodes in two dimensional array B[u,v], where $0 \leq u \leq R-1$ and $0 \leq v \leq C-1$ if $(r+c) mod 4 = 0$ *or* 2 (i.e., nodes that transmit blocks along a row and a column in phases 1 and 2, respectively), or $0 \leq u \leq C-1$ and $0 \leq v \leq R-1$ if $(r+c) mod 4 = 1$ *or* 3 (i.e., nodes that transmit blocks along a column and a row in phases 1 and 2, respectively). We assume that the array is ordered in column major, and if blocks to be transmitted are not contiguous, then they should be rearranged before transmission. The initial data structure of a node is dependent upon the communication pattern in phases 1 and 2. A block destined for the node that is u hops away from the node along the direction that the node takes in phase 1 is located in B[u,0]. In B[u,v], a block destined for the node that is v hops away from the node in B[u,0] along the direction the node takes in phase 2 is located.

In step i, $1 \leq i \leq \frac{C}{4}-1$, of phase 1, each node transmits blocks in columns $4i$ through $C-1$ to its destination node, while receiving the same number of blocks: In step 1, each node transmits all blocks except those to be transmitted by itself in phases 2, 3, and 4 (i.e., blocks in the first four columns). Among the blocks received in step 1, each node extracts the blocks to be transmitted by itself in following phases (i.e., blocks in the 5th through 8th columns), then transmits the remaining blocks to its destination node in step 2. This procedure repeats until the last step of phase 1.

In step j, $1 \leq j \leq \frac{C}{4}-1$, of phase 2, each node transmits blocks in rows $4j$ through $C-1$ to its destination node in phase 2, while receiving the same number of blocks from its source node in phase 2: In step 1, each node transmits all blocks except those will be transmitted by itself in phases 3 and 4 (i.e., blocks in the first four rows). Among the blocks received in step 1, each node extracts the blocks to be transmitted by itself in phases 3 and 4 (i.e., blocks in the 5th through 8th rows) then transmits the remaining blocks to its destination node in step 2. This procedure repeats until the last step of phase 2.

After phase 2, each node in a 4×4 submesh has RC blocks originated from all nodes in the same group ($\frac{RC}{16}$ nodes) destined for nodes in the 4×4 submesh to which the node belongs. But blocks destined for each node in the 4×4 submesh are distributed. Thus, before phase 3, the blocks are rearranged: If we divide a 4×4 submesh into 2×2 submeshes, there are four 2×2 submeshes - one includes a node P (e.g., S0), another includes the partner node in step1 of phase 3 (e.g., S1), another includes the partner node in step 2 of phase 3 (e.g., S2), and the other submesh (e.g., S3). Blocks destined for S0, S1, S3, and S2 (e.g., B0, B1, B3, and B2, respectively) are arranged in that order in data array of node P. In step 1 of phase 3, node P sends blocks destined for S1 and S3 (i.e., B1 and B3) while receiving the same number of blocks, B0 and B2, from the partner node in step1 of phase 3. Now, blocks in node P's data array are B0, B0, B2, and B2, in that order. In the next step, node P sends B2's while receiving B0's.

After phase 3, each node in a 2×2 submesh has RC blocks originated from all nodes in four node groups destined for four nodes in the submesh to which the node belongs, and the blocks are distributed. Thus, before phase 4, the blocks are rearranged: blocks destined for the node itself (e.g., N0), partner node in step 1 of phase 4 (e.g., N1), partner node in step 2 of phase 4 (e.g., N2), and the other node (e.g., N3). Blocks destined for N0, N1, N3, and N2 are arranged in that order in data array of node N0, and the block transmissions in phase 4 are performed in the same manner as those in phase 3. Now, after phase 4, every node has RC blocks, one block from every node in the network.

3.4 Complexity Analysis

In this subsection, we analyze the time costs required by the proposed algorithm in terms of startup cost, message-transmission cost, data-rearrangement cost, and message propagation cost.

(a) Startup cost: For an $R \times C$ 2D torus, $\frac{C}{4} - 1$ steps per phase are required in phases 1 and 2, and two steps per phase are required in phases 3 and 4. Thus, a total of $\frac{C}{2} + 2$ steps are required.

(b) Message-transmission cost: In step p of phase 1, where $1 \le p \le \frac{C}{4} - 1$, $R(C-4p)$ blocks (since $R \le C$) are transmitted. In step q of phase 2, where $1 \le q \le \frac{C}{4} - 1$, $R(C-4q)$ blocks are transmitted. In phases 3 and 4, there are four steps and $\frac{RC}{2}$ blocks are transmitted in each step. Thus, the total number of transmitted blocks is $\frac{RC}{4}(C+4)$.

(c) Data-rearrangement cost: At the end of each phase blocks are rearranged to prepare for the next phase. Since there are four phases, three data-rearrangement steps are required. Thus, the total data-rearrangement cost is $3(RC)m\rho$.

(d) Message propagation cost: In phases 1 and 2, there are $\frac{C}{2} - 2$ steps. In each step, the number of hops to the destination is four. In each of two steps in phases 3 and 4, the number of hops to the destination is two and one, respec-

tively. Thus, the total number of hops is $2C - 2$ and the message propagation cost is expressed as $2(C-1)t_l$.

4. Algorithm for *n*-Dimensional Tori

The algorithm for 2D tori can be extended to *n*-dimensional tori in a straightforward manner. Before describing the general *n*-dimensional algorithm, it may be helpful to first describe a 3D algorithm.

4.1 Algorithm for 3D Tori

For an $a_1 \times a_2 \times a_3$ 3D torus, where a_1, a_2, a_3 are a multiple of four and $a_1 \ge a_2 \ge a_3$, each node is labeled with $P(X, Y, Z)$, where $0 \le X \le a_1-1$, $0 \le Y \le a_2-1$, and $0 \le Z \le a_3-1$. Each node is included in one of 64 node groups according to the following rule:

IF *X mod4=i, Y mod4=j,* and *Z mod4=k*, P(X,Y,Z) is included in group *ijk*.

Communication Pattern:
The proposed algorithm requires five phases. In phase 1, the following operations are performed:

Phase 1:
IF *(X+Y) mod 4 =0* and *Z mod 4=0 or 2*, P(X,Y,Z) → P((X+4) *mod a₁*,Y,Z).
IF *(X+Y) mod 4 =1* and *Z mod 4=0 or 2*, P(X,Y,Z) → P(X,(Y+4) *mod a₂*,Z).
IF *(X+Y) mod 4 =2* and *Z mod 4=0 or 2*, P(X,Y,Z) → P((X-4) *mod a₁*,Y,Z).
IF *(X+Y) mod 4 =3* and *Z mod 4=0 or 2*, P(X,Y,Z) → P(X,(Y-4) *mod a₂*,Z).
IF *Z mod 4=1*, P(X,Y,Z) → P(X,Y,(Z+4) *mod a₃*).
IF *Z mod 4=3*, P(X,Y,Z) → P(X,Y,(Z-4) *mod a₃*).

The communication pattern of phase 1 in a 2D torus (*pattern A*) is performed in even numbered X-Y planes, while inter-plane communications (*pattern C*) are performed among nodes in odd numbered planes (see Figure 2(a)). There are $\frac{a_1}{4} - 1$ steps in phase 1.

In phase 2, the following operations are performed:

Phase 2:
IF *(X+Y) mod 4 =0*, P(X,Y,Z) → P(X,(Y+4) *mod a₂*,Z).
IF *(X+Y) mod 4 =1*, P(X,Y,Z) → P((X+4) *mod a₁*,Y,Z).
IF *(X+Y) mod 4 =2*, P(X,Y,Z) → P(X,(Y-4) *mod a₂*,Z).
IF *(X+Y) mod 4 =3*, P(X,Y,Z) → P((X-4) *mod a₁*,Y,Z).

In phase 2, every node in each X-Y plane follows the communication pattern of phase 2 in a 2D torus (*pattern B*) as shown in Figure 2(b). There are also $\frac{a_1}{4} - 1$ steps in phase 2.

In phase 3, the following operations are performed:

Phase 3:
IF *(X+Y) mod 4 =0* and *Z mod 4=1 or 3*, P(X,Y,Z) → P((X+4) *mod a₁*,Y,Z).
IF *(X+Y) mod 4 =1* and *Z mod 4=1 or 3*, P(X,Y,Z) → P(X,(Y+4) *mod a₂*,Z).
IF *(X+Y) mod 4 =2* and *Z mod 4=1 or 3*, P(X,Y,Z) → P((X-4) *mod a₁*,Y,Z).
IF *(X+Y) mod 4 =3* and *Z mod 4=1 or 3*, P(X,Y,Z) → P(X,(Y-4) *mod a₂*,Z).
IF *Z mod 4=0*, then P(X,Y,Z) → P(X,Y, (Z+4) *mod a₃*).
IF *Z mod 4=2*, then P(X,Y,Z) → P(X,Y, (Z-4) *mod a₃*).

In phase 3, nodes in even numbered planes follow *pattern C* while nodes in the other planes follow *pattern A* as

472

shown in Figure 2(c). In phase 3, there too are $\frac{a_1}{4}-1$ steps.

After phase 3, the network is divided into $\frac{a_1a_2a_3}{4^3}$ $4 \times 4 \times 4$ submeshes. Now, phase 4 initiates and has three steps. The following operations are performed in each step of phase 4 (see Figures 2(d)-(f), where only one $4 \times 4 \times 4$ submesh is shown):

Step 1 of Phase 4:
IF *(X+Y) mod 2=0*, *Y mod 4=0 or 1*, and *Z mod 2=0*, P(X,Y,Z) → P(X+2,Y,Z).
IF *(X+Y) mod 2=0*, *Y mod 4=2 or 3*, and *Z mod 2=0*, P(X,Y,Z) → P(X-2,Y,Z).
IF *(X+Y) mod 2=1*, *X mod 4=0 or 1*, and *Z mod 2=0*, P(X,Y,Z) → P(X,Y+2,Z).
IF *(X+Y) mod 2=1*, *X mod 4=2 or 3*, and *Z mod 2=0*, P(X,Y,Z) → P(X,Y-2,Z).
IF *Z mod 4=1*, P(X,Y,Z) → P(X,Y,Z+2).
IF *Z mod 4=3*, P(X,Y,Z) → P(X,Y,Z-2).
Step 2 of Phase 4:
IF *(X+Y) mod 2=0* and *X mod 4=0 or 1*, P(X,Y,Z) → P(X,Y+2,Z).
IF *(X+Y) mod 2=0* and *X mod 4=2 or 3*, P(X,Y,Z) → P(X,Y-2,Z).
IF *(X+Y) mod 2=1* and *Y mod 4=0 or 1*, P(X,Y,Z) → P(X+2,Y,Z).
IF *(X+Y) mod 2=1* and *Y mod 4=2 or 3*, P(X,Y,Z) → P(X-2,Y,Z).
Step 3 of Phase 4:
IF *(X+Y) mod 2=0*, *Y mod 4=0 or 1*, and *Z mod 2=1*, P(X,Y,Z) → P(X+2,Y,Z).
IF *(X+Y) mod 2=0*, *Y mod 4=2 or 3*, and *Z mod 2=1*, P(X,Y,Z) → P(X-2,Y,Z).
IF *(X+Y) mod 2=1*, *X mod 4=0 or 1*, and *Z mod 2=1*, P(X,Y,Z) → P(X,Y+2,Z).
IF *(X+Y) mod 2=1*, *X mod 4=2 or 3*, and *Z mod 2=1*, P(X,Y,Z) → P(X,Y-2,Z).
IF *Z mod 4=0*, P(X,Y,Z) → P(X,Y,Z+2).
IF *Z mod 4=2*, P(X,Y,Z) → P(X,Y,Z-2).

After phase 4, the network is further divided into $\frac{a_1a_2a_3}{8}$ $2 \times 2 \times 2$ submeshes. Now, phase 5 is initiated and there are

three steps. In each step, every node exchanges messages along X-, Y-, and Z-dimension, respectively (see Figures 2(g)-(i), where only one $2 \times 2 \times 2$ submesh is shown). That is, the following operations are performed in each step of phase 5:

Step 1 of Phase 5:
IF *X mod 2=0*, P(X,Y,Z) → P(X+1,Y,Z).
IF *X mod 2=1*, P(X,Y,Z) → P(X-1,Y,Z).
Step 2 of Phase 5:
IF *Y mod 2=0*, P(X,Y,Z) → P(X,Y+1,Z).
IF *Y mod 2=1*, P(X,Y,Z) → P(X,Y-1,Z).
Step 3 of Phase 5:
IF *Z mod 2=0*, P(X,Y,Z) → P(X,Y,Z+1).
IF *Z mod 2=1*, P(X,Y,Z) → P(X,Y,Z-1).

Data Array:

Now, consider the data array of each node. Initially each node has $a_1a_2a_3$ distinct blocks in a three dimensional array B[u,v,w], where $0 \le u \le a_1-1$, $0 \le v \le a_2-1$, and $0 \le w \le a_3-1$. Since the data array structure in 3D tori is very similar to that in 2D tori and can be extended in a straightforward manner, we just examine the communication requirements in node P(0,0,0). In step 1 of phase 1, P(0,0,0) sends to P(4,0,0) blocks B[4..a_1-1,*,*], while receiving the same number of blocks from node P(a_1-4,0,0). The notation B[4..a_1-1,*,*] identifies all blocks from B[4,0,0] to B[a_1-1,a_2-1,a_3-1]. In the next step, P(0,0,0) transmits blocks B[8..a_1-1,*,*] to P(4,0,0). In general, in step s_1 of phase 1, $1 \le s_1 \le \frac{a_1}{4}-1$, P(0,0,0) transmits blocks B[4s_1..a_1-1,*,*]. In step s_2 of phase 2, $1 \le s_2 \le \frac{a_2}{4}-1$, P(0,0,0) transmits blocks B[*, 4s_2..a_2-1,*] to P(0,4,0). In step s_3 of phase 3, $1 \le s_3 \le \frac{a_3}{4}-1$, P(0,0,0) transmits blocks B[*,*, 4s_3..a_3-1]. The blocks transmitted by node P(0,0,0) in each step of phases 1, 2, and 3 in a $12 \times 12 \times 12$ torus are shown in Figure 3. After

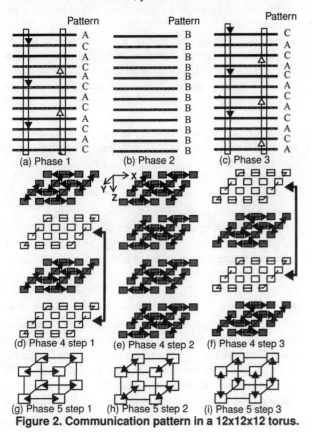

(a) Phase 1   (b) Phase 2   (c) Phase 3

(d) Phase 4 step 1   (e) Phase 4 step 2   (f) Phase 4 step 3

(g) Phase 5 step 1   (h) Phase 5 step 2   (i) Phase 5 step 3

Figure 2. Communication pattern in a 12x12x12 torus.

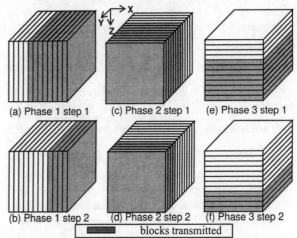

(a) Phase 1 step 1   (c) Phase 2 step 1   (e) Phase 3 step 1

(b) Phase 1 step 2   (d) Phase 2 step 2   (f) Phase 3 step 2

blocks transmitted

Figure 3. Blocks transmitted in each step in phases 1, 2, and 3 for a 12x12x12 torus.

phase 3, blocks originated from nodes in the same group destined for nodes in the $4 \times 4 \times 4$ submesh in which $P(0,0,0)$ is included are gathered in $P(0,0,0)$. Thus, in six steps in phases 4 and 5, the blocks destined for the other nodes in the $4 \times 4 \times 4$ submesh are transmitted.

4.2 Extension to *n*-Dimensional Tori

Now, we describe a general *n*-dimensional algorithm. Since the extension for *n*-dimensional tori can be made similarly to the 2D-3D extension, we describe the *n*-dimensional algorithm briefly in this subsection.

For an $a_1 \times \ldots \times a_n$ *n*-dimensional tori, where $a_1, \ldots, a_n$ are a multiple of four and $a_1 \geq \ldots \geq a_n$, there are $n+2$ phases. In the first *n* phases, messages are transmitted among nodes in the same group which form an $\frac{a_1}{4} \times \ldots \times \frac{a_n}{4}$ sub-torus. To avoid channel contention, the dimensions in which messages are transmitted are distributed in each phase. In general, for *n*-dimensional tori, nodes in the even numbered unit along the dimension *n* follow the communication patterns of $(n-1)$-dimensional networks during the first $n-1$ phases and then perform the communications along the last dimension (i.e., dimension *n*) in phase *n*, while the other nodes perform the communications along the dimension *n* in phase 1 and then follow the communications of $(n-1)$-dimensional networks during the remaining $n-1$ phases. In phases $n+1$ and $n+2$, message exchanges are performed among nodes in $4 \times \ldots \times 4$ and $2 \times \ldots \times 2$ *n*-dimensional submeshes, respectively.

4.3 Complexity Analysis

In this subsection, we analyze the time cost required by the proposed algorithm.

(a) Startup cost: For an $a_1 \times \ldots \times a_n$ *n*-dimensional torus, $a_1 \geq \ldots \geq a_n$, there are $n+2$ phases. In the first *n* phases, $\frac{a_1}{4} - 1$ steps per phase are required. In phases $n+1$ and $n+2$, *n* steps are required in each phase. Thus, a total of $n\left(\frac{a_1}{4}+1\right)$ steps is required.

(b) Message-transmission cost: In step s, $1 \leq s \leq \frac{a_1}{4} - 1$, in each of the first *n* phases, $(a_1 - 4 \cdot s)(a_2 \ldots a_n)$ blocks are transmitted (since $a_1 \geq a_2 \geq \ldots \geq a_n$). In each step of phases $n+1$ and $n+2$, $\frac{1}{2}(a_1 a_2 \ldots a_n)$ blocks are transmitted. Thus, the total number of transmitted blocks is $\frac{n}{8}(a_1 + 4)(a_1 \ldots a_n)$.

(c) Data-rearrangement cost: At the end of each phase blocks are rearranged to prepare for the next phase. Since there are $n+2$ phases, $n+1$ data-rearrangement steps are required. Thus, the total data-rearrangement cost is $(n+1)(a_1 a_2 \ldots a_n)m\rho$.

(d) Message propagation cost: In the first *n* phases, there

are $\frac{a_1}{4} - 1$ steps per phase. In each step, the number of hops to the destination is four. In phases $n+1$ and $n+2$, *n* steps are required in each phase and the number of hops to the destination is two and one, respectively. Thus, message propagation cost is expressed as $n(a_1 - 1)t_l$.

5. Performance Evaluation

Thus far, we analyzed the time cost required by the proposed algorithm in terms of startup cost, message-transmission cost, data-rearrangement cost, and message propagation cost. In this section, the performance of the proposed algorithms are evaluated and compared with that of existing algorithms.

Network	$R \times C$ torus	$a_1 \times \ldots \times a_n$ torus
Startup Cost	$\left(\frac{C}{2} + 2\right)t_s$	$n\left(\frac{a_1}{4} + 1\right)t_s$
Message Trans. Cost	$\frac{RC}{4}(C+4)mt_c$	$\frac{n}{8}(a_1 + 4)(a_1 a_2 \ldots a_n)mt_c$
Data-Rearrangement Cost	$3(RC)m\rho$	$(n+1)(a_1 a_2 \ldots a_n)m\rho$
Propagation Cost	$2(C-1)t_l$	$n(a_1 - 1)t_l$

Table 1: Performance summary of the proposed algorithms.

The time complexities of the proposed algorithms are summarized in Table 1. We are not aware of any existing message-combining algorithms for *n*-dimensional tori, where the number of nodes in each dimension is not power-of-two. For 2D tori, Tseng et al. [13] proposed an algorithm using message combining. In the algorithm, the tori are assumed to be power-of-two square networks. If we apply the proposed 2D algorithm to power-of-two square tori, the startup time and message-transmission time are equivalent to those in [13] (see Table 2). But, the proposed algorithm is advantageous with respect to data-rearrangement time and message propagation time. In the proposed 2D algorithm, data rearrangement is required between phases to prepare for the next phase. In a $2^d \times 2^d$ torus, there are four phases in the proposed algorithm, thus only three rearrangement steps are required, regardless of the network size. However, in the algorithm [13], data rearrangement is required between steps rather than phases (in our physical model of data array: if non-contiguous blocks are transmitted, the blocks should be rearranged or copied). Thus, the algorithm [13] requires $2^{d-1} + 1$ data-rearrangement steps. With respect to the total propagation delay, the proposed algorithm requires four hops (in phases 1 and 2), two hops (in phase 3), and one hop (in phase 4) per step, regardless of the network size. Thus, this algorithm which exhibits time complexity of $O(2^d)$ compares favorably to the algorithm [13] which exhibits time com-

Network	[13]	[9]	Proposed
Startup Cost	$(2^{d-1}+2)t_s$	$(3d-3)t_s$	$(2^{d-1}+2)t_s$
Message-Transmission Cost	$(2^{3d-2}+2^{2d})mt_c$	$\{9\cdot2^{3d-4}+(d^2-5d+3)2^{2d-1}\}mt_c$	$(2^{3d-2}+2^{2d})mt_c$
Data-Rearrangement Cost	$(2^{d-1}+1)2^{2d}m\rho$	$\{9\cdot2^{3d-4}+(d^2-5d+3)2^{2d-1}\}m\rho$	$(3)2^{2d}m\rho$
Propagation Cost	$\frac{1}{3}(2^{2d-1}+10)t_l$	$(13\cdot2^{d-2}-3d-3)t_l$	$(2^{d+1}-2)t_l$

Table 2: Comparison of completion time in two algorithms for a 2^dx2^d torus.

plexity of $O(2^{2d})$ due to propagation time. Thus, overall the proposed algorithm exhibits better performance than the existing algorithm [13] for power-of-two and square tori, even though the proposed algorithm is targeted at the networks whose size of each dimension need not be power-of-two and square. In [9], Suh and Yalamanchili proposed an algorithm using message combining for power-of-two tori. For a $2^d \times 2^d$ torus, message startup cost is $O(d)$ for the algorithm [9] while it is $O(2^d)$ for the proposed algorithm. The message-transmission cost of the proposed algorithm is $O(2^{3d})$ as the algorithm [9] but lower than that of the algorithm [9]. The time complexity due to data rearrangement for the algorithm [9] is $O(2^{3d})$, while that of the proposed algorithm is $O(2^{2d})$. With respect to the total propagation time, the proposed algorithm exhibits time complexity of $O(2^d)$ as the algorithm [9], but a little lower than that of the algorithm [9]. Thus, the proposed algorithm is advantageous over the algorithm [9] in all parameters except the startup cost.

6. Conclusions

This paper has proposed new algorithms for all-to-all personalized exchange for multidimensional torus-connected networks. Although the algorithms targeted at wormhole-switched networks, they can be efficiently used in virtual cut-through or circuit-switched networks. The proposed algorithms utilize message combining to reduce the time complexity of message startups. Unlike existing message-combining algorithms, the proposed algorithms accommodate non-power-of-two networks of arbitrary dimensions. In addition, destinations remain fixed over a larger number of steps in the proposed algorithms, thus making them amenable to optimizations. Finally, the data structures used are simple and hence make substantial saving of message-rearrangement time.

Although we assumed that the number of nodes in each dimension is multiple of four, the proposed algorithms can be used in tori with an arbitrary number of nodes in each dimension. If the number of nodes in each dimension is not a multiple of four, the proposed algorithms can be used by adding virtual nodes, then having every node perform communication steps as proposed in this paper.

When applied to power-of-two square tori, the proposed algorithms exhibit better performance than the algorithm [13], but the algorithm [9] shows much lower startup costs than that of the proposed algorithm although the proposed algorithms are favorable in other parameters. Thus, it may be interesting to study the comparative performance of the proposed algorithms and the algorithm [9].

References

[1] S. H. Bokhari and H. Berryman, "Complete Exchange on a Circuit Switched Mesh," *Scalable High Performance Computing Conference*, pp. 300-306, 1992.

[2] S. H. Bokhari, "Multiphase Complete Exchange on Paragon, SP2, and CS-2," *IEEE Parallel & Distributed Technology*, pp. 45-59, Fall 1996.

[3] W. J. Dally, "Performance Analysis of *k*-ary *n*-cube Interconnection Networks," *IEEE Trans. on Computer*, vol. 39, no. 6, pp. 775-785, June 1992.

[4] P. K. McKinley and Y.-J. Tsai and D. Robinson, "Collective Communication in Wormhole-routed Massively Parallel Computers," IEEE Computer, pp. 39-50, December 1995.

[5] L. M. Ni and P. K. McKinley, "A Survey of Wormhole Routing Techniques in Direct Networks," *IEEE Computer*, vol. 26, pp. 62-76, February 1993.

[6] D. K. Panda, "Issues in Designing Efficient and Practical Algorithms for Collective Communication on Wormhole-Routed Systems," Technical Report TR-25, Dept. of Computer and Information Science, Ohio State University.

[7] D. S. Scott, "Efficient All-to-All Communication Patterns in Hypercube and Mesh Topologies," *Proceedings of 6th Conference. Distributed Memory Concurrent Computers*, pp. 398-403, 1991.

[8] Y. J. Suh and S. Yalamanchili, "Algorithms for All-to-All Personalized Exchange in 2D and 3D Tori," Proceedings of the 10th International Parallel Processing Symposium, pp. 808-814, April 1996.

[9] Y. J. Suh and S. Yalamanchili, "All-to-All Communication with Minimum Start-Up Costs in 2D/3D Tori and Meshes," IEEE Transactions on Parallel and Distributed Systems, Vol. 9, No. 5, pp. 442-458, May 1998.

[10] N. S. Sundar, D. N. Jayasimha, D. K. Panda, and P. Sadayappan, "Complete Exchange in 2D Meshes," *Scalable High Performance Computing Conference*, pp. 406-413, 1994.

[11] R. Thakur and A. Choudhary, "All-to-All Communication on Meshes with Wormhole Routing," *Proceedings of 8th International Parallel Processing Symposium*, pp. 561-565, 1994.

[12] Y.-C. Tseng and S. Gupta, "All-to-All Personalized Communication in a Wormhole-Routed Torus," *Proc. of International Conference on Parallel Processing*, vol. 1, pp. 76-79, 1995.

[13] Y.-C. Tseng, S. Gupta, and D. Panda, "An Efficient Scheme for Complete Exchange in 2D Tori," *Proceedings of International Parallel Processing Symposium*, pp. 532-536, 1995.

[14] Message Passing Interface Forum, "MPI: A Message-Passing Interface Standard," Technical Report CS-93-214, University of Tennessee, April 1994.

[15] Cray T3D, *System Architecture Overview*, 1994.

Session 7A
Software Techniques

Chair: Matthew O'Keefe
University of Minnesota

Techniques for delayed binding of monitoring mechanisms to application-specific instrumentation points

Jeffrey Vetter*
Department of Computer Science
University of Illinois at Urbana-Champaign
Urbana, IL, USA, 61801

Karsten Schwan
College of Computing
Georgia Institute of Technology
Atlanta, Georgia, USA, 30332

Abstract

Online interaction with computer systems and applications allows developers to monitor, experiment with, and debug long-running, resource-intensive applications at runtime. Traditionally, developers statically bind a monitoring mechanism to each application-specific instrumentation point. This approach has shortcomings for online, interactive monitoring. Namely, static binding limits portability among monitoring systems; it may mismatch monitoring mechanisms to interactive requests for monitoring data; and, predictions for the performance and execution paths of instrumentation for static bindings are left to the developer. To address these concerns, we have created a new technique called **monitoring assertions** *that allows monitoring systems to delay binding of monitoring mechanisms to application-specific instrumentation points until runtime. Our empirical results show that we can alter the performance of both the application and the monitoring system by removing static binding requirement of application-specific monitoring systems.*

1. Interactive monitoring systems

Interactive monitoring systems permit users to interact with the monitoring system during the execution of the target application. Users can enable, disable, and reconfigure the monitoring system to suit their exploration of the application [19, 17, 9, 6]. These interactive monitoring systems complement other forms of monitoring that use post-mortem analysis [25, 18, 16, 2, 3], but they share with such systems the need to analyze and display monitoring data [20, 11, 12, 4]. The interactive monitoring systems investigated by our group are those that permit end-users to capture *application-specific* information from targets, such as the position and velocity of molecules, or values of a solution matrix in a multi-grid solver. Some online monitoring systems, which include Paradyn, Quartz, and EEL [17, 2, 3], use modified compilers or executable editing to interrogate the application for performance-relevant information. However, we do not employ these techniques because they are limited in the types of information they can provide to the user [19], especially when executables are highly-optimized [7, 24]. Alternatively, users of application-specific monitoring systems annotate their application source code to supplement information available from these other monitoring methods. Our particular form of application-specific monitoring, called *event-based* monitoring [13, 4, 14], produces streams of events that represent observed application state; the user analyzes these streams judge target system behavior.

Motivation. Application instrumentation is a primary component of any application-specific monitoring system. Across a wide variety of systems [23, 9], instrumentation support may be described as follows. (1) The developer chooses basic instrumentation mechanisms and annotates the source code. (2) At runtime, the monitoring system receives data from this instrumentation. (3) The monitoring server has limited runtime control over the instrumentation such that it typically relies on instrumentation placement to produce interesting data at appropriate rates. This *static binding* of monitoring mechanisms to instrumentation points is unacceptable for interactive monitoring systems because it is not easy to reasonably predict the interactor's exploration scenario when deciding upon instrumentation mechanisms. The developer must also predict the interactor's exploration scenario to help maintain consistent (or meaningful) data views of the target application.

This paper introduces **monitoring assertions** that allow developers to instrument applications without forcing them to predict how monitoring data might later be used and without forcing them to judge *a-priori* which mechanisms

*NASA financially supported Vetter with a Graduate Student Researchers Program Fellowship while he was a Ph.D. candidate at Georgia Tech. This work was also funded, in part, by NSF equipment grants CDA-9501637, CDA-9422033, and ECS-9411846.

are most appropriate. These assertions annotate *what* application data is available and *when* it is accessible to the monitoring system.

Related work. *Monitoring assertions* are code annotations; we propose these assertions could be used by any monitoring system in place of their application-specific instrumentation. Then, the monitoring system would query and control the instrumentation using the 'monitoring assertions' library API. Our earlier annotated bibliography provides many references to these instrumentation systems [10].

Tools like gprof[8] and Quartz[2] provide the user with valuable information about execution frequency; they assign elapsed time to static, syntactic units, such as procedures or statements. Additional work by Ammons and colleagues [1] extends this work to use flow and context information for performance counters. Paradyn [17] provides similar control-based application performance information; it delays the insertion of instrumentation until requested by the interactor, whether it is a query driven by a human or by Paradyn's performance consultant. These systems [8, 2, 1, 17] rely on information stored within the executable by the compiler—either the instrumentation itself or instrumentation targets such as procedure entry points. In many cases, this limitation prohibits the use of executable editing to observe application-specific data. An example of this shortcoming is described in §3.

Application-specific monitoring systems such as Falcon[9] and Autopilot [21] provide their own instrumentation libraries and instrumentation controls. Developers insert this instrumentation into their application source code and then, capture and analyze data produced by the instrumentation at runtime. Unfortunately, most every application-specific monitoring system has its own non-portable instrumentation library. In this respect, monitoring assertions could provide a common instrumentation tool for both application developers and tool developers. While these earlier instrumentation techniques propose various instrumentation mechanisms [19, 5, 16, 23], they focus primarily on the design of the monitoring system itself.

Research contributions. The novel idea of this work is to generalize instrumentation so that the binding of specific monitoring mechanisms to instrumentation points in target applications is delayed until more is known about the expected use of the monitoring information (i.e., at runtime). Note that executable editing allows the monitoring system to delay binding until runtime; however, it then can only bind to a limited scope of application attributes, such as procedure entry points. Whereas, monitoring assertions allows developers to introduce as many application-specific binding points as necessary. (1) **Monitoring assertions** capture the desired properties of application-specific instrumentation of *what data to monitor* and *when to monitor that*

data without the requirement of static binding to particular monitoring mechanisms. (2) **Instrumentation signatures** result in our system's ability to predict monitoring overheads and thereby enable runtime choices in instrumentation bindings based on observed patterns in instrumentation flow and frequencies. These signatures are derived from reference executions of instrumented applications. (3) Empirical evaluations of monitoring assertions and instrumentation signatures demonstrate the utility of delaying mechanism binding until runtime.

Sample applications. Two applications demonstrate our ideas. *Heat diffusion* is a 27-point, 3D-stencil, time-stepped simulation [22] implemented with kernel-level threads for SMP platforms. This simulation exhibits nearest neighbor sharing common to many simulations of physical systems. A more complex example is provided by the Splash 2 *OCEAN* benchmark. The Ocean benchmark simulates eddy and boundary currents in a cuboidal ocean basin. The application uses finite differencing CFD with a regular grid. The algorithm uses a red-black Gauss-Seidel multi-grid equation solver; each time-step of the simulation involves setting up and solving a set of spatial partial differential equations.

Experiment platform. The experimental platform is a network of 4 two-processor Sun Ultra 2 Model 2148s (148 MHz UltraSPARC CPU). Each system has 128MB of main memory and they run Solaris 2.5.1. Although this work focuses on shared memory architectures, we are not aware of any fundamental design restrictions such that monitoring assertions could not work in a message passing environment.

Paper outline. §2 reviews application instrumentation including various mechanisms and characteristics. §3 and §4 explain the technique of monitoring assertions and instrumentation signatures, respectively. §5 reveals our concluding thoughts and some future research issues.

2. Background: application instrumentation

Typical online monitoring systems have four basic components as illustrated in Fig. 1: system software, application, monitoring server, and interactor. Systems that broadly fit this model include Paradyn [17], Falcon [9], Magellan [22], Avatar [20], Vista [23], and various debuggers. We assume no special operating system, special compilers, or hardware. The interactor controls the server; it specifically provides user interface and visualization capabilities. The server is generally a separate process or thread that communicates with the application via shared memory or IPC.

Application-specific instrumentation is represented as software statements added to the target application [19, 5, 16]. This instrumentation gathers data about the application's execution, packages it, and sends it to some higher-level monitoring system. This instrumentation has two basic objectives: (1) instrumentation identifies *which* application

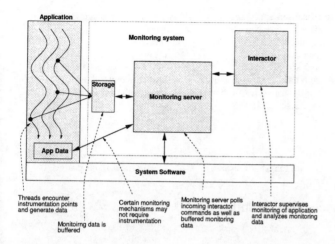

Application

Monitoring system

Interactor

Storage

Monitoring server

App Data

System Software

Threads encounter instrumentation points and generate data

Monitoirng data is buffered

Certain monitoring mechanisms may not require instrumentation

Monitoring server polls incoming interactor commands as well as buffered monitoring data

Interactor supervises monitoring of application and analyzes monitoring data

Figure 1. Typical model for an interactive monitoring system.

data the monitoring system can observe; and, (2) instrumentation identifies *when* the monitoring server can safely observe application data; thereby addressing both the validity of the each observed data item as well as the consistency of multiple data items.

The following code illustrates application-specific monitoring instrumentation for the Magellan computational steering system, which supports interactive monitoring. This code is taken from the Splash 2 Ocean benchmark.

```
AS_RegisterObject(steer, "residual norm",
   &multi->err_multi, AST_DOUBLE, 0, &sResNorm);
AS_Sense(sResNorm);
```

During initialization, the Magellan instrumentation registers target data using the call `AS_RegisterObject` and providing the name, type, size, and address to the runtime Magellan server. Next, a sensor is placed in the loop using `AS_Sense` to provide controlled access to these registered objects. Magellan need only enable these `AS_Sense` instrumentation points to receive periodic updates for this application variable.

To reason more specifically about instrumentation points, we now introduce some terminology. A **static instrumentation point** is uniquely identified by its location within the source code: a filename and line number. $IP_{file,line}$ describes this static instrumentation point. For convenience, we collapse $IP_{file,line}$ into a unique identifier: sid.

At runtime, however, this static description does not provide enough information to the monitoring system. In one scenario, multiple threads can execute the same instrumentation point, so the instrumentation point must also provide a thread (or process) identifier tid and context (or stack frame) information–sf–for scoping and recursion. Without

additional compiler support, we currently do not explore use of sf to extend sid. Adding tid, a **runtime instrumentation point (rid)** is uniquely identified by sid and tid; or, $f(sid, tid) \rightarrow rid$.

In addition to the information generated by instrumentation points, the monitoring system may also accumulate and observe information about the instrumentation itself. The monitoring system tracks the number of times instrumentation points are encountered by application threads as well as the number of times data items are actually observed by each instrumentation point. A **hit** occurs when an instrumentation point is encountered by an application thread. $Hits(sid)$ gives the number of total hits on sid by any thread while $Hits(sid, tid)$ gives the number of total hits on sid by thread tid. For example, every time any thread executes the `AS_Sense` instrumentation point, it counts as one *hit*. A **capture** is a hit where the instrumentation point observes application state and forwards it to the monitoring system. $Captures(sid)$ gives the number of total captures on sid by any thread while $Captures(sid, tid)$ gives the number of total captures on sid by thread tid. All captures are necessarily hits; however, hits are not necessarily captures.

An **event** ϵ_{eid} is a quad-tuple containing an event class descriptor ($class$), a timestamp (TS), a location (loc) and state (S): $\epsilon_{eid} = (class, TS, loc, S)$. A unique event identifier (eid) identifies each event. $Timestamp(\epsilon_{eid})$ furnishes the timestamp of the event ϵ_{eid}. The instrumentation point generates the event timestamp when it creates the event. $Loc(\epsilon_{eid})$ furnishes the originating location of ϵ_{eid} which includes the tid as well as sid. $State(\epsilon_{eid})$ allows the monitoring system to access the event's state. State sizes vary for different event classes, so $Size(\epsilon_{eid})$ furnishes the state size of the event ϵ_{eid}.

2.1. Instrumentation mechanisms

We consider four types of instrumentation mechanisms: tracing sensors, sampling sensors, snapshot sensors, and synchronous probes. For these definitions, assume that each of the mechanisms are enabled and that rid has $Hit(rid) = n$.

A *tracing sensor* installed at rid captures n events ϵ and forwards each event to the monitoring server via a FIFO shared buffer. $Captures(rid) = Hits(rid) = n$. Fig. 2(a) furnishes the pseudo code for a tracing sensor instrumentation point. All events generated by a tracing sensor are consumed by the monitoring server. The application thread must contend with the monitoring server for exclusive access to the FIFO buffer. If the non-blocking `buffer insert` fails, then the application must retry the insert. The `buffer insert` could fail because either the FIFO is currently locked or it is full.

A *sampling sensor* captures $(Hits(sid)/\omega_{sampling})$

```
trace-sensor ( datahandle )        sampling-sensor ( datahandle )      snapshot-sensor ( datahandle )     synch-probe ( datahandle )
  hits++                             hits++                              hits++                            hits++
  if enabled                         if enabled                         if enabled                        if enabled
  captures++                          if (hit % samplfreq) == 0           captures++                         captures++
  allocate event                       captures++                        lock shared area                  mondata = datahandle
  copy datahandle to event             allocate event                    copy datahandle to shared area    barrier (monitor thread)
  package event                        copy datahandle to event          update shared area attributes     barrier (monitor thread)
  while buffer insert fails            package event                     unlock shared area                return
   buffer insert event                 while buffer insert fails        return
  return                                buffer insert event
                                      return

      (a) tracing                          (b) sampling                      (c) snapshot sensor               (d) synchronous probe
```

Figure 2. Monitoring mechanism pseudo-code.

events and forwards these events to the monitoring server via a FIFO shared buffer. With $\omega_{sampling} > 1$, $Captures(rid) \leq \frac{Hits(rid)}{\omega_{sampling}}$. A tracing sensor is a sampling sensor where $\omega_{sampling} = 1$. Fig. 2(b) outlines the operation for a sampling sensor. $\omega_{sampling}$ can change dynamically.

Fig. 2(c) defines the operation of a *snapshot sensor* that captures n events but stores only one event in a shared location instead of placing it in a FIFO buffer. The application instrumentation overwrites this stored event with the most recent event. The monitoring server then reads this shared location to find this event.

A *probe* directly reads application memory without synchronizing with the application through an instrumentation point. Original probes[19] have no corresponding rid. The monitoring system copies the data immediately upon request. This lack of synchronization limits probe state size to machine-dependent data sizes. Due to this limitation, we do not study normal probes in detail; however, we do introduce synchronous probes as an alternative.

A *synchronous probe* synchronizes execution of the monitoring server and the application thread at rid. Once the synchronization occurs, the monitoring server copies ϵ_{eid} directly from the stalled application. No data is buffered between the application and the monitoring server. Fig. 2(d) illustrates the primary differences in operation of a synchronous probe from the previous constructs.

2.2. Instrumentation characteristics

Each of these instrumentation mechanisms have quantifiable impacts on the application and the monitoring system including application perturbation, monitoring latency, potential monitoring frequency, and the consistency of the monitoring information. We define γ as a global clock available to the application, instrumentation points, the monitoring server, and the interactor.

Each rid has a time associated with its execution. *Instrumentation point execution time*, $\Delta_{Execution}(rid) =$ $\gamma_{stop} - \gamma_{start}$, is the difference in time from the call to the return of the instrumentation point rid. This $\Delta_{Execution}(rid)$ captures the time the instrumentation waits on mutex locks, full buffers or other costs.

Small changes in application instruction sequences from this instrumentation can result in substantial aggregate performance perturbation[15]. We measure this aggregate perturbation instead of the execution time of each individual instrumentation point. *Application runtime*, $\tau_{application} = \gamma_{stop}^{application} - \gamma_{start}^{application}$, is the runtime of the original application without any instrumentation points. Instrumented application runtime, $\tau_{instrumented} = \gamma_{stop}^{instrumented} - \gamma_{start}^{instrumented}$, is the runtime of the instrumented application. *Application perturbation*, $\Delta_{Perturbation} = \tau_{instrumented} - \tau_{application}$, is the difference in the runtime of the instrumented application minus the runtime of the original application. *Application perturbation slowdown* is the ratio of instrumented runtime to original application runtime: $\frac{\tau_{instrumented}}{\tau_{application}}$. $\Delta_{Perturbation}$ is a function instrumentation mechanisms used throughout the exploration of the target application. It is our experience that aggregate $\Delta_{Perturbation} > 0$ and perturbation slowdown is greater than 1. For our evaluation, we lock the instrumentation points to one mechanism for each benchmark's duration.

Tab. 1 details these measurements for two example applications. Each application used two processors. *Optimized* mode used compiler option -O; *debug* mode using compiler option -g; *gprof* mode used option -xpg -O on the SUNWspro compiler. *Optimized/ma* mode is the performance of the optimized application with additional monitoring assertions instrumentation. As we expected, debug mode increased the runtimes of each application considerably. Gprof has a aggregate perturbation of 28-33%. Monitoring assertions produced on 1-3% aggregate perturbation on the target applications. **Total hits** represents the cumulative sum of all assertion hits during execution of the application. We certainly expect a more thoroughly instrumented version of either application to produce more perturbation;

Application	State	Avg Runtime (sec)	Total hits	Ratio
OCEAN	Opt	336	-	1
	Opt/ma	337	3110	1.01
	Opt/gprof	430	-	1.28
	Debug	697	-	2.07
Stencil	Opt	124	-	1
	Opt/ma	128	202	1.03
	Opt/gprof	165	-	1.33
	Debug	252	-	2.03

Table 1. Application performance under different instrumentation scenarios.

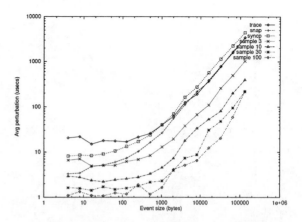

Figure 3. Average perturbation per instrumentation point versus event size.

however, this analysis demonstrates that the perturbation from monitoring assertions is not inherently limiting.

Online monitoring systems obviously require some latency to capture, transport, and analyze their data. This latency is a function of many factors including instrumentation mechanisms. Here, we are primarily interested in the latency between the event generation by application instrumentation and event consumption by the monitoring server. Buffer management can also alter the latency of the system[9, 23]; we hold buffer parameters constant across our evaluations.

Event latency, $\Delta_{Latency}^{eid} = \gamma - TS(\epsilon_{eid})$, is the difference of the current time from the timestamp on the event ϵ_{eid} as observed by the monitoring server. Assuming a correct globally consistent clock with infinite resolution, $\gamma > TS(\epsilon_{eid})$ and $\Delta_{Latency}^{eid} > 0$.

2.3. Perturbation and latency evaluation

Each of our earlier defined mechanisms have different perturbation and latency characteristics. To measure these characteristics, we have created micro-benchmarks and then, monitored those micro-benchmarks with the Magellan system[22]. As the code below illustrates, the benchmark is a loop that accesses array with size datasize.

```
int array[datasize]
start timer
for ITER
do
  incr all elements of array
  Instrumentation point(array)
  delay
done
stop timer
```

Perturbation is measured by subtracting the wall-clock time of the uninstrumented loop from the wall-clock time of the instrumented loop. The monitoring server calculates *latency* with each ϵ_{eid} timestamp and the same machine clock. This clock's resolution is microseconds.

Figs. 3 and 4 illustrate the clear differences in the perturbation and latency characteristics of tracing sensors, sampling sensors ($\omega_{sampling} = 30$), snapshot sensors, and synchronous probes. Characteristics such as buffer properties and interference have been studied by Waheed and associates, and Gu and colleagues [23, 9]. We recognize these issues by assuming a reasonable buffer size and a steady-state computer system.

From this analysis, we see that all perturbation increases with data size. Tracing sensors impose the highest perturbation on the application while sampling sensors have the lowest overall perturbation. However, this sampling sensor perturbation varies with $\omega_{sampling}$. Event latency for tracing and sampling sensors is almost identical regardless of data size because the underlying data structures are similar. the latency for synchronous probes and snapshot sensors is very predictable, increases with data size, and is almost two orders of magnitude better than either tracing or sampling sensors.

Given these clear differences, it is best to match the appropriate mechanism to current interactive monitoring requests. Our monitoring assertions allow dynamic binding of these mechanisms to the appropriate instrumentation points for each monitoring request. The monitoring system can choose which mechanism to employ.

3. Monitoring assertions

As in the earlier Magellan example, the instrumentation mechanisms are bound at compile time. AS_Sense dictates that the mechanism used to monitor sResNorm, etc. is always a sensor. If the interactive monitoring system needs a different type of mechanism such as a synchronous probe to minimize latency, then the user would have to re-instrument the application and recompile.

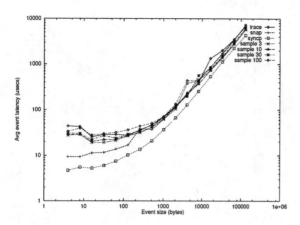

Figure 4. Average latency per event versus event size.

Monitoring assertions help solve this problem by providing the monitoring system with a method for dynamically binding these mechanisms to the assertions. Monitoring assertions allow the developer to generally instrument their application by identifying *which* data is available for monitoring and *when* this data is observable. They are annotations that a developer adds to source code. So, as a result of the scenario depicted in the Magellan example, that code becomes Fig. 5, where mechanisms are replaced by assertions. Developers can also limit the types of mechanisms that can be used at individual assertions that further limit the choices available to the monitoring system when selecting mechanisms.

Given our earlier analysis of different monitoring mechanisms, the following scenario illuminates the advantages of monitoring assertions over previously-discussed monitoring instrumentation. In Fig.5, the monitoring system can make different choices about which monitoring mechanisms to use at `AAA_Access` based on interactive requests.

If the user needs to track a variable such as `resNorm` with size 8 bytes, then the monitoring system could easily choose a snapshot sensor because it provides the best perturbation (from Fig. 3) with the second best latency of 7 microseconds (see Fig. 4). Synchronous probes provide the best latency at 8 bytes; however, the latency improvement is very small and synchronous probe perturbation is higher.

If the user wants to display a larger data item or additional data items, then the monitoring system must reevaluate its instrumentation choices. If the user requests the variable `f` with size 4112, the monitoring system can choose sampling sensors ($\omega_{sampling} = 30$) with the best perturbation. At large data sizes, the data copying dominates the latency costs; therefore, all mechanism latencies converge toward a common latency cost. This fact effectively reduces the mon-

```
AAA_double(multi->err_multi); /* resNorm */
AAA_int(k);      /* level */
while (((!flag1) && (!flag2)) {
  /* ...code omitted... */
  AAA_Access(multi->err_multi,wu,iter,
  k,f,tolerance);}
```

Figure 5. Splash2 Ocean with monitoring assertions.

itoring system's choice dimensions to perturbation, which favors sampling sensors for this example.

Without monitoring assertions, the monitoring system would be unable to combine interactive monitoring requests with its knowledge about application instrumentation to provide these optimized solutions.

Localized application de-optimization. Most large-scale, high performance applications have thousands of data items of which only a small portion are useful for monitoring. Using application-specific knowledge, the developer chooses which data to make available and when. By placing the monitoring assertions in the code, the developer also chooses how to localize de-optimizations. Namely, in contrast to de-optimizations performed when using general debug options (e.g., `-g`) provided by compilers, monitoring assertions result in de-optimizations only for the specific code components where they are placed. Monitoring assertions can be easily disabled with command line switches or preprocessor directives.

The developer controls the tradeoff between the availability of monitoring data at runtime and compiler optimizations. If the developer wants access to certain data at runtime, then such a de-optimization may be acceptable. In fact, the extraction of such data from highly-optimized code may be extremely difficult and even misleading[7, 24] without these local de-optimizations.

3.1. Source code annotations

Monitoring assertions have two different forms: one to declare data and one to access declared data. An application first must declare which application-specific data is available for interactive monitoring; then, at various places throughout the code, the application allows access to that declared data via assertions.

Declarations. Declarations provide monitoring assertions with type and scoping information while limiting the amount of data items available to the interactor. Compiler support for declarations would reduce the instrumentation for this declaration statement to a simple tag on the language variable declaration (e.g., `monitor int iter;`). Figs. 5 illustrates a declaration sequence for a set of variables. As in Fig.5, these declarations are currently preprocessor directives, `AAA_int(k)`, that expand into a procedure call with parameters for name, type, address, size, thread identifier, filename and line number:

```
aaa_decl_data("k", AAA_INT, &k,
  sizeof(k), tid, "slave1.c", 689)
```

The declaration for each `name` must occur prior to any access points using that name.

When this call is executed by the application with monitoring assertions, it stores this information. Later, this information can be written to an instrumentation signatures history file (see §4). The `aaa_decl_data` call first checks `name` to determine if it is already registered. If `name` does not exist, then it creates a table entry and initializes statistics for that name. If it does exist, then it verifies the instrumentation location (i.e., line number and file name). If `name` has been defined at another instrumentation location, `aaa_decl_data` indicates a name collision and does not register the offending name. If the static instrumentation location (sid) verifies, then it checks the thread identifier tid. If tid exists, then just the statistics are updated. Otherwise, monitoring assertions creates a new runtime instrumentation location (rid) and adds this information to the existing static instrumentation location in the registry.

Access points. Once data has been declared, monitoring assertions require control flow information about how the monitoring system can 'safely' access these data items at runtime. An assertion tells the monitoring system when the data is semantically meaningful as defined by the developer as well as when it is not being accessed by the current thread. These assertions are currently preprocessor directives that expand into a procedure call with parameters for thread identifier, filename, line number and a list of pairs of name and address. In Fig. 5, `AAA_Access(multi->err_multi, wu, iter, k, f, tolerance)` expands to

```
aaa_access(tid,"slave1.c",704,
  "multi->err_multi", &(multi->err_multi),
  "wu", &(wu), ... , NULL );
```

When this call is executed by the application with monitoring assertions, `aaa_access` acts like a declaration. The `aaa_access` call checks the static instrumentation location (sid) to determine if it is already registered. If sid does not exist, then it creates a table entry and initializes statistics for that location, else it checks the thread identifier tid as well as the data items in the list. If tid exists, then only the statistics are updated. Otherwise, the monitoring assertion creates a new runtime instrumentation location (rid) and adds it to the static instrumentation location in the registry. Essentially, an unlimited number of declared data items can be listed with each `aaa_access` call. At each appearance of a new sid, the system verifies the data items are previously declared using `name` to scan the declared data table. This provides the sid with type and size information.

4. Instrumentation signatures

Instrumentation signatures further augment monitoring assertions by providing a runtime history of an application's instrumentation. These signature files capture three basic characteristics: declarations, instrumentation points, and per-thread statistics about the number of hits on each instrumentation point (i.e., $Hits(sid, tid)$ and $Hits(sid)$). The monitoring system can use this information to determine how to bind mechanisms to access points so that performance is optimized. Signatures are generated when the target system is executed in *reference run* mode; signatures are then used at runtime to determine what data is available and to help predict which instrumentation points best satisfy data rates for the interactive requests. Instrumentation signatures do provide information unavailable with compile-time analysis and executable editing. In general, instrumentation signatures are a function of the application, its particular monitoring assertions, input data, and other system conditions such as the number of threads used by the application.

A *reference run* will produce only an initial guess about the instrumentation signatures value. For the relatively stable scientific applications considered in our research, this guess is reasonable and is not subject to frequent changes.

Declarations. The *declaration* section details an application component's name, location, type, size and its unique identifier. Declarations provide type and size information to monitoring assertions.

Instrumentation points. The *instrumentation points* section details all instrumentation points encountered during the reference run. Each line contains the location of the instrumentation point, a unique identifier and all the declared application components that are available at that instrumentation point. Using this knowledge, an interactive monitoring system can quickly determine what data is available and at what rates.

Statistics. The *statistics* section provides frequencies of execution of each instrumentation point including total hits $Hits(sid)$ as well as hits per thread $Hits(sid, tid)$—both raw and normalized statistics. Using this information, a monitoring system can choose instrumentation points based on their expected $Hits(sid)$.

5. Conclusions

We have introduced monitoring assertions and instrumentation signatures as two new techniques to help improve the efficiency and usability of monitoring systems. Monitoring assertions generalize application-specific instrumentation so that monitoring systems can dynamically control the binding of instrumentation points to monitoring mechanisms. Dynamic binding and the use of consistency information can improve application perturbation and monitoring latencies. In addition, instrumentation signatures may be used to predict the frequencies and performance of instrumentation. Currently, a C library allows tools to dynamically bind mechanisms to these assertions.

Compiler integration of monitoring assertions could drastically alter their utility and efficiency. Application-specific instrumentation usually must supplement information gathered from other compiler-provided sources. If our monitoring assertions were integrated with a compiler, they could provide the following advantages: (1) use of compile-time type information to automate the instrumentation process; (2) integrate data dependency information with monitoring assertions to rearrange and combine assertions to improve performance; and, (3) use stack frame information to make monitoring assertions more precise.

References

[1] G. Ammons, T. Ball, and J. Larus. Exploiting hardware performance counters with flow and context sensitive profiling. In *Proc. ACM SIGPLAN Programming Language Design and Implementation (PLDI)*, 1997.

[2] T. Anderson and E. Lazowska. Quartz: A tool for tuning parallel program performance. In *Proc. 1990 SIGMETRICS Conf. Measurement and Modeling Computer Systems*, pages 115–125, Boston, 1990.

[3] T. Ball and J. Larus. Optimally profiling and tracing programs. *ACM Trans. Programming Languages and Systems*, 16(4):1319–60, 1994.

[4] P. Bates. Debugging heterogeneous distributed systems using event-based models of behavior. *ACM Trans. Computer Systems*, 13(1):1–31, 1995.

[5] D. Bhatt. Scalable parallel instrumentation (SPI): an environment for developing parallel system instrumentation. In *Proc. Intel Supercomputer Users Group Conf.*, pages 98–104, 1994.

[6] D. Brown, S. Hackstadt, A. Malony, B. Mohr, J. Dongarra, and B. Tourancheau. Program analysis environments for parallel language systems: the tau environment. In *Proc. Second Workshop on Environments and Tools for Parallel Scientific Computing*, pages 162–71, 1994.

[7] M. Copperman and C. McDowell. A further note on hennessy's 'symbolic debugging of optimized code'. *ACM Trans. Programming Languages and Systems*, 15(2):357–65, 1993.

[8] S. Graham, P. Kessler, and M. McKusick. Gprof: A call graph execution profiler. *SIGPLAN Notices (SIGPLAN '82 Symp. Compiler Construction)*, 17(6):120–126, 1982.

[9] W. Gu, G. Eisenhauer, E. Kraemer, K. Schwan, J. Stasko, J. Vetter, and N. Mallavarupu. Falcon: On-line monitoring and steering of large-scale parallel programs. In *Proc. Frontiers of Massively Parallel Computation*, 1995.

[10] W. Gu, J. Vetter, and K. Schwan. An annotated bibliography of interactive program steering. *SIGPLAN Notices*, 29(9):140–8, 1994.

[11] S. Hackstadt, A. Malony, L. Bouge, P. Fraigniaud, A. Mignotte, and Y. Robert. Distributed array query and visualization for high performance fortran. In *Proc. Euro-Par '96 Parallel Processing.*, pages 55–63, 1996.

[12] E. Kraemer and J. Stasko. The visualization of parallel systems: An overview. *Jour. Parallel and Distributed Computing*, 18(2):105–117, 1993.

[13] J. Kundu and J. Cuny. A scalable, visual interface for debugging with event-based behavioral abstraction. In *Proc. Fifth Symp. the Frontiers of Massively Parallel Computation*, pages 472–9, 1995.

[14] A. Malony. Event-based performance perturbation: a case study. *SIGPLAN Notices (Third ACM SIGPLAN Symp. Principles and Practice of Parallel Programming)*, 26(7):201–12, 1991.

[15] A. Malony, D. Reed, and H. Wijshoff. Performance measurement intrusion and perturbation analysis. *IEEE Trans. Parallel and Distributed Systems*, 3(4):433–50, 1992.

[16] D. Marinescu, H. Siegel, J. Lumpp, and T. Casavant. Models for monitoring and debugging tools for parallel and distributed software. *Jour. Parallel and Distributed Computing*, 9:171–184, 1990.

[17] B. Miller, M. Callaghan, J. Cargille, J. Hollingsworth, R. Irvin, K. Karavanic, K. Kunchithapadam, and T. Newhall. The paradyn parallel performance measurement tool. *Computer*, 28(11):37–46, 1995.

[18] B. Miller, M. Clark, J. Hollingsworth, S. Kierstead, S.-S. Lim, and T. Torzewski. IPS-2: The second generation of a parallel program measurement system. *IEEE Trans. Parallel and Distributed Systems*, 1:206–217, 1990.

[19] D. Ogle, K. Schwan, and R. Snodgrass. Application-dependent dynamic monitoring of distributed and parallel systems. *IEEE Trans. Parallel and Distributed Systems*, 4(7):762–778, 1993.

[20] D. Reed, K. Shields, W. Scullin, L. Tavera, and C. Elford. Virtual reality and parallel systems performance analysis. *Computer*, 28(11):57–67, 1995.

[21] R. Ribler, J. Vetter, H. Simitci, and D. Reed. Autopilot: adaptive control of distributed applications. In *Proc. Seventh IEEE Int'l Symp. High Performance Distributed Computing*, 1998.

[22] J. Vetter and K. Schwan. High performance computational steering of physical simulations. In *Proc. Int'l Parallel Processing Symp.*, pages 128–132, Geneva, 1997.

[23] A. Waheed and D. Rover. A structured approach to instrumentation system development and evaluation. In *Proc. Supercomputing 95*, pages 1–1, 1995.

[24] R. Wismuller. Debugging of globally optimized programs using data flow analysis. *SIGPLAN Notices (ACM SIGPLAN '94 Conf. Programming Language Design and Implementation)*, 29(6):278–89, 1994.

[25] J. Yan, E. Hesham, and B. Shriver. Performance tuning with AIMS-an automated instrumentation and monitoring system for multicomputers. In *Proc. Twenty-Seventh Hawaii Int'l Conf. System Sciences. Vol.II: Software Technology*, pages 625–33, 1994.

Optimizing Distributed Data Structures Using Application-Specific Network Interface Software*

Raoul A.F. Bhoedjang   John W. Romein   Henri E. Bal
Vrije Universiteit, Amsterdam, The Netherlands
{raoul, john, bal}@cs.vu.nl

Abstract

Network interfaces that contain a programmable processor offer much flexibility, which so far has mainly been used to optimize message passing libraries. We show that high performance gains can be achieved by implementing support for application-specific shared data structures on the network interface processors. As a case study, we have implemented shared transposition tables on a Myrinet network, using customized software that runs partly on the network processor and partly on the host. The customized software greatly reduces the overhead of interactions between the network interface and the host. Also, the software exploits application semantics to obtain a simple and efficient communication protocol. Performance measurements indicate that applications that run application-specific code on the network interface are up to 2.5 times as fast as those that use generic message-passing software.

1. Introduction

Several modern workstation clusters and multicomputers have a network interface with a programmable processor, which controls the message transfers between the host and the network. Customizing this network interface software to a specific message passing layer can result in large performance improvements [2, 3, 5, 12, 13]. Research on customizing network interface software has focused on optimizing message passing performance. In this paper, we take a different approach and investigate if programmable network interface processors can also be used to implement *shared data structures* efficiently. Existing systems layer shared data structures on top of a general-purpose messaging layer. The main problem with such messaging layers is that they do not allow remote memory to be accessed without transferring control to a remote process. Our approach

is to use the network interface to avoid control transfers and to perform simple, but application-specific tasks. Our goal is to investigate whether this approach makes it possible to efficiently implement frequently-accessed shared data structures on a distributed system.

To evaluate this idea, we have implemented (shared) *transposition tables* on a 64-node Myrinet [1] cluster. Transposition tables are used in heuristic search algorithms to memorize subproblems that have already been solved. The performance of applications like computer chess critically depends on an efficient transposition table implementation.

Transposition tables are accessed at a high rate, up to 10,000s of (remote) accesses per second. Moreover, many accesses modify the table, and these write operations are issued by different processors. Also, the access pattern to the table is dynamic and unpredictable. Because of these characteristics, traditional optimizations such as replication and message combining are insufficient to implement shared transposition tables efficiently.

The contributions of this paper are twofold. First, we outline a novel approach for implementing shared data structures efficiently on stock hardware using application-specific network interface software (Section 4). Second, we report on our experiences with this approach for partitioned and replicated transposition tables and compare performance with a message-passing implementation on a 64-node Myrinet cluster (Section 5). Our performance measurements indicate that the applications that run application-specific network interface software are up to 2.5 times as fast as those that use the generic message-passing software. In addition, the application-specific implementation of partitioned transposition tables scales better than the corresponding message-passing implementation.

2. Related work

Distributed-memory clusters using a fast interconnect and shared-memory NUMA architectures like the Origin2000 [14] have converged significantly at the hardware

---

*This research is supported in part by a PIONIER grant from the Netherlands Organization for Scientific Research (N.W.O.).

level; they differ mainly in the memory model offered to the programmer. The remote memory access latency of the Origin2000 ($\approx$ 500 ns [14]) is only one order of magnitude lower than the minimum message-passing latency reported for a Myrinet cluster ($\approx$ 5 μs [8]). This relatively small difference has led to the development of software systems for distributed-memory architectures that give fast access to remote memory. Below, we discuss several of these systems.

The separation of data and control transfer, proposed in [11], eliminates the overheads associated with the use of standard Remote Procedure Call techniques to access remote memory. The authors argue that the transfer of *control* to the remote address space can often be avoided and unnecessarily adds to remote-memory access overhead. One way to avoid control transfer overheads is to let the network interface handle remote-memory requests.

Hamlyn [2], a Myrinet prototype of a sender-based communication system, allows processes to store data in a remote address space. For each data transfer, the sender of the data specifies a destination in a dedicated, pinned segment in the receiver's address space. Hamlyn allows data to be stored in (but not read from) remote memory; control transfer is optional.

VMMC-2 [3] is a virtual memory-mapped communication system that allows a process to transfer data to and from another process's virtual memory. In contrast with Hamlyn, users can transfer data to and from any page in their address space. Pages are pinned and unpinned by a user-level library, so that the operating system will not swap them out during data transfers. The network interface, which needs to know the physical addresses of user pages, caches translations of pages that were pinned by user processes.

All three remote-memory systems described above allow a process to access a remote address space without transferring control to that address space. Our work differs from these systems in that we do not aim to build a general-purpose data transfer facility. Instead, we investigate the performance impact of adding application-specific processing to remote-memory requests that are processed by the network interface rather than the host.

The SPINE [4] project provides a safe execution environment for running user code directly on the network processor through the use of a type-safe language. An extensible SPINE interface allows applications to download protocol stacks like Active Messages and MPI, as well as customized application code onto the network interface.

3. Transposition tables

Game-playing programs search a game tree to find the best move in a given board position. The name "game tree" is actually a misnomer, because the search space is a graph rather than a tree. The reason is that it can contain dupli-

cate nodes (called transpositions) which are reached through a different sequence of moves. In chess, for example, the opening moves d4–Nf6–e3 yield the same position as e3–Nf6–d4. The transposition table [15] is a well-known technique to detect and exploit transpositions. Each time a position has been searched, the results of the search are stored in the transposition table. Before searching a new position, the position is looked up in the table to see if a previous search has already computed the results for that position.

The transposition table is implemented as a large hash table and looks like a set-associative cache. Each board position is hashed to an n-bit value called the *signature*, which is subsequently mapped to an index of the table. For each index, there are a number of entries in the table, which together form a *line*. Each entry contains a tag and some search-strategy specific fields, such as the result of the position that has been searched (an integer that indicates the quality of the position), the best move from that position, and the depth to which the position has been searched.

Transposition tables differ from computer memory caches in two ways. First, hit ratios are much lower (5–50%), but the benefits of a hit are higher because the search of an entire subtree can be avoided. Second, transposition table reads may return stale data. In fact, writes may be completely discarded without affecting correctness. This will usually result in more search overhead (see Section 5), but not in an incorrect answer.

We use transposition tables in *Multigame*, an application-oriented language for writing board games [9]. Multigame uses 64-bit signatures and 2-way associative tables (two entries per line). Some search algorithms stop using the transposition table when the search reaches a certain depth, because the benefits of lookups may no longer outweigh the costs. For this paper, Multigame uses the transposition table for all nodes.

Multigame either *partitions* or *replicates* transposition tables. With partitioned transposition tables, each processor stores part of the table. The number of table entries increases when more processors are added, due to the increasing amount of memory available for transposition table storage. To access an entry stored on another processor, a process sends a lookup or update request to that processor. Since asynchronous lookups are hard to implement, Multigame executes lookups synchronously. Switching to another thread during lookups is possible, but thread switches are relatively expensive. Instead, while waiting for the result of the lookup request, Multigame polls the network and processes incoming requests.

With replicated transposition tables, all processors store the entire table in main memory. Lookups are executed locally, but updates are broadcast. The main advantage of replication is that lookups are executed without communication. The disadvantages are that the transposition table can hold fewer entries than a partitioned table and that updates generate more traffic.

Which of the two representations (partitioned or replicated) is most efficient depends on the hardware (CPU speed, network speed, amount of memory) and the game for which the tables are used. We have therefore implemented customized network interface software for both schemes.

4. Distributed Transposition Tables on Myrinet

4.1. Programmable network interface processors

Most systems with a programmable network interface processor use a network interface card that is part of the host machine. This network interface (NI) contains a processor and some memory to which we will refer as the *Network Processor* (NP) and the *NP memory*. We assume that the NP communicates with the host CPU through the I/O bus.

For our research, we use Myrinet [1], a switched, wormhole-routed network technology which conforms to the model described above. Since the error rate of the Myrinet links is extremely low, we treat the network as being reliable. The Myrinet NP is a relatively slow 37.5 MHz RISC processor which can be programmed in C.

In our system, the NP's memory is mapped into user-space on the host, so the host CPU can access it using either DMA or programmed I/O, without making a system call. The NP can use only DMA to transfer data to and from host memory. To prevent the operating system from paging to or from the memory regions that the NP accesses by means of DMA, we pin these regions to physical memory. Both our application-specific transposition table implementations and the Fast Messages [5] system that we use for our performance comparison lack protection. Protection issues are addressed by other research projects [2, 3, 4, 13].

A problem with the conventional network architecture in which the network interface resides on the I/O bus is the lack of hardware support for synchronizing the host and the NP. Neither the host nor the NP can do an indivisible read-modify-write operation (e.g., test-and-set) on the other's memory. To support atomic operations on shared data, we have implemented lock variables, using Peterson's algorithm [6]. The host's lock/unlock operations are expensive, however, because multiple uncached memory references across the I/O bus are needed to access a lock.

4.2. Table storage

All transposition table entries are stored in host memory. The NP memory is too small to store all entries. Also, since there is little locality in transposition table accesses, it makes no sense to cache entries in NP memory.

Each host allocates space for its part of the transposition table and pins the table's virtual memory pages so that the NP can safely access those pages by means of DMA transfers. Since the DMA engine uses physical addresses, we export the virtual-to-physical mappings to a page table in NP memory. The NP uses this table to map transposition table indices to physical addresses.

4.3. Partitioned transposition tables

With partitioned transposition tables, both updates and lookups can result in communication. If the table is divided evenly among all P processors and a good hash function is used, then most accesses ($\frac{N(P-1)}{P}$ out of N) will be remote.

To look up a board position, the host hashes the position to a transposition table index. The upper bits of this index determine on which processor the entry for the position is stored. In the case of a local access, the host locks the transposition table, updates or reads the entry, and unlocks the table. Since the NP may attempt to access the table concurrently, the table lock is shared between the host and the NP (see Section 4.1). Thus, local accesses are handled entirely by the host but contend with the NP for the table lock.

To access a remote entry, the host builds a request message (using programmed I/O) in a request queue in its NP's memory. The request specifies a type (lookup or update), the network address of the remote node, the offset of the line that contains the desired table entry, and (for updates only), a new value. The NP regularly polls the request queue and transmits any request it finds in that queue.

The receiving NP maintains two queues for incoming lookup and update requests (see Figure 1). When the NP finds a new lookup request in its lookup request queue, it locks the transpositions table and fetches (using DMA) the line that contains the desired entry from host memory. The NP always retrieves a complete line (two entries) and stores it in the lookup request message. The request is transformed into a reply and sent back to the node that issued the request.

Upon receiving the requested line, the host determines if one of the two entries in the line has a signature that matches the signature of the board position that the host is interested in. If there is no match, the host evaluates the board itself.

Update requests arrive in the update request queue and remain there until they are read (using programmed I/O) by the host. Unlike lookups, updates are asynchronous; no acknowledgement is sent to the requesting host.

The host processor regularly polls the update request queue and processes pending updates as follows. For each update the host dequeues, it locks the transposition table and determines if an existing entry must be replaced by this update. If necessary, the update is performed. Finally, the host unlocks the table. The replacement decision could be taken by the NP, so that the receiving host processor would

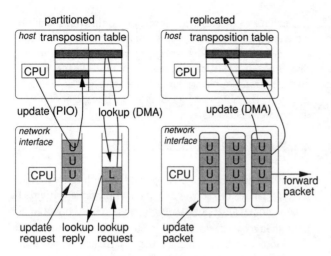

partitioned   replicated

host transposition table   *host* transposition table

CPU   CPU

update (PIO)   lookup (DMA)   update (DMA)

network interface   network interface

CPU   CPU   forward packet

update   lookup   lookup   update
request   reply   request   packet

Figure 1. Receiver processing for partitioned (l) and replicated (r) tables.

never have to handle update requests. The decision algorithm, however, can be complex, so we let the host processor handle the update.

Using a single lock to achieve mutual exclusion between the NP and the host does not lead to significant lock contention. With a high lookup/update ratio, most (lookup) table accesses are performed by the NP, but these accesses are not generated at a high rate, because lookups are performed synchronously. With a low lookup/update ratio, the access rate will be higher, but most accesses will be updates which are always performed by a host processor.

Without flow control, both the lookup and the update request queue may overflow. We avoid overflow of the lookup request queue by allowing each host to have at most one outstanding (unacknowledged) request to a particular node. No lookup request queue will ever contain more requests than the number of processors (P), so by using a queue of size P, we prevent overflow.

Since update requests are transmitted asynchronously, this solution does not work for updates. Instead, we exploit the weak-coherence semantics of transposition tables: whenever appending a new update request would overflow the update request queue, we simply discard the request. While this does not affect correctness, it may lead to increased search overhead. Since the update request queue is fairly large (1024 entries), however, very few updates are dropped in practice. In those cases where updates were dropped, we have not noticed a significant increase of the number of nodes searched.

Finally, to avoid network congestion, our current implementation allows no more than four outstanding requests to different destinations.

4.4. Replicated transposition tables

In the replicated implementation, lookups are executed locally. To look up a board position, the host hashes the board position to an index in the local copy of the transposition table and locks the transposition table. Since the NP may concurrently access the table (see below), the lock is shared between the host and the NP. After locking the table, the host looks up the line identified by the index and checks if any of the entries in the line matches the signature of the board. If there is a match, the data in the entry is copied out of the table. Finally, the host unlocks the table.

To update a position, the host first updates its local copy of the table and then broadcasts the new value, its table index, and its position in the line. The table replicas are not updated atomically. Two processes may concurrently update their local copy of the table and broadcast two different new values. Receivers of these two broadcasts may process these broadcasts in any order, so two replicas may wind up with different values in corresponding table entries. This can be avoided by using an ordered broadcast algorithm or an invalidation-based software cache coherence protocol. Transposition tables, however, do not require strict coherence, so a simple broadcast suffices.

Updates are broadcast as follows. After updating its local copy of the transposition table, the host processor writes the new value and its table address to a *store buffer*. This buffer is used to accumulate update requests; it is located in NP memory and accessed with programmed I/O. In our current implementation, the store buffer can hold up to 128 update requests. When the NP has no other work to do, it will broadcast all updates that are stored in the buffer. When the buffer is full, the host's next write to the buffer is blocked until the NP has broadcast the buffer. Using a store buffer instead of immediately broadcasting each update increases the latency of individual updates, but reduces the per-update overhead and thus increases throughput.

Since the Myrinet hardware does not support broadcasting, we have implemented a store-and-forward broadcast in software. To achieve high throughput, we use a Hamiltonian ring. Each NP forwards the updates in its store buffer to its successor in the ring. The successor forwards the updates again and delivers them to its local host by DMA-ing each update to its position in the local copy of the transposition table (see Figure 1). Note that the decision to perform the update and in which position in the line to store the new value are all taken by the host that initiated the broadcast.

All incoming broadcast messages are stored in a queue in NP memory. To avoid overflow of this queue, we use a simple flow control scheme. Each NP is given a fixed number (four) of send credits. When the NP broadcasts a buffer, it uses one credit. When the message has traveled round the ring and returns to the sender, the credit is returned. Since updates are delivered locally before being forwarded to the successor in the ring, this guarantees that a message which has returned to its original sender does not occupy any buffers on other nodes.

5. Performance

To evaluate our approach we compare the performance of two different transposition table implementations. The first implementation, FM-mci, was built on top of an efficient message-passing layer (based on Illinois Fast Messages 1.1 [5]). We extended Fast Messages with a reliable multicast primitive [12], which is used to update replicated transposition tables. The second implementation, custom, extends FM-mci with customized network interface software, as described in Section 4.

Both for custom and FM-mci, we reserve 6 MB of transposition table space on each host and use 12 bytes per table entry. For partitioned tables, FM-mci uses small active messages for remote table accesses. These messages are always processed by the remote host. For replicated tables, FM-mci uses a store buffer, just like the application-specific implementation. The store buffer resides in host memory. When it is full, it is broadcast using FM-mci's broadcast primitive. This is an efficient spanning-tree broadcast primitive, which forwards broadcast packets on the network interface [12].

All experiments were performed on a cluster of 64 200 MHz Pentium Pros.[1] Each node has 64 MB of DRAM and runs version 3.0 of the BSD/OS operating system.

Each NI has a 37.5 MHz LANai4.1 processor and 1 MB of SRAM. The NIs are interconnected in a hypercube topology using 16 switches and 2×1.28 Gbit/s cables. The NIs are attached to the host's PCI bus (33 MHz, 32 bits wide). DMA transfers between NI memory and host memory are cache-coherent, so there is no need to flush or disable the cache when using DMA transfers.

5.1. Microbenchmarks

Below, we use various synthetic benchmarks to compare the transposition table access latencies and throughputs achieved by custom and FM-mci, both for partitioned and replicated transposition tables. Table 1 shows the remote-access latencies for a partitioned table, using 12-byte table entries. All latencies were measured using straightforward ping-pong benchmarks. All timings for custom include acquiring and releasing the Peterson lock that is used to synchronize host and NP accesses to the transposition table. On the host, a single lock/unlock pair costs approximately 1.3 µs (when the lock is free).

benchmark	FM-mci	custom
lookup/poll	30 µs	19 µs
lookup/intr	61 µs	N/A
update/poll	15 µs	15 µs
update/intr	46 µs	N/A

Table 1. Remote access latencies.

Requests are received either through polling (*lookup/poll* and *update/poll*) or via interrupts (*lookup/intr* and *update/intr*). Interrupts are only generated for lookup and update requests; lookup replies are always received through polling. This is realistic, because a process that issues a lookup knows a reply will be sent to it soon. Using interrupts adds 31 µs to the latency of lookups and updates; this time is used by the operating system to process the network interrupt and to dispatch a user-level signal handler. With custom, no network interrupts occur, because lookup requests are always handled by the NP and because custom does not generate network interrupts for update requests (which are handled by the host). The lack of network interrupts for updates has not been a problem, because the update request queue is large (1024 entries) and because updates are executed asynchronously.

A remote lookup with custom (19 µs) is 1.6 times faster than FM-mci's *lookup/poll* and 3.2 times faster than *lookup/intr*. With custom, the host processor is never involved in processing the lookup request. Also, FM-mci sends fixed-size, 256-byte packets, whereas custom sends smaller, (44-byte) packets.

The update latency for custom equals the latency for FM-mci. In contrast with lookups, the receiving host participates in processing update requests by locking the table and copying a value into it.

In the replicated case, lookups are executed locally, without communication. The only difference between custom and FM-mci is that custom needs to perform an extra lock operation, which costs 1.3 µs. Measuring the latency of a single store is difficult, because stores are buffered.

An important metric for applications that frequently access the transposition table is the maximum table access rate under contention. We measured this rate using two benchmarks, one for partitioned and one for replicated transposition tables, in which all processes randomly access the distributed transposition table. We fix the lookup/update ratio by means of a lookup percentage. In both benchmarks, each processor randomly issues lookup and updates, but favors one over the other such that the percentage of lookups will eventually match the percentage that was fixed beforehand. In the case of partitioned transposition tables, processors also pick a random destination for their requests.

Figure 2 shows the results for both benchmarks. It is

---

[1] At the time of writing, only 63 processors were available.

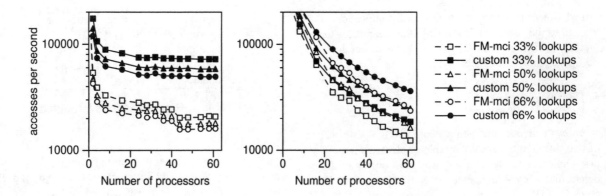

Figure 2. Access throughput (per processor) for partitioned (l) and replicated (r) transposition tables.

clear that contention affects the peak access rate: the more processors, the lower the maximum access rate. In the partitioned case, the access rate drops when the percentage of lookups increases, because lookups are executed synchronously, whereas updates can be pipelined. Both FM-mci and custom suffer from this effect, but custom stabilizes at substantially higher rates than FM-mci. On 61 processors, for example, custom processes 72,000 accesses per processor per second versus 21,000 for FM-mci.

In the replicated case, the gains obtained by using custom are smaller. The store buffer allows FM-mci to amortize communication costs over many updates. Also, custom's lookups are more expensive than FM-mci's, because an extra Peterson lock is used to synchronize the host and the NP. Nevertheless, custom's broadcast scheme outperforms FM-mci's general-purpose broadcast.

5.2. Application performance

We wrote several games in the Multigame [9] language, and embedded the application-specific network firmware in the Multigame runtime system. We performed measurements using the following games: the 15-puzzle, the 14-puzzle, and checkers. All measurements were done using custom and FM-mci and using partitioned and replicated transposition tables. In the case of FM-mci, we used only polling to receive messages, to avoid the high interrupt-processing overheads.

The three games that we use for our performance evaluation have very different characteristics, as explained below. The 15-puzzle, the well known sliding-tile puzzle, was used to stress-test the transposition table. Although the 15-puzzle contains few transpositions, it does a large number of transposition table operations. We repeatedly searched the hardest position from Korf's testset, using a parallel variant of the IDA* search algorithm.

The 14-puzzle is a variant of the 15-puzzle where we removed the "15"-tile, leaving two positions blank. This slight modification increases the number of transpositions substantially, because two consecutive moves involving the two blanks can usually be interchanged, resulting in the same position.

The third game we tested is checkers. The static evaluation function for this program is a high-quality, compute-intensive function, taken from the Chinook [10] world-championship program. The search engine (parallel MTD(f) [7] with young-brothers-wait) spends much time in this evaluation function, and therefore searches considerably fewer nodes per second than the sliding tile puzzles. Consequently, it does fewer transposition table lookups and updates. Nevertheless, a fast transposition table implementation is crucial, because checkers has many transpositions. Also, the MTD(f) search algorithm tends to visit the same tree node many times, assuming that the search results of the previous visit can be found in the transposition table.

The different properties of the applications are reflected in Table 2. Table 2 shows the number of table accesses (lookups and updates) per second per processor measured on 63 processors, as well as the execution time and hit ratio, both with the FM-mci and custom implementation. Note the differences between the applications: the 14-puzzle has a high lookup/update ratio, and checkers does significantly fewer table accesses than the 14- and 15-puzzle. With replicated tables, the hit ratios are lower than for the partioned variants, because the partioned variant contains 63 times as many transposition table entries.

Tables 2 also shows that custom achieves better execution times than FM-mci. Application performance across a larger range of processors is shown in Figure 3, which shows the speedups for every application using custom and FM-mci. Note that on more than 16 processors custom always achieves better speedups than FM-mci, for

distribution	application	FM-mci				custom			
		time (s)	lookups	updates	hit ratio	time (s)	lookups	updates	hit ratio
partitioned	15-puzzle	56.1	8414	4430	14.82%	**20.9**	22666	11938	14.74%
	14-puzzle	115.7	9453	2212	23.37%	**47.6**	23516	5548	22.06%
	checkers	57.5	4800	4058	23.49%	**45.5**	5798	4895	23.13%
replicated	15-puzzle	74.3	7980	4209	4.94%	**29.8**	19894	10492	4.99%
	14-puzzle	80.2	17389	4180	20.49%	**44.8**	34627	8331	20.08%
	checkers	71.4	3997	3501	12.84%	**50.2**	5401	4713	13.50%

Table 2. Application statistics on 63 processors. Lookups and updates are per processor per second.

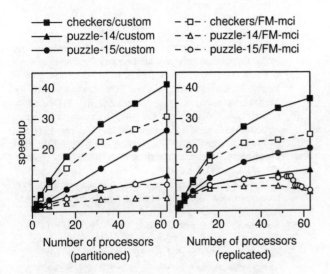

Figure 3. Applications speedups.

both the partitioned and replicated variants of all games.

Figure 3 also shows that checkers achieves the best speedups. The exact speedups depend on many factors, but one of them is the relatively coarse grain size of checkers. The checkers program spends much time in the evaluation function and therefore is less communication-intensive than the 14- and 15-puzzle. The 14-puzzle achieves lower speedups than the 15-puzzle because the 14-puzzle suffers from a considerable search overhead,[2] while the search overhead of the 15-puzzle is very modest.

Although there are other reasons for search overhead, partitioned tables generally decrease the amount of search overhead. This is due to the increasing number of entries that becomes available when more processors are added. We noticed that especially checkers suffered from capacity misses when a very small number of processors is used. Replicated tables tend to increase the search overhead slightly when more processors are added: due to the buffer-

---
[2]Search overhead is the percentage of extra tree nodes compared to a sequential program.

ing of update messages it takes some time before replicas become coherent.

The speedups for the partitioned custom version of the 14- and 15-puzzle increase linearly. In contrast, the speedup curves for FM-mci taper off when the number of processors in increased. With 63 processors, the 15-puzzle makes $8414 + 4430 = 12844$ accesses per second (see Table 2), and has a lookup percentage of 66%. For this lookup percentage, Figure 2 predicts a peak access rate of approximately 18,000 accesses per second. The application, however, suffers from congestion at a lower access rate because it does not access the transposition table during all phases of its execution; for example, part of the execution time is spent on work distribution and synchronization.

With replicated tables, both the custom and the FM-mci versions of the 14- and 15-puzzle suffer from decreasing efficiencies, although the custom implementation performs better than the FM-mci implementation. The decreasing efficiencies are mainly the result of the increase in network traffic produced by the broadcasting of updates.

When the number of processors is increased, the speedup curves for checkers taper off both for FM-mci and custom. This is not due to bandwidth limitations of the communication system, but to search overhead of MTD(f)'s speculative search.

The dip in the speedup curve of the 15-puzzle (replicated case) can be explained as follows. The 15-puzzle is the most communication-intensive of the three applications; it generates so much broadcast traffic that it triggers a buffer overflow mechanism in the broadcast implementation of FM-mci. Under heavy load, this mechanism temporarily swaps network interface buffers to host memory [12].

Summarizing our application measurements, we find that for larger numbers of processors custom always achieves better speedups than FM-mci. In the partitioned case, the 14-puzzle and 15-puzzle benefit most from using custom instead of FM-mci. On 63 processors, for the 15-puzzle, custom is more than 2.5 times faster than FM-mci. Checkers is relatively coarse-grained; the program benefits from the lower lookup latencies, but not from the increase in access throughput. The 15-puzzle, in contrast, is limited by `FM-mci`'s peak access throughput.

In the replicated case, the specialized firmware is slower than `FM-mci` for fewer than 16 processors, because the locking overhead of the Peterson lock does not outweigh the increased communication performance. On more than 16 processors, `custom` achieves better speedups. Again, `custom` obtains a 2.5 fold speedup for the 15-puzzle with respect to `FM-mci`, but this is partly due to `FM-mci`'s buffer swapping mechanism.

6. Conclusions

We have investigated how customized network interface software can improve the performance of operations on shared data structures in a distributed-memory system. We have studied the transposition table, a data structure that is accessed very frequently and lacks locality, but that allows an implementation with a weakly-coherent memory model.

We have implemented shared transposition tables on Myrinet, by customizing the software on the network interface boards. For comparison, we have implemented the same data structure on top of an existing messaging layer, using identical hardware. The comparison shows that significant performance gains are possible for both the basic operations on the data structure and for search programs that use it. For remote lookup operations, the customized network interface software is 1.6 times faster. At the application level, the gains are substantial: 2.5 times faster.

The performance improvements of the customized network interface software can be attributed to two factors. First, we reduce the overhead of interactions between the host and network interface processor. Second, we exploit application semantics to obtain a specialized and efficient communication protocol. Flow control, for example, is easier, because we are allowed to drop updates.

We have also identified some problems with customizing network interface software. A well-known problem with many networks is that the interface processor is slow compared to the host processor. As a result, expensive computations can only be run on the host. In our case, transposition table updates involve the host processor. Another problem is the lack of hardware primitives for synchronization between the host and the network interface processor, which forced us to implement slow software locks. Despite these problems, the performance improvements are substantial. An interesting issue is for which other data structures or applications our approach is applicable.

Acknowledgments. We thank Aske Plaat, Koen Langendoen, Tim Rühl, and the anonymous reviewers for their comments on this paper. Jonathan Schaeffer kindly provided us with the sources of Chinook. We thank Andrew Chien and Scott Pakin for making FM available to us.

References

[1] N. Boden, D. Cohen, R. Felderman, A. Kulawik, C. Seitz, J. Seizovic, and W. Su. Myrinet: A Gigabit-per-second Local Area Network. *IEEE Micro*, 15(1):29–36, Feb. 1995.

[2] G. Buzzard, D. Jacobson, M. MacKey, S. Marovich, and J. Wilkes. An Implementation of the Hamlyn Sender-managed Interface Architecture. In *Proc. of the 2nd Symp. on Operating Systems Design and Implementation*, pages 245–259, Seattle, WA, Oct. 1996.

[3] C. Dubnicki, A. Bilas, Y. Chen, S. Damianakis, and K. Li. VMMC-2: Efficient Support for Reliable, Connection-Oriented Communication. In *Hot Interconnects '97*, Stanford, CA, Apr. 1997.

[4] M. Fiuczynski. SPINE: Safe Programmable Integrated Network Environment. http://www.cs.washington.edu/homes/mef/research/spine/.

[5] S. Pakin, M. Lauria, and A. Chien. High Performance Messaging on Workstations: Illinois Fast Messages (FM) for Myrinet. In *Supercomputing '95*, San Diego, CA, Dec. 1995.

[6] G. Peterson. Myths about the Mutual Exclusion Problem. *Information Processing Letters*, 12:115–116, June 1981.

[7] A. Plaat, J. Schaeffer, W. Pijls, and A. de Bruin. Best-First Fixed-Depth Minimax Algorithms. *Artificial Intelligence*, 87(1-2):255–293, Nov. 1996.

[8] L. Prylli and B. Tourancheau. Protocol Design for High Performance Networking: A Myrinet Experience. Technical Report 97-22, LIP-ENS Lyon, July 1997.

[9] J. Romein, H. Bal, and D. Grune. An Application Domain Oriented Language for Describing Board Games. In *Proc. of the Int. Conf. on Parallel and Distributed Processing Techniques and Applications '97*, pages 305–314, Las Vegas, NV, June 1997.

[10] J. Schaeffer, J. Culberson, N. Treloar, B. Knight, P. Lu, and D. Szafron. A World Championship Caliber Checkers Program. *Artificial Intelligence*, 53:273–289, 1992.

[11] C. Thekkath, H. Levy, and E. Lazowska. Separating Data and Control Transfer in Distributed Operating Systems. In *Proc. of the 6th Int. Conf. on Architectural Support for Programming Languages and Operating Systems*, pages 2–11, San Jose, CA, Oct. 1994.

[12] K. Verstoep, K. Langendoen, and H. Bal. Efficient Reliable Multicast on Myrinet. In *Proc. 1996 Int. Conf. Parallel Processing (Vol. III)*, pages 156–165, Bloomingdale, IL, Aug. 1996.

[13] T. von Eicken, A. Basu, V. Buch, and W. Vogels. U-Net: A User-Level Network Interface for Parallel and Distributed Computing. In *ACM Symp. on Operating System Principles*, pages 303–316, Copper Mountain, CO, Dec. 1995.

[14] H. Wasserman, O. Lubeck, Y. Luo, and F. Bassetti. Performance Evaluation of the SGI Origin2000: A Memory-Centric Characterization of LANL ASCI Applications. In *Supercomputing '97*, San Jose, CA, Nov. 1997.

[15] A. Zobrist. A New Hashing Method with Application for Game Playing. Technical Report 88, Computer Science Department, University of Wisconsin, Madison, 1970. Reprinted in: *ICCA Journal*, 13(2):69–73, 1990.

Performance Implications of Architectural and Software Techniques on I/O-Intensive Applications*

Meenakshi A. Kandaswamy
EECS Dept.
Syracuse University
Syracuse, NY, 13244
meena@ece.nwu.edu

Mahmut Kandemir
EECS Dept.
Syracuse University
Syracuse, NY, 13244
mtk@ece.nwu.edu

Alok Choudhary
ECE Dept.
Northwestern University
Evanston, I L, 60208-3118
choudhar@ece.nwu.edu

David E. Bernholdt
NPAC
Syracuse University
Syracuse, NY, 13244
bernhold@npac.syr.edu

Abstract

Many large scale applications, have significant I/O requirements as well as computational and memory requirements. Unfortunately, limited number of I/O nodes provided by the contemporary message-passing distributed-memory architectures such as Intel Paragon and IBM SP-2 limits the I/O performance of these applications severely. In this paper, we examine some software optimization techniques and architectural scalability and evaluate the effect of them in five I/O intensive applications from both small and large application domains. Our goals in this study are twofold: First, we want to understand the behavior of large-scale data intensive applications and the impact of I/O subsystem on their performance and vice-versa. Second, and more importantly, we strive to determine the solutions for improving the applications' performance by a mix of architectural and software solutions. Our results reveal that the different applications can benefit from different optimizations. For example, we found that some applications benefit from file layout optimizations whereas some others benefit from collective I/O. A combination of architectural and software solutions is normally needed to obtain good I/O performance. For example, we show that with limited number of I/O resources, it is possible to obtain good performance by using appropriate software optimizations. We also show that beyond a certain level, imbalance in the architecture results in performance degradation even when using optimized software, thereby indicating the necessity of increase in I/O resources.

1 Introduction

Large scale parallel scientific applications in general tend to be computationally intensive as well as data intensive. The advances in I/O systems both in hardware and software, are much behind compared to those in processors and interconnection networks; resulting in poor performance for I/O-intensive applications. In this paper, we investigate the I/O performance of five different I/O-intensive applications. Our experiments confirm that, for all of these applications, poor I/O performance limits the overall performance of the application. This impact is sometime so severe that when a certain number of compute nodes (processors) is reached,

the execution time increases. Although such a situation can sometime occur with computationally intensive applications as well, the main problem with the programs in our application suite is the limited number of I/O nodes and unoptimized I/O performed by the programs. Therefore, beyond a certain point increasing the number of compute nodes has a negative impact in I/O as well as execution times. A typical high-performance parallel computer consists of compute nodes and I/O nodes (which have disks and/or disk arrays attached to them). A combination of architectural and software solutions is normally needed to obtain good I/O performance. For example, we show that with limited number of I/O resources, it is possible to obtain good performance by using appropriate software optimizations including layout transformations, collective I/O and prefetching. We also show that beyond a certain level, imbalance in the architecture results in performance degradation even when using optimized software.

We show that several optimizations are very effective on the I/O performance. For instance, we found that performance of some applications can be substantially improved by changing the file layout of the out-of-core arrays involved. For some other application, we found collective I/O to be very useful. For yet another application, we found prefetching to be effective. While many of these optimizations are not new, we show here that the different applications can benefit from different optimizations.

In this paper we investigate the software optimizations and resource scalability issues in detail. In particular, we address the following questions:

- How much improvement can be obtained by optimizing the I/O software; and what kind of optimization techniques can be used?

- How much improvement can be obtained by increasing I/O resources (e.g. number of I/O nodes) thereby making the architecture more balanced?

- How do the hardware and software improvements compare to each other?

- Do different I/O intensive applications have different improvements when the I/O resources are increased and/or the software is improved?

The rest of this paper is organized as follows. In Section 2 we describe the applications in our experimental suite. In Section 3 we discuss the Intel Paragon and IBM SP-2 machines' salient I/O features. In Section 4 we present the experimental data obtained from

*This work was supported in part by NSF Young Investigator Award CCR-9357840, NSF CCR-9509143, NSF ASC-9707074, Sandia National Labs Contract AV-6193, and in part by the Scalable I/O Initiative, contract number DABT63-94-C-0049 from Defense Advanced Research Projects Agency(DARPA) administered by US Army at Fort Huachuca. Dr. D.E.Bernholdt was supported by the Alex G. Nason Fellowship at Syracuse University.

original (unoptimized) programs, discuss the individual optimizations and explain how they improve the I/O as well as the overall performance of the applications. In Section 5 we discuss the related work and present the conclusions of the paper.

2 Applications

In this study we focus on five different I/O intensive parallel applications written in Fortran by using message-passing constructs, ranging from 500 lines of code to 19,000 lines (up to 538,000 lines if accompanying libraries are included). The important characteristics of these applications are given in Table 1. SCF 1.1 and SCF 3.0 are from computational chemistry domain and are very large applications [8]. AST is an astrophysics code; BTIO is disk-based version of a flow-solver program from NAS benchmarks [4]; and FFT is a 2-D out-of-core FFT program. More details on the applications can be found in [6]. Below, we give a summary of the various applications.

SCF 1.1 The Hartree-Fock method obtains the energy and wave function of a molecular system by iterating over two basic steps until self-consistency (SCF) is obtained. At the heart of the Hartree-Fock method is the construction of the Fock matrix F and in the process about $\mathcal{N}^4$ integrals must be evaluated, where $\mathcal{N}$ is the dimension of the basis set of the input. The values of these integrals remain constant throughout the iterations and evaluating each integral is a non-trivial computation, involving 300–500 floating point operations, on average. To lend perspective to these figures, it is worth mentioning that the design goal for SCF 1.1's SCF module is calculations of 1,000 atoms with basis sets of 10,000 functions, which would involve as many as 10^{16} integrals. In the HF algorithm, the integrals constitute the largest volume of data and a sizable computational expense. In a disk-based implementation, the integrals are computed on the first iteration and written to disk, then read from disk rather than being recomputed for each subsequent iteration. In the write phase, each node writes a private file of the integrals it evaluated during first construction of the Fock matrix. The read phase, on the other hand, consists of several iterations. In each iteration, each processor reads its private file in its entirety. SCF 1.1 application code consists of about 16,500 lines of code and about 225,000 lines when supporting libraries are included.

SCF 3.0 The SCF 3.0 parallel computational chemistry package encompasses a broad range of functionality, including the self-consistent field (SCF) module. In SCF 1.1, calculations could be either "direct", meaning that integrals are re-computed for every iteration of the SCF algorithm, or "disk-based", meaning that integrals are evaluated once and written to disk during the first iteration, then read from disk on every subsequent iteration. The semi-direct SCF 3.0 approach is a compromise between the two, where limits may be specified on the size of disk files, and any integrals which are not stored on disk are recomputed. Some attempt is made to arrange the integral evaluation from most to least expensive, so that those integrals which must be recomputed on every iteration are generally less expensive than those kept on disk. Finally, to help account for the difference in load balance between the evaluation of integrals (on the first iteration) and reading them from disk (subsequent iterations), the sizes of the integral files are balanced (currently to within 10% or 1 MB, whichever is larger) after writing is complete. In addition to change in the SCF module itself, there have also been changes to the I/O part of the application from the 1.1 to 3.0 releases.

FFT The fast Fourier Transform (FFT) is widely used in many areas such as digital signal processing, partial differential equation solutions and various other scientific and engineering problems. We implemented 2-D out-of-core FFT on the Intel Paragon. The 2-D out-of-core FFT consists of three steps: (1) 1-D out-of-core FFT, (2) 2-D out-of-core transpose, and (3) 1-D out-of-core FFT. The 1-D FFT steps consist of reading data from the two-dimensional out-of-core array and applying 1-D FFT on each of the columns. In order to perform 1-D out-of-core FFTs, the data on disk is strip-mined into memories of compute nodes. This step is highly parallel, limited in general only by the size of the available memory and individual processor speeds. After this, the processed columns are written to file. In the transpose step, the out-of-core array is staged into memory, transposed and written to a file. This step is very expensive in terms of both I/O and communication. The innermost loop of the transpose routine uses two disk resident files one of them is transposed into the other.

BTIO BTIO application simulates the I/O required by a pseudo-time-stepping flow solver. It is a disk-based version of a program from NAS parallel benchmark suite [4]. The main operation in the code is periodic writes performed by all processors to a multi-dimensional array stored in a file. Note that periodic write operations are used by such applications for check-pointing and/or off-line visualization and analysis of data. The code contains a lot of seek operations which in turn causes the performance to be poor. It represents the class of write dominant I/O intensive applications.

AST The astrophysics application [11] performs a study of highly turbulent convective layers of late-type stars such as the sun. The application simulates the gravitational collapse of self-gravitating gaseous clouds due to the Jeans instability process. This is the fundamental mechanism through which inter-galactic gases condense to form stars. It uses the piecewise parabolic method to solve the compressible Euler equations and a multi-grid elliptic solver to compute the gravitational potential. The application uses several distributed arrays and processes them and writes them on to the disk to one common shared file. The reasons that this application performs I/O is threefold, namely, check-pointing [1], data analysis, and visualization. All the three cases make the I/O mainly write-intensive, except when there is a restart of the application from previously check-pointed data, it becomes read-intensive. The application uses several data arrays that are processed during the course of the application and are stored on disk in one file in column-major order for data analysis and check-pointing purposes. For visualization purposes several shared files are created by the application. The original application performs I/O accesses in small non-contiguous chunks.

3 Platforms

In this Section we summarize some of the salient characteristics of our platforms, Intel Paragon and IBM SP-2, emphasizing the I/O capabilities. The reason that we use these platforms is the fact that both machines represent a class of distributed-memory message-passing architectures that present the user with scalable I/O architectures. Also the parallel file systems (PFS [9] in Paragon and PIOFS [3] in SP-2) on these machines are versatile and enable the users to code a variety of optimization techniques. The large scale applications in our experimental suite are available to us at these machines. Finally, these architectures are widely used by the scientists, so represent natural targets in our experimental study.

Table 1: Applications in our experimental suite and their important characteristics.

Application	Source	Lines	Description	Platform	Type of I/O
SCF 1.1	PNL	16,500	self consistent field computation	Paragon	writes integrals to disk, and reads them
SCF 3.0	PNL	19,000	self consistent field computation	Paragon	writes integrals to disk, and reads them
FFT	authors	500	2D out-of-core FFT	Paragon	reads and writes two matrices
BTIO	NASA Ames	6713	simulates the I/O required by a flow solver	SP-2	periodic writes of arrays
AST	Univ. of Chicago	17000	simulates gravitational collapses of clouds	Paragon	writes arrays for check-pointing

Table 2: I/O Summary of the original version of SCF 1.1 for LARGE input : 4 processors [Total I/O time is 4.4 Hours].

Oper	Oper Count	I/O Time (Sec)	Vol (GB)	% of I/O time	% of exec time
Open	19	1.97		0.00	0.00
Read	566,315	60,284.31	37	95.56	51.66
Seek	994	8.01		0.01	0.01
Write	40,331	2,792.11	2.5	4.43	2.39
Flush	49	0.25		0.00	0.00
Close	14	0.46		0.00	0.00
All I/O	607,722	63,087.11	39.5	100.00	54.06

Table 3: I/O Summary of PASSION version of SCF 1.1 for LARGE input : 4 processors [Total I/O time is 2.5 Hours].

Oper	Oper Count	I/O Time (Sec)	Vol (GB)	% of I/O time	% of exec time
Open	19	0.65		0.00	0.00
Read	566,330	33,805.21	37	95.38	37.73
Seek	604,342	256.56		0.72	0.29
Write	40,336	1,380.79	2.5	3.90	1.54
Flush	49	0.15		0.00	0.00
Close	14	0.37		0.00	0.00
All I/O	1,211,090	35,443.72	39.5	100.00	39.56

Intel Paragon The Paragon that we use for FFT experiments consists of 56 compute nodes, 3 service nodes, and 1 HIPPI node. The compute nodes are arranged in a two-dimensional mesh comprised of 14 rows and 4 columns. The compute nodes use the Intel i860 XP microprocessor and have 32 MBytes of memory each. The i860 has a peak performance of 75 MFlops, yielding a system peak speed of 4.2 GFlops. The total memory capacity of the compute partition is around 1.8 GBytes. For the other experiments except BTIO we use a Paragon machine with 512 compute nodes, and has service (I/O) partitions of sizes 12, 16 and 64. The compute node topology is mesh and the processor characteristics are the same as the small Paragon mentioned above. In the experiments, we use 12, 16 and 64 node I/O partitions. In both machines, the parallel file system, PFS, stripes the user files across the available I/O nodes in a round-robin fashion. The default stripe unit size, which is 64 KB, is used in all of our experiments, except SCF 1.1 where we make experiments with different stripe unit sizes.

IBM SP-2 For BTIO application, we use an SP-2 with 80 nodes. All nodes that are used in the experiments were RS/6000 Model 390 nodes with at least 256 MB memory. The parallel file system, PIOFS [3], distributes the files across multiple I/O nodes. Only four out of the five I/O nodes are available for the user files, and each such node has four 9 GB SSA disks attached to it. The fifth node is the directory server. The striping unit (called BSU in the PIOFS) is 32 KB.

4 Optimizations and Performance Comparison

In this section, we present experimental results on our program suite, and explain some of the techniques which improve the I/O performance of the applications.

4.1 Experimental Methodology

Our experimental methodology is as follows: For each application, we applied several software optimizations but due to lack of space we present only the results of most effective optimizations. Based on the platform on which we ran the application on we also changed the number of I/O nodes to observe its impact on the application's I/O behavior. In the small Paragon machine we used 2 and 4 I/O node subsystems, the only available partitions. In the large Paragon, we used 12, 16, and 64 I/O node partitions. In the SP-2, on the other hand, the number of I/O nodes is fixed at four, which is the only available partition.

4.2 SCF 1.1: effect of efficient interface and prefetching

We investigated the performance of SCF 1.1 for small as well as large number of compute nodes separately. The results for the small number of compute nodes are summarized in three bar charts given in Figure 1. In fact, that figure presents a summary of an incremental evaluation of the I/O optimizations that we performed for this application for small processor sizes. We consider three representative inputs which we call SMALL, MEDIUM and LARGE. An important observation about this application is that the programmers have reasonably optimized the I/O related parts of the programs. Instead of directly using the access pattern imposed by the application, they first pack the data to be written onto disk in larger chunks and then write the packed chunk in a single I/O call. While this effort renders further I/O optimizations difficult, it makes the applications' I/O pattern amenable to prefetching. In these experiments, we evaluated three versions of the application: (1) original version [8] with Fortran I/O. This version was obtained from PNL; (2) an optimized version which uses PASSION [10] (from Northwestern University) I/O calls; (3) an optimized version which uses PASSION prefetch calls. We represent each optimization combination in Figure 1 with a five-tuple of (V,P,M,Su,Sf) where, V is the version used (O - original version with Fortran I/O calls, P - optimized version with PASSION I/O calls, F - optimized version with

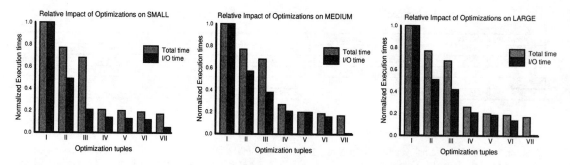

Figure 1: Impact of optimizations on different input sizes for SCF 1.1 on Intel Paragon. The number of basis functions ($\mathcal{N}$ – problem size) for SMALL, MEDIUM and LARGE are 108, 140 and 285 respectively. The configuration tuples are : I - (O,4,64,64,12); II - (P,4,64,64,12); III - (F,4,64,64,12); IV - (F,32,64,64,12); V - (F,32,256,64,12); VI - (F,32,256,128,12); VII - (F,32,256,128,16). [For small number of processors, the application-related factors are more effective than system-related factors].

(a)   (b)

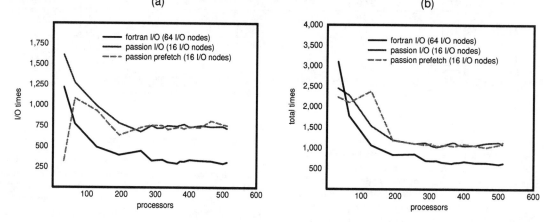

Figure 2: Performance summary for SCF 1.1 for LARGE input on Intel Paragon [Up to 64 compute nodes optimized versions perform well; beyond 64 compute nodes the unoptimized version with larger number of I/O nodes performs better].

PASSION prefetch calls); P is the number of processors; M is the available memory to the application (in KB); Su is the stripe unit size (in KB); and Sf is the stripe factor (number of I/O nodes in this case). The tuple (O,4,64,64,12) corresponds to the default configuration. For the measurement of the I/O times in the prefetching versions, we take into account the I/O, wait and copy times also. The results shown in Figure 1 summarize our evaluations. The important point to note is that the effect of the optimizations is quite similar in all three input sizes. It is easy to see that the factors that can be modified from within the software are much more effective than the system-related factors like number of compute nodes and number of I/O nodes within this experimental domain. In general, we can conclude that when the number of processors used are small in number the application-related factors have a much higher impact on the execution and I/O times of the application than the system-related factors. Tables 2 and 3 show a detailed quantitative breakdown of the various I/O operations performed by the application on four processors for the Original and PASSION version using the Pablo I/O tracing library [2]. We clearly see that the SCF 1.1 is extremely read intensive and by using a different interface to the file system (Table 3) we obtain better read and write times thereby reducing the total time. We must mention that the tracing library we used obtained results from the application level and we used it mainly in runs using small number of processors. Also for the larger number of processors cases, we were more interested in studying the scalability of the application.

The results for the larger processor case are presented in Figures 2 and 3. We notice from Figure 2(b) that up to 64 processors, the software optimizations are more effective in the overall performance; however beyond 64 processors, the lack of I/O resources dominates, and the unoptimized version with 64 I/O nodes outperforms the optimized versions with 16 I/O nodes. From Figure 3, we infer that as the number of processors or compute nodes used increases so does the contention at the I/O nodes. We observe that the increase in I/O nodes translates into reduced I/O contention and results in improved total execution times, especially when we use larger number of compute nodes.

4.3 SCF 3.0: effect of balanced I/O

We evaluated the I/O and overall performance of the SCF 3.0 from both hardware and software points of view. As in SCF 1.1, we have found an efficient interface and prefetching quite useful. Since we discussed those issues with SCF 1.1, due to lack of space, here we do not elaborate on them. Instead, we focus on another optimization technique, which we call balanced I/O which is made possible by the application programmers. In contrast to SCF 1.1, the application programmers of the SCF 3.0 give the user the opportunity of balancing I/O versus computation. That is, the user can specify what percentage of the integrals are to be cached on disk and what percentage are to be re-computed when necessary. We found that the ratio can make a critical difference in

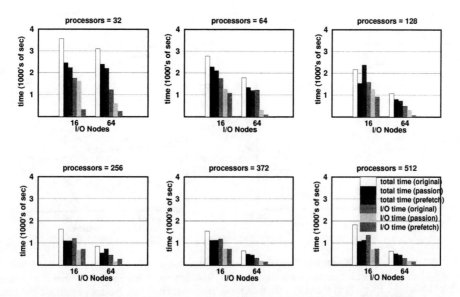

Figure 3: Effect of increasing the number of I/O nodes on SCF 1.1 on Intel Paragon.

the overall performance of the application. The problem, however, is that the best ratio is dependent on the input size. Therefore, it is almost impossible to make an educated guess beforehand.

Figure 4 shows the overall performance of the application on 16 and 64 I/O nodes respectively for different processor sizes and percentages of cached integrals. The first observation is that the number of I/O nodes is not very effective on the overall performance. The other two factors, however, namely the number of compute nodes and percentage of cached integrals do make a difference as shown in the figures. This is in contrast to SCF 1.1 where the number of I/O nodes is a critical factor. The reason is that, in SCF 3.0 I/O is not as dominant as in SCF 1.1. Another point to note is that changing the number of compute nodes makes a big difference, especially with the low percentages of cached data.

The capability of changing the percentage of the cached integrals presents the user with some opportunities. In order to improve the performance, either the number of processors or the percentage of the cached integrals can be increased. The choice depends on the availability of extra disk space versus additional number of compute nodes. For the platform (Intel Paragon) on which these experiments were conducted we found that increasing the percentage of integrals stored on the disk gave better performance. For example, when the percentage of integrals cached is around 90% or so, (for the 64 I/O nodes case), we found that even increasing the number of processors from 32 to 256, did not give any observable performance gain in the execution time. But if the disk space is limited and can only partially fit the integrals, then using larger number of processors to reduce the load of re-computation per processor is beneficial in decreasing the total execution times. From the results, we can conclude that for SCF 3.0, the amount of disk space available for caching is more important followed by the number of processors. Only in the event of the less disk space, increasing the number of processors would be desirable.

4.4 FFT: effect of layout optimization

Figure 5(a) shows the I/O times (in seconds) for three different versions of FFT application on the Intel Paragon: two versions of the original program with 2 and 4 I/O nodes, and an optimized version on 2 I/O nodes. The results show that the I/O performance of the unoptimized program is very poor. In the original unoptimized (2

I/O node case) version, the I/O time actually increases when we use more than 4 compute nodes. When we increase the number of I/O nodes to 4, the increase in the I/O time happens after 8 compute nodes. We note that this trend in the I/O time almost identically reflects on the total execution time (see Figure 5(b)). The reason for this is that the I/O time for this application constitutes 90%-95% of the execution time and therefore is the dominant factor in the overall behavior of the application.

The most costly operation in the 2-D out-of-core FFT is a 2-D out-of-core local transpose performed by each processor. In the original program, file layout for these two arrays is column-major. The transpose is performed by reading a rectangular chunk from one of the files, transposing it in the local memory, and writing it in the other file. Since both files are column-major, optimizing the block dimension for one array has a negative impact on I/O performance of the other array, resulting in poor I/O performance observed in Figure 5. On the other hand, if we store one of the arrays in row-major order the I/O performance of both the arrays improves. This is evident from Figure 5 where the optimized version of the program on two I/O nodes outperforms the unoptimized program on four I/O nodes for all processor sizes. For this example, within this experimental domain, we can conclude that the layout optimizations are very effective, and the optimized version outperforms the unoptimized version which uses more number of I/O nodes.

An important point about those types of layout optimizations is that they can sometimes be detected by parallelizing compilers by using suitable linear algebraic techniques. For example, reference [7] shows how the data layout optimizations can be automatized within a parallelizing compiler. The main idea is to choose the appropriate file layouts for disk-resident arrays referenced in an I/O intensive program. To achieve this goal, an optimizing compiler employs a suitable analysis to detect the access pattern of the individual loop nests in the program at compile-time, then depending on the collected information decides which layout to choose for each disk-resident array.

4.5 BTIO: effect of collective I/O

As mentioned earlier, the base version of the application uses MPI-2 I/O as a UNIX style interface and contains a lot of seek opera-

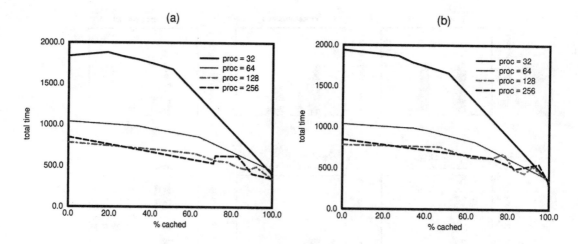

Figure 4: Performance of SCF 3.0 for different percentages of cached integrals for MEDIUM input on the Intel Paragon (a) with 16 I/O nodes and (b) with 64 I/O nodes [Note that for the full recompute version (0% cached), increasing the number of processors is very effective whereas for the full disk version (100% cached) increasing the number of processors does not make a significant difference].

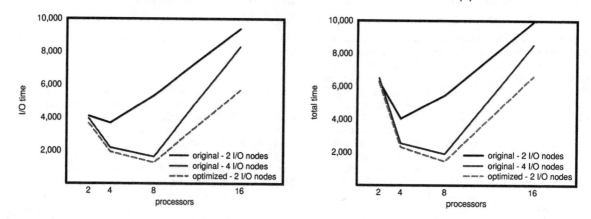

Figure 5: Performance of FFT on Intel Paragon [1.5GB total I/O amount].

tions. The I/O performance of BTIO for the input Class A is shown in Figure 6(a) and the overall performance is shown in Figure 6(b), respectively. In contrast to FFT, BTIO is not as I/O dominant. From Figure 6(a), it is easy to see that the I/O time in the unoptimized program changes drastically with the increasing number of processors. This, in turn, causes a hump in the execution time when 36 processors are used. The main problem with this application is that each node performs its I/O independently from the others. For example, if a node needs 12 chunks of data, it will issue 12 separate I/O calls, one for each of the chunks. While this approach simplifies the programming, it incurs a substantial overhead, as the number of I/O calls is the dominant factor in the I/O time. This behavior was observed with other classes of inputs as well.

The reference [10] discuss a technique called *two-phase I/O* (a form of collective I/O) which means that each processor reads the portion of the disk data that is least costly for it; and then the processors use the available interconnection network to exchange the parts of the data so that each processor gets what it needs. Although this approach slightly increases the communication time of the program, it generally minimizes the number of I/O calls which in turn reduces the execution time significantly. In two-phase I/O, the processors cooperate in accessing the data on disks. The aim

is to combine several I/O requests into fewer larger granularity requests, and reorder requests such that the file will be accessed in a close-sequential fashion. Additionally, the total I/O workload can be partitioned among the processors dynamically [10].

The optimized version of BTIO uses the two-phase I/O. The solution vector is completely described by using MPI data types. Figure 6(a) show that the I/O time is reduced significantly in the optimized version, and it does not behave unpredictably with the increasing number of compute nodes. The reason is that in the unoptimized program, increasing the number of compute nodes will decrease the volume of data processed by a processor; but, in general, does not change the number of I/O calls per processor. Consequently, the total number of I/O calls in the program increases substantially. On the other hand, in the optimized program, the increase in the number of I/O calls is equal to the increase in the number of processors as each processor issues a single I/O request from the application. The impact of the two-phase I/O in the overall performance is shown in Figure 6(b). As an example, with 36 and 64 processors, there is 46% and 49% reduction in the overall execution time respectively. Similar trend is observed in the Class B input and other inputs as well.

We also measure the I/O bandwidth of the original and the opti-

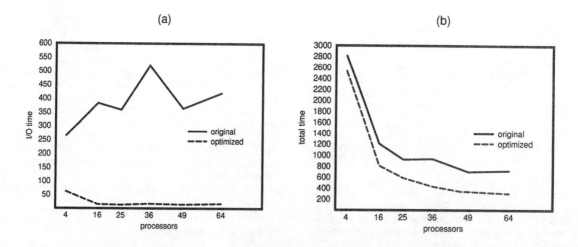

Figure 6: Performance of BTIO on IBM SP-2 for Class A input. (a) I/O time and (b) Total time. (408.9 MB total I/O amount)

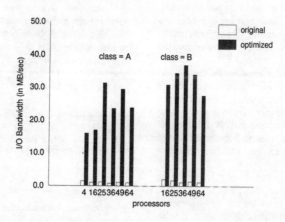

Figure 7: I/O bandwidths of the original and optimized versions of BTIO on IBM SP-2 for Class A and Class B inputs

mized versions. The results are given in Figure 7 as bar charts. The I/O bandwidth of the original program is between 0.97 MB/sec and 1.5 MB/sec while the I/O bandwidth of the optimized version is between 6.6 MB/sec and 31.4 MB/sec. In summary, BTIO is an example of a class of I/O intensive programs whose the I/O performance can be improved by software optimizations, but since the I/O does not constitute a large bulk of the execution time, the impact of the optimizations on the overall performance is limited.

4.6 AST: effect of collective I/O

The results of astrophysics application for a reasonably large input array size of 2K × 2K elements is presented in the Table 4 for 16 and 64 I/O nodes on the Intel Paragon. As mentioned earlier, the astrophysics application performs I/O for data analysis, check-pointing and visualization purposes. At every dump point, data for the three purposes are written by the various processors onto one shared file. To be specific, the snapshots of the input array are written to disk at fixed dump points for check-pointing and data analysis. And data are also processed and written out for the purposes of visualization. We compare two different implementations of the code: (1) I/O done using the Chameleon library and (2) I/O done using a run-time system library performing two-phase I/O (which is a form of collective I/O: please refer to BTIO section of the paper for further details on two-phase I/O). We see a significant perfor-

Table 4: Execution times for AST. [The I/O amount is 2.2 GBytes].

Num of procs	Unoptimized		Optimized	
	16 I/O nodes	64 I/O nodes	16 I/O nodes	64 I/O nodes
16	2,557	2,546	428	399
32	1,203	1,199	100	97
64	638	628	76	69
128	385	369	86	77

mance improvement in the overall execution time in the optimized case due to huge reduction in the I/O time. The Chameleon library makes I/O in smaller non-contiguous chunks and also has a bottle-neck of all I/O performed by a single node and this adds to the I/O time. Whereas the two-phase I/O approach eliminates small I/O requests by performing large chunks of sequential I/O. Therefore, in this application we see that this factor is more important (within our experimental domain) than increasing of the I/O nodes as shown in the Table 4.

499

Table 5: Applications and effective optimization techniques. A tick-mark is entered in the table on the effective optimization.

Application	Optimization techniques				
	collective I/O	file layout	efficient interface	prefetching	balanced I/O
SCF 1.1			✓	✓	
SCF 3.0			✓	✓	✓
FFT		✓			
BTIO	✓				
AST	✓				

5 Related Work and Conclusions

Several different works have been published in the study of I/O intensive parallel applications. Three I/O-intensive applications from the Scalable I/O Initiative Application Suite are studied in [2]. Thakur et. al. [11] evaluate the I/O performance of the IBM SP and the Intel Paragon using an astrophysics application, and concluded that IBM SP2 is faster with read operations and Paragon for writes. In [5], Foster et. al, optimize BTIO on small number of processors using remote I/O. In the area of check-pointing, Chen, Plank and Li in [1], develop a library to implement rollback recovery of parallel applications.

To summarize, from our experiments we observe the following: The I/O intensive applications in our experimental suite deliver poor performance mostly due to I/O bottleneck. This bottleneck originates from both hardware and software. From the hardware, the limited number of I/O nodes in Paragon and SP-2 limits the performance of such applications. The problem becomes so severe that beyond a number of compute nodes, the execution times actually increase. As an example, while the users of SCF 1.1, for small number of compute nodes, use the version of the code which makes I/O instead of the version which re-computes the integrals; for large number of compute nodes, they tend to use the re-compute version, as the I/O version performs very poorly. An obvious solution to this problem is to increase the number of I/O nodes. In this paper, we experimentally evaluated the impact of the increase in number of I/O nodes on the I/O as well as the overall performance of the applications.

From the software point of view, the I/O software is not easy to use and is not portable at all. For example, both PFS and PIOFS have different I/O modes which make the programming for I/O very difficult for the user. Unfortunately, the compiler techniques for I/O are not robust enough to attack the problem either. Throughout the years, several I/O optimization techniques have been developed, but they have been either tested on specific applications or specific machines. In this paper, we applied several I/O optimization techniques to the programs in our experimental suite. The results are summarized in Table 5. We have two main observations to make: First, different I/O intensive applications are amenable to different types of optimizations. The second observation is that for up to a number of compute nodes, the software techniques are competitive and sometimes more successful than merely increasing the number of I/O nodes. Beyond a certain point however, we still need to increase the number of I/O nodes for further improvement.

An important question from the software point of view is how to select a proper sequence of optimizations, given an application. Although for the I/O intensive programs it is hard to generalize the optimization process; from our experiments in this paper, we infer the following: First, the I/O access pattern of the individual compute nodes should be improved. That is, instead of doing I/O whenever they need, each compute node should consider the I/O

requirements of the other nodes as well. Here the techniques like collective I/O and buffering I/O requests are proven to be useful. For example, for BTIO and AST, the individual nodes' I/O pattern are improved by collective I/O substantially. For SCF 1.1 and SCF 3.0, the individual nodes first buffer the data that they are going to write into their private files, minimizing the number of I/O accesses substantially. After a good access pattern for the individual compute nodes are obtained, then the performance can be further improved by determining the most suitable file layouts for the disk resident data. As an example, assigning different file layouts to different disk resident arrays in the FFT improves the performance substantially. In addition, the remaining I/O time can sometimes be hidden by prefetching one or more data chunks in advance. Both SCF 1.1 and SCF 3.0 benefit from prefetching substantially.

6 Acknowledgments

A modified version of SCF 1.1 and SCF 3.0, as developed and distributed by Pacific Northwest National Laboratory, P. O. Box 999, Richland, Washington 99352, USA, and funded by the U. S. Department of Energy, was used to obtain some of these results. We also thank Evgenia Smirni for her help in using the Pablo instrumentation library. We would like to thank Rajeev Thakur for his assistance in running BTIO. We are grateful to Caltech and Argonne National Laboratory for allowing us to use their parallel machines for conducting our experiments.

References

[1] Y. Chen, J. Plank, and K. Li CLIP: A Check-pointing Tool for Message-Passing Parallel Programs (1997) In *Proceedings of SuperComputing '97*, San Jose, California.

[2] P. E. Crandall, R. A. Aydt, A. A. Chien and D. A. Reed. Input/output characteristics of scalable parallel applications. In *Proc. Supercomputing '95*.

[3] P. Corbett, D. Feitelson, J. Prost, G. Almasi, S. Baylor, A. Bolmarcich, Y. Hsu, J. Satran, M. Snir, R. Colao, B. Herr, J. Kavaky, T. Morgan, and A. Zlotek. Parallel file systems for the IBM SP computers. *IBM Systems Journal*, 34(2):222-248, January 1995

[4] S. Fineberg. Implementing the NHT-1 application I/O benchmark. In *Proceedings of the IPPS '93 Workshop on Input/Output in Parallel Computer Systems*, pages 37-55, Newport Beach, CA, 1993. Also published in Computer Architecture News 21(5), December 1993, pages 23-30.

[5] I. Foster, D. Kohr, R. Krishnaiyer, and J. Mogill. Remote I/O: fast Access to Distant Storage. In *Proc. Fifth Workshop on I/O in Parallel and Distributed Systems (IOPADS)*, pages 14–25, San Jose, CA, Nov 1997.

[6] Meenakshi A. Kandaswamy. Design and Evaluation of Optimizations in I/O-Intensive Applications, *Ph.D. Thesis, EECS Department*, Syracuse University, May 1998.

[7] M. Kandemir, J. Ramanujam, and A. Choudhary. Improving the Performance of Out-of-Core Computations. In *Proc. 1997 International Conference on Parallel Processing*, pages 128–136, Bloomingdale, IL, August 1997.

[8] NWChem, a computational chemistry package for parallel computers, version 1.1, 1995. *High Performance Computational Chemistry Group*, Pacific Northwest Laboratory, Richland, Washington 99352, USA.

[9] B. Rullman. Paragon Parallel File System, External Product Specification, Intel Supercomputer Systems Division.

[10] R. Thakur, A. Choudhary, R. Bordawekar, S. More and S. Kuditipudi, PASSION: optimized I/O for parallel applications, In *IEEE Computer*, IEEE Computer Society, June 1996.

[11] R. Thakur, W. Gropp, and E. Lusk. An experimental evaluation of the parallel I/O systems of the IBM SP and Intel Paragon using a production application. In *Proc. the Third International Conference of the Austrian Center for Parallel Computation (ACPC)*, pages 24-35, September 1996.

Session 7B
Load Balancing/Performance

Chair: Chita R. Das
Pennsylvania State University

Parallel Processing of Adaptive Meshes with Load Balancing

Sajal K. Das and Daniel J. Harvey

Department of Computer Sciences
University of North Texas
P.O. Box 311366
Denton, TX 76203-1366
E-mail:{das,harvey}@cs.unt.edu

Rupak Biswas

MRJ Technology Solutions
NASA Ames Research Center
Mail Stop T27A-1
Moffett Field, CA 94035-1000
E-mail: rbiswas@nas.nasa.gov

Abstract

Many scientific applications involve grids that lack a uniform underlying structure. These applications are often also dynamic in nature in the sense that the grid structure significantly changes between successive phases of execution. In parallel computing environments, mesh adaptation of unstructured grids through selective refinement/coarsening has proven to be an effective approach. However, achieving load balance while minimizing interprocessor communication and redistribution costs is a difficult problem. Traditional dynamic load balancers are mostly inadequate because they lack a global view of system loads across processors. In this paper, we present a novel, general-purpose load balancer that utilizes symmetric broadcast networks (SBN) as the underlying communication topology. The experimental results on the IBM SP2 demonstrate that performance of the SBN-based load balancer is comparable to results achieved under PLUM, a global load balancing environment created to handle adaptive unstructured applications.

1 Introduction

Mesh partitioning is a common approach to processing many scientific applications in parallel. These applications are generally modeled discretely using a mesh (or grid) of vertices and edges. For maximum (parallel) efficiency, the computational workloads on the processors have to be balanced and the number of edges that are cut (and hence the overall interprocessor communication cost at runtime) needs to be minimized [11, 13]. For this purpose, each vertex is usually assigned a weight that indicates the amount of computation required to process it. Similarly, each edge in the mesh has an associated weight indicating the amount of interaction between adjacent vertices. To achieve load balance dynamically, portions of the mesh have to be migrated among the processors during the course of a computation. Thus, in a multiprocessing environment, the vertex weight contains an additional component that models the cost of redistributing the vertex from one processor to another. These weights are used to minimize the data redistribution cost during the remapping phase.

In adaptive meshes, the grid topology changes during the course of a computation. Traditionally, this class of problems is processed by load balancing the mesh after each adaptation. A number of partitioners designed for this purpose has been proposed in the literature [9, 10, 11, 14, 18, 20, 23]. A majority of the successful partitioners are based on a multilevel approach that has proven to be extremely effective in producing good partitions at reasonable execution cost. In this approach, the grid graph is first contracted to a small number of vertices and edges, and the coarsened graph is then partitioned and successively refined using a Kernighan-Lin replacement algorithm [15]. For an excellent survey on other partitioning methods, refer to [1].

Although several dynamic load balancers have been proposed for multiprocessor platforms [3, 4, 6, 12, 16, 21, 22], most of them are inadequate for adaptive mesh applications because they lack a global view of system loads across processors. Also, job migration in these approaches does not take into account the structure of the adaptive grid. In this paper, we overcome these deficiencies by modifying the load balancer proposed earlier by us [6]. Our load balancer makes use of a symmetric broadcast network (SBN) which is a robust and topology-independent communication pattern among processors [7]. The proposed SBN-based load balancer can be classified as:

- **Adaptive:** Processing automatically adjusts to the number of jobs that are queued.
- **Decentralized:** Responsibility for load balancing is shared by all the nodes of the system. Any

502

node can initiate load balancing activity.

- **Stable:** Excessive load-balancing traffic does not burden the network, especially under extremely light or heavy system loads.

- **Effective:** System performance does not degrade because of load balancing activities.

In an earlier work [6], we have shown that our approach achieves superior load balance when compared to other popular load balancing techniques such as Random, Gradient, Receiver Initiated, Sender Initiated, and Adaptive Contracting.

Recently, experiments that measure the effectiveness of load balancing adaptive meshes have been conducted using an automatic portable environment, called PLUM [17], that was developed at NASA Ames Research Center. PLUM uses a novel balancing strategy consisting of two separate phases: repartitioning and remapping. After each mesh adaptation step, the computational grid is globally repartitioned if the workload distribution is unacceptable. The new partitions are then reassigned among the processors in a way that minimizes the cost of data movement. Only if the remapping cost is compensated by the computational gain that would be achieved with balanced partitions, is the necessary data appropriately redistributed. Otherwise, the new partitioning is discarded. Notice that data is not physically migrated unless the cost estimates indicate that doing so is beneficial.

The SBN-based load balancer differs from PLUM in several ways as discussed below:

- Processing is temporarily halted under PLUM while the load is being balanced. During the suspension, a new k-way partitioning is generated and data is redistributed among the nodes of the network. The SBN approach, on the other hand, allows processing to continue while the load is dynamically balanced. This feature also allows for the possibility of utilizing latency tolerance techniques to hide the communication and redistribution costs during processing.

- Under PLUM, suspension of processing and subsequent repartitioning does not guarantee an improvement in the quality of load balance. If it is determined that the estimated remapping cost exceeds the expected computational gain that is to be achieved by a load balancing operation, processing continues using the original mesh assignment. This could result in unnecessary idle time. In contrast, the SBN approach will always result in improved load balance among processors.

- PLUM redistributes all necessary data to the appropriate nodes immediately before processing continues. SBN, however, distributes in a "lazy" manner. Data is migrated to a processor only when it is ready to process the data, thus reducing redistribution and communication overhead.

We have performed extensive experiments on an IBM SP2 to compare the performance of our SBN load balancer to the results obtained under PLUM in [2]. The results demonstrate that the proposed approach achieves excellent load balance and also significantly reduces the redistribution cost compared to those obtained by using the `PMeTiS` or `DMeTiS` partitioners under PLUM. However, the edge cut percentages are higher than those for `PMeTiS`, indicating that the SBN strategy reduces the redistribution cost at the expense of a higher communication cost. For example, with a network of 32 processors, the redistribution cost using the SBN strategy is approximately half of the cost incurred under PLUM. However, total communication is almost doubled.

This paper is organized as follows. Section 2 reviews the definition of SBN and a basic load balancing algorithm. Section 3 describes the modifications made to incorporate a global view needed for adaptive mesh applications. Section 4 presents an overview of PLUM and the partitioners operating under that environment that are used for comparisons. Section 5 presents experimental results and a comparative performance analysis. Section 6 concludes the paper.

2 Symmetric Broadcast Networks

A *symmetric broadcast network* (SBN), proposed by Prasad and first presented in [7], defines a communication pattern (logical or physical) among the P processors in a multicomputer system. This communication pattern can be efficiently embedded into different parallel architectures in a topology-independent manner [5, 8]. Let us first give a brief overview of SBN and outline how to use it for load balancing.

Definition 1 *An SBN of dimension $d \geq 0$, denoted as SBN(d), is a $(d+1)$-stage interconnection network with $P = 2^d$ processors in each stage. It is constructed recursively as follows. A single node forms the basis network SBN(0). For $d > 0$, an SBN(d) is obtained from a pair of SBN(d − 1)s by adding a communication stage in the front with the following additional interprocessor connections:*

- *Node i in stage 0, is made adjacent to node $j = (i + P/2) \bmod P$ of stage 1; and*

- *Node j in stage 1 is made adjacent to the node in stage 2 which was the stage 0 successor of node i in SBN(d − 1).*

Figure 1 depicts an SBN(2), recursively constructed from two SBN(1)s.

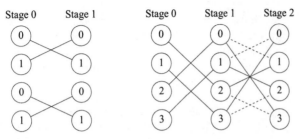

Figure 1: Construction of SBN(2) from a pair of SBN(1)s. The new connections are shown by solid lines and the original connections by dashed lines

By definition, each node in every stage s, for $1 \leq s \leq d-1$, of SBN(d) has exactly two successors; whereas a node in stage 0 has only one successor and a node in stage d has no successor. The SBN(d) defines unique communication patterns (or broadcast trees) among the nodes in the network. Precisely, for any source node or root x at stage 0, where $0 \leq x < P$, there exists a unique broadcast tree T_x of height $d = \log P$ such that each of the 2^d nodes appears exactly once.

Lemma 1 *Let n_x^s be a node at stage s in the broadcast tree T_x having the root node x (at stage 0), where $0 \leq x < P$. Then $n_x^s = n_0^s \oplus x$, where $\oplus$ is the exclusive-OR operator, thus leading to $T_x = T_0 \oplus x$.*

Thus, all SBN communication patterns can be derived from the template tree with node 0 as the root. As an example, consider two communication patterns T_0 and T_5 in SBN(3) as shown in Figs. 2(a) and 2(b) respectively. By our convention, n_0^s denotes a node at stage s in Fig. 2(a) while n_5^s is the corresponding node in Fig. 2(b). Furthermore, $n_5^s = n_0^s \oplus 5$.

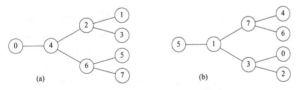

Figure 2: Examples of SBN communication patterns in SBN(3)

The predecessor and successors of each node can be uniquely defined by specifying the root x and the communication stage s so that messages from x can be appropriately routed to the other nodes.

Lemma 2 *The predecessor and successors of node n_0^s can be computed as:*

$$Predecessor = (n_0^s - 2^{d-s}) \vee 2^{d-s+1}.$$

$$Successor\_1 = n_0^s + 2^{d-s-1}, \quad for \ 0 \leq s < d.$$

$$Successor\_2 = n_0^s - 2^{d-s-1}, \quad for \ 1 \leq s < d.$$

2.1 SBN-Based Load Balancing

This section outlines the basic SBN-based load balancer, proposed by us in [6], which processes two types of messages. The first type is a *load balancing* message that is broadcast when a node n determines that the number, QLen(n), of locally queued jobs falls below the minimum threshold, MinTh. A load balancing message will also be broadcast if QLen(n) exceeds the maximum threshold, MaxTh, or if distributing the excess jobs will result in other processors exceeding MaxTh. As the load balancing message passes from one node to another, values for the global number of jobs queued (GLen) and the average number of jobs queued per node or the system load level (SysLL) are computed.

The second type of messages is called *job distribution* messages which are used to distribute jobs when QLen(n) > MaxTh. Distribution messages are also used to complete the load balancing process. After the SysLL value is calculated, a distribution message is broadcast through the network when jobs are routed to the lightly loaded processors and the threshold values (MinTh and MaxTh) are updated. As a result, the workload at all nodes is balanced.

3 Modified SBN Load Balancer

In order to provide a global view of the system and make it effective for adaptive mesh applications, we have made a series of modifications to the basic SBN load balancer [6], just outlined. These modifications are described in the following subsections.

3.1 Weighted Queue Length

The local queue length, QLen(p), as used by the basic SBN approach is assumed to be an estimate of the amount of processing to be performed by p. However, this parameter is inadequate for situations where the mesh is adapted because it does not accurately reflect the total processing load at p. To achieve a better balance, we must take into account the system variables like computation, communication, and redistribution costs, that affect the processing of a local queue. Therefore, we define a new metric called weighted queue length, $QWgt(p)$, to estimate the total time required to completely service the vertices in the local queue of p.

Let Wgt^v be the computational cost to process a vertex v, $Comm_p^v$ be the communication cost to interact with the vertices adjacent to v but whose data sets are not local to p, and $Remap_p^v$ be the redistribution cost to copy the data set for v to p from another processor. These factors vary widely from one vertex to another in a given mesh. $QWgt(p)$ is defined as:

$$QWgt(p) = \sum_{v=1}^{QLen(p)} (Wgt^v + Comm_p^v + Remap_p^v).$$

Clearly, if the data set for v is already assigned to p, no redistribution cost is incurred, i.e., $Remap_p^v = 0$. Similarly, if the data sets of all the vertices adjacent to v are also already assigned to p, the communication cost, $Comm_p^v$, is 0.

The threshold values, MinTh and MaxTh, must now be based on $QWgt(p)$ instead of $QLen(p)$ to accommodate the redefinition of processing load. In our experiments, MinTh, was set to reflect a 0.1 second processing load.

3.2 Weighted System Load

The weighted system load level is computed as:

$$WSysLL = \left\lceil \frac{1}{P} \sum_{i=1}^{P} QWgt(i) \right\rceil,$$

where P is the total number of processors used.

Assuming that the load is perfectly balanced among the processors, WSysLL estimates the time required to process the mesh and reflects the processing, communication, and redistribution costs in the current mesh-to-processor assignment. Hence, a global view of the system is captured that is otherwise not reflected using SysLL in the basic SBN load balancer.

3.3 Prioritized Vertex Selection

The basic SBN balancing approach does not consider the mesh connectivity when selecting vertices to be processed. Therefore, boundary vertices that could otherwise be migrated for more efficient execution, are as likely to be executed locally as internal vertices. The modified SBN load balancer takes advantage of the underlying mesh structure and defers execution of boundary vertices as long as possible.

Thus, the next queued vertex is selected for execution so as to minimize the overall cut size of the adapted mesh. A priority min-queue is maintained for this purpose, where the priority of a vertex v in processor p is given by $(Comm_p^v + Remap_p^v)/Wgt^v$.

Therefore, vertices with no communication and redistribution costs are executed first. Those with low communication or redistribution overhead relative to their computational weight are processed next. Conceptually, internal vertices are processed before those on partition boundaries.

3.4 Differential Edge Cut

For balancing the system load among processors, an optimal policy for vertex migration needs to be established. When vertices are being moved, assume that processor p is about to reassign some of its vertices to another processor q. The modified SBN load balancer running on p randomly picks a subset of vertices from those queued locally. For each selected vertex v, the differential edge cut[1], ΔCut, is calculated as follows:

$$\Delta Cut = Remap_q^v - Remap_p^v + 2 \times (Comm_q^v - Comm_p^v).$$

If $\Delta Cut > 0$, it is normalized as $\Delta Cut/Wgt^v$.

When a vertex is reassigned from one processor to another, the change in the communication cost must be applied to both processors. Hence, the change in the communication cost is doubled in the ΔCut formula. The parameters $Remap_p^v$ and $Remap_q^v$ will either be 0 or equal to the redistribution cost of moving the data for v from p to q. For example, assume $p = 3$, $q = 6$, the data for v reside on $p = 1$, and its redistribution cost is 8. In this case, $Remap_p^v = Remap_q^v = 8$. Similarly, if the data for v resides on $p = 3$, then $Remap_p^v = 0$ but $Remap_q^v = 8$.

A positive ΔCut indicates that an increase in communication and redistribution costs will result if v is migrated from p to q. Therefore, the formula favors migrating vertices with the smallest increase in communication cost per unit computational weight. In contrast, negative ΔCut values indicate a reduction in communication and redistribution costs, hence favoring the migration of vertices with the largest absolute reduction in communication and redistribution costs.

Once ΔCut is calculated for all the randomly chosen vertices, the vertex MinV with the smallest value of ΔCut is chosen for migration. Next, following a breadth-first search, the SBN balancer selects the vertices adjacent to MinV that are also queued locally for processing at p. The breadth-first search stops either when no adjacent vertices are queued for local processing at p, or if a sufficient number of vertices have been found for migration. If more vertices still need to be migrated, another subset of vertices are randomly chosen and the procedure is repeated. This migration

---

[1] Here we are deviating from the usual definition of edge cut to account for the dynamic nature of the SBN load balancer.

policy strives to maintain or improve the cut size during the execution of the load balancing algorithm. In contrast, the original SBN algorithms do not consider cut size and hence are likely to experience larger cut sizes as execution proceeds.

3.5 Data Redistribution Policy

The redistribution of data is performed in a "lazy" manner. Namely, the data set for a given vertex v in a processor p is not moved to q until the latter processor is about to execute v. Furthermore, the data sets of all vertices adjacent to v that are assigned to q are migrated as well. This policy greatly reduces both the redistribution and communication costs by avoiding multiple migrations of data sets and having resident all adjacent vertices that are assigned to processor q while v is being processed.

We implement data migration by broadcasting a job migration message when a vertex is about to be processed and its corresponding data set is not resident on the local processor. A locate-message is then broadcast to indicate the new location of the data set.

This policy is expected to maximize the number of adjacent vertices that are local when a grid point is processed. Hence, by considering the underlying mesh structure, the communication overhead is reduced compared to that for the basic SBN algorithm.

4 The PLUM Environment

We experimentally compare the performance of our SBN-based load balancer to PLUM [17] – a portable and parallel load balancing framework for adaptive unstructured grids. For the sake of completeness, the features of PLUM are summarized below.

Figure 3 provides an overview of PLUM. After an initial partitioning, a Solver executes several iterations of the application. When the grid-to-processor mapping becomes unbalanced due to mesh adaptation, PLUM gains control to determine if the workload among the processors has become unbalanced and to take appropriate action if so required. Mesh repartitioning and processor reassignment are then performed. If the estimated remapping cost exceeds the expected computational gain to be achieved, execution continues without remapping. Otherwise, the grid is remapped among the processors before the computation is resumed.

As the computational mesh is adapted and the processor workloads need to be rebalanced, PLUM can use any general purpose partitioner. In [2], two state-of-the-art partitioners, PMeTiS [14] and DMeTiS [20], were used. Both partitioners are parallelized and highly optimized for maximum efficiency, and have

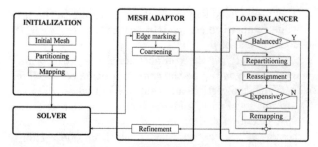

Figure 3: Overview of PLUM, a framework for globally load balancing parallel adaptive computations

proven effective for adaptive grids. DMeTiS is a diffusive scheme designed to modify existing partitions, while PMeTiS is a global partitioner that makes no assumptions on how the mesh is initially distributed.

Both DMeTiS and PMeTiS are k-way multi-level algorithms that operate in three phases: (i) in the initial coarsening phase, the original mesh, M_0, is reduced by collapsing adjacent vertices or edges through a series of smaller and smaller meshes to M_k, such that M_k has a sufficiently small number of vertices; (ii) in the partitioning phase, the mesh workload is balanced among the processors and the edge cut size is minimized; and (iii) in the projection phase, the partitioned mesh M_k is gradually restored to its original size M_0.

5 Experimental Study

The SBN-based load balancing algorithm has been implemented using MPI on the wide-node IBM SP2 located at NASA Ames Research Center, and tested with actual workloads obtained from adaptive calculations. The computational mesh used for the experiments simulates an unsteady environment where the adapted region is strongly time-dependent. This goal is achieved by propagating a simulated shock wave through the initial mesh shown in Fig. 4. The test case is generated by refining all elements within a cylindrical volume moving left to right across the domain with constant velocity, while coarsening previously-refined elements in its wake. Performance is measured at nine successive adaptation levels. The weighted sum of vertices increased from 50,000 to 1,833,730 over the nine levels of adaptation. This test case was chosen so that the results could be compared to those compiled in [2] using the PLUM environment.

5.1 Performance Metrics

The following metrics are chosen to evaluate the effectiveness of the SBN load balancer when processing an unsteady adaptive mesh. Recall that v denotes a vertex to be processed and P is the number of processors.

Figure 4: Initial and adapted meshes (after levels 1 and 5) for the simulated unsteady experiment

• **Maximum redistribution cost:** The goal is to capture the total cost of packing and unpacking data, separated by a barrier synchronization. Since a processor can either be sending or receiving data, the overhead of these two phases is modeled as a sum of two costs in this metric:

$$\text{MaxSR} = \max_{p \in P}\left\{\sum_{v \text{ sent from } p} Remap_p^v\right\} + \max_{p \in P}\left\{\sum_{v \text{ recv by } p} Remap_p^v\right\}.$$

Since MaxSR pertains to the processor that incurs the maximum redistribution cost, a reduction in the total data redistribution overhead can be guaranteed by minimizing MaxSR.

• **Load imbalance factor:** It is formulated as:

$$\text{LoadImb} = \max_{p \in P} \text{QWgt}(p) \,/\, \text{WSysLL}.$$

This factor should be as close to unity as possible.

• **Cut percentage:** The runtime interaction between adjacent vertices residing on different processors is represented by this metric as:

$$\text{Cut\%} = 100 \sum_{p \in P} \sum_{v \text{ assigned to } p} Comm_p^v \Big/ \sum_{e \text{ in mesh}} Edge^e,$$

where $Edge^e$ is the weight of edge e in the adaptive mesh. The Cut% value should be as small as possible.

Pre-Exec Cut% in Tables 1, 2, and 3 initially projects the mesh edge cut before processing an adaptation level but after the previous adaptation level has been processed.

Post-Exec Cut% is the actual cut realized after processing a given adaptation level.

Table 1 presents the results of processing the adaptive mesh with the SBN load balancer. Tables 2 and 3 respectively chart the results obtained using the PMeTiS and DMeTiS partitioners within the PLUM environment. Note that Tables 2 and 3 do not show results corresponding to all values of $P = 2$, 4, 8, 16, and 32. We have included only those data sets that were available to us.

5.2 Summary of Results

The SBN-based approach achieves excellent load balance. For example, LoadImb = 1.02 for $P = 32$ (see Table 1). When $P \leq 8$, an ideal load imbalance factor of 1.00 is achieved for most of the adaptation levels. In contrast, this factor using PMeTiS and DMeTiS under the PLUM environment is 1.04 and 1.59 respectively (cf. Tables 2 and 3).

The MaxSR metric indicates the amount of redistribution cost incurred while processing the adaptive mesh. The SBN "lazy" approach to migration of vertex data sets produces significantly lower values than those achieved by PMeTiS or DMeTiS under PLUM. For example, for $P = 32$, Table 1 shows MaxSR = 28,031, which is significantly less than the corresponding value in Table 2 (Maxsr = 63,270) and in Table 3 (MaxSR = 62,542).

Table 1 shows an SBN cut percentage that is almost triple compared to those reported by PMeTiS (30.58% compared to 10.94% for $P = 32$). This difference in the cut percentage is significantly lower when compared to the results obtained with DMeTiS (30.58% compared to 20.30%).

In conclusion, these experimental results demonstrate that the proposed SBN-based dynamic load balancer is effective in processing adaptive mesh applications, thus providing a global view across processors. In many mesh applications in which the cost of data redistribution dominates the cost of communication and processing, the SBN balancer would be preferred.

6 Future Work

Currently, we are experimenting on the SGI Origin 2000 (a distributed shared-memory architecture) to test the consistency of our results and implement additional performance refinements to reduce communication cost. It would also be interesting to apply the SBN balancer to adaptive mesh applications using a heterogeneous network of workstations in which P is not necessarily a power of 2. Since low-cost processing power is readily available, it would be desirable to explore the effect of adding latency-tolerant techniques to the load balancing method. This research also includes techniques to adapt the processing to situations where some of processors in a network environment

Table 1: Mesh adaptation results using SBN balancer

Adaptation Level	Pre-Exec Cut %	Post-Exec Cut %	MaxSR	LoadImb
P=2				
1	0.09%	4.64%	6,974	1.00
2	3.14%	6.18%	30,538	1.00
3	5.36%	6.08%	57,724	1.00
4	3.93%	3.86%	20,646	1.00
5	2.91%	5.32%	76,893	1.00
6	2.33%	4.62%	103,544	1.00
7	2.23%	5.86%	140,904	1.00
8	2.83%	6.14%	153,735	1.00
9	3.10%	6.89%	129,374	1.00
Avg	3.14%	5.54%	80,037	1.00
P=4				
1	2.26%	8.15%	4,078	1.00
2	7.22%	10.01%	26,187	1.00
3	9.44%	11.69%	64,110	1.00
4	9.16%	9.48%	46,406	1.00
5	6.60%	11.86%	149,042	1.00
6	9.83%	10.89%	94,269	1.00
7	6.58%	8.00%	50,337	1.00
8	2.79%	15.31%	170,408	1.00
9	11.53%	11.48%	85,152	1.00
Avg	7.86%	11.17%	76,665	1.00
P=8				
1	6.66%	10.77%	2,518	1.01
2	13.93%	14.98%	11,109	1.00
3	15.11%	18.16%	46,088	1.00
4	14.65%	15.83%	53,032	1.00
5	11.09%	16.48%	69,583	1.00
6	11.02%	15.91%	85,982	1.00
7	13.75%	18.13%	105,946	1.00
8	12.84%	19.51%	28,974	1.00
9	15.34%	17.35%	80,477	1.00
Avg	13.30%	17.18%	53,745	1.00
P=16				
1	15.36%	20.61%	1,767	1.01
2	24.82%	25.56%	7,259	1.00
3	24.40%	27.45%	36,031	1.01
4	20.60%	22.77%	43,943	1.01
5	16.11%	24.27%	71,736	1.01
6	17.83%	22.28%	66,211	1.01
7	19.75%	25.00%	55,361	1.01
8	17.83%	25.30%	64,796	1.01
9	17.87%	21.59%	74,316	1.01
Avg	19.19%	24.02%	46,825	1.01
P=32				
1	21.59%	26.74%	1,184	1.01
2	30.35%	32.32%	4,387	1.02
3	30.06%	34.04%	8,445	1.02
4	27.28%	31.43%	41,783	1.01
5	21.35%	29.40%	42,843	1.01
6	24.04%	29.42%	42,688	1.01
7	22.35%	30.45%	41,347	1.02
8	20.59%	30.48%	37,006	1.02
9	22.19%	29.43%	32,594	1.02
Avg	23.97%	30.58%	28,031	1.02

Table 2: Mesh adaptation results using PMeTiS under the PLUM environment

Adaptation Level	Pre-Exec Cut %	Post-Exec Cut %	MaxSR	LoadImb
P=16				
1	3.16%	4.38%	10,088	1.02
2	5.34%	7.20%	25,875	1.02
3	7.27%	9.71%	58,887	1.03
4	5.24%	8.62%	134,808	1.03
5	5.77%	8.17%	153,154	1.04
6	4.70%	8.06%	122,151	1.02
7	4.47%	8.45%	159,037	1.02
8	5.31%	7.97%	132,987	1.01
9	4.18%	7.75%	130,824	1.01
Avg	5.05%	7.81%	103,090	1.02
P=32				
1	4.78%	6.45%	5,097	1.01
2	7.56%	10.05%	16,758	1.02
3	10.28%	13.13%	39,565	1.05
4	8.14%	11.60%	73,074	1.06
5	7.59%	11.13%	92,581	1.05
6	6.51%	11.60%	82,751	1.06
7	6.66%	11.43%	88,642	1.03
8	6.88%	11.39%	91,301	1.05
9	6.19%	11.66%	79,662	1.04
Avg	7.18%	10.94%	63,270	1.04

Table 3: Mesh adaptation results using DMeTiS under the PLUM environment

Adaptation Level	Pre-Exec Cut %	Post-Exec Cut %	MAXSR	LoadImb
P=32				
1	4.65%	15.70%	5,047	1.88
2	19.26%	20.50%	17,393	2.12
3	21.14%	25.26%	44,413	2.12
4	17.13%	28.21%	99,232	1.87
5	29.08%	26.46%	97,280	1.68
6	25.31%	24.38%	86,204	1.41
7	20.55%	14.17%	78,312	1.11
8	10.04%	13.08%	72,474	1.05
9	9.41%	14.18%	62,522	1.05
Avg	17.40%	20.30%	62,542	1.59

are not available. Fault tolerance would allow applications to make use of resources that are constantly changing during execution.

Acknowledgements

This work is supported by Texas Advanced Research Program Grant Number TARP-97-003594-013 and by NASA under Contract Number NAS 2-14303 with MRJ Technology Solutions.

References

[1] C. Alpert and A. Kahng, "Recent directions in netlist partitioning," *Integration, the VLSI Journal*, 19(1-2) (1995), pp. 1–81.

[2] R. Biswas and L. Oliker, "Experiments with repartitioning and load balancing adaptive

508

meshes," NASA Ames Research Center, Moffett Field (1997), Tech Rep NAS-97-021.

[3] N. Chrisochoides, "Multithreaded model for the dynamic load balancing of parallel adaptive PDE computations," *Applied Numerical Mathematics*, 20 (1996), pp. 321–336.

[4] G. Cybenko, "Dynamic load balancing for distributed-memory multiprocessors," *Journal of Parallel and Distributed Computing*, 7 (1989), pp. 279–301.

[5] S.K. Das and D.J. Harvey, "Performance analysis of an adaptive symmetric broadcast load balancing algorithm on the hypercube," Dept Computer Science, Univ North Texas, Denton (1995), Tech Rep CRPDC-95-1.

[6] S.K. Das, D.J. Harvey, and R. Biswas, "Adaptive load balancing algorithms using symmetric broadcast networks: Performance study on an IBM SP2", *Proc. 26th International Conference on Parallel Processing* (1997), pp. 360–367.

[7] S.K. Das and S.K. Prasad, "Implementing task ready queues in a multiprocessing environment," *Proc. International Conference on Parallel Computing* (1990), pp. 132–140.

[8] S.K. Das, S.K. Prasad, C-Q. Yang, and N.M. Leung, "Symmetric broadcast networks for implementing global task queues and load balancing in a multiprocessor environment," Dept Computer Science, Univ North Texas, Denton (1992), Tech Rep CRPDC-92-1.

[9] J. Garbers, H.J. Promel, and A. Steger, "Finding clusters in VLSI circuits," *Proc. IEEE International Conference on Computer Aided Design* (1990), pp. 520–523.

[10] L. Hagen and A. Kahng, "A new approach to effective circuit clustering," *Proc. IEEE International Conference on Computer Aided Design*, (1992), pp. 422-427.

[11] B. Hendrickson and R. Leland, "A multilevel algorithm for partitioning graphs," Sandia National Laboratories, Albuquerque (1993), Tech Rep SABD83-1391M.

[12] G. Horton, "A multi-level diffusion method for dynamic load balancing", *Parallel Computing*, 19 (1993), pp. 209–229.

[13] G. Karypis and V. Kumar, "Analysis of multilevel graph partitioning," Dept Computer Science, Univ Minnesota, Minneapolis (1995), Tech Rep 95-037.

[14] G. Karypis and V. Kumar, "Parallel multilevel K-way partitioning scheme for irregular graphs," Dept Computer Science, Univ Minnesota, Minneapolis (1996), Tech Rep 96-036.

[15] B.W. Kernighan and S. Lin, "An efficient heuristic procedure for partitioning graphs", *Bell Systems Tech. Journal*, 49 (1970), pp. 291–307.

[16] G.A. Kohring, "Dynamic load balancing for parallelized particle simulations on MIMD computers," *Parallel Computing*, 21(1995), pp. 683–693.

[17] L. Oliker and R. Biswas, "PLUM: Parallel load balancing for adaptive unstructured meshes," NASA Ames Research Center, Moffett Field (1997), Tech Rep NAS-97-020.

[18] R. Ponnusamy, N. Mansour, A. Choudhary, and G.C. Fox, "Graph contraction and physical optimization methods: a quality-cost tradeoff for mapping data on parallel computers," *Proc. 7th Int'l Conf on Supercomputing* (1993).

[19] S. Pulidas, D. Towsley, and J.A. Stankovic, "Embedding gradient estimators in load balancing algorithms," *Proc. Int'l Conf on Distributed Computer Systems* (1988), pp. 488–490.

[20] K. Schloegel, G. Karypis, and V. Kumar, "Multilevel diffusion schemes for repartitioning of adaptive meshes," Dept Computer Science, Univ Minnesota, Minneapolis (1997), Tech Rep 97-013.

[21] R. Van Driessche and D. Roose, "Load balancing computational fluid dynamics calculations on unstructured grids," *Parallel Computing in CFD*, AGARD-R-807 (1995), pp. 2.1–2.26.

[22] A. Vidwans, Y. Kallinderis, and V. Venkatakrishnan, "Parallel dynamic load balancing algorithm for three-dimensional adaptive unstructured grids," *AIAA Journal*, 32 (1994), pp. 495–505.

[23] C. Walshaw, M. Cross, and M.G. Everett, "Parallel dynamic graph-partitioning for unstructured meshes," School of Computing and Mathematical Sciences, Univ of Greenwich, London (1997), Tech Rep 97/1M/20.

A Prefix Code Matching Parallel Load-Balancing Method for Solution-Adaptive Unstructured Finite Element Graphs on Distributed Memory Multicomputers[1]

Yeh-Ching Chung[2] and Ching-Jung Liao[3]

[2] Department of Information Engineering
Feng Chia University, Taichung, Taiwan 407, R.O.C
[3] Department of Accounting and Statistics
The Overseas Chinese College of Commerce, Taichung, Taiwan 407, R.O.C
Email: ychung, cjliao@cray.pdplab.iecs.fcu.edu.tw

Abstract

In this paper, we propose a prefix code matching parallel load-balancing method (PCMPLB) to efficiently deal with the load unbalancing problems of solution-adaptive finite element application programs on distributed memory multicomputers. The main idea of the PCMPLB method is first to construct a prefix code tree for processors. Based on the prefix code tree, a schedule for performing load transfer among processors can be determined by concurrently and recursively dividing the tree into two subtrees and finding a maximum matching for processors in the two subtrees until the leaves of the prefix code tree are reached. The experimental results show that the execution time of an application program under the PCMPLB method is less than that of the direct diffusion method and the multilevel diffusion method.

1. Introduction

To efficiently execute a finite element application program on a distributed memory multicomputer, we need to map nodes of the corresponding finite element graph to processors of a distributed memory multicomputer such that each processor has approximately the same amount of computational load and the communication among processors is minimized. Since this mapping problem is known to be NP-completeness [7], many heuristic methods were proposed to find satisfactory sub-optimal solutions [2, 4, 6, 8, 12-14, 19-20]. If the number of nodes of a finite element graph will not be increased during the execution of a finite element application program, the mapping algorithm only needs to be performed once. For a solution-adaptive finite element

application program, the number of nodes will be increased discretely due to the refinement of some finite elements during the execution of a finite element application program. This will result in load unbalancing of processors. A node remapping or a load-balancing algorithm has to be performed many times in order to balance the computational load of processors while keeping the communication cost among processors as low as possible. Since node remapping or load-balancing algorithms were performed at run-time, their execution must be fast and efficient.

Many load-balancing methods have been proposed in the literature [5, 9-10, 15, 17-18, 21-22, 24]. In this paper, we propose a *prefix code matching parallel load-balancing* (PCMPLB) method to efficiently deal with the load unbalancing problems of solution-adaptive finite element application programs on distributed memory multicomputers with fully-connected interconnection networks such as multistage interconnection networks, crossbar networks, etc. The main idea of the PCMPLB method is first to construct a prefix code tree for processors according to the processor graph, where the leaves of the prefix code tree are processors. Based on the prefix code tree, a schedule for performing load transfer among processors can be determined by concurrently and recursively dividing the tree into two subtrees and finding a maximum matching for processors in the two subtrees until the leaves of the prefix code tree are reached.

To evaluate the performance of the PCMPLB method, we have implemented the PCMPLB method along with two load-balancing methods, the direct diffusion method [5, 21] and the multilevel diffusion method [9, 17-18], and five mapping methods, AE/MC [4], AE/ORB [4], JOSTLE-MS [20-21], MLkP [12], and PARTY [16] on an

---

[1] The work of this paper was partially supported by NSC of R.O.C. under contract NSC-87-2231-E-035-010.
[2] Correspondence addressee.

SP2 parallel machine. The experimental results show that (1) if a mapping method is used for the initial partitioning and this mapping method or a load-balancing method is used in each refinement, the execution time of an application program under a load-balancing method is always less than that of the mapping method. (2) The execution time of an application program under the PCMPLB method is less than that of the direct diffusion method and the multilevel diffusion method.

2. The Prefix Code Matching Parallel Load-Balancing Method

The PCMPLB method can be divided into the following four phases.

Phase 1: Obtain a processor graph G from the initial partition.

Phase 2: Construct a prefix code tree for processors in G.

Phase 3: Determine the load transfer sequence by using matching theorem.

Phase 4: Perform the load transfer.

In the following, we will describe them in details.

2.1. The Processor Graph

When nodes of a solution-adaptive finite element graph were distributed to processors by some mapping algorithms, according to the communication property of the finite element graph, we can get a processor graph from the partition. In a processor graph, nodes represent the processors and edges represent the communication needed among processors. The weights associated with nodes and edges denote the computation and the communication costs, respectively. We now give an example to explain it.

EXAMPLE 1: Figure 1 shows an example of a processor graph. Figure 1(a) shows an initial partition of a 100-node finite element graph on 10 processors by using the MLkP method. In Figure 1(a), all processors are assigned 10 finite element nodes. After the refinement, the number of nodes assigned to processors P_0, P_1, P_2, P_3, P_4, P_5, P_6, P_7, P_8, and P_9 are 10, 11, 11, 12, 10, 19, 16, 13, 13, and 13, respectively, and is shown in Figure 1(b). The corresponding processor graph of Figure 1(b) is shown in Figure 1(c).

2.2. The Construction of a Prefix Code Tree

Based on the processor graph, we can construct a prefix code tree. The construction of a prefix code tree T_{Prefix} is based on the Huffman's algorithm [11] and is given as follows:

Step 1: Let V be a set of P isolated vertices, where P is

the number of processors in G. Each vertex P_i in V is the root of a complete binary tree (of height 0) with a weight $w_i = 1$.

Step 2: While $|V| > 1$, perform the following:

(a) Find a tree T in V with the smallest root weight w. If there are two or more candidates, choose the one whose leaf nodes have the smallest degree in G.

(b) For trees in V whose leaf nodes are adjacent to those in T, find a tree T' with the smallest root weight w'. If there are two or more candidates, choose the one whose leaf nodes have the smallest degree in G.

(c) Create a new (complete binary) tree T^* with root weight $w^* = w + w'$ and having T and T' as its left and right substrees, respectively.

(d) Place T^* in V and delete T and T'.

(e) Repeat (a) to (d) until $V' = 1$.

We now give an example to explain the above description.

EXAMPLE 2: An example of step by step construction of a prefix code tree from the processor graph shown in Figure 1(c) is given in Figure 2. The degrees of processors P_0, P_1, P_2, P_3, P_4, P_5, P_6, P_7, P_8, and P_9 are 2, 4, 4, 5, 3, 3, 3, 4, 4, and 6, respectively. The initial configuration is shown in Figure 2(a). Initially, P_5 has the smallest degree. P_5 and P_6 are combined as a tree and we obtain a new configuration as shown in Figure 2(b). By applying Steps 2(a)-2(e), we can obtain Figures 2(c)-2(j). Once the construction of a prefix code tree is completed, each processor is assigned a prefix code word, that is, $P_0 = 1000$, $P_1 = 1001$, $P_2 = 1010$, $P_3 = 111$, $P_4 = 1011$, $P_5 = 000$, $P_6 = 001$, $P_7 = 010$, $P_8 = 110$, and $P_9 = 011$.

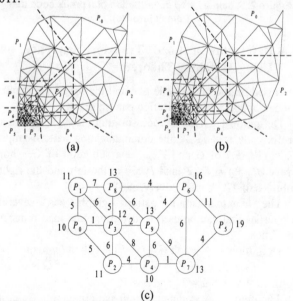

(a)   (b)

(c)

Figure 1: An example of a processor graph. (a) The initial partitioned finite element graph. (b) The finite element graph after a refinement. (c) The corresponding processor graph obtained from (b).

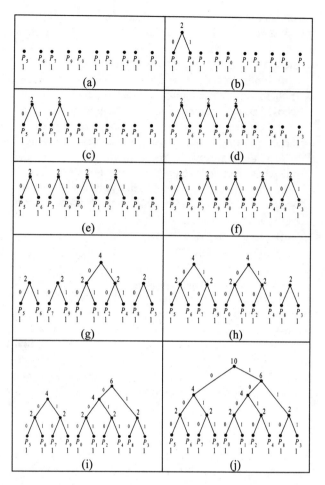

Figure 2: A step by step construction of a prefix code tree from Figure 1(c).

2.3. Determine a Load Transfer Sequence by Using Matching Theorem

Based on the prefix code tree and the processor graph, we can obtain a communication pattern graph.

Definition 1: Given a processor graph $G = (V, E)$ and a prefix code tree T_{Prefix}, the communication pattern graph $G_c = (V_c, E_c)$ of G and T_{Prefix} is a subgraph of G. For every $(P_i, P_j) \in E_c$, P_i and P_j are in the left and the right subtrees of T_{Prefix}, respectively, and $P_i, P_j \in V_c$.

The communication pattern graph has several properties that can be used to determine the load transfer sequence.

Definition 2: A graph $G = (V, E)$ is called *bipartite* if $V = V_1 \cup V_2$ with $V_1 \cap V_2 = \phi$, and every edge of G is of the form $\{a, b\}$ with $a \in V_1$ and $b \in V_2$.

Theorem 1: A communication pattern graph G_c is bipartite graph.

Proof: According to Definition 1, for every $(P_i, P_j) \in E_c$, P_i and P_j are in the left and right subtrees of T_{Prefix}, respectively. Therefore G_c is a bipartite graph. ∎

Definition 3: A subset M of E is called a *matching* in G if its elements are edges and no two of them are adjacent in G; the two ends of an edge in M are said to be matched under M. M is a *maximum matching* if G has no matching M' with $|M'| > |M|$.

Theorem 2: Let $G = (V, E)$ be a bipartite graph with bipartition (V_1, V_2). Then G contains a matching that saturates every vertex in V_1 if and only if $|N(S)| \geq |S|$ for all $S \subseteq V_1$, where $N(S)$ is the set of all neighbors of vertices in S.

Proof: The proof can be found in [3]. ∎

Corollary 1: Let $G_c = (V_c, E_c)$ be a communication pattern graph and V_L and V_R are the sets of processors in the left and the right subtrees of T_{Prefix}, respectively, where $V_L, V_R \subseteq V_c$. Then we can find a maximum matching M from G_c such that for every element $(P_i, P_j) \in M$, $P_i \in V_L$ and $P_j \in V_R$.

Proof: From Definition 3 and Hungarian method [3], we know that a maximum matching M from G_c can be found. ∎

From the communication pattern graph, we can determine a load transfer sequence for processors in the left and the right subtrees of a prefix code tree by using the matching theorem to find a maximum matching among the edges of the communication pattern graph. Due to the construction process used in Phase 2, we can also obtain communication pattern graphs from the left and the right subtrees of a prefix code tree. A load transfer sequence can be determined by concurrently and recursively dividing a prefix code tree into two subtrees, constructing the corresponding communication pattern graph, finding a maximum matching for the communication pattern graph, and determining the number of finite element nodes need to be transferred among processors until a tree contains one vertex. Assume that there are P processors in a processor graph and N nodes in a refined finite element graph. We define N/P as the average load of a processor. The load of a processor is defined as the number of finite element nodes assigned to it. The load transfer sequence is determined as follows:

Step 1: Let S be a set that contains the prefix code tree obtained in Phase 2.

Step 2: While $|S| < P$, for each tree T_{Prefix} in S and the number of vertices in T_{Prefix} is greater than 1, perform the following:

(a) Let T_L and T_R be the left and the right subtrees of T_{Prefix}, respectively. P_L and P_R represent the number of processors (leaf nodes) in T_L and T_R, respectively. Find the communication pattern graph G_c from the processor graph G and the prefix code tree T_{Prefix}.

(b) Find a maximum matching $M = \{(P_i, Q_i)|$ P_i and Q_i are processors in T_L and T_R, respectively, and P_i and Q_i are adjacent in $G\}$ from G_c.

(c) Calculate $quota(T_L)$, $quota(T_R)$, $load(T_L)$ and

$load(T_R)$, where $quota(T_L)$ and $quota(T_R)$ denote the sum of the average load of processors in T_L and T_R, respectively; and $load(T_L)$ and $load(T_R)$ represent the sum of the load of processors in T_L and T_R, respectively.

(d) If $load(T_R) > quota(T_R)$, processors in T_R need to send $m = load(T_R) - quota(T_R)$ finite element nodes to processors in T_L. If $load(T_R) < quota(T_R)$, processors in T_L need to send $m = load(T_L) - quota(T_L)$ finite element nodes to processors in T_R. If $load(T_R) = quota(T_R)$, go to step 2(g).

(e) For each element (P_i, Q_i) in M, determine the number of finite element nodes that P_i (Q_i) needs to send to Q_i (P_i) based on $|M|$, the load of P_i (Q_i), and the value of m. Assume that $M = \{(P_1, Q_1), (P_2, Q_2), \dots , (P_k, Q_k)\}$ and $load(T_R) > quota(T_R)$. The number of finite element nodes that Q_i needs to send to P_i is $w_i = m \times load(Q_i)/\sum_{j=1}^{k}load(Q_j)$, where $load(Q_i)$ is the number of finite element nodes assigned to processor Q_i. If $load(Q_i) < w_i$, an exception handling procedure is carried out by moving finite element nodes from processors in T_R to Q_i to ensure that $load(Q_i) \geq w_i$.

(f) Place T_L and T_R in S and delete T_{Prefix} from S.

(g) Repeat (a) to (f) until $|S| = P$.

We now give an example to explain the above description.

EXAMPLE 3: Figure 3 shows the communication pattern graphs and their corresponding maximum matching for the examples shown in Figures 1 and 2 step by step when performing the procedure described in this subsection. Figure 1(a) shows the communication pattern graph for the prefix code tree with root at level 1. In Figure 3(a), an arrow is an element of a matching. The number associated with an arrow denotes the number of finite element nodes that a processor needs to send to the other processor. Figure 3(b) to Figure 3(d) show the communication pattern graphs for the prefix code trees with roots at levels 2, 3, and 4, respectively. When the matching of each communication pattern graph is found, the load transfer sequence can be determined as follows.

Step 1: $P_6 \xrightarrow{4} P_8, P_7 \xrightarrow{3} P_4, P_9 \xrightarrow{3} P_3$;

Step 2: $P_5 \xrightarrow{3} P_7, P_6 \xrightarrow{2} P_9, P_3 \xrightarrow{3} P_0, P_8 \xrightarrow{4} P_1$;

Step 3: $P_5 \xrightarrow{3} P_6, P_0 \xrightarrow{2} P_2, P_8 \xrightarrow{1} P_3$;

Step 4: $P_1 \xrightarrow{2} P_0$.

2.4. Perform the Load Transfer

After the determination of the load transfer sequence, the physical load transfer can be carried out among the processors according to the load transfer sequence in parallel. The goals of the physical load transfer are to balance the load of processors and to minimize the communication cost among processors. By following the load transfer sequence, the goal of load balancing can be achieved easily. Assume that processor P_i needs to send m finite element nodes to processor Q_i. To minimize the communication cost between processors P_i and Q_i, P_i sends finite element nodes that are adjacent to those in Q_i (we called these nodes as boundary nodes) to Q_i. If the number of boundary nodes is greater than m, nodes with smaller degrees will be sent from P_i and Q_i. If the number of boundary nodes is less than m, the boundary nodes and nodes that are adjacent to the boundary nodes will be sent from P_i and Q_i.

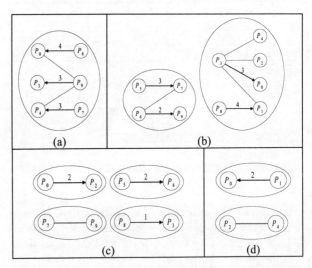

Figure 3: The matching of the communication pattern graph. (a) The first matching. (b) The second matching. (c) The third matching. (d) The fourth matching.

3. Performance Evaluation and Experimental Results

To evaluate the performance of the proposed method, we have implemented the PCMPLB method along with two load-balancing methods, the direct diffusion method (DD) and the multilevel diffusion method (MD), and five mapping methods, the AE/MC method, the AE/ORB method, the JOSTLE-MS method, the MLkP method, and the PARTY library method, on an SP2 parallel machine. All algorithms were written in C with MPI communication primitives. Three criteria, the execution time of mapping/load-balancing methods, the computation time of an application program under different mapping/load-balancing methods, and the speedups achieved by the mapping/load-balancing methods for an application program, are used for the performance evaluation.

In dealing with the unstructured finite element graphs, the distributed irregular mesh environment (DIME) [23] is used. In this paper, we only use DIME to generate the initial test sample. From the initial test graph, we use our refining algorithms and data structures to generate the desired test graphs. The initial test graph used for the performance evaluation is shown in Figure 4. The number of nodes and elements for the test graph after each refinement are shown in Table 1. For the presentation purpose, the number of nodes and the number of finite elements shown in Figure 4 are less than those shown in Table 2.

Table 1. The number of nodes and elements of the test graph *truss*.

Refine *Truss*	Initial (0)	1	2	3	4	5
node #	18407	23570	29202	36622	46817	57081
Element #	35817	46028	57181	71895	92101	112494

Figure 4. The test sample *truss* (7325 nodes, 14024 elements).

To emulate the execution of a solution-adaptive finite element application program on an SP2 parallel machine, we have the following steps. First, read the initial finite element graph. Then use the AE/MC method or the AE/ORB method or the JOSTLE-MS method or the ML*k*P method or the PARTY library method to map nodes of the initial finite element graph to processors. After the mapping, the computation of each processor is carried out. In our example, the computation is to solve Laplaces equation (Laplace solver). The algorithm of solving Laplaces equation is similar to that of [1]. Since it is difficult to predict the number of iterations for the convergence of a Laplace solver, we assume that the maximum number of iterations executed by our Laplace solver is 1000. When the computation is converged, the first refined finite element graph is read. To balance the computational load of processors, the AE/MC method or the AE/ORB method or the JOSTLE-MS method or the ML*k*P method or the PARTY library method or the direct diffusion method or the multilevel diffusion method or the PCMPLB method is applied. After a mapping/load-balancing method is performed, the computation for each processor is carried out. The procedures of mesh refinement, load balancing, and computation processes are performed in turn until the execution of a solution-adaptive finite element application program is completed.

By combining the initial mapping methods and methods for load balancing, there are twenty methods used for the performance evaluation. For examples, the AE/ORB method uses AE/ORB to perform the initial mapping and AE/ORB to balance the computational load of processors in each refinement. The AE/ORB/PCMPLB method use AE/ORB to perform the initial mapping and PCMPLB to balance the computational load of processors in each refinement.

3.1. Comparisons of the Execution Time of Mapping/Load-Balancing Methods

The execution time of different mapping/load-balancing methods for the test unstructured finite element graph *truss* on an SP2 parallel machine with 10, 30, and 50 processors are shown in Table 2. In Table 2, we list the initial mapping time and the refinement time for mapping/load-balancing methods. The initial mapping time is the execution time of mapping methods to map finite element nodes of the initial test sample to processors. The refinement time is the sum of the execution time of mapping/load-balancing methods to balance the load of processors after each refinement. Since we deal with the load balancing issue in this paper, we will focus on the refinement time comparison of mapping/load-balancing methods. From Table 2, we can see that, in general, the refinement time of load-balancing methods is shorter than that of the mapping methods. The reasons are (1) the mapping methods has higher time complexity than those of the load-balancing methods; and (2) the mapping methods need to perform gather-scatter operations that are time consuming in each refinement.

For the same initial mapping method, the refinement time of the PCMPLB method, in general, is shorter than that of the direct diffusion and the multilevel diffusion methods. The reasons are as follows:

(1) The PCMPLB method has less time complexity than those of the direct diffusion and the multilevel diffusion methods.
(2) The physical load transfer is performed in parallel in the PCMPLB method.
(3) The number of data movement steps among processors in the PCMPLB method is less than those of the direct diffusion and the multilevel diffusion methods.

3.2. Comparisons of the Execution Time of the Test Sample under Different Mapping/ Load-Balancing Methods

The time of a Laplace solver to execute one iteration (computation + communication) for the test sample under different mapping/load-balancing methods on an SP2 parallel machine with 10, 30, and 50 processors are shown in Figure 5, Figure 6, and Figure 7, respectively. Since we assume a synchronous mode of communication in our model, the total time for a Laplace solver to complete its job is the sum of the computation time and the communication time. From Figure 5 to Figure 7, we can see that if the initial mapping is performed by a mapping method (for example AE/ORB) and the same mapping method or a load-balancing method (DD, MD, PCMPLB) is performed for each refinement, the execution time of a Laplace solver under the proposed load-balancing method is shorter than that of other methods. The reasons are as follows:

(1) The PCMPLB method uses the maximum matching to determine the load transfer sequence. Data migration can be done between adjacent processors. This local data migration ability can greatly reduce the amount of global data migration and therefore reduce the communication cost of a Laplace Solver.

(2) In the physical load transfer, the PCMPLB method tries to transfer boundary nodes between processors. This will also reduce the communication overheads of a Laplace Solver.

3.3. Comparisons of the Speedups under the Mapping/Load-Balancing Methods for the Test Sample

The speedups and the maximum speedups under the mapping/load-balancing methods on an SP2 parallel machine with 10, 30, and 50 processors for the test sample are shown in Table 3 and Table 4, respectively. The maximum speedup is defined as the ratio of the execution time of a sequential Laplace solver to the execution time of a parallel Laplace solver. From Table 3, we can see that if the initial mapping is performed by a mapping method (for example AE/ORB) and the same mapping method or a load-balancing method (DD, MD, PCMPLB) is performed for each refinement, the proposed load-balancing method has the best speedup among mapping/load-balancing methods.

From Table 4, we can see that if the initial mapping is performed by a mapping method (for example AE/ORB) and the same mapping method or a load-balancing method (DD, MD, PCMPLB) is performed for each refinement, the proposed load-balancing method has the best maximum speedup among mapping/load-balancing methods. For the mapping methods, AE/MC has the best maximum speedups for test samples. For the load-balancing methods, AE/MC/PCMPLB has the best maximum speedups for test samples. From Table 4, we can see that a better initial mapping method is used, a better maximum speedup can be expected when the PCMPLB method is used in each refinement.

4. Conclusions

In this paper, we have proposed a prefix code matching parallel load-balancing method, the PCMPLB method, to deal with the load unbalancing problems of solution-adaptive finite element application programs. To evaluate the performance of the proposed method, we have implemented this method along with two load-balancing methods, the direct diffusion method and the multilevel diffusion method, and five mapping methods, AE/MC, AE/ORB, JOSTLE-MS, MLkP, and PARTY, on an SP2 parallel machine. The unstructured finite element graph *truss* is used as test sample. Three criteria, the execution time of mapping/load-balancing methods, the execution time of a solution-adaptive finite element application program under different mapping/load-balancing methods, and the speedups under mapping/load-balancing methods for a solution-adaptive finite element application program, are used for the performance evaluation. The experimental results show that (1) if a mapping method is used for the initial partitioning and this mapping method or a load-balancing method is used in each refinement, the execution time of an application program under a load-balancing method is always shorter than that of the mapping method. (2) The execution time of an application program under the PCMPLB method is less than that of the direct diffusion method and the multilevel diffusion method.

References

[1] I.G. Angus, G.C. Fox, J.S. Kim, and D.W. Walker, *Solving Problems on Concurrent Processors*, Vol. 2, N. J.: Prentice-Hall, Englewood Cliffs, 1990.

[2] S.T. Barnard and H.D. Simon, "Fast Multilevel Implementation of Recursive Spectral Bisection for Partitioning Unstructured Problems," *Concurrency: Practice and Experience*, Vol. 6, No. 2, pp. 101-117, Apr. 1994.

[3] J.A. Bondy and U.S.R. Murty, *Graph Theory with Applications*, New York: Elsevier North Holland, 1976.

[4] Y.C. Chung and C.J. Liao, "A Processor Oriented Partitioning Method for Mapping Unstructured Finite Element Graphs on SP2 Parallel Machines," Technical Report, Institute of Information Engineering, Feng Chia University, Taichung, Taiwan, Sep. 1996.

[5] G. Cybenko, "Dynamic Load Balancing for Distributed Memory Multiprocessors," *Journal of Parallel and Distributed Computing*, Vol. 7, No. 2, pp. 279-301, Oct. 1989.

[6] F. Ercal, J. Ramanujam, and P. Sadayappan, "Task Allocation onto a Hypercube by Recursive Mincut Bipartitioning," *Journal of Parallel and Distributed Computing*, Vol. 10, pp. 35-44, 1990.

[7] M.R. Garey and D.S. Johnson, Computers and Intractability, A Guide to Theory of NP-Completeness. San Francisco, CA: Freeman, 1979.

[8] B. Hendrickson and R. Leland, "An Improved Spectral Graph Partitioning Algorithm for Mapping Parallel Computations," *SIAM Journal on Scientific Computing*,

Vol. 16, No.2, pp. 452-469, 1995.

[9] G. Horton, "A Multi-level Diffusion Method for Dynamic Load Balancing, " *Parallel Computing*, Vol. 19, pp. 209-218, 1993.

[10] Y. F. Hu and R. J. Blake, An Optimal Dynamic Load Balancing Algorithm, Technical Report DL-P-95-011, Daresbury Laboratory, Warrington, UK, 1995.

[11] D.A. Huffman, "A Method for the Construction of Minimum Redundancy Codes," *Proceedings of the IRE 40*, pp. 1098-1101, 1952.

[12] G. Karypis and V. Kumar, "Multilevel *k*-way Partitioning Scheme for Irregular Graphs," Technical Report 95-064, Department of Computer Science, University of Minnesota, Minneapolis, 1995.

[13] G. Karypis and V. Kumar, "A Fast and High Quality Multilevel Scheme for Partitioning Irregular Graphs," Technical Report 95-035, Department of Computer Science, University of Minnesota, Minneapolis, 1995.

[14] B.W. Kernigham and S. Lin, "An Efficient Heuristic Procedure for Partitioning Graphs," *Bell Syst. Tech. J.*, Vol. 49, No. 2, pp. 292-370, Feb. 1970.

[15] C.W. Ou and S. Ranka, "Parallel Incremental Graph Partitioning," *IEEE Trans. Parallel and Distributed Systems*, Vol. 8, No. 8, pp. 884-896, Aug. 1997.

[16] R. Preis and R. Diekmann, "The PARTY Partitioning – Library User Guide – Version 1.1," HENIZ NIXDORF INSTITUTE Universität Paderborn, Germany, Sep. 1996.

[17] K. Schloegel, G. Karypis, and V. Kumar, Parallel Multilevel Diffusion Algorithms for Repartitioning of Adaptive Meshes, Technical Report #97-014, University of Minnesota, Department of Computer Science and Army HPC Center, 1997.

[18] K. Schloegel, G. Karypis, and V. Kumar, Multilevel Diffusion Schemes for Repartitioning of Adaptive Meshes, Technical Report #97-013, University of Minnesota, Department of Computer Science, Jun. 1997.

[19] H.D. Simon, "Partitioning of Unstructured Problems for Parallel Processing," *Computing Systems in Engineering*, Vol. 2, No. 2/3, pp. 135-148, 1991.

[20] C.H. Walshaw, M. Cross, and M.G. Everett, "A Localized Algorithm for Optimizing Unstructured Mesh Partitions," *The International Journal of Supercomputer Applications*, Vol. 9, No. 4, pp. 280-295, Winter 1995.

[21] C. Walshaw, M. Cross, and M. G. Everett, Dynamic Load-Balancing for Parallel Adaptive Unstructured Meshes, In M. Heath et al. Editor, *Parallel Processing for Scientific Computing*, SIAM, Philadelphia, 1997.

[22] C. Walshaw, M. Cross, and M. G. Everett, "Dynamic Mesh Partitioning: A Unified Optimisation and Load-Balancing Algorithm," Technical Report 95/IM/06, University of Greenwich, London, London SE18 6PF, UK, Dec. 1995.

[23] R.D. Williams, *DIME: Distributed Irregular Mesh Environment*, California Institute of Technology, 1990.

[24] M.Y. Wu, "On Runtime Parallel Scheduling for Processor Load Balancing," *IEEE Trans. Parallel and Distributed Systems*, Vol. 8, No. 2, pp. 173-186, Feb. 1997.

Table 2: The execution time of different mapping/load-balancing methods for the test sample on different numbers of processors.

# of processors / Method	10		30		50	
	initial mapping	refinement	initial mapping	refinement	Initial Mapping	refinement
AE/MC	5.054	37.563	7.964	67.061	10.256	129.929
AE/MC/DD	5.035	1.571	7.671	1.383	10.041	1.585
AE/MC/MD	5.035	7.231	7.671	4.043	10.041	4.245
AE/MC/PCMPLB	5.035	0.444	7.671	0.652	10.041	0.458
AE/ORB	0.633	7.493	0.637	6.713	0.742	6.938
AE/ORB/DD	0.614	1.607	0.614	2.086	0.586	2.763
AE/ORB/MD	0.614	4.586	0.614	5.028	0.586	6.013
AE/ORB/PCMPLB	0.614	0.474	0.614	0.769	0.586	1.475
JOSTLE-MS	1.055	3.459	1.02	4.426	2.26	5.763
JOSTLE-MS/DD	1.036	0.741	0.997	1.968	0.704	2.954
JOSTLE-MS/MD	1.036	3.45	0.997	4.838	0.704	6.173
JOSTLE-MS/PCMPLB	1.036	0.483	0.997	1.57	0.704	0.922
MLkP	0.567	4.96	0.589	5.279	0.771	5.908
MLkP/DD	0.548	1.289	0.566	1.872	0.621	2.295
MLkP/MD	0.548	4.142	0.566	4.867	0.621	5.612
MLkP/PCMPLB	0.548	1.083	0.566	0.684	0.621	1.233
PARTY	1.969	18.195	1.809	19.6	1.752	19.262
PARTY/DD	1.937	1.347	1.786	2.009	1.577	2.578
PARTY/MD	1.937	4.255	1.786	5.157	1.577	6.278
PARTY/PCMPLB	1.937	1.58	1.786	1.09	1.577	0.941

Time unit: seconds

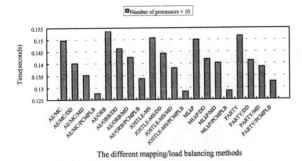

Figure 7: The time for Laplace solver to execute one iteration (computation + communication) for the test sample under different mapping/load-balancing methods on 10 processors.

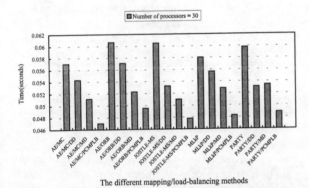

Figure 6: The time for Laplace solver to execute one iteration (computation + communication) for the test sample under different mapping/load-balancing methods on 30 processors.

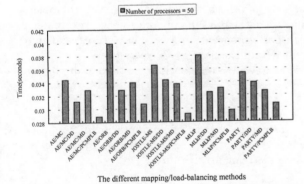

Figure 7: The time for Laplace solver to execute one iteration (computation + communication) for the test sample under different mapping/load-balancing methods on 50 processors.

Table 3: The speedups under the mapping/load-balancing methods for the test sample on an SP2 parallel machine.

Method \ # of processors	10	30	50
AE/MC	5.18	7.54	5.71
AE/MC/DD	6.79	15.73	23.28
AE/MC/MD	6.9	15.85	21.78
AE/MC/PCMPLB	7.48	18.13	25.32
AE/ORB	6.16	14.65	20.95
AE/ORB/DD	6.71	16.66	27.52
AE/ORB/MD	6.74	17.2	24.57
AE/ORB/PCMPLB	7.39	19.57	30.38
JOSTLE-MS	6.42	15.11	22.35
JOSTLE-MS/DD	6.82	17.73	26.22
JOSTLE-MS/MD	6.99	17.53	25.65
JOSTLE-MS/PCMPLB	7.67	19.8	32.31
MLkP	6.41	15.59	22.27
MLkP/DD	6.93	17.16	28.19
MLkP/MD	6.87	17.1	25.85
MLkP/PCMPLB	7.65	20.11	31.59
PARTY	5.8	12.27	17.68
PARTY/DD	6.9	17.52	26.21
PARTY/MD	6.88	16.5	25.13
PARTY/PCMPLB	7.33	19.27	30.04

Table 4: The maximum speedups under the mapping/load-balancing methods for the test sample on an SP2 parallel machine.

Method \ # of processors	10	30	50
AE/MC	6.66	17.47	28.92
AE/MC/DD	7.11	18.35	31.96
AE/MC/MD	7.37	19.48	31.67
AE/MC/PCMPLB	7.8	21.19	34.53
AE/ORB	6.49	16.43	24.98
AE/ORB/DD	6.81	17.45	30.32
AE/ORB/MD	6.98	19.05	29.35
AE/ORB/PCMPLB	7.45	20.11	32.41
JOSTLE-MS	6.61	16.47	27.25
JOSTLE-MS/DD	6.91	18.72	29.01
JOSTLE-MS/MD	7.21	19.53	31.17
JOSTLE-MS/PCMPLB	7.77	20.86	34.1
MLkP	6.64	17.17	26.18
MLkP/DD	7.02	17.91	30.72
MLkP/MD	7.1	18.85	30.83
MLkP/PCMPLB	7.75	20.64	33.56
PARTY	6.57	16.66	28.19
PARTY/DD	7.06	18.77	29.43
PARTY/MD	7.19	18.65	31.34
PARTY/PCMPLB	7.52	20.4	32.5

Performance Forecasting: Towards a Methodology for Characterizing Large Computational Applications*

Brian Armstrong   Rudolf Eigenmann
School of Electrical and Computer Engineering
Purdue University

Abstract

We present a methodology that can identify and formulate performance characteristics of a computational application and uncover program performance trends on very large, future computer architectures and problem sizes. Based on this methodology we present "performance forecast diagrams" that predict the scalability of a large seismology application suite on a terabyte data set. We find that the applications scale well up to a large number of processors, given an interconnection network similar to the one of the SGI/Cray Origin architecture. However we find that if we increase the computation-to-communication speed ratio by a factor of 100, the different applications of the seismic suite start exhibiting architectural "sweet spots", at which the communication overhead starts to dominate computation time.

The presented methodology has proven to be useful in characterizing large computational applications. It is being applied in a project to create a repository of realistic programs and their characteristics.

1. Introduction

The motivation for the work presented in this paper is twofold. One of our long-term goals is to develop facilities that enable computer systems research teams to use large computational applications for evaluating and guiding their work. Such applications need to be characterized in meaningful ways. Methodologies for performing such characterizations are not well developed, and there is a lack of tools that help gather the necessary information from programs and their machine environments. In this paper we will contribute to the development of such methodologies and tools.

A second goal is to develop next-generation computer architectures. We need methods for predicting performance trends of relevant applications on new machine concepts and system configurations. In related work we are using simulator tools to evaluate new architectures [5]. Simulators can perform detailed evaluations of small to mid-size programs. However, while it is already challenging to execute large-scope applications with large data sets on current high-performance machines (e.g, Dataset 6 requires 100 GB of disk space), the simulation of such programs on future architectures and problem sizes is not feasible. This paper develops methods to find performance trends where simulations are beyond reach.

For our project, we studied a large computational application suite used by the petroleum industry in the search for oil and gas. The application, called "Seismic," is also part of SPEChpc96, a benchmark suite of large-scope industrial applications [7]. Relatively little is known about the performance behavior of these codes. Our work will contribute to the characterization of this suite, hence facilitating its use for both our projects and those of related groups. We will make specific use of these results in our project to evaluate very-high-performance computer architectures that may be built within the next 10–20 years [4].

The specific contributions presented in this paper are

- a new method for describing and formulating performance trends of computational applications, parameterized by dataset sizes and variables of the underlying architectures,

- a description of tool technology that can help determine these trends,

- a discussion of the accuracy of these methods and their comparison with measured application timings on current computer systems,

- discussion of several "performance forecast diagrams" that show the behavior of the seismic pro-

*This work was supported in part by U. S. Army contract DABT63-92-C-0033, NSF award ASC-9612133, and an NSF CAREER award. This work is not necessarily representative of the positions or policies of the U. S. Army or the Government.

cessing suite on future architectures under several "hardware assumptions."

Our work differs from related projects in several respects. Our goal is to develop methods and techniques that apply to large-scope computational applications. Many methods that apply to small and mid-range problems are not feasible for large programs and datasets. One example is the limitation of simulation methods, mentioned above. Second, for our performance prediction methods we make use of advanced symbolic program analysis techniques available in optimizing compilers. We attempt to determine program characteristics from the given application, even where other approaches may resort to user queries [3]. Third, our performance prediction is based on the computed volume of computation, communication, and I/O plus factoring in measured effective parameters of sample program runs. This contrasts with related approaches that use kernel benchmarks for determining computation and communication speeds [2] or that are based on counting the number of program statements [14]. It also contrasts with approaches that concentrate of the measurement of parallel overhead factors in order to predict extrapolated performance [6]. Fourth, an important goal of our prediction methodology is to capture performance trends for future computer architectures. This is different from and complementary to approaches that model performance with the goal of improving application speeds [1], capturing communication behavior [15], benchmarking current machines [8], and creating performance measurement tools [9, 12].

2. SPECseis96: A Seismic Processing Application Suite

In this paper we concentrate on the seismic processing suite SPECseis96. This suite is available as part of a benchmarking effort by the SPEC/High-Performance Group [7] for both machine benchmarking and scientific study. It is a code used in the petroleum industry for the prospecting of oil and gas, consisting of four applications, referred to as four "phases," which perform the seismic processes: *data generation, stacking of data, time migration*, and *depth migration*. Each of the four phases have distinct computation, communication, and disk IO characteristics. The entire suite contains 20,000 lines of Fortran and C and includes intensive communication as well as intensive disk IO.

Several datasets are available, ranging from a 17 MB dataset to sizes that are larger than current machines can handle (4 TB.) The data space consists of seismic samples in traces along a number of so-called lines [10]. Temporary disk space is required for the file of traces, which are records of signal amplitudes at specific 3D coordinates. The data size depends on the number of samples in a trace, the number of traces in a line, and the number of lines. The traces are collected into groups according to a traces-per-group parameter allowing the data to be passed between seismic processes as a two-dimensional array of traces.

The phases are designed to execute in sequence, though the third and fourth phases can be executed simultaneously. Within each phase, a main-loop performs a series of functions on each trace. Phases 2, 3, and 4 require data to be processed and passed across the processors throughout the phase. Phase 1 requires communication only to decompose at the start of the phase and join the data at the phase's completion. Each processor writes a disjoint segment of the data file allowing for writing to occur simultaneously among processors without blocking.

Communication is implemented using a message-passing layer. Sends and receives are blocking, hence the total time a processor spends communicating can be separated from the time it spends computing. Thus, both communication and disk IO can be captured using time-stamps at the beginning and end of the read and write functions. All time spent outside of the disk IO and communication routines is considered time spent in computation.

3. Methodology

We have defined analytical models for the components of the execution time, which relate the loads placed on the machine's resources with the code structures that create these loads. We simplify the loads placed on a machine's resources into three categories: computation, communication, and disk IO. Our breakdown of the execution time makes the simplifying assumption that the number and size of processor-to-processor messages and disk reads and writes contribute the majority of overheads. All other effects are not separated from the above three in our analysis. Specifically, our analysis only implicitly models the behavior of the cache. While the presented measurements will show good accuracy of our predictions, extending the models is an ongoing effort, which will increase the range of applicable programs.

3.1. Modeling Computation

The computation time is modeled for each loop in a program based on the execution time of the loop body and the number of loop iterations. The iteration number of a loop is expressed in terms of the application's input parameters and the number of processors. This allows us to scale the number of iterations a loop executes with respect to meaningful dataset and architecture parameters. The forecasted execution time of a loop i ($FORE\_Time_{loop-i}$) is the number of times the loop is expected to execute ($FORE\_Calls_{loop-i}$) multiplied by an expression describing the average number of iterations the loop executes per call (named $FORE\_Iter_{loop-i}$) combined with the average *measured* time to execute a single iteration, (referred to as a base measurement, $BASE_{loop-i}$.) We obtain measured times by surrounding the loop with time stamps and summing the loop times exclusive of any time spent in inner-loops, for a specific program run. This sum ($MEAS\_Time_{loop-i}$,) is divided by the recorded number of iterations executed over the entire phase ($MEAS\_Iter_{loop-i}$,) to give a measured, average time per iteration of the loop. For *Seismic*, we used times from a run of Dataset 3a on four processors of the SGI/Cray Origin2000[1] as a base measurement.

$$BASE_{loop-i} = \frac{MEAS\_Time_{loop-i}}{MEAS\_Iter_{loop-i}}$$

$$FORE\_Time_{loop-i} = FORE\_Calls_{loop-i}$$

$$\times FORE\_Iter_{loop-i} \times BASE_{loop-i}$$

3.2. Modeling External Resources

Loads on resources other than the CPU that are accessed using explicit external commands, (such as communication sends/receives and disk reads/writes,) are described by (1) their position within the loop structure, (2) the size of the data that the commands operate on, and (3) architectural parameters, such as the number of processors. Commands to external resources are located within the loop structure of the application, yielding the expression that describes the number of times these commands occur during program execution. We only consider explicit communication and disk IO commands.

External commands also have parameters that describe the size of the data they operate on, (the size of the message or of the read/written data.) These parameters are expressed in terms of the application and the program's input parameters, just like the loop range expressions. The time taken to access an external resource over the course of the program is defined using the function for the number of commands which access this resource and the size of the data accessed by each command.

The performance of the interconnect and the disk are greatly affected by their runtime environment. Since we are approaching performance from a static perspective, we do not simulate or measure dynamic events, which make up such performance issues as communication contention. Yet, we can grasp the volume

of explicit disk accesses and communications. Our models combine characteristics of the code with the structure of the machine.

To account for the overhead of a message-passing layer or a file access, we use measured data as a basis. We determine the latencies used in our communication and disk IO performance models for each application phase separately. This gives us an effective communication latency, or a measure of the overhead in executing a communication call within a certain application (a phase of *Seismic*.)

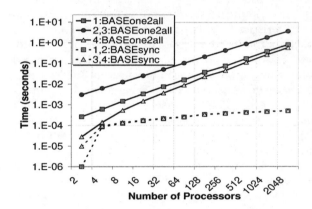

Figure 1. The base times for one-to-all broadcasts and barrier synchronizations are shown in this graph for each phase. The phase is given to the left side in the legend. These times are recorded in a lookup table for each phase. Then, a communication latency is calculated by the type of communication (all-to-all, synchronization, or master-slave gather,) and the number of processors.

Modeling Communication We include three latencies in our model, based on the SGI/Cray Origin hypercube-like interconnect:

$COMM_{su}$: a startup latency for a single communication command, obtained by calculating the average latency per message from measured data; a measure of the overhead for a communication call not including the size of the system.

$COMM_{hub}$: a Hub latency for a processor-to-processor connection, obtained by fitting forecasted to measured data.

$COMM_{router}$: a router latency for a hub-to-hub connection, also obtained by fitting forecasted to measured data.

Given a network topology, we sum the number of Routers ($One2All - Routers_p$) and Hubs ($One2All -$

---

[1]We used modi3, at the time, a 32-processor node of an SGI/Cray Origin2000 dedicated to single-user jobs, courtesy of NCSA at the University of Illinois.

Example: A forecast formula for the execution time of a loop is given below. *loop-273* in subroutine `vfill` steps through a vector, with a given stride, setting elements of the vector to a given constant. This loop is called to initialize the working array for accumulating a local image sum in order to propagate the wave field one depth step—part of the depth migration of the fourth phase of Seismic. The following values give the measured time and recorded number of iterations that *loop-273* executes during Phase 4 as well as the expressions used to forecast the kb of calls and iterations of this loop.

$MEAS\_Time_{loop-273}$	4.643	milliseconds
$MEAS\_Iter_{loop-273}$	486,400	iterations
$FORE\_Calls_{loop-273}$	$1 + \lfloor \frac{ZMAX}{10} \rfloor$	calls
$FORE\_Iter_{loop-273}$	$NX \times NLINE$	iterations-per-call

These values and expressions are used to formulate our model of *loop-273*'s execution time.

$BASE_{loop-273} = \frac{0.004643 \ seconds}{486,400 \ iterations} = 9.55 \ nanoseconds$

$FORE\_Time_{loop-273} = \left(1 + \lfloor \frac{ZMAX}{10} \rfloor\right) \times (NX \times NLINE) \times (9.55 \ nanoseconds)$

This expression describing the execution time of *loop-273* can then be used to forecast how long the loop will execute for Dataset 8 by plugging in the values for the application-specific parameters accordingly: $ZMAX \rightarrow 10,000$, $NX \rightarrow 2,168$, $NLINES \rightarrow 1,024$. The forecasted time for *loop-273* with Dataset 8, $FORE\_Time_{loop-273}$, is 21 seconds.

$Hubs_p$) that all the messages originating from a communication command executed on one processor must pass through. We describe how the latency of a communication command varies with the number of processors using these sums. Only two types of communication are done within *Seismic*: barrier synchronizations and all-to-all broadcasts.

The number of Hubs and Routers traversed by all messages sent in a one-to-all broadcast is determined for every number of processors (of a power of two) and placed in a lookup table. The base time for a one-to-all broadcast, ($BASE_{one2all-P}$,) is calculated from the number of Hub, Router, and startup latencies required to perform a one-to-all broadcast. $FORE\_Time_{all2all-i}$, the time for an all-to-all broadcast, is found by multiplying the base time by a factor of $2 \times (P-1)$, because the all-to-all communication command consists of a blocking send and receive with every other processor. Messages longer than a threshold are divided into multiple messages using the message size, $FORE\_Size_{all2all-i}$, and the maximum allowable message size, $COMM_{max-size}$, which we set to the 4 KB threshold of our MPI implementation. The time for one all-to-all broadcast is multiplied by the number of times this specific, explicit command is called within the seismic phase, labeled $FORE\_Calls_{all2all-i}$.

$FORE\_Time_{all2all-i} = FORE\_Calls_{all2all-i}$

$$\times 2 \times (P-1) \times \left(\begin{array}{c} BASE_{one2all-P} \\ + \ \lceil \frac{FORE\_Size_{all2all-i}}{COMM_{max-size}} \rceil \end{array} \right)$$

Barrier synchronizations take advantage of the hypercube structure to synchronize all processors in a tree

fashion. Their latencies are calculated for every number of processors (of a power of two) by counting the number of Routers and Hubs traversed by the messages. The resulting model for the time of a synchronization command, ($FORE\_Time_{sync-i}$,) includes the number of times the specific synchronization command is executed, ($FORE\_Calls_{sync-i}$,) and the base time, ($BASE_{sync-P}$.)

$FORE\_Time_{sync-i} =$

$$FORE\_Calls_{sync-i} \times BASE_{sync-P}$$

The base measurements for the all-to-all and synchronization commands for all four phases are graphed in Figure 1, showing how the measured averages affect the effective latencies.

Modeling Disk IO Our disk model considers explicit IO commands within the code. They are modeled as a startup latency, which depends on the logarithm of the number of processors, and a transmission latency per byte of the disk access. The startup and transmission latencies are calculated separately for each application phase and also separately for reads and writes from measured data. Separating latencies for reads from latencies for writes is significant in Phase 2, which reads from the disk file in large strides (using "transposed" reads where one sample is read from each trace.) The startup latency per read is the average time per read ($READ_{Startup}$) times the logarithm of the number of processors. The transmission latency per read ($READ_{Transmit}$) is the average time per byte of the read accesses. Latencies for writes are calculated in the same manner.

$$FORE\_Time_{read-i} = FORE\_Calls_{read-i}$$

$$\times \left(\begin{array}{c} READ_{Startup} \times (\log P + 1) \\ + \dfrac{FORE\_Size_{read-i}}{READ_{Transmit}} \end{array} \right)$$

Our communication and disk IO performance models represent simple approximations, corresponding to our goal of capturing important aspects of an application's performance behavior. Though our model cannot incorporate detailed runtime effects, it gives trends for the scalability of the features we can calculate statically and estimate in terms of application and machine-relevant parameters. The analytical models are used to determine how the loads produced by the application and the underlying machine configuration scale with the size of the dataset, structure of the data, and machine parameters.

4. Precision of Forecasts

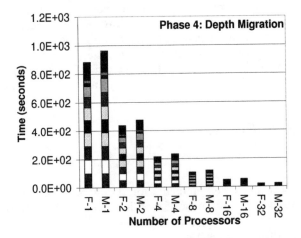

Figure 2. Loop-by-Loop Comparison of Forecasted to Measured Computation Times, dependent on Machine Size. These values are for Phase 4 of *Seismic* using Dataset 1, run on one 32 processor node of an SGI/Cray Origin 2000. The forecasts are compared to the measured times for 1,2,4,8,16, and 32 processors. The bars labeled "F-" correspond to the forecasts; the bars labeled "M-" are measured values. The top ten loops are given as different patterns and the black segment refers to the remaining loops. Discrepancies between our forecasts and what we measure can be localized within loop boundaries.

To verify the method we used in characterizing the performance of a large application suite we compared the scalability forecasted by our execution time model with actual measurements. Our model's scalability was tested as processors were added, keeping the data space

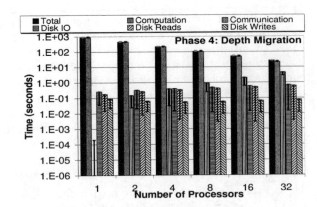

Figure 3. Comparison of Forecasted to Measured Times for the Components of Execution Time, dependent on Machine Size. These values are also for Dataset 1, run on a 32-processor node of an SGI/Cray Origin2000. Unlike the previous figure, here we include the total execution time broken down by component: computation, communication, disk reads, and disk writes. The graph shows results for the fourth seismic phase as the number of processors is increased from 1 to 32. The bars display the forecasted times of: Total Time, Computation Time, Disk IO Time, Disk Read Time, and Disk Write Time. The difference between the forecasted and measured times for each component are shown as error bars at the top of each bar. From the graphs we see that computation time is the most accurately modeled component.

constant. Some results of these tests are displayed in Figure 2 and Figure 3.

Since we predict the performance of each loop in the program individually, we can pinpoint the loops whose forecasts do not scale the same as our measurements. Figure 2 shows that for the majority of loops measured and predicted times agree well, while for a few loops there are discrepancies. Further refining of the performance expressions for the problematic loops can be done to make the forecasts more accurate. Cache effects and operating system latencies are indirectly included in the execution times for an iteration of each loop, which comes from measured data (Dataset 3a run on 4 processors.) While our tests using the first three datasets and a 32-processor machine show the predictions to be reasonably precise, improving the models is an ongoing project. Of particular interest is the more accurate formulation of cache effects and network contention.

The less predictable aspects of the *Seismic*'s performance are the times for communication and disk IO. Figure 3 shows a breakdown of Phase 4's execution time into time spent in computations, communications, and disk accesses. Separating computation time from time spent servicing external devices (communication

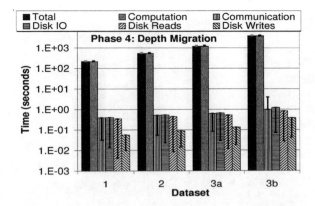

Figure 4. Comparison of Forecasted to Measured Times for the Components of Execution Time, dependent on Data Size. The dataset is varied with increasing dataset size; Dataset 1 requires 17 MB to store all the traces and Dataset 3b uses 137 MB to do so. In each case, four processors of a 32-processor SGI/Cray Origin2000 node are used. The graph shows results for the fourth seismic phase. The total execution time is broken down into four components: computation, communication, disk read, and disk write time. The difference between the forecasted and measured times for each component are shown as error bars at the top of each bar. Dataset 3a and Dataset 3b are very similar except for a few parameters: Dataset 3b has twice as many samples per trace and half as many groups per line. Also, Dataset 3b's x-y-z values for velocity sampling are larger than those of Dataset 3a's and its number of depth steps is increased by one half (this parameter only affects this seismic phase.)

and disk IO) reveals that the computation time can be accurately predicted by our simple model. The differences between the forecasted and measured times, seen in Figure 2, are consistent as the number of processors is increased—i.e., the error in the forecasts for loop execution times stays within tight bounds as the number of processors is increased.

We also varied the dataset size in Figure 4. The data space is increased from 17 MB to 137 MB. The data space is scaled consistently from Dataset 1 to Dataset 3a. Dataset 3b differs from Dataset 3a by keeping the overall amount of space required to store all traces relatively constant, increasing one dimension (the number of samples in a single receiver's trace) and decreasing another (the number of groups of traces in a line.) We include both Dataset 3a and Dataset 3b to investigate how well our forecasting model grasps changes to individual application parameters as opposed to increasing the data space in a consistent manner. The computation time does not vary much (relative to the times for Dataset 3a) for the first three phases despite this modification. However, Phase 4's time increases be-

cause Phase 4's computations are dependent upon the number of depth steps, which is 50% larger than with Dataset 3a.

5. Performance Forecast for *Seismic*

Given the methodology and tools introduced in the previous sections we now predict the performance of *Seismic* when using a very large dataset of several terabytes (Dataset 8.) The totals per phase are shown in Figure 5. The forecasts reveal that the computation time remains the major component of the execution time with large datasets, even when using up to 2,048 processors, meaning that *Seismic* is expected to perform very well under aggressive parallelization. Extrapolating for Dataset 8 distinguishes the major characteristics of the seismic processing phases.

- Phase 1 is highly parallel and performs a significant amount of disk writing.

- Phase 2 performs hours of communication as well as spends much time in disk IO. The majority of disk IO is spent reading from the disk.

- Phase 3 remains the shortest phase. Its communication depends upon two synchronizations. Its disk IO occurs within a matter of minutes.

- Phase 4 is computationally intensive, taking approximately ten times longer than the computations in Phase 2. The communication of Phase 4 is approximately ten times that of Phase 2, but their communication curves exhibit similar characteristics. The disk IO remains relatively constant, in minutes.

Current trends in processor technology favors CPU speed over communication speed; i.e., processor performance is increasing with new technology quicker than communication speed and the speed of disk accesses. To model these trends we scale up the computation speed by a factor of 100 without changing the communication performance. The forecast of *Seismic* under these hardware assumptions is given in Figure 6. The characteristics we can extract from this study are:

- Phase 1 and 4 benefit from higher processing power.

- The performance of Phases 1 and 2 are dependent upon the disk access latencies. However, Phase 1 requires twice as much computation and half the disk IO as that of Phase 2.

- Also, Phase 2's disk IO consists of reads while Phase 1's consists of writes.

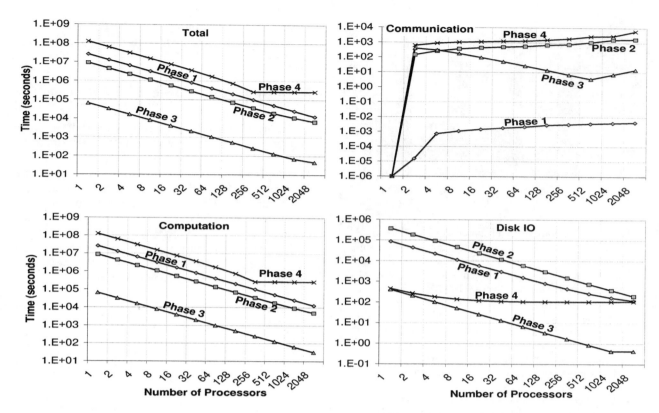

Figure 5. Forecasted Times for the Components of Execution Time, Extrapolating Machine Size. The forecasts are for Dataset 8 (which requires 4 terabytes to store all the traces.) The machine being forecasted is an SGI/Cray Origin2000 which allows configurations of up to 2,048 processors. Each graph displays the trend of each seismic phase for a component of the execution time as the number of processors is increased. These graphs show how intensive the computation, communication, and disk IO of the phases are in relation to each other. The communication of phases 2 and 4 occurs throughout the execution of these phases, which is why their communication patterns are similar. In contrast, phases 1 and 3 do a fixed number of communications for a given dataset, regardless of the number of processors. Using *transposed* reads (where a single trace is read from each group instead of every trace in a group being read sequentially) in Phase 2 makes its disk IO time the highest of all the phases.

- Phases 2 and 4 will eventually become communication dominated as more processors are added.

- Disk IO can be parallelized in all phases except in Phase 4, where it decreases to a limit around 32 processors.

The "sweet spots" in this figure are the minimum total execution times for each phase. Each phase has a sweet-spot after which its communication starts dominating the execution time. These points vary among the phases since the relative importance (in terms of time) of the execution time components differs across the phases.

6. Conclusions

We have developed a methodology for characterizing large computational applications in terms of their performance trends for large datasets and on large system configurations. We will use this methodology for analyzing and documenting a series of applications, which will be made available to other research groups. "Performance forecasting" is one of several methodologies for describing application programs such that research teams developing computer systems technology may find it easier to work with large, realistic applications and to do performance evaluation based on these programs. A repository that makes this information publicly available is being built [11].

Tools to support the described methodology in an automatic manner are partially available. Currently, several manual steps must be performed for creating performance diagrams as shown in this paper. In part, these manual steps compensate for current shortcomings of available tools, (such as limited compiler analysis techniques,) as well as combine the results of the

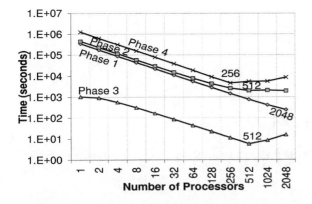

Figure 6. Forecasted Execution Time for Dataset 8 on a machine with Faster CPU Performance. The CPU performance is improved by 100 times, (roughly corresponding to 20-gigahertz CPU's,) and the totals for all four seismic processing phases are given in a single graph. The interprocessor network is the same as the hypercube network used by the SGI/Cray Origin2000 design. This models trends that CPU performance increases faster than communication performance.

various tools. Building an integrated environment is a long-term goal.

Using the described methodology we have identified performance trends of a large-scope seismic processing application suite. We have done this analysis using datasets that are larger than could be executed on any existing computer system. We have found that the applications scale well up to about 2000 processors, after which the current data partitioning scheme limits the available parallelism. When assuming a computation-to-communication speed ratio of 100 times the one of a SGI/Cray Origin2000 machine we have seen that the application begins to exhibit "sweet spots". These distinct, best-architecture points for the various seismic processing phases point out the key bottlenecks in each phase for architectures in which processing power dominates communication speed. Increasing the number of processors beyond these points will negatively impact the overall performance due to communication and IO overheads.

Extending the described models to a larger application class is an ongoing effort. *Seismic* is a regular application, for which it is relatively easy to determine and formulate the volumes of computation, communication and I/O. Furthermore, we have included cache behavior only implicitly, by factoring it into the overall computation speed. There is good agreement for our applications between predicted performance and the measurements up to 32 processors on the SGI/Cray Origin2000. Further studies with other applications are needed to demonstrate the applicable scope of the

described methods and identify future extensions.

References

[1] G. Abandah and E. S. Davidson. Configuration independent analysis for characterizing shared-memory applications. In *12th Int'l. Parallel Processing Symp.*, Mar. 1998.

[2] G. A. Abandah and E. S. Davidson. Modeling the communication performance of the IBM SP2. 10th Int'l Parallel Processing Symp. (IPPS'96), Apr. 1996.

[3] V. Balasundaram, G. Fox, and et al. A static performance estimator to guide data partitioning decisions. 3rd ACM SIGPLAN Symp. on Principles and Practice of Parallel Programming, pages 213–221, Apr. 1991.

[4] Z. Ben-Miled, R. Eigenmann, and et al. Hierarchical processors-and-memory architecture for high performance computing. In *Proc. of Frontiers'96 Conf.*, pages 355–362, Oct. 96.

[5] Z. Ben-Miled, J. A. B. Fortes, R. Eigenmann, and et al. A simulation-based cost-efficiency study of hierarchical heterogeneous machines for compiler and hand parallelized applications. *9th Int. Conf. on Par. and Dist. Computing and Systems*, pages 168–175, Oct. 1997.

[6] M. E. Crovella and T. J. LeBlanc. Parallel performance prediction using lost cycles analysis. In IEEE, editor, *Proc., Supercomputing '94: Washington, DC, November 14–18, 1994*, Supercomputing, pages 600–609. IEEE Computer Society Press, 1994.

[7] R. Eigenmann and S. Hassanzadeh. Benchmarking with real industrial applications: The SPEC High-Performance Group. *IEEE Computational Science & Engineering*, 3(1):18–23, Spring 1996.

[8] J. Gustafson and Q. Snell. HINT: A new way to measure computer performance. In *Proc. of the Twenty-eight Annual Hawaii Int'l Conf. on System Sciences*, volume II, pages 392–401, 95.

[9] B. P. Miller, M. D. Callaghan, and et al. The Paradyn parallel performance measurement tools. *IEEE Computer*, 28(11), Nov. 1995.

[10] C. C. Mosher and S. Hassanzadeh. ARCO seismic processing performance evaluation suite, User's Guide. ARCO, Plano, TX, 1993.

[11] I. Park and R. Eigenmann. URSA MAJOR: Exploring Web technology for design and evaluation of high-performance systems. In *Int'l Conf. on High-Performance Computing and Networking, HPCN Europe'98*, pages 535–544, Apr. 98.

[12] D. A. Reed. Experimental performance analysis of parallel systems: Techniques and open problems. In *7th Int' Conf on Modelling Techniques and Tools for Computer Performance Evaluation*, pages 25–51, 1994.

[13] R. H. Saavedra and A. J. Smith. Performance characterization of optimizing compilers. *IEEE Trans. on Software Engineering*, 21(7):615–628, July 1995.

[14] R. H. Saavedra and A. J. Smith. Analysis of benchmark characteristics and benchmark performance prediction. *ACM Trans. on Comp. Sys.*, 14(4), Nov. 1996.

[15] M. R. Steed and M. J. Clement. Performance prediction of PVM programs. 10th Int'l Parallel Processing Symp., Honolulu, HI, Apr. 1996, pages 803–807.

Session 7C
Wormhole Networks

Chair: Craig Stunkel
IBM T.J. Watson Research

A Real-Time Communication Method for Wormhole Switching Networks [*]

Byungjae Kim
Access Network Research Laboratory
Korea Telecom
62-1, Whaam-dong, Yusung-gu
Taejeon, Korea
E-mail: bjkim@access.kotel.co.kr

Jong Kim, Sungje Hong, and Sunggu Lee[†]
Dept. of Computer Science and Engineering
[†]Dept. of Electronic and Electrical Engineering
Pohang University of Science and Technology
San 31 Hyoja Dong, Pohang 790-784, KOREA
E-mail: jkim@postech.ac.kr

Abstract

In this paper, we propose a real-time communication scheme that can be used in general point-to-point real-time multicomputer systems with wormhole switching. Real-time communication should satisfy the two requirements of predictability and priority handling. Since traditional wormhole switching does not support priority handling, which is essential in real-time computing, flit-level preemption is adopted in our wormhole switching. Also, we develop an algorithm to determine the message transmission delay upper bound to predict worst-case message delay. Simulation results show that the delay upper bounds calculated using the proposed algorithm are very close to actual average message transmission delays for messages with high priorities.

1. Introduction

Real-time applications have two very stringent requirements, known as correct result and timing. Real-time tasks should honor the timing requirements of real-time applications to make the result effective. To determine whether real-time tasks satisfy their timing requirements, it is necessary to know the execution time of each real-time task. The execution time analysis of real-time tasks have been studied for a long time. One important factor which makes the analysis difficult is communication. Since communication is in general not bounded in time, it is hard to predict maximum message transmission delays and to guarantee that messages are delivered within their message transmission delay limit (or deadline) if it is given. Real-time communication enables us to either predict the maximum message transmission delay for a given message or to guarantee the

delivery of messages within their delivery timing requirements.

In multiprocessor systems, several cooperating tasks running on different processing nodes have to communicate with each other, and if these tasks have timing constraints such as deadlines, unpredictable delay of message transmission can adversely affect the execution of the tasks dependent on the messages, possibly resulting in missed deadlines. Thus real-time multiprocessor systems must support real-time communication, which means the timely delivery of inter-task messages. A popular communication switching method used in multiprocessor systems is wormhole switching. In wormhole switching, it is very hard to guarantee the timely delivery of messages, since wormhole switching is based on a hold-and-wait technique. Therefore, real-time communication in wormhole networks has received growing attention in recent years.

Real-time communication in multi-hop networks has been studied widely. Ferrari and Verma proposed the *real-time channel* concept, which is an enhancement of a traditional packet-switched network to provide delay bound guarantees to real-time message traffic [3, 4]. A real-time channel is a unidirectional virtual connection that traverses one or more network links. The necessary network bandwidth and other resources are reserved using real-time channel establishment procedure [1]. When real-time channels are to be established, the schedulability problem (given a set of real-time channels, can all packets in these channels be delivered before their requested delay bound[4]?) is essential. Kandlur *et al.* established the sufficient conditions for the schedulability problem [1] and Zheng and Shin derived the necessary and sufficient conditions for the same problem [4]. Research results on a fault tolerant version of the real-time channel [2] and a router architecture designed to support real-time channel have been reported recently [7].

Real-time communication in wormhole switching networks was addressed by Li [8], Mutka [9], and Song [10] recently. In Li's approach, there are as many virtual chan-

---

[*]This research was supported in part by KOSEF under Grant 96-0101-09-01-3.

nels as priority levels and each virtual channel is assigned a unique priority level. A packet can request virtual channels which are numbered lower than or equal to its priority. By doing this, the probability that a higher priority packet can obtain a virtual channel is higher than that of lower priority packets [8]. Song proposed a new flow control method for real-time communications in wormhole networks. With a special router architecture, flit-level preemption of physical channels among prioritized packets can be implemented using a smaller number of virtual channels [10]. While Song's and Li's methods are concerned only with priority handling in wormhole switching networks, Mutka has addressed how to guarantee deadlines of packets in wormhole networks. By using previous research results on rate monotonic scheduling technology, he studied how to check the schedulability of a given set of real-time periodic traffic flows [9]. However, because of the blocking characteristic of wormhole networks, mere application of the rate monotonic algorithm to real-time message traffic is not appropriate.

In this paper, we propose a communication structure and algorithm that provides message transmission delay upper bounds (U) in wormhole switching networks. For a given set of real-time communication requests, if all of their U values are less than or equal to the corresponding deadlines, the requests can be met. Traditional wormhole switching networks do not have a priority handling method, which is essential in order to make the communication have a bounded delay. Hence, we assume a flit-level preemptive wormhole switching method. Additionally, we show the relationship between the number of real-time communication requests and the number of possible priority levels using simulation experiments.

The remainder of this paper is organized as follows. In Section 2, we define the problem and describe the system model considered in this paper. Section 3 treats priority handling in wormhole switching networks. Section 4 gives the proposed algorithm and an example. Section 5 provides simulation results. Finally, in Section 6, we summarize and conclude this paper.

2. System model and problem definition

A general real-time multiprocessor system considered in this paper is shown in Figure 1. As shown in Figure 1, the system consists of a special processor, called the host processor, and several nodes for job execution. The host processor is in charge of overall system management such as job scheduling, node allocation, and schedulability testing of real-time jobs. Also, the host downloads jobs to allocated nodes. Each node in Figure 1 contains its own processor and local memory. Each real-time job is downloaded into a group of allocated nodes and these nodes communicate with

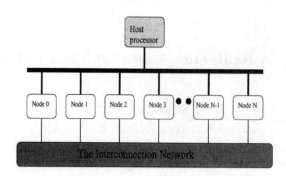

Figure 1. A general multiprocessor system

each other by sending messages through an interconnection network. The interconnection network connects the nodes in a topology, such as a hypercube or a mesh.

We assume most message traffic which require timely delivery are periodic as in [9]. A real-time application consists of several cooperating jobs, and each job is executed on a different processing node. Real-time message traffic flows are required between such jobs. We assume that the minimum communication frequency between jobs is known. The host processor calculates the upper bound of message transmission delay for all messages and compares it with the required delay limit.

Prior to the formal description of the problem discussed in this paper, we present a few definitions.

- *Network latency* [5] : The time taken to deliver a message when no other traffic is present.

- *Message stream* (M_i) : The continuous message traffic between a source and destination node pair. Each message stream is characterized by minimum message inter-generation time (T_i), maximum message length (C_i), deadline (D_i), and priority (P_i).

- L_i : The maximum *network latency* of messages belonging to M_i

- U_i : The transmission delay upper bound of messages belonging to M_i

One message stream denotes a message traffic flow between a source and destination node pair. Each *message stream* M_i has a priority value P_i representing the importance of the message stream. Every message that belongs to the *message stream* M_i inherits the corresponding P_i value. D_i is the requested delay limit and U_i is the calculated delay upper bound. In other words, D_i is the deadline within which the message should be delivered, and U_i is the guaranteed delivery delay.

The following is the formal definition of the problem.
Instance : A multiprocessor system such as shown in Figure 1 with a wormhole switching interconnection network

and a set of message streams $M = \{M_1, M_2, M_3, ..., M_n\}$. A message stream M_i is characterized by a seven-tuple $(S_{id}, R_{id}, P_i, T_i, C_i, D_i, L_i)$, where S_{id} and R_{id} are the source node and the destination node, respectively. The routing path of each message stream is statically determined by using a deterministic routing algorithm such as X-Y routing for meshes.

Problem : Determine whether all message streams in M satisfy the condition that U_i for a given M_i is less than or equal to its corresponding D_i ($U_i \leq D_i$ for all M_i).

To be able to solve the above problem, we should have an algorithm that finds the delay upper bound of all message streams when all real-time message streams are defined for a given job. We will call the above problem *message stream feasibility testing*. The calculation of U_i is the kernel of this problem. The mapping of real-time jobs to processing nodes should be preceded for this problem to be meaningful. The jobs which communicate each other frequently could be mapped to relatively nearby processing nodes. But job allocation is another problem and we do not consider in this paper.

Predictability and priority handling are two cardinal issues in real-time computing. Determining the delay upper bound U for all M_i's is the predictability issue. Without having a priority handling scheme, no difference in delay upper bound will be shown between higher priority messages and lower priority messages. Higher priority messages should be delivered as fast as possible at the cost of lower priority messages and the delay upper bound of higher priority messages should be closer to the actual message transmission delay than that of lower priority messages.

In a classical wormhole switching network, there is no priority handling method. In the following section, we introduce a priority handling method for wormhole switching networks.

3. Priority handling in wormhole switching networks

Early multi-hop networks used store-and-forward switching. In this approach, the entire packet is stored in a packet buffer when a packet reaches an intermediate node. On the other hand, cut-through switching is a switching technique which does not buffer packets in an intermediate node if the next output channel is available. It just forwards the received data to a selected neighboring node without buffering. Wormhole switching is a special case of cut-through switching. A packet (or message) is divided into a number of *flits*. The header flit governs the route. As the header advances along the specified route, the remaining flits follow in a pipeline fashion. If the header flit encounters a channel that is already being

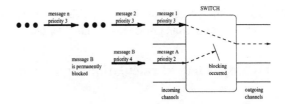

Figure 2. An example of priority inversion

used, it is blocked until the channel becomes available [5]. This blocking is a major difference with other cut-through switching variations, such as circuit switching and virtual cut-through. Because of the blocking and waiting for channels, deadlock situation may occur in wormhole switching. Deadlock can be avoided by some deterministic path selection schemes, such as X-Y routing for meshes. Hence, we assume deadlock situation never occur.

Priority inversion can occur in handling real-time communication messages in wormhole switching. *Priority inversion* [6] is a situation where low-priority messages block higher priority messages. Priority inversion occurs when the physical channel in the switch is arbitrated by priorities of messages and non-preemptable. An example of priority inversion is shown in Figure 2. In Figure 2, message B, which has the highest priority, is permanently blocked.

We assume flit-level preemptive wormhole switching. If higher priority messages can preempt the blocking lower priority messages, the priority inversion problem can be easily resolved. This is an ideal priority handling method. However, flit-level preemption is not easy to implement in classical wormhole switching networks because only the header flit has the routing information. Preemption may cause messages to become lost in the network.

As previously mentioned, Song proposed a real-time traffic flow control method based on flit-level preemption [10]. However, the proposed method requires special router development. Hence, we use a flit-level preemption method implemented by using virtual channels. Several virtual channels can exist in one physical channel. We assume there are as many virtual channels as priority levels. Each virtual channel is assigned a different priority level. The arbitration for the physical channel is based on priorities. A virtual channel V_i associated with priority level i can obtain physical channel bandwidth if all virtual channels associated with priorities higher than i are free. A message with priority i can only request the virtual channel associated with priority value i. This method works identically with Song's scheme from the viewpoint of real-time message arrival [10].

Although more virtual channels guarantee a wider range of priorities, it is difficult to have too many virtual channels due to practical resource constraints. Hence, we simulate a multi-hop network with the assumed flit-level preemption method to find the effect of the number of virtual channels (or the number of different priorities) on the U value.

4. Delay upper bound calculation algorithm

In this section, we first present a delay upper bound calculation algorithm and then give a simple example of the algorithm.

4.1. Overview of the proposed algorithm

Messages in a preemptive and prioritized network are blocked only when higher priority messages use a part of the path to be used by the blocked messages. To determine the maximum delay, known as the delay upper bound, of the blocked messages, information on higher priority messages that may affect the blocked messages is required. So the first step is determining which message streams affect the given message stream. Next, we calculate the delay upper bound by considering the message generation interval, maximum message size, and blocking relationships between message streams. Let us describe how to determine which message streams affect the given message stream. The host processor has all the information about message streams. For each message stream from higher priority to lower priority, the set of all affecting higher priority messages, denoted as the HP set, is constructed. The HP set of the given message stream is constructed by combining the HP sets of higher priority message streams that pass through a part of the path to be used by the given message stream. An example is shown in Figure 3. In Figure 3, the message D which has the highest priority cannot be blocked or preempted by any other message. Thus its HP set is empty. In the case of messages B and C, both messages can be blocked or preempted by the message D and they are mutually influential. So the HP set of the message B consists of messages D and C, and the HP set of the message C consists of messages D and B. All elements in these sets are marked as *direct*. In the case of the message A, it can be blocked or preempted by messages B or C. But the message D can block the message A indirectly through messages B or C. So the HP set of message A consists of messages B and C which are marked as *direct* and the message D which is marked as *indirect*. For each *indirect* element, the list of intermediate message streams are maintained. Messages B and C are intermediate message streams of message D. Using dependencies between message streams we can draw a blocking dependency graph for each message stream. We define the following terms.

- *Direct blocking* : the case that paths of two message streams are overlapping

- *Indirect blocking* : the case that paths of two message streams do not overlap but there is(are) intervening message stream(s) between given two message streams

- *Blocking chain* : the list of intervening message streams when an *indirect* blocking occurs

More than one blocking chain can be defined for an *indirect* blocking. For example, the *indirect* blocking between message A and message D in Figure 3 defines two blocking chains. Message D can indirectly block message A through message B *or* message C. So the two blocking chains are (M_B) and (M_C). Using HP sets and derived blocking dependency graphs, we can calculate how frequently *direct* or *indirect* blockings occur. Then we can determine the worst case transmission delay (or delay upper bound).

Every message has *network latency*. Network latency is defined as the time to complete transmission when no other traffic is present. If there is only one message, the delay upper bound of that messages equals the network latency. But we must consider the case where there are more than one message that can be mutually influential. The basic idea in calculating the delay upper bound for a message stream is shown in Figure 4.

In Figure 4, there are four message streams. Message streams are listed in decreasing order of their priorities, i.e., (M_1, M_2, M_3, M_4). The shaded area shows the time slot occupied by a message and dotted area shows the time slot preempted by higher priority messages. For messages M_1, M_2, and M_3, message generation interval T and message length C are given. Let us assume that the HP set of M_4 is (M_1, M_2, M_3) and all elements are marked as *direct*. As time advances, there are free time slots that are not used by message streams in the HP set of M_4. These time slots can be used by M_4. The delay upper bound of M_4 is the time when the summation of all these free time slots equals the network latency. For example, if the network latency of M_4 is 6, then time 26 is the delay upper bound of M_4. If M_1 and M_2 in HP set of M_4 are marked as *indirect* and their intermediate message streams are M_2 and M_3 respectively, then their blocking dependency graph is like Figure 5. Figure 6 presents a timing diagram for delay upper bound calculation. As shown in Figure 6, the second and the third instance of M_1 in Figure 4 are removed since M_2, which is the intermediate message stream of M_1, does not exist in that time period. Thus the delay upper bound of M_4 is reduced to time 22.

4.2. Data structure

The proposed algorithm constructs the set HP_i for each message stream M_i. It also creates $GList[]$, which is a set

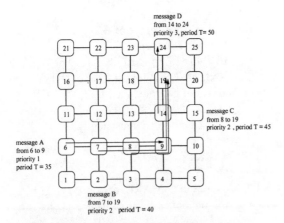

Figure 3. HP **set construction example**

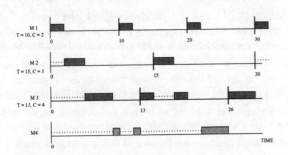

Figure 4. U **calculation for an** *direct* **blocking**

Figure 5. The blocking dependency graph for an *indirect* **blocking**

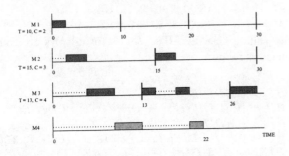

Figure 6. U **calculation for an** *indirect* **blocking**

of message streams that have a same priority. HP_i is a set of the structure variable that has following fields.

- M_{id} field : stores message stream id

- $Mode$ field : can have one of the values (DIRECT, INDIRECT)

- IN field : stores the set of message stream id

The M_{id} field stores the message stream id which affects the given message stream, the $Mode$ field indicates whether M_{id} affects it directly or indirectly, and the IN field keeps the list of intermediate message stream(s) when the $Mode$ field is set to INDIRECT.

After generating HP sets, the proposed algorithm creates the blocking dependency graph(BDG) in the form of adjacency matrix and the timing diagram in the form of two-dimensional array structure for each message stream. The column index of timing diagram corresponds to time and the row index corresponds to message streams. Cells of timing diagram can have one of the values (FREE, BUSY, WAITING, ALLOCATED). FREE means that time slot is usable. BUSY indicates that a higher priority message stream is using that time slot, so this time slot is not usable. WAITING means preempted state and ALLOCATED means that time slot is allocated to a message stream specified by the row index.

4.3. Algorithm

The input to the algorithm is the instance of *message stream feasibility testing* and the output is either *success* or *fail*, which indicates whether the given real-time communication requests can be satisfied or not. The proposed algorithm is as follows.

Determine-Feasibility(M)

```
1   plevel = the number of priority level;
2   N = the number of message streams;
3   FOR i = 0 TO N − 1
4       GList[Pi] ⇐ Mi;  /* add a element to a set */
5   FOR i = plevel − 1 DOWNTO 0
6       FOR each element Mj in GList[i]
7           Generate_HP(i, j);
8       FOR each element Mj in GList[i]
9           Uj = Cal_U(j);
10  IF Ui < 0 for any i
11      RETURN fail;
12  ELSE RETURN success;
```

Global variables and $GList[]$ are initialized from line 1 to line 4. Then HP sets are constructed. Because the host processor has all traffic information, generating HP set for each message stream is not difficult. So, we omit the detail of Generate_HP() function code. Delay upper bound for each message stream is calculated by Cal_U() function and the determination of the feasibility result follows.

Cal_U(j)

1   HP_j -= an element that has M_j as an M_{id} field;
2    $required = L_j$; $dtime = D_j$; $gtime = 0$;
3   ne = the number of elements in HP_j;
4    $T\_diagram$ = allocate $[0..ne][1..dtime]$;
5   Generate_Init_Diagram($T\_diagram,j,dtime$);
6   IF there is an INDIRECT element in HP_j
7   Generate BDG G of HP_j;
8   Modify_Diagram($T\_diagram,j,G,ne$);
9   FOR i = 1 TO $dtime$
10   IF $T\_diagram[ne][i]$ == FREE
11   IF ++$gtime$ == $required$ RETURN i;
12   RETURN -1;

Generate_Init_Diagram($T\_d,j,dtime$)

1    $mi = 0$;
2   Sort HP_j in non-increasing order of priority
3   FOR each K in HP_j
4   FOR i = 0 TO $\lceil dtime/T_{K.M_{id}}\rceil$
5            $alloctime = 0$;
6   FOR l = 0 TO $T_{K.M_{id}}$
7   IF $T\_d[mi][i \times T_{K.M_{id}} + l]$==FREE
8                    $alloctime$++;
9                    $T\_d[mi][i \times T_{K.M_{id}} + l]$=ALLOCATED;
10                   $T\_d[mi + 1..ne][i \times T_{K.M_{id}} + l]$=BUSY;
11   ELSE IF $T\_d[mi][i \times T_{K.M_{id}} + l]$==BUSY
12                   $T\_d[mi][i \times T_{K.M_{id}} + l]$=WAITING;
13   IF $alloctime$ == $C_{K.M_{id}}$ BREAK;
14   mi++;

Modify_Diagram(T_d,j,G,ne)

1    $G = G^T$; /*transpose*/
2    $s = pre$ = the node M_j in G;
3   Allocate $vc[ne]$ and initialize to 0;
4   DO
5   cur=BFS(pre,s,G); /*breadth first search*/

6   ni = the order of M_{cur} in sorted HP_j;
7   IF M_{cur} INDIRECTly affects
8   IF ++$vc[ni]$==(indegree of M_{cur} in G)
9   FOR i = 1 TO $dtime$
10   IF $T\_d[ni][i]$==ALLOCATED or WAITING
11   AND all $T\_d[r][i]$==FREE or BUSY
12   (r is the indexes of intermediate M. of M_{cur})
13                       $T\_d[ni][i]$=FREE
14   Update T_d consistently;
15   MARK M_{cur};
16   ELSE MARK M_{cur}; /*DIRECT*/
17       $pre = cur$;
18   UNTIL all nodes in G MARKed;

The function Generate_Init_Diagram() creates the timing diagram of a given HP set assuming all elements are *direct*. When one or more *indirect* elements exist, after generating blocking dependency graph, the proposed algorithm calls Modify_Diagram(). A time slot used by an *indirect* element can be freed if all of the intermediate message streams do not request that time slot. A released time slot can be reused by other message streams. Free slots at the last row of timing diagram can be used by the given message stream and the time at which the summation of these time slots is equal to the network latency of the message stream is the *delay upper bound* of that message stream.

4.4. An example of the algorithm

We show a simple example of the proposed algorithm in this subsection. We assume that nodes are interconnected in a two-dimensional mesh topology and deadlock is avoided by using X-Y routing. The given set of message streams are as follows. Each message stream is presented in the form $M_i = (S_{id}, R_{id}, P_i, T_i, C_i, D_i, L_i)$
$M = \{M_0, M_1, M_2, M_3, M_4\}$,
where $M_0 = ((7,3),(7,7),5,15,4,15,7)$
    $M_1 = ((1,1),(5,4),4,10,2,10,8)$
    $M_2 = ((2,1),(7,5),3,40,4,40,12)$
    $M_3 = ((4,1),(8,5),2,45,9,45,16)$
    $M_4 = ((6,1),(9,3),1,50,6,50,10)$
After calling Generate_HP(), HP_i's for all M_is are constructed as follows.

$HP_0 = \{(0, DIRECT,)\}$
$HP_1 = \{(1, DIRECT,)\}$
$HP_2 = \{(0, DIRECT,),(1, DIRECT,),(2, DIRECT,)\}$
$HP_3 = \{(1, DIRECT,),(3, DIRECT,)\}$
$HP_4 = \{(0, INDIRECT, (2)),(1, INDIRECT, (2,3)),$
$(2, DIRECT,),(3, DIRECT,),(4, DIRECT,)\}$

During execution of Cal_DUB(), timing diagrams of all HP sets are constructed and U values are determined. Among the HP sets, only HP_4 has *indirect* elements.

Figure 7 shows the initial timing diagram of HP_4 generated

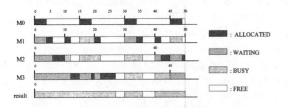

Figure 7. The initial timing diagram of HP_4

assuming all elements are *direct*. There are 7 free time slots at the last row. Because the network latency of M_4 is 10, deadline can not be guaranteed. Using blocking

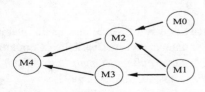

Figure 8. The blocking dependency graph of HP_4

dependency graph of HP_4 as shown in Figure 8, the algorithm modifies the initial timing diagram considering *indirect* elements. The final timing diagram of HP_4 is shown in Figure 9. As Figure 9 shows, the second and the third instance of M_0 and the fourth instance of M_1 are removed. Because of the released time slots, the first instance of M_3 is compacted and there exist enough free time slots to guarantee the deadline of M_4. The U_i's for all M_is are determined as follows.

$U_0 = 7$, $U_1 = 8$, $U_2 = 26$, $U_3 = 20$, $U_4 = 33$

Since all U_i's are smaller than their corresponding D_i's, it returns *success*.

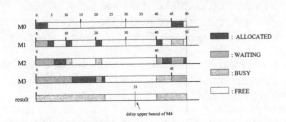

Figure 9. The final timing diagram of HP_4

5. Simulation

In this section, we show the ratio between the delay upper bound found using the proposed algorithm and the ac-

Table 1. 1 priority level, 20 message streams

	avg. U	avg. latency	ratio
P : 1	67.315002	31.064676	0.461482

tual latency changing the number of priority levels. In this simulation study, we assume the following environment.

- PNs are interconnected in a 10×10 two dimensional mesh and X-Y routing is used.

- Each PN is a source of at most one message stream and the corresponding destination node is selected using a spatial uniform distribution.

- The total simulation time is 30000 flit time, omitting 2000 start-up time units. One flit time unit is the time for a flit to be transmitted to a selected neighbor node.

- The maximum message size C_i is uniformly distributed between 10 and 40.

- All message streams are periodic. Minimum message inter-generation time T_i is uniformly distributed between 400 and 900. If the calculated U_i is larger then T_i, we increased T_i to accommodate all generated traffics.

We performed simulation by changing the number of priority levels and total number of message streams. Each message stream has a priority value P_i with probability $\frac{1}{the\ number\ of\ prioriy\ levels}$.

Table 1 shows the result when only one priority level is allowed and the total number of message streams is 20. The ratio between the calculated delay upper bound and the actual latency is less than 0.5. If more message streams are generated, the ratio is extremely exacerbated as shown in Table 2.

The results of simulation when more than one priority level is allowed are presented in Tables 3, 4, and 5.

As we can see from the tables, the more priority levels are allowed, the better the result we can get. From simulation results including not presented here, we found that at least $\frac{1}{4}|M|$ priority levels are needed to have the ratio of the highest priority level be higher than 0.9. $|M|$ represents the total number of message streams. In addition, when more priority levels are allowed, the ratio value of the lowest priority one also increases as shown in Tables 1, 3, and 4.

6. Conclusion

In this paper, we presented a real-time communication method that can be used in general point-to-point real-time multicomputer systems with wormhole switching. We

Table 2. 1 priority level, 60 message streams

	avg. U	avg. latency	ratio
P : 1	801.142456	32.076866	0.040039

Table 3. 4 priority levels, 20 message streams

	avg. U	avg. latency	ratio
P : 4	34.711800	29.970371	0.863406
P : 3	42.384201	30.540106	0.720554
P : 2	50.759399	30.731548	0.605436
P : 1	58.535999	31.127224	0.531762

Table 4. 5 priority levels, 20 message streams

	avg. U	avg. latency	ratio
P : 5	33.465000	30.239433	0.903614
P : 4	39.832500	30.570595	0.767479
P : 3	46.442501	30.845715	0.664170
P : 2	50.389999	31.661804	0.628335
P : 1	57.739998	32.161690	0.557008

Table 5. 15 priority levels, 60 message streams

	avg. U	avg. latency	ratio
P : 15	32.912498	30.037508	0.912647
P : 14	38.294998	30.413145	0.794181
P : 13	44.100002	30.645300	0.694905
P : 12	52.564999	30.852299	0.586936
P : 11	56.217499	31.154004	0.554169
P : 10	67.767502	31.654676	0.467107
P : 9	75.150002	31.706261	0.421906
P : 8	84.472504	31.717149	0.375473
P : 7	93.457504	31.820578	0.340482
P : 6	102.337502	32.584705	0.318404
P : 5	115.849991	32.809212	0.283204
P : 4	130.330002	32.910263	0.252515
P : 3	147.065002	33.209141	0.225813
P : 2	160.862488	33.310387	0.207074
P : 1	190.454987	33.808067	0.177512

addressed two important issues in real-time communication: predictability and priority handling. For priority handling, we assume a flit-level preemptive wormhole switching method. We also provided an algorithm to compute message transmission delay upper bounds assuming that this priority handling method is used. Using simulation, we show that reasonable number of priority levels are required to obtain meaningful delay upper bounds.

References

[1] D. D. Kandlur, K. G. Shin, and D. Ferrari, "Real-time communication in multi-hop networks," *Proc. 11-th Int'l. Conf. on Distributed Computing Systems*, 1991, pp. 300-307.

[2] Qin Zheng and Kang G. Shin, "Fault-Tolerant Real-Time Communication in Distributed Computing Systems," *22nd International Symposium on Fault Tolerant Computing*, Boston, MA, Jul., 1992.

[3] D. Ferrari and D. C. Verma, "A Scheme for Real-Time Channel Establishment in Wide-Area Networks," *IEEE J. Selected Areas Communication*, 1990, pp. 368-379

[4] Qin Zheng, and Kang G. Shin, "On the Ability of Establishing Real-Time Channels in Point-to-Point Packet-Switched Networks," *IEEE Tran. on Communications*, Vol. 42, No. 2/3/4, February/March/April 1994.

[5] Lionel M. Ni and Philip K. McKinley, "A Survey of Wormhole Routing Techniques in Direct Networks," *IEEE Computer*, February, 1993, pp. 62-76.

[6] K. Toda, K. Nishida, S. Sakai, and T. Shimada, "A Priority Forwarding Scheme for Real-Time Multistage Interconnection Networks," *Proc. of Real-Time Systems Symp.*, pp. 208-217, December 1992.

[7] Jennifer Rexford, John Hall, and Kang G. Shin, "A Router Architecture for Real-Time Point-to-Point Networks," *Int'l. Symp. on Computer Architecture*, 1996.

[8] J. P. Li and M. W. Mutka, "Priority Based Real-Time Communication for Large Scale Wormhole Networks," *Proc. of the IPPS*, 1994.

[9] M. W. Mutka, "Using Rate Monotonic Scheduling Technology for Real-Time Communication in a Wormhole Network," technical report, Department of Computer Science, Michigan State University, 1993

[10] H. Song, B. Kwon, and H. Yoon, "Throttle and Preempt: A New Flow Control for Real-Time Communications in Wormhole Networks," *Proc. of the ICPP*, 1997

DRIL: **D**ynamically **R**educed Message **I**njection **L**imitation Mechanism for Wormhole Networks*

P. López, J. M. Martínez and J. Duato
Depto. Informática de Sistemas y Computadores
Universidad Politécnica de Valencia
Camino de Vera s/n, 46071 - Valencia, SPAIN
E-mail: {plopez,jmmr,jduato}@gap.upv.es

Abstract

Deadlock avoidance [11] and recovery techniques [3] are alternatives to deal with the interconnection network deadlock problem. Both techniques allow fully adaptive routing on some set of resources while providing dedicated resources to escape from deadlock. They mainly differ in the way they supply escape paths and when those paths are used. As the escape paths only provide limited bandwidth to escape from deadlocks, both techniques suffer from severe performance degradation when the network is close to saturation. On the other hand, deadlock recovery is based on the assumption that deadlocks are rare. Several studies show that deadlocks are more prone when the network is close to or beyond saturation.

In this paper we propose a new mechanism that prevents network saturation by dynamically adjusting message injection limitation into the network. As a consequence, this mechanism will avoid the performance degradation problem that typically occurs in both deadlock avoidance and recovery techniques, making fully adaptive feasible. Also, it will guarantee that the frequency of deadlock is really negligible, allowing the use of simple low-cost recovery strategies.

1. Introduction

Wormhole [9] has become the most widely used switching technique for multicomputers [4] and distributed shared-memory multiprocessors [17], and it is also being used for networks of workstations [5]. In wormhole, each message is serialized into a sequence of flits. The flit at the head of a message governs the route. As the header flit advances along the specified route, the remaining flits follow it in a pipeline fashion. If the header encounters a channel already in use, it is blocked until the channel is freed; the flow control within the network blocks the trailing flits. Wormhole switching only requires small buffers in the nodes through which messages are routed, avoiding storage bandwidth usage in the intermediate nodes. Also, it makes the message latency largely insensitive to the distance in the network. See [13] for a detailed analysis of wormhole.

However, the main drawback of wormhole is the low network throughput achieved due to message blocking. In order to reduce the impact of message blocking, physical channels can be split into virtual channels [10] by providing a separate buffer for each virtual channel and by multiplexing physical channel bandwidth. Dynamically sharing the physical bandwidth among several messages increases throughput considerably. However, virtual channels are expensive because they complicate routing decision block and channel control, increasing the router complexity and node delay [8]. So, the number of virtual channels per physical channel should be kept small. The use of adaptive routing [13] (usually combined with virtual channels) improves network performance even more.

One of the most important interconnection network design issues is deadlock handling. A deadlock occurs when some packets cannot advance toward their destination because all of them are requesting resources held by other packets in a cyclic way. The size of the buffers strongly influences the probability of reaching a deadlocked configuration. In wormhole switching, buffers are relatively small, being more deadlock-prone than packet switching. In the wormhole context, there are two strategies for deadlock handling [13]: deadlock avoidance and deadlock recovery.

In deadlock avoidance, resources are requested while packets advance through the network, granting them to a packet only if the resulting global state is safe. A common technique consists of establishing an ordering between re-

*This work was supported by the Spanish CICYT under Grant TIC97–0897–C04–01

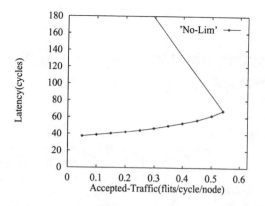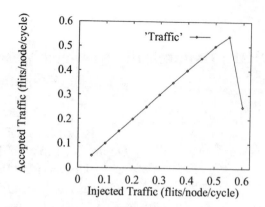

Figure 1. Performance degradation of a true fully adaptive routing algorithm with 3 virtual channels per physical channel. 512-node 3-D torus. Uniform distribution of message destinations. 16-flit messages.

sources and granting resources to each packet in decreasing order. This is the case for routing algorithms that restrict routing so that there are no cyclic dependencies between channels [9]. A more efficient approach that also fits into this category consists of allowing the existence of cyclic dependencies between channels while providing some escape paths to avoid deadlock, therefore increasing routing flexibility [11, 12].

However, deadlock avoidance techniques require dedicated resources to provide those escape paths. Usually, those dedicated resources are virtual channels, thus preventing the use of all the virtual channels for fully adaptive routing. Deadlock recovery strategies [25, 15, 2, 3] allow the use of unrestricted fully adaptive routing, potentially outperforming deadlock avoidance techniques. However, these strategies require a deadlock detection mechanism and a deadlock recovery mechanism that is able to recover from deadlocks faster than they occur. The frequency of packets recovering from deadlock plays an important role when considering the deadlock handling mechanism. Only when this frequency drops to a very low value is possible to use a simple, low-cost recovery mechanism that does not affect normal router behavior. An example of this simple recovery mechanism can be found in the software-base deadlock recovery technique proposed in [21].

Both techniques, deadlock avoidance and recovery may produce severe performance degradation when the network is close to saturation [11, 2]. This problem is illustrated in Figure 1, and can be stated as follows. Latency increases with network traffic until certain point, at which latency value goes up while traffic decreases. Average traffic matches flit injection rate until the performance degradation point is reached, then traffic noticeably decreases.

Performance degradation is produced because both deadlock avoidance and recovery strategies allow cyclic de-

pendencies between some channels provided that there are some escape paths or a recovery mechanism. When message injection rate becomes high, messages block cyclically faster than they are drained by the escape paths or the deadlock recovery mechanism, thus increasing latency and decreasing the number of messages delivered per time unit. It must be noticed that messages do not deadlock, but they spend a long time in the network.

This problem has already been studied in [11, 18, 19]. Although degradation can be removed by adding enough virtual channels per physical channel, this solution is expensive and may lead to an excessive number of virtual channels for most topologies. An alternative approach was proposed in [18, 19]. The basic mechanism [18] consists of preventing network saturation by limiting new message injection when network traffic exceeds a given level. The main drawback of this approach is that the mechanism must be properly tuned according to the expected network load, which is not known in advance. In [19] a mechanism to circumvent this drawback was presented. Although it was able to prevent network saturation under all the network loads analyzed, the mechanism did not achieve the best results for each individual traffic pattern considered.

Concerning deadlock recovery techniques, some studies [26, 24] have measured the frequency of deadlock occurrence on k-ary n-cubes using a true fully adaptive minimal routing algorithm, showing that deadlocks only occur when the network is close to or beyond saturation. Again, preventing network saturation is crucial in order to keep the frequency of deadlock occurrence, and, thereafter, invocations of the recovery mechanism under negligible values.

Thus, considering the importance of preventing network saturation in making stable the behavior of the interconnection network at high loads and also in order to make simple and low-cost deadlock recovery mechanisms feasible, this paper proposes a new mechanism to avoid network saturation. It is based in the basic idea proposed in [18], making it more robust. The main goal of the new mechanism is to dynamically adjust message injection limitation as a function of network load, reducing injection automatically to the proper level as soon as saturation is detected. On the other hand, in order to improve the mechanism proposed in [19], the new approach should allow the routing algorithm to achieve the maximum performance for every network load.

Section 2 describes the mechanism proposed in [18] to prevent network saturation, which is the starting point for the new one. The new mechanism is described in Section 3. Performance evaluation results of the new mechanism for different message destination distributions and lengths are presented in Section 4. Finally, some conclusions are drawn.

2. Basic Message Injection Limitation Mechanism

In this section we briefly summarize the message injection limitation mechanism proposed in [18], as it is the basis for the new one. Consider again Figure 1. As can be seen, network behavior is only poor if traffic surpasses the performance degradation point (when the network is saturated). Thus, the basic idea of this mechanism is to control network traffic by limiting the injection of messages into the network, keeping it under the saturation point. This increases the time that messages spend at the source node when they are not injected into the network at once, but the average message latency is actually lower than the one obtained by the same routing algorithm without the injection limitation mechanism because of the degradation previously mentioned.

However, the problem is how to precisely measure the actual network traffic, as it is a global magnitude. The used solution is to estimate network traffic locally at each node by counting the number of busy virtual output channels. For instance, Figure 2 shows the number of busy virtual output channels versus traffic for a 512-node 3-D torus with true fully adaptive routing and 3 virtual channels per physical channel. Uniform distribution of message destinations and 16-flit messages were used. Other message destination distribution plots have similar shape. As shown, there is a useful correlation between the number of busy virtual output channels and network traffic.

Thus, the basic mechanism works as follows. If the number of busy output channels surpasses a threshold value, the router prevents the injection of new messages, keeping them at their source node. Threshold value must be properly selected, according to the number of busy output channels just before entering saturation. For instance, threshold value for

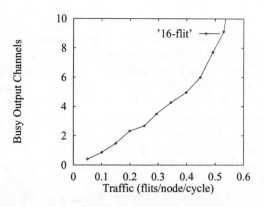

Figure 2. Busy virtual output channels versus traffic for a 512-node 3-D torus with a fully adaptive routing algorithm and 3 virtual channels per physical channel.

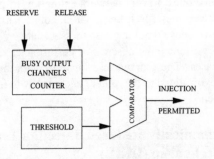

Figure 3. Hardware required for the basic message injection limitation mechanism.

the network analyzed in Figure 2 is around 9.

In order to implement this mechanism (Figure 3), each router requires a register to hold the threshold value, a comparator and a counter, which are not in the critical path. The counter is incremented each time a successful route is established (another output virtual channel becomes occupied) and is decremented when the tail of a message leaves the router. Before routing a message generated at the source node, the number of busy output channels is compared against the threshold. If this number exceeds the threshold, the message is queued. Otherwise, injection is permitted. Every time a channel is freed, queued messages are checked in order to inject them into the network. In addition, queued messages have greater priority than newly generated messages.

The main drawback of this mechanism is that optimal threshold value varies according to the message distribution and message length currently in the network. Thus, in order to use this mechanism, a complete analysis of its behavior for several network loads should be done, leading to a set of different "optimal" thresholds. If we use the threshold value imposing the maximum restrictions, there will be a performance penalty when a lower limitation is really required. On the other hand, if we tune the threshold imposing a lower limitation than it is really required, the mechanism does not work, and the network will reach saturation and the performance degradation point.

In [19] a mechanism was proposed in order to overcome this problem. The basic idea is to dynamically update the threshold used in the comparison according to a guess of the message destination distribution currently in the network. In particular, the number of network dimensions that a newly injected message has to cross to reach its destination is used to distinguish between different distributions. Based on this information, a new threshold is computed using a linear function.

Again, several linear functions can be used. The most restrictive ones prevent network saturation in most cases, but increase message latency. On the other hand, the least restrictive ones do not increase message latency but are not able to guarantee the absence of performance degradation in all cases. These drawbacks, together with the hardware complexity added to the router suggested us to find a better approach.

3. Dynamically Reduced Injection Limitation mechanism (DRIL)

The main goal of the new message injection limitation mechanism is to automatically adapt to the current network load, adjusting limitation to the precise value required. Thus, the key point is that the mechanism should not depend on message destination distribution, message length and saturation traffic.

Traffic is estimated by counting the number of busy virtual output channels, and injection of a newly generated message is prevented if traffic surpasses a threshold. In addition, a variable threshold as in [19] is used. In this case, threshold value is dynamically updated as a function of network load. In section 2, threshold value has been computed by counting the number of busy virtual output channels when the network traffic is close to saturation, just before the performance degradation point is reached. The idea is to dynamically take this count locally at each node at this precise moment. Thus, the value just read will exactly match the actual network load conditions. Moreover, every node computes its own busy output channel count.

To do so, every node must detect in a distributed way when the network is just entering saturation. At this moment, all the useful output channels required by a newly

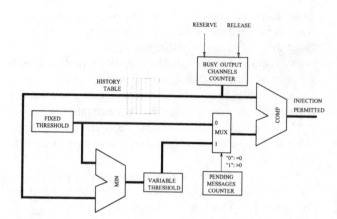

Figure 4. Hardware required for the DRIL mechanism.

generated message will be occupied, so that its routing will not be successful. These messages will be buffered at the source node in a pending message queue. Thus, the number of messages buffered in this queue can be used as an indication that the network is possibly just reaching saturation.

When the local pending message queue surpasses a threshold (for instance, when it has one or more pending messages), the busy output channel counting is performed. The obtained value will be used as the new threshold used in the comparison. The newly computed threshold value will be used for limitation purposes until traffic decreases below the saturation point. If this occurs, a fixed low threshold value that imposes lower restrictions to inject a message will be used instead. Notice that threshold is computed once every time the network reaches saturation, maintaining its value until traffic decreases. Computing the threshold only once avoids positive feedback effects that will lead to a null message injection. On the other hand, returning the threshold value to a fixed one when the network is no longer saturated allows the mechanism to work even with traffic patterns that change over time.

However, in some cases we have observed that, when the network is just entering saturation, the number of busy virtual output channels tends to be higher than the optimum one that prevents saturation, leading to an insufficient limitation. Thus, the newly computed threshold value should be used only if its value is lower than the fixed one (i.e., if it leads to a more restricted injection policy). In other words, there is an upper bound for the threshold value that should be used in any case.

On the other hand, threshold value should be greater than a minimum value (for instance 1) that guarantees the possibility of message injection, and thus the absence of starvation.

Figure 4 shows the hardware required to implement the mechanism. In order to more precisely compute the new threshold, information for not only one sample, but for the last m samples of the number of busy output channels can be used. In this case, each time a message is successfully routed, the number of busy output channels is stored in a table. By averaging table contents, the average number of busy output channels sampled for the last m routed messages is computed. This value will be used as the new threshold value when the network is presumed to be saturated, if it is lower than the fixed threshold value. Network saturation is indicated by a non-zero count of the pending messages counter.

Notice that the comparison between the number of busy virtual output channels and the threshold is done before message injection into the network. This slightly increases message latency when the network is not saturated and the limitation mechanism is not really needed. On the other hand, if a table with m samples is used, the average of table contents and calculation of the threshold value can be done between message routing operations. Thus, the hardware required to implement the DRIL mechanism is not in the critical path.

4. Performance Evaluation

In this section, we will evaluate by simulation the behavior of the DRIL mechanism. The evaluation methodology used is based on the one proposed in [11]. The most important performance measures are latency (time required to deliver a message, including the time spent in the source queue) and throughput (maximum traffic accepted by the network). Traffic is the flit reception rate. Latency is measured in clock cycles. Traffic is measured in flits per node per cycle.

In order to evaluate DRIL robustness, several network load conditions have been analyzed. In particular, each node generates messages independently according to an exponential distribution. Destinations are chosen according to the following traffic patterns: *Uniform, Bit-reversal, Perfect-Shuffle* and *Butterfly*. These traffic patterns illustrate different features. The uniform one is the standard benchmark used in network routing studies [10, 7, 6]. The other patterns have been selected taking into account the permutations that are usually performed in parallel numerical algorithms [23, 14, 16]. Notice that we have not evaluated the uniform destination distribution with locality because the low distance traversed drastically reduces the number of cyclic dependencies so that no performance degradation is observed. For message length, 16-flit and 64-flit messages were considered. In addition, an hybrid load composed of 60 % of 16-flit messages and 40 % of 64-flit messages has also been used.

4.1. Network Model

The network model considered consists of a four port architecture [22], a true fully adaptive router (TFAR) [26, 24, 21] with three virtual channels per physical channel, a crossbar switch and channels. Routing time and transmission time across the crossbar and a channel are all assumed to be equal to one clock cycle. There is also a four-flit buffer associated with each virtual channel. The software-based deadlock recovery technique proposed in [21] is used. In this strategy, deadlocked messages are removed from the network at the current node, and injected again at a later time. It is used together with the deadlock detection mechanism proposed in [20]. Finally, the DRIL mechanism described in Section 3 is used. In order to evaluate the performance of the mechanism with the simplest hardware complexity, no history table was used. On the other hand, the fixed threshold required by the mechanism has been set equal to 9 busy virtual output channels. This value is the optimal threshold for the uniform distribution of message destinations [18].

Taking into account the sizes of current multicomputers and the studies about the optimal number of dimensions [1], we have evaluated the performance of the DRIL mechanism on a 8-ary 3-cube network (512 nodes).

4.2. Performance Comparison

In this section, we will analyze the results obtained by the TFAR routing algorithm with the DRIL mechanism. For comparison purposes, we will also show the results obtained with the previous message injection limitation mechanisms, the basic one (**Basic**) [18] and the one that computes threshold based on the number of network dimensions that a newly injected message has to cross using a linear function (**Linear Function**) [19]. Finally, results without any injection limitation mechanism (**No-Lim**) are also shown.

Figures 5 and 6 show the results for the uniform distribution of message destinations. Due to the little differences observed, only the results for 16-flit messages are shown. As we can see, there is a severe performance degradation when the network reaches saturation if no message injection limitation is used. When any message injection limitation mechanism is used, performance degradation of the network is avoided. The performance of all the mechanisms is almost the same because the threshold returned by all of them is almost identical. Average latency as well as its standard deviation is slightly increased when any injection limitation mechanism is used and the network is just entering saturation. This is due to the increased time that messages spend at the source nodes. Among all the limitation mechanisms, DRIL achieves both the lowest average latency and

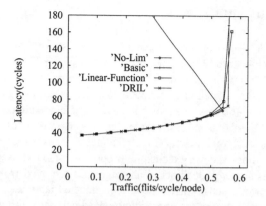

Figure 5. Average message latency versus traffic. Uniform distribution for message destinations. 16-flit messages.

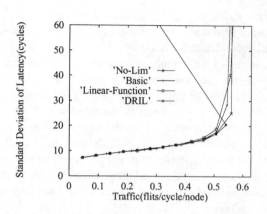

Figure 6. Standard deviation of message latency versus traffic. Uniform distribution for message destinations. 16-flit messages.

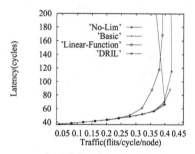

Figure 7. Average message latency versus traffic. Bit-reversal pattern. 16-flit messages.

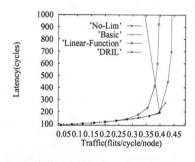

Figure 8. Average message latency versus traffic. Bit-reversal pattern. 64-flit messages.

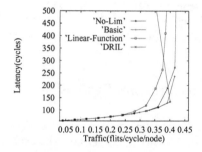

Figure 9. Average message latency versus traffic. Bit-reversal pattern. 60% 16-flit and 40% 64-flit messages.

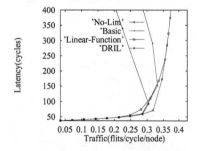

Figure 10. Average message latency versus traffic. Perfect-shuffle pattern. 16-flit messages.

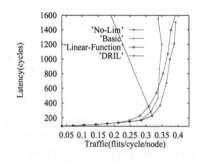

Figure 11. Average message latency versus traffic. Perfect-shuffle pattern. 64-flit messages.

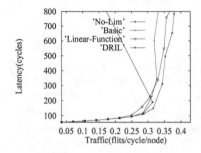

Figure 12. Average message latency versus traffic. Perfect-shuffle pattern. 60% 16-flit and 40% 64-flit messages.

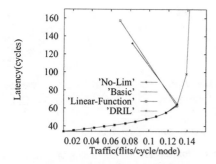

Figure 13. Average message latency versus traffic. Butterfly pattern. 16-flit messages.

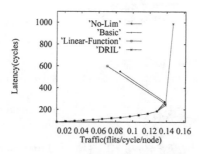

Figure 14. Average message latency versus traffic. Butterfly pattern. 64-flit messages.

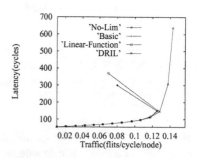

Figure 15. Average message latency versus traffic. Butterfly pattern. 60% 16-flit and 40% 64-flit messages.

standard deviation values.

Figures 7 to 15 show the results for the permutation-based traffic patterns analyzed. As can be seen, message injection limitation is also mandatory. Otherwise, severe performance degradation is reached. The **Basic** message injection limitation mechanism based on a fixed threshold does not prevent performance degradation in all cases. Notice that the value currently used for the threshold is the same as in the uniform distribution for message destinations. Clearly, more limitation is required for these traffic patterns. In this way, the variable threshold **Linear-Function** mechanism improves the results over the basic one. It avoids performance degradation for all traffic patterns but the Butterfly one. However, average message latency is increased over the results without injection limitation or **Basic** limitation mechanism, because more limitation that is strictly needed is applied.

The new message injection limitation mechanism proposed in this paper, DRIL, avoids performance degradation for all the traffic patterns analyzed. In addition, DRIL outperforms in terms of network throughput and average message latency our previous variable threshold proposal (**Linear-Function**), for all traffic patterns. On the other hand, DRIL does not introduce any penalty in latency when the network is not saturated. The key issue is the ability of the new mechanism to dynamically reduce its threshold at each node according to the load that is currently measured.

5. Conclusions

In this paper we have proposed a new message injection limitation (DRIL) mechanism to prevent network saturation. By doing so, the performance degradation suffered by fully adaptive routing algorithms with cyclic dependen-

cies between channels is avoided. This include both deadlock avoidance-based and recovery-based routing. In addition, when deadlock recovery mechanisms are used, the frequency of deadlock is reduced to negligible values.

The proposed mechanism consists of limiting new message injection into the network when the number of busy virtual output channels exceeds a threshold. This threshold is dynamically updated based on the network load. As a consequence, the mechanism is more robust than previous approaches, being almost independent of destination distribution and message length. On the other hand, the mechanism neither increases average latency when traffic is far from saturation nor reduces network throughput. Finally, the proposed mechanism needs to be implemented in the routing control unit but it does not affect clock frequency, because it is not in the critical path.

As future work, we plan to analyze the effect of injection limitation on real applications. Although the proposed mechanism could lead to starvation at some nodes while other nodes continue injecting messages at the maximum rate, this should not be the case for real applications because messages are not independent of each other.

References

[1] A. Agarwal, "Limits on interconnection network performance", *IEEE Transactions on Parallel Distributed Systems*, vol. 2, no. 4, pp. 398–412, Oct. 1991.

[2] Anjan K. V. and T. M. Pinkston, An efficient fully adaptive deadlock recovery scheme: DISHA," in *Proceedings of the 22nd International Symposium on Computer Architecture*, June 1995.

[3] Anjan K. V., T. M. Pinkston and J. Duato, "Generalized theory for deadlock-free adaptive routing and

its application to Disha Concurrent," in *Proceedings of the 10th International Parallel Processing Symposium*, April 1996.

[4] W. C. Athas and C. L. Seitz, "Multicomputers: Message-passing concurrent computers," *IEEE Computer*, vol. 21, no. 8, pp. 9–24, August 1988.

[5] N. J. Boden, D. Cohen, R. E. Felderman, A. E. Kulawik, C. L. Seitz, J. Seizovic and W. Su, "Myrinet - A gigabit per second local area network," *IEEE Micro*, pp. 29–36, February 1995.

[6] R. V. Boppana and S. Chalasani, "A comparison of adaptive wormhole routing algorithms," in *Proceedings of the 20th International Symposium on Computer Architecture*, May 1993.

[7] A. A. Chien and J. H. Kim, "Planar-adaptive routing: Low-cost adaptive networks for multiprocessors," in *Proceedings of the 19th International Symposium on Computer Architecture*, May 1992.

[8] A. A. Chien, "A cost and speed model for k-ary n-cube wormhole routers," in *Proceedings of Hot Interconnects '93*, August 1993.

[9] W. J. Dally and C. L. Seitz, "Deadlock-free message routing in multiprocessor interconnection networks," *IEEE Transactions on Computers*, vol. C–36, no. 5, pp. 547–553, May 1987.

[10] W. J. Dally, "Virtual-channel flow control," *IEEE Transactions on Parallel and Distributed Systems*, vol. 3, no. 2, pp. 194–205, March 1992.

[11] J. Duato, "A new theory of deadlock-free adaptive routing in wormhole networks," *IEEE Transactions on Parallel and Distributed Systems*, vol. 4, no. 12, pp. 1320–1331, December 1993.

[12] J. Duato, "A necessary and sufficient condition for deadlock-free adaptive routing in wormhole networks," *IEEE Transactions on Parallel and Distributed Systems*, vol. 6, no. 10, pp. 1055–1067, October 1995.

[13] J. Duato, S. Yalamanchili and L.M. Ni, *Interconnection Networks: An Engineering Approach*, IEEE Computer Society Press, 1997.

[14] J. Kim, A.Chien, "An evaluation of the planar/adaptive routing," in *Proc. 4th IEEE Int. Symp. Parallel Distributed Processing*, 1992.

[15] J. H. Kim, Z. Liu and A. A. Chien, "Compressionless routing: A framework for adaptive and fault-tolerant routing," in *Proceedings of the 21st International Symposium on Computer Architecture*, April 1994.

[16] F. T. Leighton, *Introduction to Parallel Algorithms and Architectures: Arrays, Trees, Hypercubes*. San Mateo, CA, USA, Morgan Kaufmann Publishers, 1992.

[17] D. Lenoski, J. Laudon, K. Gharachorloo, W. Weber, A. Gupta, J. Hennessy, M. Horowitz and M. Lam, "The Stanford DASH multiprocessor," *IEEE Computer*, vol. 25, no. 3, pp. 63–79, March 1992.

[18] P. López and J. Duato, "Deadlock-free adaptive routing algorithms for the 3D-torus: Limitations and solutions," in *Proceedings of Parallel Architectures and Languages Europe 93*, June 1993.

[19] P. López, J.M. Martínez, J. Duato and F. Petrini, "On the Reduction of Deadlock Frequency by Limiting Message Injection in Wormhole Networks," in *Proceedings of Parallel Computer Routing and Communication Workshop*, June 1997.

[20] P. López, J.M. Martínez and J. Duato, "A Very Efficient Distributed Deadlock Detection Mechanism for Wormhole Networks," in *Proceedings of High Performance Computer Architecture Workshop*, February 1998.

[21] J.M. Martínez, P. López, J. Duato and T.M. Pinkston, "Software-Based Deadlock Recovery Technique for True Fully Adaptive Routing in Wormhole Networks," *1997 International Conference Parallel Processing*, 1997.

[22] P.K. McKinley, H. Xu, A. Esfahanian and L.M. Ni, "Unicast-based multicast communication in wormhole-routed networks," in *Proceedings 1992 International Conference Parallel Processing*, Aug. 1992.

[23] P.R. Miller, "Efficient communications for fine-grain distributed computers," Ph.D Thesis, Southampton University, 1991.

[24] T.M. Pinkston and S. Warnakulasuriya, "On Deadlocks in Interconnection Networks", to appear in *the 24th International Symposium on Computer Architecture*, June 1997.

[25] D. S. Reeves, E. F. Gehringer and A. Chandiramani, "Adaptive routing and deadlock recovery: A simulation study," in *Proceedings of the 4th Conference on Hypercube, Concurrent Computers & Applications*, March 1989.

[26] S. Warnakulasuriya and T.M. Pinkston, "Characterization of deadlocks in interconnection networks," in *Proceedings of the 11th International Parallel Processing Symposium*, April 1997.

Algebraic Foundations and Broadcasting Algorithms for Wormhole-Routed All-Port Tori[*]

San-Yuan Wang and Yu-Chee Tseng
Department of Computer Science and Information Engineering
National Central University
Chung-Li, 32054, Taiwan
E-mail: { sywang, yctseng }@csie.ncu.edu.tw

Abstract

The one-to-all broadcast is the most primary collective communication pattern in a multicomputer network. We consider this problem in a wormhole-routed torus which uses all-port and dimension-ordered routing model. We derive our routing algorithms based on the concept of "span of vector spaces" in linear algebra. For instance, in a 3-D torus, the nodes receiving the broadcast message will be "spanned" from the source node to a line of nodes, to a plane of nodes, and then to a cube of nodes. Our results require at most $2(k-1)$ steps more than the optimal number of steps for any square k-D torus. Existing results, as compared to ours, can only be applied to tori of very restricted dimensions or sizes, and either rely on an undesirable non-dimension-ordered routing or require more numbers of steps.

1. Introduction

One-to-all broadcast is an essential communication operator in multicomputer networks, which has many applications, such as algebraic problems, barrier synchronization, parallel graph and matrix algorithms, cache coherence in distributed-share-memory systems, and data re-distribution in HPF. Wormhole routing [1, 4] is characterized with low communication latency due to its pipelined nature and is quite insensitive to routing distance in the absence of link contention. Machines adopting such technology include the Intel Touchstone DELTA, Intel Paragon, MIT J-machine, Caltech MOSAIC, nCUBE 3, and Cray T3D and T3E.

In this paper, we study the scheduling of message distribution for one-to-all broadcast in a wormhole-

routed torus, which type of architecture has been adopted by parallel machines such as Cray T3D and T3E (3-D tori). The network is assumed to use the *all-port* model[1] and the popular *dimension-ordered* routing. Following the formulation in many works [2, 6, 8, 10, 12, 13], this is achieved by constructing a sequence of steps, where a *step* consists of a set of congestion-free communication paths each indicating a message delivery. The goal is to minimize the total number of steps used.

The same problem has been studied in several works. In [9, 10], schedules following the dimension-ordered routing are proposed for 2-D $2^n \times 2^n$ and 3-D $2^n \times 2^n \times z$ tori using n and $n + m + 2$ steps, respectively, where $7 \times 6^m + 1 \leq z \leq 7 \times 6^{m+1}$. The numbers of steps used are at least $\log_4 5$ and $\log_6 7$ times, i.e., about 16% and 8.6% more than, the optimal numbers of steps, respectively (refer to the lower bounds in Lemma 1). A schedule using the optimal number of steps is proposed in [8] for any 2-D torus of size $5^p \times 5^p$ or $(2 \times 5^p) \times (2 \times 5^p)$, where p is any integer. The works in [6, 7] remain optimal, but can be applied to any square k-D torus with $(2k + 1)^p$ nodes on each side. However, the disadvantages of [6, 7, 8] include : (i) the tori must be square, (ii) very few network sizes are solvable (e.g., for 2-D tori, the possible sizes are 5×5, 10×10, 25×25, 50×50, 125×125, 250×250, etc.), and (iii) the routing is not dimension-ordered (we comment that unfortunately most current torus machines use dimension-ordered routing). These drawbacks would greatly limit the applicability of [6, 7, 8]. Generalization to tori supporting multi-port capability is shown in [3]; however, the routing is still non-dimension-ordered. Recently, these deficiencies were eliminated by [11], which can

---

[*]This work is supported by the National Science Council of the Republic of China under Grant # NSC87-2213-E-008-012 and #NSC87-2213-E-008-016.

---

[1]The reverse of this is the *one-port* model, in which case the broadcast problem can be trivially solved by a recursive-doubling technique.

be applied to 2-D tori of any size using dimension-ordered routing; at most 2 (resp., 5) communication steps more than the optimum are required when the torus is square (resp., non-square). However, it still remains as an open problem how to extend this scheme to higher-dimensional tori.

One interesting technique used in [11] is the concept of *diagonal* in a 2-D torus. In this paper, we extend the work of [11] and show how to perform one-to-all broadcast in a torus of any dimension. For practical consideration, the routing should still follow the dimension-ordered restriction. The extension turns out to need some mathematical foundations when higher-dimensional tori are considered. Our schemes are based on the concept of "span of vector spaces" in linear algebra. For instance, in a 3-D torus, the nodes receiving the broadcast message will be "spanned" from the source node to a line of nodes, to a plane of nodes, and then to a cube of nodes. We develop the algebraic foundations to solve this problem for any k-D torus of size n on each dimension. Our results require at most $2(k-1)$ steps more than any optimal scheduling. Existing results, as compared to ours, can only be applied to tori of very restricted dimensions or sizes, and either rely on an undesirable non-dimension-ordered routing or require more numbers of steps.

2. Preliminaries

A k-D torus of size n is an undirected graph denoted as $T_{n \times \cdots \times n}$. Each node is denoted as $p_{x_1, x_2, \cdots, x_k}$, $0 \le x_i < n$, $1 \le i \le k$. Each node is of degree $2k$. Node $p_{x_1, x_2, \cdots, x_k}$ has an edge connecting to $p_{(x_1 \pm 1) \bmod n, x_2, \cdots, x_k}$ along dimension one, an edge to $p_{x_1, (x_2 \pm 1) \bmod n, \cdots, x_k}$ along dimension two, and so on. (Hereafter, we will omit saying "mod n" whenever the context is clear.)

We will map the torus into an Euclidean integer space $\mathbb{Z}^k$. Note that instead of being the normal integer set, $\mathbb{Z}$ is in the domain $\{0, 1, \ldots, n-1\}$. A node $p_{x_1, x_2, \cdots, x_k}$ in the torus can be regarded as a point $(x_1, x_2, \ldots, x_k)$ in $\mathbb{Z}^k$. A vector in $\mathbb{Z}^k$ is a k-tuple $\vec{v} = (v_1, v_2, \ldots, v_k)$. As a convention, the *$i$-th positive (resp., negative) elementary vector* $\vec{e}_i$ (resp., $\vec{e}_{-i}$) of $\mathbb{Z}^k$, $i = 1..k$, is the one with all entries being 0, except the i-th entry being 1 (resp., -1). We may write $\vec{e}_{i_1} + \vec{e}_{i_2}$ as $\vec{e}_{i_1, i_2}$, $\vec{e}_{i_1} - \vec{e}_{i_2}$ ($= \vec{e}_{i_1} + \vec{e}_{-i_2}$) as $\vec{e}_{i_1, -i_2}$, and similarly $\vec{e}_{i_1} + \cdots + \vec{e}_{i_m}$ as $\vec{e}_{i_1, \ldots, i_m}$. For instance, $\vec{e}_{1,3} = \vec{e}_1 + \vec{e}_3$ and $\vec{e}_{1,-3} = \vec{e}_1 - \vec{e}_3$. The *linear combination* of vectors (say $a_1 \vec{v}_1 + a_2 \vec{v}_2$, where a_1 and a_2 are integers) follows directly from the typical definition of vector addition, except that a "mod n" operation is implicitly applied.

Definition 1 In $\mathbb{Z}^k$, given a node x, an m-tuple of vectors $B = (\vec{b}_1, \vec{b}_2, \ldots, \vec{b}_m)$, and an m-tuple of integers $N = (n_1, n_2, \ldots, n_m)$, we define the *span of x by vectors B and distances N* as

$$SPAN(x, B, N) = \{x + \sum_{i=1}^{m} a_i \vec{b}_i | 0 \le a_i < n_i\}.$$

Note that the above definition is different from the typical definition of SPAN in linear algebra [5]. The main purpose here is to identify a portion of the torus. For instances, the main diagonals of $T_{n \times n}$ and $T_{n \times n \times n}$ can be written as $SPAN(p_{0,0}, (\vec{e}_{1,2}), (n))$ and $SPAN(p_{0,0,0}, (\vec{e}_{1,2,3}), (n))$, respectively; an XY-plane passing node $p_{0,0,i}$ in $T_{n \times n \times n}$ can be written as $SPAN(p_{0,0,i}, (\vec{e}_1, \vec{e}_2), (n, n))$.

In the *one-to-all* broadcast problem, a source node needs to send a message to the rest of the network. The *all-port* model will be assumed, in which a node can simultaneously send and receive messages along all outgoing and incoming channels. Since the node degree is $2k$, in the best case one may multiply the number of nodes owning the broadcast message by $2k + 1$ after each step. This leads to the following lemma.

Lemma 1 In a k-D all-port torus $T_{n \times \cdots \times n}$, a lower bound on the number of steps to achieve one-to-all broadcast is $\lceil \log_{2k+1} n^k \rceil$.

3. Broadcasting in 2-D Tori

In this section, we review the broadcasting scheme for 2-D tori in [11]. This will be helpful to understand our algorithms for higher-dimensional tori later. Consider any 2-D torus $T_{n \times n}$. As the network is symmetric, we let, without loss of generality, the source node be $p_{0,0}$. We denote by M the message to be broadcast. The scheme is derived in two stages.

Stage 1: In this stage, message M will be sent to the main diagonal, $SPAN(p_{0,0}, (\vec{e}_{1,2}), (n))$. This is achieved by two parts.

Stage 1.1 (Distribution): In this part, M will be recursively distributed to one of the nodes in each row. For easy of representation, let $n = 5t$. First, we regard $p_{0,0}$ as the center of the torus and horizontally and evenly slice the torus into five strips. In one step, we let $p_{0,0}$ send four copies of M to nodes $p_{0,-2t}$, $p_{-t,-t}$, $p_{t,t}$, and $p_{0,2t}$. The above five nodes are located at the center rows of the five strips and the routing is clearly congestion-free, as illustrated in Fig. 1(a). Then, by regarding these five nodes as the source node of the five strips, we can recursively send M to more rows. Fig. 1(b) illustrates the routing in the second step. This is repeated until the height of each strip reduces to one or zero. At the end, along each row in the torus,

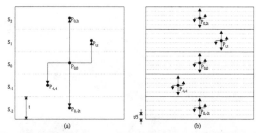

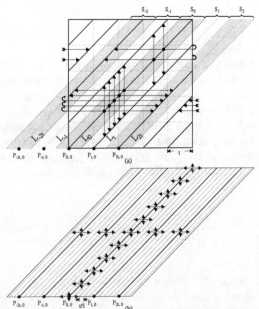

Figure 1. Stage 1.1 of broadcast in a 2-D torus: (a) the first step, and (b) the second step.

Figure 2. Stage 2 of broadcast in a 2-D torus: (a) the first step, and (b) the second step. Note that for clarity only typical communication paths are shown.

exactly one node will have received M. Overall, this stage takes $\lceil \log_5 n \rceil$ steps to complete.

Stage 1.2 (Alignment): For each node $p_{i,j}$ holding message M, $p_{i,j}$ sends M along the first dimension to $p_{j,j}$ if $i \neq j$. So all nodes on the main diagonal will own M. This requires only one step.

Stage 2: In this stage, the torus is viewed as n diagonals $(i = -\lfloor \frac{n-1}{2} \rfloor, -\lfloor \frac{n-1}{2} \rfloor + 1, \ldots, \lceil \frac{n-1}{2} \rceil)$

$$L_i = SPAN(p_{i,0}, (\vec{e}_{1,2}), (n)). \quad (1)$$

We evenly partition the torus into 5 strips $S_i, i = -2..2$ each contains t diagonals. This is illustrated in Fig. 2(a).

In the first step, M will be sent to 4 other diagonals L_{-2t}, L_{-t}, L_t, and L_{2t}. This can be done by having each node $p_{i,i}$ in L_0 send M to nodes $p_{i-2t,i}$, $p_{i,i+t}$, $p_{i,i-t}$, and $p_{i+2t,i}$. The communication, as illustrated in Fig. 2(a), is clearly congestion-free.

In the second step, we can regard the diagonal L_{it} as the source of strip S_i, $i = -2..2$, and recursively perform the above diagonal-to-diagonal message distribution in S_i. (refer to Fig. 2(b)). The recursion terminates when each strips contains one or zero diagonal. This stage takes $\lceil \log_5 n \rceil$ steps to complete. Hence, broadcast can be done in $2\lceil \log_5 n \rceil + 1$ steps, which number of steps is at most 2 steps more than the lower bound in Lemma 1.

4. Broadcasting in 3-D Tori

Now we develop our algorithm for a $T_{n \times n \times n}$ with any n. Without loss of generality, let $p_{0,0,0}$ be the source node. The basic idea is to distribute the broadcast message M in three stages: (i) from $p_{0,0,0}$ to a line $SPAN(p_{0,0,0}, (\vec{e}_{1,3}), (n))$, (ii) from the above line to a plane $SPAN(p_{0,0,0}, (\vec{e}_{1,3}, \vec{e}_{1,2}), (n,n))$, and then (iii) from the above plane to the whole torus. These stages will use $\lceil \log_7 n \rceil + 1$, $\lceil \log_7 n \rceil + 1$, and $\lceil \log_7 n \rceil$ steps, respectively. For simplicity, we may use X-, Y-, and Z-axes to refer to the first, second, and third dimensions, respectively.

4.1. Stage 1: From the Source Node to a Line

Again, this stage is divided into two parts. In the first part, M will be distributed to one representative node on each of the n XY-planes. In the second part, M will be forwarded to the line $SPAN(p_{0,0,0}, (\vec{e}_{1,3}), (n))$.

4.1.1 Stage 1.1 (Distribution)

For simplicity, let n be a multiple of 7, $n = 7t$. We view the torus as consisting of the following n XY-planes $(i = -\lfloor \frac{n-1}{2} \rfloor, -\lfloor \frac{n-1}{2} \rfloor + 1, \ldots, -\lceil \frac{n-1}{2} \rceil)$:

$$SPAN(p_{0,0,i}, (\vec{e}_1, \vec{e}_2), (n,n)). \quad (2)$$

We then partition the torus horizontally into 7 cubes $C_i, i = -3..3$, such that the first cube consists of the first t XY-planes in Eq. (2), the second cube the next t XY-planes, etc. Let's identify the following nodes:

$$m_0 = p_{0,0,0},$$
$$m_1 = p_{t,0,t}, \qquad m_{-1} = p_{-t,0,-t},$$
$$m_2 = p_{0,2t,2t}, \qquad m_{-2} = p_{0,-2t,-2t},$$
$$m_3 = p_{0,0,3t}, \qquad m_{-3} = p_{0,0,-3t}.$$

In one step, node m_0 can forward M to $m_i, i = \pm 1, \pm 2, \pm 3$, without congestion. The communication paths are illustrated in Fig. 3(a).

Now, observe that each m_i is located at the central XY-plane of the cube $C_i, i = -3..3$. So we can regard m_i as the source of C_i and recursively perform broadcasting in C_i, until each cube reduces to only one

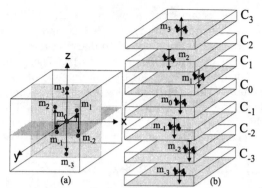

Figure 3. Stage 1.1 of broadcast in a 3-D torus: (a) the first step, and (b) the second step.

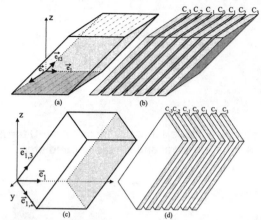

Figure 4. Stage 2 of broadcast in a 3-D torus: (a) viewing the torus from the perspective $SPAN(p_{0,0,0}, (\vec{e}_{1,3}, \vec{e}_2, \vec{e}_1), (n, n, n))$, and (b) partitioning the torus into 7 cubes $C_i, i = -3..3$. Stage 3 of broadcast in a 3D torus: (c) viewing the torus from the perspective $SPAN(p_{0,0,0}, (\vec{e}_{1,3}, \vec{e}_{1,2}, \vec{e}_1), (n, n, n))$, and (d) partitioning the torus into 7 cubes $C_i, i = -3..3$.

or zero XY-plane. The second step is illustrated in Fig. 3(b).

At this point, we would introduce some notations to facilitate our later presentation.

Definition 2 Consider a k-D torus. A *routing matrix* $R = [r_{i,j}]_{k \times k}$ is a matrix with entries $-1, 0$, or 1 such that each row indicates a message delivery; if $r_{i,j} = 1$ (resp. -1), the corresponding message will travel along the positive (resp. negative) direction of dimension j; if $r_{i,j} = 0$, the message will not travel along dimension j. A *distance matrix* $D = [d_{i,j}]_{k \times k}$ is an integer diagonal matrix (all non-diagonal elements are 0); $d_{i,i}$ represents the distance to be traveled by the i-th message described in R along each dimension.

For instance, the six message deliveries in Fig. 3(a) have three directions and thus can be represented by a routing matrix:

$$R_1 = \begin{bmatrix} \vec{e}_{1,3} \\ \vec{e}_{2,3} \\ \vec{e}_3 \end{bmatrix} = \begin{bmatrix} 1 & 0 & 1 \\ 0 & 1 & 1 \\ 0 & 0 & 1 \end{bmatrix}. \tag{3}$$

In general, the six nodes receiving M are $p_{\alpha_1,0,\alpha_1}, p_{0,\alpha_2,\alpha_2}, p_{0,0,\alpha_3}, p_{\alpha_{-1},0,\alpha_{-1}}, p_{0,\alpha_{-2},\alpha_{-2}}, p_{0,0,\alpha_{-3}}$, (note that $\alpha_{\pm i} \approx \pm\frac{in}{7}$; see [14] for details about deriving $\alpha_{\pm i}$). So we can use two distance matrices:

$$D^+ = \begin{bmatrix} \alpha_1 & 0 & 0 \\ 0 & \alpha_2 & 0 \\ 0 & 0 & \alpha_3 \end{bmatrix}, D^- = \begin{bmatrix} \alpha_{-1} & 0 & 0 \\ 0 & \alpha_{-2} & 0 \\ 0 & 0 & \alpha_{-3} \end{bmatrix} \tag{4}$$

and represent the 6 message deliveries in Fig. 3(a) by matrix multiplication:

$$D^+ \times R_1 = \begin{bmatrix} \alpha_1 & 0 & \alpha_1 \\ 0 & \alpha_2 & \alpha_2 \\ 0 & 0 & \alpha_3 \end{bmatrix}, \text{ and } D^- \times R_1 = \begin{bmatrix} \alpha_{-1} & 0 & \alpha_{-1} \\ 0 & \alpha_{-2} & \alpha_{-2} \\ 0 & 0 & \alpha_{-3} \end{bmatrix},$$

where each row represents one routing path.

4.1.2 Stage 1.2 (Alignment)

The goal is to "align" the nodes receiving M to the line $SPAN(p_{0,0,0}, (\vec{e}_{1,3}), (n))$. This can be done in one step by having every $p_{x,y,z}$ holding M send to $p_{z,0,z}$ along

the path $p_{x,y,z} \to p_{z,y,z} \to p_{z,0,z}$. This is congestion-free as communications only happen in individual XY-planes.

4.2. Stage 2: From a Line to a Plane

In this stage, we will view the torus from a different perspective:

$$SPAN(p_{0,0,0}, (\vec{e}_{1,3}, \vec{e}_2, \vec{e}_1), (n, n, n)). \tag{5}$$

See Fig. 4(a) for an illustration. With this view, we partition the network along the direction $\vec{e}_1$ into the following n planes ($i = -\lfloor\frac{n-1}{2}\rfloor, -\lfloor\frac{n-1}{2}\rfloor + 1, \ldots, \lceil\frac{n-1}{2}\rceil$):

$$SPAN(p_{i,0,0}, (\vec{e}_{1,3}, \vec{e}_2), (n, n)). \tag{6}$$

The message M will be sent from the line $SPAN(p_{0,0,0}, (\vec{e}_{1,3}), (n))$ to $n - 1$ other lines, each spanned along the same direction $\vec{e}_{1,3}$ but located on a different plane in Eq. (6). Finally, we will align these lines to a plane $SPAN(p_{0,0,0}, (\vec{e}_{1,3}, \vec{e}_{1,2}), (n, n))$.

It is easy to send messages from a line of nodes to another parallel line in one communication step. For instance, to deliver messages from line $SPAN(p_{0,0,0}, (\vec{e}_{1,3}), (n))$ to line $SPAN(p_{2,3,4}, (\vec{e}_{1,3}), (n))$, we simply let each $p_{i,0,i}$ (of the former line) send to $p_{i+2,3,i+4}$ (of the latter line). One can easily generalize this to a line sending to six other parallel lines in one step.

4.2.1 Stage 2.1 (Distribution)

This stage is based on a recursive structure as follows. For simplicity, let $n = 7t$. We partition the torus into 7

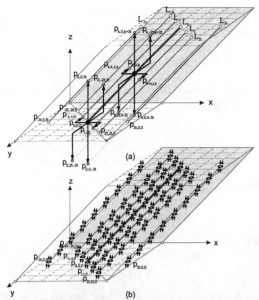

Figure 5. Stage 2 of broadcast in a 3-D torus: (a) the first step, and (b) the second step.

cubes $C_i, i = -3..3$, such that C_{-3} consists of the first t planes in Eq. (6), C_{-2} the next t planes, etc. (refer to Fig. 4(b)).

Let $L_0 = SPAN(p_{0,0,0}, (\vec{e}_{1,3}), (n))$ be the line already owning M. By having each $p_{i,0,i} \in L_0$ send M to the following six nodes:

$$p_{i+t,t,i}, \quad p_{i,2t,i-2t}, \quad p_{i,0,i-3t}, \quad p_{i-t,-t,i}, \quad p_{i,-2t,i+2t}, \quad p_{i,0,i+3t},$$

we can distribute M to six other lines in one step:

$$L_{\pm t} = SPAN(p_{\pm t, \pm t, 0}, (\vec{e}_{1,3}), (n))$$
$$L_{\pm 2t} = SPAN(p_{0, \pm 2t, \mp 2t}, (\vec{e}_{1,3}), (n))$$
$$L_{\pm 3t} = SPAN(p_{0,0,\mp 3t}, (\vec{e}_{1,3}), (n))$$

This communication step, as illustrated in Fig. 5(a), is congestion-free. The resulting line L_{it} is on the central plane of C_i for all $i = -3..3$. To see this, let's prove the case of L_{2t}:

$$L_{2t} = SPAN(p_{0,2t,-2t}, (\vec{e}_{1,3}), (n))$$
$$\in SPAN(p_{0,2t,-2t}, (\vec{e}_{1,3}, \vec{e}_2), (n,n))$$
$$= SPAN(p_{0,2t,-2t} + 2t\vec{e}_{1,3} - 2t\vec{e}_2, (\vec{e}_{1,3}, \vec{e}_2), (n,n))$$
$$= SPAN(p_{2t,0,0}, (\vec{e}_{1,3}, \vec{e}_2), (n,n)),$$

which is indeed the central plane of C_2. The other cases can be proved similarly. The routing matrix can be written as:

$$R_2 = \begin{bmatrix} 1 & 1 & 0 \\ 0 & 1 & -1 \\ 0 & 0 & -1 \end{bmatrix}.$$

Using the distance matrices in Eq. (4), the six routing paths in Fig. 5(a) can be described by the six rows in $D^+ \times R_2$ and $D^- \times R_2$.

Next, we can recursively perform the similar line-to-line distribution in each C_i using L_{it} as the source. The next step is shown in Fig. 5(b).

4.2.2 Stage 2.2 (Alignment)

From stage 2.1, on each plane $SPAN(p_{i,0,0}, (\vec{e}_{1,3}, \vec{e}_2), (n,n))$, $i = 0..n-1$, some line $L = SPAN(p_{i,j,0}, (\vec{e}_{1,3}), (n))$ already owns M. The goal is to "align" these n lines to the plane $SPAN(p_{0,0,0}, (\vec{e}_{1,3}, \vec{e}_{1,2}), (n,n))$. This can be done by having each node $\in L$ send M along the second dimension by $i - j$ hops, which is obviously congestion-free. This will forward M to the lines

$$SPAN(p_{i,i,0}, (\vec{e}_{1,3}), (n)) = SPAN(p_{0,0,0} + i\vec{e}_{1,2}, (\vec{e}_{1,3}), (n))$$

for $i = 0..n-1$. Clearly, these n lines constitute the plane $SPAN(p_{0,0,0}, (\vec{e}_{1,3}, \vec{e}_{1,2}), (n,n))$. Only one step is used in this stage.

4.3. Stage 3: From a Plane to More Planes

In this stage, we view the torus from another perspective:

$$SPAN(p_{0,0,0}, (\vec{e}_{1,3}, \vec{e}_{1,2}, \vec{e}_1), (n,n,n)), \qquad (7)$$

which is illustrated in Fig. 4(c). With this view, we partition the torus along the direction $\vec{e}_1$ into n planes $(i = -\lfloor \frac{n-1}{2} \rfloor, \ldots, \lceil \frac{n-1}{2} \rceil)$:

$$SPAN(p_{i,0,0}, (\vec{e}_{1,3}, \vec{e}_{1,2}), (n,n)). \qquad (8)$$

For simplicity, let $n = 7t$. Following the same philosophy as before, we divide the torus into 7 cubes $C_i, i = -3..3$, such as the first cube consists of the first t planes, the second cube the next t planes, etc. This is shown in Fig. 4(d).

The central plane in Eq. (8) already owns message M. In this stage, plane-to-plane message distribution will be performed. For instance, if every node on plane $SPAN(p_{0,0,0}, (\vec{e}_{1,3}, \vec{e}_{1,2}), (n,n))$ sends M along the Y- and Z-axes to nodes that are $+3$ and $+5$ hops way, respectively, then two planes will receive M:

$$SPAN(p_{0,3,0}, (\vec{e}_{1,3}, \vec{e}_{1,2}), (n,n)) = SPAN(p_{-3,0,0}, (\vec{e}_{1,3}, \vec{e}_{1,2}), (n,n))$$
$$SPAN(p_{0,0,5}, (\vec{e}_{1,3}, \vec{e}_{1,2}), (n,n)) = SPAN(p_{-5,0,0}, (\vec{e}_{1,3}, \vec{e}_{1,2}), (n,n)),$$

which are -3 and -5 planes next to the source plane. Specifically, we will use the routing matrix:

$$R_3 = \begin{bmatrix} 1 & 0 & 0 \\ 0 & -1 & 0 \\ 0 & 0 & -1 \end{bmatrix}.$$

The distance D^+ and D^- remain the same. The resulting 6 routing paths can be represented by the 6 rows in the following matrices:

$$D^+ \times R_3 = \begin{bmatrix} t & 0 & 0 \\ 0 & -2t & 0 \\ 0 & 0 & -3t \end{bmatrix} \begin{matrix} \text{// the next } t \text{ planes} \\ \text{// the next } 2t \text{ planes} \\ \text{// the next } 3t \text{ planes} \end{matrix}$$

$$D^- \times R_3 = \begin{bmatrix} -t & 0 & 0 \\ 0 & 2t & 0 \\ 0 & 0 & 3t \end{bmatrix} \begin{matrix} \text{// the next } -t \text{ planes} \\ \text{// the next } -2t \text{ planes} \\ \text{// the next } -3t \text{ planes} \end{matrix}.$$

Now we have 7 planes owning M on the centers of the cubes $C_i, i = -3..3$, so the recursion can be proceeded, until each C_i reduces to one or zero plane. Totally $\lceil \log_7 n \rceil$ steps will be used in this stage.

Theorem 1 *In a 3-D $T_{n \times n \times n}$ torus with dimension-ordered routing and all-port capability, broadcast can be done in $3\lceil \log_7 n \rceil + 2$ steps, which number of steps is at most 4 steps more than optimum.*

5. Broadcasting in k-D Tori

In this section, we extend our broadcasting algorithm to a k-D $T_{n \times \cdots \times n}$ torus. Following the same philosophy as before, broadcasting in $\mathbb{Z}^k$ (a k-D torus) will be achieved by distributing the broadcast message M in k stages: from the source to a line, from a line to a plane, from a plane to a cube, from a cube to a 4-D cube, etc. In the following, we discuss in general how stage i works, $i = 1..k$. Still, this has two parts: *distribution* and *alignment*. Throughout this section, we let $\vec{0} = p_{0,\ldots,0}$ be the source node and N_i be a vector of length i equal to $(n, n, \ldots, n)$.

5.1. Distribution Sub-stage

First, we need to define the set of nodes receiving the broadcast message after stage i.

Definition 3 The set of nodes receiving message M after stage i is defined to be:

$$U_i = SPAN(\vec{0}, \Omega_i, N_i),$$

where $\Omega_i = (\vec{e}_{1,k}, \vec{e}_{1,k-1}, \cdots, \vec{e}_{1,k-i+1})$.

The number of nodes in U_i is n times that of U_{i-1}. Also, we can think of U_i as n copies of U_{i-1} expanding along the vector $\vec{e}_{1,k-i+1}$, i.e.,

$$U_i = \bigcup_{j=0..n-1} (j\vec{e}_{1,k-i+1} + U_{i-1}), \quad (9)$$

where a vector $\vec{v}$ plus a set of nodes S ($\vec{v} + S$) means a "translation" operation which moves each node of S to a node relative to the former by a vector of $\vec{v}$. The following lemma guarantees that M will really be received by all nodes after stage k.

Lemma 2 $U_k = \mathbb{Z}^k$.

The way Ω_i being selected is to insure the following two lemmas, which are important later to guarantee our routing to be congestion-free. The following two lemmas can be simply proved by the Gaussian Elimination method.

Lemma 3 *For any i and j such that $1 \leq i \leq k - 1$ and $1 \leq j \leq k$, the union of Ω_i and the vector $\vec{e}_j$ is linearly independent.*

Lemma 4 *For any i, j_1, and j_2 such that $1 \leq i \leq k - 1$ and $2 \leq j_1, j_2 \leq k - i + 1$, the union of Ω_i and $\{\vec{e}_k, \vec{e}_{j_1}, \vec{e}_{j_2}\}$ is linearly independent.*

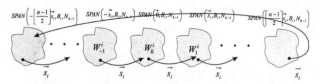

Figure 6. Partitioning V_i along $\vec{s}_i$ into a "super linear path".

To expand U_{i-1} to U_i, we need to view the torus from a different perspective defined as follows.

Definition 4 In stage i, we view the torus as:

$$V_i = SPAN(\vec{0}, B_i \cdot \vec{s}_i, N_k),$$

where

$$B_i = \begin{cases} (\vec{e}_{k-1}, \vec{e}_{k-2}, \cdots, \vec{e}_2, \vec{e}_1) & i = 1 \\ \Omega_{i-1} \cdot (\vec{e}_{k-i+1}, \vec{e}_{k-i}, \cdots, \vec{e}_2) & 2 \leq i \leq k \end{cases}$$

$$\vec{s}_i = \begin{cases} \vec{e}_k & i = 1 \\ \vec{e}_1 & 2 \leq i \leq k. \end{cases}$$

(Here "." means the concatenation of two sequences.)

The earlier perspectives Fig. 3(a), Fig. 4(a) and (c) of a 3-D torus are derived based on this formula. The above perspective provides us a way to partition the torus. As we have seen earlier, partitioning is used to solve our problem in a recursive manner.

Definition 5 In stage i, V_i is partitioned along direction $\vec{s}_i$ into the following n sub-networks ($j = -\lfloor \frac{n-1}{2} \rfloor, -\lfloor \frac{n-1}{2} \rfloor + 1, \ldots, \lceil \frac{n-1}{2} \rceil$):

$$W_j^i = SPAN(j\vec{s}_i, B_i, N_{k-1}).$$

The partitioning is illustrated in Fig. 6. Examples of such partitioning of a 3-D torus at different stages can be seen in Fig. 3(b), Fig. 4(b) and (d). We can imagine W_j^i as a "super-node" which is connected through a vector $\vec{s}_i$ to two "super-nodes" W_{j-1}^i and W_{j+1}^i in a *wrap-around* manner. So these super-nodes actually form a "super linear path" of length n. Also note that U_{i-1} (which already has the message M) is resident in the central super-node W_0^i. In the distribution sub-stage, we try to send M from W_0^i to the other $n - 1$ super-nodes; the sets of nodes receiving M in each super-node will have a shape "isomorphic" to U_{i-1}. This is done based on the following recursive structure: (i) partition the linear path into $2k + 1$ segments, (ii) send M to a representative super-node in each segment, and then (iii) perform the distribution in each segment recursively.

Given a segment of super-nodes of length m, we use a routing matrix and two distance matrices to describe the routing in one recursive step.

548

Definition 6 In stage i, the *routing matrix* is a $k \times k$ matrix defined as:

$$R_1 = \begin{bmatrix} \vec{e}_{1,k} \\ \vec{e}_{2,k} \\ \vdots \\ \vec{e}_{k-1,k} \\ \vec{e}_k \end{bmatrix} = \begin{bmatrix} 1 & 0 & \cdots & 0 & 1 \\ 0 & 1 & \cdots & 0 & 1 \\ \vdots & \vdots & \ddots & \vdots & \vdots \\ 0 & 0 & \cdots & 1 & 1 \\ 0 & 0 & \cdots & 0 & 1 \end{bmatrix}$$

$$R_i = \begin{bmatrix} \vec{e}_1 \\ \vec{e}_{2,-k} \\ \vdots \\ \vec{e}_{k-i+1,-k} \\ -\vec{e}_{k-i+2} \\ \vdots \\ -\vec{e}_k \end{bmatrix} = \left[\begin{array}{c|c} \mathbf{I}_{k-i+1} & \begin{matrix} 0 & \cdots & 0 & 0 \\ 0 & \cdots & 0 & -1 \\ \vdots & \ddots & \vdots & \vdots \\ 0 & \cdots & 0 & -1 \end{matrix} \\ \hline \mathbf{0} & -\mathbf{I}_{i-1} \end{array} \right], 2 \le i \le k.$$

Definition 7 In stage i, given a segment of super-nodes of length m, the *distance matrices* with respect to m are (intuitively, $\alpha_{\pm i} \approx \pm\frac{im}{2k+1}$; their precise values are derived in [14]):

$$D_m^+ = \begin{bmatrix} \alpha_1 \vec{e}_1 \\ \alpha_2 \vec{e}_2 \\ \vdots \\ \alpha_k \vec{e}_k \end{bmatrix} \approx \begin{bmatrix} \frac{m}{2k+1} & 0 & \cdots & 0 \\ 0 & \frac{2m}{2k+1} & \cdots & 0 \\ \vdots & \vdots & \ddots & \vdots \\ 0 & 0 & \cdots & \frac{km}{2k+1} \end{bmatrix}$$

$$D_m^- = \begin{bmatrix} \alpha_{-1} \vec{e}_1 \\ \alpha_{-2} \vec{e}_2 \\ \vdots \\ \alpha_{-k} \vec{e}_k \end{bmatrix} \approx \begin{bmatrix} \frac{-m}{2k+1} & 0 & \cdots & 0 \\ 0 & \frac{-2m}{2k+1} & \cdots & 0 \\ \vdots & \vdots & \ddots & \vdots \\ 0 & 0 & \cdots & \frac{-km}{2k+1} \end{bmatrix}$$

Using these matrices, the intuitive meanings of routing paths in one recursive step can be described by the $2k$ rows through the following matrix multiplication:

$$D_m^+ \times R_i = \begin{bmatrix} \text{routing paths to } W_{\alpha_1}^i (\alpha_1 \approx \frac{m}{2k+1}) \\ \text{routing paths to } W_{\alpha_2}^i (\alpha_2 \approx \frac{2m}{2k+1}) \\ \text{routing paths to } W_{\alpha_3}^i (\alpha_3 \approx \frac{3m}{2k+1}) \\ \vdots \\ \text{routing paths to } W_{\alpha_k}^i (\alpha_k \approx \frac{km}{2k+1}) \end{bmatrix} \quad (10)$$

$$D_m^- \times R_i = \begin{bmatrix} \text{routing paths to } W_{\alpha_{-1}}^i (\alpha_{-1} \approx \frac{-m}{2k+1}) \\ \text{routing paths to } W_{\alpha_{-2}}^i (\alpha_{-2} \approx \frac{-2m}{2k+1}) \\ \text{routing paths to } W_{\alpha_{-3}}^i (\alpha_{-3} \approx \frac{-3m}{2k+1}) \\ \vdots \\ \text{routing paths to } W_{\alpha_{-k}}^i (\alpha_{-k} \approx \frac{-km}{2k+1}) \end{bmatrix} \quad (11)$$

Consider the first communication step where U_{i-1} (resident in W_0^i) sends M following the second row of $D_m^+ \times R_i$ (which is equal to $\alpha_2 \vec{e}_{2,-k}$). Then, the message M will be sent to:

$$\begin{aligned} & \alpha_2 \vec{e}_{2,-k} + U_{i-1} \\ =\ & \alpha_2 \vec{e}_{2,-k} + \alpha_2 \vec{e}_{1,k} + U_{i-1} \ // \ \vec{e}_{1,k} \in \Omega_{i-1} \\ =\ & \alpha_2 \vec{e}_{1,2} + U_{i-1} \\ \in\ & SAPN(\alpha_2 \vec{e}_{1,2}, B_i, N_{k-1}) \\ =\ & SAPN(\alpha_2 \vec{e}_{1,2} - \alpha_2 \vec{e}_2, B_i, N_{k-1}) \ // \ \vec{e}_2 \in B_i \\ =\ & W_{\alpha_2}^i. \end{aligned}$$

The meanings of routing paths in the other rows can be proved similarly, so we omit the details.

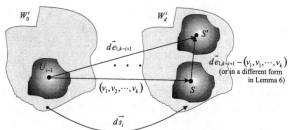

Figure 7. Aligning S to S' in W_d^i.

Lemma 5 *[14]In the distribution sub-stage of stage i, each communication step is congestion-free.*

5.2. Alignment Sub-stage

Now each super-node $W_d^i, d = 0..n-1$, already has a set of nodes (of shape isomorphic to U_{i-1}) owning M. The next job is to align these n sets to form U_i. In the following, we show the routing in W_d^i. Suppose the set of nodes owning M after the distribution sub-stage in W_d^i is S. As S is isomorphic to U_{i-1}, we can write S as $(v_1, v_2, \dots, v_k) + U_{i-1}$. Also, recall that U_i consists of n copies U_{i-1}'s (Eq. (9)) spanned along direction $\vec{e}_{1,k-i+1}$. So the set of nodes that we expect to own M in W_d^i should be $S' = d\vec{e}_{1,k-i+1} + U_{i-1}$ (see the illustration in Fig. 7).

If $(v_1, v_2, \dots, v_k) = d\vec{e}_{1,k-i+1}$, then $S = S'$ and there is no need of alignment. Otherwise, some alignment may be necessary. Intuitively, if we take a difference of these two vectors:

$$d\vec{e}_{1,k-i+1} - (v_1, v_2, \dots, v_k),$$

then the resulting vector can be used to represent the routing paths leading S to S'. However, such a routing may not be congestion-free. The following lemma shows that S in fact can be rewritten in a different form.

Lemma 6

$$\begin{aligned} S\ &=\ (v_1, v_2, \dots, v_k) + U_{i-1} \\ &= \begin{cases} (\underbrace{*, \dots, *}_{k-1}, d) * U_{i-1} & i = 1 \\ (d, \underbrace{*, *, \dots, *}_{k-i}, \underbrace{0, 0, \dots, 0}_{i-1}) * U_{i-1} & 2 \le i \le k \end{cases} \end{aligned}$$

where $*$ means a "don't care".

Using the new form in Lemma 6, we perform the following subtractions:

$$d\vec{e}_{1,k} - (\underbrace{*, *, \dots, *}_{k-1}, d) = (\underbrace{*, *, \dots, *}_{k-1}, 0) \quad i = 1 \quad (12)$$

$$\begin{aligned} & d\vec{e}_{1,k-i+1} - (d, \underbrace{*, *, \dots, *}_{k-i}, \underbrace{0, 0, \dots, 0}_{i-1}) \\ & = (0, \underbrace{*, *, \dots, *}_{k-i}, \underbrace{0, 0, \dots, 0}_{i-1}) \quad 2 \le i \le k \end{aligned} \quad (13)$$

The resulting vectors indicate how to align S to S'. When $i = 1$, the alignment may go along dimensions $\vec{e}_1, \vec{e}_2, \ldots, \vec{e}_{k-1}$ (by observing the locations where $*$'s appear in Eq. (12)). As $\vec{e}_1, \vec{e}_2, \ldots, \vec{e}_{k-1} \in B_1$, the routing only happens inside W_d^1. Thus, we only need to prove that the routing for the alignment inside individual W_d^1's is congestion-free. The proof is similar to that of Lemma 5, so we omit the details. Similarly, when $i > 1$, the alignment may go along dimensions $\vec{e}_2, \vec{e}_3, \ldots, \vec{e}_{k-i+1}$ (by observing the locations where $*$'s appear in Eq. (13)). As $\vec{e}_2, \vec{e}_3, \ldots, \vec{e}_{k-i+1} \in B_i$, the routing only happens inside W_d^i.

Also note that when $i = k$, Eq. (13) reduces to a zero vector, which means no need of alignment sub-stage in stage k. This leads to the following theorem.

Theorem 2 *In a k-D $T_{n \times \cdots \times n}$ torus with dimension-ordered routing and all-port capability, broadcast can be done in $k\lceil \log_{2k+1} n \rceil + k - 1$ steps, which number of steps is at most $2(k - 1)$ steps more than optimum.*

6. Conclusions

We compare our scheme for 3-D tori against two other known schemes: (i) Tsai and McKinley [10], which works for $T_{2^d \times 2^d \times z}$ and requires $d+1$ or $d+m+2$ steps when $2 \leq z \leq 7$ or $7 \times 6^m + 1 \leq z \leq 7 \times 6^{m+1}$, respectively, and (ii) Park *et al.* [6, 7], which works for $T_{7^i \times 7^i \times 7^i}$ and requires $3i$ steps. In Fig. 8, we draw the numbers of communication steps required by these and our schemes in a $T_{n \times n \times n}$ torus.

We make the following observations. First, in terms of the numbers of steps uses, the Park scheme is the best and always coincides with the lower bound; the TM scheme is better than ours when n is small, but is outperformed by ours as n becomes larger. Second, in terms of network sizes allowed, ours has the broadest applicability because any n is allowed; the TM and the Park schemes have quite limited applicability, and the situation is getting worse especially when n becomes larger. Third, in terms of communication capability, both TM and our schemes assume a dimension-ordered routing, while the Park scheme assumes a stronger non-dimension-ordered routing.

We are currently trying to extend our result to other port models such as [3].

References

[1] W. Dally and C. Seitz. The torus routing chip. *J. of Distributed Computing*, 1(3):187–196, 1986.

[2] C.-T. Ho and M.-Y. Kao. Optimal broadcasting in all-port wormhole-routed hypercubes. *IEEE Trans. on Paral. and Distrib. Sys.*, 6(2):200–204, Feb. 1995.

[3] S.-K. Lee and J.-Y. Lee. Optimal broadcast in α-port wormhole-routed mesh networks. In *Int'l Conf. on Paral. and Distrib. Sys.*, pages 109–114, 1997.

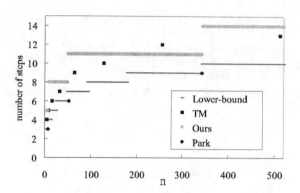

Figure 8. Comparison on the numbers of communication steps required to perform one-to-all broadcast in a $T_{n \times n \times n}$ torus.

[4] L. M. Ni and P. K. McKinley. A survey of wormhole routing techniques in directed network. *IEEE Computers*, 26(2):62–76, Feb. 1993.

[5] W. K. Nicholson. *Linear Algebra with Applications*. PWS Publishing Company, 3 edition, 1995.

[6] J. L. Park and H.-A. Choi. Circuit-switched broadcasting in tori and meshes networks. *IEEE Trans. on Paral. and Distrib. Sys.*, 7(2):184–190, Feb. 1996.

[7] J. L. Park, S.-K. Lee, and H.-A. Choi. Circuit-switched broadcasting in d-dimensional torus and mesh networks. In *Int'l Parallel Processing Symp.*, pages 26–29, 1994.

[8] J. G. Peters and M. Syska. Circuit-switched broadcasting in torus networks. *IEEE Trans. on Paral. and Distrib. Sys.*, 7(3):246–255, March 1996.

[9] Y.-J. Tsai and P. K. McKinley. A broadcasting algorithm for all-port wormhole-routed torus networks. In *Symp. on Frontiers of Massively Parallel Computation*, pages 529–536, 1995.

[10] Y.-J. Tsai and P. K. McKinley. A broadcasting algorithm for all-port wormhole-routed torus networks. *IEEE Trans. on Paral. and Distrib. Sys.*, 7(8):876–885, Aug. 1996.

[11] Y.-C. Tseng. A dilated-diagonal-based scheme for broadcast in a wormhole-routed 2d torus. *IEEE Trans. on Comput.*, 46:947–952, Aug. 1997.

[12] Y.-C. Tseng and S. K. S. Gupta. All-to-all personalized communication in a wormhole-routed torus. *IEEE Trans. on Paral. and Distrib. Sys.*, 7(5):498–505, May 1996.

[13] C.-M. Wang and C.-Y. Ku. A near-optimal broadcasting algorithm in all-port wormhole-routed hypercubes. In *ACM Int'l Conf. on Supercomputing*, pages 147–153, 1995.

[14] S.-Y. Wang and Y.-C. Tseng. Algebraic foundations and broadcasting algorithms for wormhole-routed tori. Technical report, Dept. of Computer Science and Information Eng., National Central Univ., Jan. 1998.

Session 8A
Protocols

Chair: Kang G. Shin
University of Michigan

PastSet - An Efficient High Level Inter Process Communication Mechanism[Ψ]

Brian Vinter, Otto J. Anshus and Tore Larsen
Department of Computer Science, University of Tromsø, Norway

Abstract

A new high level IPC mechanism, PastSet, is presented. PastSet supports partial causal ordered logging of synchronization and communication events. Communicated data are represented as tuples and stored in a common repository accessible by all processes. In the repository, tuples of the same template are causally ordered While being equivalent to semaphores, messages and pipes, PastSet also offer a powerful abstraction suitable for knapsack type parallel applications as well as applications that require state logging. An implementation on uniprocessors and four-way multiprocessors running Linux. The mechanism is integrated into the Linux kernel alongside existing Sys V mechanisms. PastSet gives up to 40% faster synchronization and up to 56% better small package bandwidths than achieved with Linux semaphores, messages, and pipes. Although being a higher abstraction level mechanism, PastSet proves to consistently outperform existing Linux Sys V interprocess communication mechanisms on multiprocessors and to a large extend also on uniprocessors.

1 Introduction

This paper describes an efficient implementation of PastSet, a high-level inter-process communication (IPC) mechanism. The current PastSet implementation is for Intel-based uni- and symmetrical multiprocessors running Linux 2.0.30. All performance measurements are done on these platforms. The work demonstrates the feasibility of PastSet IPC and documents that this high abstraction-level IPC mechanism may perform as efficiently as more simple mechanisms on the same platform..

An IPC mechanism should provide the means to perform efficient, secure and reliable communication between potentially non-trusted processes in the system. The mechanism should also allow the programmer to decide whether a process is in ready or waiting state. [14] is a classical early study of IPC primitives. Several IPC mechanisms has been investigated such as message passing [11], semaphores [7], and shared memory [1]. Mechanisms for message passing, semaphores, and shared memory are provided in most modern operating systems.

More advanced IPC mechanisms include lightweight remote procedure calls [3] and local procedure calls [6]. The latter mechanism offers semantics similar to those of RPC [5], but is optimized for execution within one machine.

In distributed computing the initial overhead for performing communication is much higher than for centralized systems. Because of this imperative overhead, research has been done into supplying more powerful IPC, as a means to reduce the number of costly IPC operations. Advanced IPC mechanisms suggested for distributed computing include Horus [13], Linda [8], and ISIS [4]. Because distributed IPC mechanisms differ so much in nature from standard IPC mechanisms, these will not be discussed further in this paper.

For the reminder of the paper, we will first briefly discuss the PastSet communication model and compare it to the standard IPC mechanisms in Linux. Further, our implementation is described and discussed, and performance numbers are presented, discussed and compared with the performance of Linux 2.0.30 standard IPC. Finally conclusions are drawn and future work is outlined.

2 PastSet

PastSet was first introduced as an inter process communication paradigm in [2]. The paradigm resembles that of Linda, but with some significant differences. Tuples are generated dynamically based on tuple templates that may also be generated dynamically. A tuple template is an ordered set of types. Tuples based on a particular template has an ordered set of variables matching the types in the template. Each type in a tuple template has an associated value-space, or dimension, describing the set of all possible values for that type in this template. Taken together, the types in a template spawns a space encompassing all conceivable type-value combinations for tuples based on that template. A tuple with all singular values represents a singular point in this space. As with Linda, PastSet supports writing (called move) tuples into tuple-space and reading (called observe) tuples that reside in tuple space. Contrary to Linda reads,

[Ψ] This work is in part supported by the Research Council of Norway, grants no. 107625/24, 116591/410 and others.

PastSet observes do *not* remove tuples from tuple space. No mechanism is provided to remove individual tuples from PastSet. In PastSet, each set of tuples based on the same or identical templates is denoted an element of PastSet. An element may be seen as representing a trace of interprocess communications in the multidimensional space spawned by the tuple template. PastSet preserves the causal order among all operations on tuples based on the same or identical templates. There is no ordering between tuples of different elements.

In effect, PastSet keeps a causally ordered log of all tuples of the same or identical templates that has existed in the system. This also allows the processes to re-read previously read tuples.

It is the intention that the added semantics of PastSet will allow programmers to more easily create parallel programs that are not of the traditional 'bag of tasks' type. Validating this intent is beyond the scope of this paper. Currently, our focus is on creating an efficient implementation of PastSet that allows us to experiment with porting and developing parallel applications using PastSet.

In addition to a set of causally ordered tuples, two pointers First and Last are associated with each element. First refers to the elements oldest unread tuple. Last refers to the elements last (newest) tuple. A third parameter, DeltaValue, defines the maximum allowed number of tuples between First and Last. DeltaValue may be set by a process at any time. The move and observe operators update First and Last, and obey the restrictions imposed by DeltaValue for each element in PastSet.

Functionality is provided to truncate PastSet on a per element basis, permanently removing all tuples that are older than a given tuple.

2.1 The Enter-operator

To be allowed to operate on an element a process must perform an *enter* operation, this is done by issuing an 'enter dimensions' specifying the specific space that the element covers. Any tuple may have a tag as its first data; this tag can be used to differentiate between otherwise similar elements. In addition, by using an appropriately complex tag it can function as a security mechanism to avoid unauthorized access to the element. This is equivalent with having a large and sparse name space. In addition to the tag the parameters for the *enter*-operator are; the size of the tuple excluding the tag, an initial DeltaValue and an identifier for a pair of filter functions (described below). The *enter*-operator will return an integer that identifies the element and which is used when accessing the element. If no existing element fits the given space, a new element of PastSet will be created. If the system does not have, enough memory to create the element an ENOMEM-error code will be returned. Each process can exist in at most 1024 spaces, if this limit has been reached the *enter*-operator returns a EMFILE error.

2.2 The Move operator

To add tuples to an element the *move*-operator is used. It is semantically similar to the 'out' operator in Linda but has a different syntax because under PastSet, the element must also be identified in the operation. The *move*-operator takes an element identifier and a pointer to the tuple as parameters. The tuples are strongly typed, and a string for instance must have a fixed length.

The *move*-operator returns when the operation has completed. If the move operation would break the boundary defined by the DeltaValue, the operation will block. If this happens the process remains blocked until one of two things happen. Either another process executes an observe operation that increases the First pointer by one, thereby allowing the move operation to continue, or a process changes the DeltaValue to a value that allows the move. A blocked move operation may also be terminated if the element it works on is deleted, see the *axe*-operator below.

2.3 The Observe operator

The *observe*-operator reads a tuple value from an element, and makes it available to the process. The *observe*-operator does not directly compare to either of Linda's operators; **in** and **read**. Because the tuple is still available for reading after an observe it is not as 'destructive' as **in** and because it can change the First pointer it is not totally invisible as **read**. Observe may be called with two or three parameters. The element identifier must be specified, as must a pointer to a tuple memory region. The tuple memory region is where any information on the requested tuple is stored; this information could be used to do 'pattern' matching as in Linda or other ways to further specify the desired tuple, i.e. a virtual timestamp for rollback in optimistic execution or a given checkpoint for error recovery. The same space is also where the result of the observe will eventually be stored. The third and optional parameter is an absolute number that specifies which tuple to read. If no tuple number is specified the observe operator reads the value of the tuple pointed to by the First pointer, and atomically increases the First pointer by one. If First=Last, the process will be blocked until another process issues a *move*. This case represents the situation where no unobserved tuples exist in the element. An *observe* may also block if no tuple in the element fits the requirements passed as a pattern.

If a tuple number is specified that specific tuple value is read into the passed tuple memory region. If the tuple does not exist, the process will be blocked until it does. Reading specific tuples does not alter the First pointer, even if the specified tuple is the one pointed to by the First pointer. If the specified tuple does not exist in the element any more, see the *Axe* operator below, an EDEADLK error-message will be returned.

2.4 The X-function

The *X-function* is a set of function pairs from which the programmer can choose one to associate with an element. Any *X-function* comes as two parts called *X-in* and *X-out*. When a *move* operation is executed the tuple data is filtered through the *X-in* function and then stored according to the *X-in* result. When an *observe*-operation is issued, the *X-out* function is called with the input tuple as parameter, the *X-out* returns a specific tuple to return.

The *X-functions* may potentially perform many semantic operations, but are primarily intended to supply the following features: alternatives to causal ordering; pattern matching; and general tuple manipulation. Alternative ordering may be used for achieving any number of alternative ordering in tuples, this may be ordering by a real-time time-stamp in the tuple, ordinary sorting or for supporting priorities in 'bag of job' type applications.

Pattern matching as supplied by Linda can also be supplied via an *X-function*, as the *X-in* function can build a lookup table, i.e., a hash table, and the *X-out* function can then easily perform pattern matching. For this ordinary database algorithms may be used, with the usual space/speed tradeoff considerations.

General tuple manipulation may be used for a large number of things, in the extreme most of the applications functionality may be performed via *X-functions*. A example of such tuple manipulation could be a graphical application where moves and observes to an element would be bitmapped frames for an animation, but the *X-in* function would mpeg compress the frames before storing them, and *X-out* would decompress the frames when they were observed.

2.5 The Axe operator

As all tuples that are moved into an element in principle will exist there forever, the size of these elements may grow unreasonably; this is especially problematic if the old data will never be used again. To solve this the *axe*-operator supplies an option to denounce a part of the element. The *axe*-operator takes only two parameters. The element which should be truncated and the absolute number of the last tuple that may never again be available. The PastSet can then reuse the space used by this and previous tuples when needed. The *axe* operation does not guarantee that the tuples are removed by the time the *axe* operation returns, only that they may disappear at any time thereafter. For cleaning up after execution a *DelElement* operator is supplied, this operation totally removes the element that is passed as the parameter.

2.6 The First, Last and Delta operators

The PastSet also allows the programmer to directly monitor the value of the `First` and `Last` pointers of an element, as well as allowing the `DeltaValue` to be monitored or modified. *First* and *Last* simply takes the element id as the parameter and returns the respective value. *Delta* also requires the element id, and may also take a second parameter, i.e., the new `DeltaValue`. If the new `DeltaValue` is smaller than the current `Last-First`, this is simply accepted and if this is still the case when the next *move* operation arrives it will be blocked. If the new `DeltaValue` allows blocked move operations to perform, these processes will be woken.

3 Comparing Sys V and PastSet

The reminder of this paper will focus on performance differences between standard Sys V IPC and PastSet, but before we start to compare numbers we should compare the semantics of Sys V and PastSet. Because pipes are often used instead of Sys V IPC for special cases where only two processes are communicating, pipes are also included in this overview and the numbers following this section. The shared memory model which is also included in Sys V IPC is not included as it provides no primitives for synchronization, and communication is plain memory copying so that the user himself is responsible for checking that both source and destination buffers are valid.

IPC	#processes	Carries semantic value	Max # of operations pr. call	Interpret message semantics[1]	Supports priorities	Write once read many	Monitor state
Semaphores	N/a	No	32 (Typical)	No	No	No	Yes
Messages	N/a	Yes	1	No	Yes	No	Yes
Pipes	2	Yes	1	No	No	No	No
PastSet	N/a	Yes	1	Yes	Yes[2]	Yes[3]	Yes

Table 1: Comparing the semantics of IPC mechanisms.

---

[1] What this means is: May the IPC mechanism read the value of the data and act correspondingly?
[2] Priorities must implemented via an X-function
[3] Read once read many may be done by a move and then indexed observes.

As table 1 indicates the only parameter where PastSet provides less powerful semantics than Sys V, is the fact that Sys V can manipulate several semaphores at one time. The availability of such a operation block facility for PastSet was discussed but agreed against, because the added user complexity seemed to outweigh the advantage of saving one or more system calls. When one looks at the semantics of the compared IPC mechanisms, it should be clear that PastSet can easily model the functionality of the others, the only functionality that is not provided by PastSet is non-blocking operations.

4 Implementation

The PastSet implementation described here is done in the Linux 2.0.30 kernel. The implementation is only approximately 1000 lines of C code.

Because of our initial expectation, that more complex IPC mechanisms by nature are slower than relatively simple mechanisms, much effort was placed into speed considerations in the implementation. Some of the guidelines that were made for the implementation were:

1. The size of all data structures must be a multiple of pages[4]
2. The newest data must be expected to be most likely to be read
3. Where ever possible fixed indexing should be preferred to list structures.
4. Data structures should be build in a way that maximizes the utilization of the cache line width, i.e. variables that are used in conjunction should be placed on the same cache line.

Elements are handled in a manor very similar to a Unix I-node structure, only with a reverse ordering, so that the newest tuples are most easily retrieved, ad. point 2. To meet point 1, the structure that describes an element, holds the data that describes an element, such as tag, First, Last, ... After these data, the structure has two pointers to user tuple storrage, one that points to a page of pointers to data blocks of size one page, and one that points to a page of pointers that points to pages of pointers to pages of user data. After these, the structure is simply filled with pointes to data pages up until the page boundary. This way data can be accessed directly, indirected by one pointer and indirected by two pointers. New data is always stored via the direct pointers, once these are filled the oldest is migrated to a single indirect pointer, which in turn when full migrates the oldest pointer to a double indirect pointer. The double indirected part of the structure can in it's own hold 4GB of data, twice the available address space under Linux. Naturally, no space is allocated until needed.

The position of an existing tuple can easily be calculated, from it's index the size of the tuples in the element and the Last pointer. Thus even with this fully flexible structure

we meet requirement 3. The only part of the PastSet code that does not use indexing is the X functions which has to utilize linked lists to be able to insert tuple indexes in arbitrary order. By sacrificing memory these could also be optimized on. These speed/space tradeoffs must be considered depending on the nature of the X function, i.e., reverse arrival order is efficiently handled with linked lists whereas sorting the tuples from their data contents can defend using more memory for more entry points into the linked list.

All PastSet code is placed inside the kernel for two reasons. One reason is to ensure protection of the elements so that tuples that have been moved into the PastSet are not modified, and are only read via *observe*. The other reason to place the code in the kernel is to achieve performance results that can be compared with System V IPC mechanisms, without having to consider any other parameters. The PastSet code does not include any compile time optimizations for single- or multiprocessing, the PastSet code is identical whether or not the kernel is build with SMP support.

The interface for calling PastSet is a direct extension of Linux's System V calling interface, this is not inherently efficient but makes the PastSet data more comparable to the standard IPC measurements. Adding a new system-call for PastSet was slightly faster than integrating the call in standard IPC. We have chosen to keep PastSet directly in the standard IPC demultiplexer anyway to achieve more directly comparable results.

Only a limited set of *X-functions* has been implemented up until now. These include one that implements reverse arrival order, and one that sorts the tuples, according to their data values. These *X-functions* are implemented to demonstrate the functionality and to allow measurements for elements that use *X-functions*.

5 Performance

To compare the performance of PastSet with the performance of standard IPC we have measured the time to do a roundtrip (sending a minimal sized packet from the sender to the receiver and back again) as a measure for the time to do one synchronization. We have also measured the communication bandwidth for several packet sizes. Micro benchmarks have been written that measures the performance of semaphores, messages, pipes and the PastSet. Pipes are included because piped communication often outperforms the corresponding functionality of the Sys V IPC mechanisms. And thus in some cases pipes are the mechanism that performance should be compared to, it is important to stress that pipes cannot replace IPC mechanisms for many applications as they are far less flexible. Shared memory has not been included, as the performance of shared memory is extremely dependent on the number of CPU's and the load of the system, and because shared memory does not provide any suspend-wakeup support. Because the footprint of the PastSet can

---

[4] On the Intel x86 architecture a page is 4KB

grow large, we also measure the IPC performance between threads as well as processes. If our page alignment policy does not work, PastSet could prove to be less efficient between threads than processes.

All experiments were run on a Quad CPU 166MHz Pentium Pro box with 128 MB RAM. The operating system was Linux 2.0.30 patched with the PastSet functionality. Two versions of the kernel was used, one with SMP support and one without, without SMP support the machine functions as an uni-processor. For all benchmarks the PastSet 'Delta-value' has been set to 10^6, to model an unconstrained element. All loops are iterated 1000 times to achieve measurements that are insensitive to noise. All benchmark results are the mean of ten runs.

5.1 Synchronization Performance

To measure the synchronization performance we run two processes in step-lock. The advantage of this scenario is that it, besides testing the basic performance of the mechanisms, also tests the efficiency of suspending and waking processes. Efficient suspend-wake mechanisms are important for all applications where the processing of the communicated data is of minor importance relative to the communication itself. Linux's text-mode based mouse-copy-and-paste driver, GPM, is an example of such an application. Pseudo code for the benchmark is:

Parent	Child
Synchronize	Synchronize
for(1000 iterations)	for(1000 iterations)
start=timestamp;	read(package);
write(package);	write(package);
read(package);	
stop=timestamp;	
time+=stop-start;	

The step-locking applications are all very simple, the parent process forks off a child and the two processes synchronize to ensure that both are ready to run. The child then starts out by reading a package[5] from the parent-process, then sends a package back to the parent-process and loops these operations a fixed number of times.

After forking the parent process synchronizes with the child. Then for a fixed number of times take a timestamp[6], sends a package to the child-process, receives a package from the child-process and takes another timestamp. The measured time for the roundtrip is calculated and added to the total time for the 1000 iterations. Finally the parent-process calculates the average latency for a roundtrip step-lock and from that the context-switching overhead for the IPC mechanism in question. For the IPC mechanisms that transfer user defined data, a minimal package size has

---

[5] Reading a package can be reading from a stream, locking a semaphore, receiving a message or observing a tuple. Writing a package can mean writing to a stream, unlocking a semaphore, sending a message or moving a tuple.
[6] Timestamps are taken with the cycle counters available in Pentium processors and above.

been chosen: 1 byte for pipes and 0 bytes for messages and PastSet.

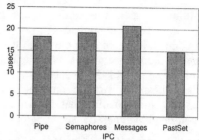

Figure 1: Context switching overhead between processes on a uni-processor.

It is interesting to see that even though PastSet is a more complex IPC mechanism than semaphores, on the single CPU box the current implementation is 29% faster than semaphores. Although pipes are faster than semaphores also, PastSet is still 23% faster than the fastest solution available under standard Linux. Sys V messages are 40% slower than the PastSet.

For threads the situation is about the same. PastSet is 22% faster than pipes and still 29% faster than semaphores. Messages improve their relative performance slightly and now PastSet is only 37% faster. The fact that there is no significant change in the relative performance between the IPC mechanisms is not surprising as all of them should have a relative small footprint with message size zero or one byte. None of the mechanisms trigger more TLB reloads than the others.

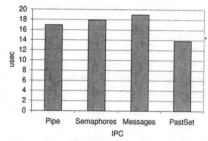

Figure 2: Context switching overhead between threads on a uni-processor.

On the SMP box, results are generally poorer than on the single CPU. This is largely because of additional overhead that is imperative on SMP systems. In addition, because Linux versions 2.0.xx are particularly bad at handling symmetrical multiprocessing, a more optimized SMP handling will be found in the Linux 2.1.xx kernels. However, none of these was stable enough that we would venture into these for our current implementation. While context switching processes in SMP mode, the advantage for PastSet shrinks to 11% on semaphores and 4% on pipes. Also, messages improve their relative performance so that PastSet now only has an 18% advantage on them. This change in relative performance is because the system-call overhead and the OS level context-switching overhead takes up a larger portion of the overall latency than in a single CPU system. Thus, the absolute gain has not decreased however the relative performance has.

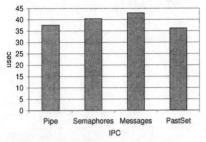

Figure 3: Context switching overhead between processes on a SMP machine.

Under SMP, the performance of threading becomes increasingly interesting. The same picture that showed for threading on a single CPU repeats here, thus the advantage of PastSet shrinks to 2% on pipes and 17% on messages. Interestingly semaphores loose a bit and are now 12% slower than PastSet.

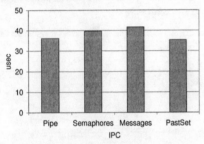

Figure 4: Context switching overhead between threads on a SMP machine.

5.2 Bandwidth

The step-lock benchmarks test the IPC mechanism's basic speed of operation and its efficiency of handling suspend-wakeup. As the packages that are sent and received in the step-lock benchmarks are minimized to show just these parameters, these benchmarks does not give any impression of the mechanisms ability to transfer data. For this purpose, another benchmark, testing communication bandwidth, has been derived. Pseudo code for the benchmark is:

Parent	Child
synchronize	Synchronize
start=timestamp;	for(1000 iterations)
for(1000 iterations)	read(package);
write(package);	stop=timestamp;
read(stop);	write(stop);
time+=stop-start;	

The bandwidth benchmarks are somewhat similar in structure to the step-lock benchmarks, but after synchronizing, the child-process only reads data, and the parent-process only writes data. When the parent-process has written all the data, it reads the timestamp that the child took when it had finished reading the last package, and then calculates a communication bandwidth between

the processes. The package size is varied to test the different mechanisms under different conditions. As semaphores cannot carry semantic information, they are not included in this benchmark suite.

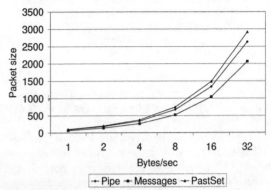

Figure 5: Uniprocessor process communication bandwidth using small packages.

The bandwidth results are presented in four pairs of graphs here. In each pair, one graph shows bandwidth for small packages, and one that shows for all package sizes up till 2048 bytes. The zooming on small packages allows one to see performance characteristics for small packages, which is often used for IPC. When communicating between processes on the uni-processor PastSet is slightly faster than any of the standard IPC mechanisms supplied by Linux for small packages. This would encourage the use of PastSet over the standard IPC mechanisms, at 32-byte package size PastSet delivers 41% better bandwidth than messages and 11% better than pipes. On the SMP box, this difference shrinks to 9% improvement on pipes. Messages however, perform rather poorly under SMP and the advantage of PastSet grows to 55%. The fact that PastSet and messages looses ground to pipes on SMP is probably due to the fact that pipes need not manage a queue of waiting processes as only one process can read from a given pipe descriptor.

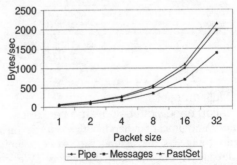

Figure 6:Multi processor process communication bandwidth using small packages.

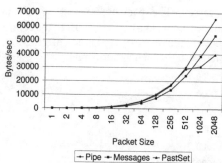

Figure 7:Uniprocessor process communication bandwidth using large packages

When increasing the package size PastSet starts to loose performance relative to the other IPC mechanisms, on the single CPU experiment. The crossover point is between 256 and 512 bytes per package for pipes and between 512 and 1024 bytes for messages. The explanation to why PastSet, after this point, has a slower speedup rate than the others is because the PastSet stores all of the communicated data in the data element. As the package size increases, PastSet must more often allocate more memory. This requires some pointer handling and memory clearing. On the SMP experiment the crossover point is pushed closer to 512 byte packages for pipes, and now the pipe performance advantage don't grow as large as with the uni-processor. Most likely this is because only two CPU's are being kept busy by the experiment, which allows the other two to keep ahead with the memory management. Messages continue to perform poorly under SMP, and now PastSet consistently outperforms messages, at packet size 2048 PastSet is a full 28% better than messages. Exactly why messages perform so badly under SMP is hard to determine, but one must expect that the implementation is not optimized for SMP usage.

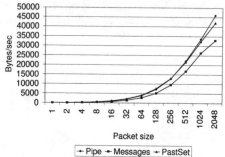

Figure 8: Multi processor inter-process communication bandwidth using large packages.

Testing the communication bandwidth between threads might seem strange as the natural way to communicate between threads is through shared memory. We do it anyway however, because we want to test the performance of PastSet once it's footprint really starts to grow. For small packages we would expect to see a slight improvement for all the tested mechanisms, simply as a result of the smaller context switching overhead imposed on threads relative to processes. Surprisingly messages

show a slight decrease in bandwidth, which however is very small. Pipes and PastSet has practically the same bandwidth with threads as with processes.

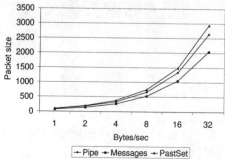

Figure 9:Single processor inter thread communication bandwidth using small packages.

Under SMP PastSet decreases it's relative performance to pipes, so that the advantage of PastSet while communicating between threads is only 6%. Messages continue to perform poorly, so that PastSet performs 54% better than messages.

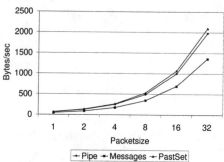

Figure 10:Multi processor inter thread communication bandwidth using small packages.

Large packet communication between threads on the uni-processor behaves exactly as it did between processes, even the peek bandwidth is roughly the same. This indicates that the page alignment policy of PastSet works and causes no more TLB reloads than the other two mechanisms.

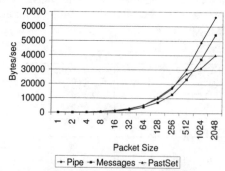

Figure 11:Single processor inter thread communication bandwidth using large packages.

Inter thread communication, under SMP, with large packages is interesting. Pipes have the same performance as with processes, whereas both messages and PastSet performs poorer than they did with processes. The explanation for this is that either the scheduler treats threads waiting for pipes differently or the C-library has an optimization for stream handling that somehow pins the threads onto the same CPU, thereby avoiding copying the data over the bus. At 2048 bytes pr. package, PastSet is 37% slower than pipes and 33% faster than messages.

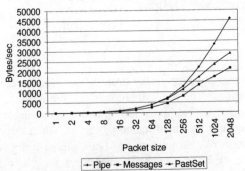

Figure 12:Multi processor inter thread communication bandwidth using small packages.

6   Review of other systems

Little work has been done lately on IPC mechanisms, and of the work that is done very little is comparable with our work on the PastSet. Most IPC mechanism research is an integral part of a custom operating system, which makes comparisons to other IPC's difficult.

Eros[12] shows IPC bandwidth that is approximately twice as high as Linux pipes. The Eros work is done under the framework of a totally new operating system, and their IPC work is targeted mainly against speed, and not so much a more powerful IPC mechanism.

L3, L4 and L5 are work into efficient micro-kernel design, for this means a very fast IPC mechanism has been developed[10]. The L3 IPC is shown to be much faster than the IPC of Mach, which in return is faster than that of Linux. The L3 IPC is directly targeted towards micro-kernel functionality and does not introduce any new IPC semantics.

MPI[9] is a very powerful message passing API, which contain many of the features found in PastSet, plus quite a lot more. The MPI API is a supported standard and is targeted MPP and networks, more than small SMP machines as described in this paper. Until PastSet becomes a distributed IPC the comparison to MPI is not really fair.

7   Conclusion

PastSet is a more powerful IPC mechanism when compared to ordinary System V IPC, yet the added semantics results in no performance penalty, except in sustained bandwidth when working with large packages. We have shown that a well considered design and an efficient implementation is able to outperform the standard Linux synchronization mechanism by 2-40%. In addition, provide a sustained bandwidth up to 56% better than standard communication primitives do. The few primitives supported by PastSet are enough to perform any desired communication primitive, and the guaranteed causal consistency supported by PastSet is a powerful addition from the point of the programmer.

The PastSet specifically targeted a high performance in multiprocessor systems.   We have shown results that indicate that our page alignment policy results in no more TLB reloads than the other IPC mechanisms, even though PastSet may have a radically larger footprint. PastSet is significantly better that System V messages on multiprocessors, and should be a clear advantage in applications that does not simply pipe data through processes.

We have shown that the functionality of ordinary System V IPC can be easily modeled by PastSet and not loose any performance, still utilizing the extra features of PastSet comes at no extra performance cost.

Reference

[1] An Evaluation of Directory Schemes for Cache Coherence, Argawal et al., Proc 15'th SoCA

[2] *MacroScope: The Abstractions of a Distributed Operating System*, Anshus O. J., Larsen T., Norsk Informatikk Konferanse 1992, October 1992.

[3] *Lightweight Remote Procedure Call*, B. N. Bershad, Proc. 12th ACM Symposium on Operating System Principles, December 1989, pp. 102-113.

[4] Reliable Communication in the Presence of Faliures, Birman, K. P. and Joseph, T., Proc. OSP 1987

[5] *Implementing Remote Procedure Calls*, A. D. Birrel, B. Nelson, ACM Transactions on Computer Systems. Febuary 1984, pp. 39-59

[6] *Inside Windows NT*, Hellen Custer, Microsoft Press 1993, pp.155-16

[7] *Co-operating Sequential Processes*, Programming Languages, Genuys,F.(Ed), London Academic Press, 1665

[8] *Generative Communication in Linda*. ACM Trans. On Programming Languages and Systems, vol 7. 1985.

[9] *The MPI Standard for Message Passing*, Lecture Notes in Computer Science, vol 797, 1994 pp. 247-252

[10] *Improving IPC by Kernel Design, Improving IPC by Kernel Design*, 14th Symposium on Operating System Principles (SOSP), Asheville, NC, 1993

[11] *Understanding and using Asynchronous Message passing Primitives*, Proc. Symposium of Distributed Computing, 1982.

[12] *The Measured Performance of a Fast Local IPC*, Jonathan S. Shapiro, David J. Farber, and Jonathan M. Smith, 5th International Workshop on Object-Orientation in Operating Systems

[13] *Horus : a flexible group communication system*, Robbert van Renesse, Kenneth P. Birman and Silvano Maffeis, Communications of the ACM Vol.39, No. 4 (April 1996), pp. 76-83.

[14] Processes, Tasks and Monitors: A Comparative Study of Concurrent Programming Primitives, Wegner P and Smolka S. A., IEEE trans. On Software Engeneering, 1983.

Efficient Sleep/Wake-up Protocols for User-Level IPC

Ronald C. Unrau
Department of Computing Science
University of Alberta, CANADA
unrau@cs.ualberta.ca

Orran Krieger
IBM T.J. Watson Research Centre
Yorktown Heights, New York
okrieg@watson.ibm.com

Abstract

We present a new facility for cross-address space IPC that exploits queues in memory shared between the client and server address space. The facility employs only widely available operating system mechanisms, and is hence easily portable to different commercial operating systems. It incorporates blocking semantics to avoid wasting processor cycles, and still achieves almost twice the throughput of the native kernel-mediated IPC facilities on SGI and IBM uniprocessors. In addition, we demonstrate significantly higher performance gains on an SGI multiprocessor. We argue that co-operating tasks will be better served if the operating system is aware of the co-operation, and propose an interface for a hand-off scheduling mechanism. Finally, we report initial performance results from a Linux implementation of our proposal.

1. Introduction

The performance of Inter-Process Communication (IPC) is crucial to many applications. For this reason, there has been a great deal of research into developing IPC facilities that perform well [1, 4, 6, 7, 10, 13]. However, most of this work was in the context of either user-level thread packages or research operating systems; it is of little relevance to the developer trying to implement, for example, a high performance data base server on an existing commercial system.

One promising strategy for implementing IPC on current systems is to use memory shared between the client and server address spaces to implement the communication protocol — we refer to this strategy as *User-level IPC* because the communication is not kernel mediated. User-level IPC is attractive for several reasons: first, the number of (expensive) system calls can be reduced; second, the amount of copying into and out of the kernel address space is reduced; third, custom protocols that take advantage of application-specific knowledge can be used; and fourth, User-level IPC uses only widely available mechanisms, and is therefore portable to many commercial systems.

Under ideal circumstances, user-level IPC can achieve round-trip latencies on the order of tens (or hundreds) of instructions. The ideal situation is when a message transfer is achieved by simply adding and/or removing requests from queues in shared memory; that is, when there is no need to invoke kernel services. On a shared-memory multiprocessor, if the client and server are running on different processors (and are willing to spin for a time) this efficient situation may be common. On a uniprocessor, this efficient situation can be common if the IPC is asynchronous. In this case a client process can enqueue multiple asynchronous messages on to a shared queue without blocking waiting for a response. Similarly, when the server gets the opportunity to run, it can handle requests and respond without invoking kernel services until all pending requests are processed.

The challenge for user-level IPC is to handle synchronous message passing efficiently, especially on a uniprocessor. In this case, when a queue is empty (or full) the process should block (i.e., yield the processor) both to avoid wasting processor cycles and to give other processes the opportunity to process requests from the shared queues. A consumer process that finds its queue empty should put itself to sleep until there is work to do; a producer process should enqueue its work and then wake-up the consumer so that response latency is minimized. Kernel services must be invoked in the sleep/wake-up part of the protocol, and the challenge is to achieve performance better than the native IPC facilities provided by the operating system.

In this paper, we present and evaluate several user-level IPC protocols that use shared FIFO queues to implement cross-address space client-server communication. We develop a user-level IPC protocol that incorporates sleep/wake-up (Section 3), but show that because of interactions with the operating system scheduling policy the protocol has worse performance than standard kernel-mediated IPC. We then give two enhancements to the protocol that improve performance (Section 4), and demonstrate that for even the tough case of synchronous IPC, user-level IPC can out perform traditional kernel mediated IPC. The mechanisms we employ are available on most commercial operating systems, and we show improved performance on SGI IRIX and IBM AIX uniprocessors, and on an SGI multiprocessor. Finally, in Section 6 we argue that even better per-

```
void Send( Msg *msg, Msg *ans ) {
  while( !enqueue( Q[srv], msg ) )
    sleep( 1 ); /* queue full */

  while( !dequeue( Q[clnt], ans ) )
    busy_wait(); /* wait for reply */
}

void Receive( Msg *msg ) {
  while( !dequeue( Q[srv], msg ) )
    busy_wait(); /* queue empty */
}

void Reply( int clnt, Msg *msg ) {
  while( !enqueue( Q[clnt], msg )
    sleep( 1 ); /* queue full */
}
```

Figure 1. **Both Sides Spin**: A Send/Receive/Reply interface with fixed sized messages and busy waiting using shared memory queues.

formance can be achieved if the operating system is made aware that the processes are co-operating through IPC. We propose a hand-off scheduling mechanism, and report initial performance from an implementation in Linux.

The purpose of this paper is to examine the performance issues associated with user-level IPC, and due to space limitations we do not deal with security issues. Servers can protect themselves from clients by careful access to the shared memory queues. Clients can be protected from other clients by placing only recoverable control information in the queues shared by other clients; all sensitive state is maintained in mapped regions isolated from the other clients.

2. IPC Primitives

We start by presenting and examining a simple user-level IPC mechanism based on concurrent uni-directional queues [12] implemented in shared memory. Using a Send/Receive/Reply interface and a busy-wait implementation, we can explore the factors affecting the performance of subsequent blocking user-level IPC algorithms.

2.1. Busy-Waiting User-Level IPC

Figure 1 shows the implementation of a synchronous Send/Receive/Reply interface over the base queue interface[1]. We refer to this basic implementation as **Both Sides Spin (BSS)**. We use fixed sized messages to permit efficient free-pool management. Variable sized (and sensitive) messages are accommodated by using fields of the fixed sized message to refer to variable sized components in memory separately shared between the client and server.

The implementation in Figure 1 uses a receive queue at the server for incoming messages, and a reply queue for responses back to the client. Each client has a separate reply queue which the server determines by the id of the requesting client. The busy_wait function of Figure 1 is implemented as a null function on a multiprocessor to minimize latency, and as a yield() on a uniprocessor to allow other processes to progress. Also, though the sleep(1) on queue full conditions may seem long, the condition seldom occurs and the implication is that the consumer is saturated; waiting a full second should allow it to reduce the backlog of outstanding messages.

2.2. Performance

To evaluate the protocol, we implemented a simple client-server system where up to n clients connect to a single-threaded server and make requests using our user-level IPC interface. The clients connect to the server, barrier, and then enter a tight loop where they barrage the server with many thousands of message requests. Each message contains 24 bytes which includes both header and data. The server is placed in a tight Receive/Reply loop that accepts connections and processes requests, where (in these experiments) the processing per request is simply to echo the data back to the client.

Figure 2 shows the measured server throughput (ie. larger numbers are better) in messages per millisecond for 1 to 6 clients on two different uniprocessor systems. The results in the left graph of the figure were obtained from an SGI Indy running IRIX 6.2 on a 133 MHz MIPS R4000 processor; the results on the right are from an IBM P4 running AIX 4.1 on a 133 MHz PowerPC 604 processor. Both systems are configured with a 32 KByte split L1 cache, and a 512 KByte combined L2 cache.

Each of the graphs in Figure 2 contains three curves, however, we shall focus on the bottom two curves of each graph for now. The middle curve is the measured server throughput for the Both Sides Spin algorithm of Figure 1. For comparison purposes, we also show the measured server throughput using System V message queues[2]. As a kernel mediated IPC mechanism, SYSV message queues represent a lower-bound on acceptable user-level IPC performance. The performance is a lower bound in the sense that while there may be many advantages to using shared-memory based communication, performance is usually the primary motivator.

We can see from Figure 2 that a simple spinning implementation of user-level IPC can, in fact, result in much better peformance than kernel-mediated IPC. The throughput of user-level IPC outperforms kernel-mediated IPC by factors of more than 1.5 and 1.8 for the SGI and IBM sys-

---

[1] The implementation of asynchronous Send is functionally identical to Reply.

[2] We also tried Unix pipes, and found their performance was similar to SYSV message queues.

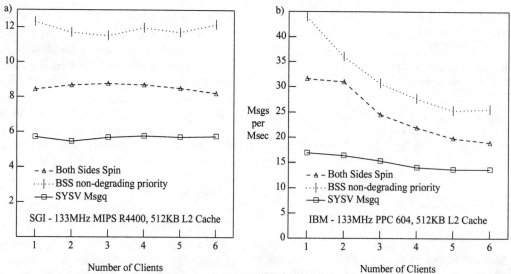

Figure 2. Measured uniprocessor Server Throughput in messages/millisecond for varying numbers of client processes. The left and right graphs are measured throughputs from 133MHz SGI and IBM machines, respectively. The middle curve in each plot is the throughput for the BSS algorithm; the lower curve shows the throughput when SYSV message queues are used; and the top curve is the throughput when non-degrading priorities are used.

tems, respectively. However, quite a bit can be learned by examining these results in more detail. When multiple clients run simultaneously, one would intuitively expect server throughput to *decrease*, because many processes are actively wasting processor cycles context switching and waiting for their request to complete. We see this expected behaviour on AIX (Figure 2b), but on SGI (Figure 2a) the BSS curve exhibits the counter-intuitive effect of *increasing* throughput as the number of clients increases. The reason is that the server can avoid context switches if there are multiple messages on its input queue when the server is given its time slice, and hence the overall number of context switches is actually reduced. This behavior was confirmed using the `getrusage` system call to obtain the number of voluntary and involuntary context switches. The number of voluntary context switches at the server remained the same with either 1 or 2 clients.

While the performance of the BSS algorithm is good, we expected it to be even better. Instrumentation of the code revealed that each process on the SGI was performing approximately 2.5 context switches per round-trip message exchange. This suggests that the degrading priority scheme used by the operating system for scheduling is preventing the process that just enqueued a message from yielding the CPU to the waiting process. Note that since both the client and server are busy-waiting, the operating system always sees both processes as ready; it is only after the active process has accumulated sufficient execution time that its priority is degraded enough to warrant a full context switch.

To test the hypothesis that priority aging by the operating system is impacting performance, we set both the server and client priorities to be non-degrading. The top curve of Fig-

ure 2 shows that the throughput is increased by 50% on the SGIs, and 30% on the IBMs. We also reran the SYSV Message Queue implementation with fixed priority scheduling, and found no appreciable difference in performance.

Unfortunately, running with fixed-priority is not practical, except possibly for real-time applications. On both the SGI and the IBM, the system call to set fixed-priority scheduling requires super-user privileges – primarily because the system can be deadlocked by careless use of non-degrading priority scheduling. Of course, the problem is not with the priorities *per sé*, the problem is that even though the CPU is explicitly `yielded`, there is no guarantee that any other process will run. This behavior suggests a fundamentally different scheduling approach is needed for user-level IPC. The reason is that schedulers normally view all ready processes as *competing* for the CPU, however, processes involved in user-level IPC are *co-operating* towards a common goal. What we desire is a user-level call to effect hand-off scheduling from the client to the server or *vice versa*. We explore this possibility further in Section 6.

3. Incorporating Sleep/Wake-Up

In this section we show how the busy-wait implementation of user-level IPC presented in Figure 1 can be extended to incorporate blocking. Since kernel-mediated IPC can be accomplished in only 4 system calls per round-trip message (ie. client send, server receive, server reply, client receive), any sleep/wake-up protocol must avoid unnecessary system calls and even extraneous context switches to be efficient.

Figure 3 shows how sleep/wake-up (implemented in the figure as `P` and `V` operations on counting semaphores, re-

```
void Send( Msg *msg, Msg *ans ) {                    void Receive( Msg *msg ) {
  while( !enqueue( Q[srv], msg ) )                     while( !dequeue( Q[srv], msg ) ) {
    sleep( 1 ); /* queue full */                         Q[srv]->awake = 0;
                                                          if( !dequeue( Q[srv], msg ) ) {
  if( !tas( &(Q[srv]->awake) ) )                            P( srv ); /* Wait for client */
    V( srv ); /* Wake-up server */                          Q[srv]->awake = 1;
                                                          }
  /* Wait for reply */                                    else { /* not empty */
  while( !dequeue(Q[clnt],ans) ) {                          if( tas( &(Q[srv]->awake) ) ) P(srv);
    Q[clnt]->awake = 0;                                     break;
    if( !dequeue(Q[clnt],ans) ) {                         }
      P( clnt ); /* Wait for server */                 } /* end while */
      Q[clnt]->awake = 1;                             }
    }
    else { /* reply ready */                          void Reply( int clnt, Msg *msg ) {
      if( tas( &(Q[clnt]->awake) ) )                    while( !enqueue( clnt, msg ) )
        P( clnt ); /* Fix race condition */               sleep( 1 ); /* queue full */
      break;
    }                                                   if( !tas( &(Q[clnt]->awake) ) )
  } /* end while */                                       V( clnt ); /* Wake-up client */
}                                                     }
```

Figure 3. **Both Sides Wait**: A Send/Receive/Reply interface that uses counting semaphores to incorporate sleep/wake-up.

spectively) can be incorporated into the basic IPC algorithm of Figure 1. In particular, the server sleeps if there are no client requests outstanding and the clients need not compete for resources if they sleep while waiting for their reply. The difficulty in incorporating sleep/wake-up is that the consumer should only block if the queue is empty, and therefore the producer must determine if the consumer should be awoken when new work has been enqueued. It is important that the consumer only block if the queue is empty and that the producer only wake the consumer if it is sleeping, because sleep and wake-up are system calls. If these system calls are made for every enqueue/dequeue then the performance advantage of user-level IPC is lost. In the best case user-level IPC requires no system calls, which happens if the server and client never see their respective queues empty. In the worst case, blocking user-level IPC may need four system calls: the client sends and wakes up server, then sleeps waiting for the reply; the server processes the request and wakes up the client, then blocks waiting for the next request. The challenge is to find and exploit situations where the client and/or server need not explicitly block – this saves 2 system calls because no wake-up is needed if no sleep was performed.

A further complexity in designing a sleep/wake-up protocol is that two "incompatible" operations must be performed atomically. On detecting an empty queue, a thread: (1) indicates that it *may* be going to sleep (by setting awake to 0 in Figure 3); (2) executes the kernel call to do so (the P operation in the figure). These two steps cannot be made atomic using a lock, since the thread cannot release the lock once it is asleep. Consequently, the sleep/wake-up protocols presented here have race conditions[3]. Race conditions

are not necessarily harmful, in the sense of causing incorrect behavior. However, they may have an impact on performance if left unchecked. Conversely, the work-arounds to prevent race conditions can also degrade performance.

There are three race conditions handled by the **Both Sides Wait (BSW)** algorithm of Figure 3. For brevity, we will not describe the races or the work-arounds here – the interested reader is referred to [14].

3.1. Initial Performance

The performance of the BSW algorithm is plotted with respect to BSS and SYSV message queues in Figure 4. The performance more or less matches the performance of kernel mediated IPC. This could be considered positive, since if user-level IPC is as good as kernel mediated IPC, and has advantages for asynchronous IPC, specialized protocols, and multiprocessors, then it is overall a win. However, we do not consider this sufficiently good since synchronous IPC on uniprocessors is the most important workload today.

The reason for the poor performance is that the V operation that wakes up the consumer does not force a rescheduling decision. Thus, if the server is blocked when the client places something in the queue, the client "ups" the semaphore but then must block on the reply. At this point, the operating system can restart the server, who enqueues the reply and "ups" the client semaphore. The server then blocks waiting for the next request. The result is four system calls per round-trip: two V operations and two P operations. Since we used System V semaphores, which are of similar weight to the four System V message queue calls, there is no advantage to the shared memory solution at all.

---

[3]The race conditions could be resolved with an extended operating system interface [9]. For example, SymUnix [3] allows user processes to indicate when they are executing a critical section, and should therefore not be pre-empted.

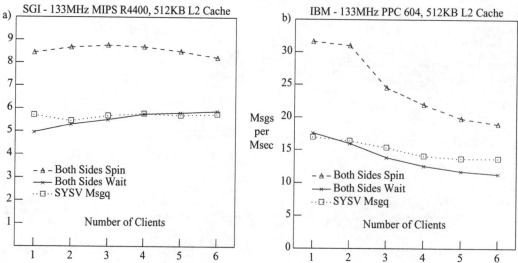

Figure 4. Measured uniprocessor Server Throughput in Messages/millisecond for varying numbers of client processes. The solid curve in each figure represents the throughput for the **Both Sides Wait** algorithm.

4. Performance Improvements

In this section, we first show where `yield` calls can be added to suggest hand-off points to the operating system scheduler. We find that this improves performance dramatically when used with fixed priority scheduling, and argue that this performance could be obtained with a hand-off scheduling policy. Until such a policy is implemented, we then introduce limited spinning on both the client and server sides, and report the performance on commercial systems.

4.1. Simulating Hand-off Scheduling

What we desire is a hand-off scheduling policy such that when the client executes the system call to wake the server, the server is readied and run immediately instead of returning to the client. If the server can process the request in a single quantum, it would not block until it tried to dequeue the next request. At that time, the client (who was blocked as part of the wake-up system call) could continue, find its reply already available, and continue processing. Adding up the costs, we see that hand-off scheduling reduces the number of system calls from 4 to 2 per round-trip.

Figure 5 shows the **BSW** algorithm of Figure 3 modified to include `busy_wait`/`yield` calls to suggest hand-off scheduling to the operating system. On the client side, the `busy_wait` calls are added after the client returns from waking the server, and after the client first finds the reply queue is empty. Note that we used `busy_wait` instead of `yield` directly, so that the algorithm could port transparently between multiprocessor and uniprocessor implementations. On both architectures the `V( srv )` call readies the server. However, on a multiprocessor the server will likely execute on a different processor (assuming one is available), while on a uniprocessor the semaphore oper-

ation does not force a rescheduling decision and the client continues. Thus, on a multiprocessor the `busy_wait` will delay the client while the server processes the request, so that the reply can be ready when the client attempts to dequeue it. On uniprocessors where `busy_wait` is implemented as `yield`, the operating system is forced to at least re-evaluate whether the client or server should run.

Since the wake-up operation is only executed if the server is already blocked, the second `busy_wait` is executed if the client finds the reply queue is empty. In this case, the `busy_wait` attempts to give the server one last chance to prepare a reply before the client puts itself to sleep.

Figure 5 also shows a `yield()` system call added in the Receive implementation of the server to allow the clients to process their replies and (possibly) enqueue their next request. Note that the server only yields if a dequeue attempt results in a queue empty condition. The reason for this extra dequeue is again for scalability with multiple clients. In particular, with multiple clients there is a higher probability that the server's queue has multiple outstanding entries, and it is more productive to continue processing than to give up the processor after every reply.

Figure 6 shows how the hand-off suggestions of the **BSWY** algorithm affect performance on a uniprocessor. The solid curves in the figure show the server throughput when the default scheduling mechanisms are used. The curves show that the `busy_wait` calls are effective for one or two clients, but that the performance degrades as concurrency is increased further. The reason is that the `yield` contains no hint about which process should be favored, and so *any* ready process, including the yielding process, could be scheduled as a result. Unless control is actually transferred to the server, the client will still block, in which case

```
void Send( Msg *msg, Msg *ans ) {          void Receive( Msg *msg ) {
  while( !enqueue( Q[srv],msg ) )            if( dequeue( Q[srv], msg ) ) return;
    sleep( 1 ); /* queue full */
                                             yield(); /* Let clients run */
  if( !tas( &(Q[srv]->awake) ) ) {
    V( srv ); /* Wakeup server */            while( !dequeue( Q[srv], msg ) ) {
    busy_wait(); /* and let it run */          Q[srv]->awake = 0;
  }                                            if( !dequeue( Q[srv], msg ) ) {
                                                 P( srv ); /* Wait for client */
  /* Wait for reply */                          Q[srv]->awake = 1;
  while( !dequeue(Q[clnt],ans) ) {             }
    busy_wait(); /* Try to handoff */          else { /* not empty */
    Q[clnt]->awake = 0;                          if( tas( &(Q[srv]->awake) ) ) P(srv);
    if( !dequeue(Q[clnt],ans) ) {               break;
      P( clnt ); /* Wait for server */         }
      Q[clnt]->awake = 1;                     } /* end while */
    }                                       }
    else { /* reply ready */
      if( tas(&(Q[clnt]->awake)) )          void Reply( int clnt, Msg *msg ) {
        P( clnt ); /* Fix race condition */   while( !enqueue(Q[clnt],msg) )
      break;                                    sleep( 1 ); /* queue full */
    }
  } /* end while */                           if( !tas( &(Q[clnt]->awake) ) ) V(clnt);
}                                           }
```

Figure 5. Both Sides Wait and Yield

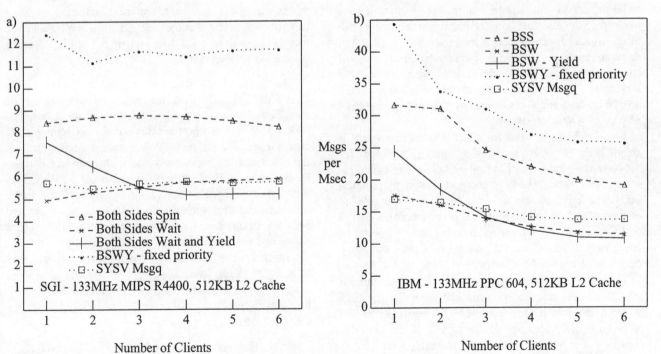

Figure 6. Measured uniprocessor Server Throughput in Messages/millisecond for varying numbers of client processes. The solid curve in each figure represents the throughput for the **Both Sides Wait and Yield** algorithm of Figure 5.

the `yield` calls have no benefit and actually contribute to the critical path latency.

To demonstrate the potential if hand-off scheduling were implemented, the top dotted curves of Figure 6 show the performance of **BSWY** when fixed-priority scheduling is used. The throughput with this scheduling policy basically matches the performance of the busy-waiting **BSS** algorithm under the same scheduling policy (see Figure 2).

4.2. Adding Limited Busy-Waiting

The **BSWY** algorithm of Figure 5 shows some promise in that it seems to be able to effect a hand-off to the consumer for small numbers of clients. However, Figure 6 shows that real hand-off scheduling, as approximated by the fixed priority scheduler, could do much better. Remember that in Section 2.2 we found it took 2.5 `yield` calls (on average) before the default scheduler actually performed a context switch. It is therefore reasonable to conclude that the **BSWY** algorithm is unable to reach its full potential because the single hand-off suggestions (`yields`) inserted in the algorithm do not necessarily result in the desired context switch.

The **Both Sides Limited Spin (BSLS)** algorithm of Figure 7 incorporates a loop around the hand-off attempts. Note that both the server and client spin, the rationale is that the client is anxiously awaiting a reply; and it is cheaper to let the server spin a little than to wake it up if it goes to sleep. Note also that both the client and server can still block, which happens if there is no activity after MAX_SPIN dequeue attempts. The BSLS algorithm also makes use of an `empty` test that checks the head of the queue without locking it. The `poll_queue` subroutine is implemented as `yield` on a uniprocessor, and as a delay loop that calls `empty` on a multiprocessor.

Picking the right value for MAX_SPIN is important: it should be large enough so that the client will not block for the (common) case where the server has an immediate response; and it should be large enough to ensure that a hand-off will be effected. On the other hand, too large a value of MAX_SPIN will waste resources if the server has had to do I/O or is already busy handling other local requests. In either case the client should get out of the way and allow other useful work to be accomplished.

Figure 8 shows the sensitivity of the algorithm to MAX_SPIN. As expected, performance generally improves as the number of tries is increased. We verified that this is because the probability of falling out of the loop decreases as the number of hand-off attempts increases. At a MAX_SPIN value of 20, a single client only blocks 3% of the time, and gets an answer back within 2 iterations on average. Even with six clients, the numbers rise to: 10% of the loops fall-through; and 4 iterations of the loop are executed on average.

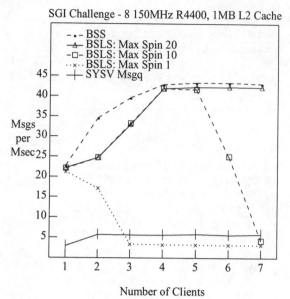

Figure 9. Measured multiprocessor Server Throughput in Messages/millisecond for varying numbers of client processes.

5. Multiprocessor Performance

Figure 9 shows the performance of the various algorithms on an 8-processor SGI Challenge. The code used in this experiment is identical to that used for the uniprocessor experiments, except that the `poll_queue` implementation uses a busy wait loop (25 μsec) where the `empty` check is made on every iteration.

The figure shows five curves: the top curve is the Both Sides Spin algorithm, the middle three curves are the Both Sides Limited Spin algorithm with different values of MAX_SPIN, and the bottom curve is for System V message queues. We see that SYSV message queues perform the worst and are unable to scale with increased concurrency demands. The best performance is for the BSS algorithm, whose throughput increases rapidly until the server saturates, and then stays stable. The Both Sides Limited Spin algorithms have similar performance to BSS up to a point, and then performance degrades rapidly. The reason for this is that as soon as a client spins for longer than MAX_SPIN, the server must pay the extra overhead to wake it up, which increases the load on the server and as a result increases the probability of other clients spinning for longer than MAX_SPIN.

We could break the positive feedback in the BSLS algorithm by having the server recognize the fact that it is overloaded, and limit the number of clients it wakes up at any given time. The challenge is constraining the concurrency in this fashion while guaranteeing that starvation doesn't occur. We leave this for future work.

```
void Send( Msg *msg, Msg *ans ) {              void Receive( Msg *msg ) {
  while( !enqueue( Q[srv],msg ) )                spincnt = 0;
    sleep( 1 ); /* queue full */                 while( empty(Q[srv]) && spincnt++<MAX_SPIN )
                                                    poll_queue( Q[srv] ); /* Try to handoff */
  if( !tas(&(Q[srv]->awake)) ) V(srv);
                                                 while( !dequeue( Q[srv], msg ) ) {
  spincnt = 0;                                     Q[srv]->awake = 0;
  while(empty(Q[clnt]) && spincnt++<MAX_SPIN)      if( !dequeue( Q[srv], msg ) ) {
    poll_queue( Q[clnt] );  /* Try to handoff */     P( srv ); /* Wait for client */
                                                      Q[srv]->awake = 1;
  while( !dequeue(Q[clnt],ans) ) {                 }
    busy_wait(); /* Try to handoff */              else { /* not empty */
    Q[clnt]->awake = 0;                              if( tas( &(Q[srv]->awake) ) ) P(srv);
    if( !dequeue(Q[clnt],ans) ) {                    break;
      P( clnt ); /* Wait for server */             }
      Q[clnt]->awake = 1;                         } /* end while */
    }                                            }
    else { /* reply ready */
      if( tas(&(Q[clnt]->awake)) )               void Reply( int clnt, Msg *msg ) {
        P( clnt ); /* Fix race condition */        while( !enqueue(Q[clnt],msg) )
      break;                                         sleep( 1 ); /* queue full */
    }
  } /* end while */                                if( !tas( &(Q[clnt]->awake) ) ) V(clnt);
}                                                }
```

Figure 7. Both Sides Limited Spin (**BSLS**)

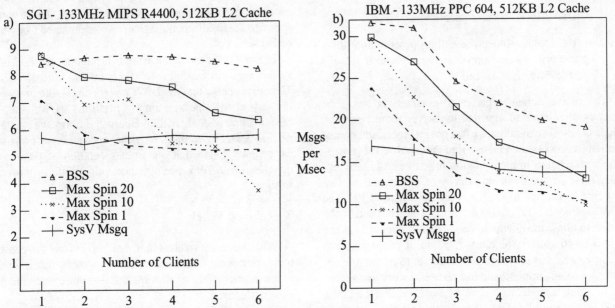

Figure 8. Measured uniprocessor Server Throughput in Messages/millisecond for varying numbers of client processes. The curves show the effect of different MAX_SPIN values for the **Both Sides Limited Spin** algorithm.

6. Modifying `yield` in Linux

Earlier sections have shown that fixed-priority scheduling substantially increases performance when the algorithms incorporate `yield` calls to suggest hand-off scheduling to the system scheduler. We would like to prove that a hand-off scheduling policy would indeed achieve the same performance as a fixed-priority policy, but without the deadlock and priority inversion problems that forces users of real-time scheduling to have super-user privileges.

Fundamentally, an operating system scheduler views multiple ready processes as *competing* for CPU resources. For this workload, the dynamically degrading priorities of typical schedulers will maximize throughput while still preventing starvation. However, since user-level IPC processes are *co-operating* instead of competing, overall system throughput would be best served with a hand-off scheduling policy. A similar mechanism has been used in L4 [8], and in [5] but we seek a minimum number of modifications to existing commercial operating systems. In the remainder of this section, we suggest an interface and implementation for a hand-off scheduling policy.

Ideally, a `handoff` system call would take a single `pid_t` argument (say, `pid`) that would be interpreted as follows:

`pid = some_pid` - hand-off to the specified `some_pid`. `some_pid` must already be in the ready queue to be eligible for execution.

`pid = PID_SELF` - same semantics as `yield`.

`pid = PID_ANY` - block the calling process and allow highest priority ready process to run, *even* if it has a lower priority than the caller.

The first argument type (`pid=some_pid`) would be used by the clients to *hint* that the server should execute. Since hand-off scheduling is often not incorporated because malicious processes could use it to monopolize the processor, a reasonable implementation might be to logarithmically increase the dynamic priority of `some_pid` so that it would be favored to run but could not hog the CPU. The third argument style (`pid=PID_ANY`) would be used by the server to allow the clients to run. The server could use the first form to specify the client to whom it just responded, but in general it is sufficient for the server to inform the operating system simply that it has no useful work to do.

We implemented this `handoff` system call in the Linux 1.0.32 Slackware Release. It turns out that this version of Linux has a relatively simplistic scheduler that does not exhibit all of the characteristics of the other commercial operating systems we looked at. In particular, the support for fixed-priority scheduling was too immature to run the busy-waiting algorithms at all. Even with the default scheduler,

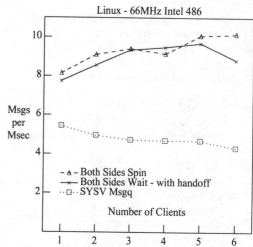

Figure 10. Measured uniprocessor Server Throughput in Messages/millisecond for varying numbers of client processes. The solid curve is the **BSWY** algorithm of Figure 5 with the modified `sched_yield` implementation.

we found that the response time for the busy-wait algorithm (**BSS**) was on the order of 33 *milliseconds* instead of the 120 microseconds we were expecting. The problem appeared to be in the way the dynamic priority was aged, so to fix it, we changed the `sched_yield` call to expire the caller's quantum and force a context switch. This change brought the latency back to 120 μsec on a 66MHz 486 machine. Of course, this is exactly the way we would like the commercial unix schedulers to treat `yield`, and so the results we obtain from the busy-wait algorithm in Linux should correspond to the fixed-scheduling curves we obtained from AIX or IRIX.

Figure 10 shows the measured throughput on the Linux system with our modified `sched_yield` implementation. The curves show that the **BSWY** algorithm — the one *without* any client side spinning — performs as well as the busy-waiting **BSS** algorithm. Because the way we changed `sched_yield` brought us near maximal performance, we actually found that our implementation of `handoff` matched the **BSWY** performance, but did not improve it further.

7. Related Work

With the recent interest in micro-kernels and the general trend in moving traditional operating system functionality to the user level, we were surprised that more work did not exist in this area.

The issues of fast user-level IPC arise in user-level thread packages [13], but since these packages also include the thread scheduler, system calls are not needed to sleep and wake-up threads. Also, the race conditions that we encounter as a result of crossing the kernel boundary do not have to occur in a user-level thread package because the interface can allow a thread to atomically sleep and set a flag to inform others that it is doing so.

Fast IPC has also been the focus of microkernel architecture research, and solutions based on hand-off scheduling have been proposed in Bershad's LRPC [1], Gamsa's PPC [6], Spring doors [7], and Liedtke's L3 and L4 systems [10, 11]. However, all these systems are based on kernel mechanisms to support client upcalls and server registration of entry points.

Bershad's URPC system [2] is mostly implemented at the user level, but depends on a high degree of concurrency in the client to batch calls or tolerate latency when control must be handed to the server. In contrast, our work does not assume concurrency within a single client, and focuses on achieving low latency for the case where the server data is cached locally.

Many of the race conditions and scheduling considerations could be resolved with an extended operating system interface [9]. For example, SymUnix [3] allows user processes to indicate when they are executing a critical section, and should therefore not be pre-empted. We would welcome extensions such as our proposed `handoff(pid_t p)`, which could allow a client to suggest that the server be scheduled after a request has been enqueued. For example, the CPU Inheritance Scheduling mechanism proposed by Ford [5] could be used by the clients to donate the unused portion of their quantums to the server. However, their `schedule` operation has so far only been implemented in a user-level threading package.

8. Conclusion

The performance of IPC is crucial to many applications, and there has been a great deal of work done on developing IPC facilities for new operating systems that perform well. In this paper we have shown how, using user-level IPC, good performance can be achieved on current commercial operating systems. We showed that we could achieve throughputs on uniprocessors that are twice as high as the kernel mediated IPC facilities, and demonstrated that even better performance improvements can arise in multiprocessors. Also, we show that with minor changes to the operating system interface, even better performance is possible.

Our work has so far mainly concentrated on achieving good performance for synchronous IPC on a uniprocessor, since this is the most challenging situation. In the future we intend to explore in more detail the other benefits of user-level IPC, namely, asynchronous IPC, specialized protocols, and multiprocessor performance. Also, more work is required on the security issues that arise when user-level IPC is used.

While the results in this paper are based on unrealistic micro-benchmarks, the motivation for this work comes from the performance and functionality limitations we found in current IPC facilities when developing a new data base server. This data base server exploits not only the improved performance of user-level IPC for synchronous IPC, but also the optimizations available for asynchronous IPC and customized protocols.

The source used to generate the results in this paper is freely available and can be obtained via anonymous ftp from `ftp.cs.ualberta.ca:pub/TechReports/1997-/TR97-08/ipc.tar.Z`

References

[1] B. Bershad, T. Anderson, E. Lazowska, and H. Levy. "Lightweight Remote Procedure Call". *ACM TOCS*, 8(1):37–55, Feb 1990.

[2] B. Bershad, T. Anderson, E. Lazowska, and H. Levy. "User-Level Interprocess Communication for Shared Memory Multiprocessors". *ACM TOCS*, 9(2):175–198, May 1991.

[3] J. Edler, J. Lipkis, and E. Schonberg. "Process Management for Highly Parallel UNIX Systems". In *Proc. USENIX Workshop on Unix and SuperComputers*, Pittsburgh, PA, Sept 1988.

[4] D. Engler, F. Kaashoek, and J. O. Jr. "Exokernel: An Operating System Architecture for Application-level Resource Management. In *Proc. 15th SOSP*, pages 251–267, Copper Mountain Resort, CO, Dec 1995.

[5] B. Ford and S. Susarla. "CPU Inheritance Scheduling". In *Proc. 2nd OSDI*, pages 91–105, Seattle, Wa, Oct 1996.

[6] B. Gamsa, O. Krieger, and M. Stumm. "Optimizing IPC Performance for Shared-Memory Multiprocessors". In *Proc. ICPP*, volume 2, pages 208–211, Aug 1994.

[7] G. Hamilton and P. Kougiouris. "The Spring nucleus: A microkernel for objects". In *Proc. Summer USENIX*, pages 147–159, June 1993.

[8] H. Härtig, M. Hohmuth, J. Liedtke, S. Schönberg, and J. Walter. "The Performance of μ-Kernel Based Systems". In *Proc. 16th SOSP*, Saint-Malo, France, Oct 1997.

[9] L. Kontothanassis, R. Wisniewski, and M. Scott. Scheduler Conscious Synchronization. Technical Report TR 550, Dept. Comp. Sci., University of Rochester, Rochester, NY, 1994.

[10] J. Liedtke. "Improving IPC by Kernel Design". In *Proc. 14th SOSP*, pages 175–188, Dec 1993.

[11] J. Liedtke. "On μ-Kernel Construction". In *Proc. 15th SOSP*, Dec 1995.

[12] M. Michael and M. Scott. "Simple, Fast, and Practical Non-Blocking and Blocking Concurrent Queue Algorithms". In *15th ACM PODC*, 1996.

[13] D. Ritchie and G. Neufeld. "User Level IPC and Device Management in the Raven Kernel". In *Proc. USENIX Microkernels and Other Kernel Arhcitecures*, Sept 1993.

[14] R. Unrau and O. Krieger. Adding sleep/wake-up to user-level IPC. Technical Report TR97-08, Dept. Comp. Sci., University of Alberta, Edmonton, Canada, T6G 2H1, 1997.

Group Protocol for Distributed Replicated Objects

Tomoya Enokido, Hiroaki Higaki, and Makoto Takizawa
Dept. of Computers and Systems Engineering
Tokyo Denki University
Ishizaka, Hatoyama, Saitama 350-0394, Japan
Email {eno, hig, taki}@takilab.k.dendai.ac.jp

Abstract

In group protocols, larger computation and communication are consumed to causally order all messages transmitted in the network. Transactions in clients manipulate objects in servers by sending read and write requests to the servers. In this paper, we define significant messages, which are to be ordered at the application level, by using a conflicting relation among the transactions. We newly propose an object vector to causally order only the significant messages. The scheme of the object vector is invariant in the change of the group membership. We also show a TBCO (transaction-based causally ordered) protocol adopting the object vector, by which the number of messages to be causally ordered are reduced.

1 Introduction

In distributed applications, a *group* of multiple objects are cooperating. Here, messages sent by objects have to be reliably delivered to the destination objects in the group. Many group protocols[3, 8, 9, 10] are discussed to causally order messages transmitted in the network. However, the group protocols imply $O(n)$ to $O(n^2)$ computation and communication overhead[10]. Cheriton[4] points out that it is meaningless to causally order all the messages transmitted from the application point of view. Agrawal[6] discusses a rollback algorithm where only processes computing significant requests are rolled back if the senders of the significant requests are rolled back. Tachikawa and Takizawa[13] define the *object-based causality* among messages based on the conflicting relation among operations supported by the objects in the presence of the nested invocation of operations. Raynal[1] discusses a way to relex the traditional message-based causality based on the write-semantics for a group of the replicas.

In this paper, we introduce a *transaction*[2] concept to define a causality among messages which are significant for the applications. A transaction T in a client processor issues *read* and *write* requests to server processors. The server processor reads and writes objects stored and sends back responses to the client. Thus, a *subtransaction* of T is a sequence of requests of T computed in a server. Data read from an object is written to another object if *read* and *write* are computed in a transaction. A message m_1 may carry information in m_2 if a transaction sends m_1 after receiving or sending m_2. Thus, the messages received and sent by one transaction are related. Suppose a transaction T_1 sends m_2 after T_2 receives m_1 in the same processor. m_1 and m_2 are not related unless T_1 and T_2 manipulate same objects. In order to define messages to be causally ordered, we have to consider what subtransactions send and receive messages. Hence, the group is required to be composed of multiple subtransactions and servers. In this paper, we define how read and write messages are causally related in a context of transactions. In addition, each object is replicated in order to increase the reliability, availability, and performance of the system. We define *significant* messages to be causally ordered based on the transaction concept.

In most group protocols discussed so far, messages are causally ordered by using the *vector clock*[7] where a group is composed of processors and messages are causally delivered to the processors. In order to causally order messages sent and received by transactions, a group is required to be composed of subtransactions and clients. Hence, each time transactions are randomly initiated and terminated, the size of the vector clock is required to change. In this paper, we newly propose an *object vector* whose size is given by the number of objects, not the number of transactions. We discuss a TBCO (transaction-based causally ordered) protocol which uses the object vector to causally order only significant messages. In the TBCO protocol, only significant messages can be delivered without waiting for insignificant messages preceding the significant messages.

We present transactions and messages in section 2. In section 3, we present the *object vector* and the TBCO protocol. In section 4, we evaluate the TBCO protocol.

2 Transactions Messages

2.1 Transactions

A system is composed of processors $p_1, \ldots, p_N$ ($N \geq 1$) interconnected by a communication network. Objects $o_1, \ldots, o_M$ are distributed in the processors. The objects are replicated in order to increase the reliability and availability of the system. Each replica of an object is allocated in one processor. Let o_a^t denote a replica of o_a in a processor p_t. On receipt of a request message m with an operation op_a, o_a^t computes op_a. On completion of op_a, o_a^t sends back the response message to the sender of m. In the network, messages may be lost and may be delivered out of order.

A transaction T_i in one *client* processor p_s issues *read* and *write* requests to the *server* processors to manipulate replicas of an object o_a. A processor p_s sends a *read* request to one processor p_t which has a replica of o_a. p_t sends p_s back the response with the data derived. p_s sends *write* requests to all the replicas of o_a. That is, the *read-one-write-all* principle is adopted. Here, $op_1 \rightarrow_{T_i} op_2$ shows that an operation op_1 precedes op_2 in T_i. T_i commits (c^i) or *aborts* (a^i) at the end of T_i. T_i commits if all the operations invoked by T_i complete successfully. If at least one operation fails in T_i, T_i aborts. Thus, T_i is an atomic sequence of *read* and *write* operations[2]. Let $op_t^i(x)$ denote an operation op for a replica x in p_t which is issued by T_i. Here, op shows an operation type r (*read*) or w (*write*). A subsequence of operations of T_i on the replicas in a processor p_t is named a *subtransaction* T_{it} of T_i in p_t. $op_1 \rightarrow_{T_{it}} op_2$ iff op_1 precedes op_2 in T_{it}. The interleaved computation of subtransactions in p_t is a *local history* H_t of p_t. op_1 *precedes* op_2 in p_t ($op_1 \rightarrow_{H_t} op_2$) iff op_1 is computed before op_2 in p_t. A global history H of T is a collection of the local histories $H_1, \ldots, H_N$. op_1 precedes op_2 in H ($op_1 \rightarrow_H op_2$) if and only if (iff) $op_1 \rightarrow_{H_t} op_2$, $op_1 \rightarrow_{T_i} op_2$, or $op_1 \rightarrow_H op_3 \rightarrow_H op_2$ for some p_t, T_i, and op_3. Here, op_1 conflicts with op_2 iff op_1 and op_2 are operations for manipulating an object and the results obtained by computing op_1 and op_2 depend on the computation order of op_1 and op_2. T_i *precedes* T_j iff op_i issued by T_i conflicts with op_j issued by T_j and $op_i \rightarrow_{H_t} op_j$ in some p_t. H is serializable if all the transactions are totally ordered by the precedent relation. H has to be *serializable*[2] to keep the replicas consistent. That is, the conflicting operations, i.e. *write* and *read*, *write* and *write* on the same object have to be computed in the same order as some serial history.

Each transaction T_i is given a unique identifier $t(T_i)$ in order to totally order the transactions. In the *time stamp ordering* (TO) concurrency control[2], every pair of conflicting operations are computed in the order of the transaction identifiers, i.e. time stamps. That is, if an operation op_i of T_i conflicts with op_j of T_j in p_t and $t(T_i) < t(T_j)$, op_i

is computed before op_j in p_t. On the other hand, in the two-phase locking[2], the replicas are locked before they are manipulated.

2.2 Omissible messages

A processor p_t may not receive messages or may receive messages out of order. For example, if p_t loses a message sent by p_u, p_u resends the message to p_t. Hence, after p_t receives a message m, p_t has to *wait* for all messages causally preceding m.

[**Example 1**] Suppose $w_t^1(x^t)$, $w_s^1(x^s)$, and $w_u^1(x^u)$ are initiated by a request message m_1, $r_t^2(x^t)$ is by m_2, $w_s^3(x^s)$, $w_t^3(x^t)$, and $w_u^3(x^u)$ are by m_3, and $r_u^4(x^u)$ is by m_4 as shown in Figure 1. $w_t^3(x^t)$ is computed after $r_t^2(x^t)$ in p_t. Here, suppose p_u receives m_3 before m_1. In the traditional group protocols, p_u has to wait for m_1 without delivering m_3. That is, p_u has to compute $w_s^1(x^s)$, $w_u^3(x^u)$, and $r_u^4(x^u)$ in this sequence. $r_u^4(x^u)$ reads x from $w_u^3(x^u)$ but not from $w_s^1(x^s)$. Here, suppose $w_u^1(x^u)$, $w_u^3(x^u)$, and $r_u^4(x^u)$ are still stored in the receipt queue RQ_u of p_u due to the communication delay although the operations complete in p_s and p_t. Since $r_u^4(x^u)$ reads from $w_u^3(x^u)$, $w_u^1(x^u)$ does not need to be computed, i.e. $w_s^1(x^s)$ can be omitted. □

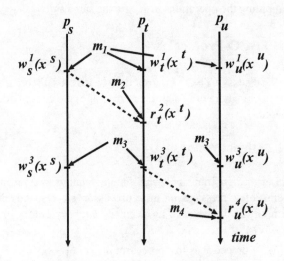

Figure 1. Omissible messages.

[**Example 2**] Suppose p_t receives read requests r_t^i, r_t^j, and r_t^k from transactions T_i, T_j, and T_k, respectively. p_t reads a value from a replica x and sends back the response with data each time p_t receives a read request. Here, p_t computes read operations on x three times. If p_t reads x once and sends the response back to T_i, T_j, and T_k, the number of operations computed can be reduced. That is, $r_t^j(x)$ and r_t^k can be removed from RQ_t if r_t^i is computed. □

The first example shows that some write requests can be omitted. Suppose $w_t^i(x) \rightarrow_H w_t^j(x)$. If there is no read $r_t^k(x)$ such that $w_t^i(x) \rightarrow_H r_t^k(x) \rightarrow_H w_t^j(x)$, p_t does not need to receive $w_t^i(x)$. This means p_t can compute $w_t^j(x)$ without waiting for $w_t^i(x)$. p_t can further reject $w_t^i(x)$ if p_t receives $w_t^i(x)$ after computing $w_t^j(x)$. The second example shows that some *read* requests can be omitted. We discuss what messages can be omitted.

[**Definition**] A message m is *omissible* iff the following conditions hold :

(1) If $m = r_t^i(x)$, there is some read $r_t^j(x)$ in H such that $r_t^j(x)$ precedes $r_t^i(x)$ and there is no write $w_t^k(x)$ between $r_t^j(x)$ and $r_t^i(x)$ in H.

(2) If $m = w_t^i(x)$, there is some write $w_t^j(x)$ in H such that $w_t^i(x)$ precedes $w_t^j(x)$ and there is no read $r_t^k(x)$ between $w_t^i(x)$ and $w_t^j(x)$ in H. □

In Figure 1, suppose p_u receives messages $m_1 = w_u^1(x^u)$, $m_3 = w_u^3(x^u)$, and $m_4 = r_u^4(x^u)$. Here, m_3 and m_4 are not omissible but m_1 is omissible in p_u. Omissible messages can be omitted from H.

It is straightforward that the following theorem holds.

[**Theorem 1**] Let R_t be a sequence of messages in the receipt queue RQ_t of p_t. Let R_t' be a subsequence of R_t which includes no omissible messages. Here, the state of p_t and the sequence of output values of read requests obtained by computing the operations in R_t' are the same as R_t. □

3 TBCO Protocol

We discuss a TBCO (transaction–based causally ordered) protocol where only significant messages are causally delivered.

3.1 Object vector

Let $snd_t[m]$ and $rcv_t[m]$ denote sending and receipt events of a message m in a processor p_t, respectively. Lamport[5] defines that an event e_1 *happens before* e_2 ($e_1 \rightarrow e_2$) iff

(1) e_1 precedes e_2 in a processor p_t, i.e. $e_1 \rightarrow_{H_t} e_2$,

(2) $e_1 = snd_s[m]$ and $e_2 = rcv_t[m]$, or

(3) $e_1 \rightarrow e_3 \rightarrow e_2$ for some event e_3.

A message m_1 *causally precedes* m_2 ($m_1 \rightarrow m_2$) iff $snd_s[m_1] \rightarrow snd_t[m_2]$[3]. p_t has to receive m_1 before m_2 if $m_1 \rightarrow m_2$. The *vector clock*[7] $V = \langle V_1, \ldots, V_N \rangle$ is used to causally order the messages received. Each element V_t in V is initially 0 ($t = 1, \ldots, N$). p_t increments V_t by one each time p_t sends a message m. m carries a field $m.V$ which shows the vector clock of p_t when p_t sends m. On receipt of m, p_s changes V as $V_t = \max(V_t, m.V_t)$ for $t = 1, \ldots, N$ and $s \neq t$. $m_1 \rightarrow m_2$ iff $m_1.V < m_2.V$. If the group

membership changes, the vector clocks of all the processors have to be synchronized[3, 4, 5, 6, 7, 13].

We consider a way to order only messages which are significant for transactions by using the conflicting and precedent relations among transactions.

[**Definition**] A request message m_1 *significantly precedes* m_2 (or m_2 *significantly follows* m_1) iff

(1) m_1 is issued before m_2 by a transaction and the operations of m_1 and m_2 conflict with one another, or

(2) m_1 and m_2 are issued by different transactions T_1 and T_2, respectively, and T_1 precedes T_2. □

It is straightforward for the following proposition to hold.

[**Proposition 2**] A message m_1 causally precedes m_2 ($m_1 \rightarrow m_2$) if m_1 significantly precedes m_2 □

[**Definition**] A message m is *significant* iff m significantly precedes or follows some message. □

In order to significantly order messages, we have to consider which transactions issue the messages. Hence, a group is considered to be composed of subtransactions and servers. The membership of the group changes each time a transaction is initiated and terminated. If the vector clock is used, the group has to be frequently resynchronized. The vector clock can be used to causally order messages sent by processors at the network level but not by transactions at the application level. In this paper, we newly propose an *object vector* to causally order only significant messages sent by transactions. The object vector V is $\langle V_1, \ldots, V_M \rangle$ where each element V_a shows a version number of an object o_a ($a = 1, \ldots, M$). Each replica o_a^t of an object o_a in p_t has a version number $v(o_a^t)$. $v(o_a^t)$ is updated each time o_a^t is updated by a write operation. Each operation op issued by a transaction has a unique identifier $tno(op)$ which satisfies the following properties:

(1) $tno(op_1) < tno(op_2)$ if op_1 is issued before op_2 by a transaction and one of op_1 and op_2 is write.

(2) $tno(op_1) < tno(op_2)$ if op_1 and op_2 are issued by different transactions[T_1 and T_2, respectively, and T_1 starts before T_2 in the system.

We discuss how $tno(op)$ is calculated in the succeeding subsection.

Each replica o_a^t of an object o_a in a processor p_t manipulates the version number $v(o_a^t)$ by using the operation identifier $tno(op)$ each time op is computed in o_a^t as follows:

(1) If $v(o_a^t) < tno(op)$, $v(o_a^t) := tno(op)$ if op is *write*.

(2) If $v(o_a^t) \geq tno(op)$, op is rejected.

o_a^t does not change $v(o_a^t)$ for *read* operations.

Each processor p_t has an object vector $V = \langle V_1, \ldots, V_M \rangle$. If p_t has a replica o_a^t of an object o_a, V_a is $v(o_a^t)$. When p_t sends a message m, p_t includes V in m. $m.V$ shows the object vector carried by m.

On receipt of a message m from p_u, p_t manipulates V as follows;

$V_a := \max(V_a, m.V_a)$ for $a = 1, \ldots, M$.

[**Theorem 3**] A message m_1 significantly precedes m_2 if $m_1.V < m_2.V$.

[**Proof**] Assume $m_1.V < m_2.V$ and m_1 does not significantly precede m_2. Suppose that a processor p_s sends a write message m_1 to replicas x^t and x^u in p_t and p_u. p_t sends a request message m_2 to p_u. On receipt of m_1, the object vector V of x is changed and V_x is incremented. m_2 carries the object vector V. Here, $m_1.V < m_2.V$. According to the definition, m_1 significantly precedes m_2. It contradicts the assumption. $\square$

3.2 Operation identifier

We discuss how to realize the operation identifiers which are used in the object vector. Each transaction T_i has a unique identifier $t(T_i)$ satisfying the following properties :

(1) If T_i starts before T_j in a processor, $t(T_i) < t(T_j)$.
(2) If a processor p_t initiates T_i after receiving a message from T_j, $t(T_i) > t(T_j)$.

The transaction identifier is generated by using the linear clock[5]. Each processor p_t manipulates a variable tid showing the linear clock whose initial value is 0 as follows :

(1) $tid := tid + 1$ if a transaction is initiated in p_t.
(2) On receipt of a message from T_j, $tid := \max(tid, tid(T_j))$.

When T_i is initiated in p_t, $t(T_i)$ is given a concatenation of tid and the processor number $pno(p_t)$ of p_t. Here, let $tid(T_i)$ denote tid given to T_i. $t(T_i) = \langle\, tid(T_i), pno(p_t) \,\rangle$. For every pair of transactions T_i and T_j initiated at p_t and p_u, respectively, $tid(T_i) > tid(T_j)$ if (1) $t(T_i) > t(T_j)$ or (2) $t(T_i) = t(T_j)$ and $pno(p_t) > pno(p_u)$. It is clear that every transaction T_i has a unique identifier $t(T_i)$. In stead of the linear clock, we can use the vector clock[7]. In order to make the implementation simple, the linear clock is used here.

[**Proposition 4**] $t(T_i) < t(T_j)$ if a transaction T_i precedes T_j. $\square$

Each event e occurring in T_i is given an event number $no(e)$ as follows :

(1) If e_1 is the initial event of T_i, $no(e_1) = 0$.
(2) If e_2 is write and $e_1 \rightarrow e_2$ in T_i, $no(e_1) < no(e_2)$.
(3) If e_2 is read and there is no write event e_3 such that $e_1 \rightarrow_{T_i} e_3 \rightarrow_{T_i} e_2$, $no(e_1) = no(e_2)$.

T_i manipulates a variable no_i to give the event number to each event to occur in T_i. no_i is incremented by one each time a write event occurs in T_i. The event number $no(e)$ of the event e is given as $no(e) := no_i$. Each event e in T_i is given a global event number $tno(e)$ as the concatenation of $t(T_i)$ and $no(e)$, i.e. $tno(e) = \langle\, t(T_i), no(e) \,\rangle$. Each operation op issued by T_i is given the global event number $tno(op)$ which is named an operation identifier.

3.3 Message transmission and receipt

A message m exchanged among processors is composed of the following fields :

$m.src$ = sender processor of m, i.e. p_s.

$m.dst$ = set of destination processors.

$m.op$ = type of message, i.e. $op \in \{read, write, commit, abort, response\}$.

$m.tno$ = global event number $\langle m.t, m.no \rangle$, i.e. $tno(op)$.

$m.o$ = object to be manipulated by $m.op$.

$m.V$ = object vector $\langle V_1, \ldots, V_M \rangle$.

$m.SQ$ = vector of sequence numbers $\langle sq_1, \ldots, sq_N \rangle$.

$m.d$ = data.

Suppose that a transaction T_h invokes an operation op_h to manipulate an object o_a. A processor p_s constructs a request message m with op_h as follows :

$m.tno = \langle m.t, m.no \rangle := tno(op_h) = \langle t(T_h), no(op_h) \rangle$;

$m.op := op_h$; $m.o := o_a$;

$m.src := p_s$;

$m.dst = p_t$ if op_h is $read$, otherwise all the replicas.

If $op_h = read$, one replica o_a^t in a processor p_t is selected to be the destination. If $m.op = write$, $m.dst$ shows all the processors which have the replicas of o_a. That is, a transaction reads one replica while writing all the replicas.

A processor p_s manipulates variables $sq_1, \ldots, sq_N$ to sequence messages which p_s sends. Each time p_s sends a message to p_t, sq_t is incremented by one. Then, p_s sends m to every destination p_t in $m.dst$. m carries sq_u in a field $m.sq_u$, $(u = 1, \ldots, N)$.

$sq_t := sq_t + 1$ for every p_t in $m.dst$;

$m.sq_u := sq_u$ $(u = 1, \ldots, N)$;

A processor p_t has to detect a gap between messages received from p_s by checking the sequence number sq_t, i.e. messages lost or unexpectedly delayed. p_t manipulates variables $rsq_1, \ldots, rsq_N$ to detect the gap. On receipt of a message m from p_s, there is no gap between m and messages sent before m if $m.sq_t = rsq_s$. If $m.sq_t > rsq_s$, there is a gap m' where $m.sq_t > m'.sq_t \geq rsq_s$. That is, p_t does not receive m' which is sent by p_s. m is *correctly* received by p_t if p_t receives every message m' where $m'.sq_t < m.sq_t$. That is, p_t receives every message which p_s sends to p_t before m. p_t enqueues m in the receipt queue RQ_t. p_t has an object vector $V = \langle V_1, \ldots, V_M \rangle$. p_t manipulates the object vector V as $V_a = \max(V_a, m.V_a)$ for $a = 1, \ldots, M$.

If $m.op$ completes to manipulate a replica o_a^t, p_t sends back a response m' of m to p_s. If $m.op = read$, m' carries data derived from o_a^t in the field $m'.d$ and the version number $v(o_a^t)$ of o_a^t in $m.V$. The object vector V is updated as $V_a = v(o_a^t)$. The response message m' carries V including not only the current version number $v(o_a^t)$ but also the version numbers of the other replicas which p_t knows. If $m.op = write$, the version number $v(o_a^t)$ is updated, i.e. $v(o_a^t) := tno(op)$ as presented in the preceding subsection.

$$m'.tno := m.tno; \qquad m'.o := o_a;$$
$$m'.op := response;$$
$$m'.V := V;$$

3.4 Message delivery

As discussed before, m_1 significantly precedes m_2 if $m_1.V < m_2.V$. $m_1.V < m_2.V$ means that m_1 has to precede m_2 from the transaction point of view since there might be some information flow between m_1 and m_2, e.g. through read and write relations. Suppose that two transactions T_1 and T_2 issue requests m_1 and m_2 to replicas x^s in a processor p_s and x^t in p_t. If $m_1.V = m_2.V$ or $m_1.V$ and $m_2.V$ are not comparable, p_s and p_t may compute $m_1.op$ and $m_2.op$ in different orders. If m_1 and m_2 are $write$ operations, x^s and x^t get inconsistent. Hence, m_1 and m_2 have to be ordered if $m_1.op$ and $m_2.op$ conflict. A pair of messages m_1 and m_2 are ordered as "m_1 precedes m_2 ($m_1 \Rightarrow m_2$)" according to the following ordering rule.

[**Ordering rules**]

(1) If $m_1.V < m_2.V$, $m_1 \Rightarrow m_2$.

(2) If $m_1.V = m_2.V$, $m_1 \Rightarrow m_2$ if $m_1.t < m_2.t$ and $m_1.op$ conflicts with $m_2.op$.

(3) If $m_1.V$ and $m_2.V$ are not comparable and $m_1.o = m_2.o$ ($= o_a$),

    (3.1) if $m_1.V_a < m_2.V_a$, $m_1 \Rightarrow m_2$,

    (3.2) if $m_1.V_a = m_2.V_a$, $m_1 \Rightarrow m_2$ if $m_1.t < m_2.t$ and $m_1.op$ conflicts with $m_2.op$.

Messages received by p_u are stored in the receipt queue RQ_u in the order "$\Rightarrow$". If m_1 and m_2 are not ordered by the ordering rule, m_1 and m_2 are stored in RQ_u in the receipt order.

[**Example 3**] In Figure 2, $\langle \alpha, \beta \rangle$ shows an object vector where α and β are values of variables V_x and V_y showing the versions of objects x and y, respectively. Initially $\langle 0, 0 \rangle$ in every processor. x and y are in every processor in Figure 2. A transaction T_{1s} is computed in p_s. Here, $t(T_{1s}) = 1s$ where s is the processor number of p_s and 1 is the local linear clock of p_s. T_{1s} sends a $write$ request m_1 of x to p_s, p_t, and p_u. Here, $m_1.V = \langle 1s0, 0 \rangle$, $m_1.op = write$, and $m_1.o = x$. T_{2s} is initiated after T_{1s} completes in p_s where "2" shows a linear clock of p_s. T_{3s} is initiated after T_{2s} is started in p_s, i.e. T_{2s} and T_{3s} are interleaved. In addition, p_t initiates a transaction T_{2t} after receiving a message m_1 from p_s. T_{2s} sends a $read$ request m_2 of x to p_u. After T_{2s} sends m_2, T_{3s} sends a $read$ request m_3 of y to p_t. After receiving m_3, T_{2t} sends a $read$ request m_4 of x to p_u. Here, $m_1.V = m_2.V = m_3.V = m_4.V = \langle 1s0, 0 \rangle$. $m_2.op = m_3.op =$

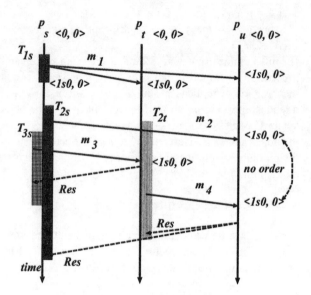

Figure 2. Message ordering.

$m_4.op = read$. $m_2.o = m_4.o = x$ and $m_3.o = y$. p_u receives three messages m_1, m_2, and m_4. In the traditional group protocols, $m_1 \to m_4$ since m_1 causally precedes m_2 ($m_1 \to m_2$) and $m_2 \to m_4$. p_u has to receive m_1, m_2, and m_4 in this order. In this paper, the messages received in a receipt queue RQ_u are ordered by using the ordering rule. Here, m_1 precedes m_2 ($m_1 \Rightarrow m_2$) and $m_1 \Rightarrow m_4$ in p_u. $m_1.op$ conflict with $m_2.op$ and $m_4.op$ and T_{1s} precedes T_{3s} and T_{2t}. Since $m_2.V = m_4.V$ ($= \langle 1s0, 0 \rangle$) and $m_2.t$ ($= 2s$) $< m_4.t$ ($= 2t$) but $m_2.op$ is compatible with $m_4.op$, m_2 and m_4 are neither $m_2 \not\Rightarrow m_4$ nor $m_4 \not\Rightarrow m_2$ in p_u by the ordering rule. Therefore, if p_u receives m_4 before m_2, p_u delivers m_4 to the application object without waiting for m_2. □

This example shows that m_2 causally precedes m_4 ($m_2 \to m_4$) although m_2 and m_4 are not ordered by the ordering rule. That is, p_u can deliver m_4 if p_u receives m_4 before m_2 due to the delay or loss of m_2.

[**Theorem 5**] For every pair of significant messages m_1 and m_2, m_1 and m_2 are ordered in the same order $\Rightarrow$ in every pair of common destination processors of m_1 and m_2 by the ordering rule.

[**Proof**] From theorem 3, m_1 significantly precedes m_2 if $m_1.V < m_2.V$. If $m_1.V = m_2.V$ and $m_1.V$ and $m_2.V$ are not comparable, m_1 and m_2 are ordered by the identifiers of the transactions issuing m_1 and m_2. From proposition 4, m_1 and m_2 are ordered by the transaction identifiers. □

Messages in the receipt queue RQ_t are ordered in "$\Rightarrow$" by the ordering rule. m is a top message in RQ_t iff there is no message m_1 in RQ_t such that $m_1 \Rightarrow m$. Each top message m_1 in RQ_t still cannot be delivered because p_t may not yet have received some message m_2 causally preceding m_1 due to the unexpected delay. We discuss what messages in RQ_t can be delivered.

[**Definition**] Let m be a message sent by p_u to p_t and stored in the receipt queue RQ_t. m is *stable* in p_t iff

(1) p_t has received a message m_1 from p_u in RQ_t where $m_1.sq_t = m.sq_t + 1$, and

(2) p_t correctly receives a message m_1 in RQ_t from every p_u where $m \Rightarrow m_1$. □

The top message m in RQ_t can be delivered if m is stable, because every message causally preceding m from the transaction point of view is surely delivered in RQ_t.

[**Definition**] A top message m in the receipt queue RQ_t is *ready* in p_t if p_t computes no operation conflicting with $m.op$ in a replica $m.o$. □

In addition, only significant messages which are not omissible in RQ_t are delivered from RQ_t by the following delivery procedure in order to reduce time for delivering messages.

[**Delivery procedure**] While each top message m in RQ_t is stable and ready,

   { m is dequeued from RQ_t;

     m is neglected if m is omissible,

     otherwise m is delivered; }. □

[**Example 4**] In Figure 3, two transactions T_{1s} and T_{2s} are computed in p_s while T_{3t} and T_{4t} are in p_t. T_{1s}, T_{2s}, and T_{3t} issue write requests $w^{1s}(x)$, $w^{2s}(x)$, and $w^{3t}(x)$. $w^{1s}(x)$ arrives at neither p_t nor p_u. $w^{2s}(x)$ does not arrive at p_u. Since $w^{1s}(x)$ and $w^{2s}(x)$ are omissible in p_u, they are omitted. □

If p_t receives read requests $r^1(x)$, ..., $r^h(x)$ ($h > 1$), p_t computes $r(x)$ once and then sends the response to all the source processors of $r^1(x)$, ..., $r^h(x)$. Thus, the number of operations computed can be reduced.

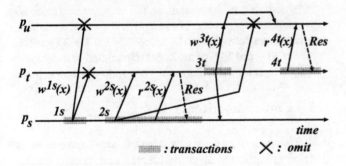

Figure 3. Omission of write operations.

Each p_t has variables D_1, ..., D_M where each D_a shows the version number of an object o_a to deliver messages ($a = 1$, ..., M). Each time a message m is delivered, $D_a := m.t$ if $m.o = o_a$ and $m.t \geq D_a$. Here, if $m.t < D_a$, m is omitted.

If some p_u sends no message to p_t, the messages in RQ_t cannot be stable. In order to resolve this problem, each p_u sends a message without data to p_t if p_u had not sent any message to p_t for some predetermined δ time units. δ is defined to be proportional to delay time between the processors. p_t considers that p_t loses a message from p_u if (1) p_t does not receive any message from p_u for δ time units or (2) p_t detects a gap in the receipt sequence of messages. Here, p_t requires p_u to resend m. p_u considers that p_t may lose m unless p_u receives the receipt confirmation of m from p_t in 2δ after p_u sends m to p_t.

4   Evaluation

In the TBCO protocol, messages are ordered by the *object vector* whose size is the number M of objects, not the number of processes, i.e. the number of servers and subtransactions in the group. On the other hand, the size of the vector clock is given by the number of processes. Messages sent and received by a transaction are related but messages exchanged among transactions may not be related. Hence, it is critical to consider a group to be composed of subtransactions to order only significant messages. Each time a transaction is initiated and terminated, the scheme of the vector clock has to change, i.e. subtransactions and servers have to be resynchronized. Since the object vector only depends on the number of the objects but not on the number of transactions, the TBCO protocol can be adopted to transaction-oriented applications.

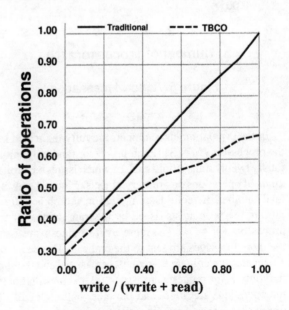

Figure 4. Ratio of operations.

In the TBCO protocol, only significant messages are

causally ordered but not all the messages transmitted in the network. We evaluate the TBCO protocol in terms of the number of messages causally ordered compared with the traditional message-based group protocol. The TBCO protocol is realized in threads of a Super Server 6400 with 10 Ultra Sparcs in the evaluation. Each processor p_t is bound to one Ultra Sparc ($t = 1, \ldots, N$). TCP[15] is used to exchange messages among the processors. Each processor randomly creates transactions each of which randomly manipulates objects by *read* and *write*.

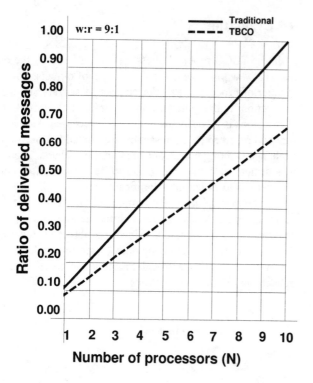

Figure 5. Ratio of messages.

In the evaluation, three objects are fully replicated in all the processors ($M = 3$). Each processor randomly initiates totally twenty transactions each of which issues ten arbitrary kinds of operations on arbitrary objects. Figure 4 shows the total number of requests computed in the objects for the ratio of *write* requests issued by the transactions for three processors ($N = 3$). The more *write* requests are issued, the more messages are sent to the replicas. The *write* ratio 1.0 means that only *write* requests are issued and 0.0 shows that only *read* requests are issued. 0.5 shows that half of the operations are *write* and the other half are *read*. The figure shows that the more write messages are issued, the more messages can be omitted. For example, only 68% of the messages transmitted in the message-based protocol are transmitted in the TBCO protocol in case that all the

messages are writes, i.e. the write ratio is 1.0 while 50% for the write ratio 0.4 and 90% for the write ratio 0.0.

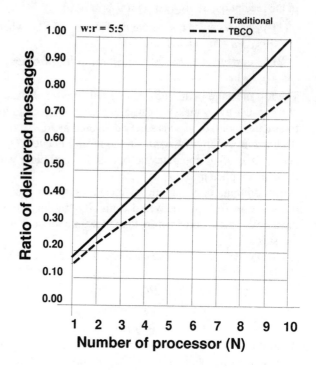

Figure 6. Ratio of messages.

In Figures 5 and 6, the vertical axis indicates the ratio of the number of messages delivered to the number of messages transmitted in case of ten processors ($N = 10$) in the traditional message-based protocol. The dotted line shows TBCO and the solid line indicates the traditional message-based protocol. Figures 5 and 6 show cases that 90% and 50% of the operations issued by each transaction are writes, respectively. These figures show that the number of messages delivered can be reduced by the TBCO protocol. About 30% and 20% of messages transmitted in the network are reduced for the write ratios 90% and 50%, respectively.

5 Concluding Remarks

This paper has discussed what messages have to be ordered in replicated objects with read and write operations from the application point of view. We have proposed the novel *object vector* for significantly ordering messages based on the transaction concept. The scheme of the object vector depends on the number of the objects, not the number of the processes. Here, the object vector is invariant in change of the group membership, i.e. transactions. In the TBCO protocol, only the messages to be significantly preceded for the applications can be ordered. We have also discussed a way for omitting messages which are not significant for the applications. We have shown that the TBCO protocol implies fewer operations computed than the protocols which causally order all the messages transmitted in the network.

References

[1] Ahamad, M., Raynal, M., and Thia-Kime, G., An Adaptive Protocol for Implementing Causally Consistent Distributed Services. *Proc. of the 18th IEEE Int'l Conf. on Distributed Computing Systems (ICDCS-18)*, : 86–93, 1998.

[2] Bernstein, P. A., Hadzilacos, V., and Goodman, N., Concurrency Control and Recovery in Database Systems. *Addison-Wesley*, 1987.

[3] Birman, K., Lightweight Causal and Atomic Group Multicast. *ACM Trans. on Computer Systems,* : 272–290, 1991.

[4] Cheriton, D. R. and Skeen, D., Understanding the Limitations of Causally and Totally Ordered Communication. *Proc. of the ACM SIGOPS'93*, : 44–57, 1993.

[5] Lamport, L., Time, Clocks, and the Ordering of Events in a Distributed System. *Comm. ACM*, 21(7): 558–565, 1978.

[6] Leong, H. V. and Agrawal, D., Using Message Semantics to Reduce Rollback in Optimistic Message Logging Recovery Schemes. *Proc. of IEEE ICDCS-14*, : 227–234, 1994.

[7] Mattern, F., Virtual Time and Global States of Distributed Systems. *Parallel and Distributed Algorithms* (Cosnard, M. and Quinton, P. eds.), *North-Holland*, : 215–226, 1989.

[8] Melliar-Smith, P. M., Moser, L. E., and Agrawala, V., Broadcast Protocols for Distributed Systems. *IEEE Trans. on Parallel and Distributed Systems*, 1(1): 17–25, 1990.

[9] Nakamura, A. and Takizawa, M., Reliable Broadcast Protocol for Selectively Ordering PDUs. *Proc. of IEEE ICDCS-11*, : 239–246, 1991.

[10] Nakamura, A., Tachikawa, T., and Takizawa, M., Causally Ordering Broadcast Protocol. *Proc. of IEEE ICDCS-14*, : 48–55, 1994.

[11] Object Management Group Inc., The Common Object Request Broker Architecture and Specification. *Rev.* 2.0, 1995.

[12] Tachikawa, T. and Takizawa, M., Distributed Protocol for Selective Intra-group Communication. *Proc. of IEEE ICNP-95*, : 234–241, 1995.

[13] Tachikawa, T. and Takizawa, M., Object-Based Message Ordering in Group Communication. *Proc. of the IEEE 3rd Int'l Workshop on Object-oriented Real-time Dependable Systems (WORDS'97)*, : 315–322, 1997.

[14] Tachikawa, T., Higaki, H., and Takizawa, M., Group Communication Protocol for Realtime Applications. *Proc. of the 18th IEEE Int'l Conf. on Distributed Computing Systems (ICDCS-18)*, : 40–93, 1998.

[15] Transmission Control Protocol. RFC793, : 1–26, 1981.

Session 8B
Compiler III:
Automatic Restructuring and Parallelization

Chair: Pen-Chung Yew
University of Minnesota

Automatic Generation of Provably Correct Parallelizing Compilers*

Gopal Gupta, Enrico Pontelli, Amado Lara-Rodriguez, Roberto Felix-Cardenas
Department of Computer Science
New Mexico State University
Las Cruces, NM 88003, USA
http://www.cs.nmsu.edu/lldap

Abstract

We show how parallelizing compilers can be automatically derived from denotational definitions of programming languages. In our approach, the denotational definition is expressed using definite clause grammars (syntax specification) and Horn Logic or Constraint Logic (semantic specification). The conditions for executing two or more statements in parallel (e.g., GCD test, Banerjee test, or exact test) are included as part of the (parallel) denotational semantics of the language. Solutions of Diophantine equations, needed for parallelizing DO loops, can be expressed in constraint logic as well, and are thus easily incorporated in our denotational framework. This parallel denotational specification of the language is executable, and thus automatically yields a parallel interpreter. This interpreter can be partially evaluated with respect to a given program to automatically obtain (provably correct) parallel compiled code. In addition, the various syntactic and semantic restructuring transformations that have been proposed to expose more parallelism in sequential programs can also be expressed in our denotational framework.

1. Introduction

We present a denotational semantics based framework for deriving parallelizing compilers from language specifications. Denotational semantics is a well-established methodology for language design and specification [14]. We automatically derive parallel compiled code from the specification of a language (the language considered in this paper is Fortran, though any imperative language can be used). Essentially, we automatically obtain a parallelizing compiler that is provably correct. Two statements in a program can be parallelized if they are *independent*. We assume that the definition of independence is made part of the language specification, i.e., the notion of independence employed is part of the semantic specification of the language. Using *Horn logic* (or *Constraint-logic*) based denotational semantics [3], we are able to derive parallel code from this extended semantics through partial evaluation. This becomes possible because the use of Horn/Constraint logic renders *semantic specification executable* [3].

Traditionally, in imperative languages (e.g., Fortran), parallelism is extracted by executing DO loops in parallel. Different iterations of a DO loop can be executed in parallel if certain independence conditions hold. These conditions boil down to non-existence of solutions of Diophantine equations [18], that arise from equating array references. These equations are constraints over the index variables of the DO loops, and are expressible and solvable in Constraint-logic. Thus, Horn/Constraint-logic framework is powerful enough to express semantics of computations as well as for capturing the notions of independence.

Using the implementation technology developed for solving constraints [16, 4], independence tests such as the *I* test [12] are also automatically incorporated. More advanced tests can also be constructed on the fly during program execution. Additionally, in our approach constraint solving needed to detect independence can be done in parallel using a parallel constraint logic programming system [10, 17]. Partial evaluators for Horn Logic are written in Horn Logic languages (i.e., logic programming languages) themselves. It is well known that parallelism can be automatically exploited from logic programs [10]. Thus, partial evaluation for obtaining the parallel code can be done in parallel itself. In effect, *this means that compilation of the program to parallel code is done in parallel*. So even if exact test is used to solve the Diophantine equations, parallelism exploited should keep the time for compilation low.

Our denotational approach also provides a semantic framework for restructuring transformations. Restructuring transformations are semantics preserving transformations applied to programs to expose more parallelism. They can be expressed as mappings from one semantic domain to

* Authors are partially supported by NSF grants CCR 96-25358, INT 95-15256, CDA 97-29848, HRD 96-28450, and HRD 98-00209.

579

another, and are expressible in a denotational framework.

Our work makes several contributions: (i) it shows how constraint logic can be usefully employed to solve many problems encountered in building parallelizing compilers; (ii) it presents a denotational semantics based framework which can be used for specifying parallel computations, restructuring loop transformations, (iii) it shows how provably correct parallelizing compilers can be derived from the semantic specification of a language. We assume that the reader is familiar with denotational semantics (e.g., [14]), parallelizing compilers (e.g., [18]), and constraint logic programming (e.g., [4]). In the rest of the paper we will use the terms Horn Logic and Constraint Logic interchangeably. By Horn Logic we mean Logic Programming (or pure Prolog). Constraint Logic is a generalization of Horn Logic which includes constraints and constraint solving [4].

2. Horn Logic Denotations

Denotational semantics [14] of a language has three parts: (i) *syntax*: typically specified as a context free grammar; (ii) *semantic algebra*: these are the basic domains along with associated operations; meaning of a program is expressed in terms of these basic domains. (iii) *valuation function*: these are mappings from patterns of parse trees and the global state (which itself is modeled as a semantic algebra) to values in the basic domains in the semantic algebra. Traditional denotational definitions express syntax in the BNF format, and the semantic algebras and valuation function in λ-calculus. However, in the traditional approach, while the semantic algebra and the valuation functions could be made executable, syntax checking and generation of parse trees cannot. This disadvantages disappears if the formalism of logic programming (with its formal basis in Horn logic, a subset of predicate logic) is used, since syntax can be directly specified as a Definite Clause Grammar to automatically obtain a parser [15] and the semantic algebras and valuation functions expressed as logic programs. Thus, both *syntax and semantics become executable, automatically producing an interpreter for the language*.

Consider a simple subset of Fortran (BNF shown below). For simplicity, assume that the only possible variable names allowed are w, x, y and z, and that the only data-type allowed is integer, and that constants appearing in the program are only 1 digit long.

```
Program ::= C.
C ::= C1;C2 | loop while B C endloop while |
      if B then C1 else C2 endif | I = E
E ::= N | Identifier | E1 + E2 |
      E1 - E2 | E1 * E2 | (E)
N ::= 0 | 1 | 2 | ... | 9
Identifier ::= w | x | y | z
```

This BNF is easily transformed into a definite clause grammar (DCG) by a simple change in syntax [15] (plus removal of left-recursion, required for recursive descent parsing). The DCG is a logic program, and when executed, a parser is automatically obtained that can also generate a parse tree.

```
SYNTAX:
program(p(X)) --> cmd(X), [.].

cmd(X) --> cmd(X).
cmd(comb(X,Y)) --> cmd1(X),[;],cmd(Y).
cmd1(assign(I,E)) --> id(I),[=],expn(E).
cmd1(ce(X,Y,Z)) --> [if],expn(X),[then],
           cmd(Y),[else],cmd(Z), [endif].
cmd1(while(B,C)) --> [loop, while], bool(B),
           cmd(C), [endloop, while].
expn1(id(X)) --> id(X).
expn1(num(X)) --> n(X).
expn1(e(X)) --> ['('],expn(X),[')'].
expn(X) --> expn1(X).
expn(add(X,Y)) --> expn1(X),[+],expn1(Y).
expn(sub(X,Y)) --> expn1(X),[-],expn1(Y).
expn(multi(X,Y)) --> expn1(X),[*],expn1(Y).
bool(equal(X,Y)) --> expn(X),[=],expn(Y).
bool(greater(X,Y)) --> expn(X),[>],expn(Y).
bool(less(X,Y)) --> expn(X),[<],expn(Y).
id(x) --> [w].        id(x) --> [x].
id(y) --> [y].        id(z) --> [z].
n(0) --> [0].         n(1) --> [1].
n(2) --> [2].         n(3) --> [3].
....
```

The above grammar specification serves as a parser for the language considered. Thus, the query to parse the program for computing the value y^x and placing it in the variable z:

```
?- program(P, [z,=,1,;, w,=,x,;,
            loop, while,w,>,0,
               z,=,z, *, y,;, w,=,w,-,1,
            endloop, while], []).
```

will parse that program, and produce the parse tree:

```
P = p(comb(assign(z,num(1)),comb(assign(w,id(x)),
        while(greater(id(w),num(0)), comb(
          assign(z,multi(id(z),id(y))),
          assign(w,sub(id(w),num(1))))))))
```

The denotational semantics is defined next, by expressing the semantic algebra and the valuation functions as logic programs. We assume that the input is initially found in variables x and y. The answer is computed and placed in the variable z. The semantic algebra consists simply of the store domain, realized as an association list of the form [(Id, Value) ...] with operations for creating, accessing, and updating the store:

```
SEMANTIC ALGEBRA 1:
  init_store([]).
  access(Id,[],0). %return 0 if uninitialized
  access(Id,[(Id,Val)|_],Val).
  access(Id,[_|R],Val) :- access(Id,R,Val).
  update(Id,NewV,[(Id,_)|R],[(Id,NewV)|R]).
  update(Id,NewV,[P|R],[P|R1]) :-
                  update(Id,NewV,R,R1).
```

Next, the valuation functions, that impart meaning to the language are specified, again as logic programs. These valuation predicates relate the current store, a parse tree pattern whose meaning is to be specified, and the new store that results on executing the program fragment specified by the parse tree pattern. These valuation predicates are shown below; the very first valuation predicate takes the two input values, that are placed in the store locations corresponding to x and y.

```
SEMANTICS: VALUATION PREDICATES
prog_eval(p(Comm), Val_x, Val_y, Output) :-
  init_store(Store),
  update(x, Val_x, Store, Midstore),
  update(y, Val_y, Midstore, Nextstore),
  comm(Comm, Nextstore, Newstore),
  access(z, Newstore, Output).
comm(comb(C1, C2), Store, Outstore) :-
  comm(C1, Store, Newstore),
  comm(C2, Newstore, Outstore).
comm(while(B, C), Store, Outstore) :-
  (bool(B, Store) -> comm(C, Store, Newstore),
     comm(while(B, C), Newstore, Outstore);
   Outstore=Store).
comm(ce(B, C1, C2), Store, Outstore) :-
  (bool(B, Store) -> comm(C1, Store, Outstore);
        comm(C2, Store, Outstore)).
comm(assign(I, E), Store, Outstore) :-
  expr(E, Store, Val),
  update(I, Val, Store, Outstore).
expr(add(E1, E2), Store, Result) :-
  expr(E1, Store, Val_1), expr(E2, Store, Val_2),
  Result is Val_+Val_2.
expr(sub(E1, E2), Store, Result) :-
  expr(E1, Store, Val_1), expr(E2, Store, Val_2),
  Result is Val_1-Val_2.
expr(multi(E1, E2), Store, Result) :-
  expr(E1, Store, Val_1), expr(E2, Store, Val_2),
  Result is Val_1*Val_2.
expr(id(X), Store, Result) :-
  access(X, Store, Result).
expr(num(X), _, X).
bool(greater(E1, E2), Store) :-
  expr(E1, Store, Eval1),
  expr(E2, Store, Eval2), Eval1 > Eval2.
bool(less(E1, E2), Store) :-
  expr(E1, Store, Eval1),
  expr(E2, Store, Eval2), Eval1 < Eval2.
bool(equal(E1, E2), Store) :-
  expr(E1, Store, Eval), expr(E2, Store, Eval).
```

Once the syntax, semantic algebras, and valuation predicates are defined, an interpreter is immediately obtained. Now for both parsing and interpreting the program, define:

```
main(ValX, ValY, A) :-
  program(P, [z,=,1,;, w,=,x,;,
              loop, while,w,>,0,
                 z,=,z, *, y,;,w,=,w,-,1,
              endloop,while], []),
  prog_eval(P,ValX,ValY,A).
```

If the above syntax and semantics rules are loaded in a logic programming system and the query ?- main(5,2,A)

for computing the value of 2^5 posed, then the value of A will be computed as 32. Notice that use of logic programming for specifying semantics results in a complete interpreter.

In the semantics above, we assumed that the store is maintained as an association list, which is passed around as an argument. This does not exactly model imperative languages in which the memory store is treated as a global entity. Given that logic programs can support global data structures through their database facility (the assert and retract built-ins [15]), it is better to model the store as a collection of dynamic facts manipulated using assert and retract. If we decide to adopt this point of view, the only change that will take place will be in the store algebra, which transforms to:

```
SEMANTIC ALGEBRA 2 (globalized):
access(Var,Val) :-
       (store(Var,Val) -> true; Val = 0).
update(Var,Val) :- retractall(store(Var,_)),
                   assert(store(Var,Val)).
```

Now, both the input and the output store arguments can be eliminated in the semantic valuation predicates. However, note that assert and retract are extra-logical built-ins of Prolog, hence our denotational semantics becomes less declarative (though the good thing is that these built-ins are confined to a single semantic algebra).

3. Provably Correct Compilation

It is well known in partial evaluation [5] that compiled code for a program $\mathcal{P}$ written in language $\mathcal{L}$ can be obtained by partially evaluating $\mathcal{P}$ w.r.t. the interpreter for $\mathcal{L}$. We have already obtained an interpreter for the language from its denotational specification. Removal of the semantic algebra for the store from our definition, followed by partial evaluation of the interpreter w.r.t. the program for computing y^x, results in "compiled" code. Our goal is to treat the semantic algebra operations as primitives, and hide their implementation from the partial evaluator. Using the Mixtus partial evaluation system from the Swedish Institute of Computer Science [13], the program that results after partially evaluating the query ?- main(5,2,A) (using SEMANTIC ALGEBRA 1) is the following:

```
main(5,2,A) :-          commandwhile(A,B) :-
  init_store(B),          (access(w,A,C),
  update(a,5,B,C),        C>0 ->
  update(b,2,C,D),        access(z,A,D),
  update(z,1,D,E),        access(y,A,E),
  access(x,E,F),          F is D*E,
  update(w,F,E,G),        update(z,F,A,G),
  commandwhile(G,H),      access(w,G,H),
  access(z,H,A).          I is H-1,
                          update(w,I,G,J),
                          commandwhile(J,B)
                        ; B=A).
```

Note the similarity of this resulting program to compiled code. Essentially, a series of memory `access`, memory `update`, arithmetic and comparison operations are left, that correspond to `load`, `store`, arithmetic, and comparison operations of a machine language. The while-loop, whose meaning was expressed using recursion, will (always) partially evaluate to a *tail-recursive* call that is easily converted to an iterative structure using jumps. Note that the update and access operations are also parameterized on the store name (in contrast, load and store operations of any machine architecture do not take the whole store as an argument). This parameter can easily be eliminated through globalization [14] (using `assert` and `retract` discussed above). Thus, compiled machine code is just one or two very simple transformation steps away. Thus, provably correct compiled code is trivially obtained (of course, assuming that the partial evaluator has been proven correct).

4. Derivation of a Parallelizing Compiler

A denotational definition of a language $\mathcal{L}$ is a complete specification of the syntax and semantics of $\mathcal{L}$. A parallel semantics can also be given to the language, within the same framework. For instance, in Fortran programs, parallelism is mainly exploited in the DO loops. Iterations of a DO loop can be executed in parallel only if certain conditions are satisfied. These conditions essentially boil down to checking if linear Diophantine equations do not have integer solutions within the range of loop limits [18]. These conditions (the non-existence of integer solutions to the Diophantine equations) can be made part of the semantics of the DO loops. These conditions will be evaluated during partial evaluation. During this evaluation, if no solutions for these Diophantine equations are found, then parallel code will be generated. If solutions are indeed found, then code for parallelizing dependent iterations is generated. We give an example next.

Consider a slightly larger subset of Fortran with declarations, DO loops, and (single dimensional) arrays. The grammar of this subset can be straightforwardly coded as the DCG below (details such as structure of identifiers, etc., are omitted for brevity):

```
program(prog(O,X))  -->  [program], [cr],
  specification_part(O), exec_part(X),
  [end], [program], [cr].
specification_part(spec_part(DC)) -->
  decl_construct_list(DC).

decl_construct_list(DC) --> type_decl(DC), [cr].
decl_construct_list((DC,DCL)) -->
  type_decl(DC), [cr], decl_construct_list(DCL).
decl_construct_list([]).
type_decl(type_decl(TS,[EDL])) -->
  type_spec(TS), simple_identifier(EDL).
type_decl(type_decl(TS,dim(AS),[EDL])) -->
  type_spec(TS), [dimension], ['('],
```

```
  array_spec(AS), [')'], simple_identifier(EDL).
type_spec(type_spec(integer)) --> [integer].
array_spec(array_spec(ASL)) -->
  array_spec_list(ASL).
array_spec_list(PN) --> positive_number(PN).
array_spec_list((PN,ASL)) --> numeral(PN),
  [','], array_spec_list(ASL).

exec_part(exec_part(EPC)) --> exec_p_c(EPC).
exec_p_c(exec_p_c(EPL)) --> exec_part_list(EPL).
exec_part_list(AS) --> action_stmt(AS), [cr].
exec_part_list([]).
exec_part_list((AS,EPL)) --> action_stmt(AS),
  [cr], exec_part_list(EPL).

action_stmt(do(I,Z1,Z2,EPC)) --> [do],
  simple_identifier(I), [=], expr(Z1), [','],
  expr(Z2), [cr], exec_p_c(EPC), [enddo].
action_stmt(assign(I,E)) -->
  identifier(I), [=], expr(E).

expression_list([X|R]) --> expr(X),[','],
  expression_list(R).
expression_list([E]) --> expr(E).
identifier_list([]).
identifier_list([I|R]) --> identifier(I),[','],
  identifier_list(R).
expr(E) --> expr4(E).
expr4(E) --> expr5(E).
expr4(plus(E1,E2)) --> expr5(E1),['+'],expr4(E2).
expr5(E) --> expr6(E).
expr5(times(E1,E2)) --> expr6(E1),['*'],expr5(E2).
expr6(E) --> expr7(E).
expr6(E) --> ['('],expr4(E),[')'].
expr7(V) --> numeral(V); identifier(V).

identifier(I) --> array_identifier(I);
  simple_identifier(I).
array_identifier(array(I,EL)) -->
  simple_identifier(ident(I)),
  ['('], expression_list(EL), [')'].
```

The (parallel) semantics can be next given. For each grammar rule in the Definite Clause Grammar, there is one semantic valuation function. These semantic functions are predicated on parse trees and the global state and compute the meaning of the program in terms of domains defined in the semantic algebra. Before we define the semantic valuation function, let us define the semantic algebras needed for the parallel semantics. Mainly, we need the semantic algebra for the store, similar to semantic algebra 2 in example above, since parallel tasks may access the store concurrently.

```
SEMANTIC ALGEBRA:
access(Var,Val) :-
    (store(Var,Val) -> true; Val = 0).
update(Var,Val) :- retractall(store(Var,_)),
    assert(store(Var,Val)).
update_arr(Name,E,V) :- retractall(store(Name,E,_)),
    assert(store(Name,E,V)).
access_arr(Name,E,V) :-
    (store(Name,E,V) -> true; V = 0).
```

Next we define the various semantic functions. These semantic functions specify the meaning of each construct in the language. The most significant is the (parallel) semantics of the DO loop construct and is discussed next. Code for some of the valuation predicates have been omitted for simplicity.

```
par_program_sem(prog(Spec,Exec)) :-
  process_declarations(Spec), exec_comms(Exec).
exec_comms(exec_part(exec_p_c(Seq))) :-
  process_commands(Seq,[]).
process_commands((C1,C2),S) :-
  comm(C1,S), process_commands(C2,S).
process_commands(C,S) :- comm(C,S).

comm(assign(I,E),S) :-
  expr_val(E,V1,S), update_loc(I,V1,S).
comm(do(ident(I),E1,E2,exec_p_c(Seq)),S) :-
  expr_val(E1,V1,S), expr_val(E2,V2,S),
  collect_exp(Seq,Left,Right),
  create_equations(Left,Right,Eqs),
  solutions(Eqs,Sols),
  execute_body(V1,V2,Seq,Sols,I,S).

/*Begin: auxiliary predicates used
  by semantic predicates of DO*/
execute_body(Start,End,Seq,Sols,I,S) :-
  ( Start > End -> true; par_begin(task1,task2),
      task1(task1,Sols,Start,Seq,I,S),
      task2(task2,End,Start,Seq,Sols,I,S),
      par_end).

task1(T1,Sols,Value,Seq,I,S) :-
  start_task(T1), enforce_deps_big(Sols,Value),
  process_commands(Seq,[(I,Value)|S]),
  enforce_deps_small(Sols,Value),
  end_task(T1).
task2(T2,End,Start,Seq,Sols,I,S) :-
  start_task(T2), Start1 is Start + 1,
  execute_body(Start1,End,Seq,Sols,I,S),
  end_task(T2).

enforce_deps_big([],_).
enforce_deps_big([(D1,D2)|Rest],Value) :-
  max(D1,D2,D3), min(D1,D2,D4),
  (D3 = D4 -> true;
      (Value = D3 -> wait(D4); true)),
  enforce_deps_big(Rest,Value).
enforce_deps_small([],_).
enforce_deps_small([(D1,D2)|Rest],Value) :-
  min(D1,D2,D3), max(D1,D2,D4),
  (D3 = D4 -> true;
      (Value = D3 -> signal(D4); true)),
  enforce_deps_small(Rest,Value).
/*end: auxiliary functions used by DO*/

/*begin: auxiliary predicates for '='*/
update_loc(array(Name,[Express]),Value,S) :-
    expr_val(Express,E1,S),
    update_arr(Name,E1,Value).
update_loc(J,Value,_) :-
  (J = ident(I) -> update(I,Value);
    J = array(_,_) -> fail; update(J,Value)).
/*end: auxiliary predicates for '='*/

expr_val(plus(E1,E2),Val,S) :-
  expr_val(E1,V1,S),
```

```
  expr_val(E2,V2,S), Val is V1+V2.
expr_val(times(E1,E2),Val,S) :-
  expr_val(E1,V1,S),
  expr_val(E2,V2,S), Val is V1*V2.
expr_val(integer(N),N,_).
expr_val(array(Name,[Arg]),Val,S) :-
  expr_val(Arg,Pos,S),
  access_arr(Name,Pos,Val).
expr_val(ident(Name),Val,S) :-
  (find_local(Name,Val,S) -> true;
      access(Name,Val)).

find_local(Name,Val,[(Name1,Val2)|R]) :-
  (Name =  Name1 -> Val = Val2;
          find_local(Name,Val,R)).
```

Consider the valuation predicate for the DO loop (comm(do(ident(I),...) :- ..). The first argument is the parse tree for the DO loop construct. The parse tree contains the index variable (ident(I)), the starting value (E1), ending value (E2), and the parse tree of the loop body (Seq). For simplicity we assume in the semantics that the increment to the index variable is always 1. The start value expression and the end value expressions are evaluated. A local store is maintained by each iteration, where the value of the index variable is kept. This is needed since all iterations are being executed in parallel. The final value of the index variable should be copied into the main store at the end of the DO loop execution, however, for simplicity in our semantics we discard the local stores at the end of the execution of the DO loop. The body of the DO loop is examined, and the array subscript expressions are collected (collect_exp goal). The subscript expressions are equated to generate all the Diophantine equations that need to be solved to check for independence of loops (create_equations). These Diophantine equations are then solved (in the goal solutions) and the list of solutions is computed in Sols. If there are no solutions, this list is empty, otherwise it contains pairs of the form (n, m). Each pair is a solution to one of the Diophantine equations. If (n, m) is a solution to the equations, then it means that iteration n must be executed before iteration m. This list is passed to the predicate execute_body that specifies the parallel semantics of the DO loop. Note that in our case we assume that the solutions predicate solves the Diophantine equation exactly, taking the lower and upper limits of the loop into account. We could use any independence test that we choose. For instance, we could employ the GCD test, an approximate test, if we wish to be conservative in exploiting parallelism. Likewise, Banerjee test, or any other desired approximate or exact test could be used.

Consider the execute_body function above. The execute_body function is a recursive function whose arguments are the starting value, ending value, the parse tree of the body of the DO loop, the (possibly empty) list of solutions to the Diophantine equations, the current value of the index variable, and the local store to be used by that iteration. The last argument is the output store produced by the body of the DO loop. If the value of the index variable exceeds the end value expression, `execute_body` terminates. Otherwise, the execution of the current iteration is begun in parallel with rest of the iterations after updating the index variable in the local store of the current iteration with the new value. Maintaining a local store where the current value of the index variable for that particular iteration is stored is, we believe, the best way to model the actual execution semantics of the parallel DO loop. Appropriate `wait` and `signal` operations should be called, given the solutions of the Diophantine equations. If (n, m) is present as a solution, then iteration n at the end of its execution should call `signal(m)`, indicating that iteration m can now proceed. Likewise, iteration m should call the `wait(n)` instruction before it begins execution to ensure that execution of iteration n is over. This is exactly what is specified in the `enforce_deps_small` and `enforce_deps_bigs` predicates. Parallelism is indicated using the `par_begin/par_end` construct. The tasks to be executed in parallel inside a `par_begin/par_end` parallel construct are identified by the `start_task/end_task` construct. Consider the following simple program below (the program is represented as a list of tokens; `cr` denotes carriage return):

```
ex([program,cr,
    integer,length,',',width,',',area,',',i,cr,
    integer,dimension,'(',100,')',arr,cr,
    length,=,12,cr, width,=,3,cr,
    do,i,=,1,',',8,cr,
    arr,'(',2,*,i,+,0,')',=,length,+,1,cr,
    length,=,arr,'(',1,*,i,+,1,')',cr, enddo,cr,
    end,program,cr]).
```

Calling the parser routine for this program:
    `?- ex(Prog),program(ParseTree,Prog,[]).`
yields a parse tree (not shown), that is passed to the interpreter (by calling `par_program_sem`) for execution. If `par_begin/par_end` are implemented (so that the tasks enclosed within them are executed in parallel) along with `wait` and `signal`, then parallel execution takes place.

We next partially evaluate the parallel interpreter w.r.t. the Fortran program above. We will remove the semantic algebra for the store and the array domain, so that evaluation stops when a store or an array operation is reached. The Diophantine equations are solved during partial evaluation (the `solutions` predicate is defined in our semantics so as to solve the Diophantine equations exactly). The Diophantine equation generated is $2i_1 = i_2 + 1$. Note that the variables i_1 and i_2 are constrained by the loop limits, i.e., $1 \le i_1 \le 8, 1 \le i_2 \le 8$ and $i_1 \ne i_2$. These constraints can also be included in the semantics (in the definition of the solutions/4 predicate). Solving these constraints, the list of solutions obtained is: $[(4,7),(3,5),(2,3)]$. The partial evaluator produces the following code, shown below.

Notice that each call in the code below essentially corresponds to a machine instruction. The compiled code produced has iterations numbers 7, 5, and 3 waiting for iterations 4, 3, 2 respectively. Note that all recursive procedures (e.g., `executed_body1`) are tail-recursive (`end_task` and `par_end` are really markers), and hence can be automatically transformed into iterative loops. The empty goal `true` translates to noop, which can be optimized away. Thus, machine code can be now obtained by simple mechanical transformations.

```
go1 :- create_store,
       update(length, _),
       update(width, _),
       update(area, _),
       update(i, _),
       update(length, 12),
       update(width, 3),
       execute_body1(1).
execute_body1(A) :-
       (A>8 -> true ;
        par_begin(task1, task2),
        start_task(task1),
          ( A=7 -> wait(4) ; true ),
          ( A=5 -> wait(3) ; true ),
          ( A=3 -> wait(2); true ),
          access(length, B),
          C is B+1,
          D is 2*A,
          E is D,
          update_arr(arr, E, C),
          F is A,
          G is F+1,
          access_arr(arr, G, H),
          update(length, H),
          ( A=4 -> signal(7) ; true ),
          ( A=3 -> signal(5) ; true ),
          ( A=2 -> signal(3) ; true ),
        end_task(task1),
        start_task(task2),
          I is A+1,
          execute_body1(I),
        end_task(task2),
        par_end).
```

Consider the same program as above, except that the array expressions involved are $2 * i_1 + 1$ and $2i_2$. The Diophantine equation $2 * i_1 + 1 = 2 * i_2$ has no integer solutions. Hence, no `wait`s or `signal`s are generated, as all iterations can be executed in parallel. This can be seen in the compiled code obtained through partial evaluation that is shown below (only the code for `execute_body1` is shown).

```
execute_body1(A) :-
     (A>8 -> true ;
             par_begin(task1, task2),
               start_task(task1),
               access(length, B), C is B+1,
               D is 2*A, E is D,
               update_arr(arr, E, C),
               F is A, G is F+1,
               access_arr(arr, G, H),
```

584

```
        update(length, H),
        end_task(task1),
        start_task(task2),
        I is A+1,
        execute_body1(I),
        end_task(task2),
    par_end).
```

Note that in above discussion, the partial evaluator applied to the parallel interpreter (obtained from the specification of the language) serves as a parallelizing compiler.

5. The I test

As shown above, the conditions for independence of loops are included as part of the parallel semantics of the language. If we have a partial evaluator for a constraint logic programming language, then these constraints can be evaluated during partial evaluation. The constraints framework needed for this purpose is that of CLP(FD) [16]. The CLP(FD) framework is capable of directly solving constraints of the form: $a*i_1+b*i_2 = c, k_1 \leq i_1, i_2, \leq k_2$ (several other types of constraints can also be solved, but these do not concern us here). CLP(FD) solves these constraints assuming the variables involved have finite domains. Thus, the Diophantine equations of the above form are solved with domain of the variables i_1, i_2 set to $k_1..k_2$. If we use the CLP(FD) framework, and we use a partial evaluator for CLP(FD) then we can obtain parallel compiled code in a way similar to the above, the only difference will be that the constraints will be solved using the implementation mechanisms used in CLP(FD) (in the example in the previous section, a simple solver for Diophantine equations was also included in the semantic specification, in the `solutions` predicate, as Mixtus does not support constraints solving).

An interesting thing happens when CLP(FD) is used: *the I test* [12], as well as the *Direction Vector I test* [11], is incorporated automatically. This is because the mechanisms used in the *I* tests have long been known in the constraint programming community and are incorporated in the constraint solving systems (see page 87 in [16]). Consider a linear equation of the form: $a_1x_1+...+a_nx_n = c$ where c and x_is are unknown but whose ranges are known (in CLP(FD) terminology, they are termed *finite domain variables*). Assume, for simplicity, that a_is are natural numbers ($a_i \geq 0$). Suppose the range of c is $[min..max]$, where min, max are integers. Recall that both in parallelizing compilers as well as in CLP(FD) we are only interested in integer solutions of the above linear equation. Suppose the finite domain of each x_i is $[min_i..max_i]$. Then, the following holds $a_ix_i \geq low_i$ and $a_ix_i \leq high_i$, where

$$low_i = min - (\sum_{k=1, k\neq i}^{n}(a_k max_k))$$
$$high_i = max - (\sum_{k=1, k\neq i}^{n}(a_k min_k))$$

Thus, the new domain of x_i can be computed as $[low_i..high_i]$. If the original domain of x_i, namely, $[min_i..max_i]$ does not overlap with the new computed domain $[low_i..high_i]$, then the constraints are unsolvable. If they do overlap, then the domain of x_i can be narrowed to the intersection of the two ranges. Computing integer solutions with this narrowed domain is considerably more efficient. The above constraint solving facility is present in most constraint solving systems (e.g., CHIP [16] and ALICE [7]). This technique has been used in the parallelizing compiler community as well and is known as the I-test [12].

If there are further constraints on x_i, then these will be used in constraint programming systems to narrow the domains of x_i's further. Thus, if constraints imposed by direction vectors were included, then these constraints will just be included as new constraints in a CLP(FD) system and used during finite domain constraint solving. This extended constraint solving mechanism is known by the name of *Direction Vector I* test in the parallelizing compiler community [11]. The above discussion is easily extended to the case where a_i's are integers (the way low_i and hi_i are computed will change).

If we used a CLP(FD) system to execute our semantics (CLP(FD) systems are Prolog systems extended with finite domain constraint solving [16]), then the *I test* will automatically be included. What is more, other advanced forms of constraint solving that are found in CLP(FD) systems will also be available.

6. Restructuring Transformations

Restructuring transformations can also be expressed in our denotational semantics framework. A restructuring transformation specifies how one or more DO loop (call the set of loops S_1) that has a specific structure is to be transformed to one or more loops (call this set of loops S_2), such that the semantics of the program is preserved. The transformation is done with the hope that the transformed set of loops S_2 will expose more parallelism.

Denotational semantics serves as a good uniform framework for specifying these restructuring transformations. A restructuring transformation can be thought of as transforming the parse tree of the set of loops S_1 to the parse tree of the set of loops S_2. In the denotational framework, parse tree of S_2 is regarded as the meaning of the parse tree of S_1. Thus, the semantic algebra employs domains that range over parse trees, and the valuation predicates give the denotation of a given loop structure in terms of the transformed loop structure expressed using these domains. Given that semantics is executable in our logical denotational framework, the semantic specification of the transformation yields a program transformer automatically.

The dependence information that usually needs to be preserved during restructuring transformation can be computed from the parse trees, and included as part of the semantic specification.

The intended framework is as follows. Loop restructuring transformations are specified as described above. Given a program, the transformer maps this program to transformed code. The transformed code is partially evaluated (in the manner described in previous sections) to obtain parallel compiled code. We next take the example of *Index Set Splitting Transformation* and show how it can be expressed in this denotational framework. The Index Set Splitting transformation splits the index set of a loop into two parts in order to remove a conditional statement. For example, consider the loop shown below to the left, and its transformed version to the right.

```
DO I=1,100              DO I=1,28
  IF 2*I+4 > 60            A[I] = I+5
    THEN A[I-20] = I+2  ENDDO
    ELSE A[I] = I+5     DO I=29,100
  ENDIF                   A[I-20] = I+2
ENDDO                   ENDDO
```

This transformation can be symbolically described in our denotational framework as shown below. Essentially, we employ the power of logical variables of logic programming to express patterns of parse-trees. We assume that the `Condition` is an affine expression [18] involving only loop indices and symbolic constants, of the form `a*I + b > c`, or of the form `a*I+b < c` (we place this restriction only for simplicity of presentation, the most general case in which the condition is an arbitrary conjunction/disjunction of affine expressions can be easily handled). The predicate `affine_expression` takes the parse tree of this condition as an argument and produces the index value around which the loop is to be split. It also computes if the condition is true in the first part of the split loop or the second part. The code for `affine_expression`, `split` and `combine` predicates is obvious, and is not included for simplicity. Most other restructuring transformations can be specified in a similar way.

```
comm(do(ident(i),E1,E2,Stmt),S) :-
  split(Stmt,Stmt1,Stmt2,Stmt3),
  Stmt2 = if(Condition,Then-part,Else-part),
  affine_expr(Condition,SplitIndex,Dir),
  combine(Stmt1,Then-part,Stmt3,B1),
  combine(Stmt1,Else-part,Stmt3,B2),
  (Dir = first -> Body1 = B1, Body2 = B2;
                  Body1 = B2, Body2 = B1),
  S = (do(ident(i),E1,SplitIndex,Body1),
       do(ident(i),SplitIndex+1,E2,Body2)).
```

7. Conclusions and Related Work

For many critical applications, correctness of the parallel code is important. Our constraint logic denotational framework produces provably correct compiled code. Our work also provides a uniform framework for restructuring transformation [6, 9]. Our Horn/Constraint logic based denotational framework can be put to further use. The problem of

scheduling parallel tasks on a given architecture is NP complete. Constraint logic is a good framework for specifying and solving such problems (powerful heuristics are automatically applied to considerably narrow the search space whenever possible). Given that our denotational specification is based on a constraint logic framework, the parallel architecture on which the program is to run can be included as part of the semantic specification. Parallel code tailored to the particular architecture can then be automatically generated from this specification through partial evaluation. Similar ideas can be applied for computing an optimal data-placement on a given parallel architecture.

Previous work in semantics based study of parallelizing compiler includes the work of Parsons [8] and Felleisen [1]. Fritzson [2] uses semantics based approaches to generate code for a data-parallel language. Research has also been done in developing unified frameworks for restructuring transformations [9, 6]. In contrast to their approach, our framework is based on denotational semantics. A major advantage of our approach is that the same framework suffices for most aspects of compilation and transformation of parallel programs.

References

[1] M. Felleisen, R. Cartwright. A Semantic Foundation for Program Optimization. Internal Report, Rice Univ. 1988.

[2] J. Ringstrom et al. Generating an Efficient Compiler for a Data Parallel Language from a Denotational Specification, Springer, LNCS, 786, pp. 248-262, 1994.

[3] G. Gupta. Horn Logic Denotations and Their Applications. Technical Report, NMSU, Dec. 1997.

[4] K. Marriott, P. Stuckey, Constraint Programming. MIT Press, 1998.

[5] N. Jones. Introduction to Partial Evaluation. In *ACM Computing Surveys*. 28(3):480-503.

[6] W. Kelly, W. Pugh. A Unifying Framework for Iteration Reordering Transformations. CS-TR-3430, Univ. of Maryland, 1995.

[7] J-L. Lauriere. A Language and a Program for Stating and Solving Combinatorial Problems. *Artificial Intelligence*, 10(1):29-127, 1978.

[8] R. Parsons. A Rewriting Semantics for Program Dependence Graphs. 16th POPL, ACM Press, 1989.

[9] W. Li, K. Pingali. A Singular Loop Transformation Framework based on Nonsingular Matrices. In *Int'l J. of Parallel Prog.*, 22(2), 1994.

[10] E. Pontelli, G. Gupta. Parallel Symbolic Computation with ACE. In *Annals of AI and Mathematics*. Dec. 97. (Summary in http://www.cs.nmsu.edu/lldap/ace/ace.html).

[11] K. Psarris, et al. The Direction Vector I Test. *IEEE Trans. on Par. and Distr. Sys.*, 4(11), 1993.

[12] K. Psarris, et al. The I Test: An Improved Dependence Test for Automatic Parallelization. *IEEE Trans. on Par. and Distr. Sys.*, 2(3), 1991.

[13] D. Sahlin. An Automatic Partial Evaluator for Full Prolog. Ph.D. Thesis. 1994. Royal Institute of Technology, Sweden.

[14] D. Schmidt. *Denotational Semantics: a Methodology for Language Development.* W.C. Brown Publishers, 1986.

[15] L. Sterling & S. Shapiro. The Art of Prolog. MIT Press, '94.

[16] P. van Hentenryck. *Constraint Handling in Prolog.* MIT Press, 1988.

[17] P. van Hentenryck. Parallel Constraint Satisfaction in Logic Programming. *Proc. Int. Conf. on Logic Prog.*, MIT Press, 1989.

[18] M. Wolfe. *High Performance Compiler for Parallel Computing*, Addison Wesley, 1996.

Automatic Data Partitioning for Irregular and Adaptive Applications

Gagan Agrawal
Department of Computer and Information Sciences
University of Delaware Newark DE 19716
(302)-831-2783
agrawal@cis.udel.edu

Abstract

An important component in compiling for distributed memory machines is data partitioning. While a number of automatic analysis techniques have been proposed for this phase, none of them is applicable for irregular problems. In this paper, we present compile-time analysis for determining data partitioning for such applications. We have developed a set of cost functions for determining communication and redistribution costs in irregular codes. We first determine the appropriate distributions for a single data parallel statement, and then use the cost functions with a greedy algorithm for computing distributions for the full program. Initial performance results on a 16 processor IBM SP-2 are also presented.

1. Introduction

In recent years, there have been major efforts in developing language and compiler support for programming distributed memory machines. Compilers for High Performance Fortran (HPF) are now available from several vendors. Several academic projects have proposed further extensions to HPF and it is likely that the future versions of these compilers will be able to generate efficient code for wider classes of applications.

Compiling for distributed memory machines has three major components: data partitioning, computation partitioning and communication generation. Data parallel languages like HPF [14] require the programmers to specify the data partitioning explicitly, using *decompositions* or *templates*. The current commercial compilers for HPF, as well as the prototype academic compilers like Fortran D [11] or Vienna Fortran, focus mostly on communication generation. These compilers use programmer specified data distributions and determine computation partitioning from the data distribution, using the *owner computes* rule [11].

Specifying data distribution using language directives can be difficult for application programmers, and it is important for the compilers to automatically compute the appropriate data distribution for a data parallel code. Data distribution analysis has been an important area of research within the compiler community for several years [3, 4, 8, 16]. A number of different techniques like integer programming, dynamic programming or greedy algorithms are used, which widely vary in the accuracy and costs of analysis.

Traditionally, data parallel languages like HPF are considered the most suited for programming *regular* applications, i.e. the applications in which the data accesses can be determined at compile-time. Current HPF compilers are restricted to optimizing the communication for regular applications only. However, several academic projects have made considerable progress in the area of compiling *irregular applications* [6, 10, 15, 17, 18]. These projects have successfully demonstrated that with the use of additional language directives and appropriate runtime libraries, communication can be optimized for irregular applications and code with good efficiency can be generated. It is expected that the future versions of HPF compilers will incorporate these techniques and generate efficient code for irregular applications.

An important limitation of the current work in compiling for irregular applications has been data distribution analysis. The proposed techniques for automatic data distribution are all restricted to codes in which all array accesses are *affine* functions of loop indices, i.e., the regular applications. The prototype compilers which have successfully handled irregular applications require the programmers to explicitly insert runtime calls to data partitioning routines [17], or build map arrays and use value based distributions [9]. We believe that neither of these approaches give the programmers the level of automation that they desire.

In this paper, we present an automatic data distribution technique which analyzes codes with indirection arrays. We believe that this is the first proposed technique for automatic data distribution in irregular codes. The main difficulty in the automatic data distribution for irregular applications is

```
Real   X(m), Y(n)   ! data arrays
Integer IA(m)        ! indirection array
forall i = 1, m
       X(i) = X(i) + Y(IA(i))
```

Figure 1. A Data Parallel Irregular Loop

that the costs of using different distributions cannot be assessed accurately at compile-time. We propose heuristic cost functions for assessing the communication costs associated with different candidate distributions and of redistribution directives. Our initial analysis considers a single data parallel statement and suggests distribution functions for the arrays which are either used as indirection arrays or are accessed using indirection arrays. The second phase of our algorithm uses a greedy algorithm to choose between different candidate distributions and to decide the placement of redistribution statements.

The rest of the paper is organized as follows. In Section 2, we give an overview of the current state of art in the area of compiling irregular applications and define the automatic data distribution problem for such applications. The technique is presented in Section 3. Preliminary experimental evaluation of our work is presented in Section 4. We conclude in Section 5.

2. Compiling Irregular Applications

In this paper, we are primarily concerned with the irregular problems which can be expressed in HPF-like languages. Such irregular problems use *indirection arrays* for accessing data. Consider, for example, the code presented in Figure 1. In this simple data parallel loop, the contents of the array X are updated using the contents of the array Y. Array Y is accessed using an *indirection array*, IA. The communication required in this code depends upon the contents of the indirection array, which are not known at compile-time. However, by developing runtime libraries like CHAOS and PARTI [13], and by compiler techniques which automatically insert these runtime routines [2, 1, 6, 10], efficient SPMD code has been generated for such applications.

The main steps involved in the executing such a loop on message passing machines are:

I. Distributing the arrays across different processors (known as *data partitioning*).

II. Distributing the loop iterations (work) between processors (known as *computation partitioning*).

III. Determining the communication requirements and optimizing the communication.

Our goal here is to automate the steps I and II above. Commonly, after data distribution has been defined, work

distribution can be defined using the data distribution and the owners compute rule. Therefore, in this paper, we focus on the data distribution problem only. Before presenting our technique in the next section, we first discuss existing techniques for the communication optimization step. In the example code, it is clear that the arrays X and IA can be partitioned in *block* fashion, i.e. each processor can be allocated consecutive m/p elements, where m is the size of the array and p is the number of processors. Accordingly, the computation partitioning can be done by allocating m/p consecutive iterations of the loop to each processor. The main difficulty in the above loop arises in the distribution of array Y. If the array Y is distributed in a *regular* fashion, (i.e. using standard block, cyclic or block-cyclic distributions), then it is likely that the number of off-processor references will be very high for this loop. This situation can be improved by an *irregular* partitioning of the array Y, at runtime, when the contents of the array IA are known.

A similar problem arises in determining the communication requirements in this loop. Once the distribution of array Y has been determined, the off-processor elements of array Y depends upon the contents of array IA again. There is no method available for aggregating communication at compile-time for such a loop. This leaves the compilers/programmers with two options, either to use *runtime resolution* and have one message per iteration of the loop, or use runtime preprocessing for aggregating communication. Clearly, because of the high communication latencies, runtime resolution cannot achieve acceptable performance, and, therefore, runtime preprocessing is used.

2.1. Overview of the Runtime, Language and Compiler Support

We now present a brief outline of the runtime and compiler techniques used for irregular compilation. Runtime libraries like PARTI and CHAOS have been developed to provide the routines required for efficient execution of irregular applications [13]. Runtime routines supported by these libraries can broadly be divided into two categories:

- Routines for determining data and computation partitioning

- Routines for communication preprocessing and optimizing communication

A basic data structure commonly used is the *communication schedule*. A communication schedule is generated by processing an indirection array at runtime, and determines the communication required between different processors for a particular parallel loop involving indirect accesses. A communication schedule is then used by a *collective communication* routine, which performs the actual communication required. The principal reason for separating the the communication preprocessing step (i.e. the generation

```
          Real   X(m), Y(n)    ! data arrays
          Integer IA(m)        ! indirection array
     C    COMPILED CODE
     C    Distributed array Y
          Irreg_distr(Y, IA)
     C    Build the required schedule
          Sched  =  Irreg_Sched(.. parameters ..)
     C    Commnicate data using the schedule build above
          Call Data_Move(Y,Sched)
     C    Actual Loop
          do 10 i =   1, m_local
          X(i) = X(i) + Y(IA_local(i))
     10   continue
```

Figure 2. Compiling a HPF irregular loop

of the communication schedule) from data communication step is that by reusing a communication schedule several times, the cost of generating the communication schedule can be amortized.

Parallelization of the loop presented earlier in Figure 1 is shown in Figure 2. We will visit the details of *Irreg_distr(Y, IA)* later while discussing language support issues. The communication schedule *Sched* is built at runtime and is used later by the *Data_Move* routine.

In recent years, considerable effort has been put into compiling irregular application written in HPF-like languages [6, 10, 15, 17, 18]. Most of the work has focussed on optimizing communication for irregular applications. Earlier versions of the compilers focussed largely on recognizing irregular patterns and inserting appropriate communication preprocessing and collective communication routines [15, 17, 18]. Prototype extensions to both the Rice Fortran D system and the Syracuse 90D system were implemented with this functionality. In more recent work, the communication was further optimized using more aggressive compiler analysis. Hanxleden proposed a new communication placement framework: Give-N-Take [10], and implemented it as part of the Fortran D system. This framework involves intraprocedural analysis for placement of communication, so as to avoid any redundant message traffic in the code. Das used slicing technique for generating communication in codes which involve multiple levels of indirection [6]. Agrawal extensively used interprocedural analysis for performing aggressive placement of communication preprocessing routines and communication routines [2, 1].

We now give the overview of the language support proposed for irregular distributions, and then define the automatic data partitioning problem we are addressing. Hanxleden proposed the notion of *value-based distributions* and implemented these as part of the Fortran D system [9]. Consider the code presented earlier in Figure 1. In the irregular loop, we will like to distribute the array Y based upon

the *value* of array IA. Obviously, this distribution can be done only at runtime, when the contents of the array IA are known. However, programmer can specify that he/she expects the distribution of X and IA to be done in the block fashion and the distribution of Y to be done based upon the value of IA. Specifying block distribution is part of the HPF language, and is commonly used for a variety of applications. The syntax proposed for value-based distributions is as follows:

```
DIST Y(VALUE(IA))
```

The implementation of value-based distributions requires that the programmer provides such a directive explicitly in the source code. Once such a directive has been provided, the compiler can generate appropriate runtime routines for partitioning the array Y using values of the array IA using the techniques described by Hanxleden [9]. Our analysis focuses on generating value based distributions from the source code.

2.2. Problem Description

We now informally define the compilation problem we are interested in addressing. We described in the previous subsection how the language directives could be used for specifying irregular distributions. Our goal is to ease the programming of irregular applications by automatically generating the value-based distribution directives from the source code. Unlike the simple loop presented in the previous subsection, this problem can be much more difficult for a real code, for one or more of the following reasons:

- If the same array accesses data using different indirection arrays in different parallel loops, then the ideal distributions will be different for these two loops. However, using different distributions in different parts of the code may involve frequent redistributions which may have high costs associated with them. Thus, a trade-off needs to be made about the choice of suitable distributions

- The values of the indirection arrays may change themselves during different iterations of a single loop. This may involve making the choice of either redistributing the array frequently, or paying high communication costs.

3. Analysis for Data Partitioning

In this section, we present our analysis for data partitioning for irregular applications. Our analysis has three major components: analysis at a single data parallel statement, calculating communication and redistribution costs, and global analysis for final distributions using a greedy algorithm.

Consider any HPF program. The arrays used in the programs can be classified into two classes:

- Arrays which are either

  - Used for indirect accesses or,

  - Accessed indirectly or,

  - Accessed in a statement where one or more arrays are accessed through indirection.

- Arrays which do not fall into any of the above categories.

The arrays in the second category can be analyzed for data distribution using standard techniques from the automatic data distribution literature, and we assume that their data distribution has been decided previously using these techniques. So, for our presentation, we focus on the arrays in the first category, and look for data-parallel statements in which indirect accesses are made.

3.1. Analysis for a Single Statement

Consider a single array assignment statement in which one or more arrays are accessed using indirection. The analysis can be trivially extended to a forall loop. Later in this section, we discuss how the analysis can be extended for a program comprising of several data parallel loops.

We assume that in our source program, no array is accessed through indirection in more than one dimension and multiple levels of indirection do not occur in this statement. Loops in which more than one dimension of a single array is accessed through indirection are beyond the scope of this paper. We do not consider spread operations.

Consider any array expression in the left-hand-side or right-hand-side of this assignment statement. This array is either accessed through indirection, and has the form

$$X(IA(l_1 : h_1, i), l_2 : h_2)$$

or is accessed without indirection, and has the form

$$Y(l_1 : h_1, l_2 : h_2)$$

Note that the notation $(l_1 : h_1)$ implies a lower bound of l_1 and an upper bound of h_1. We are considering only two dimensional arrays since the analysis can be trivially extended to arrays with more than two dimensions. One dimensional arrays can be viewed as special case of two dimensional arrays. Without loss of generality, we have assumed that indirection is used along the first dimension.

We have the following distribution tasks:

1. Distributions of the arrays which are not accessed through indirection

2. Distributions of indirection arrays

3. Distribution of the arrays which are accessed through indirection, along the dimension indirection is not used

4. Distribution of the arrays which are accessed through indirection, along the dimension indirection is used

Consider the array expression $X(IA(l_1 : h_1 : s_1, i), l_2 : h_2 : s_2)$. The distribution choice for the array X along the second dimension does not depend upon the contents of indirection array. Similarly, the distribution choice of the array IA itself does not depend upon the values of array IA. Clearly, the distribution of the array Y above again does not depend upon the values in the indirection array. So, in summary, the contents of the indirection array does not affect the choice of distribution for the tasks 1, 2 and 3 above. The analysis used for regular codes can be applied for determining distributions for these array dimensions. For most of the common loops, block partitioning results in optimal performance.

The existing techniques in literature for regular codes do not apply for determining distribution of the arrays dimensions, along which indirection is used. Suppose, we have a total of k arrays which are accessed using indirection arrays, and let these indirection array sections be $IA_1(l_1 : h_1, i_1), \ldots, IA_k(l_k : h_k, i_k)$. We create a template T, and distribute this template as follows:

```
DIST T(VALUE(IA_1(l_1 : h_1, i_1),...,
    IA_k(l_k : h_k, i_k) ))
```

For each of the arrays accessed through indirection, the dimension accessed through indirection can now be aligned with the above template T.

3.2. Cost Functions and Candidate Distributions

After deciding the ideal distribution of each array in a single data parallel statement, we are interested in deciding data distributions for the entire program. To be able to compare different choices of distributions, we have developed a set of heuristic cost functions. Consider a loop which accesses data using indirection array, e.g. the code presented in Figure 1. We refer to the arrays X and Y as the data arrays and the array IA as the indirection array.

We assume that the cost of communication depends upon the maximum number of off-processor elements required by any processor. This implies that sufficient number of communication channels are available for all the processors to be communicating simultaneously. Further, we assume that after message aggregation has been done, the messages sent are sufficiently large so that the effect of latency of communication is not significant on the communication costs. We believe that these two assumptions model the behavior of irregular applications on current parallel machines reasonably well, and keep our cost models simple enough for analysis.

We introduce the following terminology for our presentation:

p : Number of processors
C_{comm} : Cost of communication per element
C_{sched} : Cost of generating a communication schedule per element

Consider again the loop in Figure 1. Data partitioning can be done so that that no off-processor references are involved for arrays IA and X. Number of off-processor references in accessing Y depends both upon the distribution of Y chosen and the values in array IA. Therefore, it is not possible to accurately determine the number of off-processor references for the array Y at compile-time. However, we can approximate these values based upon the experiences with irregular applications [5, 12]. Typically, the arrays X and Y represent elements of a two-dimensional or three-dimensional geometric structure, and the indirection array represents neighbor relationship between elements of such a structure. In such a case, after a value based distribution for array Y, each processor can be viewed as owning a continuous square or cubical section of the structure. The number of off-processor elements of Y accessed by each processor will then be the ratio of perimeter to the area (for two-dimensional structure) or the ratio of surface area to the volume (for three-dimensional structure).

In the two-dimensional case, assume that problem geometry comprises of $m^{1/2} \times m^{1/2}$ elements. Then, each processor owns $(m/p)^{1/2} \times (m/p)^{1/2}$ elements. The number of off-processor elements required by each processor will be the same as the perimeter of the area owned by each processor, which equals:

$$4 \times (m/p)^{1/2}$$

Similarly, the number of off-processor elements required if the problem geometry is three-dimensional is

$$8 \times (m/p)^{1/3}$$

The communication costs for the above two cases will be:

$$4 \times C_{comm} \times (m/p)^{1/2}$$

and

$$8 \times C_{comm} \times (m/p)^{1/3}$$

Now, consider the case when the distribution of array Y was not done based upon the values of IA, i.e. either Y has been distributed in a regular fashion, or an irregular distribution based upon another indirection array has been done. In such a case, we cannot expect to see any regularity in the elements of Y that are owned by a single processor. Each processor accesses m/p elements of the array Y and let us assume that there are no duplicate elements in those.

If the allocation of the elements of Y is completely random, then each element has equal probability of being owned by any of the p processors. Therefore, of the m/p elements of the array Y accessed, we will expect $(m/p) \times (p-1)/p$ off-processor accesses. So, the communication cost will be:

$$C_{comm} \times (m/p) \times (p-1)/p$$

Next, we estimate the costs of redistribution. Consider any array which is distributed in a block fashion or using an indirection array IA. For a different data parallel statement, we will like a value based distribution of this array using a different indirection array. Consider any element of this array, which is on a particular processor. If there is no regularity between the two distributions, we will expect that this element is equally likely to be in any of the p processors after redistribution. So, the cost of redistribution will be:

$$C_{comm} \times (m/p) \times (p-1)/p$$

In presenting the costs of communication and redistribution, we have so far not taken into account the time taken by preprocessing step. If a particular communication schedule is used several times, then we need to amortize the cost of preprocessing appropriately. Suppose an indirection array is of size m and each processor owns m/p elements of this array. Experience with PARTI/CHAOS routines has shown that the cost of preprocessing is typically linear in the size of indirection array owned by each processor [7]. So, the cost of preprocessing will be:

$$C_{sched} \times m/p$$

3.3. Greedy Algorithm

We now present global analysis for determining the distributions for the entire program. This problem involves natural trade-offs, since the ideal distribution for an array may be different for different data parallel statements, however, frequently modifying the distributions in the program will lead to high costs of data redistribution. For this purpose, we use the cost models presented in the previous subsection, and a heuristic greedy algorithm.

To illustrate this, we have shown a code sequence in Figure 3. Array X is accessed using two different indirection arrays IB and IA in two different data parallel loops. For reducing the communication costs in the first loop, we will like to distribute the array X based upon the values in array IB, and similarly, we will like to have a distribution based upon IA for the second loop. However, this will involve frequent redistributions of the array X, and is therefore, not likely to give best performance.

To solve this problem, we model the communication and redistribution costs in the program by a graph, and apply a greedy algorithm. We model the redistribution and communication costs by a graph $G = (V, E)$. Each node in the

```
      Real   X(10000), Y(10000)   ! data arrays
      Integer IA(20000,2)          ! indirection array
      Integer IB(10000,2)          ! indirection array
C     Time Step Loop
      do 40  l = 1,50
C            First Loop
             do 10 i =   1, 2500
             X(IB(i,1)) = X(IB(i,1))  + Y(i)
             X(IB(i,2)) = X(IB(i,2))  - Y(i)
10           continue
             do 30  k = 1,10
C                   Second Loop
                    do 20 j =   1, 5000
                    X(IA(i,1)) = X(IA(i,1))  + Y(i)
                    X(IA(i,2)) = X(IA(i,2))  - Y(i)
20                  continue
30           continue
40    continue
```

Figure 3. A Code Showing Access Through Multiple Indirection Arrays

graph $(v \in V)$, represents a data parallel statement in which data is accessed using indirection. An edge $(v, w) \in E$ represents potential data-flow between the data parallel statements v and w in the program.

Next, for each statement which involves indirect accesses, we assess the frequency of execution. Also, for each edge, we assess the frequency of execution, i.e. the number of times during the execution of the program that we expect the flow of control to be passed from the source loop of the edge to the sink loop of the edge, without passing through any other loop.

Our goal is to reduce the *total communication* costs, which is the sum of the communication costs of the individual loops and the redistribution costs. We have already calculated conforming distributions within each loop. We calculate the total communication costs of executing this loop, which is the product of the execution frequency of the loop, and the communication cost per execution calculated in the previous sub-section. We mark the nodes with the graph with these costs.

Consider an edge in the graph. If the distributions of the arrays in both the source and the sink nodes is conformal, then redistributions may be involved along this edge. We determine the cost of performing these redistributions, which will be the product of frequency of redistribution with the cost of performing redistribution once. We mark the edges in the graph with these costs.

The sum of the costs of edges and nodes in the graph shows the communication and redistribution time of the program, assuming that each array in each loop has a conformal distribution. This is likely to involve high redistri-

bution costs, and thus the total execution time of the program may be high. Our goal is to determine distributions and redistributions, so that the overall cost of the graph is minimum possible. Rather than attempting an optimal solution, which may be very expensive, we use a greedy heuristic. We proceed by *merging* nodes in the graph, which means that all arrays will have identical distribution in both the nodes, and no redistribution will be done between the nodes. We choose the pair of nodes to merge in the order they are likely to reduce the total communication costs of the program. For this purpose, we calculate the following information about all the edges $e = (v, w)$ in the graph:

- Let $C(v)$, $C(w)$, and $C(e)$ be the costs associated with the nodes v, w and the edge e.

- Compute $C'(v)$, the cost of the node v, assuming that the distribution of all the arrays in loop v is identical to the the conforming distributions in the loop nest w, and no redistributions are performed along the edge e.

- Similarly, compute $C'(w)$, the cost of the node w, assuming that the distribution of all the arrays in loop w is identical to the the conforming distributions in the loop v, and no redistributions are performed along the edge e.

- Determine $min(C'(v) + C(w), C(v) + C'(w))$. Determine the difference of $C(v) + C(w) + C(e)$ and this minimum computed above. We refer to this term as the *merge advantage* of the edge.

The merge advantage computed above shows the reduction in the total communication costs achieved by making the distributions along the nodes v and w identical, and performing no redistributions along the edge. Clearly, if this difference is positive, there is a likely advantage in merging the nodes v and w.

We use a greedy strategy, by choosing the edges with the highest merge advantage and repeating the process till no edge with positive merge advantage remains in the graph. The algorithm can be summarized as follows:

- Find the edge $e = (v, w)$ with the highest merge advantage

- Merge the nodes v and w of the graph, let the new node be u, and mark the cost of the u to be $min(C'(v)+C(w), C(v)+C'(w))$, as computed earlier

- For any edge (l, v) or (l, w), mark a new edge (l, u) and recalculate the cost of this edge

- Similarly, for any edge (v, l) or (w, l), mark a new edge (u, l) and recalculate the cost of this edge

- Recompute the *merge advantage* of all the edges and repeat the same process till there is no edge left with a positive merge advantage

3.4. Handling Adaptive Applications

In adaptive irregular applications, often some elements of the indirection array are modified after each time-step, or after certain number of time-steps. In such a case, the cost of communication is likely to increase, as the resulting indirection array, with the existing distribution, may not support a high level of locality. This creates interesting trade-offs, since redistributing the data arrays can also incur high communication costs.

Suppose, that the number of elements of the indirection array modified is l. On any given processor, we assume that l/p elements of the indirection array have been modified. Consider an array element whose value is accessed through this modified indirection array. Assuming that there is no locality in data distribution using this modified indirection array, we can estimate the increased communication cost to be

$$C_{comm} \times (l/p) \times (p-1)/p$$

Instead, if we choose to perform a data-redistribution, the cost of redistribution will be

$$C_{comm} \times (m/p) \times (p-1)/p$$

Considering the above two costs, we can choose to perform redistribution after every k iterations, such that the overall cost

$$(\Sigma_{i=1}^{k} C_{comm} \times (il/p) \times (p-1)/p + C_{comm} \times$$

$$(m/p) \times (p-1)/p)/k$$

is minimized.

4. Experimental Results

To demonstrate the efficacy of our technique, we have experimented with one template and a real application. The template has a typical irregular loop which accesses data through an indirection array. The real application we have chosen for this study is the Euler code on an unstructured grid [5]. We applied the analysis presented here and measured the performance of the code using the distribution choices made by our analysis. All our experiments were performed on a 16 processor IBM SP-2.

4.1. Irregular Template

The main computational part of the template comprises of a single loop, in which data is accessed through the use of indirection. This template simulated the basic computational features of a solver on an unstructured mesh, i.e. the indirection array is used to represent the edges between the

No. of Proc.	Block Distr. (sec.)	Irreg. (sec.) Distr.
1	55.6	55.6
2	39.3	28.6
4	31.7	15.0
8	26.9	8.1
16	21.4	4.3

Figure 4. Performance of the Template With Block and Irreg. Distributions

computational point. We ran this application on a 53K node mesh.

The experimental results from this template have been shown in Figure 4. We considered two versions of this code. In the first version, default block distribution was used for all the arrays. In the second version, using our analysis, the value based distribution was used for the arrays accessed through indirection. The version with irregular distributions is able to achieve a speedup of nearly 13 on 16 processors, while the version with block distributions speeds up by a factor of less than three. The performance achieved by version which used our analysis is the same as what could be achieved with the best hand-parallelized code.

4.2. Full Application

Our second experiment was based upon the full irregular application, which solved the Euler equation on an irregular grid. The access pattern in this application is similar to the access pattern shown for the example in the previous section. The main data arrays are accessed using two different indirection arrays in different part of the code. Our analysis determined that it was profitable to access data in one of the loop nests with a non-conformal distribution, as compared to performing frequent redistributions of the data arrays.

We considered two versions of this code, the first version performed redistribution during each iteration of the outer-most loop of the code. The second version did not have any redistributions, but used non-conforming distribution for one loop nest. We executed both the versions on a 53 K mesh. The results have been shown in Figure 5. The first version, with frequent redistributions, achieves only a speedup of 8 on 16 processors, while the second version achieves a speed up of 12 on 16 processors. This result shows that our analysis correctly predicted the benefit of using non-conforming distribution, as compared to redis-

No. of Proc.	With Redistr.	W/o Redistr.
1	209.3	209.3
2	122.4	109.6
4	72.8	58.6
8	43.6	31.7
16	26.5	17.3

Figure 5. Performance of the Euler Code With and Without Redistributions

tributing data arrays frequently.

5. Conclusions

In this paper, we have addressed the problem of determining data distributions for irregular and adaptive applications. We have presented a compile-time (static) analysis technique which computes the data distributions automatically. Our analysis generates value based distributions from the source code. The initial part of the analysis considers a single data-parallel statement and summarizes the desired distribution using the notion of value based distributions. Final distribution choices for the entire program are determined by a heuristic greedy algorithm using the cost functions we have developed.

We applied our analysis on an irregular template and a full irregular application. Our preliminary results show that our analysis can determine the appropriate distributions for achieving high performance.

Acknowledgements

The author was supported in part by NSF CAREER award.

References

[1] G. Agrawal and J. Saltz. Interprocedural compilation of irregular applications for distributed memory machines. In *Proceedings Supercomputing '95*. IEEE Computer Society Press, Dec. 1995.

[2] G. Agrawal, J. Saltz, and R. Das. Interprocedural partial redundancy elimination and its application to distributed memory compilation. In *Proceedings of the SIGPLAN '95 Conference on Programming Language Design and Implementation*, pages 258–269. ACM Press, June 1995. ACM SIGPLAN Notices, Vol. 30, No. 6.

[3] J. M. Anderson and M. S. Lam. Global optimizations for parallelism and locality on scalable parallel machines. In *Proceedings of the SIGPLAN '93 Conference on Programming Language Design and Implementation*, pages 112–125, June 1993. ACM SIGPLAN Notices, Vol. 28, No. 6.

[4] S. Chatterjee, J. R. Gilbert, R. Schreiber, and S.-H. Teng. Automatic array alignment in data-parallel programs. In *Conference Record of the Twentieth Annual ACM SIGACT/SIGPLAN Symposium on Principles of Programming Languages*, pages 16–28, Jan. 1993.

[5] R. Das, D. J. Mavriplis, J. Saltz, S. Gupta, and R. Ponnusamy. The design and implementation of a parallel unstructured Euler solver using software primitives. *AIAA Journal*, 32(3):489–496, Mar. 1994.

[6] R. Das, J. Saltz, and R. v. Hanxleden. Slicing analysis and indirect access to distributed arrays. In *Proceedings of the 6th Workshop on Languages and Compilers for Parallel Computing*, pages 152–168. Springer-Verlag, Aug. 1993. Also available as University of Maryland Technical Report CS-TR-3076 and UMIACS-TR-93-42.

[7] R. Das, M. Uysal, J. Saltz, and Y.-S. Hwang. Communication optimizations for irregular scientific computations on distributed memory architectures. *Journal of Parallel and Distributed Computing*, 22(3):462–479, Sept. 1994.

[8] M. Gupta and P. Banerjee. Demonstration of automatic data partitioning techniques for parallelizing compilers on multicomputers. *IEEE Transactions on Parallel and Distributed Systems*, 3(2):179–193, Mar. 1992.

[9] R. Hanxleden, K. Kennedy, and J. Saltz. Value-based distributions and alignments in Fortran D. *Journal of Programming Languages*, 2(3):259–282, Sept. 1994.

[10] R. v. Hanxleden and K. Kennedy. Give-n-take – a balanced code placement framework. In *Proceedings of the SIGPLAN '94 Conference on Programming Language Design and Implementation*, pages 107–120. ACM Press, June 1994. ACM SIGPLAN Notices, Vol. 29, No. 6.

[11] S. Hiranandani, K. Kennedy, and C.-W. Tseng. Compiling Fortran D for MIMD distributed-memory machines. *Communications of the ACM*, 35(8):66–80, Aug. 1992.

[12] Y.-S. Hwang, R. Das, J. H. Saltz, M. Hodoscek, and B. R. Brooks. Parallelizing molecular dynamics programs for distributed memory machines. *IEEE Computational Science & Engineering*, 2(2):18–29, Summer 1995. Also available as University of Maryland Technical Report CS-TR-3374 and UMIACS-TR-94-125.

[13] Y.-S. Hwang, B. Moon, S. D. Sharma, R. Ponnusamy, R. Das, and J. H. Saltz. Runtime and language support for compiling adaptive irregular programs. *Software–Practice and Experience*, 25(6):597–621, June 1995.

[14] C. Koelbel, D. Loveman, R. Schreiber, G. Steele, Jr., and M. Zosel. *The High Performance Fortran Handbook*. MIT Press, 1994.

[15] C. Koelbel and P. Mehrotra. Compiling global name-space parallel loops for distributed execution. *IEEE Transactions on Parallel and Distributed Systems*, 2(4):440–451, Oct. 1991.

[16] J. Li and M. Chen. Compiling communication-efficient programs for massively parallel machines. *IEEE Transactions on Parallel and Distributed Systems*, 2(3):361–376, July 1991.

[17] R. Ponnusamy, J. Saltz, and A. Choudhary. Runtime-compilation techniques for data partitioning and communication schedule reuse. In *Proceedings Supercomputing '93*, pages 361–370. IEEE Computer Society Press, Nov. 1993. Also available as University of Maryland Technical Report CS-TR-3055 and UMIACS-TR-93-32.

[18] J. Wu, R. Das, J. Saltz, H. Berryman, and S. Hiranandani. Distributed memory compiler design for sparse problems. *IEEE Transactions on Computers*, 44(6):737–753, June 1995.

Performance Range Comparison for Restructuring Compilation

Xian-He Sun*

Department of Computer Science
Louisiana State University
Baton Rouge, LA 70803-4020
sun@bit.csc.lsu.edu

Mario Pantano, Thomas Fahringer

Institute for Software Technology and
Parallel Systems, University of Vienna
Liechtensteinstr. 22 1090 Vienna, Austria
{pantano,tf}@par.univie.ac.at

Abstract

A major difficulty in restructuring compilation is how to compare parallel performance over a range of system and problem sizes. This study introduces the concept of range comparison for data-parallel programming. Unlike conventional execution time comparison in which performance is compared for a particular system and problem size, range comparison compares the performance of programs over a range of ensemble and problem sizes via scalability and performance crossing point analysis. An algorithm is developed to predict the crossing point automatically. The correctness of the algorithm is proved and a methodology is developed to integrate range comparison into restructuring compilations. A preliminary prototype of the methodology is implemented and tested under Vienna Fortran Compilation System. Experimental results demonstrate that range comparison is feasible and effective.

1 Introduction

Traditionally, Highly parallel scalable MultiProcessing Systems (HMPs) have been programmed using message passing where the user is responsible for explicitly inserting communication statements into a sequential program. The development of parallel languages such as Vienna Fortran, Fortran D and High Performance Fortran (HPF) [1, 2] improved the situation by providing high-level features for the specification of data distributions. However, current technology of code restructuring systems inherently lacks the power to fully exploit the performance offered by HMPs. The primary motivation of parallel processing is high performance. Effectiveness and efficiency of restructuring compilation are the current barriers for the success of a simple, high-level programming model approach.

Restructuring a program can be seen as an iterative process in which a parallel program is transformed at each iteration. The performance of the current parallel program is analyzed and predicted at each iteration. Then, based on the performance result, the next restructuring transformation is selected for improving the performance of the current parallel program. This iterative process terminates when certain predefined performance criteria are met or as a result of explicit user intervention. Integrating performance analysis with a restructuring system is critical to support automatic performance tuning in the iterative restructuring process. The development of a fully compiler integrated performance system for scalable parallel machines is especially challenging. In a scalable environment, the performance of a program may vary with data distribution, number of processors (system ensemble size), and problem size. Predicting the performance variations and integrating the performance indices automatically into a restructuring compiler are two major challenges facing researchers in the field [3].

A key question of restructuring is how to predict and compare the scaled relative performances of a small number of data distributions and transformations automatically, so that appropriate optimization decisions can be made. In order to compare relative performance over a range of problem and ensemble sizes, scalability prediction is proposed as a solution in this study. A restructured code with a smaller initial execution time and a larger scalability will be a clear

* This author was supported in part by National Science Foundation under NSF grant ASC-9720215 and by LSU 1998 COR award.

winner over the scalable range. Otherwise, the superior range of the implementation will end at the first fast/slow crossing point. We introduce a technique called range comparison, which is concerned with locating the crossing point. An iterative algorithm is first derived to predict the scalability and crossing point on a given parallel platform. Then, the connection between the iterative algorithm and an existing static performance estimator, P^3T, [4] is discussed. A preliminary prototype of automatic range comparison is implemented under the Vienna Fortran Compilation System (VFCS). Finally, two applications are tested with two different data distributions to verify the correctness and feasibility of the range comparison approach. While current experimental results are primitive, they clearly demonstrate the feasibility and effectiveness of the range comparison approach for program restructuring.

2 VFCS and P^3T

Vienna Fortran Compilation System (VFCS) consists of a parallelizing compiler for Vienna Fortran/HPF and tools for program analysis and transformation. The parallelization techniques of VFCS are based upon the *Single-Program-Multiple-Data (SPMD)* paradigm. Currently two parallelization techniques, the *overlap* strategy and the *inspector-executor* strategy [5] are implemented. The overlap strategy is targeted towards regular computations, like stencil computations, and relies heavily on compile-time analysis and compile-time optimization. The second parallelization strategy, a run-time technique based on the inspector-executor strategy, is targeted towards irregular computations, which are characterized by loops exhibiting irregular access patterns (using indirection arrays) that are dependent on run-time data.

P^3T [4] is a static, interactive performance estimator that assists users in performance tuning of regular programs. P^3T is based on a single profile run to obtain characteristic data for branching probabilities, statement and loop execution counts. The shortcoming of P^3T is the lack of information on the influence of data distribution, especially for scalable computing. Communication overhead is an important metric in choosing an appropriate data distribution. It consists of two parts: number of data transfers and amount of data transferred. For the sake of brevity, only issues of static estimation of communication overhead are discussed in this section. Interested readers may refer to [4] for more information regarding the other performance parameters of P^3T.

2.1 Number of Data Transfers

The number of data transfers is a critical parameter which reflects the high message startup costs on most distributed memory architectures. Commonly the overhead for communication is decreasing if it can be hoisted outside of a nested loop. Moreover, communication inside of a specific loop body in many cases implies that the loop is sequentialized due to synchronization between the processors involved in the communication. P^3T carefully models the loop nesting level at which a communication is placed, array access patterns, data dependences and distribution, control flow, and compiler communication optimizations (e.g., communication vectorization and fusion) in order to determine the number of data transfers with high accuracy.

For communication that can be hoisted outside a loop nest we assume the loosely synchronous communication model [6] which implies that all involved processors communicate simultaneously. For such a communication statement the number of data transfers is determined by the maximum number of data transfers across all involved processors. For communication that cannot be hoisted outside a loop nest due to a data dependence we assume that it sequentializes the loop at which the communication is placed as well as all data transfers implied by the communication. The number of data transfers for such a communication is given by the sum of data transfers across all processors involved in the communication.

2.2 Amount of Data Transferred

The current generation of distributed memory architectures reduces the impact of the message length on the communication overhead. For applications that transmit small data volumes, the startup cost is the predominate communication cost factor. However, for increasing data volumes transmitted, the message transfer time per byte and in turn the amount of data transferred becomes the first order performance effect. In order to provide a highly accurate estimate for the amount of data transferred (given in bytes) as induced by a parallel program, P^3T estimates the number of non-local data elements accessed and incorporates machine specific data type sizes. For this purpose, P^3T examines the loop nesting level at which a communication is placed, array access patterns, data dependences and distributions, control flow, and compiler communication optimizations.

As the compiler specifies the communication pattern at the source code level, the target architecture can be for the most part – except for data type sizes – ignored. Consequently, this parameter ports easily to a large class of distributed memory architectures.

3 Performance Range Comparison

While execution time is an important performance metric for restructuring compilations, its comparison bonds to a specific pair of system and problem size. Execution time alone is not sufficient for performance comparison over a range of system and problem sizes. Scalability has been recognized as an important property of parallel algorithms and machines in recent years. Several scalability metrics have been proposed [7, 8, 9]. However, scalability has been traditionally studied separately as an independent property. Only very recently has the relation of scalability and execution time been studied [10]. Based on these relations, the concepts of crossing point analysis and range comparison are introduced [11]. To fully understand the concept of range comparison, some background for scalability and crossing point analysis needs to be introduced.

3.1 Isospeed Scalability

In this paper, problem size refers to the work to be performed. The following definition was given in [7].

Definition 1 (Isospeed Scalability) *An algorithm-machine combination is scalable if the achieved average speed of the algorithm on the given machine can remain constant with the increasing number of processors, provided the problem size can be increased with the system size.*

For a large class of Algorithm-Machine Combinations (AMCs), the average speed can be maintained by increasing the problem size. The necessary problem size increase varies with algorithm-machine combinations. This variation provides a quantitative measurement for scalability. Let W be the amount of work of an algorithm when p processors are employed in a machine, and let W' be the amount of work of the algorithm when $p' > p$ processors are employed to maintain the average speed, then the scalability from system size p to system size p' of the algorithm-machine combination is:

$$\psi(p, p') = \frac{p' \cdot W}{p \cdot W'} \tag{1}$$

Where the work W' is determined by the isospeed constraint. Finally, let $T_p(W)$ be the time for computing W work on a p processors system, equation (2) shows how parallel execution time could be computed from scalability,

$$T_{p'}(W') = \psi^{-1}(p, p') \cdot T_p(W). \tag{2}$$

Three approaches have been proposed to determine scalabilities [7]. They are: *computing* the relation between problem size and speed, directly *measuring* the scalability, and *predicting* scalability with certain predetermined parameters. Among them, scalability prediction seems to be the most useful for data-parallel compilation systems.

The parallel execution time $T_p(W)$ can be divided into two parts: the ideal parallel processing time and parallel processing overhead, T_o.

$$T_p(W) = \frac{T_s}{p} + T_o = \frac{W \cdot \Delta}{p} + T_o, \tag{3}$$

where T_s is the sequential execution time. The parallel processing overhead T_o contains the load imbalance overhead, communication overhead, and other possible parallelism degradations. By the definition of scalability (see (1)), scalability can be predicted if and only if the scaled work size, W', can be predicted. A prediction formula has been given in [12] to compute W':

$$W' = \frac{a \cdot p' \cdot T_o(W')}{1 - a\Delta} \tag{4}$$

where a is the average speed, Δ is the computing rate of a single processor, and $T_o(W')$ is the parallel processing overhead on p' processors. Parallel processing overhead $T_o(W')$ in general is a function of problem size. With unknowns on both sides of the equation, using formula (4) for scalability prediction is not a straightforward task.

3.2 Performance Crossing Point and Range Comparison

Theorem 1 gives a relation between scalability and execution time of two different algorithm-machine combinations [10].

Theorem 1 *If algorithm-machine combinations 1 and 2 have execution time $\alpha \cdot T$ and T, respectively, at the same initial state (the same initial ensemble and problem size), then combination 1 has a higher scalability than combination 2 at a scaled ensemble size if and only if the execution time of combination 1 is smaller than the α multiple of the execution time of* *combination 2 for solving W' at the scaled ensemble size, where W' is the scaled problem size of combination 1.*

Theorem 1 shows that if an AMC is faster at the initial state and has a better scalability than that of others then it will remain faster over the scalable range. Range comparison becomes more difficult when the initially faster AMC has a smaller scalability. When the system ensemble size scales up, an originally faster code with lower scalability can become slower than another code with a better scalability. Finding the fast/slow crossing point is critical for choosing efficient program transformations in a data-parallel environment. Finding the superiority/inferiority crossing point, however, is very difficult and is depending on the view of scalable computing [11]. Definition 2 gives a formal definition of crossing point based on the isospeed scalability.

Definition 2 (scaled crossing point) *For any $\alpha > 1$, if algorithm-machine combinations 1 and 2 have execution time $\alpha \dot{T}$ and T respectively at the same initial state, then we say a scaled ensemble size p' is a crossing point of combinations 1 and 2 if the ratio of the isospeed scalability of combination 1 and combination 2 is greater than α at p'.*

Let AMC 1 have execution time t, scalability $\Phi(p, p')$, and scaled problem size W'. Let AMC 2 have execution time T, scalability $\Psi(p, p')$, and scaled problem size W^*. By Definition 2, p' is the crossing point of AMC 1 and 2 if and only if

$$\frac{\Phi(p, p')}{\Psi(p, p')} > \alpha. \tag{5}$$

In fact, as proven by Theorem 2, when $\Phi(p, p') \geq \alpha \Psi(p, p')$ we have $t_{p'}(W') \leq T_{p'}(W^*)$. Notice that since $\alpha > 1$ combination 2 has a smaller execution time at the initial state, $t_p(W) > T_p(W)$. This superiority/inferiority changing in execution time gives the meaning of performance crossing point. The correctness of Theorems 2 is proved in [11].

Theorem 2 *If algorithm-machine combination 1 has a larger execution time than algorithm-machine combination 2 at the same initial state, then, for any scaled ensemble size p', p' is a scaled crossing point if and only if combination 1 has a smaller scaled execution time than that of combination 2.*

Based on the above theoretical findings Figure 1 gives the range comparison algorithm in terms of scalability.

```
Assumption: Assume algorithm-machine combina-
tions 1 and 2 have execution time αT and T respec-
tively at the same initial state, where α > 1.
Objective: Find the superior range of combination
2

    Range Comparison
    Begin
    p' = p;
    Repeat
        p' = p' + 1;
        Find the Scalability of comb. 1 Φ(p,p');
        Find the Scalability of comb. 2 Ψ(p,p');
    Until(Φ(p,p') > αΨ(p,p') or p' = the up-limit)
    If Φ(p,p') > αΨ(p,p') then
        p' is the smallest scaled crossing point
        Comb. 2 is superior over range < p,p'−1 >;
    Else
        Comb. 2 is superior over range < p,p' >
    End{If}
    End{Range Comparison }
```

Figure 1: Range Comparison Via Performance Crossing point

3.3 Automatic Crossing-Point Prediction

The range comparison algorithm listed in Figure 1 is in terms of scalability. Scalabilities of different code implementations, or different algorithm-machine combinations in general, still need to be determined for range comparison. In this paper we propose an iterative method listed in Figure 2 to compute W' and to predict the scalability automatically. We assume that the underlying application is scalable and its problem size (computation work) is a monotonically increasing function of a scaling parameter n (input data size). We also assume that parallel overhead T_o is either independent of parameter n or is monotonically increasing with n. Function $\phi(W)$ is implied by equation (4). Mathematically, the iterative algorithm is to find a fixed point of $\phi(W)$ such that $W = \phi(W)$. A proof of correctness of the algorithm is provided in [13].

Like most iterative methods, the convergence rate of the algorithm is application dependent. It depends on the properties of function $f(n)$. For most scientific computations, $f(n)$ is a low degree polynomial function and the algorithm converges very fast. Our experimental results show that the algorithm only requires three to five iterations to converge to a solution with an error bound of 10^{-2}.

`Assumption:` Assume work W and overhead T_o are increasing functions of the scaling parameter n, $W = f(n)$ and $T_o = g(n)$, or $T_o = g(n)$ is a constant, and assume the parallel code under study has been executed on the target machine with W work and p processors.
`Objective:` Compute the scalability from machine ensemble size p to machine ensemble size p', where $p' > p$, with an error of $\epsilon > 0$.

```
Iterative Method
Begin
Initial Value: W_0 = p'·W / p;
Compute φ(W_0);
If φ(W_0) := W_0 do
   W' = W_0;
Elseif φ(W_0) > W_0 do
   Begin Iteration (k=0; k++)
      W_{k+1} = φ(W_k);
   until ||W_{k+1} − W_k|| < ε;
   W' = W_{k+1};
Else do
   Begin Iteration (k=0; k++)
      W_{k+1} = φ^{-1}(W_k)
   until ||W_{k+1} − W_k|| < ε
   W' = W_{k+1};
End{If}
End{Iterative Method}

Subroutine φ(W)
   Solve f(n) = W for n;
   Compute T_o = g(n);
   Compute φ(W) = a·p·T_o / (1−a·Δ);
Subroutine φ^{-1}(W)
   Compute T_o = (1−a·Δ)/(a·p) W;
   Solve g(n) = T_o for n;
   Compute φ^{-1}(W) = f(n);
```

Figure 2: An Iterative Method for Predicting Scalability

4 Integrated Range Comparison Under VFCS

Scientific applications have been tested under VFCS to confirm the correctness and efficiency of the proposed range comparison. The experiments have been carried out on an iPSC/860 hypercube with 16 processors. The parallel processing overhead T_o used in the scalability iteration algorithm contains communication overhead and load imbalance. Limited by the current functionality of P^3T, we choose two codes, Jacobi and Redblack, which have good load balance. T_o, therefore, contains only the communication time that can be obtained by the formula

$$T_o = Z(\alpha + (\beta \cdot D) + \gamma \cdot h), \quad (6)$$

where Z - the number of data transfers - and D - the amount of data transferred - can be predicted at compile time for any problem size W using P^3T. α and β are the startup time and the transfer time per message byte, respectively. γ represents the additional overhead for each network hop and h is the number of hops.

Jacobi and Redblack, have been parallelized with VFCS and their performance measured on 4 processors. The performance indices obtained, and needed for computing the initial state of the scalability prediction, are W, T_p, T_c, Z, D, T_o, where T_c is the computation time. Based on equation (3), the execution models of Jacobi and Redblack are:

$$T_p = \frac{W}{p} * \Delta + T_o = 11 * \frac{(n-2)^2}{p} \Delta + T_o$$

and

$$T_p = \frac{W}{p} * \Delta + T_o = 6 * \frac{(n-1)^2}{p} \Delta + T_o$$

respectively. Computation is uniformly distributed across all processors. $T_c = \frac{W}{p} * \Delta$. The computing rate $\Delta = \frac{T_c * p}{W}$ and the average speed $a = \frac{W}{p * T_p(W)}$ can be determined by the measured computing time and total execution time. The initial value of the prediction algorithm, $W_0 = \frac{p' * W}{p}$, is computed based on the work, W, performed on 4 processors. Starting with iteration $k = 0$, a new input data size $n_k = f^{-1}(W)$ is computed for $k > 0$. The original source code is then modified and automatically parallelized by using VFCS. After parallelization, P^3T automatically estimates the number of transfers Z and the amount of data transferred D. The communication overhead T_o' and the scaled work W_k' are predicted using (6) and

(4), respectively. Scalability from processors p to processors p' is determined when the terminating condition $\|W_k - W_{k-1}\| < \epsilon$ is satisfied for a fixed $\epsilon > 0$ ($\epsilon = 0.01$ is used in our experiments). Otherwise the method iterates with the new parameter n_{k+1}. Figure 3 depicts the path for predicting the scalability by using VFCS and P^3T.

Tables 1 and 2 show the measured and predicted scalability of Jacobi algorithm with two different data distribution strategies: two-dimensional block distribution (Jacobi_2D) and one-dimensional (column) distribution (Jacobi_C) of all program arrays to a two-dimensional and one-dimensional processors array, respectively. The experimental results confirm that

$\psi(p,p')$	$p' = 8$			$p' = 16$		
	Pred	Meas	diff	Pred	Meas	diff
p=4	0.718	0.738	2.7%	0.605	0.617	1.9 %
p=8	1.000	1.000	0%	0.842	0.819	2.7%
p=16				1.000	1.000	0%

Table 1: Jacobi: 2D distribution, predicted and measured scalability

$\psi(p,p')$	$p' = 8$			$p' = 16$		
	Pred	Meas	diff	Pred	Meas	diff
p=4	0.721	0.739	2.4%	0.576	0.581	0.8 %
p=8	1.000	1.000	0%	0.796	0.808	1.5%
p=16				1.000	1.000	0%

Table 2: Jacobi: column distribution, predicted and measured scalability

our predicted scalabilities are very accurate and the variations of scaled performance for various data distributions are also captured.

Table 3 shows the predicted and measured scalability values of the Redblack algorithm with 2D distribution. Indeed, scalability can be used to predict execution time by using (2). Table 4 presents the predicted execution times versus the measured ones.

The execution time of Redblack can be written as $\alpha * T_4(64) = \alpha * 1869 = 5560\ \mu sec$ and for Jacobi $T_4(64) = 1869\ \mu sec$. α is 2.975. According to Tables 1, 2, and 3, the scalability of Jacobi algorithm is higher than that of Redblack algorithm. Therefore, by Theorem 1, the smaller initial execution time and larger scalability show that Jacobi scales better than

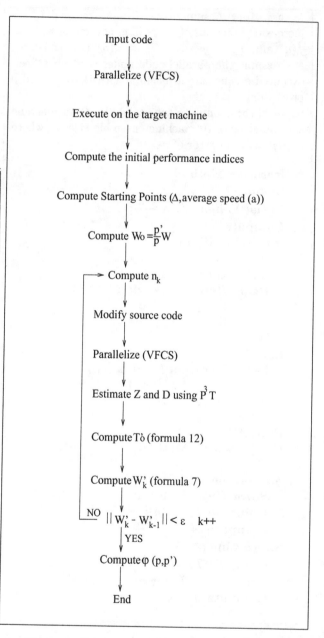

Figure 3: Predicting scalability under VFCS

$\psi(p,p')$	$p'=8$			$p'=16$		
	Pred	Meas	diff	Pred	Meas	diff
p=4	0.524	0.565	7.8 %	0.445	0.477	7.1 %
p=8	1.000	1.000	0%	0.851	0.846	0.5%
p=16				1.000	1.000	0%

Table 3: Redblack: 2D distribution, Predicted and Measured Scalability

Alg.	p=8			p=16		
	Pred	Meas	diff	Pred	Meas	diff
J_2D	2603	2532	2.7%	3089	3066	0.7%
J_C	2373	2313	2.5%	2971	2944	0.9%
R_2D	10611	9840	7.2%	11324	11641	2.7%

Table 4: Predicted and Measured Execution times (in $\mu secs$)

Redblack, which is confirmed by measured results as given in Table 4.

A more interesting result is given by the two different versions of the Jacobi algorithm. From Tables 1 and 2, we can see that the 2D distribution implementation has a larger initial execution time and a better scalability, on $p = 16$, than that of column distribution. According to Theorem 2, there will be a crossing point at some scaled ensemble size p'. However, in this case the crossing point is greater than 16 and cannot be confirmed by our testing environment. Table 5 shows the scaled input data sizes (parameter n) for Jacobi with the two data distribution strategies used. As we see, at $p = 8$ the isospeed scalability

Algorithm	p=4	p=8	p=16
Jacobi_2D	64	105	161
Jacobi_C	64	105	165

Table 5: Scaled input data sizes

is maintained at the same data size ($n = 105$). The initial problem size used in Tables 1, 2, and 3 is determined by the asymptotic speed [12] for best performance, where $n = 64$ is chosen. As pointed out in [12], the difference of isospeed scalability between "good" and "bad" algorithms increases with the communication/computation ratio. For Jacobi, the communication/computation ratio increases with the decrease in

problem size. At the initial state $p = 4$, and $n = 20$, the execution time for Jacobi with column distribution strategy is $T_4(20) = 594$ μsec and for Jacobi with 2D distribution it is $\alpha * T_4(20) = 753$ μsec, where $\alpha = 1.267$. Considering the scalability results of Table 6, we see that for $p' = 8$, the 2D distribution (Table 6a) scales better than that of column distribution (Table 6b). The ratio between the two predicted scalabilities, $\frac{0.652}{0.373} = 1.747$, is greater than α. Therefore, by Definition 2, $p' = 8$ is a crossing point where the execution time of 2D distribution becomes less than that of column distribution implementation. This performance crossing is due to the communication behavior involved on iPSC/860 for $p' = 8$ and is confirmed by measured performance as shown in Figure 4. Table 7

	$\psi(p,p')$	$p'=4$	$p'=8$	$p'=16$
(a)	p=4	1.000	0.652	0.548
	p=8		1.000	0.840
	p=16			1.000

	$\psi(p,p')$	$p'=4$	$p'=8$	$p'=16$
(b)	p=4	1.000	0.373	0.333
	p=8		1.000	0.893
	p=16			1.000

Table 6: Predicted scalability for Jacobi with (a) 2D distribution and (b) column distribution

presents the scaled input data sizes for Jacobi starting the scalability prediction with $n = 20$.

Algorithm	p=4	p=8	p=16
Jacobi_2D	20	33	50
Jacobi_C	20	43	64

Table 7: Scaled input data sizes for crossing-point testing

5 Conclusion

There are many ways to parallelize an application, and the relative performance of different parallelizations vary with problem size and system ensemble size. Comparing the performance of different implementations over a range of system and problem sizes is crucial in developing effective restructuring compilation

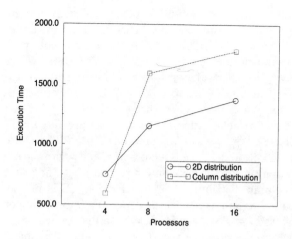

Figure 4: Scaled crossing point of the Jacobi with n=20

systems and ultimately in reducing the burden of parallel programming. In this study a practical methodology is developed and tested for automatic range comparison in a data-parallel compilation system. The proposed methodology is built on rigorous analytical models. Experimental results confirm its effectiveness in a restructuring system.

This work is a part of our current effort in development of the SCALA (SCALability Analyzer), an integrated performance analysis system. SCALA is an advanced system that is comprised of performance prediction techniques, advanced post-execution, and scalability analysis to compute performance indices that reflect the behavior of scalable parallel programs. It is integrated into restructuring systems in order to exploit knowledge from the compiler and guide the user as well as the compiler in the selection of restructuring transformations and optimization strategies.

References

[1] B. Chapman, P. Mehrotra, and H. Zima, "Programming in Vienna Fortran," *Scientific Programming*, vol. 1, pp. 31–50, 1992.

[2] H. P. Fortran Forum, "High performance Fortran language specification version 1.0." Technical Report, Department of Computer Science, Rice University, May 1993.

[3] V. S. Adve, J. M. Crummey, M. Anderson, K. Kennedy, J.-C. Wang, and D. A. Reed, "An integrated compilation performance analysis environment for data parallel programs," in *Proc. of Supercomputing*, (San Diego, CA), Dec. 1995.

[4] T. Fahringer, *Automatic Performance Prediction of Parallel Programs* . Kluwer Academic Publishers, Boston, USA, ISBN 0-7923-9708-8, March 1996.

[5] S. Benkner, S. Andel, R. Blasko, P. Brezany, A. Celic, B. Chapman, M. Egg, T. Fahringer, J. Hulman, Y. Hou, E. Kelc, E. Mehofer, H. Moritsch, M. Paul, K. Sanjari, V. Sipkova, B. Velkov, B. Wender, and H. Zima, *Vienna Fortran Compilation System - Version 2.0 - User's Guide*, October 1995.

[6] G. Fox, M. Johnson, G. Lyzenga, S. Otto, J. Salmon, and D. Walker, *Solving Problems on Concurrent Processors*, vol. 1. and 2. Englewood Cliffs, NY: Prentice Hall, 1988.

[7] X.-H. Sun and D. Rover, "Scalability of parallel algorithm-machine combinations," *IEEE Transactions on Parallel and Distributed Systems*, pp. 599–613, June 1994.

[8] V. Kumar, A. Grama, A. Gupta, and G. Karypis, *Introduction to Parallel Computing, Design and Analysis of Algorithms*. The Benjamin/Cummings Publishing Company, Inc., 1994.

[9] S. Sahni and V. Thanvantri, "Performance metrics: Keeping the focus on runtime," *IEEE Parallel & Distributed Technology*, pp. 43–56, Spring 1996.

[10] X.-H. Sun, "The relation of scalability and execution time," in *Proc. of the International Parallel Processing Symposium'96*, April 1996.

[11] X.-H. Sun, "Performance range comparison via crossing point analysis," in *Lecture Notes in Computer Science, No 1388* (J. Rolim, ed.), Springer, march 1998.

[12] X.-H. Sun and J. Zhu, "Performance prediction: A case study using a scalable shared-virtual-memory machine," *IEEE Parallel & Distributed Technology*, pp. 36–49, Winter 1996.

[13] X.-H. Sun, M. Pantano, and T. Fahringer, "Integrated range comparison for data-parallel compilation systems." Technical Report #97-004, Department of Computer Science, Apr. 1997.

Session 8C
Interconnection Networks

Chair: Yoshitaka Shibata
Iwate Prefectural University, Japan

nD-dBPN: New Self-Routing Permutation Networks Based On the de Bruijn Digraphs

Azman Samsudin and Kyungsook Y. Lee
Dept. of Mathematics and Computer Science
University of Denver, Denver, CO 80208-0189
e-mail: asamsudi@cs.du.edu, klee@cs.du.edu

Abstract

A new class of self-routing permutation networks based on the de Bruijn digraphs is proposed. The new networks are modular and scalable, and have an optimal cross-point complexity. Compared to the crossbar switches of the same size, nD-dBPN uses less cross-points, and operates faster. With its optimal configuration, the new network uses $O(N \log N)$ cross-points compared to $O(N^2)$ cross-points of the crossbar switches. The 2D-dBPN has the same cross-point complexity as the 3-stage Clos network, but it has a constant control complexity compared to $\Omega(N^{3/2})$ of the Clos network.

Keywords: Non-blocking Networks, Permutation Networks, de Bruijn Digraphs, and Banyan Networks.

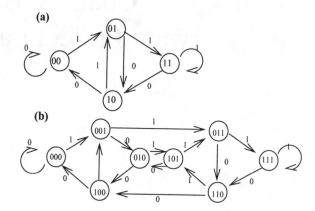

Figure 1. (a) dB(2,2). (b) dB(2,3)

1. Introduction

The crossbar switches, the Clos networks [1], and the Benes networks [2] are well-known permutation networks. The $(N \times N)$ crossbar switches have N^2 cross-points and a constant control complexity. The $(N \times N)$ 3-stage Clos network has the $O(N^{3/2})$ cross-point and control complexities. The Benes network, based on $(d \times d)$ crossbar switches, has the $O(N \log_d N)$ cross-point and control complexities.

In this paper, a new class of self-routing, packet switched permutation networks with an $O(N \log_d N)$ cross-point complexity is presented. The new permutation networks, nD-dBPN, are based on the de Bruijn digraphs. The 2D-dBPN has a cross-point complexity comparable to that of the 3-stage Clos network but without the complex control algorithm required by the Clos networks.

This paper is organized as follows. Section 2 presents the de Bruijn digraphs. Section 3 presents the 1D-dBPN and 2D-dBPN. In Section 4, we explore variations of 2D-dBPN. The nD-dBPN is presented in Section 5, and Section 6 concludes.

2. de Bruijn Digraphs

A de Bruijn digraph, dB(d,n), has d^n nodes and d^{n+1} directed edges, [3]. The address for each node is represented as a sequence of n digits from the d-ary number system. Each node has d outgoing edges and d incoming edges, and the network diameter is n. Node $u = (u_0, u_2, \ldots, u_{n-1})$ has a directed edge to node $v = (v_0, v_2, \ldots, v_{n-1})$ if and only if $v_i = u_{i+1}$, for $0 \le i \le n-2$. Figure 1 shows dB(2,2) and dB(2,3). A directed edge is identified by the least significant digit of the destination node address. The routing in the de Bruijn digraphs is simple, and is based on the destination address.

For example, the routing path from source node 00 to destination 11 in dB(2,2) in Figure 1(a) is $00 \xrightarrow{1} 01 \xrightarrow{1} 11$. For a large network, dB(5,4), the routing path from source node 2043 to destination node 0123 is $2043 \xrightarrow{0} 0430 \xrightarrow{1} 4301 \xrightarrow{2} 3012 \xrightarrow{3} 0123$.

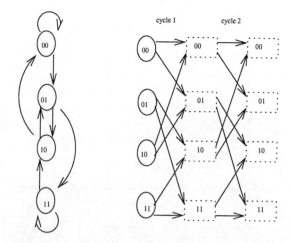

Figure 2. (a) dB(2,2). (b) A permutation can be performed in two network cycles represented as two additional columns.

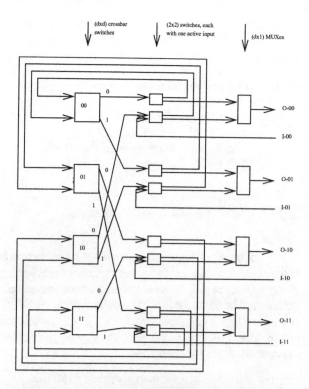

Figure 3. A (4×4) **1D-dBPN(d),** $d = 2$**. I-xx are the input links to the network, and O-xx are the output links from the network.**

3. 1D-dBPN and 2D-dBPN

3.1. Non-Blocking Property Of dB(d,2) as a Permutation Network

The de Bruijn digraphs were originally proposed as multi-hop networks [4] where each of d^2 nodes sends and receives arbitrary packets. When dB(d,2) is used as a permutation network, d^2 nodes send d^2 packets whose destinations form a permutation of $(0, 1, \ldots, d^2 - 1)$. These packets are generated synchronously during a network cycle with one packet generated per node. The following theorem proves that dB(d,2) as a synchronous permutation network performs a permutation in two network cycles.

Theorem 1 *A synchronous permutation network dB(d,2) is non-blocking with two network cycles.*

Proof: Based on the routing path generated by the routing algorithm in the previous section, each packet in dB(d,2) traverses exactly two edges before reaching its destination node. In the first cycle, each packet has d edges to choose from, and therefore, the first cycle is conflict-free. In the second cycle, each node might receive up to d packets. However, each of these packets chooses a distinct edge, since in the second cycle each packet is routed to its destination node which is distinct.

dB(2,2) is redrawn with nodes in a column in Figure 2(a). The two network cycles required to perform a permutation on dB(2,2) are represented as two additional columns in dashed lines in Figure 2(b).

3.2. $(N \times N)$ **1D-dBPN(d),** $N = d^2$

The $(d^2 \times d^2)$ 1D-dBPN(d) is a single-stage network consisting of d^2 crossbar switches of size $(d \times d)$, labeled corresponding to the d^2 nodes in dB(d,2). Figures 3 shows a (4×4) 1D-dBPN(2). Each crossbar switch has d input and d output links, which are used to connect the crossbar switches in dB(d,2). The output links are labeled corresponding to the least significant digit of the destination address of the crossbar switches. Each output link of a crossbar switch is connected to a (2×2) switch, which provides two paths for a packet arriving at its input link: one for routing and the other for leaving the network when the packet reaches its destination. The d network output links of each group of d (2×2) switches are connected to a $(d \times 1)$ multiplexer whose output link is a network output. Each group of d (2×2) switches also has a network input link.

The packets within a 1D-dBPN(d) are required to cycle the network exactly twice to reach their destinations. A packet is injected at a network input link of a (2×2) switch. Each $(d \times d)$ crossbar switch is connected to d (2×2) switches whose d upper output links connect the crossbar switches in dB(d,2).

Since there are d (2×2) switches for every network output link, a $(d \times 1)$ multiplexer is needed for each network output link. Note that only one packet may exit from each group of d (2×2) switches every two network cycles.

Algorithm to determine the routing tag for 1D-dBPN(d)

Let $S = s_0 s_1$: source node address,
  $D = d_0 d_1$: destination node address,
  P^{cr} : crossbar routing tag from S to D, and
  P^{sw} : (2×2) routing tag from S to D.

$P^{cr} = d_0 d_1$;
$P^{sw} = 101$. /* '1' for cross, '0' for straight */

An important characteristics of non-blocking networks is the network depth, defined as the number of cross-points along the longest path between the source node and destination node. The depth for $(d \times d)$ crossbar switches is $2d - 1$. If we use a (2×2) crossbar switch for a (2×2) switch, and assume that a $(d \times 1)$ multiplexer has d cross-points, then the network depth for 1D-dBPN(d) is:

$$((2 \times 2) \text{ switch}) + (2 \text{ internal cycles}) + (\text{MUX})$$
$$= (3) + (2(2d - 1 + 3)) + (d)$$
$$= 5d + 7. \qquad (1)$$

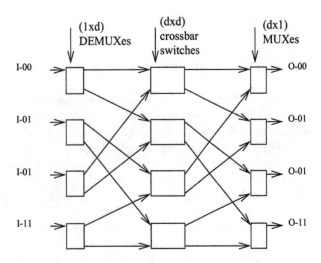

Figure 4. A (4×4) **Pipelined 1D-dBPN(d),** $d = 2$.

3.3. Pipelined 1D-dBPN(d), $N = d^2$

A pipelined 1D-dBPN(d) can be designed with a stage of $(1 \times d)$ DEMUXes, followed by a stage of $(d \times d)$ crossbar switches and a stage of $(d \times 1)$ MUXes as shown in Figure 4. Three different sets of data packets occupy the pipelined

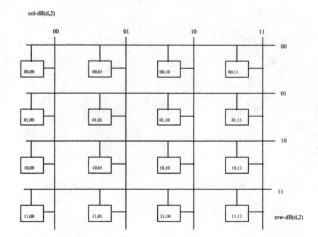

Figure 5. (16×16) **2D-dBPN(2) as 2-dimensional dB(2,2)'s.**

1D-dBPN(d) at any given time. It requires $d^4 + 2d^3$ cross-points.

3.4. $(N \times N)$ **2D-dBPN(d)**, $N = (d^2)^2$

The $(d^4 \times d^4)$ 2D-dBPN(d) consists of two $(d^2 \times d^2)$ square arrays of $(d \times d)$ crossbar switches. The crossbar switches in each column/row are connected as a dB(d,2): col-dB(d,2) or row-dB(d,2). A (16×16) 2D-dBPN(2) is shown in Figure 5. Each crossbar switch is connected to a col-dB(d,2) and a row-dB(d,2), and is labeled as row-dB no., col-dB no. in the d-ary number system.

Figure 6 and Figure 7 show col-dB(2,2) 00 and row-dB(2,2) 00 of (16×16) 2D-dBPN(2), respectively. The output links of the $(d \times d)$ crossbar switches are prefixed with either 'R' for row or 'C' for column connections. The network input links to 2D-dBPN(d) are connected to col-dB(d,2)'s, and are labeled as 'I-row-dB no., col-dB no.' in Figure 6. The network output links from 2D-dBPN(d) are connected from row-dB(d,2)'s, and are labeled as 'O-row-dB no., col-dB no.' in Figure 7.

The routing algorithm for 2D-dBPN(d) consists of two phases: one to send a packet to its destintion row and the other to send a packet to its destination column. The row or column routing is simply the 1D-dBPN(d) routing. Each 1D-dBPN(d) requires two network cycles for routing. To simplify the following discussion, 1 1D-dB-network cycle is defined as the 2 network cycles required by the 1D-dBPN(d).

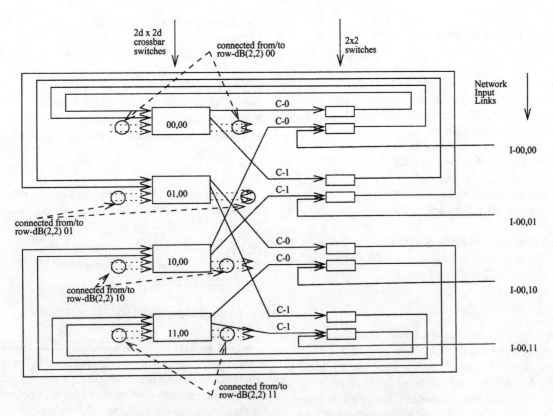

Figure 6. Col-dB(d,2) 00 of the (16×16) **2D-dBPN(d),** $d = 2$.

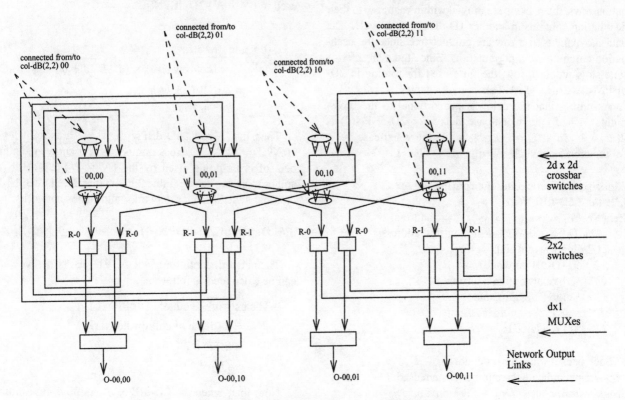

Figure 7. Row-dB(d,2) 00 of the (16×16) **2D-dBPN(d),** $d = 2$.

Pseudo routing algorithm for $(d^4 \times d^4)$
2D-dBPN(d)

1 For $i \leftarrow (1$ to $d^2 - 1)$ do
   /* During, time-slot i, all packets i rows
   away from their destination rows are routed
   to their final destinations */
2   If $[((\text{src-row} + i) \bmod d^2) = \text{dest-row}]$
3   route data to (dest-row, src-col)
        via col-dB(d,2) of src-col;
4   route data to (dest-row, dest-col)
        via row-dB(d,2) of dest-row;
5   else
6   idle for 2 1D-dB-network cycles.
      /* 1 1D-dB-network cycle of col-dB(d,2)
      and 1 1D-dB-network cycle of
      row-dB(d,2). */

During time-slot i, all packets i rows away from their destination rows move to the destination rows in every column. These moves of packets within a column are a uniform shift of distance i and can be realized in 1 1D-dB-network cycle of col-dB(d,2) networks. Data packets move to a new row only if the new row is the destination row. After all these packets from each column reach their destination rows, the packets are moved within each row to their destination columns in another 1D-dB-network cycle. The data movements in a row are conflict-free since the destination columns are a permutation. Since there are $d^2 - 1$ time-slots within a row, the time used for routing in 2D-dBPN(d)is $2(d^2 - 1)$ 1D-dB-network cycles.

Assuming that the delay is proportional to the cross-points visited, the worst-case delay for 2D-dBPN(d) is $2(d^2 - 1)(5d + 7) = O(d^3)$, while the worst-case delay for the crossbar switch is $2(d^4 - 1) = O(d^4)$.

Algorithm to determine the routing tag for
$(d^4 \times d^4)$ **2D-dBPN(d)**

Let $(Sr, Sc) = (sr_0 sr_1, sc_0 sc_1)$: src address,
   $(Dr, Dc) = (dr_0 dr_1, dc_0 dc_1)$: dest address,
   /* 2 digit row/col address for
   2-hop 1D-dB-network */
   P^{cr} : crossbar routing tag from
   (Sr, Sc) to (Dr, Dc), and
   P^{sw} : (2×2) routing tag from
   (Sr, Sc) to (Dr, Dc).

/* Each packet waits for time-slot $D_r - D_s$.
   Subscripts indicate the number-system used. */
$RowDistance_{10} = (Dr_d - Sr_d) \bmod d$;
Wait for $(2 \times RowDistance_{10} - 1)$ time-slots;

/* Routing tag for (2×2) switches in each
   col-dB or row-dB is always 1001. */
$P^{sw} = 10011001$;

/* Column routing to D_r via the crossbar
   switch output links $C - dc_0$ and $C - dc_1$.
   Row routing to D_c via the crossbar switch
   output links $R - dr_0$ and $R - dr_1$. */
$P^{cr} = (C\text{-}dc_0, C\text{-}dc_1, R\text{-}dr_0, R\text{-}dr_1)$.

For example, if the source address is (00,00) and the destination address is (11,11), then the routing path is $(00, 00) \xrightarrow{C-dc_0} (01, 00) \xrightarrow{C-dc_1} (11, 00) \xrightarrow{R-dr_0} (11, 01) \xrightarrow{R-dr_1} (11, 11)$. Since the $RowDistance = (11_2 - 00_2) = 11_2 = 3_{10}$, the packet from (00,00) is routed after 2 time-slot delay.

3.5. Cross-Points Used By 2D-dBPN(d)

As can be seen in Figures 6 and 7, there are three different kinds of switching components in $(d^4 \times d^4)$ 2D-dBPN(d): $(d \times d)$ crossbar switches, (2×2) switches, and $(d \times 1)$ multiplexers. The number of cross-points required for these switches are d^2, 4, and d, respectively. Summing up all the cross-points required, the number of cross-points used in $(N \times N)$ 2D-dBPN(d), $N = d^4$:

(col and row arrays)
$$\times \text{(col/row size)} \times (d^2 + 4d + d)$$
$$= 2(d^4)(d^2 + 5d)$$
$$= 2d^6 + 10d^5 \tag{2}$$

Thus, the $(N \times N)$ 2D-dBPN(d), $N = d^4$, uses $2N^{3/2} + 10N^{5/4} = O(N^{3/2})$ cross-points. Table 1 shows the numbers of cross-points used by the $(N \times N)$ 2D-dBPN(d) and crossbar switches. Table 2 compares the 2D-dBPN(d), crossbar switches, Clos networks, and Benes networks.

3.6. Depth of 2D-dBPN(d)

The network depth for $(N \times N)$ 2D-dBPN(d), $N = d^4$, can be calculated as follows:

The network depth of 2D-dBPN(d)
$$= 2 \text{ (depth of col/row network)}$$
$$= 2(5d + 7)$$
$$= O(N^{1/4}) \tag{3}$$

Note that, since the 2D-dBPN(d) employs time multiplexing in the first dimension, the network delays for 2D-dBPN(d) is higher than the network depth. The network

Networks	Cross-points	Control complexity	Network depth
2D-dBPNs	$2N^{3/2} + 10N^{5/4}$	$O(1)$	$O(N^{1/4})$
Crossbar switches	N^2	$O(1)$	$O(N)$
3-Stage Clos	$6N^{3/2} - 3N$	$O(N^{3/2})$	$O(N^{1/2})$
Benes	$2N(2(\log_2 N) - 1)^\dagger$	$O(N \log N)^\ddagger$	$O(\log N)$

† Assuming 2×2 crossbar switches. ‡ Looping algorithm.

Table 2. Comparison of different permutation networks.

Size	Cross-points used	
	2D-DBPN(d)	$(N \times N)$ Crossbar switches
$d = 2, N = 16$	448	256
$d = 3, N = 81$	3,888	6,561
$d = 4, N = 256$	18,432	65,536
$d = 5, N = 625$	62,500	390,625
$d = 10, N = 10,000$	3,000,000	100,000,000

Table 1. Cross-points used for the $(N \times N)$ 2D-dBPN(d) and crossbar switches.

d_c	d_r	$(N \times N)$ 2D-dBPN(d_r,d_c)
4	4	256
4	5	400
4	6	576
5	5	625

Table 3. Network sizes available for 2D-dBPN(d_r,d_c).

d_r, all packets in a row can be routed in one 1D-dB-network cycle of row-dB(d,2) networks. However, 2D-dBPN(d_r,d_c) is hardware efficient when $d_r = d_c$, i.e., when it reverts to 2D-dBPN(d). Table 3 shows examples of extra network sizes available in 2D-dBPN(d_r,d_c).

The network delay, including the buffering time for 2D-dBPN(d_r,d_c), is $(d_c^2)((5d_c + 7) + (5d_r + 7))$ cross-point delays. The number of cross-points used in 2D-dBPN(d_r,d_c) is $(d_c^2 d_r^2)((d_c^2 + 5d_c) + (d_r^2 + 5d_r))$.

4.2. $(N \times N)$ 2D-BdBPN(d), $N = d^4$

We can improve 2D-dBPN(d) by using Banyan networks [5] for the column networks. The function of col-dB's of the 2D-dBPN is a uniform shift. This uniform shift within a column can be handled by a Banyan network without a conflict.

The advantages of using Banyan networks for the column networks are twofold: a reduction in the cross-points used and the capability for pipelining. If the pipelining is used in the Banyan networks, then row-dB(d,2)'s should also use pipelining (pipelined 1D-dBPN), so that both column and row networks can be pipelined synchronously.

The $(N \times N)$ Banyan networks based on (2×2) switching elements have $(\log_2 N)$ stages, with each stage consisting of $N/2$, (2×2) switching elements. The Banyan networks are bit-controlled with the destination address.

The $(d^4 \times d^4)$ 2D-BdBPN(d) is shown in Figure 8. Each column network is a $(d^2 \times d^2)$ Banyan network. The outputs from these Banyan networks are directed to the de Bruijn

delays for 2D-dBPN(d) is $O(N^{3/4})$ as shown below:

$$
\begin{aligned}
&\text{The network delay of 2D-dBPN(d)} \\
&= (d^2 - 1) \times (2(\text{1D-dBPN(d)})) \\
&= (d^2 - 1)(2(5d + 7)) \\
&= 10d^3 + 14d^2 - 10d - 14 \\
&= 10N^{3/4} + 14N^{1/2} - 10N^{1/4} - 14 \\
&= O(N^{3/4}) \quad\quad\quad\quad\quad\quad\quad\quad\quad (4)
\end{aligned}
$$

4. Variations Of 2D-dBPN(d)

4.1. $(N \times N)$ 2D-dBPN(d_r,d_c), $N = d_r^2 d_c^2$

While the 2D-dBPN(d) is based on two square arrays of $(d \times d)$ crossbar switches, the $(N \times N)$ 2D-dBPN(d_r,d_c), $N = d_r^2 d_c^2$, is based on two $(d_r^2 \times d_c^2)$ rectangular arrays of crossbar switches. The rectangular array of col-dB(d,2)'s consists of $(d_c \times d_r)$ crossbar switches and the rectangular array of row-dB(d,2)'s consists of $(d_r \times d_r)$ crossbar switches.

The routing algorithm for 2D-dBPN(d_r,d_c) is the same as the routing algorithm for 2D-dBPN(d) in Section 3.3. The only difference is that the col-dB and row-dB network cycles may be different for 2D-dBPN(d_r,d_c). Based on the algorithm, it is more efficient if $d_c < d_r$ since regardless of

row-networks. Within a de Bruijn network, data are routed without a conflict since the destination addresses of the data within a row are a permutation.

Algorithm to determine the routing tag for 2D-BdBPN(d)

Let $(Sr, Sc) = (sr_0sr_1, sc_0sc_1)$: src address,

$(Dr, Dc) = (dr_0dr_1, dc_0dc_1)$: dest address,

P^B : routing tag used by Banyan networks,

P^{dBcr} : crossbar routing tag used by row-dB(d,2)'s, and

P^{dBsw} : (2×2) routing tag used by row-dB(d,2)'s.

$RowDist_{10} = (Dr_d - Sr_d) \bmod d^2$;

wait $(3(\log_2 d^2) \times RowDist_{10})$ cross-point delays;

$P^B = (Dc)_{base\ 2}$;

$P^{dBcr} = Dr$ and $P^{dBsw} = 101$.

More choices of network sizes can also be obtained by using different network degrees for column and row networks, similar to 2D-dBPN(d_r,d_c). The number of cross-points used in 2D-BdBPN(d) are:

(Cross-points in Banyan networks)+

(Cross-points in de Bruijn networks)

$$= \left((d^2)\left(\frac{4d^2}{2}\log_2 d^2\right) \right) + ((d^4)(d^2 + 5d))$$

$$= d^4(4(\log_2 d) + d^2 + 5d) \qquad (5)$$

The network depth of 2D-BdBPN(d) is better than the network depth of the 2D-dBPN(d). This is because the depth of the de Bruijn row-networks in 2D-dBPN(d), $5d+7$, is replaced by the depth of the Banyan networks in 2D-BdBPN(d), $2(\log_2 d)$. The 2D-BdBPN(d) has a better delay than the same size crossbar switch: $O(d^3)$ versus $O(d^4)$. Note that the amortized delay for 2D-BdBPN(d) can be improved if pipelining is used.

The network delay for 2D-BdBPN(d)

$$= \text{(Number of rows)} \times$$

$$((\text{Banyan network delay}) +$$

$$(\text{de Bruijn network delay}))$$

$$= d^2 \left(3(\log_2 d^2) + (5d + 7)\right)$$

$$= 6d^2(\log_2 d) + 5d^3 + 7d^2 \qquad (6)$$

5. n-Dimensional dBPN: nD-dBPN(d)

The n-dimensional dBPN(d) can be constructed similar to the construction of 2D-dBPN(d). There are $N = (d^2)^n$

Network Size $(N = 2^{64})$	Cross-points used	Network delays
2D-dBPN(d=2^{16})	1.58×10^{29}	2.81×10^{15}
4D-dBPN(d=2^8)	4.93×10^{24}	1.45×10^{18}
8D-dBPN(d=2^4)	4.96×10^{22}	5.02×10^{19}
16D-dBPN(d=2^2)	1.06×10^{22}	4.98×10^{20}
Crossbar Switches	3.40×10^{38}	3.69×10^{19}
3-Stage Clos Networks	4.76×10^{29}	4.29×10^{10}

Table 4. Cross-points used for $(2^{64} \times 2^{64})$, $2 \le n \le 16$.

input/output nodes in the nD-dBPN. In 3D-dBPN(d), the first-dimension networks and the second-dimension networks are the column networks and the row networks of 2D-dBPN(d), respectively. In 3D-dBPN(d), the outputs from the second-dimension networks are routed to the inputs of the third-dimension networks. The process can be repeated for the n dimensional dBPN, $n > 3$.

The number of cross-points used in nD-dBPN(d) is shown in Equation 7. Table 4 shows examples of various nD-dBPN(d) for network size $N = 2^{64}$ and their corresponding cross-point requirements. In terms of hardware, the table implies that for a given network size, it is better to choose a big n and a small d.

Number of cross-points used in nD-dBPN(d)

$$= \text{(no. of dimensions)} \times \text{(network size)} \times$$

$$(d^2 + 5d)$$

$$= nd^{2n}(d^2 + 5d)$$

$$= n(N^{\frac{1}{2n}})^{2n}\left((N^{\frac{1}{2n}})^2 + 5(N^{\frac{1}{2n}})\right)$$

$$= nN(N^{\frac{1}{n}} + 5N^{\frac{1}{2n}})$$

$$= n(N^{\frac{n+1}{n}} + 5N^{\frac{n+1}{2n}}) \qquad (7)$$

If we choose n such that $n = \log_m N$, for some integer m, Equation 7 becomes:

$$(\log_m N)\left(mN + 5(mN)^{\frac{1}{2}}\right)$$

$$= O(N \log N). \qquad (8)$$

Note that for a high n, the range of the variables involved are as follows: $(d, n = 2, 3, \ldots)$, $(m = d^2..d^{2n})$, $(N = d^{2n})$.

The cross-point delay for nD-dBPN(d) is shown in Equation 9. Table 4 shows the cross-points used and the network delays for the various nD-dBPN(d)'s for the network size of $N = 2^{64}$. The table shows that the larger the n is, the longer the delay is.

Cross-point delay for nD-dBPN(d)

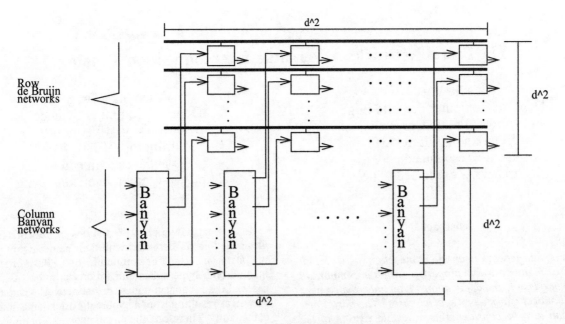

Figure 8. $(N \times N)$ **2D-BdBPN(d)**, $N = d^4$.

$$= ((d^2)^{n-1}) \times (n \times 1\text{D-dBPN(d)})$$
$$= d^{2(n-1)}(n(5d + 7))$$
$$= 5nd^{2n-1} + 7nd^{2n-2}$$
$$= 5nN^{\frac{2n-1}{2n}} + 7nN^{\frac{2n-2}{2n}} \quad (9)$$

If we choose n such that $n = \log_m N$, for some integer m, Equation 9 becomes:

$$\frac{N}{m}(\log_m N)\left(5m^{\frac{1}{2}} + 7\right)$$
$$= O(N \log N). \quad (10)$$

Note that the delay shown in Equation 10 includes the buffering time before the data enters the network. The network depth for nD-dBPN(d) is only $O(\log N)$ as shown in the following:

Network depth for nD-dBPN(d)
$$= (n) \times (\text{depth of each dimension})$$
$$= n \times (5d + 7)$$
$$= 5nd + 7n$$
$$= 5nN^{\frac{1}{2n}} + 7n$$
$$= (\log_m N)\left(5m^{\frac{1}{2}} + 7\right), \text{ for some } m$$
$$= O(\log N) \quad (11)$$

6. Conclusion

This paper introduced new permutation networks based on the de Bruijn digraphs. The new permutation networks,

nD-dBPN, are self-routing, scalable and have an optimal cross-point complexity. Compared to the crossbar switches of the same size, nD-dBPN uses less cross-points and operates faster. With its optimal configuration, the new network uses $O(N \log N)$ cross-points compared to $O(N^2)$ cross-points of the crossbar switches. The 2D-dBPN has the same cross-point complexity as the 3-stage Clos network, but it has a constant control complexity compared to $\Omega(N^{3/2})$ of the Clos network.

References

[1] C. Clos, "A Study of non-blocking switching networks," *Bell System Technical Journal*, 32, pp. 406-424, 1953.

[2] V.E. Benes, "Permutation groups, complexes, and rearrangeable multistage connecting networks," *Bell System Technical Journal*, 43, pp. 1619-1640, 1964.

[3] N.G de Bruijn, "A combinatorial problem," *Proc. Akademe Van Weteschappen*, vol 49., part 2, pp. 758-764, 1946.

[4] K. Sivarajan and R. Ramaswami, "Multihop Lightwave Networks Based on de Bruijn Graphs," *Proc. INFOCOM'91*, pp. 1001-1011, Apr. 1991.

[5] L. Goke and G. Lipovski, "Banyan networks for partitioning multiprocessor systems," *Proc. of 1st Annual Symp. on Computer Architecture*, pp. 21-28, Dec. 1973.

The Postal Network: A Versatile Interconnection Topology*

Jie Wu
Dept. of Computer Sci. and Eng.
Florida Atlantic University
Boca Raton, FL 33431
jie@cse.fau.edu
http://www.cse.fau.edu/~jie

Yuanyuan Yang
Dept. of Computer Science
University of Vermont
Burlington, VT 05405
yang@cs.uvm.edu
http://www.emba.uvm.edu/~yang

Abstract

The postal network is an interconnection network that possesses many desirable properties which are important in network design and applications. It includes hypercubes and Fibonacci cubes as its special cases. The postal network can also be considered as a flexible version of the hypercube which relaxes the restriction on the number of nodes and thus makes it possible to construct multicomputers with arbitrary sizes. Basically, the postal network forms a series (with series number λ) that is based on the sequence $N_\lambda(n) = N_\lambda(n-1) + N_\lambda(n-\lambda)$, where n is the dimension and $N_\lambda(n)$ represents the number of nodes in an n-dimensional postal network in series λ. In this paper, we study topological properties of postal networks and relationships between different postal networks. One application of postal networks is also shown in implementing barrier synchronization using a special spanning tree called a postal tree.

1 Introduction

The use of undirected graphs as interconnection topologies for large multicomputer systems has been an active research area in the past decades. The hypercube has been a popular topology because of its strong connectivity, regularity, symmetry, and ability to embed many other topologies. Unfortunately, the number of nodes 2^n in an n-dimensional hypercube (n-cube) grows rapidly as n increases. This limits considerably the choice of the number of nodes in the graph. The Fibonacci cube (FC) proposed by Hsu [4] is a special subcube of a hypercube based on Fibonacci numbers. It has been shown that the Fibonacci cube can efficiently emulate many hypercube algorithms. Fibonacci cubes use fewer links than comparable hypercubes and their size does not increase as fast as hypercubes. The structural analysis of the Fibonacci cube has been extensively studied in [4], its applications in [2], and its extensions in [6].

In this paper, we propose a series of network topologies called *postal networks* with their names coming from the *postal model* [1] of communication. Postal networks include both hypercubes and Fibonacci cubes as special cases. Like Fibonacci cubes, postal networks can also be viewed as resulting from a hypercube after some nodes become faulty. Therefore, the postal network not only allows the construction of multicomputers of arbitrary sizes but also exposes the nature of hypercubes operating in a gracefully degraded mode. Basically, the n-dimensional postal network in series λ, $PN_\lambda(n)$, is based on the generalized Fibonacci sequence $N_\lambda(n) = N_\lambda(n-1) + N_\lambda(n-\lambda)$. The postal network series can also be considered as a flexible version of the hypercube which relaxes the restriction on the number of nodes and thus makes it possible to construct multicomputers with arbitrary sizes.

We show that the postal network series still maintains many desirable properties of hypercubes, such as existence of a Hamming distance path between any two nodes and a simple routing algorithm. Moreover, postal networks support efficient collective communication using the postal model [1] which can fine tune the communication structure based on network latency in the underlying system. Specifically, this model incorporates a latency parameter λ measuring the inverse of the ratio between the time it takes an originator of a message to send it and the time that passes until the recipient of the message receives it. If $N_\lambda(n)$ represents the maximum number of nodes that can be reached in time n on a one-port model exhibiting λ. Then the following equation holds:

$$N_\lambda(n) = \begin{cases} N_\lambda(n-1) + N_\lambda(n-\lambda), & \text{if } n \geq \lambda \\ 1, & \text{otherwise} \end{cases}$$

Therefore, if λ in the postal network is selected based on the given latency parameter in the underlying network, efficient broadcast and gather operations can be carried out, i.e., a broadcast (gather) operation can be done in a minimum of steps.

The main features of the postal network can be summarized as follows:

- The series of postal networks allows more choices in constructing systems of different sizes.

- The series contains both hypercubes and Fibonacci cubes as its special cases.

*Research supported by the U.S. National Science Foundation under Grant No. OSR-9350540 and the U.S. Army Research Office under Grant No. DAAH04-96-1-0234.

612

- The series number λ can be carefully selected to match the latency parameter in the underlying communication network to support efficient collective communication.

Our study focuses on topological properties and communication aspects of the postal network. Relationships between different postal networks are also studied. The purpose of this study is not just to propose a "new" interconnection network, but to extend the existing ones such as hypercubes and Fibonacci cubes. We try to gain some insights on these popular networks, operated under certain relaxed conditions and/or degraded modes, by studying their topological properties, routing capability, and the ability of simulating other structures through embedding.

2 Postal Networks

Normally, a graph model is used to represent a point-to-point multicomputer topology. We use graph $G = (V, E)$ to represent an interconnection network, where V is a vertex set with each element representing a processor (also called a node) and E is an edge set with each element corresponding to a communication link connecting two nodes. Let $b_{(m)}$ represent m consecutive bits of b; for example, $0_{(4)} = 0000$, and symbol $\|$ denote a concatenation operation; for example, $01\|\{0, 1\} = \{010, 011\}$ and $0_{(2)}1\|\{01, 10\} = \{00101, 00110\}$.

Definition 1: *Assume that graphs $PN_\lambda(n) = (V_\lambda(n), E_\lambda(n))$, $PN_\lambda(n-1) = (V_\lambda(n-1), E_\lambda(n-1))$, and $PN_\lambda(n-\lambda) = (V_\lambda(n-\lambda), E_\lambda(n-\lambda))$. Then $V_\lambda(n) = 0\|V_\lambda(n-1) \cup 10_{(\lambda-1)}\|V_\lambda(n-\lambda)$ for $n > \lambda$. As initial conditions for recursion, $V_\lambda(n) = \{0_{(n)}, 0_{(n-1)}1, ..., 010_{(n-2)}, 10_{(n-1)}\}$, $1 \leq n \leq \lambda$. Two nodes in $PN_\lambda(n)$ are connected by an edge in $E_\lambda(n)$ if and only if their labels differ in exactly one bit position.*

A $PN_\lambda(n)$ is called a *postal network* with dimension n and series number λ. The number of bits in a node address is the same as its dimension. Figure 1 shows examples of $PN_3(n)$ for $n = 1, 2, 3, 4, 5$. A PN_3 of dimension n consists of one PN_3 of dimension $n - 1$ and one PN_3 of dimension $n - 3$. Figure 2 shows examples of $PN_4(n)$ for $n = 1, 2, 3, 4, 5, 6$.

Theorem 1: *A $PN_1(n)$ is an n-cube $Q(n)$ and a $PN_2(n)$ is an n-dimensional Fibonacci cube $FC(n)$.*

Proof: When $\lambda = 1$, $V_1(n) = 0\|V_1(n-1) \cup 1\|V_1(n-1)$. Therefore, $PN_1(n)$ matches exactly the definition of the n-cube $Q(n)$. Similarly, when $\lambda = 2$, $V_2(n) = 0\|V_2(n-1) \cup 10\|V_2(n-2)$. Recall that the Fibonacci cube is defined as follows [4]: Assume that graphs $FC(n) = (V(n), E(n))$, $FC(n-1) = (V(n-1), E(n-1))$, and $FC(n-2) = (V(n-2), E(n-2))$. Then $V(n) = 0\|V(n-1) \cup 10\|V(n-2)$. Two nodes in $FC(n)$ are connected by an edge in $E(n)$ if and only if their labels differ in exactly one bit position. As initial conditions for

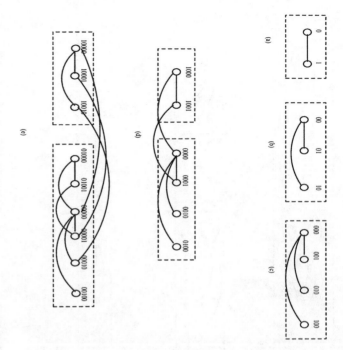

Figure 1: Postal network PN_3: (a) $n = 1$, (b) $n = 2$, (c) $n = 3$, (d) $n = 4$, (e) $n = 5$.

recursion, $V(2) = \{\}$, $V(3) = \{0, 1\}$. Therefore, $PN_2(n)$ also matches the definition of the n-dimensional Fibonacci cube $FC(n)$. ∎

Despite its asymmetric structure, the postal network still maintains many desirable properties from the hypercube network. Based on the definition of the postal network, the vertex set $V_\lambda(k)$ of $PN_\lambda(k)$ can be partitioned into $10_{(\lambda-1)}\|V_\lambda(k-\lambda)$ and $0\|V_\lambda(k-1)$. The following lemma shows the relationship between these two vertex sets.

Lemma: *For each node in $10_{(\lambda-1)}\|V_\lambda(k-\lambda)$ there is exactly one neighbor in $0\|V_\lambda(k-1)$, i.e., the addresses of these two nodes differ in exactly one bit.*

Proof: Randomly pick a node in $10_{(\lambda-1)}\|V_\lambda(k-\lambda)$. This node comes from a node in $V_\lambda(k-\lambda)$ with $10_{(\lambda-1)}$ attached in front. Based on the recursive definition of the postal network, $0_{(\lambda-1)}\|V_\lambda(k-\lambda)$ is a subset of $V_\lambda(k-1)$ and it always appears as the first term of the recursive definition of $V_\lambda(k-1)$ until $V_\lambda(k-1)$ is resolved into $V_\lambda(k-\lambda)$. Therefore, there is at least one node in $0\|V_\lambda(k-1)$ that is the neighbor of the selected node in $10_{(\lambda-1)}\|V_\lambda(k-\lambda)$. In addition, each node in $10_{(\lambda-1)}\|V_\lambda(k-\lambda)$ has exactly one neighbor in $0\|V_\lambda(k-1)$, because the address of each node in $10_{(\lambda-1)}\|V_\lambda(k-\lambda)$ starts with 1 while the one in $0\|V_\lambda(k-1)$ starts with 0. ∎

Theorem 2: *There exists a Hamming distance path for any two nodes in $PN_\lambda(n)$.*

Proof: We prove this theorem by induction on n for any λ. We first show that this theorem holds for $n = 1, 2, ..., \lambda$. Since each of these networks is a two-level tree that con-

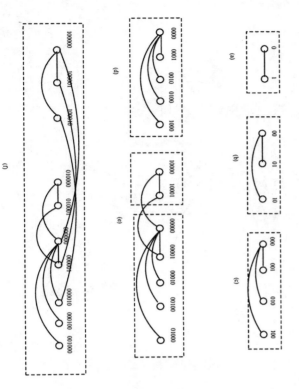

Figure 2: Postal network PN_4: (a) $n = 1$, (b) $n = 2$, (c) $n = 3$, (d) $n = 4$, (e) $n = 5$, (f) $n = 6$.

tains n nodes: $0_{(n)}, 0_{(n-1)}1, ..., 010_{(n-2)}, 10_{(n-1)}$. Obviously, the root node $0_{(n)}$ directly connects to all the other nodes. Since any two leaf nodes differ in two bits, they are two Hamming distance apart and a Hamming distance path exists between any two leaf nodes, since each leaf node can reach another leaf node via the root node.

Assume that this theorem holds for all $n < k$ (for $k > \lambda$, since we have proved the theorem for $n = 1, 2, ..., \lambda$). When $n = k$, $V_\lambda(k) = 0\|V_\lambda(k-1) \cup 10_{(\lambda-1)}\|V_\lambda(k-\lambda)$. Therefore, nodes in $V_\lambda(k)$ can be partitioned into $0\|V_\lambda(k-1)$ and $10_{(\lambda-1)}\|V_\lambda(k-\lambda)$.

We randomly select two nodes, if both nodes belong to $0\|V_\lambda(k-1)$ (or $10_{(\lambda-1)}\|V_\lambda(k-\lambda)$) this theorem holds based on the induction assumption. We only need to consider cases when one node is in $0\|V_\lambda(k-1)$ and the other is in $10_{(\lambda-1)}\|V_\lambda(k-\lambda)$. Based on Lemma, for each node in $10_{(\lambda-1)}\|V_\lambda(k-\lambda)$ there is exactly one neighbor in $0\|V_\lambda(k-1)$. The Hamming distance path can be constructed recursively the following two cases:

(1) If the source is in $10_{(\lambda-1)}\|V_\lambda(k-\lambda)$, the first link in the path should connect the source to its neighbor in $0\|V_\lambda(k-1)$. The rest of the links in the path can be determined recursively in $0\|V_\lambda(k-1)$.

(2) If the source is in $0\|V_\lambda(k-1)$, we first determine a Hamming distance path within $0\|V_\lambda(k-1)$ that connects the source to the neighbor of the destination in $0\|V_\lambda(k-1)$. The last link connects the neighbor of the destination in $0\|V_\lambda(k-1)$ to the destination node which

is in $10_{(\lambda-1)}\|V_\lambda(k-\lambda)$. ∎

Theorem 3: *The diameter of $PN_\lambda(n)$ is the following:*

$$d(PN_\lambda(n)) = \begin{cases} n & \lambda = 1 \\ 2\lceil\frac{n}{\lambda}\rceil - 1 & \lambda \neq 1 \text{ and } (n-1 \bmod \lambda) = 0 \\ 2\lceil\frac{n}{\lambda}\rceil & \lambda \neq 1 \text{ and } (n-1 \bmod \lambda) \neq 0 \end{cases}$$

Proof: When $\lambda = 1$, $PN_\lambda(n)$ is an n-cube $Q(n)$ which has a diameter of n. We only need to consider cases when $\lambda \neq 1$, i.e., there are no adjacent 1 bits in a node address. Based on the recursive definition of the postal network, the maximum number of 1 bits in a node address increases by one when n increases for λ, i.e., the distance between two 1 bits is at least λ and there are at most $\lceil\frac{n}{\lambda}\rceil$ 1 bits in a node address. In the extreme case, the positions of 1 bits in two nodes are all different. When $(n - 1 \bmod \lambda) \neq 0$, it is possible that both nodes have $\lceil\frac{n}{\lambda}\rceil$ 1 bits. When $(n - 1 \bmod \lambda) = 0$, only one node may have $\lceil\frac{n}{\lambda}\rceil$ bits and the other node may have at most $\lceil\frac{n}{\lambda}\rceil - 1$ 1 bits at different bit positions. The above two situations correspond to two nodes that have the longest Hamming distance in the network, i.e., their distance corresponds to the diameter of the network. ∎

Based on the above result, the diameter of a postal network is a fraction of its dimension n. However, postal networks with a large λ contain fewer nodes than the ones with a small λ under the same dimension condition. The number of nodes and links in a given postal network is given in the following theorem.

Theorem 4: *Let $N_\lambda(n)$ and $L_\lambda(n)$ be the number of nodes and links in $PN_\lambda(n)$, respectively, then*

$$N_\lambda(n) = \begin{cases} n+1 & n \leq \lambda \\ N_\lambda(n-1) + N_\lambda(n-\lambda) & n > \lambda \end{cases}$$

and

$$L_\lambda(n) = \begin{cases} n & n \leq \lambda \\ L_\lambda(n-1) + L_\lambda(n-\lambda) + N_\lambda(n-\lambda) & n > \lambda \end{cases}$$

Proof: The expression for $N_\lambda(n)$ is straightforward from the definition of the postal network. The number of links $L_\lambda(n)$ in $PN_\lambda(n)$ is the summation of the number of links $L_\lambda(n-1)$ in $PN_\lambda(n-1)$ and the number of links $L_\lambda(n-\lambda)$ in $PN_\lambda(n-\lambda)$. In addition, we should include links that connect $PN_\lambda(n-1)$ to $PN_\lambda(n-\lambda)$. Based on Lemma, we know that for each node in $PN_\lambda(n-\lambda)$ there exists exactly one neighbor in $PN_\lambda(n-1)$. That is, exactly $N_\lambda(n-\lambda)$ links exist, each of which connects one node in $PN_\lambda(n-1)$ to one node in $PN_\lambda(n-\lambda)$. ∎

Note that $N_\lambda(n)$ belongs to a recurrence relation of form

$$\begin{aligned} f(n) &= C_0 N(n) + C_1 N(n-1) + C_2 N(n-2) + \cdots \\ &\quad + C_\lambda N(n-\lambda) \end{aligned} \tag{1}$$

where C_i's are constants. It is also called a *linear recurrence relation with constant coefficients*. It is also known

614

Table 1: Number of nodes in $Q = PN_1$, $FC = PN_2$, PN_3, and PN_4.

k	1	2	3	4	5	6	7	8	9
$N_1(k)$	2	4	8	16	32	64	128	256	512
$N_2(k)$	2	3	5	8	13	21	34	55	89
$N_3(k)$	2	3	4	6	9	13	19	28	41
$N_4(k)$	2	3	4	5	7	10	14	19	26

Table 2: Number of links in $Q = PN_1$, $FC = PN_2$, PN_3, and PN_4.

k	1	2	3	4	5	6	7	8	9
$L_1(k)$	1	4	12	32	80	192	448	1024	2304
$L_2(k)$	1	2	5	10	20	38	71	130	235
$L_3(k)$	1	2	3	6	11	18	30	50	81
$L_4(k)$	1	2	3	4	7	12	19	28	42

as a λth-*order recurrence relation*. Assume that r_i's are distinct roots of the *characteristic equation*

$$C_0 N^{\lambda} + C_1 N^{\lambda-1} + C_2 N^{\lambda-2} + \cdots + C_{\lambda} = 0 \qquad (2)$$

Then

$$N(n) = A_1 r_1^n + A_2 r_2^n + A_3 r_3^n + \cdots + A_{\lambda} r_{\lambda}^n \qquad (3)$$

where $A_1, A_2, A_3, ..., A_{\lambda}$ are constants which are to be determined by the boundary conditions, i.e., the known values of $N(i)$'s. For example, when $\lambda = 2$,

$$N_2(n) = N_2(n-1) + N_2(n-2)$$

The corresponding characteristic equation is $N^2 - N - 1 = 0$ which has the two distinct roots $r_1 = \frac{1+\sqrt{5}}{2}$, $r_2 = \frac{1-\sqrt{5}}{2}$. It follows that

$$N_2(n) = A_1 \left(\frac{1+\sqrt{5}}{2} \right)^n + A_2 \left(\frac{1-\sqrt{5}}{2} \right)^n$$

is the solution, where A_1 and A_2 are to be determined from the boundary conditions $N_2(1) = 1$ and $N_2(2) = 2$. Note that if the characteristic equation (2) has multiple roots (i.e., not all roots are distinct), $N(n)$ is calculated differently. See [3] for details.

There is no general procedure for determining the solution of a difference equation, especially for a high-order equation. That is, for a large value of λ, a closed form expression for either $N_{\lambda}(n)$ or $L_{\lambda}(n)$ is unlikely. Tables 1 and 2 show $N_{\lambda}(n)$ and $L_{\lambda}(n)$ for different λ's and n's. From these tables, we can see that when series number λ increases, the increase rates for the number of nodes and links both reduce. To estimate $N_{\lambda}(n)$, we have $N_{\lambda}(n) = N_{\lambda}(n-1) + N_{\lambda}(n-\lambda) \leq N_{\lambda}(n-1) + N_{\lambda}(n-1) \leq 2^n$. Also, we have $N_{\lambda}(n) = N_{\lambda}(n-1) + N_{\lambda}(n-\lambda) \geq N_{\lambda}(n-\lambda) + N_{\lambda}(n-\lambda) \geq 2^{\lfloor \frac{n}{\lambda} \rfloor}$. Combining the above two conditions, we have $2^{\lfloor \frac{n}{\lambda} \rfloor} \leq N_{\lambda}(n) \leq 2^n$

Furthermore, we can obtain a tighter upper bound on $N_{\lambda}(n)$ when $\lambda > 1$ as given in the following theorem. The theorem indicates that as λ gets larger, the number of nodes in a $PN_{\lambda}(n)$, $N_{\lambda}(n) = O\left(\left(1 + \frac{1}{\sqrt{\lambda-1}} \right)^{n-1} \right)$, is much smaller than that of a hypercube, $N_1(n) = 2^n$.

Theorem 5: *When* $\lambda > 1$,

$$N_{\lambda}(n) \leq (\lambda+1) \left(1 + \frac{1}{\sqrt{\lambda-1}} \right)^{n-1}$$

Proof: We prove this theorem by induction on n for any given $\lambda > 1$. First, for $1 \leq n \leq \lambda$, we have

$$N_{\lambda}(n) = n + 1 \leq \lambda + 1 \leq (\lambda+1) \left(1 + \frac{1}{\sqrt{\lambda-1}} \right)^{n-1}$$

Now, suppose the upper bound holds for $n = k-1, k-2, \ldots, k-\lambda$ $(k > \lambda)$. We prove that it also holds for $n = k$. Note that

$$N_{\lambda}(k) = N_{\lambda}(k-1) + N_{\lambda}(k-\lambda)$$
$$\leq (\lambda+1) \left[\left(1 + \frac{1}{\sqrt{\lambda-1}} \right)^{k-2} + \left(1 + \frac{1}{\sqrt{\lambda-1}} \right)^{k-\lambda-1} \right]$$
$$= (\lambda+1) \left(1 + \frac{1}{\sqrt{\lambda-1}} \right)^{k-\lambda-1} \left[\left(1 + \frac{1}{\sqrt{\lambda-1}} \right)^{\lambda-1} + 1 \right]$$

only need to show that

$$\left(1 + \frac{1}{\sqrt{\lambda-1}} \right)^{\lambda-1} + 1 \leq \left(1 + \frac{1}{\sqrt{\lambda-1}} \right)^{\lambda}$$

Or equivalently,

$$\left(1 + \frac{1}{\sqrt{\lambda-1}} \right)^{\lambda} - \left(1 + \frac{1}{\sqrt{\lambda-1}} \right)^{\lambda-1} \geq 1 \qquad (4)$$

In fact, from the left hand side of (4), we have

$$\left(1 + \frac{1}{\sqrt{\lambda-1}} \right)^{\lambda-1} \left(\frac{1}{\sqrt{\lambda-1}} \right) \geq \left(1 + \frac{\lambda-1}{\sqrt{\lambda-1}} \right) \frac{1}{\sqrt{\lambda-1}} \geq 1$$

Thus, Theorem 5 holds. ∎

Similarly, we can estimate $L_{\lambda}(n)$. The following theorem gives the relationship between $L_{\lambda}(n)$ and $N_{\lambda}(n)$ and an upper on $L_{\lambda}(n)$.

Theorem 6: *When* $\lambda > 1$,

$$L_{\lambda}(n) < \left(\frac{n-2}{\lambda+1} + 1 \right) N_{\lambda}(n) \leq (n+\lambda-1) \left(1 + \frac{1}{\sqrt{\lambda-1}} \right)^{n-1}$$

Proof: We prove this theorem by induction on n for any given $n > 1$. First, when $n = 1$, $L_{\lambda}(1) = 1$ and $N_{\lambda}(1) =$

2. Clearly, $L_\lambda(n) < (\frac{n-2}{\lambda+1} + 1)N_\lambda(n)$ given $\lambda > 1$. When $2 \leq n \leq \lambda$, we have

$$L_\lambda(n) = N_\lambda(n) - 1 < \left(\frac{n-2}{\lambda+1} + 1\right) N_\lambda(n)$$

Now, suppose the upper bound holds for $n = k - 1, k - 2, \ldots, k - \lambda$ $(k > \lambda)$. We will prove it also holds for $n = k$. Note that

$$
\begin{aligned}
L_\lambda(k) &= L_\lambda(k-1) + L_\lambda(k-\lambda) + N_\lambda(k-\lambda) \\
&< \left[\frac{(k-1)-2}{\lambda+1} + 1\right] N_\lambda(k-1) + \\
&\quad \left[\frac{(k-\lambda)-2}{\lambda+1} + 1\right] N_\lambda(k-\lambda) + N_\lambda(k-\lambda) \\
&= \left(\frac{k-2}{\lambda+1} + 1\right) [N_\lambda(k-1) + N_\lambda(k-\lambda)] - \\
&\quad \frac{1}{\lambda+1}[N_\lambda(k-1) + N_\lambda(k-\lambda)] \\
&< \left(\frac{k-2}{\lambda+1} + 1\right) [N_\lambda(k-1) + N_\lambda(k-\lambda)] \\
&= \left(\frac{k-2}{\lambda+1} + 1\right) N_\lambda(k)
\end{aligned}
$$

Thus, we have

$$L_\lambda(n) < \left(\frac{n-2}{\lambda+1} + 1\right) N_\lambda(n)$$

Moreover, by Theorem 5, we obtain an upper bound on $L_\lambda(n)$:

$$
\begin{aligned}
L_\lambda(n) &< \left(\frac{n-2}{\lambda+1} + 1\right)(\lambda+1)\left(1 + \frac{1}{\sqrt{\lambda-1}}\right)^{n-1} \\
&= (n + \lambda - 1)\left(1 + \frac{1}{\sqrt{\lambda-1}}\right)^{n-1}
\end{aligned}
$$

∎

3 Routing

In this section, we study routing algorithms for the postal network. Efficient interprocessor communication is a key to the performance of a point-to-point multicomputer system. We consider here *unicasting*, which is a one-to-one communication between a source and a destination. Although the postal network is asymmetric, a simple routing algorithm can still be constructed based on the following result that determines whether a given bit sequence belongs to a node address in a postal network.

Theorem 7: *An n-bit sequence is the address of a node in $PN_\lambda(n)$ if and only if any two 1 bits (if any) are separated by at least λ bit positions.*

Proof: Let's consider a systematic way of generating all the possible n-bit sequences such that any two 1 bits (if

any) are separated by at least λ bit positions. Assume that we have constructed $S_\lambda(i)$'s for all $i < n$, where $S_\lambda(i)$ stands for all the possible i-bit sequences such that any two 1 bits (if any) are separated by at least λ bit positions. Let's consider the leftmost bit (the 1st bit) of the nodes in $S_\lambda(n)$: If it is 0, then the number of different arrangements for the rest of $n - 1$ bits should all be in $S_\lambda(n - 1)$. If it is 1, then based on the constraint that any two 1 bits must be separated by at least λ bit positions, the next $\lambda - 1$ bits must be all 0's. The number of different arrangements for the rest of $n - \lambda$ bits should all be in $S_\lambda(n - \lambda)$. Based on the above observation, it is clear that $PN_\lambda(n)$ and $S_\lambda(n)$ are the same. ∎

The above result provides a simple way of defining a postal network and more importantly it offers a simple way of generating all the nodes in a postal network. For example, nodes in $PN_4(6)$ are 000000, 000001, 000010, 000100, 001000, 010000, 100000, 010001, 100001, 100010. Among these nodes, the node addresses have two 1 bits or less that are separated by at least 4 bit positions. We use $distance_1(node)$ to represent minimum distance between 1 bits in a given node address. When there is at most one 1 bit in a node address, the $distance_1$ of the corresponding node is ∞. For example, $distance_1(000100) = \infty$ and $distance_1(010001) = 4$.

We consider here adaptive and minimal routing. An adaptive routing algorithm allows all messages to use any minimal paths. The challenge is to exploit all the possible routes while still keeping routing distance minimum. Since the postal network can be considered as an incomplete hypercube with several missing nodes, the traditional dimension-ordered routing is no longer applicable here. For example, consider two nodes 01000 (the source s) and 10010 (the destination d), the exclusive-or of their addresses is $01000 \oplus 10010 = 11010$. If the dimensions are resolved following an increasing order of dimensions: 1, 2 and 4, an illegal intermediate node 11000 (with two neighboring 1 bits) will be generated in the corresponding path: $01000 \to 11000 \to 10000 \to 10010$.

In order to avoid generating illegal intermediate nodes, we should ensure that each intermediate node is legal. That is, the distance between two 1 bits (if any) in the node address should be at least λ. To make the routing algorithm adaptive, no additional constraint is added, i.e., a dimension can be randomly selected as long as it meets the above requirement.

Consider a unicasting from s to d in $PN_\lambda(n)$. Let s^i denote complementing the ith bit of s, for example $10010^2 = 11010$, and $r(i)$ denote the ith bit of r. The adaptive and minimal routing algorithm for the postal network is the following:

For source node s with message m:

1. $r := s \oplus d$; /* calculate relative address r */
2. randomly select i such that $r(i) = 1$ and $distance_1(s^i) \geq \lambda$; /* select a neighbor */
3. **send** (m, r^i) **to** s^i.
   /* send message m together with the updated

relative address to the selected neighbor */

For all intermediate nodes t (including destination d):

1. **receive** (m, r); /* receive message m together with relative address r */
2. **if** $r = 0$ **then** node t is the destination and **stop**;
3. randomly select i such that $r(i) = 1$ and $distance_1(t^i) \geq \lambda$;
4. **send** (m, r^i) **to** t^i.

To carry out step 3 of the above procedure, we first pick up a neighbor. If the address of this neighbor meets the condition in Theorem 7 (this can be done in constant time), it is done; otherwise, another neighbor is selected. In the worst case, all the neighbors, except the last one, fail the condition. That is, if the current node is k distance away from the destination, it may need $k - 1$ selection steps. Thus, step 3 may need $O(n)$ time in the worst case.

Consider $(s, d) = (100010, 000001)$ with $r = 100011$ in $PN_4(6)$. At the first step, two legal neighbors (of s) are 100000 and 000010. 100011 is an illegal neighbor, since its $distance_1(10001) = 1$ which is less than $\lambda = 4$. During the second step, at node 100000, there are two choices of the next intermediate node: 100001 and 000000; at node 000010, there is only one choice which is node 000000. Therefore, three minimal routing paths can be generated:

$$100010 \rightarrow 100000 \rightarrow 100001 \rightarrow 000001$$

$$100010 \rightarrow 100000 \rightarrow 000000 \rightarrow 000001$$

$$100010 \rightarrow 000010 \rightarrow 000000 \rightarrow 000001$$

Note that if $distance_1(s \oplus d = r) \geq \lambda$, there is no constraint on selecting intermediate nodes. Routing will be the same as in a regular hypercube. For example, consider $(s, d) = (10000, 00001)$ in $PN_3(5)$, i.e., $\lambda = 3$. Clearly, $distance_1(s \oplus d = 10001) \geq 3$. The e-cube routing in hypercubes can be applied for this case. In fact, s and d are contained in 2-cube $*000*$, where $*$ is a don't care. $*000*$ contains four nodes 00000, 00001, 10000, and 10001. The following theorem shows a general case.

Theorem 8: *In a* $PN_\lambda(n)$, *if* $distance_1(s \oplus d) \geq \lambda$ *then* s *and* d *are two nodes in a* k-*cube, where* $k \geq H(s, d)$.

The above theorem can be easily derived from the above observation. To determine the smallest cube that contains s and d, assuming that $distance_1(s \oplus d) \geq \lambda$, one simple approach is to replace all the 1 bits in $s \oplus d$ by $*$ and the remaining bits are replaced by the corresponding bits in s (or d). For example, $s \oplus d = 11011 \oplus 01001 = 10010$, the smallest cube that contains s and d is $*10 * 1$.

The minimal routing approach can be easily extended to the one for non-minimal routing. For example in non-minimal routing, we can separate 1's (called *preferred dimensions*) from 0's (called *spare dimensions*) in $r = s \oplus d$. In minimal routing, only preferred dimensions are resolved by changing each of them to 0. In non-minimal routing, spare dimensions can also be used which are changed from

0's and 1's, but to reach the destination, these 1's still need to be changed back to 0's. At each step, the $distance_1$ condition still needs to be enforced to ensure that each intermediate node is legal. Consider a unicasting from $s = 100000$ to $d = 000000$ in PN_4, $s \oplus d = 100000$, a non-minimal routing that uses preferred dimension 1 and spare dimension 6 generates the following path $100000 \rightarrow 100001 \rightarrow 000001 \rightarrow 000000$.

4 Embedding

In this section, we study relationships between regular hypercubes, Fibonacci cubes, and postal networks. Efficient embedding of a guest network G into a host network H is important in parallel/distributed processing, especially for a newly proposed network used as a host network. Not only do embedding results demonstrate computational equivalence (or near-equivalence) between networks of different topology, but efficient embeddings lead to efficient simulations of algorithms originally designed for G on host H.

Based on the definition of the postal network series, link connections follow the same rule: Two nodes are connected if and only if their addresses differ in exactly one bit position. Therefore, to show that one postal network contains another postal network as its subgraph, we only need to show that the vertex set of the former contains the vertex set of the latter. Specifically, a graph H contains a graph G if one of the following two conditions holds: (1) $V(H)$ contains $V(G)$. (2) $V'(H)$ contains $V(G)$, where $V'(H)$ is derived from $V(H)$ by removing certain bit positions of all the nodes in $V(H)$.

For example, $PN_2(4)$ contains $PN_3(4)$ based on Condition (1), because $V(PN_2(4)) = \{0000, 0001, 0010, 0100, 0101, 1000, 1001, 1010\}$ contains $V(PN_3(4)) = \{0000, 0001, 0010, 0100, 1000, 1001\}$. Also, $PN_2(4)$ contains $PN_2(3)$ based on Condition (2), because $V(PN_2(3)) = \{000, 001, 010, 100, 101\}$ is derived by removing either the 1st or 4th bit of all the nodes in $V(PN_2(4))$.

The following theorem shows relationships between postal networks within the same series.

Theorem 9: $PN_{\lambda_1}(n_1)$ *contains* $PN_{\lambda_1}(n_2)$ *as its subgraph if and only if* $n_1 > n_2$.

Proof: Based on the definition of the postal network, $PN_{\lambda_1}(n_1)$ contains $PN_{\lambda-1}(n_1 - 1)$. Clearly $PN_{\lambda_1}(n_1)$ also contains $PN_{\lambda-1}(n_2)$, where $n_1 > n_2$. ∎

The following theorem shows that for a given dimension n_1, a network with a small series number (with a small λ value) contains a network with a large series number.

Theorem 10: $PN_{\lambda_1}(n_1)$ *contains* $PN_{\lambda_2}(n_1)$ *as its subgraph if and only if* $\lambda_1 < \lambda_2$.

Proof: We prove this theorem by induction. When $n_1 \leq \lambda_1$, $PN_{\lambda_1}(n_1) = PN_{\lambda_2}(n_1)$. When $\lambda_1 < n_1 \leq \lambda_2$, we can easily verify that $PN_{\lambda_1}(n_1)$ contains $PN_{\lambda_2}(n_1)$. When $n_1 > \lambda_2$, based on the recursive definition of both series and the induction assumption, $PN_{\lambda_1}(n_1)$ contains $PN_{\lambda_2}(n_1)$. ∎

The following theorem shows that under certain conditions a network with a large series number contains a network with a small series number.

Theorem 11: *Given $PN_{\lambda_1}(n_1)$, $PN_{\lambda_2}(n_2)$, and $\lambda_1 > \lambda_2$. If $\lceil \frac{n_1}{\lambda_1} \rceil > \lceil \frac{n_2}{\lambda_2} \rceil$ then $PN_{\lambda_1}(n_1)$ contains $PN_{\lambda_2}(n_2)$ as its subgraph. If $\lceil \frac{n_1}{\lambda_2} \rceil = \lceil \frac{n_2}{\lambda_2} \rceil$ and $n_1 - c\lambda_1 \geq n_2 - c\lambda_2$ then $PN_{\lambda_1}(n_1)$ contains $PN_{\lambda_2}(n_2)$ as its subgraph, where c is a constant.*

Proof: We reorganize postal networks in series λ in groups, each of which contains λ consecutive networks, i.e., the nth network in series λ is in group $\lceil \frac{n}{\lambda} \rceil$. For example, in series $PN_3(n)$, $\{PN_3(1), PN_3(2), PN_3(3)\}$ forms group 1, $\{PN_3(4), PN_3(5), PN_3(6)\}$ forms group 2, and so on. Therefore, each network in the series has a group number $\lceil \frac{n}{\lambda} \rceil$ and a number within the group $n - (\lceil \frac{n}{\lambda} \rceil - 1)\lambda$. The theorem is reduced to prove the following: Consider two networks from different series with the same group number and the same number within the group, the one with a larger series number contains the one with a smaller series number. The above fact can be proved by induction from group to group using the following fact: The ith network in group j ($j > 1$) is constructed from the network that just precedes it and the ith network in group $j - 1$. ∎

Corollary: $PN_\lambda(n_1)$ *contains the n_2-cube $Q(n_2)$ as its subgraph if and only if $n_1 + \lceil \frac{n_1}{\lambda_1} \rceil (1 - \lambda_1) \geq n_2$.*

This corollary is derived directly from Theorem 11 and can be used to derive the largest hypercube as a subgraph of a given postal network. For example, for $PN_2(9)$ the largest hypercube is an n_2-cube such that $9 + \lceil \frac{9}{2} \rceil (1 - 2) \geq n_2$, i.e., $n_2 = 4$.

We have the following simple process to determine all the largest subcubes in $PN_\lambda(n_1)$: We start with an n_1-bit of 0's and then replace n_2 bits (which is determined from the above Corollary) of 0's by $*$'s such that any two $*$'s are separated by at least λ. For example, given $PN_4(6)$, based on the above Corollary, the largest subcube is a 2-cube. All the possible 2-cubes in $PN_4(6)$ are $*0000*$, $0 * 000*$, and $*000 * 0$.

5 Application: Barrier Synchronization Using Postal Trees

In this section, we first study the *postal tree*, $PT_\lambda(n)$, which is a special spanning tree of the postal network $PN_\lambda(n)$. We then look at one of its applications in implementing barrier synchronization, an important type of collective communication in a multicomputer system.

Many numerical problems can be solved using iterative algorithms that successively compute better approximations to an answer, terminating when either the final answer has been computed or the final answer has converged. These algorithms normally require all the iterative processes to be synchronized at the end of each iteration.

More specifically, these processes, $process(i)$, can be described by the following algorithm:

```
do not_converged →
   code to implement process i
   barrier (wait for all n processes to complete)
od
```

In the above algorithm, **barrier** represents a barrier synchronization point which waits for all n processes to complete. This type of synchronization is called *barrier synchronization* [5] because the delay point at the end of each iteration represents a barrier that all processes have to arrive at before any of them is allowed to pass. There are many ways of implementing barriers, among them *tree barrier* [7] is the widely used one. In this approach, two phases are used. In the *reduction* phase, all participating processes engage in a reduction operation by sending and/or receiving synchronization messages following a tree structure where the root node eventually receives the reduced message and decides that all the processes have arrived at the barrier. In the next phase which is called distribution phase, the root node broadcasts a synchronization message following the same tree to inform all the processes to proceed. Normally, the reduction phase is carried out by a collective communication called gather and the distribution phase is implemented by another collective communication called broadcast. Both of which use a spanning tree in the given network to collect and distribute messages.

In order to determine an optimal spanning tree structure for tree barrier, we have to look at the underlying communication mechanism. If communication delay is considered as part of overall performance, the *postal model* [1] can be used which is based on $\lambda = l/s$, where s is the time it takes for a node to send the next message and l is the network latency. For example, assume $s = 2$ and $l = 4$ then $\lambda = 2$. If the source node sends a message at time 0, it has to wait $s = 2$ time steps before sending the message to another neighbor at time 2. The message sent at time 0 will reach the corresponding neighbor at time $l = 4$. Similarly, the one sent at time 2 will reach another neighbor at time 6, etc. Under the one-port model (in which each node can send and receive one message at a time), the binomial tree is optimal when $\lambda = 1$. An optimal tree for a specific λ is constructed based on:

$$N_\lambda(n) = \begin{cases} N_\lambda(n-1) + N_\lambda(n-\lambda), & \text{if } n \geq \lambda \\ 1, & \text{otherwise} \end{cases}$$

where $N_\lambda(n)$ represents the maximum number of nodes that can be reached in time n on a one-port model exhibiting λ. Note that before time $n < \lambda$, only the source node has a copy of the message, although several copies have been sent from the source node since time 0 and they are still in transit. Clearly, the parameter λ in the postal model matches the series number λ in the postal network. It is easy to derive the corresponding optimal tree structure as: $PT_\lambda(n)$ is constructed out of $PT_\lambda(n-1)$ and $PT_\lambda(n-\lambda)$, with the root node of $PT_\lambda(n-\lambda)$ as the child of the root node of $PT_\lambda(n-1)$. As initial conditions,

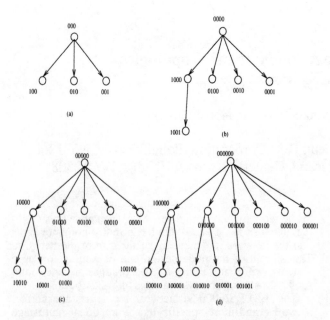

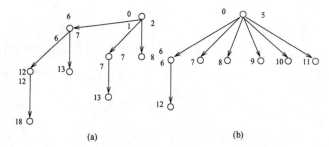

Figure 4: Comparison with $\lambda = 6$: (a) binomial trees $PT_1(3)$ and (b) optimal spanning tree $PT_6(6)$.

Figure 3: Postal trees: (a) $PT_3(3)$, (b) $PT_3(4)$, (c) $PT_3(5)$, and (d) $PT_3(6)$.

$PT_\lambda(i)$ $(1 \le i < \lambda)$ consists of $i+1$ nodes in a two-level tree. Clearly, $PT_\lambda(n)$ is a spanning tree of $PN_\lambda(n)$. More formally, we have the following definition of a postal tree.

Definition 2: *A postal tree $PT_\lambda(n)$ of $PN_\lambda(n)$ is defined as follows: (Base) $PT_\lambda(n) = PN_\lambda(n)$ for $1 \le n \le \lambda$. (Recursion) For $\lambda < n$, a $PT_\lambda(n)$ consists of $PT_\lambda(n-1)$ and $PT_\lambda(n-\lambda)$ by connecting the root of $PT_\lambda(n-\lambda)$ as the child of the root of $PT_\lambda(n-1)$.*

Figure 3 shows the structure of postal trees $PT_3(n)$ for $n = 3, 4, 5, 6$. Clearly, $PT_3(n)$ has the same vertex set as $PN_3(n)$. Hence, $PT_3(n)$ is a spanning tree of $PN_3(n)$. Figure 4 shows two different spanning trees in a fully-connected network with eight nodes, when $\lambda = 6$ with $s = 1$ and $l = 6$. Clearly, the binomial tree implementation (Figure 4 (a)) requires 18 units to complete a broadcast and it is no longer optimal. The optimal tree (Figure 4 (b)) needs only 12 units to complete a broadcast. Note that this postal model can be applied to any topology as long as it has sufficient connectivity.

Based on the above analysis, we can see that parameter λ plays an important role in selecting networks from different series. Because λ defines the ratio of the time it takes for a node to send the next message to the communication latency, it should be carefully selected to minimize communication delay especially for collective communication. For example, if we are to select a network of eight nodes from a series and $\lambda = 1$, $PN_1(3)$ is better than $PN_2(4)$. Here we simplify the selection process without considering other factors. In designing an actual multicomputer system, different factors should be considered and weighted against each other.

6 Conclusions

We have proposed a series of networks called postal networks that contain both hypercubes and Fibonacci cubes as their special cases. We have shown that these networks still maintain some desirable properties of hypercubes. Relationships between different networks have also been studied. Postal networks can be used to complement several existing network topologies such as hypercubes and Fibonacci cubes. Because each postal network can also be considered as an incomplete hypercube after some nodes become faulty, the study of postal networks will also provide some insights on the behavior of the cube-based systems operated in a degraded mode. Our future work will focus on embedding other popular structures such as binary trees in postal networks. Another interesting issue is to determine postal networks from a given faulty hypercube.

References

[1] A. Bar-Noy and S. Kionis. Designing broadcasting algorithms in the postal model for message-passing systems. *Proc. of 1992 Symposium on Parallel Algorithms and Architecture.* 1992, 13-22.

[2] B. Cong, S. Q. Zheng, and S. Sharma. On simulations of linear arrays, rings and 2-d meshes on Fibonacci cube networks. *Proc. of the 7th International Parallel Processing Symposium.* 1993, 748-751.

[3] C. L. Liu. *Elements of Discrete Mathematics.* McGraw-Hill, Inc. 1985.

[4] W. J. Hsu. Fibonacci cubes – a new interconnection topology. *IEEE Transactions on Parallel and Distributed Systems.* 4, (1), Jan. 1993, 3-12.

[5] H. F. Jordan. A special purpose architecture for finite element analysis. *Proc. of 1978 International Conference on Parallel Processing.* 1978, 263-266.

[6] J. Wu. Extended Fibonacci cubes. *IEEE Transactions on Parallel and Distributed Systems.* 8, (12), Dec. 1997, 1203-1210.

[7] P. C. Yew, N. F. Tzeng, and D. H. Lawrie. Distributing hotspot addressing in large-scale multiprocessors. *IEEE Transactions on Computers.* 36, (4), April 1987, 388-395.

IBM RS/6000 SP Interconnection Network Topologies for Large Systems

Harish Sethu[†]   Craig B. Stunkel[+]   Robert F. Stucke[†]

[†]{sethu, stucke}@us.ibm.com; Server Development, IBM Corporation, Poughkeepsie, NY 12601
[+]stunkel@watson.ibm.com; T. J. Watson Research Center, Yorktown Heights, NY 12508

Abstract

While the interconnection network topology is one of the most important determinants of the performance of a parallel system, no single topology offers an ideal cost/performance trade-off for all classes of applications in parallel processing. The modular units used in the IBM RS/6000 SP topologies allow the construction of a large variety of topologies including 4-ary fat-tree networks. In our experience, however, cost and cost/performance ratio are often the primary concerns of customers. Therefore, while fat-tree topologies offer excellent performance, they are not always the most attractive choice for customers of large-scale parallel systems. This paper presents the lower-cost RS/6000 SP topologies for large systems designed with fewer switching elements than fat-tree networks, and describes some of the rationale behind the choices made.

1 Introduction

The network topology of a parallel computer system is the pattern in which the nodes of the system are connected together for communication. Network topologies fall into two important classes—direct and indirect networks, both of which have been extensively studied. Examples of direct networks include hypercubes [10], meshes, and variants of these such as the cube-connected cycles [9], hierarchical networks [5,8], the hypernet [6] and the meshes of trees [3]. Examples of indirect networks include the fat-tree [7] and uni-directional or bidirectional multistage interconnection networks. The SGI Origin2000 network [4], with a "fat" hypercube topology, is an indirect network formed by successive stages of direct network hypercube nodes.

Direct networks, except for a completely connected system, typically rely on a user making an intelligent choice of the task-to-node mapping. For instance, with the right task-to-node mapping, the mesh network is ideal for computations that require nearest neighbor communications. However, if the mapping is arbitrary, the performance can be quite different from ideal. In a multi-user system, with nodes constantly being allocated and deallocated among tasks of several users running parallel jobs, there is a strong motivation to keep the performance of a system as independent of the task-to-node mapping as possible. Many indirect networks offer an excellent uniformity of performance with changes in the task-to-node mapping. This has an additional benefit to most general-purpose users of parallel systems, who prefer to have the topological properties of

the network hidden from them. Also, each node on an indirect network has a small number of entry points or links into the network, independent of the size of the network. This simplifies the node design and packaging for large systems, while preserving a good cost/performance ratio for the most common system sizes of 8–32 nodes.

The IBM RS/6000 SP network topologies are indirect networks, and more specifically, bidirectional multistage interconnection networks (BMINs). BMINs allow for easier packaging with each node connected to just one point on the network. In addition, they permit smaller latencies and better isolation when the traffic is locally contained within a small set of nodes connected to physically close points on the network. For example, nodes connected to the same switching element in a BMIN do not have to travel through other switching elements to communicate with each other.

A BMIN-based approach allows the design of topologies that share the good performance properties of fat-tree networks. This is best illustrated in the 128-way SP topology [12], where the network allows a potentially congestion-free path to a lowest common ancestor switching element or link, from which the traversal back down to the destination is through a unique path. Similar to the 128-way topology, it is possible to design 4-ary fat-tree topologies for 256-way and 512-way systems, using BMINs with 8x8 switching elements. The 4-ary fat-tree topologies are excellent on a number of different performance criteria, including the performance of preferred partitions, tolerance to sub-optimal partitioning and scalability in bisection bandwidth. While 4-ary fat-tree topologies can be constructed out of the switching elements used in our topologies, in our experience, the cost and the cost/performance ratio of a system have often been the primary concerns of the customers. Thus, lower-cost topologies using fewer switching elements have often been the preferred choice. This market-driven factor to reduce cost while maintaining or possibly improving the cost/performance ratio was our motivation in designing lower-cost topologies for large systems which use fewer switching elements than the 4-ary fat-tree options. These topologies are referred to in this paper as RS/6000 SP topologies or just SP topologies.

In this paper, we describe the SP topologies for systems with more than 128 nodes and explain some of the rationale behind them. For topologies of systems with 128 nodes or less, the reader is referred to [12]. We additionally evaluate each of these topologies by comparing their performance with 4-ary fat-trees. Section 2 describes the terms and conventions used in this paper. Section 3 describes some of the cost and performance criteria used in the evaluation of the topologies. Section 4 describes the SP topologies for 129–256 node systems and briefly describes the rationale behind them based on some of the criteria described in section 3. This section also compares the performance of the SP options and the 4-ary fat-tree networks for 129–256 node systems. Section 5 similarly describes the SP topologies for 257–512 node systems and compares them to the fat-tree networks. Section 6 concludes the paper.

2 Terms and Conventions

The Switch Board (SB) is the basic unit by which large SP topologies are constructed in a modular fashion. Each SB is functionally comprised of 8 switching elements (SEs), each of which is an 8-input to 8-output buffered-wormhole switch. Each SE, implemented as a single VLSI chip, contains eight receiver modules, eight sender modules, an unbuffered crossbar and a shared central buffer. The central buffer accepts packet flits from a receiver module when the desired output port is busy or when the output port has another flit waiting for it in the buffer. The central buffer stores the packet flits in FIFO order on eight linked lists, each corresponding to one of the eight output ports of the switch. The reader is referred to [12, 13] for a more detailed treatment of the functional aspects of the SE. The wiring between the SEs on an SB is as shown in Figure 1.

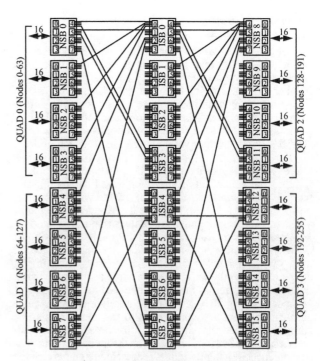

Figure 2: 256-way SP Topology
(Not all cables are shown)

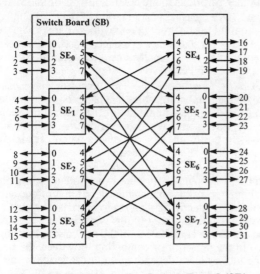

Figure 1: Wiring on the Switch Board (SB)

Using SBs rather than SEs as modular units for large system topologies allows for a smaller number of boards and a reduced number of long cables between boards, thus making the packaging easier. In addition, considering that most SP systems tend to consist of less than 32 nodes, using a single-board implementation serving up to 16 nodes also serves to make these large-volume systems more cost-efficient.

Since the SB is the basic modular unit used in the topologies in this paper, the connections within an SB will not be specified in describing the topologies under consideration. The topologies will only be described in terms of the cable links between the SBs. Note that all of the links

shown in Figure 1 are bidirectional. The ports of an SE are labelled 0 to 7 and the ports of an SB are labelled 0 to 31. Port i, $0 \le i \le 3$, of a switching element SE_k, $0 \le k \le 7$, corresponds to connection port $(4*k+i)$ in the SB. An SB that has at least one cable directly connected to a node is referred to as a Node Switch Board (NSB). An SB that is directly connected only to other SBs but not to a node is referred to as an Intermediate Switch Board (ISB). In a topology with N NSBs, the NSBs are labelled sequentially from 0 to N–1. The ISBs are also similarly labelled from 0 to N–1, where N is the total number of ISBs in a topology. Port i, $0 \le i \le 15$, of an NSB n is connected to node $(16n+i)$ in the system. A *quad* is a set of four NSBs in a system that are connected to the same set of 16 SEs in the ISBs, with each SE connected to each of the 4 NSBs. For example, NSBs 0, 1, 2 and 3 in Figure 2 of a 256-way SP system, comprise a quad. The set of nodes labelled 0-$(N/2-1)$ in a system with N nodes is referred to as a topological half of the system while the remaining $N/2$ nodes form the other topological half. Switch chips 0, 1, 2 and 3, as shown in Figure 1, are said to be on one side of the SB while switch chips 4, 5, 6 and 7 on the other side. Nodes connected to NSBs that are connected to an ISB through switch chips 0–3 but not through chips 4–7, or vice-versa, are said to be on the same side of that ISB.

3 Criteria Used to Evaluate Topologies

Several criteria were used to evaluate many proposals for SP topologies, and the decisions were made based on issues ranging from analytical performance estimations to practical considerations such as the length of cable slack possible to allow ease of installation and upgrades. This paper primarily describes the performance and cost issues that were considered.

Bisection Bandwidth—The definition of bisection bandwidth used in this paper is as follows. Consider all possible planes that divide a network into two halves with equal number of nodes in each half. Consider the maximum possible peak bandwidth available for message traffic across each of these planes. The bisection bandwidth of the network is defined as the *minimum* of these bandwidths. Consider a 32-node system with a single SB in which nodes 0 to 31 are connected, respectively, to ports 0 to 31 of the SB. (Note that this is merely an example of a network topology for illustrating the definition of bisection bandwidth and that this configuration is not one of IBM RS/6000 SP offerings). Consider a horizontal plane that divides the network into two halves: one half comprising of nodes 0–7, nodes 16–23 and SEs 0, 1, 4 and 5; the other half comprising of nodes 8–15, nodes 24–31 and SEs 2, 3, 6 and 7. There are only 8 wires that cross this plane. Therefore, assuming all the paths are available for deadlock-free routing, the bandwidth available across this plane between these two sets of 16 nodes is only 50% of the peak throughput of the communication adapter ports on each of the nodes. It may be similarly verified that the bandwidth across a vertical bisectional plane is 100% of the peak throughput. In this paper, the bisection bandwidth is represented as a percentage of the maximum aggregate peak bandwidth of the communication ports in the system. The bisection bandwidth of the 32-way example topology, therefore, is 50%, assuming all the paths in the topology are usable without restrictions.

Random Traffic Latency and Bandwidth—The average latency or the maximum sustainable bandwidth of a multistage interconnection network is highly sensitive to the traffic pattern of messages exchanged between the nodes in an application, and this sensitivity makes it extremely difficult to ascertain the performance of a given network topology without a qualifying statement about the characteristics of the message traffic injected into the network. A practical solution for analytical purposes is to evaluate the performance for a random traffic pattern. We define a random traffic pattern as the message pattern generated when each node in the set of nodes allocated to a job sends a sequence of messages to destinations that are selected randomly among all possible destinations. Random traffic can be loosely described as an "average-case" traffic pattern. It is important that this not be confused with the false assumption that most applications on the RS/6000 SP will exhibit a random traffic pattern. In other words, although the random traffic pattern is not representative of the traffic patterns of most real applications, it is a fair assumption that the performance of a topology with random traffic is indicative of the average performance of the topology measured on a wide range of real applications. For a comparative evaluation of topologies, the random traffic bandwidth numbers were generated using software simulation. We consider the random traffic bandwidth to be much closer than bisection bandwidth in being representative of the performance of real jobs on the system.

Partitioning—More often than not, the SP systems and the larger systems in particular, are expected to be used as multi-user systems with several jobs running on different partitions of the system. The performance of the system under such partitioning, therefore, is also a critical factor that

is sensitive to the topology of the network. In addition, we also had the goal of providing performance which is as independent as possible, within practical constraints, of the task-to-node mapping. We evaluate the performance of a network topology under partitioning, based both on tolerance to *sub-optimal* partitioning and on the performance of *preferred* partitions. This is to ensure that a suboptimal choice of a partition does not degrade performance beyond tolerable limits, while also allowing a sophisticated user to create ideal partitions of a desired size.

A single-NSB partition is the set of nodes that are all connected to the same NSB. In general, an *n*-NSB partition is the set of nodes that are directly connected to one of a set of *n* NSBs in the network. Note that a single-NSB partition is not the same as a 16-node partition. We qualitatively determine the tolerance to sub-optimal partitioning based on the performance of worst case 2-NSB, 4-NSB, 8-NSB and 16-NSB partitions, and the average of the bisection bandwidths of all possible 2-NSB and 2-quad partitions.

We base our analysis of the performance of preferred partitions on the performance and isolation of the best-performing 2-NSB, 4-NSB, 8-NSB, and 16-NSB partitions, and the performance of the best-isolated partitions. With regard to performance (as opposed to fault-tolerance), we consider an isolated partition to be one in which there is no possibility of interference on the links from other partitions. We do not consider as significant the interference from other partitions in the central buffers of the SEs.

Cost—We measure cost in terms of the total number of SBs required to construct the network for any given topology. This is because other associated costs such as cables, power supplies, fans, enclosures, etc., tend to be proportional to the number of SBs.

Ease of Upgradability—This criterion is measured based on the number of cables that have to be moved for an upgrade and on the complexity of the algorithms required for cable movements. We also consider the performance of the system during the upgrade mode when certain cables cannot be used for communication between nodes.

Average and maximum number of switch hops—In the absence of contention, the hardware latency through the switching network is almost an order of magnitude smaller than the total latency for a message from user space to user space. Thus, the number of hops is not a significant determinant of the overall latency in the network at low applied loads. In the presence of contention, however, the latency can be much higher depending on the severity of the contention. The latency in the presence of contention is more a function of the bandwidth available for the messages in the network, and less on the number of hops. Thus, while a lesser number of switch hops does imply a smaller latency, it often does not contribute significantly to a reduction in latency. The average or the worst-case number of switch hops, therefore, is not a very good indicator of average message transmission times on most real applications. In addition, since most of the topologies under consideration for a given system size do not differ significantly in this criterion, we give it less significance than other criteria.

All SP topologies allow deadlock-free routing with at least 4 distinct redundant paths between any two nodes that are not directly connected to the same switching element. The routing algorithm is an important component in the analysis of the bandwidths and other performance criteria.

The routing algorithm is based on a breadth-first search of all shortest paths with routes assigned thereafter with appropriate load-balancing among all the cables in the network [2]. Since the routing algorithm is not topology-specific except for certain restrictions placed to invalidate a subset of the available routes for deadlock-avoidance, this paper will not provide a detailed specification of the routing algorithm on the topologies. Instead, this paper will limit the discussion of routing to a set of examples of certain node-to-node paths that are illustrative of the routing used.

4 Topologies for 129–256-node systems

In this section, we discuss the SP topologies for 129–256 node systems, and make cost as well as performance comparisons to 4-ary fat-tree networks. The topologies of all N-node systems, where $129 \leq N \leq 255$, are constructed as subsets of 256-way systems. This is done because pure source-based shortest-path routing based on breadth-first search as in [2], does not always permit a good balance in the cable loads on odd-sized (not a power of 2) system networks and thus may degrade performance. In this range of the number of nodes, the topologies will have exactly as many ISBs as there are in a 256-way system. All upgrades within this range, therefore, only involve adding more NSBs and using up some of the unused ports on the ISBs, without disturbing the existing topology.

4.1 256-way 4-ary fat-tree

We shall first describe the 256-way 4-ary fat-tree network. The formal topology specification in pseudo-code for the 256-way 4-ary fat-tree is as follows:

```
for (i = 0; i < Number_of_NSBs; i++)
  for (j = 16; j < 32; j++)
    NSB(i), port(j) ↔ ISB(j-16), port(i);
```

In the above specification, ports 16–31 of the ISBs are open and unused. The routing on this network is illustrated by the following examples of paths traversed by packets between some source and destination nodes. Node i is represented by the notation Ni in all of the route specifications in this paper. The switch hops through the ISBs are italicized.

N16 to N0:	NSB 1, SE$_0$ → NSB 1, SE$_4$ → *ISB 0, SE$_0$* → NSB 0, SE$_4$ → NSB 0, SE$_0$.
N63 to N0:	NSB 3, SE$_3$ → NSB 3, SE$_7$ → *ISB 15, SE$_0$* → NSB 0, SE$_7$ → NSB 0, SE$_0$.
N64 to N0:	NSB 4, SE$_0$ → NSB 4, SE$_4$ → *ISB 0, SE$_1$* → *ISB 0, SE$_4$* → *ISB 0, SE$_0$* → NSB 0, SE$_4$ → NSB 0, SE$_0$.
N255 to N0:	NSB 15, SE$_3$ → NSB 15, SE$_7$ → *ISB 15, SE$_3$* → *ISB 15, SE$_7$* → *ISB 15, SE$_0$* → NSB 0, SE$_7$ → NSB 0, SE$_0$.

4.2 256-way SP Topology

The distinguishing feature of the 256-way SP topology, shown in Figure 2, as compared to the 4-ary fat-tree is that it has half as many ISBs, bringing down the cost of the system. The formal specification of the 256-way SP topology is as follows:

```
for (i = 0; i < Number_of_NSBs; i++)
  for (j = 16; j < 32; j++)
  { k = 4*(i/8) + 2*((i/4) MOD 2) + (j/4) MOD 2;
    NSB(i), port(j) ↔ ISB((j/24)*4 + j MOD 4),
                      port(k*4 + i MOD 4);
  }
```

In the above specification, k identifies the SE in the ISB to which the NSB port will be connected to. In addition, throughout this paper, in all instances of formal specification of topologies, x/y indicates the integer quotient obtained by dividing x by y. The following are a few examples to illustrate the routing algorithm.

N63 to N0:	NSB 3, SE$_3$ → NSB 3, SE$_4$ → *ISB 0, SE$_0$* → NSB 0, SE$_4$ → NSB 0, SE$_0$.
N64 to N0:	NSB 4, SE$_0$ → NSB 4, SE$_4$ → *ISB 0, SE$_2$* → *ISB 0, SE$_4$* → *ISB 0, SE$_0$* → NSB 0, SE$_4$ → NSB 0, SE$_0$.
N127 to N0:	NSB 7, SE$_3$ → NSB 7, SE$_4$ → *ISB 0, SE$_2$* → *ISB 0, SE$_6$* → *ISB 0, SE$_1$* → NSB 0, SE$_5$ → NSB 0, SE$_0$.
N128 to N0:	NSB 8, SE$_0$ → NSB 8, SE$_6$ → *ISB 7, SE$_4$* → *ISB 7, SE$_1$* → NSB 0, SE$_7$ → NSB 0, SE$_0$.
N255 to N0:	NSB 15, SE$_3$ → NSB 15, SE$_7$ → *ISB 7, SE$_7$* → *ISB 7, SE$_1$* → NSB 0, SE$_7$ → NSB 0, SE$_0$.

Note that in this topology the SEs on an ISB with direct links between them are cabled to NSBs in different quads. This increases the bandwidth between quads because packets travelling to another node in the same quad do not use the internal links of the ISBs. This is the reason we do not use a topology with a simpler interconnection scheme where port(j) of NSB(i) is connected to port($i + (j/24)*16$) of ISB(j MOD 8).

Consider two quads on the 256-way SP topology on different sides of the ISBs. Note that the 256-way SP topology provides for 4 links per ISB between these quads. Now, consider two quads that are on the same side of the ISBs. The SEs connected to these quads have no direct links between them on the ISBs. Communication between these two quads would, therefore, require two hops in the ISBs. The improvement in the bandwidth between quads, therefore, comes at the cost of an additional hop in the path of certain messages. However, as discussed earlier, the smaller number of hops only makes a difference when the applied load into the network is low, while the average latency in the midst of real traffic is determined largely by the available bandwidth.

The 2-hop turn-around paths (across 3 SEs) inside the ISBs lead to a traffic situation in the ISBs similar to that in a single-SB 32-way discussed in [1] creating a potential for deadlocks. Now, having to avoid deadlocks in the ISBs, the routing has to be chosen in such a way as to prohibit certain routes while keeping the loss in bandwidth to a minimum. In addition, we have to preserve the shortest-path routing and also the balance of bandwidths available between different sets of nodes. A simple routing strategy could be one where, for example, quads 0 and 1 always communicate only through ISBs 0–3 while quads 2 and 3 always communicate through ISBs 4–7. In this scheme, quads on different sides of the ISBs, however, would communicate through any of the 8 ISBs. While such a routing strategy is simple and provides good isolation between partitions, it provides only 50% bisection bandwidth between some partitions such as between two NSBs on different quads which are on the same side of the ISBs.

The routing used on the 256-way SP provides for significantly better bandwidth between quads, by prohibiting fewer paths than described above to eliminate the deadlocks. Note that there are a total of 96 two-hop (or three-SE) turn-around paths inside an ISB. Out of these 96, only 64 have the potential of being used in the 256-way SP network. This is because the shortest-path routing algorithm ensures that a packet with both its source and destination nodes in the same quad does not have to take a 3-SE path inside the ISBs. Now, at least four of these 64 paths are needed to create a loop and therefore a deadlock situation. Prohibiting the use of some of these 64 paths selectively can break all of the deadlocks. Table 1 lists the 16 paths that are prohibited inside ISB 0 in the 256-way SP network. A different set of 16 paths, among a total of 4 sets of paths, is prohibited in each ISB in a 256-way SP, with regard to a goal of keeping as much symmetry as possible in the routing between any two quads. This is achieved by ensuring that, among the 8 ISBs, the set of numbers of paths prohibited from an SE in a given location in an ISB, has as low a standard deviation as possible. An additional goal is that, among the 8 ISBs, the cable loads on any given link in an ISB has as low a standard deviation as possible. Nevertheless, the deadlock restrictions do introduce some asymmetry in the routing between quads. The routing algorithm, however, attempts to compensate by balancing the loads on all cables in the system for random traffic. The complete set of deadlock restrictions on all the ISBs in the system is described in [11].

Table 1: Paths Prohibited in ISB 0 in a 256-way SP Topology

SE	Paths Prohibited (Port $X \rightarrow$ Port Y)
0	$4 \rightarrow 6, 4 \rightarrow 7, 6 \rightarrow 5, 7 \rightarrow 5$
1	$5 \rightarrow 6, 5 \rightarrow 7, 6 \rightarrow 4, 7 \rightarrow 4$
4	$4 \rightarrow 6, 4 \rightarrow 7, 6 \rightarrow 5, 7 \rightarrow 5$
5	$5 \rightarrow 6, 5 \rightarrow 7, 6 \rightarrow 4, 7 \rightarrow 4$

Note that the 256-way SP topology is also chosen such as to minimize the number of cables that have to be moved in an upgrade from the 128-way topology, described in [12]. A simpler topology with the following specification, therefore, is also not used as the 256-way SP, allowing a less disruptive upgrade from a 128-way topology:

$k = (i/8)*2 + 4*((i/4) \text{ MOD } 2) + (j/24);$
$\text{NSB}(i), \text{port}(j) \leftrightarrow \text{ISB}(j \text{ MOD } 8), \text{port}(k*4 + i \text{ MOD } 4);$

Other minor variations of the 256-way topology were similarly not accepted because of practical considerations related to packaging and the slack desired in the cables necessary for ease in cable movements.

4.3 Performance Comparisons

Figure 3 shows a graph of the latency in case of random traffic on 256-way SP and a 256-way 4-ary fat-tree network. This software simulation is based on the current generation of the SP Switch, which is a successor to the SP2 High-Performance Switch [12]. In this generation of the SP

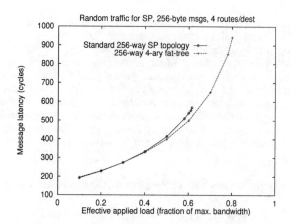

Figure 3: Latency vs. Applied load on 256-way Topologies

Switch, each output (input) port can send (receive) a 2-byte flit every 13.33 nanosecond cycle, for a maximum of 300 MB/s of bidirectional traffic over the link. For our simulations, we count latency in cycles and we assume 2-byte flits. Minimum latency through each switch is assumed to be 6 cycles, with 4 cycles required for reading data out of the input FIFO, determining the route, requesting an output port and granting of the request. For traversing the switch via the central buffer, flits are deserialized into a chunk, requiring an additional 7 cycles for the 8-flit chunks. We assume that each of the 8 input FIFOs contains 64 flits and that the central buffer contains 2,048 flits. We assume that packet flits are immediately pulled from the network upon arrival at a node, and we include the queueing time at the source node in the latency results. As with most network simulations, in our experiments, we measure latency vs. applied load and do not plot results above the saturation bandwidth. All of the simulations were done using 256-byte messages, under the assumption that the entire 256-byte message can fit within one packet. Figure 3 shows that until the saturation point in the SP system, the latencies through the two topologies are very close. The 256-way SP topology saturates at a lower input load than the 4-ary fat-tree. This, however, does not necessarily translate into a proportional difference in the performance of most real applications as is explained below.

Table 2 makes a summary comparison between the 256-way SP topology and the 256-way 4-ary fat-tree. In evaluating the cost/performance ratio, it is certainly very hard to quantify a complex criterion such as performance in a large parallel system. If one uses the maximum random traffic throughput on a 256-way job as the performance indicator, and the number of SBs as the cost indicator, Table 2 and Figure 3 clearly show that the two topologies discussed here are comparable in terms of the cost/performance ratio. However, in reality, few applications drive the network to the saturation point. In addition, the maximum throughput of the communication adapters at the network ports is typically less than the link bandwidth at the switch ports, except possibly for very large messages. Further, as shown in Table 2, the performance of partitions of 64 nodes or less is almost equal on the two topologies. Most jobs on SP systems are likely to be on smaller partitions of 16, 32 or 64 nodes. Finally, since the two topologies are equally efficient with smaller partitions, all parallel algorithms that exploit locality in message traffic patterns will exhibit almost identical performance on the two topologies. For all of the reasons above, the SP topologies are more attractive than the fat-tree networks based on both cost and the cost/performance criterion.

Table 2: 256-way Topologies — Summary

	256-way SP	256-way 4-ary Fat-tree
Number of SBs	24	32
Max. throughput with random traffic	62%	80%
BBW[a]	50%	100%
Avg. & wc # of hops	5.9, 7	6.4, 7
BBWs of wc[b] and bc[c] 2-NSB partitions	100%, 100%	100%, 100%
BBWs of wc and bc 4-NSB partitions	100%, 100%	100%, 100%
BBWs of wc and bc 8-NSB partitions	50%, 100%	100%, 100%
Average BBW of 2-NSB partitions	100%	100%
Average BBW of 2-quad partitions	58.3%	100%
Isolated n-NSB partition sizes feasible	$n = 1, 2, 4, 8$	$n = 1, 2, 4, 8$

a. Bisection Bandwidth
b. worst-case
c. best-case

The 256-way fat-tree has its advantages in addition to a consistently excellent performance of partitions. For instance, it does not require route restrictions for deadlock avoidance, permitting a more uniform routing strategy. This is because in the 256-way fat-tree topology, the ports on one side of the ISBs are unused and therefore do not give rise to a situation where the paths of packets can form a loop. That more than 75% of its routes require 7 switch hops, as compared to a maximum of 6 hops in the 256-way SP, is of little concern given the lower possibility of contention owing to the high bandwidth provided by this topology. The downside of the 256-way fat-tree, of course, is that it requires 8 more SBs than the 256-way SP network. Cost and the cost/performance ratio being the most important factors in the choice of topologies by customers, the 256-way SP ends up on a more attractive spot on the cost-performance curve despite the excellent performance of 4-ary fat-tree networks.

5 Topologies for (257–512)-node systems

For performance and upgradability reasons similar to those discussed in Section 4, all of the topologies for 257–511 nodes are constructed as proper subsets of the 512-way topologies, with the same number of ISBs as in a 512-way system. Here again, we discuss the 512-way 4-ary fat-tree and the 512-way SP topologies.

5.1 512-way 4-ary fat-tree

The 512-way 4-ary fat-tree topology is the only one among those discussed in this paper with two stages of ISBs, with 16 ISBs in each stage. This topology merely cables together two 256-way 4-ary fat-trees. With the extra stage of SBs, this topology does not have a potential for deadlock situations, and therefore, one may use a shortest-path routing algorithm with no restrictions for deadlock avoidance. The formal pseudo-code specification of the topology is as follows:

```
for (i = 0; i < 32; i++)
  for (j = 16; j < 32; j++)
    NSB(i), port(j) ↔ ISB(j - 16 + (i/16)*16),
                              port(i -(i/16)*16);
for (i = 0; i < 16; i++)
  for (j = 16; j < 32; j++)
    ISB(i), port(j) ↔ ISB(j), port(i+16);
```

Note that the 512-way 4-ary fat-tree topology requires packets headed to the other topological half of the system to go through 8 switch hops or four SBs. In addition, all packets headed to a node in a different quad require at least 7 hops. The routing on this topology is as illustrated by the following examples:

N63 to N0: NSB 3, SE_3 → NSB 3, SE_7 → *ISB 15, SE_0* → NSB 0, SE_7 → NSB 0, SE_0.

N255 to N0: NSB 15, SE_3 → NSB 15, SE_7 → *ISB 15, SE_3* → *ISB 15, SE_7* → *ISB 15, SE_0* → NSB 0, SE_7 → NSB 0, SE_0.

N256 to N0: NSB 16, SE_0 → NSB 16, SE_4 → *ISB 16, SE_0* → *ISB 16, SE_4* → *ISB 0, SE_4* → *ISB 0, SE_0* → NSB 0, SE_4 → NSB 0, SE_0.

N511 to N0: NSB 31, SE_3 → NSB 31, SE_7 → *ISB 31, SE_3* → *ISB 31, SE_7* → *ISB 15, SE_7* → *ISB 15, SE_0* → NSB 0, SE_7 → NSB 0, SE_0.

5.2 512-way SP Topology

A 512-way SP topology has 32 NSBs just as in the 512-way fat-tree, but only 16 ISBs as opposed to 32 ISBs in case of the fat-tree. Figure 4 shows the 512-way SP topology. Note that the semi-circular representation of the ISBs is merely for convenience in a planar representation of the topology on paper. The formal pseudo-code specification of the 512-way SP topology is as follows, with each of 32 NSBs connected to each of 16 ISBs.

```
for (i = 0; i < 32; i++)
  for (j = 16; j < 32; j++)
    NSB(i), port(j) ↔ ISB(j-16), port(i);
```

As in other topologies with a second stage of SBs, the packets with destinations within the same quad enter and leave the ISBs through the same SE. The packets which are headed to the other topological half of the machine go through two SEs inside the ISBs. However, packets that are headed to nodes in a different quad but in the same topological half of the machine have to go through three switch hops inside the ISBs. This leads to a deadlock scenario in-

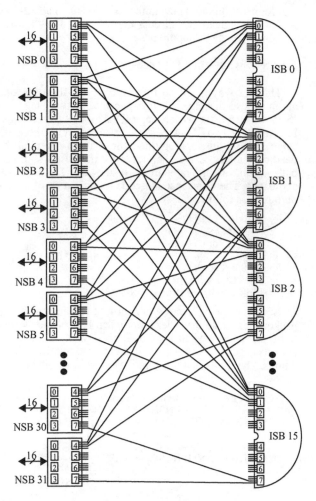

Figure 4: 512-way SP Topology
(Not all cables are shown)

N255 to N0:   NSB 15, SE_3 → NSB 15, SE_7 → *ISB 7, SE_3*
     → *ISB 7, SE_7* → *ISB 7, SE_0*
     → NSB 0, SE_5 → NSB 0, SE_0.

N256 to N0:   NSB 16, SE_0 → NSB 16, SE_4 → *ISB 0, SE_4*
     → *ISB 0, SE_0* → NSB 0, SE_4
     → NSB 0, SE_0.

N511 to N0:   NSB 31, SE_3 → NSB 31, SE_7 → *ISB 15, SE_7*
     → *ISB 15, SE_0* → NSB 0, SE_7
     → NSB 0, SE_0.

Other topologies that we considered for 512-way systems using only 16 ISBs, and which avoid the deadlock scenario, do so at the cost of reducing the bandwidth available for most partitions. For example, in a topology with the following specification, the worst-case bisection bandwidths of 4-NSB and 8-NSB partitions are as low as 25% and 12.5% respectively, significantly worse than those of the 512-way SP.

```
for (i = 0; i < 16; i++)
  for (j = 0; j < 32; j++)
    if ((i MOD 4) < 2)
      ISB(i), port(j) ↔ NSB(j), port(16 + i/4 + 4*(i MOD 4));
    else
      ISB(i), port(j)
        ↔ NSB(((i MOD 4)-2)*16 + (j/8)*4 + j MOD 4),
          port(16 + i/4 + (j/4) MOD 2 + 4*(i MOD 4));
```

The performance of a 512-way application is slightly better on a topology with the above specification, than on the 512-way SP topology. However, given that the performance of individual small partitions is important in a multi-user environment, and since most applications exhibit a high degree of locality in message traffic, we consider the 512-way SP topology to be the better choice.

5.3 Performance Comparisons

Figure 5 shows a plot of the latency on a 512-way SP topology and that on a 512-way 4-ary fat-tree with random traffic. Table 3 shows that the 512-way 4-ary fat-tree, sim-

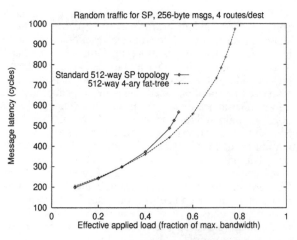

Figure 5: Latency vs. Applied load on 512-way Topologies

side the ISBs exactly similar to the one in the 256-node SP system described in Section 4.2. This deadlock scenario is handled in a manner similar to that on the 256-way SP system, by restricting the routing through the ISBs. In the 512-node case, we have a total of 96 3-SE or two-hop turn-around paths inside the ISBs that may be used by a shortest-path routing algorithm. We eliminate the potential for deadlocks in the system by prohibiting 32 of these turn-around paths inside each of the ISBs. While it is actually possible to prohibit even fewer paths than 32 and still eliminate the deadlocks, we do not do so in the interest of not unduly sacrificing the symmetry of routing between the quads. The complete set of routing restrictions is described in [11]. The routing on the 512-way SP system is illustrated by the following examples.

N16 to N0:   NSB 1, SE_0 → NSB 1, SE_4 → *ISB 0, SE_0*
     → NSB 0, SE_4 → NSB 0, SE_0.

N63 to N0:   NSB 3, SE_3 → NSB 3, SE_7 → *ISB 15, SE_0*
     → NSB 0, SE_7 → NSB 0, SE_0.

N64 to N0:   NSB 4, SE_0 → NSB 4, SE_4 → *ISB 0, SE_1*
     → *ISB 0, SE_5* → *ISB 0, SE_0*
     → NSB 0, SE_4 → NSB 0, SE_0.

ilar to the 256-way 4-ary fat-tree, offers excellent performance on all best-case as well as worst-case partitions, in addition to providing a 100% bisection bandwidth for the 512-way system as a whole. The better performance of the

512-way fat-tree comes at the cost of adding 16 additional SBs in the system. Note that the performance of preferred partitions on both the 512-way SP topology and the 512-way fat-tree is excellent.

Figure 5 shows that the latency on the 512-way SP is better or very close to that of the fat-tree for small loads because of the smaller worst-case number of hops. The 512-way SP, however, does saturate at a lower applied load than the 512-way fat-tree network. Once again, as in the case of the 256-way, if one considers the maximum random traffic throughput as the performance indicator and the number of SBs as the cost indicator, the two 512-way topologies are comparable in terms of the cost/performance criterion. However again, most SP systems will be used with several partitions of 16, 32 or 64-node jobs, and the performance on such partitions is similar on the two topologies. This and other reasons mentioned in Section 4.3 contribute to making the SP systems more attractive as regards the cost/performance criterion.

Table 3: 512-way Topologies — Summary

Criterion	512-way SP Topology	512-way 4-ary Fat-tree
Number of SBs	48	64
Max. throughput with random traffic	54%	78%
BBW	50%	100%
Avg. & wc # of hops	6.2, 7	7.2, 8
BBWs of wc and bc 2-NSB partitions	100%, 100%	100%, 100%
BBWs of wc and bc 4-NSB partitions	50%, 100%	100%, 100%
BBWs of wc and bc 8-NSB partitions	25%, 100%	100%, 100%
Avg. of 2-NSB partition BBWs	100%	100%
Average of 2-quad partition BBWs	42.9%	100%
Isolated n-NSB partitions feasible	$n = 1, 2, 4, 8$	$n = 1, 2, 4, 8, 16$

6 Conclusion

In this paper, we have described the large-system topologies used for the IBM RS/6000 SP systems, and some of the rationale behind them. In particular, we have made comparisons to 4-ary fat-tree topologies, and shown that the SP topologies are more attractive in terms of cost/performance, despite the use of a smaller number of SBs. Besides low cost, the SP topologies also satisfy a variety of other design goals such as excellent performance of preferred partitions, reasonably good independence of performance from task-to-node mapping illustrated by the random traffic results, and overall excellent system performance in both multi-user and single-job environments. The goal of excellent tolerance to sub-optimal partitioning is

also partially achieved on the SP topologies designed with fewer SBs. The SP network topologies, it should be noted, have the potential to become even more attractive in terms of the cost/performance ratio if a deadlock-avoidance strategy, such as with virtual channels, is implemented locally inside the SEs.

In this paper, we have not attempted to solve the larger theoretical problem of trying to prove that the SP topologies are optimal in performance for the given number of SBs. We do not present here a general framework by which one may arrive at topologies for parallel systems if, for e.g., constraints such as the modular unit to be used for the topologies were different. However, the criteria that we use for the evaluation of these topologies should serve well in the evaluation of the interconnection networks of all parallel systems.

Acknowledgments

We would like to thank Don Grice for several suggestions and unique insights.

References

[1] Abali, B., "A Deadlock Avoidance Method for Computer Networks", *Proc. 1st Int'l Workshop, CANPC '97*, In *Lecture Notes in Computer Science*, Vol. 1199, Springer-Verlag, 1997, pp. 61–72.

[2] Abali, B., "Routing Algorithms for IBM SP1", *Proc. 1st Int'l Workshop PCRCW '94*, In *Lecture Notes in Computer Science*, Vol. 853, Springer-Verlag, 1994, pp. 161–165.

[3] Efe, K. and Fernandez, A., "Mesh-Connected Trees: A Bridge between Grids and Meshes of Trees", *IEEE Trans. Par. Dist. Sys.*, Vol. 7, No. 12, Dec. 1996, pp. 1281–91.

[4] Galles, M., "Spider: A High-Speed Network Interconnect", *IEEE Micro*, Jan./Feb. 1997, pp. 34–39.

[5] Ghose, K. and Desai, K. R., "Hierarchical Cubic Networks", *IEEE Trans. Par. Dist. Sys.*, Vol. 6, No. 4, Apr. 1995, pp. 427–35.

[6] Hwang, K and Ghosh, J., "Hypernet: A Communication Efficient Architecture for Constructing Massively Parallel Computers", *IEEE Trans. Comput.*, Vol. C-36, pp. 1450–66, Dec. 1987.

[7] Leiserson, C. E., "Fat-trees: Universal Networks for Hardware-Efficient Supercomputing", *IEEE Trans. Comput.*, Vol. C-34, No. 10, Oct. 1985, pp. 892–901.

[8] Malluhi, Q. M. and Bayoumi, M. A., "The Hierarchical Hypercube: A New Interconnection Topology for Massively Parallel Systems", *IEEE Trans. Par. Dist. Syst.*, Vol. 5, No. 1, Jan. 1994, pp. 17–30.

[9] Preparata, F. P. and Vuillemin, J., "The Cube-Connected Cycles: A Versatile Network for Parallel Computation", *Commun. ACM*, 24, May 1981, pp. 300–309.

[10] Seitz, C. L., "The Cosmic Cube", *Commun. ACM*, Vol. 28, No. 1, Jan. 1985, pp. 22–23.

[11] Sethu, H., "Route Restrictions for Deadlock-Free Routing with Increased Bandwidth in a Multistage Cross-Point Packet Switch", patent pending, US patent number to be issued.

[12] Stunkel, C. B., et al, "The SP2 High-Performance Switch", *IBM Systems Journal*, Vol. 34, No. 2, 1995, pp. 185–204.

[13] Stunkel, C. B., Sivaram, R. and Panda, D. K., "Implementing Multidestination Worms in Switch-Based Parallel Systems: Architectural Alternatives and their Impact", *Proc. 24th Annu. Int'l Symp. on Comp. Arch.*, 1997, pp. 50–61.

Index of Authors

— *Notes* —

— *Notes* —

— *Notes* —

— *Notes* —

— *Notes* —